PROCEEDINGS OF THE ELEVENTH INTERNATIONAL CONFERENCE
ON SOIL MECHANICS AND FOUNDATION ENGINEERING
SAN FRANCISCO / 12-16 AUGUST 1985

COMPTES RENDUS DU ONZIEME CONGRES INTERNATIONAL DE
MECANIQUE DES SOLS ET DES TRAVAUX DE FONDATIONS
SAN FRANCISCO / 12-16 AOUT 1985

VOLUME 3

PROCEEDINGS OF THE ELEVENTH INTERNATIONAL CONFERENCE ON SOIL MECHANICS AND FOUNDATION ENGINEERING

SAN FRANCISCO / 12-16 AUGUST 1985

EDITOR: PUBLICATIONS COMMITTEE OF XI ICSMFE

VOLUME 3
TECHNICAL PAPERS
EXPOSES TECHNIQUES

COMPTES RENDUS DU ONZIEME CONGRES INTERNATIONAL DE MECANIQUE DES SOLS ET DES TRAVAUX DE FONDATIONS

SAN FRANCISCO / 12-16 AOUT 1985

EDITEUR: COMITE DES PUBLICATIONS DU XI CIMSTF

A.A.BALKEMA / ROTTERDAM / BOSTON / 1985

Scheme of the work / Schéma de l'ouvrage

Complete set of five volumes: / Collection complète de cinq volumes: ISBN 90 6191 560 0
Vol. 1: ISBN 90 6191 561 9 / Vol. 2: ISBN 90 6191 562 7 / Vol. 3: ISBN 90 6191 563 5 / Vol. 4: ISBN 90 6191 564 3 / Vol. 5: ISBN 90 6191 565 1

Published by: / Publié par:
A.A.Balkema, Postbus 1675, Rotterdam, Nederland / A.A.Balkema Publishers, P.O.Box 230, Accord, MA 02018, USA

Printed in the Netherlands / Imprimé aux Pays Bas

Contents
Table des matières

Session 3C

Geotechnical aspects of environmental control
Tailings dams and waste containment structures

Séance 3C

Aspects géotechniques de la réglementation de l'environnement
Barrage en déchets et structures pour l'entrepôt des déchets

Session 4A
Piles and other deep foundations
Pile foundation design methods

Séance 4A
Pieux et autres fondations profondes
Méthodes de calcul de fondation sur pieux

Session 4B

Séance 4B

Piles and other deep foundations
Pier foundations

Pieux et autres fondations profondes
Fondations sur caissons

Session 3A
Geotechnical aspects of environmental control
A. Motion of landslides and debris flows

Séance 3A
Aspects géotechniques de la réglementation de l'environnement
A. Mouvement des glissements de terrain et l'écoulement des déchets

Methodology for landslide prediction

Méthodologie pour la prédiction des glissements de talus

K. KAWAMURA, Professor of Civil Engineering, Kanazawa Institute of Technology, Kanazawa, Japan

SYNOPSIS   Landslides can be triggered by rainfall, melting snow, freezing and thawy action and seismic effect due to earthquakes in Japan. They often occur in major Tertiary mudstone and Green-tuff zones. In engineering practice, it is considered very important to be able to predict landslides in some way. This paper describes a methodology for landslide prediction based on field observations. The first half of the paper proposed a technique to make it possible not only to evaluate a landslide type either successively approaching failure or remaining in a stable state but also how to determine the characteristics of movement, such as convergence and divergence, if required. In the second half of the paper, the practical application of the proposed prediction method is discussed based on the comparisons with the results observed for actual landslides. It can be shown that this methodology is very effective and easy to use from a practical standpoint.

INTRODUCTION

The establishment of good method of prediction based on field observations has recently been recognized as one of the important matters in a series of optimum design and construction procedures for earth work, because these can make it possible to resolve various uncertainties such as inevitable analytical errors in idealization of the complicated actual behavior, variation of soil properties and insufficient imformation due to the limited number of samples. (Matsuo and Kawamura, 1975, 1980, Matsuo, Kuroda, Asaoka and Kawamura, 1977). It is also considered quite important in engineering practice that a good method of prediction of the successive behavior of landslides is available in order to either allow inhabitants near the landslide location to be evacuated to a safe place or not and to determine the most appropriate countermeasures to be taken immediately if necessary. For these reasons, a methodology of landslide prediction based on field observations has been proposed in this paper. The significant points of this methodology are the following:

(i)   it is possible to easily estimate either landslide movement to divergence indicating imminent failure or convergence no failure,

(ii)   results as shown in (i) above can be successively modified by using new imformation obtained from field observations,

(iii)   results of observations are analyzed statistically in order to make the best use of the prediction system.

Next, the applicability of the proposed methodology to practical use is examined by comprison with the actual data obtained recently from large-sized landslides. In addition, the actual result of application to a real landslide in progress is presented. Based on the results of these examinations, it has been determined that this methodology can be very effective for practical use.

PROPOSED METHODOLOGY FOR LANDSLIDE PREDICTION

Landslide movement is normally described as one of creep behavior. As the results of many observed data and numerical analyses utilizing the creep theory, an inductive model of landslide can be expressed as follows:

$$\left(\frac{dt}{dy}\right) = A \cdot (B-t) \cdot t \tag{1}$$

where y denotes the displacement or strain, t the time and A, B the constants, respectively. Solving Eq.(1) under the initial condition $t=t_0$ in $y=0$, the general solution is easily given as follows:

$$y = \frac{1}{A \cdot B} \ln \left\{ \frac{t}{B-t} \cdot \frac{B-t_0}{t_0} \right\} \tag{2}$$

As shown in Fig.(1), it can be seen that Eq.(1) under both $A>0$ and $B>0$ is regarded as a divergent y curve indicating landslide failure and while under $A<0$ and $B \doteqdot 0$ convergent y curve approaching a stable state. Accordingly, exact determination of the constants A and B based on observed data is very important in order to be able to apply Eq.(1) to actual landslide prediction.

For the purpose mentioned above, now, the j-th observed displacement or strain can be defined as $y_j = y \cdot j$ and the corresponding time t_j as $t_j = t(y_j)$, respectively, as shown in Fig. 1.

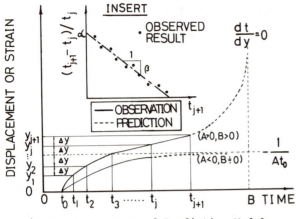

Fig. 1   Proposed Prediction Model

The defference equation equivalent to Eq.(1) can be obtained as follows:

$$\left(\frac{t_{j+1} - t_j}{t_j}\right) = \alpha - \beta t_{j+1} \tag{3}$$

where α and β are the constants. Solving Eq.(3) under same initial condition as Eq.(1), the general solution can be obtained from the following equation:

$$t_j = \frac{(1+\alpha)^j \cdot t_0}{1+[\{1+\alpha\}^j - 1] \cdot B \cdot t_0/\alpha} \tag{4}$$

Based on Eqs.(2) and (4), the following relationships between the constants A, B and α, β are determined, respectively:

$$\left.\begin{array}{l} \alpha = \exp(\Delta y \cdot A \cdot B) \\ \\ \beta = \alpha/B \end{array}\right\} \tag{5}$$

where Δy denotes the equal diving value in y as shown in the ' ted figure of Fig. 1. Arranging the observed data on the basis of Eq.(3), the constants α and β can be immediately calculated by using the method of least squares as follows:

$$\alpha = \frac{\sum_i w_i \left(\frac{t_{j+1} - t_j}{t_j}\right)_i - \beta \sum_i w_i (t_{j+1})_i}{\sum_i w_i} \tag{6}$$

$$\beta = \frac{\sum_i w_i \{\sum_i w_i (t_{j+1})_i (\frac{t_{j+1} - t_j}{t_j})_i\} - \{\sum_i w_i (\frac{t_{j+1} - t_j}{t_j})_i\}\{\sum_i w_i (t_{j+1})_i\}}{\sum_i w_i \{\sum_i w_i (t_{j+1})_i^2\} - \{\sum_i w_i (t_{j+1})_i\}^2}$$

where w_i denotes the weight of creep imformation in i-th arranged result. It is assumed that the later the data obtained will be, the larger the weight is. Finally, substituting α and β into Eq.(5), the constants A and B can be determined and consequently Eq.(1) makes it possible to predict the behavior of a landslide in the future.

APPLICATION OF PROPOSED MODEL TO LANDSLIDE PREDICTION

The most important point for this study is to be able to determine the engineering usefulness and the accuracy of the proposed methodology as follows:

Prediction of landslide failure

Initially, Fig. 2 shows a comparison between the observed data from an actual landslide failure near a Japan National Railway Line and the predicted behavior obtained by utilizing the earlist actual data in the proposed method. The table in Fig. 2 where actual field name, the observed failure time t_{fob}, the final time of observed data used for prediction t_u and the predicted failure time t_{fp} are summarized indicates the accuracy of this prediction method based on the various numbers of observed data used for prediction (each curve a, b and c under an actual field condition).

The case of the Dosan-Line shown in Fig. 2 is explained in detail. The soil conditions at this landslide location consists mainly of discontinuous Black-schist and a failure occurred in 1962. No trains were allowed to pass this landslide area for 41 days because a railway bridge was destroyed by a soil and rock landslide movement of about 60,000m^3 volume. Initially, several tension cracks with 18cm in width appeared on the surface of slope. Immediately, field observations and landslide prediction were begun. The displacement of landslide progressed rapidly

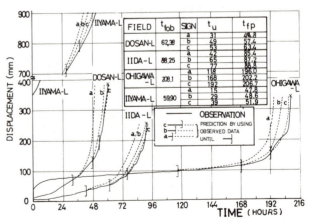

Fig. 2   Comparison between Observations and Predictions for Actual Cases of Failure

just after the observation system was completed and at that time, the rate of strain determined by a strain meter already indicated 2.68×10^{-5} /min. After a while, the rate of displacement gradually increased with time and suddenly, a definite failure occurred 62.38 hours later as shown in Fig. 2.

The landslide prediction was made by substituing the actual data up to $t_u = 31.0$ hours later into Eq.(3). The number of data is 8 for use under $\Delta y=12$mm and defining the weight w_i as i^4 in Eq.(6), the constants α and β were determined to be 0.52 and 0.011, respectively. The constants $A=7.3 \times 10^{-4}$ and $B=48.8$ from Eq.(5) and the prediction curve with $t_{fp}=48.8$ hours can be described as a dotted line a of Dosan-Line in Fig. 2. Similarly, the prediction curves obtained by using the actual data up to $t_u=49.0$ and 53.0 hours later are both shown as dotted lines b and c with $t_{fp}=57.4$ and 63.4 hours respectively.

Comparing t_{fp} with t_{fob} for several landslide areas, it becomes clear that, (1) the more data avaiable for prediction, the more exact the prediction method can be and (2) landslide prediction can be accomplished at any time with sufficient engineering accuracy.

The latter shows a difference from the conventional prediction method where t_{fp} is predicted based on the second creep rate (a constant creep rate) has been published by Saito and Uezawa. (Saito and Uezawa, 1961).

Prediction of convergent movement

A comparison between the predicted behavior obtained from the proposed methodology and the actual data from landslides where the movement have all temporarily stopped or have continuously decreased is shown in Fig. 3. In the case of Field-S where the observed convergent displacement y_{fob} is 0.12m, substituting a set of observed data up to 54 days later into Eq.(1) under the initial condition of $t_0=1.2$ days in $y_0=0$, the constants $\alpha=0.156$ and $\beta=1.55 \times 10^3$ are determined and therefore the constants $A=-0.29$ and $B=-100.3$ can be obtained from Eq.(5).

Since (dt/dy) becomes positive if the constants $A<0$ and $B<t$ in Eq.(1), Eq.(1) with a sufficiently small value of B is redefined as follows:

$$\left(\frac{dt}{dy}\right) = -A't^2 \qquad (7)$$

The difference equation equivalent to Eq.(7) can be shown as follows:

$$\left(\frac{t_{j+1}-t_j}{t_j}\right) = -\beta't_{j+1} \qquad (8)$$

Based on both general solutions of Eqs.(7) and (8), the relation between the constants β' and A' is easily given as follows:

$$\beta' = A' \cdot \Delta y \qquad (9)$$

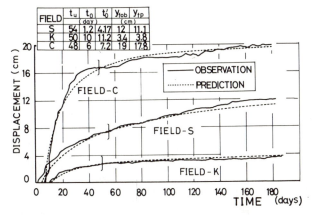

FIELD	t_u (day)	t_0 (day)	t_0' (day)	y_{fob} (cm)	y_{fp} (cm)
S	54	1.2	4.17	12	11.1
K	50	10	11.2	3.4	3.8
C	48	6	7.2	19	17.8

Fig. 3 Comparison between Observation and Predictions for Actual Cases of Non-failure

Accordingly, the convergent displacement y_{fp} can be obtained as $-(1/A' \cdot t_0')$ where t_0' denotes the initial time modified by Eq.(8).

The initial time t_0 of Field-S can be modified as $t_0'=4.17$ days and at once the predicted convergent displacement y_{fp} can be calculated to be 0.111m nearly consistent with the actual data $y_{fob}=0.12$m.

Examining other fields using the same procedure as mentioned above, it is determined from Fig. 3 that this prediction method can almost be applied to actual field conditions where the movement tends to be less than the critical state.

Example of practical application

The proposed methodology has been applied to an actual Tertial mudstone landslide area where a landslide is now in progress. Signs of landslide failure, such as a small movement along the slope and a small cracks occurrence in the rice field near the toe of slope as shown in Fig. 4, had appeared and therefore the observation system was started in August, 1982. Although some tension cracks appeared near the top of slope, heaving in the rice field and channel destruction near the toe of slope were observed in December, after some time, the movement of landslide stopped for several months. This methodology was applied for landslide prediction in May, 1983 and a failure could be forseen 13 months later from this point. Countermeasures such as a retaining structure and lateral holes for removal of ground water were immediately undertaken in July. After that, in November, the second prediction made while the countermeasures were being implemented indicated the failure would occur earlier than the first prediction. The inhabitants near the landslide area were obliged to be evacuated to safe places. Since the rate of displacement tended to countinuously increase in spite of the completion of lateral holes for removal of ground water in November, 1983, the construction of the retaining struc-

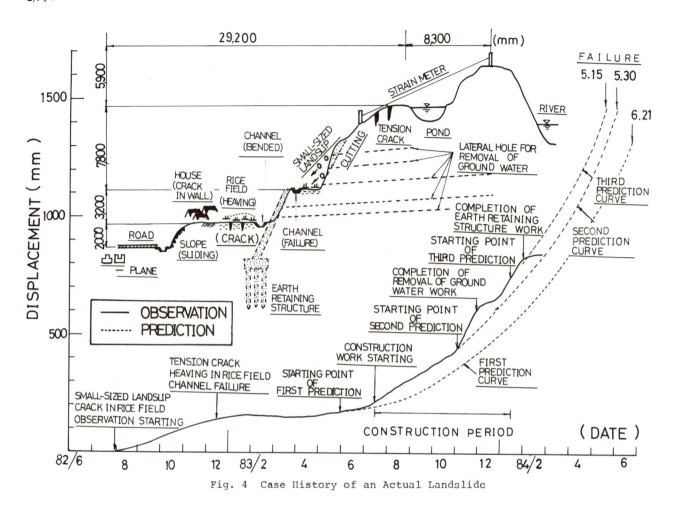

Fig. 4 Case History of an Actual Landslide

ture was undertaken more rapidly and a third prediction was made in January, 1984. This latest predicted failure based on the actual observation was found to be earlier than the previous two predictions. We are therefore observing this landslide very carefully in order to make more exact prediction.

CONCLUSIONS

Conclusions obtained from this study are summarized as follows:

(i)   The methodology for prediction of the behavior of landslides based on field observation is proposed in order to keep inhabitants near landslide field safe and to protect various structures against landslide failure.

(ii) This methodology definitely makes it possible to estimate the landslide movement not only to divergence indicating imminent failure but also to convergence stable state.

(iii) This methodology can also be applied to prediction of failure and settlement of soft cohesive clay layer under surcharge load.

ACKNOWLEDGEMENTS

The auther is grateful to Professor Minoru Matsuo and Associate Professor Akira Asaoka of Nagoya University for their valuable comments in this study.

REFERENCES

Matsuo, M., Kuroda, K., Asaoka, A., and Kawamura, K. (1977). Dynamic decision procedure of embankment construction. Proc. 9th ICSMFE, 2, 117-120, Tokyo.
Matsuo, M., and Kawamura, K. (1977). Diagram for construction control of embankment of soft ground. Soils and Found. (17), 3, 37-52.
Matsuo, M., and Kawamura, K. (1980). Prediction of failure of earth retaining structure during excavation work. Soils and Found. (20), 3, 33-44.
Saito, M., and Uezawa, H. (1961). Failure of soil due to creep. Proc. 5th ICSMFE, 1, 315-318.

Consolidation characteristics of polluted sea bottom sediments

Les caractéristiques de la consolidation des sédiments maritimes pollués

V. KUMBASAR, Professor of Civil Engineering, Istanbul Technical University, Istanbul, Turkey
I. K. ÖZAYDIN, Assoc. Prof. of Civil Engineering, University of Petroleum and Minerals, Dhahran, Saudi Arabia

SYNOPSIS   The contribution of polluted sea bottom sediments to environmental problems and investigation of possible methods of disposal for such sediments in shallow waters has become a major problem of concern in many parts of the world. This paper outlines the findings of an investigation carried out on Golden Horn bottom sediments. The organic content and the putrescibility index of the sludge samples studied are found to be higher than those encountered in similar places. The geotechnical investigations have shown that these sediments consist of fine grained soils of very high water contents and upon consolidation in a slurry consolidometer, block soil samples of medium consistency with high compressibility could be obtained. Also, it has been experimentally observed that a marked decrease in putrescibility index of the samples took place during consolidation.

INTRODUCTION

The Golden Horn bay in the city of Istanbul is a long and narrow waterway dividing the city, and the area is a site of many historic monuments as well as being a densely populated residential and industrial region. In past centuries (the days of Ottoman Sultans), the region used to be a recreational area with its picturesque surrounding. Since the turn of the century, it has been victim of over-population and uncontrolled industrial development. Today, it has long lost its beautiful image and is a typical case of man's destruction of its environment. It is been largely filled with eroded material from surrounding hills and disposal of waste, and it is highly polluted.

The area has unique soil conditions and the associated geotechnical problems have been reported elsewhere (Peynircioğlu, 1961, 1965, 1973; Toğrol, 1975; Kumbasar et.al., 1976). The present investigation was carried out to study the contribution of sea bottom sediments on the pollution problem and to study the methods of disposal for these sediments. This paper primarily deals with the consolidation behavior of these bottom sediments and associated changes in their geotechnical properties. Sea bottom sediments from various points along the Golden Horn have been tested in the laboratory and the results are presented herewith.

GEOLOGY

The geology of Golden Horn area has been the subject of many investigations (Ketin, 1953; Maden, 1975; Sayar, 1976). The southern shores Golden Horn are gently sloping to heights of 40-60 m, whereas the northern shores have steeper slopes reaching to 80-140 m heights. The oldest formations of the area consist of graywacks, clayey schists and limestones belonging to Upper Paleozoic. On this base, at higher elevations sand, gravel, clay and marl series of Neogene age are encountered. The area has been affected by Hersinien and Alpine tectonic movements. Grayawacks and clayey schist have been subject to different degrees of weathering on the surface. Aluvial deposits at the basins of Alibey and Kagithane streams flowing into the bay, and aluvial deposits of marine origin encountered along the shores and basin of Golden Horn constitute the youngest sediments of Quarternery age in the area. Along the shores a fill layer decreasing in thickness towards inlands covers the aluvial deposits.

Because the surrounding slopes are not protected, fine sand and silt size particles from the weathered graywacks and schists are carried by erosion into the bay. In addition, large quantities of sewage, solid waste and industrial pollutants have been disposed into the bay for a long period of time.

SOIL PROFILE AND THE GEOTECHNICAL PROPERTIES

In the vicinity of Golden Horn, the ground surface is covered with a fill layer of varying thickness composed of sands, silts, clays, gravels and boulders, bricks as well as organic materials. Underneath the fill layer, a brown highly plastic residual silty clay layer whose thickness decreases from end to the mouth of the bay is encountered. Below this formation, the most typical soil formation of the area, the Golden Horn clay, a gray silty clay of marine origin with shells and a large organic content is found. The thickness of this formation varies from 0-6 m at the end to 35-40 m towards the mouth of the bay. The base rock in the vicinity of Golden Horn consist of clayey schists and graywacks, the upper elevations of which are weathered and have surface slopes varying between 20° - 60°. Figure 1 illustrates a typical soil profile across the Golden Horn.

TABLE I

Average Geotechnical Properties of Soil Layers

	w_L (%)	w_P (%)	w (%)	c_u (kPa)	m_v (kPa)$^{-1}$	c_v (m^2/s)
Brown Residual Clay	50	27	34	50	3.0×10^{-4}	4×10^{-8}
Soft Gray Clay	70	35	60	25	6.5×10^{-4}	7×10^{-9}

Table I summarizes the average geotechnical properties of soil formations.

In the bottom of the bay itself, a very thick accumulation of fine silts and clays due to erosion from the surrounding slopes and two small streams that used to flow into bay (a recently built earth dam now controls their flow), plus discharge of sewage lines, solid and industrial wastes constitutes a slurry like sediment which has very high organic content and rich in pollutants. From the end of the bay up to about one third of its length the thickness of the bottom sediments reach to less than 1 m from the water surface and it decreases towards the mouth of the bay. Golden Horn bottom sediments are in the consistency of a slurry to very large depths, increasing in density and consistency gradually, and with their high contents of organic materials and pollutants they not only hinder navigation but also pose grave environmental problems.

POLLUTION CHARACTERISTICS OF SEA BOTTOM SEDIMENTS

Several investigators studied the environmental aspects of Golden Horn sea bottom sediments (Karpuzcu and San, 1975; Baykurt, 1976; Orhon, et.al., 1978). Measurements of samples from these sediments indicate very high concentrations of organic materials (between 10% - 30%) and heavy metals (Cu: 40-50 ppm, Zn: 150-200 ppm, Hg: 10-20 ppm, Pb: 60-70 ppm, Cr: 70-80 ppm). In this investigation, primarily the effect of bottom sediments on pollution of the sea water and sediment-water interactions were studied. In this respect, particular attention was paid to determination of soluble phosphorus and nitrogen transport and organic matter concentrations as well as benthic oxygen demand potential. Table II summarizes the pollution

TABLE II

Pollution Characteristics of Bottom Sediments

Solids Ratio (%)	31-66
Organic Content (%)	9-32
Putrescibility Index (mg O_2/g dry wt.)	13-94
Putrescibility Index After Consolidation (mg O_2/g dry wt.)	7-13
PO_4-P (mg/g dry wt.)	0.10-0.40
NH_3-N (mg/g dry wt.)	0.30-7.50

characteristics of bottom sediments. Also, laboratory model test were carried out to study the pollution potential of these sediments on the water above them. In these experiments, the variations in concentrations of suspended solids in water, free oxygen and putrescibity index have been measured for a period of 6 months under laboratory testing conditions. The analysis of the results of these experiments are beyond the scope of this paper, but it can be safely concluded that the pollution potential of these sediments (with respect to sediment-water interaction) is markedly decreased with consolidation pressure and time.

SLURRY CONSOLIDATION OF SEA BOTTOM SEDIMENTS

Taking into account the possibility that the sea bottom sediments may be dredged and deposited behind dikes on shores, the consolidation behavior of bottom sediments from Golden Horn and the associated changes in their engineering properties have been investigated. The bottom sediments are first consolidated in a slurry consolidometer. The settlement-time and void ratio-pressure relationships are experimentally determined. Then the block soil samples obtained

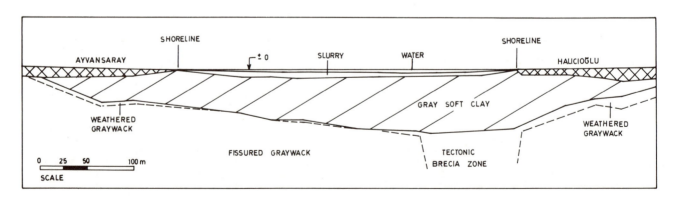

Fig.1 - A Typical Cross-Section Across the Golden Horn (Maden, 1975)

after slurry consolidation are subjected to
testing to determine their shear strength and
compression behavior.

Figure 2 illustrates the void ratio-consolidation pressure variations observed in slurry
consolidation tests. It is observed from the

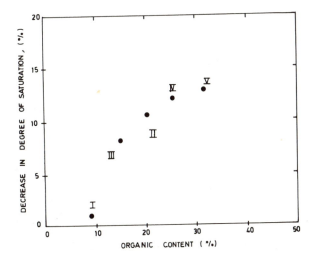

Fig.3 - The Decrease in Degree of Saturation
During Slurry Consolidation

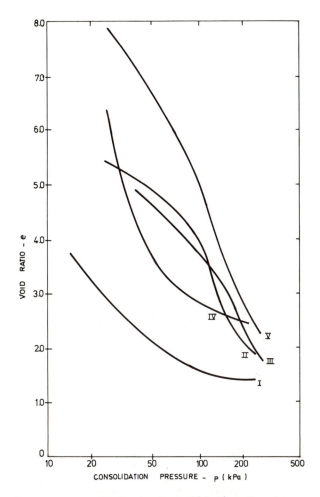

Fig.2 - The Void Ratio-Consolidation Pressure
Variations Observed in Slurry
Consolidation Tests

results of these tests that under 100 kPa
consolidation pressure the average values of
coefficient of volume change, m_v is about
$2 \times 10^{-3} (kPa)^{-1}$ and coefficient of consolidation,
c_v is about 5×10^{-8} m^2/s. An interesting (may be
peculiar) observation from the results of these
tests has been the change in degree of saturation
during consolidation. In contrast to what would
be expected, the degree of saturation has
decreased during the slurry consolidation of
these sediments rather than increasing. This is
attributed to high organic content of these
sediments and the release of gases by decay of
organic material as well as the oxygen uptake
of the mud from the water in the slurry during
the consolidation period (about 2 months). It
has been experimentally determined that a marked

decrease in putrescibility index of the
specimens took place during consolidation.
Figure 3 illustrates the decrease in degree of
saturation during consolidation with respect to
organic content.

The block soil samples obtained from the slurry
consolidation of bottom sediments have been
tested to determine their shear strength and
compression properties. Due to the limited
number of specimens that could be prepared from
these samples, their shear strength were
determined only by unconfined compression and
vane tests. Even though there is some scatter
in data due to presence of fiberous materials
in the specimens tested, the undrained shear
strength/consolidation pressure ($c_u/\bar{p}$) ratio
seems to vary linearly with the plasticity
index, the average value being about 0.23. The
slurry consolidated samples were also tested in
the oedometer device to investigate their
compression behavior. Figure 4 illustrates void
ratio-consolidation pressure relationships
obtained in these experiments. From the results
of oedometer tests, it is observed that the
average compression index for these slurry
consolidated soils is around 1.0. Variation
of average values of coefficient of consolidation and coefficient of volume change with
consolidation pressure during recompression of
slurry consolidation are shown in Fig.5.

CONCLUSIONS

Sea bottom samples taken from representative
sections of Golden Horn are studied for their
pollutional and geotechnical properties. The
organic content and putrescibility index of
these sediments are found to be considerably
higher than those commonly encountered in
similar places. Also, the high magnitude of
soluble phosphorus and nitrogen transported to the
main body of water from the sediments is found
to closely depend upon the hydraulic regime of
the medium. Experimentally determined
geotechnical properties indicate that these
sediments generally consist of fine grained

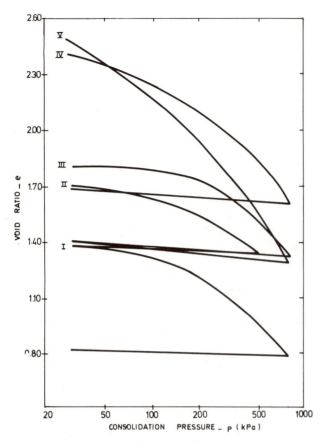

Fig.4 – The Void Ratio – Consolidation Pressure Variations During Recompression of Slurry Consolidated Samples

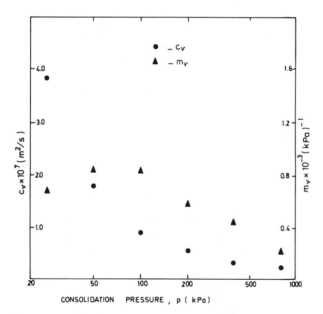

Fig.5 – Variation of Average Values of c_v and m_v With Consolidation Pressure p

soils. Their consolidation behavior studied by slurry consolidation have shown that, under suitable drainage conditions relatively thick layers of these bottom sediments can be consolidated in reasonable periods of time. Experimental results indicate that upon consolidation under final pressures of between 200-300 kPa, soil layers of medium consistency with high compressibility can be obtained if the dredgings of these sediments are stored behind dikes on shore.

ACKNOWLEDGEMENT

This investigation is a part of research project No.MAG-439 supported by the Scientific and Technical Research Council of Turkey(T.B.T.A.K.).

REFERENCES

Baykurt,F. (1976). Environmental Pollution and Golden Horn. Proc.Nat.Symp. on Problems of Golden Horn, Bosphorus Univ., İstanbul.

Karpuzcu,M. and H.A.San. (1975). Effects of Bottom Sediments on Water Quality. Proc. Golden Horn Symp., Istanbul Technical Univ. Istanbul.

Ketin,I. (1953). Tectonische Untersuchungen auf den Prinzen Inseln Nahe Istanbul. Geol. Rundschau 41, 161-172.

Kumbasar,V., R.Ülker, and F.Kip. (1976). Foundation Systems of Some Structures Along the Golden Horn. Proc.Nat.Symp. on Problems of Golden Horn, Bosphorus Univ., Istanbul.

Maden,S. (1975). Geotechnical Conditions at the Site of 3rd Golden Horn Bridge. Proc.Golden Horn Symp., Istanbul Technical Univ., Istanbul.

Orhon,D., I.K.Özaydın and O.Tünay (1975). Disposal of Polluted Sediments from Golden Horn. T.B.T.A.K. Tech.Rep.No. MAG-439, Istanbul.

Peynircioğlu,H. (1961). Settlement of Buildings in Istanbul. Proc., 5th Int.Conf.Soil Mech. Found Engg., (1), 771-775, Paris.

Peynircioğlu,H. (1965). Adjustable Box Foundation as a Measure Against Excessive Settlement and Tilting. Proc., 6th Int.Conf.Soil Mech. Found.Engg., (2), 174-177, Montreal.

Peynircioğlu,H. (1973). Performance of Very Soft Muds Under Very Light Loads and Consolidation of a Mudy Bottom Under a Wide Sand Fill. Proc., 8th Int.Conf.Soil Mech. Found.Engg., (2), 159-163, Moscow.

Sayar,C. (1976). Geology of Golden Horn Area. Proc., Nat.Symp. on Problems of Golden Horn, Bosphorus Univ., Istanbul.

Toğrol,E. (1975). Geotechnical Problems of Golden Horn Area. Proc., Golden Horn Symp., Istanbul Technical Univ., Istanbul.

A catastrophic debris flow near Gupis, Northern areas, Pakistan

Un écoulement des déchets catastrophique près de Gupis, Pakistan du Nord

D. F. T. NASH, Department of Civil Engineering, University of Bristol, UK

D. K. BRUNSDEN, Department of Geography, King's College, University of London, UK

R. E. HUGHES, International Disaster Institute, London, UK

D. K. C. JONES, Department of Geography, London School of Economics and Political Science, UK

B. F. WHALLEY, Department of Geography, Queen's University, Belfast, UK

SYNOPSIS   Debris flows, mudflows, landslides and rockfalls are a frequent occurrence in the Karakoram region of Northern Pakistan. Periodically these have been of such major proportions that they have dammed the river Indus or its tributaries. Sometimes when the dam has burst subsequently there has been serious flooding downstream. In July 1980 a catastrophic debris flow blocked the Ghizar river near Gupis, about 130 km west of Gilgit. Over a period of 30 hours waves of mud up to 5 metres high periodically surged down a side valley at estimated speeds of 100 km/hr, and formed a natural dam about 30 metres high. A lake quickly built up extending 5 km up-stream. The causes and nature of the debris flow are described together with the behaviour of the dam during the period following overtopping.

INTRODUCTION

In recent years there has been increasing attention to the causes and behaviour of debris flows so that their occurrence can be predicted and steps taken to prevent them or ameliorate their effects, (e.g. Johnson, 1970). Debris flows, landslides and rockfalls are a common occurrence in the remote high and mountainous terrain of the Karakoram region of Northern Pakistan, and a study of the geomorphological activity in the Hunza Valley was undertaken as part of the International Karakoram Project 1980 organised by the Royal Geographical Society (Goudie et al 1983). By chance a major debris flow was observed in the Ghizar Valley elsewhere in the region and this event is described here.

THE GHIZAR VALLEY

The Ghizar Valley (2000–2500m) is a deep steep-sided sediment-floored glaciated valley situated in the west of the Karakoram region (see Fig. 1a). On either side the barren mountains rise to 4500-5500m with some of the highest peaks snow covered even in summer. Near Gupis the valley floor consists of low angle fans which formed from outwash and debris flow deposits through which the river has cut a broad flood plain. In many places glacial deposits and scree slopes have formed above the fans. The valley floor is arid with a mean annual rain fall recorded at Gupis of only 117mm, and with diurnal temperatures ranging from +18°C to +32°C in July and August, and -5° to +5°C in January and February.

The Ghizar river drains a catchment of 4000 km^2, part of the Upper Indus Basin. Near its confluence with the Yasin river at Gupis it is about 50 metres wide and is a pale turquoise blue indicating a low concentration of suspended sediment, in contrast to the dirty grey of the Yasin river. As much of the flow is derived from snow and glacier melting, the discharge shows a minimum in winter and a maximum in July and August. Based on the records for the Gilgit river it is estimated that the summer discharge averages 170 cumec, and the annual discharge averages 70 cumec (equivalent to 550 mm annual precipitation).

PREVIOUS DEBRIS FLOWS IN THE REGION

The area is extremely arid, and storm generated precipitation falling on the steep poorly vegetated slopes results in rapid run off. As there is a plentiful supply of non-lithified superficial debris produced by weathering, slope degradation, and glacial and aeolian processes, there is a widespread occurrence of debris flows. These range in size from short narrow runnels on scree slopes to catastrophic events produced by flash flooding in storms or by sudden release of glacial melt-water (e.g. at Sheeshkat, Hunza 1976 (Goudie et al, 1983) and Gupis (this paper)). Such debris flows pose a major hazard to the local people, as they frequently destroy roads, housing, animals and agricultural land, and occasionally form natural dams.

Two types of natural dam are of relatively frequent occurrence in the Upper Indus Basin - landslide dams, and ice dams formed by the rapid advance of glaciers (Hewitt, 1982). Bursting of natural dams has often resulted in catastrophic flooding downstream. The principal landslide dams which have been recorded in historic times are shown in Table 1 but there is field evidence of the remains of many others.

TABLE 1

Some Landslide Dams in the Upper Indus Basin
(Hewitt, 1982, Goudie et al, 1983)

Date	River	Cause	Details
1841	Indus	landslide/ rockslide	300m high 55km long lake drained in 24 hrs on overtopping. Major floods.
1858	Hunza	landslide/ rockslide	? 100m high 45km long lake drained suddenly on overtopping. Major floods.
1931	Indus	landslide	Drained slowly.
1976	Hunza	debris flow	20m high 12km long lake persisted despite attempts to breach dam.
1980	Ghizar	debris flow	30m high 5km long lake persisted.
1981	Gilgit	debris flow	5m high 0.5km long lake drained.

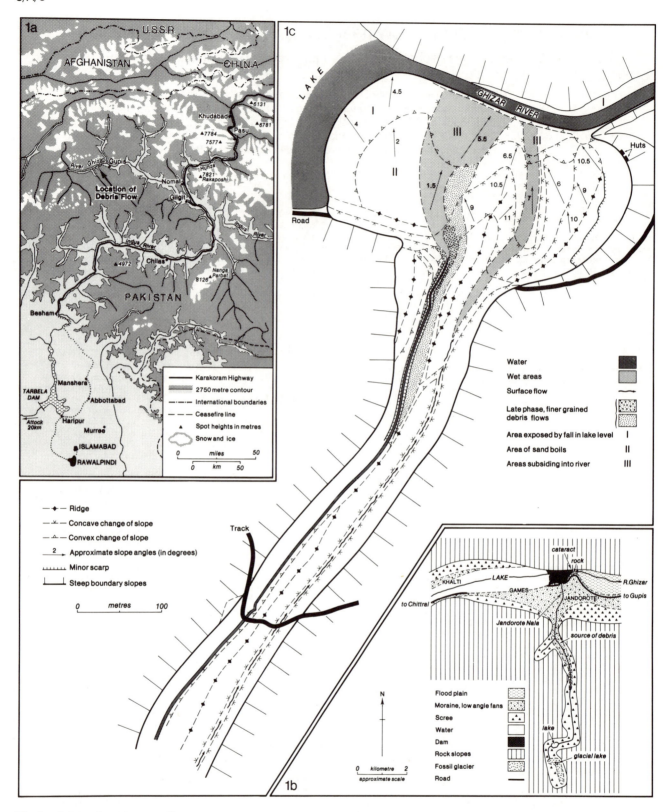

Fig 1: a) Location Plan. b) A sketch plan made before the overflow of the lake had taken place.

c) Detailed survey of the lower track, lobe and lake overflow, measured on 6th August 1980.

DESCRIPTION

The debris flow occurred about 5 km west of the confluence of the Yasin and Ghizar rivers, at a point where the Ghizar river flows through a narrow rocky cataract (see Fig. 1b). Upstream and downstream from the gorge the river crossed alluvial plains bounded by low angle fans to the south and rocky slopes to the north. Emerging from a side valley to the south, the Jandorote Nala joined the river just upstream of the cataract. With a normal summer flow similar to a mountain stream, the Nala flowed down a deep channel cut through the fan, approximately 80 metres wide at its base. Local people had constructed a dozen channels to tap the water for irrigation purposes. The road from Gilgit to Chittral crossed the Nala where it emerged into the main valley. At the time of the debris flow the weather was fine and there had been no significant rainfall in the area for some weeks previously. There were no earthquakes felt or recorded in the area that day.

At approximately 1630 hrs on 27 July 1980 a wave of mud and boulders swept down the Nala destroying crops, houses and livestock as well as the road, flowed across the alluvial plain and blocked the Ghizar river. Eye-witnesses said there was no warning and that thereafter waves of debris emerged very frequently so that the flow was almost continuous. By next morning (1100 hrs) when two authors (DN and REH) arrived the waves were arriving about four times per hour. The first indication of an approaching wave was aural giving 1½ to 2 minutes warning (the source was about 3 km away). Soon the wave

could be seen slewing from side to side of the channel as it went round bends until with a deafening roar it reached the bottom of the Nala. At this point the wave was the full 80 metres width of the channel, up to 5 metres high and travelling at speeds of perhaps 100 km/hr, throwing up debris and boulders as it passed (see photos Figs. 2, 3). The wave then spread out when it reached the surface of the landslide dam which rose and fell like jelly. The scene closely resembled a breaking wave passing through the narrow entrance to a tidal inlet. When all the movement had ceased the surface of the fresh debris was firm enough for people to cross the Nala, and the debris had the consistency of a freshly mixed concrete.

By that evening the frequency and size of the waves had diminished and a flow of water and mud had started, eroding the surface of the debris track. At this time the dam was about 30 metres high, 200 metres along its axis with the downstream toe right through the rocky gorge. The maximum slopes of the dam were determined with an Abney level as 3.5 to 4° while the average slope of the debris track was 11.7°. A lake had formed which extended upstream about 5 km covering two villages and rendering 500 people homeless. At about midnight the dam was overtopped, but the level only dropped gradually at the dam eroded. There was no flooding downstream.

Over the following three days the river cut down the surface of the dam and the lake dropped by about 1 metre. During this time the topography of the dam changed significantly and the crest slope increased to 10° near the river. Standing water appeared on the surface of the

Figs 2a), 2b): General views of landslide dam and debris track.

Figs 3a), 3b): Views of debris waves emerging from Nala and spreading across dam.

dam and in places there were numerous sand boils. The surface of the dam and the lower part of the debris track was surveyed during the period 4 to 6 August and this survey is shown in Fig. 1c.

The day after the dam overtopped a reconnaissance was made up the side valley (see Fig. 1b). The lower part of the valley was inaccessible as a 30m deep gorge had been eroded in the moraine which formed the valley floor. At this point the average slope of the valley floor was about 20^b. Further up the side valley the moraine was covered by scree and boulders and there had been little erosion. At the head of the valley there was a debris covered relic glacier within which was a lake estimated to be 80 metres in diameter. There were clear signs that the lake level had recently been 20 metres higher, at a level above the lowest part of its rim, suggesting the presence of a lake alongside the glacier. Shepherds who had been in the lower part of the side valley at the time spoke of a sudden flood which built up so quickly that people fled for their lives. They were only able to cross over again after 24 hours. By the time of the reconnaissance the Nala was back to its normal flow, which mostly came from melting of the glacier.

PROPERTIES OF DEBRIS

The debris was derived from the moraine that lined the base of the side valley. The geology of the area consists of two main units - the Rakaposhi volcanic complex forming the sides of the Ghizar valley, and the granodiorite of the Ladakh Intrusives up the side valley to the south (Tahirkheli, 1982). The moraine was derived mostly from the Ladakh granodiorites, and although the flow moved over the Rakaposhi volcanics, they were generally not incorporated.

The debris consisted of boulders cobbles and gravel in a silty micaceous sand matrix. The majority of the boulders were less than 0.5m in diameter but there were occasional boulders of at least 3m diameter. Particle size distribution analyses of samples of the matrix showed typically clay 1% silt 4-6%, sand 47-70%, gravel (<32mm) 25-47%. 100mm shear box tests on the fine fraction of the matrix (<6mm) placed wet showed a residual angle of shearing resistance at constant volume of 37°. Unfortunately it was not possible to determine the moisture content of the in-situ material, but from laboratory tests it may be inferred that the moisture content of the matrix lay in the range 15-20%.

DISCUSSION

This valley confined debris flow is similar to events described in many other arid mountain regions. Full summaries are given by Johnson (1970) and Brunsden (1979). The glacial lake at the head of the side valley appears to have burst quite suddenly with no obvious cause, the lake partially drained and then the burst closed again. Known in Iceland as a Jökulhlaup this phenomenon is thought to be caused by hydraulic fracture of the ice. Although there was no indication that it had happened before here, glacial lake bursts have recurred elsewhere causing successive debris flows. During the debris flow eyewitnesses indicated that the water flow in the side-valley was continuous for 24 hours, but there was no flow of water in the lower part of the Nala between the debris waves until the main flood higher up abated. It was not possible to observe the formation of the debris waves but at low moisture contents the debris is highly dilatant, and only when it reached a critical moisture

content would it be sufficiently mobile to flow down the 20° channel. The pronounced pulsing is a characteristic of debris flows with high sediment concentration. It can be caused by the mobile debris suddenly bursting through a bouldery snout of a debris mass. During the period of observation each pulse passed in a few seconds with a pronounced breaking wave at the front, leaving the channel firm and motionless behind it. This contrasts with the extended laminar flow that has been observed in debris flows elsewhere, e.g. at Wrightwood (Johnson, 1970).

It is clear that high pore pressures were present in the landslide dam. The limiting slope of the dam during deposition was around 4° which implies an r_u value of 0.9 if an infinite slope analysis is applied. Once the dam was overtopped the river started to cut a channel down through it, but with high pore pressures still present the debris flowed in to the channel to choke the flow. This limited the rate at which the channel could be cut down, thus avoiding catastrophic flooding downstream. After three days the pore pressures had dissipated sufficiently that the limiting slope had increased to 10°, but the river still did not deepen its channel rapidly, presumably due to the presence of boulders from the debris in the channel bed. Recent reports (1984) indicate that the dam and lake still persist, in contrast to the landslide dams of 1841 and 1858.

CONCLUSIONS

This valley confined debris flow is similar to events described in many other arid mountain regions, although few have been attributed to glacial lake bursts. The serious consequences of such flows point the need for improved warning and control measures. A recurrence of debris flows at Gupis is possible, and warning could be given by monitoring the level of the glacial lake. Drainage could be installed to limit any future rise of lake level. In the Karakoram region a remote sensing survey could be undertaken to identify potentially hazardous areas, followed by field geomorphological surveys and the preparation of hazard maps. These could then be used as part of the input to future development programmes in the region.

REFERENCES

Brunsden, D. (1979). Mass Movements. Ch5 in Process in Geomorphology, ed Embleton, C. and Thomas, J.B. Arnold.

Goudie, A.S. et al (1983). The Geomorphology of the Hunza Valley, Karakoram Mountains, Pakistan. In the Int. Karakoram Project, Vol. 2, ed Miller, K.J. Cambridge University Press.

Hewitt, K. (1982). Natural dams and outburst floods of the Karakoram Himalaya. In Hydrological Aspects of Alpine and High Mountain Areas, I.A.H.S. Publ. 138 p 259-269.

Johnson, A.M. (1970). Physical Processes in Geology. Freeman, Cooper and Co.

Tahirkheli, R.A. Khan, (1982). Geology of the Himalaya, Karakoram and Hindukush in Pakistan. Geol. Bull. Univ. of Pechawar. Spec. Issue, Vol. 15. pp 51.

Aspects of landslide mobility

Aspects de la mobilité des glissements

G. SALT, Geotechnical Engineer, Clutha Valley Development, New Zealand

SYNOPSIS

Geotechnical case histories both in New Zealand and overseas have provided more than an isolated instance where the potential for rapid acceleration of a landslide has been underestimated. Frequently, detailed survey information has been obtained but seldom have appropriate criteria been considered and pre-set for identification of a critical situation with respect to landslide mobility. While many factors may cause acceleration of a slide mass, these may be grouped as either displacement-dependent or displacement-independent mechanisms. It is apparent that the former require particular consideration when assessing the potential for a landslide to move rapidly. Laboratory evaluation of landslide materials using a ring shear apparatus operated in a stress controlled mode is an effective means of observing displacement-dependent aspects of mobility. A review of some notable landslide disasters demonstrates the enhanced predictive capacity which might have been provided through appropriate interpretation of deformation monitoring.

1. INTRODUCTION

In many landslide situations, an aspect of particular concern is not only whether movements will occur but what rates of movement are to be expected, in order to ascertain if the degree of slide mobility could present a hazard. This article attempts to collate known and conjectured mechanisms for rapid failure of slopes, to provide a rational basis for assessment of active or potentially active landslides.

2. BASIC CONCEPTS OF SOIL FAILURE

2.1 Peak and residual effective strengths.

The concepts of peak and residual strengths of soil have been discussed by Skempton (1964). Depending on the initial structure of the material, there will exist a greater or lesser separation of the peak and residual strength envelopes. Any displacement of a "first time" slide will result in a transition from the peak, towards the residual strength, leaving a net accelerating force acting on the slide mass.

Skempton (1977) suggests that movements totalling about 1 or 2 metres may be required to achieve residual strength in fine grained soils. Accordingly, the most convenient means of simulating this condition has been in a ring shear apparatus (Bishop, 1971) in which an annulus of soil may be subjected to indefinitely large displacements.

2.2 Rate dependence of residual strength.

Skempton and Hutchinson (1969) note that the strength of soils is dependent on shearing rate even when these rates are slow enough to permit full drainage. A value of about 1% increase in strength per tenfold increase in strain rate was obtained in strain controlled ring shear tests. Because landslide behaviour is stress controlled rather than strain controlled, it may be argued that Skempton and Hutchinson's data might be replotted with shear stress as the abscissa (independent variable), as shown on Figure 1.

Further results have come from stress controlled ring shear tests on schist-derived gouge from landslides in Otago. For both sands and plastic soils, strained to the residual strength condition, generally similar results were obtained, ie the nature of curve A - B (Figure 1) was confirmed. However, if the shear stress was reduced (effective normal stress being held constant) until all movement ceased (B on Fig. 1) then a significantly higher shear stress was required in order to reactivate movement (point C). Very slow creep displacement rates could then be achieved by subsequently reducing the shear stress. Obvious analogies for this aspect of soil behaviour are the thixotropy of gels and the accepted differences between static and dynamic coefficients of friction for solid surfaces.

Figure 1 gives explanation for three significant features of landslide mobility:

(i) Successive "stick-slip" movements are to be expected in a residual strength slide where the factor of safety is being slowly reduced (eg by river erosion of the toe).

(ii) If a small percentage (1 or 2%) decrease in the factor of safety occurs in a slide which is creeping slowly, the result is an

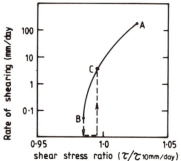

Figure 1. Rate dependence on shear stress. in stress-controlled apparatus.

acceleration until the displacement rate mobilises the appropriate higher strength.

(iii) Following from (ii), if shear stresses approach failure in a homogeneous, normally consolidated soil, greater strength will be shown by the elements through which incipient displacement is occurring thus favouring the failure of a zone of soil rather than a discrete failure surface, at least for initial movements. This aspect is discussed further in Section 4.3.4.

3. DISPLACEMENT-INDEPENDENT ACCELERATING MECHANISMS

Many external factors acting independently of slide displacement can affect the resultant force acting on a slide mass (Terzaghi, 1950). In general these factors (eg change in submergence or groundwater, redistribution of mass etc) occur slowly and more predictably than displacement dependent accelerating mechanisms (which will be discussed in detail).

4. DISPLACEMENT-DEPENDENT ACCELERATING MECHANISMS

Those factors which decrease the available resistance of a soil along a slide failure surface while displacement progresses, provide the potential for rapid movement when accelerating forces are left unbalanced. A discussion of soil characteristics which may provide displacement dependent accelerating mechanisms follows.

4.1 Reduction of effective cohesion.

Reduction or elimination of effective cohesion is the most obvious source of significant loss in strength. Failure may be very brittle with little warning, when a large proportion of available shear resistance is cohesive.

Cohesion may be present in soils previously at residual strength (with c = 0) through dessication, which has been demonstrated to create effective as well as apparent cohesion, (Allam and Sridharan, 1981).

4.2 Reduction of effective friction.

4.2.1 Peak to residual strength.

In dense sands or overconsolidated cohesionless soils, the "density component" of strength (Cornforth, 1973) can equal more than 30% of the available peak strength, allowing rapid failure after initial movements have increased the void ratio to its critical value. Normally consolidated clays can show similarly large differences between their peak and residual strengths, as platy minerals become aligned parallel to the direction of shearing.

4.2.2 Mechanical attrition.

Granular materials composed of weak rock and subjected to moderate or high normal stresses will suffer particle breakdown in shear until a sufficient matrix of fines is created to "cushion" any further degradation. Formation of such gouge invariably results in a decrease of available frictional resistance.

4.3 Increase in pore fluid pressure.

4.3.1 Shear contraction.

Excess pore pressure, resulting from densification of a soil that is above its critical void ratio, has been the mechanism involved for many catastrophic slides in both granular and cohesive 'quick' soils, eg the Aberfan disaster (Bishop, 1969).

4.3.2 Monotonic loading.

Landsliding is generally a slope reducing process which transfers load from the head of a slope to the toe. This process of slope adjustment causes a general reduction in shear stress within the soil and particularly to the soil located beneath the failure zone. If this soil is a dense granular material which was previously subjected to at least a moderate degree of shear mobilisation, the pore pressure parameter A (Skempton, 1954) would be negative, regardless of the amount of shear stress reduction (as opposed to the more common case of a reversal of the sign of A under increasing deviatoric stress). This concept was investigated in the laboratory. Figure 2 shows the stress path for a dense sand which was sheared in a drained triaxial test until a high degree of shear was mobilised and the sample was dilating rapidly. The deviatoric stress was then removed in an undrained test (to simulate rapid unloading). The resulting pore pressures were small but positive.

Skempton's B parameter also provides an explanation for pore pressure rises within a failure zone. For a typical slide, the geometry of the failing mass involves a thickening from the toe to the central regions. In the vicinity of the toe of such a slide, an element of soil close beneath the failure surface will be subjected to an increase in total confining pressure as displacements take place. Since B is always positive, any saturated or near saturated soil elements, regardless of their relative density, will incur significant excess pore pressures which can then be transmitted to the overlying failure surface.

Pore pressure responses of this nature would be most marked where failure is taking place in a low permeability soil underlain by fully saturated material.

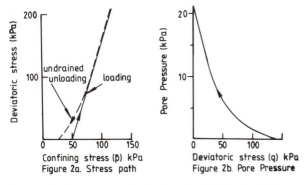

Figure 2a. Stress path

Figure 2b. Pore Pressure

Figure 2. Response of dense sand to unloading

A feature of slides which have been subjected to excess pore pressures induced during sliding is that they can only be arrested naturally by a change in slide geometry (mainly self-buttressing at the toe) which is significantly more effective than the geometry required to counter sliding in the absence of excess pore pressures. It follows that on coming to rest, the long term factor of safety of such a slide (after pore pressure dissipation) may be substantially greater than unity.

The East Abbotsford landslide (Salt et al, 1979) is a suggested example where undrained response of dense saturated soils contributed to unexpected acceleration.

4.3.3 Cyclic loading.

Pore pressure increases in both granular and cohesive soils have often been demonstrated during cyclic loading. An undulating failure surface could induce densification of either material within a slide (through cyclic shear in the vertical direction) or material beneath the failure surface (through cycling of the effective normal stress). Either case may allow transmission of excess pore pressures to the failure zone.

4.3.4 Frictional heating.

Pore pressure increase through vaporisation of fluid has been suggested as the mechanism for rapid accelerations at Vaiont, (Voight and Pariseau, 1979). However, because the coefficient of thermal expansion of water is about 8 times that of common rock forming minerals, it may be considered that even minor frictional heating without the extreme case of vaporisation could cause significant excess pore pressures.

When verifying the data in Figure 1 with the stress controlled shear apparatus, it was noticed that with low permeablility soils subject to sudden shear stress increments (of about 3% or more), acceleration from the yield state to rapid velocities (greater than 1m/sec) occurred, usually within 10 seconds. The superposed shear was then removed but stable conditions could not be readily restored. Substantial reductions (30% or more) of the shear stress level were necessary to restore creep displacement. However after sufficient

time the original shear stress could again be sustained. As this effect is most readily explained by frictional heating of pore fluid, this effect was examined further. The shear cell was adapted to take a heating element which for practical reasons had to be located closer to the base drainage platten than to the centre of the shear zone. Efficiency was hence in doubt but the effect of pore fluid heating could be crudely investigated. Figure 3 shows the comparative effects that can be obtained by heating indirectly (through friction) or directly with a similar quantity of energy applied through the heating element. For the saturated, low permeability clay tested, heat was applied at a very low intensity with convincing results.

The aspect of note with regard to increase in shear stress or fluid heating is that the rate of introducing energy must be short with respect to the soil permeability and boundary drainage conditions. If the velocity of a slide is made to increase gradually (Figure 3b) a new temperature differential from the failure zone to the surrounding soil will become established so that at no time do significant excess pore pressures develop. Excess pore pressure is dependent on a sufficiently rapid energy increment.

Thus it is apparent that a slide undergoing an acceleration for any reason will incur some frictional heating with accompanying pore pressure increases. These in turn create a greater difference between slide driving and resisting forces and lead to further acceleration.

It may be concluded that while some soils fail in a zone rather than a discrete surface, if

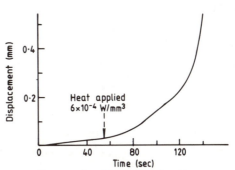

Figure 3a. Electrical heating

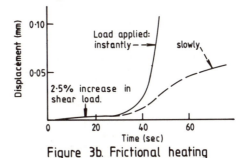

Figure 3b. Frictional heating

Figure 3. Heating effects in low permeability soil in stress controlled ring shear.

the failure zone is sufficiently restricted, then frictional heat will be confined to a small volume of soil where higher temperatures and excess pore pressures will act. The worst conceivable situation for the frictional heating mechanism is in a sequence where a thin layer of low strength material lies between layers of significantly higher strength. Such layering prohibits failure of a thick zone (Section 2.2).

For this mechanism to operate, a suggested dimension for the "thin" layer is where the failure zone is about 3 or more orders of magnitude smaller than the average overburden thickness.

As well as at Vaiont, the pore fluid heating explanation may have contributed to the accelerations of the Goldau Slide (Terzaghi, 1950) and the East Abbotsford Slide.

4.4 Coalescence of multiple slides.

When a group of individual slides merge to form common boundaries, lateral shear restraint reduces giving a means for sudden increase in the resultant accelerating force. An example is given by the Lower Baker Slide (Peck 1967).

4.5 Development of internal deformations.

The concept of internal deformations required for movement of non-circular slides has been discussed by Karal, (1979). This can lead to rapid movement if the deforming slide mass is brittle or contains saturated soil exhibiting a positive value for Skempton's A parameter. A lurching response ("stick-slip") results if the material is a low permeability saturated soil with negative A value.

4.6 Unstable failure surface geometry.

A slide containing non-homogeneous material and having a general failure surface profile which is upwardly convex, can present an unstable situation where the factor of safety decreases with displacement because the average inclination of the slope increases.

4.7 Secondary accelerating mechanisms.

Various mechanisms have been postulated to explain the very rapid movement of the Vaiont Slide, eg. hydrodynamic wave pressures (Corbyn, 1982); aquaplaning (Trollope, 1980); fluid vapourisation (Habib, 1975) and fusion (Erismann, 1979).

In most cases, velocities must be substantial before the above mechanisms can operate. Primary acceleration mechanisms are therefore regarded as being sufficent to create a hazardous situation (regardless of aggravation by secondary accelerations).

5. INFERENCES FROM DEFORMATION MONITORING

Monitoring of surface displacements has been the traditional means of predicting future activity of an incipient slide. Apart from earthquake induced slides and some failures in steep rock slopes, some warning movements typically occur. Terzahgi (1950) reports; "If a landslide comes as a surprise to eye witnesses, it would be more accurate to say that the observers failed to detect the phenomena which preceded the slide".

Consideration of events preceding the Vaiont Slide and two recent catastrophic slides in New Zealand (East Abbotsford and Ruahihi) suggests that techniques for interpretation of surface deformation monitoring have not been well documented. Three aspects requiring consideration are:-
(1) Displacement - Examination of resultant downslope displacement vectors relative to the topographic slope and position on the slide readily provides information on:
(a) how deep-seated a slide is,
(b) whether a significant non-circular motion is occurring and
(c) whether regressive segments are developing or distortion is taking place within the sliding mass. The former allows improved evaluation of remedial measures. Implications of non-circular failure surface geometry have been discussed earlier. Some attempts have been made (unsuccessfully) to predict rapid failure from displacement criteria (Voight and Kennedy, 1979). In general, this approach will be unreliable.
(2) Velocity - Creep rates preceding catastrophic failures have been documented for several notable landslides and give some measure of their future movements (although thickness and permeablility of the failure zone is of particular importance). Downslope velocities of 100 mm/day were achieved by the Vaiont, East Abbotsford and Ruahihi Slides (NZGS, in prep) some days before their final rapid movements. This leads to the suggestion that large slides in relatively low permeability materials should be regarded with particular caution if velocities approach 100 mm/day. However the significance of acceleration is considered more relevant.
(3) Acceleration - In terms of catastrophic potential, ultimate slide velocity is of particular relevance, and foresight into this aspect requires appreciation of accelerations. Clearly, until negative acceleration occurs, a slide cannot begin to slow down. It follows that adequate monitoring of landslide movement requires successive differentiation of the displacement - time record to obtain both velocity and acceleration.

This is essential in any instance where the displacement-time curve exhibits a concave upward shape. A good example of such forewarning (with the benefit of hindsight) is given by the detailed displacement monitoring carried out for the East Abbotsford Slide. Successive differentials for the latter (Figure 4) show linearly increasing acceleration for 2 weeks followed by concave upward (clearly unstable) curvature of the acceleration record for 5 days prior to rapid failure. The movement record of the Vaiont Slide may be differentiated similarly to reveal a concave upward acceleration record for the two weeks immediately preceding the catastrophic failure. Comprehensive survey monitoring is not available for the Ruahihi Slide (final readings were at weekly intervals). However, approximate interpolation suggests a concave upward acceleration curve may have been taking place for 10 days prior to the rapid failure

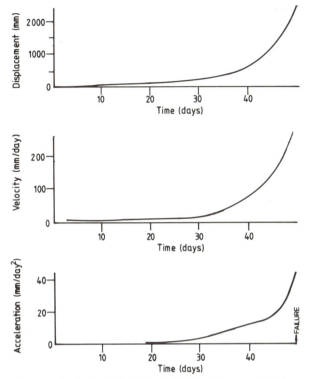

Figure 4. East Abbotsford Slide: Movement History.

(NZGS in prep.). This example highlights the need to provide sufficient survey data to determine the acceleration characteristics continuously at any stage when a hazardous slide is experiencing positive acceleration.

6. CONCLUSIONS

In establishing a policy for rational evaluation of marginally stable slopes, this discussion has endeavoured to collate known and conjectured means whereby catastrophic rates of movement could occur. While it is not possible to establish that this list of mechanisms is exhaustive, all rapid slides reviewed during the preparation of this article can be explained by conditions favouring one or more of these mechanisms.

An ideal slide which provides no attributes likely to cause rapid failure must be subject to only small increments in external forces and exhibit all of the following:-

i) thick, permeable shear zone which has no irregularities and is at residual strength;

ii) unchanged history (since the previous movement) with respect to effective stresses on the failure zone;

iii) stable failure surface geometry (concave upward) with no capacity for coalescing with adjacent slides;

iv) no capacity for development of unfavourable internal deformations.

To some extent, the potential for displacement dependent accelerating mechanisms may be quantified using standard techniques for pore pressure response under undrained loading, and by determining response to stress controlled ring shear. Further research using the latter is in progress to determine empirical criteria for predicting rapid failure from shear zone thickness, velocity and acceleration characteristics.

A review of some catastrophic slides for which deformation monitoring is available suggests that landslide mobility may be most rationally assessed through examination of all possible accelerating mechanisms, particularly those which are displacement dependent. Predicted behaviour may best be confirmed by due consideration of displacement, velocity, and most particularly, acceleration characteristics determined from downslope deformation vectors.

7. REFERENCES

Allam, M. & Sridharan, A. (1981). Effect of wetting and drying on shear strength. J. Geotech. Eng. Div. ASCE Vol 107, No GT4, 421-438.

Bishop, A.W. et al. (1969). Geotechnical investigation at Aberfan. In: A selection of technical reports submitted to the Aberfan Tribunal. Welsh Office H.M.S.O. London.

Corbyn, J.A. (1982). Failure of a partially submerged rock slope. Int. J. Rock Mech. Min. Sc. & Geomech. Vol. 19.

Cornforth, D.H. (1973). Prediction of drained strength of sands from relative density measurements. ASTM STP 523 281-303.

Erisman, T.H. (1979). Mechanism of large landslides. Rock Mechanics, Vol. 12.

Habib, P. (1975). Production of gaseous pore pressure during rockslides. Rock Mechanics, Vol.7, 193-197.

Karal, K. (1979). The energy method for soil stability analyses. ASCE J. Geotech. Eng. Div., Vol. 103. GT5, 431-445.

Peck, R.B. (1967). Stability of natural slopes. J. Soil Mech. Found. Div. ASCE, SM4.

Salt, G. Hancox, G.T. & Northey, R.D. (1980). Limit equilibrium analysis of the East Abbotsford Landslide and assessment of possible causes of the slide. N.Z. Geological Survey Report EG 341.

Skempton, A.W. (1954). The pore pressure coefficients A and B. Geotechnique, Vol. 4, 143-147.

Skempton, A.W. (1964). Long term stability of clay slopes. Geotechnique Vol. 14, No. 2, 77-102.

Skempton, A.W. (1977). Slope stability of cuttings in brown London Clay. 9th Int. Conf. Soil Mech. Found. Eng. Vol. 3, 261-270.

Skempton, A.W. & Hutchinson, J. (1969).

Stability of natural slopes and embankment
foundations.   7th Int. Conf. Soil Mech. Found.
Eng. State-of-the-Art Volume, 291-340.

Terzaghi, K. (1950). Mechanism of landslides.
In: Application of Geology to Engineering
Practice, Eng. Geol. Berkey) Vol.   Geol.
Soc. of America NY.

Trollope, D.H. (1980). The Vaiont slope failure
Rock Mechanics Vol. 13, 71-88.

Voight, B. (1979). Rockslides and Avalanches:
Basic Principles in: Rockslides and Avalanches
Vol.2, B. Voight (ed), Elsevier.

Voight, B. and Kennedy, B.A. (1979). Slope
failure of 1967-1969, Chuquicamata Mine, Chile.
in: Rockslides and Avalanches, Vol 2, B. Voight
(ed), Elsevier.

The mechanism of debris flow

Le méchanisme d'écoulement de débris

K. SASSA, Associate Professor, Disaster Prevention Research Institute, Kyoto University, Uji, Kyoto, Japan

SYNOPSIS   A new big and high speed ring shear apparatus was designed to study debris flows. The velocity control constant volume tests produced liquefaction of loose grains.   The velocity control constant normal stress tests gave the same internal friction angle independent of flow velocity, which gave no support to the existence of "flow structure" of grains proposed by Casagrande, 1976. Rotation of saturated debris in a ring channel increased the specific gravity of pore liquid due to floatation of particles. Those experiments and field observations put forward a hypothesis that debris flow is initiated by rapid loading of the loose torrent deposits due to the failed mass from slopes, then "flow" of the deposit causes a high specific gravity of pore liquid, and resulting in a low shear resistance during flow.

INTRODUCTION

The common type of debris flows is initiated in torrents, then the torrent deposit must be sheared in prior to its movement.   Torrent deposits are sandy.   "Shear" of sands is classified in four cases shown in Fig. 1.   (a), (b) are failure envelopes of dense and loose states of sands, respectively.   The stress paths of A, B are those of drained shear of loose and dense states, the stress paths of C, D are those of undrained shear of loose and dense ones, too.   The undrained shear of loose sands should be most probable for the initiation of debris flow because only its case shows a low shear resistance after failure necessary for "flow".

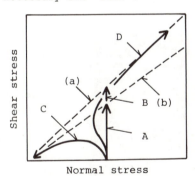

Fig. 1   Typical Stress Paths of Sands

LIQUEFACTION OF LOOSE SANDS

The undrained shear of loose sands was studied by Castro, 1969 and Casagrande, 1976 in use of the so-called load control triaxial test in which the axial load was increased by putting a weight on the load hanger.   The most typical example of liquefaction by Castro is shown in Fig. 2. A sudden failure took place at a strain less

than 1 %, a rapid flow and a very low resistance was observed, where load (stress) on sample was not controlled after failure probably because of the acceleration of weight.   Sassa & Kaibori did the similar undrained triaxial tests, where the axial load was supplied by a series of air regulator – air tank – air cylinder to avoid the acceleration effect of weight, samples of 10×25 cm in size three times larger than Castro's one were used to obtain a longer flow distance and to be able to test coarse torrent deposits.   A

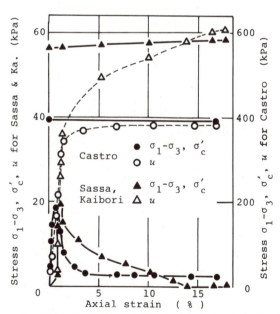

Fig. 2   Liquefaction of Sands by Triaxial Test
Castro e=0.75, D_r=27 %
Sassa & Kaibori e=0.98, D_r=0.3 %

(Void ratio e is after consolidation)

multi-pen recorder was set to take digital values of each 1.5 millisecond before/after the failure in use of trigger as well as continual analog record. Pore air was replaced by CO_2 gas for full saturation, and the lubricated ends were not used.

Fig. 2 shows one of the most typical liquefaction (Its relative density is calculated from the JSSMFE, 1979) of 25 tests in use of the Toyoura standard sand (D_{10}=0.15 mm, D_{60}=0.18 mm). Observation of Video tape at 1/30 sec. stop motion visualized that loading could not follow the samples deformation enough, especially in the greater strain. The value of pore pressure 2 kPa over the cell pressure expresses the increased specific gravity of pore liquid due to floatation of particles, which is examined in Fig. 8. In this type of tests, the stress-strain relation strongly depends on loading method, and flow distance is too small for study of a steady flow.

A NEW HIGH SPEED RING SHEAR APPARATUS

Casagrande (1976) proposed "flow structure" expressing the state which each grain rotates so as to offer a minimum frictional resistance during flow. To study the shear characteristics of grain flow, namely "flow structure", a rapid strain control test or a real stress control test having enough flow distance is desired. Sassa designed a new high speed ring shear apparatus for this purpose.

Fig. 3 illustrates its structure. In this figure the sample's size is 30 - 48 cm inside and outside diameter, 9 cm in height. The lower ring and the hatched table is rotated by a motor and gear in the speed of 0.3 mm/min. - 90.76 cm/sec. in the center of ring. While the upper ring and the dotted plate is stopped its rotation and kept still by the load cell for shear stress measurement.

Normal stress is supplied by a compressed air, and the loaded normal stress on shear plane is measured by the load cell to avoid a possible loss of stress transmission to the ring wall. The loading plate is locked for constant volume tests at three vertical rods to keep it horizontal. The edges of two rings are vertically tapered at 1:6, those are much easier to keep a minimal slit without contact of two edges and leaking of samples than the horizontal straight edges. When it is necessary, silicon rubber is sticked on the inside edge of the upper ring so as to slide on the inside edge of the lower ring with a negligible contact stress. A spring balance is used to take off a little clearence in the rotary joint and the gear of gap adjuster. Fig. 4 is a photo of the front view, where the transparent acryl for water bath is removed.

Fig. 5 is the test results of glass beads of 1 mm (Silicon rubber was used). Since the influence of suction will be negligible, tests were done in the air dry for dense and medium states, tests for the loose state were done in a damp state (1 - 3 % in water content). The results of constant volume tests are shown as three lines, their stress paths are similar to C, D of Fig. 1 and their intermediate one. The loose one was sheared by about 1 m/sec. which is the order of debris flow velocity monitored in Japan (Okuda et al, 1977), it once reached the origin and it went into a steady flow with

a very low shear resistance of 0.8 kPa. However, the undrained condition is not maintained during flow because pore water can move to the phreatic surface freely. Then, shear during a steady flow must be the drained condition, accordingly the constant normal state. To study the shear characteristics of a steady flow, the constant normal stress tests were done in various shear speeds at the medium void ratio. The results of Fig. 5 showed that all stood in the same failure envelope (the friction angle is 19°. Usual triaxial tests gave the same value, too) independent of shear speed. Therefore, it

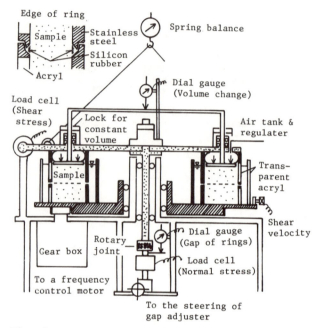

Fig. 3   Schematic Diagram of the New High Speed Ring Shear Apparatus

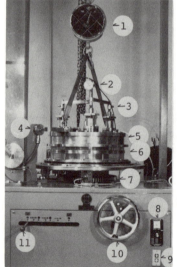

1) Spring balance
2) Dial gauge for volume change
3) Arm connecting the loading plate
4) Load cell for shear stress
5) Loading unit
6) Sample box
7) Gear for rotation
8) Electrical speed controller
9) Power switch
10) Steering of the gap adjuster of two rings
11) Change lever of gears

Fig. 4   Front View of the New Apparatus

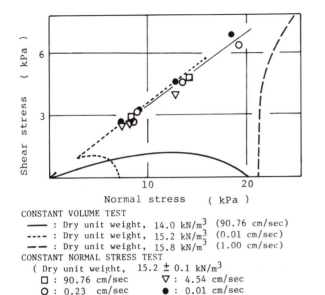

Fig. 5 Results of the New Ring Shear Apparatus

CONSTANT VOLUME TEST
—— : Dry unit weight, 14.0 kN/m³ (90.76 cm/sec)
---- : Dry unit weight, 15.2 kN/m³ (0.01 cm/sec)
-- — : Dry unit weight, 15.8 kN/m³ (1.00 cm/sec)
CONSTANT NORMAL STRESS TEST
(Dry unit weight, 15.2 ± 0.1 kN/m³
□ : 90.76 cm/sec   ▽ : 4.54 cm/sec
○ : 0.23 cm/sec   ● : 0.01 cm/sec

will be of no doubt that the reason why debris flow continues its movement until several degrees can not be explained by the special structure of grains "flow structure".

THE MECHANISM OF DEBRIS FLOWS

Fig. 6 is the mechanism of debris flows illustrated from both of field observations of over one hundred debris flows during 1975 - 1983 in Japan and laboratory liquefaction tests. Torrent deposits which have a loose and unstable structure can disjoint its structure by rapid loading due to the failed mass, accordingly the failed mass and the upper layer sits on water (1st & 2nd figure), the torrent deposit starts to flow causing liquefaction at its front and increasing its volume (3rd & 4th figure). Hutchinson & Bhandari (1971) proposed a similar mechanism for mudslides in England, and Tabata & Ichinose (1973) suggested that debris flows could be triggered by the energy of failed mass.

To give more exact supports to the hypothesis of Fig. 6, a small volcano (640 m in height) often causing debris flows was selected for a detailed study. The Usu volcano erupted in 1977, thereafter, small - medium debris flows were caused repeatedly. During a series of very heavy rains in 1981, field observation, survey, direct shear test in the field were done for 11 days. Three small debris flows took place in the investigating torrent at that period.
In the top of torrent, a talus deposited so critical that its partial submergence has to slide it, and it must have given a rapid loading on the torrent deposit according to the direct shear tests and survey. Furthermore, the torrent deposit behaved like a water cussion when the author gave a rapid loading by stamping at the saturated state in some hours before a debris flow (Sassa, 1984). Fig. 7 is the results of the so-called load control triaxial test of the torrent deposit (Grains greater than 12 mm were eliminated. Then, $D_{10}=0.13$, $D_{50}=2.7$, $D_{90}=8.0$

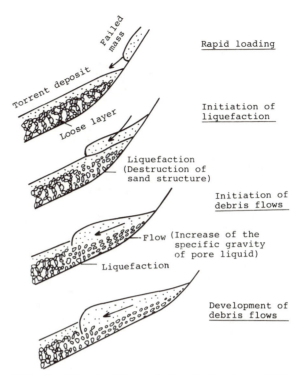

Fig. 6 Illustration of the Mechanism of Debris Flows

mm, G=2.46). 26 tests were done in the same procedure with Fig. 2, except the degree of saturation was changed.
T-1 is the result of typical liquefaction of full saturation, the void ratio is 0.74, which is in the range of the torrent deposit in field, 0.61 - 0.77. T-3 and T-4 are the tests to study the behavior of less saturated sample. T-3 showed the torrent deposit can be liquefied even if it were not fully saturated by unnatural high back pressure and use of CO_2 gas, (though the critical void ratio for liquefaction seems to change from 0.7 at the full saturation to about 0.8 at 85 % saturation).

Fig. 8 is the results of very simple experiment to look for the reason why a low shear resistance is maintained even during a steady flow. The Toyoura sand and water is poured into a small ring channel and rotated by a bar while pore pressure is measured at the bottom through a filter. During a steady flow, an excess pore pressure to cause "flow" to the phreatic surface does not exist, but the recorded pore pressure is proportional to the velocity of the bar. This is interpreted by the idea of sedimentation method for the grain size distribution. The greater the flowing velocity of sands, the greater percent of particles floats in water, then the specific gravity of pore liquid increases. It will be the reason why pore pressure exceeded the cell pressure during flow in Fig. 2.
The same tests of the Usu sample used in Fig. 7 could not be done in a wider range because of its big grain size for this channel. However, the specific gravity increased up to 1.25 at 70 cm/sec.. Usual speed of debris flows is 1 - 10 m/sec. by monitoring in Japan, therefore, the value probably will reach 1.4 or more at the

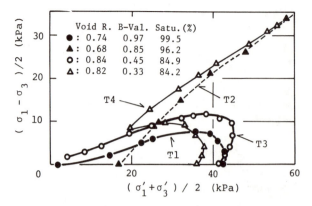

Fig. 7 Results of Undrained Triaxial Tests of
the Usu Torrent Deposit

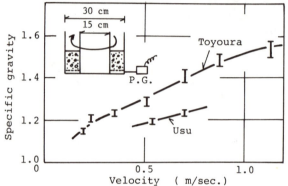

Fig. 8 Specific Gravity of Pore Liquid during
Flow
(Saturated unit weight: 17.2 - 18.6 kN/m³ for
the Toyoura, 16.9 - 17.9 kN/m³ for the Usu)

usual velocity range. At that time we will
calculate the critical angle of stoppage (θ)
by

$$\tan \theta = (\gamma_b / \gamma_t) \times \tan \phi$$

The total unit weight (γ_t) of the less disturbed
samples of torrent deposit including volcanic
porous stones at the naturally submerged state
was 16.1 kN/m³-18.0 kN/m³. The measured internal
friction angle of the torrent deposit was 32°,
the bouyant unit weight (γ_b) is γ_t - 1.4 × 9.8 in
kN/m³. It gives 5.2 - 8.5° as the critical
angle of stoppage which agrees with the real
deposit angle of debris flows in Japan and also
the Usu, 4 - 10°.

CONCLUSION

1. The so-called load control undrained triaxial
   tests can produce liquefaction, but its stress-
   strain relation depends on the loading method,
   and it is not enough to create a steady state
   of flow.
2. A new big and high speed ring shear apparatus
   was designed, and the tests of glass beads of
   1 mm showed that the loose grains are liquefied,
   when they are sheared in the constant volume

state.
3. The constant normal stress tests showed that
   the internal friction angle of grains is independent of the shearing speed in 0 - about 1
   m/sec.. Therefore, the special "flow structure"
   of grains to offer a minimum resistance proposed
   by Casagrande was not found there.
4. A simple experiment to rotate sands and water
   put forwards that pore water becomes a dense
   pore liquid having a higher specific gravity
   by floatation of fine particles during flow.
5. Field observations and laboratory tests of
   1) - 4) gave supports to the hypothesis stated
   in 6) and 7) as the mechanism of debris flows.
6. A loose torrent deposit is rapidly loaded by
   the failed mass from the top or the sides of
   torrent. The loose structure of deposit is
   destroyed and the failed mass and the upper
   layer sit on water (liquefaction), then the
   mass starts to flow. During a steady flow
   any excess pore pressure to cause "water flow"
   to the phreatic surface can not be maintained,
   because water can move freely.
7. Rapid flow of debris causes floatation of
   their particles in water, and it results in
   the increase of the specific gravity of pore
   liquid. It will be the reason of a low shear
   resistance and the low deposition angle of
   debris flows, 4° - 10°.

ACKNOWLEDGEMENT

The author acknowledges Prof. M. Shima of Kyoto
University and a graduate student Mr. M. Kaibori
for their advice and cooperation. A part of
this research was done by Grant-in-Aid for
Developmental Scientific Research No. 57860028
of the Japanese Ministry of Education, Science
and Culture.

REFERENCE

Casagrande A. (1976) Liquefaction and cyclic
deformation of sands -a critical review-.
Harvard Soil Mechanics Series, No.88, 1-27.

Castro G. (1969). Liquefaction of sands.
Harvard Soil Mechanics Series, No.81, 1-112.

Hutchinson, J.N., Bhandari, R.K. (1971). Undrained loading, a fundamental mechanism of
mudflows and other mass movements. Géotechnique
21, No.4, 353-358.

Jap. Soc. SMFE (1979). Manual of Soil Tests.
2nd Ed., 172-186.

Okuda, S. et al. (1977). Synthetic observation
on debris flow - Part 3. Disaster Prevention
Research Institute (Kyoto University), Annuals,
No.**20** B-1, 237-263.

Sassa, K. (1984). The mechanism starting liquefied landslides and debris flows. Proc. International Symposium on Landslides, under print,
Toronto.

Tabata, S., Ichinose, E. (1973). Study on the
primary factors of the mud-flow disasters in
Owase area. Jour. of the Erosion Control
Engineering Society, Japan, Shin-sabo, No.86,
20-24.

Session 3B
Geotechnical aspects of environmental control
B. Seepage control

Séance 3B
Aspects géotechniques de la réglementation de l'environnement
B. Contrôle de l'infiltration

Seepage losses from small irrigation reservoirs

Pertes par infiltration pour les réservoirs de petite capacité

R. BAKER, Senior Lecturer, Faculty of Civil Engineering, Technion, I.I.T., Haifa, Israel

SYNOPSIS

A large number of small water reservoirs have been, and are currently being built in Israel. One of the most difficult aspects of the design of such reservoirs is the estimation of the expected water loss due to seepage. In fact this consideration is frequently the decisive factor with respect to the feasibility and profitability of a proposed reservoir.

Frequently, these reservoirs have the following characteristics:
a) The permeability of the foundation soil is higher or equal to that of the embankment.
b) Water table is deep or non-existant.
c) The operational policy of the reservoir (i.e., the function h = h(t) where t is time and h denoting the height of water in the reservoir) is periodic with period of one year.

Features (a) and (b) imply that the water losses are mainly due to vertical seepage. Features (b) and (c) imply that steady state is never realized.

In the present paper a procedure for the evaluation of water losses is presented. The procedure is based on the approximation of the actual flow regime by the vertical movement of horizontal wetting front. The procedure can handle any operational policy h(t). Solutions for simple operational policies are presented in graphical form.

1. INTRODUCTION

One dimensional vertical flow from the bottom of a reservoir can be analyzed using the classical infiltration theory (Raudkivi and Callander, 1976). Such an approach suffers from two practical limitations: i) The specification of an infiltration problem requires experimental determination of two constitutive functions describing the dependence of permeability and suction on water content. The small scale of most irrigation reservoirs makes the determination of these functions for each project prohibitively expensive. ii) The infiltration equation requires numerical solution for each operation policy h(t). Such numerical solutions are cumbersome to apply on a regular basis.

There exist two observations suggesting that an alternative simplified procedure may be feasible: i) The solution of the infiltration equation is not too sensitive to the exact form of the constitutive functions (Neuman, Feddes and Bresler, 1974). ii) The resulting distribution (with depth) of water content obtained from the solution of the infiltration problem can frequently be approximated by a sharp wetting front (Ibrahim and Brutsaet, 1968).

It appears therefore that the process of water losses from the bottom of a reservoir can be approximatively modeled by studying the advance of a sharp wetting front separating an upper wet (saturated) zone from a lower unsaturated one. Similar approximation has been used by Bear (1972).

2. FORMULATION OF THE PROBLEM

Consider a simplified flow regime as shown in Fig. 1.

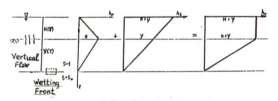

Figure 1 - Simplified Flow Regime.

On the basis of this figure it is possible to write:

$$q = k \frac{h + y}{y} \qquad (1)$$

where q is the specific discharge,
      k - coefficient of permeability
      h - height of water in the reservoir
(h = h(t) is the given operational policy of the reservoir) and y = y(t) is the depth of the wetting front at time t.

Neglecting volume change due to wetting and writing an equation for water balance at the wetting front, the following relation is obtained

$$qdt = n(S_f - S_0)dy \qquad (2)$$

where n is the porosity and S_f, S_0 are degrees of saturation above and below the wetting front. Combining equations (1) and (2) yields

$$\frac{dy}{dt} = \frac{k}{n(S_f - S_0)} \left(1 + \frac{h}{y}\right) \qquad (3)$$

It is convenient to introduce the following non-dimensional variables

$$Y = y/h_m \qquad (4.1)$$
$$H = h/h_m \qquad (4.2)$$
$$T = kt/n(S_f - S_0)h_m \qquad (4.3)$$

where h_m is the maximum value of h, so that the function H = H(T) varies between zero and one. In terms of Y, H and T, eqn. (3) becomes:

$$dY/dT = 1 + H/Y \qquad (5)$$

Equation (5) is a non-linear ordinary differential equation which controls the motion of the wetting front. The term (1 + H/Y) is the hydraulic gradient i; hence the knowledge of its solution (the function Y = Y(T) makes it possible to calculate the rate of losses from the relation q(T) = k(1 + H(t)/Y(T)). Moreover, since all water lost from the reservoir are stored behind the wetting front the cumulative losses D(T) up to the time T are given by:

$$D(T) = n(S_f - S_0)h_m Y(T) \qquad (6)$$

The boundary conditions for the solution of eqn. (5) are H(T = 0) = Y(T = 0) = 0. Notice that T = 0 is a singular point of eqn. (5) since at that time the term H/Y is not well defined (it is of the form 0/0).

For convenience, it is possible to approximate any arbitrary operational policy as a combination of linear segments as shown in Fig. (2).

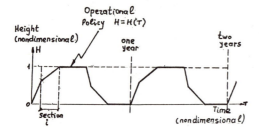

Figure 2 - Operational Policy

Hence, it is sufficient to solve eqn. (5) for the linear operational policy H(T) = aT + b using the boundary conditions $H(T = T_1) = H_1$ and $Y(T=T_1) = Y_1$. The end values of Y of the solution in one section is then taken as the initial value in the next section and the procedure is advanced section after section.

3. MATHEMATICAL ANALYSIS

Define a new variable η(T) as

$$\eta(T) = \frac{H(T)}{Y(T)} > 0 \qquad (7)$$

In terms of η, eqn. (5) becomes

$$H \frac{d\eta}{dT} = -\eta\Phi(T) \qquad (8.1)$$

where

$$\Phi(T) = \eta^2 + \eta - a \qquad (8.2)$$

In solving eqn. (8.1) one has to distinguish between the case $\Phi = \Phi(T) \neq 0$ and the case $\Phi = 0 \neq f(T)$. The first case corresponds to a regular solution of eqn. (8.1) while the second one represents a singular solution of this equation.

3a. The regular solution - Here too, it is necessary to deal separately with the case a=0 (constant water level in the reservoir) and the case a ≠ 0.

(i)   The case a ≠ 0:
In that case dT = dH/a and eqn. (8.1) becomes

$$\frac{d\eta}{\eta\Phi} = -\frac{1}{a}\frac{dH}{H} \qquad (9)$$

The solution of this equation is obtained using standard tables of integrals. This solution can be represented in the following form:

$$Y = \exp[(C - \ln|\Phi| + I(\eta))/2] \qquad (10.1)$$

with

$$I(\eta) = \begin{cases} \dfrac{U}{|U|\sqrt{4a+1}} \ln \dfrac{|U|}{\sqrt{4a+1}(2\eta+1)} & \text{for } a>-1/4 \\[2mm] -2/(2\eta+1) & \text{for } a = -1/4 \\[2mm] \dfrac{1}{\sqrt{4|a|-1}} \arctan \dfrac{2\eta+1}{\sqrt{2|a|+1}} & \text{for } a<-1/4 \end{cases} \qquad (10.2)$$

$$U(\eta) = (2\eta+1) - \sqrt{aY} + 1 \qquad (10.3)$$

and C is an integration constant. Equations(10) are implicit representations of the solution since η and Φ depend on Y, but this does not cause any serious difficulties in application. The segmented form of eqn. (10.2) may cause the impression that a = -1/4 corresponds to some change in the character of flow. A careful examination shows, however, that the solution is continuous at a = -1/4 only changing its formal mathematical representation. At T=0, H=Y=0 and η,Φ are not defined, hence it is not possible to use the information at T=0 (H=Y=0) in order to evaluate the integration constant C in eqn. (10.1). Consequently, this solution cannot be utilized in the vicinity of the singular point T=0.

(ii) The case a = 0:
In that case H=b≠f(T) and eqn. (8.1) can be written as

$$dT = -\frac{bd\eta}{\eta^2(1+\eta)} \qquad (11)$$

The solution of this equation is

$$T = Y+b \ln(1+\eta)+C \qquad (12)$$

with C an integration constant.

Obviously, this solution cannot be applied at T=0 when H(0) = 0 since in that case a=0 implies that the reservoir remains empty.

3b. The singular solution

The singular solution - The solutions presented above were based on the assumption that $\Phi \neq 0$. It was shown that these solutions do not apply in the vicinity of the point T=0. Since the boundary conditions of the problem are specified at that point, it is necessary to find a solution which is valid at T=0. Let us investigate if such a solution may be obtained on the basis of the assumption

$$\Phi = \eta^2 + \eta - 1 = 0 \qquad (13)$$

Using eqn.(13) and H=aT in eqn.(8.1) one get $aT(d\eta/dT) = 0$. Hence, eqn.(13) implies that $\eta = \eta_o = const.$ is a solution of the differential equation (8.1). The value of the constant η_o can be obtained from eqn.(13)

$$\eta_o = \frac{\sqrt{1+4a} - 1}{2} = \frac{H(T)}{Y(T)} \qquad (14)$$

Since η_o is constant. eqn.(14) implies that a must also be a constant, or in other words, this singular solution is valid only for a linear variation of H with time. Substituting H(T)=aT into eqn.(14) and solving for Y(T) yields

$$Y(T) = \beta T \qquad (15.1)$$

$$\beta = \frac{2a}{\sqrt{4a+1} - 1} \qquad (15.2)$$

Eqn. (15) shows that the wetting front advances at a constant rate. Notice that in this solution the hydraulic gradient $i = 1+H/Y = 1+a/\beta$ is well defined at the singular point T=0, H=0, Y=0.

Finally one has to establish the range of validity of the singular and regular solutions (eqns. (15) and (10)). It was seen that the singular solution is valid only as long as a = const. For this constant value $\Phi_o = \Phi = 0$. When $\Phi = 0$ the regular solution (eqn.(10.1)) cannot be applied since ln(0) does not exists. It may be concluded therefore that the singular solution is valid from the time T=0 up to the first time when the function H(T) changes its slope. From that time on the regular solution applies.

4. RESULTS AND DISCUSSIONS

The above solution was implemented on a micro-computer and checked for number of conditions. In every case reasonable results have been obtained. Comparison with field observation is in progress at the present but no conclusive results have been obtained as yet.
An example of a solution is shown in Fig. 3. This solution is based on the following input data (k = 10^{-6} cm/sec, S_o = 0.8, S_f = 1.0, n = 0.4 and h_m = 10 m) which is quite typical of conditions in Israel. For these conditions the non-dimensional time T for one year (one period) is 0.4. The solution was obtained for the periodic operational policy specified on the bottom of Fig. 3 and it is shown as the solid lines in the figure. For comparison purposes the solution by Bear (1972) which corresponds to the operational policy H=1 for T⩾0 is shown as a dashed line on the same figure.

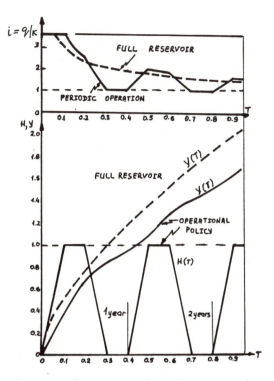

Figure 3 - Solution of an Example Problem

Following are number of observations (conclusions) which are based on the present analysis:

(a) On first filling the rate of advance of the wetting front (and hence also the rate of seepage losses) is constant (See Fig. 3). This result is fundamentally different from the one obtained by Bear (1972) which yields infinite losses at T=0.

(b) The rate of losses decreases with time and q approaches assymptotically the value of k. The decreases in the rate of seepage is rather slow and in the example shown in Fig. 3, q ≅ 1.5k after three years of operation.

(c) When the reservoir is empty (actually not empty but with minimum water level required to prevent drying and cracking) then i → 1 and q → k.

(d) If the wetting front meets a regional water table then the rate of seepage losses no longer decreases. It can be assumed that horizontal gradients in the regional aquifer adjust themselves to the inflow from the reservoir and a steady state is achieved. This observation shows clearly that the presence of high water table in the vicinity of a reservoir does not improve the situation from the stand point of seepage loss as is sometimes claimed.

REFERENCES

Bear, J. (1972). Dynamic of fluids in porous media. Elsevier Publ., Comp.

Ibrahim, H.A. and Brutsaet, W. (1968). Intermittent infiltration into soils with

hysteresis. Jour. of the Hydraulic Div.,
ASCE, Vol. 94, No. HY1, pp. 113-137.

Neuman, S.P., Feddes, R.A. and Bresler, E.
(1974).   Finite element simulation of
flow in saturated-unsaturated soils.
Research Report No. ALD-SWC-77, Technion
I.I.T., Haifa. Israel.

Raudkivi, A.J. and Callander, R.A. (1976).
Analysis of ground water flow. John Wiley
and Sons, N.Y.

Seepage control from ash lagoons

Contrôle de l'infiltration de lagunes de cendres

B. BROŚ, Professor of Civil Engineering, Agriculture University of Wrocław, Poland
K. PARYLAK, Assistant Professor, Agriculture University of Wrocław, Poland

SYNOPSIS   The results of seepage control from ash lagoon, anisotropy of shear strength and permeability of lagooned fly ashes as well as their age hardening behaviour are discussed.

INTRODUCTION

The operation of pulverized coal-fired boilers for the production of electric power results in the production of large amounts of fly ash. The major portion of this waste product is still being dumped in a slurry form in the storage lagoons, where it settles out. The economic requirement led to the development of the commonly used in Poland upstream method of ash lagoons construction with the initial dike of sand or gravel and with the use of compacted fly ash for subsequent dikes. The fly ash slurry is discharged by a uniform spigotting off the top of every dike which forms a gently sloping beach. Due to selective deposition of the coarser grains close to the discharge point, a lateral gradation of lagooned fly ash exists between this point and the outfall tower. The deposited fly ash ranges from highly stratified, alternating layers of coarse grained particles and thin layers of silt near the discharge point to less distinct stratification at the outfall tower. Compacted fly ashes as well as those deposited exhibit age hardening behaviour, i.e., time-dependent increase in strength, which has best been correlated with the presence of free lime /CaO/, anhydrite /CaSO$_4$/ and gypsum /CaSO$_4$. 2H$_2$O/ in the fly ash. The upstream methods of tailings dam construction for disposal of tailings as a waste product of the mining industry, suffer the disadvantage of being built on the layers of previously deposited, often loose and saturated tailings. Under static load there is a limiting height to which such a dam can be built without danger of shear failure in the downstream direction in unconsolidated, having limited shear strength tailings. Under earthquake loading, the upstream type of dam may be subject to failure by liquefaction, at any height. The age hardening of deposited in lagoons or compacted in dikes fly ashes combined with their complex, highly stratified structure reduces the danger of failure by sliding or by liquefaction.

FLY ASH LAGOON OF POWER PLANT

In the Silesia Region a big power plant exploits the lagoon complex covering an area of about 70 ha. At present it is the highest fly ash lagoon in use in Poland, which is now about 24 m high and will be raised in the future to the height of 35 m. The lagoon complex is located in the valley of Biały Stream and is underlain by post-glacial sands and gravels of about 15 do 25 m thick, overlying Tertiary clays. The groundwater table ranges from 0.5 m to 5 m below ground level. The initial dike was constructed from locally available borrow permeable materials. After filling initial pond, the dike was raised by borrowing material from the dried surface of the previously deposited fly ashes, i.e., from the beach and the cycle was repeated.

FIELD AND LABORATORY TESTING

A comprehensive series of laboratory and in-situ tests have been carried out on lagooned fly ash, deposited on the beach, mainly to assess drainage characteristics of material. The investigated lagooned fly ash is predominantly silt-sized material, mostly sandy silt, with the coefficient of uniformity of 14.
Density.- The density of solid particles was 2255 kg/m^3.
Dry density. - Dry density of settled lagoon fly ash from the same small area of the beach, ranged from 804 kg/m^3 to 884 kg/m^3. For the same undisturbed samples, moisture content varies from 62.0% to 70.7% and porosity from 60.8% to 64.3%.
Permeability. - In deposited artificial soils, the horizontal permeability tends to be larger than the vertical one. The method of placement and compaction in earth and artificial soils is such, that the stratifications tend to be built into the embankments. In-situ permeability tests on the beach gave the results:

Place:	ϱ_d /kg/m^3/	n/%/	k /m/s/
Compacted dike fill	1095	51	8.7 x 10^{-6}
5m from discharge point	889	61	7.0 x 10^{-5}
12m from discharge point	656	71	9.5 x 10^{-5}
40m from discharge point	741	67	1.4 x 10^{-5}

As a result of selective deposition of fly ash particles, the density and permeability of the settled solids decrease with the increasing distance from the point of discharge. The coefficients of permeability from the laboratory tests on undisturbed samples are as follows:

Direction of water flow	ϱ_d /kg/m^3/	n/%/	k /m/s/
vertical to stratification	804	64.3	1.80 x 10^{-6}
vertical to stratification	809	64.1	1.97 x 10^{-6}
vertical to stratification	804	64.3	1.79 x 10^{-6}
parallel to stratification	884	60.8	6.71 x 10^{-6}
parallel to stratification	842	62.6	1.11 x 10^{-5}
parallel to stratification	866	61.5	1.30 x 10^{-5}

Undrained triaxial compression tests have been carried out on the undisturbed samples of deposited lagoon fly ashes. The values of cohesion and angle of shearing resistance are as follows:

Axis of test:	n/%/	S$_r$ /%/	c /kPa/	ϕ°
vertical to bedding	64	88	12	39°40'
horizontal to bedding	61.5	92	12	36°20'

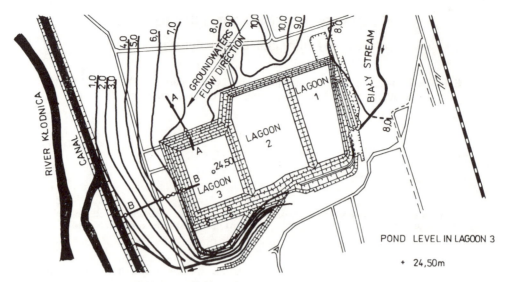

Fig. 1   Site Plan of Lagoons Complex

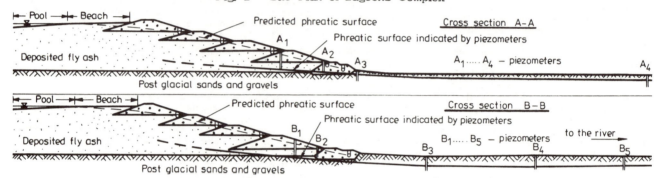

Fig. 2   Cross-Sections showing predicted and observed Phreatic Surfaces

GROUNDWATER CONDITIONS AND SEEPAGE CONTROL

A total of 60 standpipe piezometers were installed on the area adjacent to ash lagoons complex and on the embankments. The piezometers have been read and recorded regularly since 1975 to monitor the changes in the groundwater regime. Fig. 1 shows the site plan of lagoons complex with contour-line water-table map and Fig.2 presents the being observed phreatic surface in compacted fly ash embankments and that on the areas adjacent to ash lagoons, during lagoon No 3 exploitation. It has been observed that the phreatic surface indicated by piezometers was located at an increasingly greater distance from the location of predicted phreatic surface. As a result, the outside shell of lagoon embankment contributes more to stability as the height of the lagoon increases. Such formation of phreatic surface is caused by the tendency to seepage flow in the horizontal direction, towards the centre of the disposal area, due to the stratification of deposited fly ash. The analyzed lagoons complex is located on a natural watercourse and groundwater is closely related to water levels in the Kłodnica River and Canal. A groundwater mound may be observed to form underneath the leakey pond of lagoon complex. Following cessation of discharging into lagoon the groundwater level dropped in a matter of weeks to its equilibrium value, which is controlled by the water condition in the Kłodnica River. The most serious problem can develop, when the pond level rises above the level of the beach so that it is in direct contact with the dike, causing excess seepage flows with the threat of piping. Fly ashes consist of many different minerals. Because of that, the specific gravity of fly ash particles varies from about 1.90 g/cm^3 to 2.60 g/cm^3. Therefore, seepage flows, even by very small hydraulic gradient cannot prevent passage of the finest and the lightest fly ash particles into the drainage pipes. In this case, the filter zones design criteria for natural soils cannot prevent subsurface erosion and subsequent dike failure by piping.

CONCLUSIONS

The deposited in lagoon fly ashes indicate highly stratified structure as well as anisotropy of shear strength and permeability. The lagoon fly ashes exhibit age hardening behaviour and chemical cementing agents in the fly ash produce an end-product that is far more stable than at the beginning of the disposal process. The phreatic surface in fly ash embankments indicated by piezometers is situated at an increasingly greater distance from the location of predicted phreatic surface. All the above mentioned facts contribute more to the stability of the upstream method-constructed ash lagoon, as the height of the lagoon increases. The deposited or compacted fly ashes are highly susceptible to internal piping.

Prefabricated sand filter drains used at Tarbela Dam

Drains filtrants en sable préfabriqués utilisés au barrage de Tarbela

HAQ IZHARUL, Dr. M.Sc., Pakistan
ABDUL KHALIQ, M.Sc., Pakistan

SYNOPSIS   The left bank rocks of Tarbela Dam are highly fractured and contain solution channels, fissured zones and erodible gouge material. Seepage through the bed rock was controlled by grout curtain and drainage system from the galleries. Problem arose when substantial amount of fines were passed by some of the drain holes. Different types of drains such as polymer bonded filters, epoxy bonded filters and sand filtered drains were tried and finally the latter were selected.The concept of the sand filtered drain consists of two concentric slotted PVC pipes prefabricated with filter sand in the annulus.The latest design has been the result of a thorough re-appraisal of the filtered drain concept. These drains have been successfully used at Tarbela Dam.

INTRODUCTION

Seepage through bedrocks under the spillway structures and from the abutments of the Main Embankment of Tarbela Dam Project is controlled by the conventional grout curtain and drainage system. Pervious rocks extend to great depth and it was not economical to make a positive cutoff with the grout curtains. The limestone beds contain granulated lenses which will not accept portland cement grout but which will pass appreciable quantities of water. In the original design the drainholes were lined with 50 mm dia PVC pipe having 0.5 mm wide longitudinal slots. It was expected that natural filter would quickly develope around the slots and after an initial passing of some fines, further piping would stop. This did not happen and instead very heavy flows and discharge of fines were experienced. The situation especially under the auxiliary spillway and the left abutment, deteriorated fast.This paper describes the problem, the design and construction of prefabricated sand filter drains. This innovation is expected to prove very satisfactory and may be used elsewhere on similar sites.

GEOLOGY

Tarbela left bank rocks consist of low grade metamorphic limestones interbedded with phyllites and occasional layers of quartizites and basic igneous dolerites.The limestones are dolomitic, ferruginous or marly with lenses of granulated material locally called sugary limestone.The beds strike northeast and dip steeply to the southwest.Local folding of beds is common.The rocks are generally moderately to highly weathered.Fractured rock with crushed zones is frequently present.There are many shear zones containing erodible gouge material of very low shear strength.

DESIGN AND PERFORMANCE OF DRAINAGE SYSTEM

It was assumed in the original design that grouting would fill majority of the open joints, cavities and solution channels thus reducing permeabilities.The hydraulic head on the drainage curtains would thus reduce to less than 1 on 1 and will not cause piping.Migration of fines was to be prevented by use of slotted PVC pipe drains.At the left abutment,the core of the main embankment was wrapped around its u/s face and on the spillways,special u/s impervious blankets were provided under the approach slab adjacent to the headworks structure.The use of the u/s blanket would reduce the hydraulic gradient on the drains and little potential would thus exist for piping of fines.Experience showed the presence of much higher percentage of erodible material in the rock,the low effectiveness of grout curtain and inadequacy of slotted pipes to retain the migrated rock fines.

Effective angle of shearing resistance of the gouge material was found as low as 18°.Stability analysis indicated that piezometric pressures especially under the auxiliary spillway must not be allowed to rise above specified limits.Fig.1 shows schematic sketch of auxiliary spillway. Longitudinal drainage adits ASDA-2 and ASDA-3 are located in the left and right abutment rocks respectively.Both adits connect with the transverse Adit ASDA-1 under the headworks.During the initial impounding in 1974, the seepage into the drainage adits of left abutment reached 10 cusecs (0.283 cms)against the estimated value of 1.5 cusecs (0.042 cms).A number of drains discharged fines.The performance of drainage system of Auxiliary Spillway from 1975 to 78 was satisfactory.However during 1978 impounding deterioration was indicated with the discharge of significant amounts of fines from 10 drains under the headworks structure.These drains were plugged and replacement drains were installed by lowering a coaxial 50 and 75 mm diameter slotted PVC pipes down the holes from the drainage adits in 1.3 m segments.Sand filter was installed between the

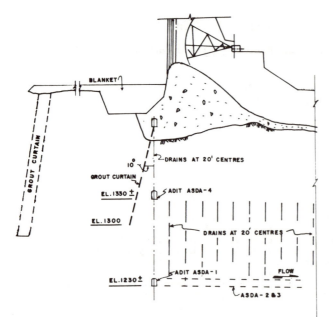

Fig.1 Drainage System For Auxiliary Spillway

PVC pipes under controlled conditions. A slightly coarser filter sand was placed in the annulus between the 75 mm PVC pipe and the wall of the hole. Performance of 1980 indicated discharge of fines from some additional drains. It was clear that the gradation of the fines was not suitable to form a natural filter pack behind the slots of the PVC pipes. The gradation of the silt sized fines is shown in Fig.2.

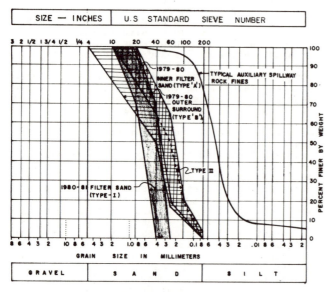

Fig.2 Gradation Of Rock Fines And Sands Tested For Use In Drains.

To prevent the movement of these fines a filter was required which would not only retain these fines but also transmit the seepage water so that pressures would not build up. Furthermore a large number of drain holes had been drilled upward from the galleries. Placement of filter sand

around the slotted PVC pipes in these holes was not possible. The construction difficulties required a workable solution.

ALTERNATIVE FILTER DRAIN SYSTEMS

In 1978, drains had been fabricated at the site. The method consisted of placing the inner sand filter continuously as the pipes were extended down the drain hole. This meant that the filter sand extended in an unbroken column from the bottom to the top of the drain. The drawback to this arrangement is that it could result in a substantial loss of sand filter, should serious damage occur to the inner PVC pipe. For the updrains various proposals for prefabricated filter drains were investigated. Initially, both prefabricated proprietory system and site-fabricated systems utilizing filter cloth were looked into. The prefabricated proprietory system, in general, comprised of slotted PVC pipes coated with a 15 mm thick epoxy bonded sand layer. The samples tested in the site laboratory were either weak in retention of fines or weak in transmissibility. Laboratory tests were also run on various filter cloth drain samples for discharge capacity and fines retention capability. The results are summarised in Fig.3 & 4. All the cloth samples tested had desirably high discharge capacities but none retained rock fines of the grading found at the site. Eventually a sandwich type drain was prepared which proved practical, dependable and economical.

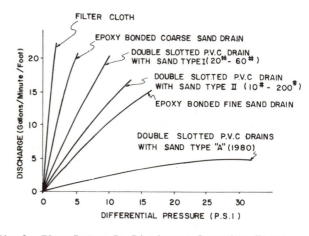

Fig.3 Flow Rates In Discharge Capacity Tests

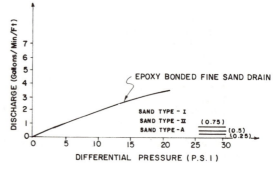

Fig.4 Flow Rates In Fines Retention Tests

FABRICATION OF SANDWICH FILTER DRAINS

Prefabricated sand filter drain consists of two concentric PVC pipes of outer dia 75 mm,inner dia 50 mm and 1.3 m length of the two pipes fabricated in the workshop Fig.5.

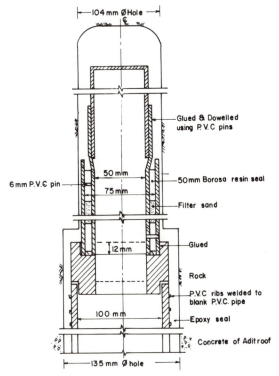

Fig.5 Sandwich Filter Drain Detail

The slots on both the pipes were 0.5 mm wide, 50 mm long and at 100 mm c/c vertically. After being filled with sand,the units were transferred to the vibrating table and were subjected to vib-rations for 3 minuts obtaining final sand density of 1.84 gm/cc.After vibration,3 number 6 mm dia PVC dowel pins inserted into predrilled holes located close to the end of the pipe and at the mid points of the area to be filled with Barosa resin to seal the ends of the unit.The average production rate during 24 hours was 160 units with a crew of 12 men.Cost per foot was $ 10. Locally obtained river sand,oven dried and speci-ally graded to conform to the requirement shown in Fig.2 was used in the annulus of the drains.

TESTS ON PREFABRICATED DRAIN

To check the flow capacity,a series of laboratory tests were conducted on the sandwich filter drains. The flow through the drain was measured and loss of filter sand through the slots was also moni-tored.Another series of tests with weights applied to the PVC pipe were conducted. This series checked whether the accumulated weight of the sand filter may cause the slots in the PVC pipe to open thus increasing flows and loss of filter sand.The loss of fines was small amounting to .05% of the filter weight.There was negligible change in flows with added weight on the filter. A series of tests were conducted witin a triaxial

cell allowing pressure to be applied from the outside of the drain such as occurs in the field.The effective permeability dropped to 0.00022 cm/sec. The drain capacity was found to be 0.049 L/Sec/m/m head.

INSTALLATION OF SAND FILTERED DRAINS

In 1980,the drains were designed so that sepa-rate drain elements were formed by each pair of slotted PVC pipes.The elements could then be prefabricated with the filter sand sealed in at the ends with putty.By isolating the sand,the consequences of damage to the inner PVC pipe were limited to the loss of filter sand from only one drain element.The limited risk of drain defects and geological features coincid-ing was a major advantage of the prefabricated drains. In 1981,the use of putty for the end seals was discontinued;instead,a Barosa resin product was selected that formed a strong per-manent seal after cooling.Other significant modifications in the drain arrangement were the improved bottom support and the strengthened junction with the upper adit.The uppermost unit of each drain was made unslotted connecting drain and capped temporarily during installa-tion.

PERFORMANCE

After the replacement of all existing drains by sand filtered drains,the performance during the subsequent years was satisfactory.There has been a substantial reduction in seepage and an improved distribution of piezometric pressures. Since 1981 remedial works,there has not been any discharge of fines from the drains.

CONCLUSIONS

Prepacked sand filter drains have proved succe-ssful not only in retaining the migration of fine silt sized rock gouge material but also in transmitting the seepage water so that pressures do not build up.These drains have been prepared from indigenous material and are economical as compared to the patented filters.

REFERENCES

Cedergren,H.R.(1977). Seepage,Drainage and Flownets 2nd Ed.,pp. 1975-220

Francis,G.M.& Raymond,J.K.(1971) Seepage Characteristics of Imperfact Cutoffs.ASCE J.SM & FD Vol.97,No.SMI pp 305-311

Karpoff,K.P.(1955) The Use of Laboratory Tests to Develop Design Criteria for Protective Filters.Proceedings ASTM Vol.55,0 1183.

Contribution to the hydraulics of tailings impoundments

Contribution à l'hydraulique des remblais en déchets granuleux

J. P. JESENÁK, Associated Professor, Institute for Geotechnics, Slovak Technical University, Bratislava, Czechoslovakia

SYNOPSIS   The paper deals with seepage through the slopes of granular tailings impoundments with continuously changing permeability either in horizontal, or both in horizontal, as well as in vertical direction. For two-dimensional seepage above a horizontal impervious base approximate analytic solutions are given, for permeability changing according to different laws. For the general case with spatial movement of water above an arbitrarily inclined base and possibly irregularly altering cross sections a simple engineering approach is presented, giving a good picture of the permeability distribution and seepage. The results can serve for prognosing future changes of the phreatic surface, for the design of additional drainage elements and for stability calculations.

INTRODUCTION

The fundamental geotechnical properties of sedimented tailings depend on the parent material, grinding and processing and the technology of transport and deposition. When these factors are relatively stable, the scatter remains within statistically acceptable margins: estimating the main parameters of seepage a simplified geotechnical model and approximate analytic solutions can lead to quite satisfactory results.

DISTRIBUTION OF PERMEABILITY

The main types of refuse impoundments are defined in standards and professional papers /e.g. WAHLER and SCHLICK,1976/. In flat regions, diked impoundments are the common type. In wide valleys, the side-hill type is advantageous. In mountainous regions, the cross-valley typ is used. For each type, the upstream, the downstream or the centerline construction method can be applied. Where hydraulic separation of the sandy fraction is not used, the permeability of the sediment changes continuously in horizontal direction, with maximum values near the outflows on the crest; gradually decreasing toward the pool. Using the centerline method, the permeability remains roughly constant in each cross section. Applying the upstream or the downstream method, the outlets of the slurry shift with raising crest of the slope in upstream, resp. in downstream direction: in the first case in vertical sections the permeability increases, in the second it decreases from the bottom to the surface. Depending from the type of the impoundment, seepage develops within the slopes either in plane or in spatial conditions. The main factor governing the movement of water is the continuous inhomogeneity of the sediment. The importance of its anisotropy - often overestimated - is secondary and can be, if necessary, respected by tranforming the flow region.

TWO-DIMENSIONAL CONDITIONS

Let us introduce the following assumptions:
1. the tailings lay upon a horizontal impervious base,
2. the permeability of sedimented tailings changes continuously in horizontal direction,
3. changes of boundary conditions are very slow and can be neglected,
4. DARCY´s law $v = k.i$ is valid,
5. DUPUIT´s simplifications are admissible,
6. the real case can be approximated by a deterministic model of permeability distribution.

For simple boundary conditions and for permeability changing according to six different laws solutions were derived for the discharge and the coordinates of the phreatic line /JESENÁK, 1983/. The equations are given in Table I. Some examples are shown in Fig.1. The deviations from the homogeneous case are important.

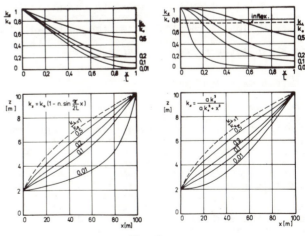

Fig. 1

TABLE I

0. $k = const.$ (Dupuit)	$q_D = k \frac{H^2 - h^2}{2L}$
	$z_D = [h^2 + \frac{2q}{k} x]^{0,5}$
1. $k_x = k_o(1 - n\frac{x}{L})$	$q = k_o \frac{H^2 - h^2}{2L} \cdot \frac{(-n)}{ln(1-n)} = q_D \frac{(-n)}{ln(1-n)}$
	$z = [h^2 + \frac{2q}{k_o} \cdot (\frac{-L}{n}) ln(1 - n\frac{x}{L})]^{0,5}$
2. $k_x = k_o \frac{1}{ax^{n+1}}$ ($n \geq 1$)	$q = k_o \frac{H^2 - h^2}{2L} \cdot \frac{n+1}{aL^n + (n+1)} = q_D \cdot \frac{n+1}{aL^n + (n+1)}$
	$z = [h^2 + \frac{2q}{k_o} (\frac{a}{n+1} x^{n+1} + x)]^{0,5}$
3. $k_x = k_o e^{-ax}$ $a = -\frac{ln\frac{k_L}{k_o}}{L}$	$q = k_o \frac{H^2 - h^2}{2L} \cdot \frac{aL}{e^{aL} - 1} = q_D \cdot \frac{aL}{e^{aL} - 1}$
	$z = [h^2 + \frac{2q}{ak_o} (e^{ax} - 1)]^{0,5}$
4. $k_x = k_o(1 - n \cdot \sin\frac{\pi x}{2L})$	$q = k_o \frac{H^2 - h^2}{2L} \cdot \frac{\pi(1-n^2)^{0,5}}{4[arctg(\frac{1-n}{1+n})^{0,5} - arctg\frac{-n}{(1-n^2)^{0,5}}]^{0,5}}$
	$z = [h^2 + \frac{2q}{k_o} \cdot \frac{4L}{\pi(1-n^2)^{0,5}} (arc\,tg\frac{tg\frac{\pi x}{4L} - n}{(1-n^2)^{0,5}} - arctg\frac{-n}{(1-n^2)^{0,5}})]^{0,5}$
5. $k_x = \frac{ak_o^3}{ak_o^2 + x^2}$	$q = k_o \frac{H^2 - h^2}{2L} \cdot \frac{3ak_o^2}{3ak_o^2 + L^2} = q_D \cdot \frac{3ak_o^2}{3ak_o^2 + L^2}$
	$z = [h^2 + \frac{2q}{k_o} (x - \frac{x^3}{3ak_o^2})]^{0,5}$
6. $k_x = \bar{k}(1 + m\cos\frac{\pi x}{L})$ $\bar{k} = \frac{k_o - k_L}{2}$ $B = (1 - m^2)^{0,5}$	$q = k_o \frac{H^2 - h^2}{2L} \cdot \frac{(1-m^2)^{0,5}}{(1+m)} = q_D \cdot \frac{(1-m^2)^{0,5}}{(1+m)}$
	$z = [h^2 + \frac{2q}{\bar{k}} (\frac{2L}{\pi B} arctg\frac{(1-m)}{B} \cdot tg\frac{\pi x}{2L})]^{0,5}$

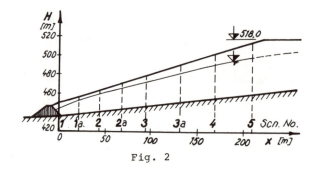

Fig. 2

Fig. 2 shows a schematic longitudinal section of the impoundment. Table II contains basic data: x-horizontal distance from cross-section No.1, H-absolute elevation of the phreatic line, D-ditto, for the impervious rock base, h-height of the phreatic line above the base, B-width of the section at the phreatic surface, A-area of the section beneath the water level, i-average hydraulic gradient between neighbouring sections.

TABLE II

	Section No.						
	1	1a	2	2a	3	3a	4
x	0	22,0	44,5	69,6	95,0	132,0	169,0
H	443,5	451,5	459,5	466,0	472,5	482,5	491,5
D	437,0	438,0	440,5	443,0	446,0	472,5	482,5
h	6,5	13,5	19,0	23,0	26,5	32,5	36,5
B	49,0	66,0	98,0	115,0	135,0	153,0	161,0
A	193	486	921	1352	1865	2497	3105
i	0,364	0,356	0,260	0,255	0,270	0,243	

Note: x,h,B in [m], H,D in m.a.s.l., A in [m²]

The assumptions correspond well with the real conditions in longer straight sections of the slopes of impoundments constructed with the centerline method. Otherwise, the coefficient of permeability represents for each vertical an average value from the base up to the phreatic level. Should the general trend of permeability distribution in vertical direction be known, the absolute values can be derived - as will be shown later - from the average.

GENERAL CASE: AN EXAMPLE

The following example, a cross-valley type copper mill tailings impoundment about 90 m high, constructed with the upstream method, represents a general case. The overall slope of the dump is 1:3, the beach is about 200 m long. The phreatic surface is controled weekly in wells situated in cross-sections. The discharge, measured at the drainage outflows, oscillates about $Q = 10$ l.s^{-1}. Up to now no drainage elements had been constructed except the drainage blanket of the basic dam, 13 m high. A detailed outline of the geotechnical properties of the tailings had been already published /JESENÁK and MASAROVIČOVÁ, 1983/.

The impundment had already reached its originally designed maximum height, and is now going to be increased by further 45 m up to a total height of 135 m. In order to obtain a realistic basis for the design of drainage elements, for the prediction of future changes of the phreatic line and for stability calculations, the distribution of permeability within the slope and the fundamental parameters of seepage were investigated.

For similar cases there are no analytic solutions: an engineering approach was developed. First of all, the average value of the coefficient of permeability between neighbouring sections was calculated, using the approximate formula of KAMENSKIJ/1943/, adapted for spatial water movement:

$$Q = \bar{k}_{ij} \frac{A_i + A_j}{2} \cdot \frac{H_j - H_i}{L_{ij}} \qquad /1/$$

where Q is the discharge, κ_{ij} the average value of k between section i and j, A_i, A_j areas of the sections, H_i, H_j absolute elevations of the phreatic surface, L_{ij} the horizontal distance between section i and j.

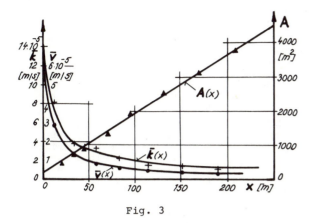

Fig. 3

The calculated values of $\bar{k}/x/$ showed a continuous decrease with increasing $\underline{x}$. After linearization in appropriate coordinates they could be expressed by hyperbolic regression functions. e.g. /Fig.3/:

$$\bar{k}/x/ = \frac{10,87.10^{-3}.Q}{1 + 0,0416.x} \quad /m.s^{-1}/ \quad /2/$$

Eq./2/ and similar others made it possible to calculate the average permeability for any arbitrary cross section. In a similar way the real phreatic line $z = z/x/$ was expressed by a parabolic equation. The hydraulic gradient $i = dz/ /dx$ could then be approximated by the term

$$i/x/ = 3,0883./x + 47,78/^{-0,5} \quad /3/$$

The dependence of the cross section areas on the horizontal coordinate gave a linear equation

$$A/x/ = 17,47.x + 157,26 \quad /m^2/ \quad /4/$$

Now, since $Q = A.k.i$, an analytic expression for the permeability $\bar{k}/x/$ could be compiled

$$\bar{k}/x/ = \frac{Q./x + 47,78/^{0,5}}{53,95.x + 485,67} \quad /m.s^{-1}/ \quad /5/$$

The average seepage velocity $\bar{v}/x/ = Q/A$ we got as

$$\bar{v}/x/ = \frac{Q}{17,47.x + 157,26} \quad /m.s^{-1}/ \quad /6/$$

Both equations /2/ and /5/ give realistic values. The advantage of eq./5/ is that it expresses the physical substance of the phenomenon,whereas eq./2/ is a mere regression formula without any physical meaning.

No analytic funktional relations can be derived, if abrupt changes either of the hydraulic gradient, or the permeability are detected, In such cases the investigations remain limited to separate parts between two neighbouring cross sections.
The following was the estimate of permeability distribution in vertical direction. The general trend is given by the construction method. More detailed informations can be obtained from direct measurements in the field, or from a study of changes of grain size in horizontal as well as in vertical direction.

In general, the assumed change of permeability in vertical direction can be approximated with a mathematical term. We introduced the simple but flexible expression

$$k /z/ = k_1 z^{\alpha} = k_h \left(\frac{z}{h}\right)^{\alpha} \quad /\alpha > 0/ \quad /7/$$

where k_1, k_z, k_h are the values of the coefficient of permeability at elevations 1 m, $\underline{z}$ and $\underline{h}$ above the bottom of the section, and α is an exponent.

If $k/z/$ decreases with $\underline{z}$, eq./7/ must be rewritten as $k/z/ = k_h (/h-z/: h)^{\alpha}$. For a homogeneous section, $k = const.$, $\alpha = 0$. For linearly increasing or decreasing permeability, $\alpha = 1$. Similarly, for the increase of b_z, the width of the valley at elevation $\underline{z}$, we have

$$b/z/ = mz^{\beta} = B \left(\frac{z}{h}\right)^{\beta} \quad /\beta > 0/ \quad /8/$$

where $m = B/h^{\beta}$ and B is the width for $z = h$.

For two-dimensional seepage $\beta = 0, b/z/ = B$, or 1 running meter. For linearly increasing width $\beta = 1$ /Fig.4/.

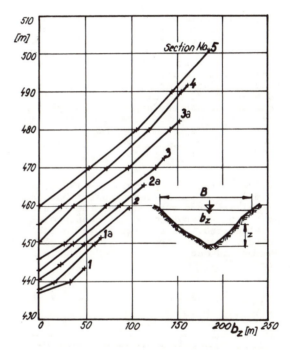

Fig. 4

By integration of $b/z/$ from $z = 0$ to $z = h$ we obtain the area of the cross section A:

$$A = \frac{B \cdot h}{\beta + 1} \quad /9/$$

If we now introduce the term $t_z = k_z.b_z$, which means the local transmissivity at elevation $\underline{z}$, and assume according to DUPUIT the hydraulic gradient to be constant throughout the whole section, we can write

$$dq/i = k/z/.b/z/.dz = t/z/.dz \quad /10/$$

Integrating eq./10/ from z = 0 to z = h we obtain

$$T = \frac{Q}{i} = k_1 \cdot \frac{B.h}{\alpha + \beta + 1} = k_h \cdot \frac{B.h^{\alpha+1}}{\alpha + \beta + 1} \qquad /11/$$

where T we called the transmissivity of the section. In eq./11/ the quantities k_1, resp. k_h are still unknown. They can be determined from the avarage value of the permeability, see eq. /1/, /2/ and /5/:

$$T = \frac{Q}{i} = \frac{A.\bar{k}.i}{i} = \frac{B \cdot h}{\beta + 1} \cdot \bar{k} \qquad /12/$$

With respect to eq. /7/ and /11/

$$k_h = \bar{k} \; \frac{\alpha + \beta + 1}{\beta + 1} \qquad /13/$$

and

$$k/z/ = \bar{k} \; \frac{\alpha + \beta + 1}{\beta + 1} \cdot \left(\frac{z}{h}\right)^\alpha \qquad /14/$$

The value given by eq./14/ is the average for the width b_z at elevation z above the bottom.

The above equations give a clear picture of the permeability distribution in vertical direction, if the general trend of the changes is known. Besides eq./7/ also other can be used. Repeating the calculation for all cross-sections, a relatively correct model of the seepage is obtained. Among others, the method can be used for predicting the changes of the phreatic level with raising height of the crest, or for an optimum design of additional drainage. The ratio of discharge through any arbitrary horizontal slice of a section can be determined as follows:

$$\frac{\Delta Q}{Q} = \frac{\int_{z_1}^{z_2} t/z/.dz}{T} = \frac{\int_{z_1}^{z_2} k/z/.b/z/.dz}{A.\bar{k}} \qquad /15/$$

As an example, for section No.3 /B = 135 m, h = 26,5 m, β = 1/, five different distributions of permeability were assumed, and the relative discharge from the bottom to different relativ levels calculated. The results shown in Table III confirm, that in impoundments built with the upstream method deep drainage elements are not economic.

Seepage through vertical slices of the section, too, can be similarly computed.

CONCLUSIONS

Approximate analytic solutions for seepage through granular tailings impoundments are possible, if changes of the grain size and the permeability are continuous.

The simplified model works with average values, and neglects not only the vertical component of the velocity vector, but also its horizontal component perpendicular to the main direction of the seepage. Comparison with FEM results and approximate solutions for radial flow confirmed fully the practical value of the method.

In practice, however, a realistic geotechnical model of the problem can be defined and succesfully solved only on the basis of realistic informations about valley geometry, phreatic surface and discharge, or about the spatial distribution of grain size, resp. permeability of the tailings.

REFERENCES

Wahler,W.,Schlick,D.P. /1976/. Mine refuse impoundments in the United States. Transactions 12th Int.Conf.on Large Dams, /I/, 279 - 319, Mexico

Jesenák,J./1983/. Contribution to the hydraulics of the continuously inhomogeneous porous medium /in Slovak/. Vodohospodársky časopis No.6, 626 - 642, Bratislava

Jesenák,J., Masarovičová, M. /1983/. Baugrundmechanische Untersuchungen des Flotationsabfalls einer Kupferhütte. Proc. 7th Danube-European Conf. Soil Mech. Found. Engg, /I/9/, 59 - 66, Kishinev

TABLE III

$\frac{z}{h}$	$\Sigma \Delta Q/Q \, [\%]$				
	1	2	3	4	5
0,1	1	0,1	0,3	0,03	0,4
0,2	4	1	1,8	0,36	1,9
0,3	9	3	4,9	1,5	4,8
0,4	16	6	10,1	4,1	9,6
0,5	25	13	17,7	8,8	16,7
0,6	36	22	27,9	16,7	26,4
0,7	49	34	41,0	28,7	39,2
0,8	64	51	57,0	45,8	55,5
0,9	81	73	76,8	69,2	75,6
1,0	100	100	100	100	100

Note:
1 - $k = const.$
2 - $k(z) = k_1 \cdot z^{0,5}$
3 - $k(z) = k_1 \cdot z^{1,5}$
4 - $k(z) = k_1 \cdot z^{1,5}$
5 - $k(z) = 0,33 k_1 \cdot h + k_1 \cdot z$

Bentonite treated colliery spoil for sealing waste disposals

Résidus traités par bentonite pour l'étanchéité de l'endroit de dépôt

H. L. JESSBERGER, Professor of Civil Engineering, Ruhr-University Bochum, FRG
W. EBEL, Dipl.-Ing., Ruhr-University Bochum, FRG
R. A. BEINE, Dipl.-Ing., Jessberger & Partner Consultants, Bochum, FRG

SYNOPSIS   In this paper a method for construction of sealing layers using colliery spoil is introduced. In mining areas colliery spoil has proved to be an economic and convenient material for sealing waste disposals after being mixed with suitable additives. These additives are bentonite and clay for sealing and sand, silt or rock powder for improving the gradation. The coefficient of permeability for recommended mixtures keeps within $2 \cdot 10^{-9}$ m/s, Darcy's law is not valid. The choice of bentonite should take into account the swelling properties and the thixotropy, the product herein called "effectivity". Useful hints for practical application are given. In an appendix the used permeameter and obtained flow rules are described for low hydraulic gradients.

INTRODUCTION

Waste disposals are producing contaminates which must not penetrate into the ground water. Therefore it is necessary to seal a waste disposal against the adjacent ground with permanently effective layers.

In mining areas colliery spoil is available which was found to be very useful for building high quality sealing layers. Fig. 1 gives the scheme of a waste disposal with a sealing layer built by mineral material which consists mainly of colliery spoil with some additives.

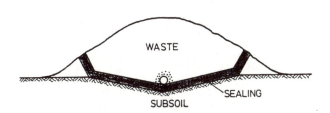

Fig. 1   Scetch of waste disposal with impervious sealing layer

This paper describes the technology of building horizontal impervious layers and gives informations about the material behaviour. In addition test results both in laboratory and in situ are presented and discussed.

THE METHOD TO BUILD MINERAL SEALING LAYERS

The mineral sealing layer is built with natural soil material, especially silt or clay. A certain amount of sand content is possible. For locations where the in situ soil conditions are not sufficient for building impermeable layers admixtures can be used. For these cases it is quite common to admix bentonite in order to decrease the permeability. The gradation can also be improved by admixing sand or silt.

This paper is dealing with the application of colliery spoil which is improved by sodiumbentonite. Hänsel (1981) published results of a major research project and he found that the permeability of a bentonite improved sealing layer is almost constant for a test period of 40 days. In addition he reported that material for impervious vertical walls consisting of artificially treated sodium-bentonite and cement is stable during a test period of 10 months.

The authorities demand that the mineral sealing layer has a coefficient of permeability not higher than $1 \cdot 10^{-8}$ or $2 \cdot 10^{-9}$ m/s respectively. The thickness of the layer has to be at least 60 cm. In addition an effective drainage system is requested in order to keep the water head restricted. Furthermore the blanket has to be trafficable during construction period and it has to be strong enough in order not to be squeezed out by overburden loads.

This demands can be met by soils or colliery spoil materials which are improved by special admixtures if necessary. The construction method is shown in Fig. 2, in which the final thickness of 60 cm is reached by building two layers of 30 cm. In the given example betonite is spread

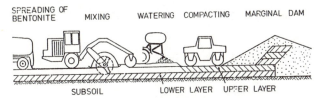

Fig. 2   Working procedures for a mineral sealing layer with bentonite

out on top of the untreated layer and than admixed to the soil using a rotary hoe. The water content of this lose material can be increased in order to reach the optimum content which allowes an effective compaction. Fig. 3 is a photo taken from the construction site showing the mix-in-place procedure.

Fig. 3   Mix-in-place technique

MATERIAL PROPERTIES OF COLLIERY SPOIL

Colliery spoil is rock hauled together with coal and then separated from the coal in washing procedures. The material can be described as shale or schist, sometimes containing sandstone. Worth to mention that schist will be disaggregated when it is exposed to the atmosphere. In general there is a broad variety of the soil mechanics properties of colliery spoil material as it is shown in Table I.

TABLE I

Soil parameters of colliery spoil

		colliery spoil			material 2
		range	mean value	
ρ_s	t/m^3	2,15-2,65	2,40	2,52
$\rho_{d\ min}^*$	t/m^3	1,15-1,35	1,25	-
$\rho_{d\ max}^*$	t/m^3	1,60-1,80	1,75	-
ρ_d^+	t/m^3	1,50-2,15	-	$\rho_{Pr} = 2,15$
w_{opt}	%	6 - 7	-	6,8
E_s	MN/m^2	25 - 47 at 95-100 % D_{Pr}	-	-
ϕ'	°	37 - 51	-	-
c'	kN/m^2	14 - 52	-	-

*laboratory
+in situ

The numbers of this table are taken from Annen and Stalmann (1968) with exception of the last column which contains the data of the material used for the tests described in this paper.

Colliery spoil is widely used for building dams, for roads and coffer dams. The coefficient of permeability is $5 \cdot 10^{-3}$ m/s for fresh and about $1 \cdot 10^{-5}$ m/s for weathered material.

Fig. 4 shows the gradation curve of two colliery spoil materials (material 1 and material 2). Material 1 is too coarse to be mixed with the rotary hoe, but material 2 is more suitable as far as the content of coarse grains is concerned and also with respect to the grain size distribution compared with the Fuller curve.

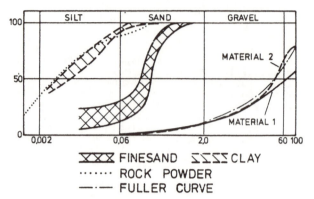

XXX FINESAND ΣΣΣΣ CLAY
······ ROCK POWDER
—·— FULLER CURVE

Fig. 4   Grain-size distribution of the investigated colliery spoil and various admixtures

The first step for reduction of the coefficient of permeability is the improvement of the gradation curve by admixing silty fine sand which filles the larger pores. The next step can be admixing clay or bentonite. In case suitable clay is available on site the admixing of clay is an economic solution. But in many cases bentonite is used because it is available with known conditions. In Fig. 4 the gradation curves of fine sand, clay and rock powder used in the herein described tests are given. Table II characterizes these materials. In Table III the amount of the various admixtures in percent of the dry colliery spoil is given.

TABLE II

Soil parameters of admixtures

additive	content (%)
silty fine sand	0/8/10/12/16
clay	0/2/4
rock powder	0/2/4
bentonite A	0/0,75/1,0/1,5
bentonite B	0/1/2

A broad variety of different brands of bentonite is available on the market. It is to be expected that the different brands do not have the same properties with respect to the behaviour of ready mixed and compacted mixture. In order to select the best bentonite with respect to effectivity and economy the special properties of bentonite like swelling and thixotropy

TABLE III

Type and amount of admixtures to colliery spoil material

Additive	clay 0,002 mm	silt 0,002 to 0,06 mm	sand 0,06 to 2,0 mm	ρ_s [t/m^3]	ρ_d	ρ	w [%]	k [m/s]
silty fine sand	-	22	78	2,65-2,66	1,63-1,65	1,91-1,93	15,6-18,5	$9,6 \cdot 10^{-7}$ $1,4 \cdot 10^{-6}$
clay	40	55	5	2,57-2,60	11,9-12,3	1,65-1,71	38,6-39,4	$2,9 \cdot 10^{-9}$ $4,0 \cdot 10^{-8}$
rock powder	35	52	13	2,72				
bentonite	75	25		2,60			7 - 12	

are to be tested. The swelling is described as the volume increase of bentonite after water adsorption. The method to determine the swelling volume ∆V is described by Jessberger et al. (1983). The intensive swelling is an advantage because it leads to closing of the pores within the mixture.

The thixotropic behaviour is described by the value $N = V_1/V_s$; V_1 is the volume of the liquid (water) and V_s is the volume of the solid substance. The value N is determined for a congelation period of 1 minute. This value N can be used as indicator of the activity of the bentonite.

For a clear distinction between various bentonite brands the so called "effectivity" is introduced as the product of N times ∆V/V. Figure 5 shows some test results for various bentonites and the different behaviour of the tested bentonites is obvious. For the investigations described in this paper bentonite A and B are used.

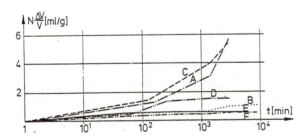

Fig. 5   "Effectivity" of various bentonites
A,C,D: activated bentonite
B: activated and natural bentonite
E,F: natural bentonite

PERMEABILITY TESTS

The decision for the amount of admixtures related to the colliery spoil material is based on the results of permeability tests. These tests are performed with constant head in modified proctor moulds. The mould has a diameter of 25 cm and a height of 18 cm in order to allow a maximum grain size of 63 mm.

The mixtures are compacted in the mould according to the compaction energy of the original proctor test. Saturation is reached by introducing a back pressure of 2 bar. After 18 hours of saturation the permeability test is performed with a water head of 500 cm which leads to i = 28.

In the appendix an advanced method for performing the permeability test is described. With a special balance a small water volume penetrating the sample can be measured and recorded automatically.

TEST RESULTS AND DISCUSSION

A series of tests were performed with two colliery spoil materials (material 1 and material 2) and two bentonites (bentonite A and bentonite B) with and without admixing fine sand or rock powder.

The test results show that the permeability of the coarse material 1 is about 4 times higher than that of the finer material 2 using 1 % bentonite A and 8 to 16 % silty fine sand as admixtures. With respect to the construction procedure on site it is advantageous that an increase of sand content in the given branch is not influencing the result. A remarkable reduction of the permeability can be produced by admixing rock powder or natural clay of about 2 to 4 % in addition to 1 % bentonite A and 8 % silty fine sand. An increase of the bentonite content of 1 to 1,5 % does not improve the impermeability considerably.

The type of the admixed bentonite is influencing the permeability in that way that the permeability of the mixtures containing bentonite A is much lower than that mixtures containing bentonite B which is in good agreement to the information of Fig. 5.

There is also a remarkable difference in the properties of the mixture with colliery spoil material 1 and material 2. The coefficient of permeability of $2 \cdot 10^{-9}$ m/s can be reached for material 1 only if bentonite and clay or rock powder is admixed. In contrary for material 2 clay or rock powder admixtures are not necessary. For a special waste disposal project the following mixture was recommended:

Colliery spoil material 2

1 % bentonite A

8 % silty fine sand

The test results indicated that there is a direct relationship between density and permeability. It was found that in some cases the requested coefficient of permeability can be reached only with a certain dry density of the mixture. During construction this density can be achieved by supplementary compaction which was performed one or two days after the moulding of the sample. The effect of this supplementary compaction is caused by the needed swelling period of the bentonite which lies in the order of 20 hours. The dry density is increased by about 3 % caused by the supplementary compaction which is in agreement with the fact that the density influences directly the permeability. Fig. 6 shows that there seems to be a limitation as far as the advantageous effect of the supplementary compaction is concerned. Obviously with the used mixtures a coefficient of permeability lower than $8 \cdot 10^{-10}$ m/s will not be reached.

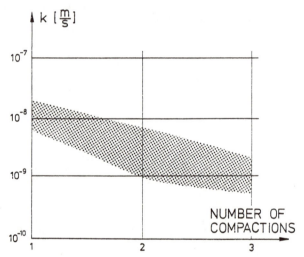

Fig. 6   Influence of supplementary compaction on the coefficient of permeability

It is important to have in mind that the water content of the mixture during compaction should be always on the wet side of the proctor curve. On the construction site enough water should be available which is needed for the swelling procedure of the bentonite. On the other hand if the water content is too high the workability and the trafficability of the sealing layer is difficult or even absent.

The long term permeability with water is investigated for two identical samples. After two days the samples were supplementary compacted with the desired effect of remarkable decrease of permeability (Fig. 7). The tests were performed during a period of 220 days with water pressure gradient of i = 11. For the repeatedly performed permeability tests during this time the short term gradient was i = 28. In the tests the k-value was increased slightly but after a while it

again decreased, probably caused by the fact that the fine grained particles close the pores. This effect was also described by Hänsel (1981).

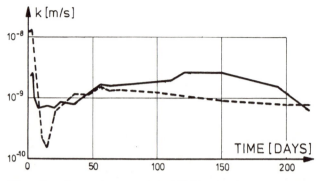

Fig. 7   Long-term permeability tests

The suitability of a mineral sealing layer is judged on the base of the flow equation which is commonly formulated as Darcy's law and gives the direct relation between flow velocity and hydraulic gradient with the k-value as constant factor.

Recently it was found that for low permeabilities there is no direct proportionality. Fig. 8 summarizes various flow equations which generally can be expressed according to Kezdi

$$v = \kappa \cdot (i - i_a)^{\alpha}$$

If the yield gradient $i_a = 0$ the curve will be a parabola penetrating the origin as proposed by Hansbo (1960).

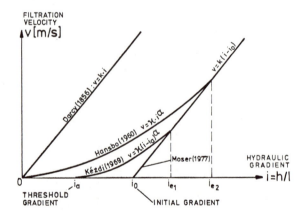

Fig. 8   Hydraulic gradient versus filtration velocity

The results of test series for investigating the flow equation of colliery spoil material, treated with silty sand and bentonite are given in Fig. 9. The results of test 1 were obtained immediately after sample preparation and saturation, whereas the measurements of test 2 and test 3 were taken 2 and 4 days after sample preparation and saturation. From Fig. 9 can be seen that only the measurements of test 1 are covering Darcy's flow equation. For test 2 and test 3 linearity between velocity and gradient is established only for i > 10. With the new test method described in the Appendix it was possible to reduce the hydraulic gradient to less than 1 and it was found for two clayey and silty soils that Darcy's law is not valid under these conditions. This finding is in agreement with the test results published by Gabener (1982).

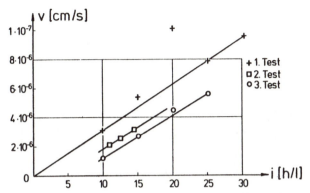

Fig. 9   Hydraulic gradient versus filtration velocity for mineral sealing material consisting of colliery spoil and various admixtures

HINTS FOR PRACTICAL APPLICATION

Referring to Fig. 2 the mineral sealing layer is constructed by building two layers of 30 cm thickness each. This two layers procedure is necessary because of the restricted working depth of commonly available mixing machines. In addition the requested density of a 30 cm thick layer can easily be achieved and also be controlled. The result of the mixing is checked by eyes in order to make sure that the mixture is homogeneous. After the first mixing the water content of the mixture is measured and if necessary increased by watering.
The watering should be done with a suitable vehicle after the surface of the mixture was made even and was slightly compacted with a static roller. After watering the area is compacted dynamically. Depending on the available equipment and the properties of the subsoil 4 runs with a dynamic roller are sufficient to reach the requested density.

For acceptance of the sealing layer it is almost impossible to perform in situ tests. Therefore the deductive method is used by measuring the in situ density and compare it with the density found by laboratory tests to be needed to meet the demands of a certain coefficient of permeability.

Following this method the acceptance procedure starts with taking a sample in situ together with measuring the in situ density. The disturbed sample is remoulded in laboratory to the in situ density and also taken for measuring the permeability. If the requested permeability is not reached, supplementary compaction is performed until the demands are met. With this procedure the in situ density is taken as measure of the permeability factor in situ. In many tests it was shown that this procedure of acceptance leads to good results and does not produce delay of the construction work.

In case of wet soil conditions the compaction can produce pore water pressure increase and reduction in the bearing capacity of the sealing layer. Under these circumstances it can be necessary to leave 1 day time interval between each run of supplementary compaction.

SUMMARY

The basic principles of the application of mineral sealing layers for waste disposals using colliery spoil material are described. The following conclusions can be drawn.

a) Colliery spoil together with suitable admixtures in small percentages can be used successfully to build mineral sealing layers.

b) The authority's regulations can be fulfilled especially the long-term impermeability.

c) The inspection for acceptance of the sealing layer can be executed with density tests.

d) In mining areas the use of colliery spoil for sealing layers of waste disposals is an effective and economic solution.

ACKNOWLEDGEMENT

The test results in this paper were performed fulfilled a contract with the Abfallbeseitigungsbetriebe Ruhrgebiet Essen. The permission to publish the results is greatfully acknowledged.

REFERENCES

Annen, G., Stalmann, N. (1968). Die Eignung von Nebengestein des Kohlenbergbaus (Waschberge) zum Bau von Deichen und Dämmen. Technisch-wissenschaftliche Mitteilungen der Emschergenossenschaft und des Lippeverbandes, Heft 7

Gabener, H.G. (1982). Über den Durchflußwiderstand feinkörniger Böden beim hydraulischen Grundbruch. Mitteilungen aus dem Fachgebiet Grundbau und Bodenmechanik, Heft 4, pp. 251-267

Hänsel, W. (1981). Prüfung der Dichtungswirkung und Beständigkeit von Deponieabdichtungen mit Bentonit und natürlichen Tonen. Vortrag Fachtagung der Südchemie AG, Bentonite im Erd- und Spezialtiefbau.

Jessberger, H.L., Beine, R.A., Ebel, W. (1983). Herstellung von Basisabdichtungen für Mülldeponien mit Waschbergen. Müll und Abfall 15(1983) pp. 193-200

APPENDIX

The permeability tests are now performed in a permeability measuring system as shown in Fig. 10. This apparatus was designed because of the experience with the flow equation shown in Fig. 9. The volume measuring system consists of a weighing apparatus, which records the volume of flow by an accuracy of 0,01 cm^3. The sample my be moulded either in a rigid wall permeameter or in a triaxial cell. It is saturated by back pressure. At low hydraulic gradients the potential drop Δh is controlled as shown in the figure.

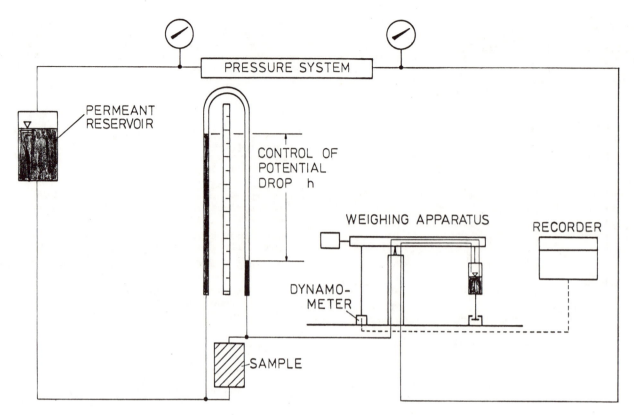

Fig. 10   Schematic diagram of the permeability measuring system

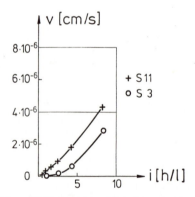

Fig. 11   Filtration velocity versus
hydraulic gradient for in situ-
samples

The results of two test series are plotted in
Fig. 11. The samples tested were taken from a
construction site. The soil in situ was a
clayey silt (S 11) and a clay (S 3) respectively. The obtained flow equations show a parabolic
curve of velocity versus hydraulic gradient. The
curvature for clay is greater than that for silt,
a threshold gradient for the silt is not evident whereas the clay seems to have a threshold
gradient in the order of 1. This fact is important for the judgement of the soils for sealing
purposes.

The effect of chemical contamination on soil strength

L'effet de la pollution chimique sur la résistance du sol

N. K. KUMAPLEY, Associate Professor of Civil Engineering, University of Science & Technology, Kumasi, Ghana
A. ISHOLA, Formerly Research Assistant, Department of Civil Engineering, University of Science & Technology, Kumasi, Ghana

SYNOPSIS   While the principle of the base exchange capacity of soils has been used extensively in civil engineering in the area of admixture stabilisation of soils, the related problem of the detrimental effects of chemical contaminants on the mechanical properties of soils has not been adequately addressed. Recent case histories of structural damage to industrial buildings resulting from chemical contamination of soils serve to emphasise the importance which needs to be attached to the consideration of the problem. Some evidence has been presented to indicate that drastic decrease in shear strength of soils could be one of the consequences of contamination which results in an increase in pH of the soil. Careful planning of storage, handling and disposal facilities for industrial chemicals and effluent has been suggested as a way of mitigating the problem.

INTRODUCTION

The principle of base exchange capacity of soils has found wide application in the fields of agronomy, ceramics and engineering following the pioneering work on the subject by Thompson (circa, 1850) and Way (1850). Until recently, however, the main application of the principle in civil engineering has been in the area of chemical stabilisation of soils for highway and air-field construction. Consequently, initial efforts were directed towards the investigation of the influence of chemical additives on the consistency limits of soils (Winterkorn, 1941; Lambe, 1953; Katti et al, 1962; Fossberg, 1963). In recent years, however, the related problem of the influence of chemical contaminants on other engineering properties of soils has began to receive considerable attention from geotechnical engineers. Sherard et al (1972) discussed the influence of pore water chemistry on the erosion susceptibility of soils. Wagener et al (1981) described an interesting case history in which the properties of a dispersive clay were altered by cation exchange in the field during the rehabilitation of a dam which failed by dispersive piping, while Anderson (1982) discussed the possibility of changes in the permeability of clay liners in industrial landfills as a result of prolonged contact with organic liquids. By comparison, however, the influence of chemical contaminants on the strength and deformation properties of soils has received relatively little attention.

This paper discusses some aspects of the effect of chemical contaminants on the mechanical properties of soils and suggests the need for geotechnical engineers to take measures to prevent possible long-term effects of chemical contamination of the subsoils resulting from careless storage, handling and disposal of industrial chemicals and effluent.

EFFECT OF CHEMICAL CONTAMINANTS ON THE MECHANICAL PROPERTIES OF SOILS

With the possible exception of efforts aimed at stabilising soft clays using the principle of base exchange (Katti et al, 1981; Matsuo and Kamon, 1981) the effect of chemical contaminants on the mechanical properties of soils does not appear to have received the attention it deserves, given current global emphasis on detailed studies addressing environmental problems relating to all aspects of the disposal of hazardous waste and other highly aggressive industrial effluents. This has resulted in some expensive foundation failures. Lukas et al (1972) gave a detailed account of the foundation failures of three industrial buildings as a result of chemical reactions between the subsoil and accidental chemical spillages, which were acidic in two of the cases and basic in the other. They attributed the large settlements recorded in each case, to soil losses as a result of the dissolution of either the limestone in glacial till or the high silica sand subsoils in the chemical contaminants. They also recorded substantial reductions in SPT blow-counts in borings made after the chemical contamination compared with the original borings. Shridharan et al (1981) also discussed a case history of extensive cracking damage to light industrial buildings in a fertilizer factory as a result of the heaving of the potentially expansive foundation soils because of acid contamination resulting from leakage of industrial effluents into the subsoils.

A similar case of accidental seepage of highly concentrated caustic soda solution and lye into the subsoils as a result of spillages, and seepage through cracked drains in an industrial establishment in Tema, Ghana, caused considerable structural damage to light industrial buildings in the factory, in addtion to localised subsidence of the affected area. The foundation soils consisted of about 1.5 m of dark-green plastic clay overlying light-brown friable silty clay containing calcium carbonate concretions - both soil types being decomposition products of the underlying granite-gneiss rock which was encountered at a depth of 8m. The ground water table at the site was struck at a depth of some 6m. The pH of the uncontaminated soil was 6.5. Measurement of pH profiles at two locations close to each other within the affected area, shown in Fig 1, indicate the appreciable rate of contamination. Trial pits sunk in the affected area also showed seepage of caustic soda at certain depths, thus implying the existence of erosion channels within the otherwise intact foundation soil.

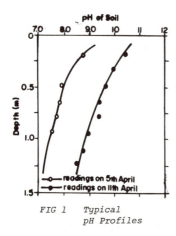

FIG 1 Typical
pH Profiles

Among the possible causes of structural distress was the deterioration in soil strength as a result of chemical reactions in the soil. In order to investigate this possibility, a laboratory investigation of the effect of caustic soda contamination on the strength and consistency limits of soils was undertaken.

LABORATORY INVESTIGATION

Materials Tested

Three different types of soil were used in the experimental work. These were;

(a) A greyish mottled clay derived from the decomposition of Accra Shales.

(b) A reddish micaceous silty clay formed as a weathering product of biotite granite from Kumasi, and

(c) an alluvial silty clay

The particle size distributions and the consistency limits of the raw soils are given in Fig 2.

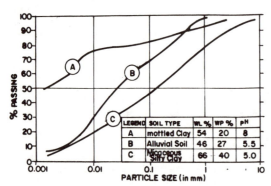

LEGEND	SOIL TYPE	WL %	WP %	pH
A	mottled Clay	54	20	8
B	Alluvial Soil	46	27	5.5
C	Micaceous Silty Clay	66	40	5.0

FIG 2 Particle Size Distribution Curves.

It has not been possible carry out chemical and mineralogical analyses on the soil samples. However, according to de Graft-Johnson et al (1967) the predominant clay mineral in the Accra Shale is kaolinite, while unpublished results of analyses carried out by the Ghana Geological Survey showed that the most common clay mineral in most of the local residual soils is kaolinite.

It is therefore reasonable to suppose that the predominant clay mineral in all three samples is kaolinite.

Sample Preparation

The minus No.36 (B.S.) sieve portion of each soil was repeatedly washed with distilled water until the pH of the supernatant water, determined after 24 hours of soaking, was approximately 7, indicating a neutral condition. In doing this, particular care was taken to ensure that loss of fines is prevented.

The soil samples so prepared were oven-dried and divided into various portions which were then mixed with caustic soda solutions of varying concentrations, produced by dissolving caustic soda pellets in distilled water. The pH of the soil-caustic soda mixtures were determined prior to their storage in plastic containers to cure for seven days before testing.

Experimental Technique

Using the GEONOR type of Cone Penetrometer device, a relationship was established between the cone penetration and moisture content, for each soil type in both the contaminated and the raw states, and for moisture contents around the liquid limits of the raw soils. The liquid limits of the contaminated soils were determined from the cone penetration values, as were the undrained shear strengths of the soils, using the relationship established by Hansbo (1957).

DISCUSSION OF RESULTS

Effect of Caustic Soda Contamination on the Liquid Limit

Increasing concentration of caustic soda contamination generally caused a decrease in the liquid limits of the soil as shown in Fig 3, with the decrease more marked in the case of the mottled clay than the other two soil types.

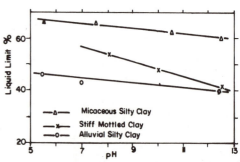

FIG 3 Variation of Liquid Limit with pH Concentration

This decrease in liquid limit with increasing degree of caustic soda contamination, also noted by other researchers, is clearly a reflection of the experimental observation that the soil samples became more friable with increasing concentrations of caustic soda contaminant.

Variation of Undrained Shear Strength with Level of Caustic Soda Contamination

All three soils types showed a general decrease in undrained shear strength with increasing pH concentration. Fig 4 shows the variation for the decomposed clay shale and the alluvial soil. In this case also, the decrease in undrained shear strength displayed by the decomposed clay shale is more marked than that shown by either the alluvial soil or the decomposed granite, both of which contained considerably less clay sized particles, and probably less clay minerals. The present study focussed only on the shear strengths of the soils around

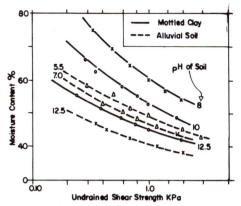

FIG 4 *Variation of Undrained shear strength with pH Concentration.*

REFERENCES

Anderson, D. (1982). Does landfill leachate make clay liners more permeable? Civil Engineering - ASCE Sept. 1982 66-69.

de Graft-Johnson, J.W.S., Bhatia, H.S. and M.D. Gidigasu (1967). The consolidation and swell characteristics of Accra Mottled Clays. Proc. 3rd Asian Reg. Conf. Soil Mech. and Found. Engg. (1) 75-80. Haifa.

Fossberg, P.E. (1963). Sulphite Lye Treatment of Gravel Roads in South Africa. Proc. 3rd African Reg. Conf. on Soil Mech. and Found. Engg. (1) 73-76, Salisbury.

Hansbo, A. (1957). A new approach to the determination of the shear strength of clay by the Fall-Cone Test. Proc. Royal Swedish Geot. Inst. No.14. Stockholm.

Katti, R.K., Dongarwar, D.W. and S.H. Patwardhan (1981). Studies of Electrochemical Hardening of Marine Clay. Proc. 10th Int. Conf. Soil Mech. and Found. Engg. (3) 717-720. Stockholm,

Katti, R.K. and A.G. Barve (1962). Effect of Inorganic Chemicals on the Consistency Properties of an Expansive Soil Sample. Bull. No.349, 1-7, H.R.B. 1962. Washington, D.C.

Lambe, T.W. (1953). The effect of Polymers on Soil Properties. Proc. 3rd Int. Conf. Soil Mech. and Found. Engg. (1). 253-257. Zurich.

Lukas, R.G. and R.J. Gnaedinger Jr. (1972). Settlement due to Chemical attack of soils. Proc. ASCE Specialty Conf. on the Performance of Earth and Earth-Supported Structures (1). Purdue Univ., Lafayette. Indiana. (1972) 1087-1104.

Matsuo, S. and M. Kamon (1981). Soil Stabilization by Multivalent Cations. Proc. 10th Int. Conf. Soil Mech. and Found. Engg. (3). 735-738. Stockholm.

Sherard, J.L., Decker, R.S. and N.L. Ryker (1972). Piping in Earth Dams of Dispersive Clay. Proc. ASCE Specialty Conf. on the Performance of Earth and Earth-Supported Structures (1). Purdue Univ., Lafayette. Indiana. 1972. 589-626.

Sridharan A., Nagaraj, T.S., and P.V. Sivapullaiah (1981) Heaving of Soil Due to Acid Contamination. Proc. 10th Int. Conf. Soil Mech. Found. Engg. (2). 383-386. Stockholm.

Thompson, H.S. (1850). On the Absorbent Power of Soils. Journal, Royal Agric. Society, Vol. 11 66-74. London.

Wagener, F.v.M., Harmse, H.J.v.M., and P. Stone (1981). Chemical Treatment of a Dispersive Clay Reservoir. Proc. 10th Int. Conf. on Soil Mech. and Found Engg. (3) 785-791. Stockholm,

Way, J.T. (1850). On the Power of Soils to absorb Manure.Journal, Royal Agric. Soc. Vol.11 313-379. London.

Winterkorn, H.F. (1941). A study of changes in Physical Properties of Putnam Soil induced by Ionic Substitution. Proc. H.R.B. (21). 415-433. Washington, D.C.

the liquid limit, mainly in a desire the obtain more uniform samples for testing. There is no reason to suppose that the trend of the results obtained will be any different at lower consistencies.

CONCLUDING REMARKS

Since the caustic soda acts as a dispersing agent, it is to be expected that increasing the pH of the soil/water system would lead to a reduction in the interparticle forces, which would, in turn account for the friable nature of the contaminated soil and the recorded reduction in undrained shear strength. Clearly, in a given situation, the extent of the deterioration in strength will be a function of the soil chemistry, the nature and concentration of the contaminant and the level of the groundwater table and its range of fluctuation, since the groundwater will not only influence the concentration of the contaminant, but would also aid the removal of some of the products of the chemical reaction. In general, the effects of chemical contamination of soils would be more serious in situations of deep water table.

It has not been possible to investigate the effect of caustic soda contamination on the compressibility characteristics of the soils under test, but it is reasonable to expect increased settlement with prolonged caustic soda contamination as a result of the reduction in equilibrium void ratios for a given stress level, particularly in the case of more heavily loaded foundations.

Storage, handling and disposal of industrial chemicals and effluents need to be carefully considered at the planning stage of industrial establishments, not only from the standpoint of environmental safety but also as a safeguard against drastic adverse changes in geotechnical properties of the foundation soils during the service life of the facility. In certain soil types, especially highly permeable formations, prolonged seepage of such contaminants into the soil could cause structural distress in many structures in the vicinity of the industrial establishment.

ACKNOWLEDGEMENT

The experimental work reported in this paper was done by the junior author in partial fulfilment of the requirements of the Bachelor of Science (Engineering) degree of the University of Science and Technology, Kumasi, Ghana.

Interaction of heat pump discharges in aquifers

Réactions de l'écoulement de pompe à chaleur en aquifères

G. V. MADABHUSHI, AWU Research Participant, US Geological Survey, WRD, WR, Menlo Park, California, USA
Y. K. KHARAKA, Research Hydrologist, US Geological Survey, WRD, WR, Menlo Park, California, USA
C. G. CLYDE, Professor of Civil Engineering, Utah State University, Logan, Utah, USA

SYNOPSIS   Studies indicate that the use of groundwater heat pumps for residential space heating and cooling conserves energy and may be more economical than many conventional heating and cooling systems. A groundwater heat pump extracts heat from groundwater during winter and discharges cold water into the aquifer. During summer the heat pump works as an air conditioner and discharges hot water into the aquifer. This paper explains the consequences of the interactions between the aquifer minerals and water injected at temperatures different from that of the groundwater. Porosity changes resulting from precipitation and/or dissolution of minerals in a typical aquifer are computed using equilibrium and mass-transfer geochemical models. Porosity changes are found to be of minor importance. Comments are offered to control adverse effects on the environment.

INTRODUCTION

Studies in many parts of the country indicate that the use of groundwater heat pumps for residential space heating and cooling conserves energy and may be more economical than many conventional heating and cooling systems (Utah Water Research Laboratory, 1979). Heat pumps are attractive because the groundwater temperature remains fairly constant throughout the year and there is no atmospheric pollution due to its usage. The groundwater heat pump extracts heat energy from incoming groundwater and delivers it into the home during the winter season. However, during the summer season the heat pump operates as an air conditioner by removing heat from the home and carrying it away by the outgoing groundwater, which is usually injected into the same aquifer through a separate well. A good description of the operation of a groundwater heat pump was given recently (Civil Engineering, 1983). A schematic representation of the groundwater heat pump operation is shown in Fig. 1.

Government regulations in many states such as Utah, require that the utilized groundwater should be re-injected back into the aquifer to conserve this precious resource, since arid conditions prevail in those areas. Monitoring of a groundwater heat pump at Logan, Utah, yielded a maximum temperature of 32°C in summer for the injected water and a minimum temperature of 4°C for the injected water during winter. The average groundwater temperature in that aquifer is 12.2°C. The temperatures of the injected water at St. Paul Energy Park in Minnesota (Civil Engineering, 1983) will be about 6°C and 30°C during winter heating and summer cooling, respectively. In this paper, we are selecting 50°C and 1°C as the maximum and minimum temperatures for the injected water.

In this study, 10 aquifers with different mineral and groundwater chemical compositions are considered. However, due to space limitations, results with respect to only one aquifer are presented. Chemical reactions which take place between the minerals of the aquifer and the injected hot or cold water are studied using equilibrium and mass-transfer geochemical models.

WATER-ROCK INTERACTIONS

Groundwater is a natural electrolyte and all the major and minor dissolved constituents are in the ionic form. It acquires these dissolved constituents principally while flowing through the unsaturated zone and from the dissolution of minerals present in the aquifer.

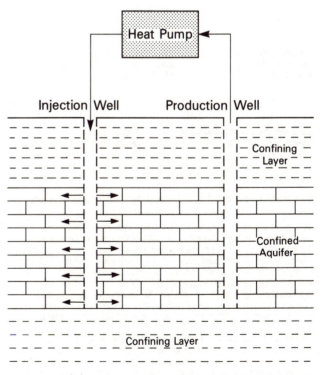

Fig. 1 Operation of Groundwater Heat Pump

Thus, a water-quality analysis is essential to gain an insight into the nature of aquifer minerals. An additional feature is that groundwater is relatively homogeneous and has fairly constant physical properties such as temperature and density. When the temperature of the groundwater is changed by the injection of hot or cold water by the heat pump, solubility of most minerals in the aquifer is affected. It is well known that the solubility of calcium carbonate in limestone aquifers decreases with increasing temperature. On the other hand, solubility of silica increases with increasing temperature. It is possible that groundwater saturated with a mineral such as calcite ($CaCO_3$) at ambient groundwater temperatures may precipitate calcite at higher temperatures. This precipitate may adhere to the aquifer material or it may become a suspended solid which could plug the pore channels in the aquifer.

In groundwater, the Gibbs free energy change (ΔG_{diff}) determines whether the water is undersaturated, saturated or supersaturated with respect to a particular mineral. The Gibbs free energy change is given by the equation:

$$\Delta G_{diff} = RT \ln\left(\frac{Q}{K}\right) \qquad (1)$$

where R is the gas constant, Q the activity product of the solutes and other species that participate in the reaction, T the absolute temperature in degrees Kelvin, and K the equilibrium constant for the reaction at a particular temperature. When the groundwater flows through a limestone aquifer containing the mineral calcite ($CaCO_3$), the reaction may be represented by

$$CaCO_{3(S)} \rightleftharpoons Ca^{2+} + CO_3^{2-}. \qquad (2)$$

For dissolution, the reaction will proceed to the right and

$$\Delta G_{diff} < 0 \qquad (3)$$

indicating undersaturation of the groundwater with respect to calcite. For precipitation of calcite, the reaction will proceed to the left and

$$\Delta G_{diff} > 0 \qquad (4)$$

indicating supersaturation of the groundwater with respect to calcite. The reaction is at equilibrium when

$$\Delta G_{diff} = 0 \qquad (5)$$

and neither precipitation nor dissolution takes place.

The equilibrium constants of all chemical reactions will be controlled by changes in temperature and pressure. In this case, the pressure may be assumed to be approximately constant, because it is a closed system and minor changes in pressure have an insignificant effect on the solubility of minerals. Thus, $\partial K/\partial P$ is treated as approximately equal to zero. However, in the present case, the temperature changes with injection of hot or cold water. The value of the equilibrium constant K generally changes significantly with temperature and $\partial K/\partial T$ can not be treated as zero. The magnitude of temperature effect depends mainly on the enthalpy of the reaction. Equilibrium positions of highly endothermic or exothermic reactions may vary with temperature more than those with small enthalpies of reaction.

Groundwaters tend to be in chemical equilibrium with the reactive minerals in the aquifer. A review of existing literature demonstrated that groundwaters in limestone aquifers tend to be in equilibrium with calcite ($CaCO_3$) and may be in equilibrium with gypsum ($CaSO_4.2H_2O$). However, at normal temperatures prevailing in aquifers, groundwaters are generally not in equilibrium with respect to silicate minerals because of their slow rates of reaction (Wollast, 1967).

Dissolution and precipitation of minerals is potentially important to the geotechnical engineer. A rise or fall in temperature of groundwater may cause dissolution or precipitation of minerals. Dissolution results in an increase of pore space and thus can cause a decrease in the fluid pressure in the aquifer. This will increase the effective stress which may cause land subsidence and consequent damage to the foundations of the overlying structures. On the other hand, precipitation will clog the pores and reduce the pore space possibly resulting in an increase of fluid pressure which will result in decrease in effective stress. This may culminate in uplift and sometimes even in an hydraulic fracture, which can cause extensive damage to the foundations of overlying structures. The main problem of clogging will be reduced yield of the aquifer. For the above reasons, it is imperative that the geotechnical engineer should be able to check whether precipitation or dissolution of minerals will occur as a result of temperature changes in groundwater.

GEOCHEMICAL MODELS USED

Two types of groundwater models are available to determine the reactions resulting from the disequilibrium between the aquifer minerals and the injected water differing in temperature. These models may be classified as follows: (1) aqueous-solution models, and (2) mass transfer models. The main difference between these two models is that, in the case of mass transfer models, it is possible to calculate the amount of precipitation or dissolution occurring in the aquifer. These models are briefly described below.

Aqueous Solution Models

Aqueous-solution models provide a technique by which measured chemical compositions of water are converted into thermodynamically significant quantities such as free ion activities. Ion activity is defined by the equation:

$$a_i = \gamma_i m_i \qquad (6)$$

where a_i, γ_i and m_i are the activity, activity coefficient, and molality of an ion i respectively. By using these models speciation of various cations and anions present in groundwater is computed, and the saturation indices of the water with respect to any mineral may be obtained. Therefore, they are also called speciation models.

In the present study, the model used for speciation is called SOLMNEQ (solution-mineral equilibria). SOLMNEQ is a computer program developed by the U.S. Geological Survey (Kharaka and Barnes, 1973) which, in its updated version, calculates equilibrium distribution of 180 inorganic aqueous species commonly present in natural waters over the temperature range of 0° to 350°C from the chemical analyses of groundwater, temperature, Eh (optional) and pH. Departures from equilibrium of the aqueous solutions with respect to 170 minerals are computed from the distribution of aqueous species and an internally consistent set of thermodynamic data. In this paper, the total value of carbon as CO_2 is computed by using the SOLMNEQ computer program with data inclusive of HCO_3 alkalinity and pH. For further details, one may refer to the original publication (Kharaka and Barnes, 1973).

Mass Transfer Models

By using mass transfer models, it is possible to calculate not only the speciation, activities and saturation indices, but also mass transfer between minerals and groundwater resulting from precipitation and dissolution. Solution reactions with mineral phases are treated in much the same way as are ion-complexation reactions in the solution itself. For each mineral reacting, a mass action expression may be written:

$$K_p = \prod_i a_i^{n_{ip}}, \; p = 1, 2, \ldots P \qquad (7)$$

where K_p is the equilibrium constant for the dissolution of phase p; a_i are the activities of dissolved free ions i; and n_{ip} is the stoichiometric coefficient of ion i in phase p. This equation in addition to the set of equations describing the solution, permits the addition of another unknown to the mass balance equations for each ion i. This additional term is the number of moles transferred between the solution and the phase p.

In the present study, the model used for mass transfer is called PHREEQE (pH-redox-equilibrium-equations). PHREEQE was developed by the U.S. Geological Survey (Parkhurst, Thorstenson, and Plummer, 1982). PHREEQE is based on an ion-pairing aqueous model. The compositions of solutions in equilibrium with multiple phases can be calculated. The model calculates pH, pe ($-\log a_e^-$), total concentration of elements, the amounts of minerals transferred into or out of the aqueous phase, distribution of aqueous species, and the saturation state of the aqueous phase with respect to specified mineral phases as a function of reaction progress. The equations used by PHREEQE are: (1) electrical neutrality (one equation), (2) conservation of electrons (one equation), (3) mass balance (one equation for each element except H and O), (4) mineral equilibrium (one equation for each mineral phase) and, (5) mass action equations for aqueous species (one for each aqueous specie). PHREEQE uses the continued fraction approach and the Newton-Raphson method to solve a set of algebraic equations by iterative techniques. For details, one may refer to the original publication (Parkhurst, Thorstenson, and Plummer, 1982).

METHOD OF CALCULATION

The following assumptions are made to make the computations as simple as possible. (1) The time taken for groundwater to travel through the heat pump system is small and the system is considered closed and the chemical composition of the groundwater is not significantly affected. (2) The amount of clay fraction in the aquifer is negligible compared to other minerals, so that, swelling and dispersion effects of the clay fraction may be ignored. (3) Kinetics are not considered. However, the time taken for precipitation or dissolution of a mineral is important for proper aquifer management.

To demonstrate the application of the models, a water-quality analysis is selected from Data of Geochemistry (White, Hem, and Waring, 1963). The aquifer is Meagher Limestone from Ennis, Montana. The composition of the groundwater and aquifer temperature are shown in Table I. PHREEQE program also requires a redox potential, in terms of pe as an input. The appropriate value of pe may be estimated roughly from the iron concentration in the water analysis using the Eh-pH diagram for iron (Hem and

TABLE I

Groundwater-Quality Analysis of
Meagher Limestone Aquifer, Ennis, Montana

Species	Concentration (mg/l)
SiO_2	11
Al	0.2
Fe	0
Mn	0
Ca	53
Mg	19
Na	2.8
K	1.6
HCO_3	187
SO_4	61
Cl	2.2
F	0.3
NO_3	1.4
PO_4	0.05
Temp	12.2°C
pH	7.8

Cropper, 1959) and the equation:

$$Eh = 0.059 \; pe. \qquad (8)$$

In this water-quality analysis the iron concentration is reported as zero, hence it can be assumed to be small. A value of pe for this sample was selected by trial and error from the range -5.0 to $+5.0$. The value selected is that for which the program converges with the least number of iterations. In this case, a value of -4.00 for pe is obtained. The total value of carbon as CO_2 is computed and the value is found to be 138.48 mg/l.

In limestone aquifers, the minerals of interest are calcite ($CaCO_3$), aragonite ($CaCO_3$), gypsum ($CaSO_4 \cdot 2H_2O$), anhydrite ($CaSO_4$), dolomite ($CaMg(CO_3)_2$), quartz, chalcedony and silica gel. As no iron is present in the water-quality analysis, iron minerals are not considered. The value of total carbon obtained using SOLMNEQ is used in the PHREEQE to compute mass transfer. The amount of mineral precipitated or dissolved is usually directly proportional to the surface area of the mineral particles present in the aquifer, therefore each mineral is assumed to equilibrate individually with hot water in summer at 50°C and cold water in winter at 1°C. This assumption will yield the worst case to be expected because individual equilibration gives the maximum amount of precipitation or dissolution of the mineral in question.

RESULTS AND DISCUSSION

Table II shows amounts of minerals precipitated or dissolved per kilogram of the water being modelled at 50°C and 1°C. These data can be used to estimate the rate at which precipitated mineral will decrease the pore space in the aquifer or the rate at which dissolution of minerals will increase the aquifer pore space especially around the injection well. From a knowledge of the porosity and thickness of the aquifer and rates of water injection and movement, the volume of the aquifer within which precipitation or dissolution will occur may be estimated.

In our problem, assuming an effective porosity of 25%, and flow velocity of 0.01 meter per day, the distance having a temperature of 50°C or 1°C on each side of the injection well may be roughly estimated to be about 2 meters (Reed and Reddell, 1980; Mercer, Faust, Miller and Pearson, Jr., 1982). Assuming an average thickness of

25 meters for the aquifer and an injection rate of 10 gpm $(3.785 \times 10^{-2}$ m^3/min)it will take about 1.8 days to fill the pore volume of the affected aquifer with water at either 50°C or 1°C. For a season of six months of winter or summer, calculations show that a maximum of 93 pore volumes will pass through the affected volume of the aquifer during every season. In this study we computed the volumes of minerals dissolved or precipitated assuming 100 pore volumes of water per season.

TABLE II

Precipitation and Dissolution from PHREEQE in moles/kg H$_2$O (-Precipitation, + Dissolution)

Mineral	Saturation Index at 12.2°C	Precipitation or Dissolution	
		50°C	1°C
Calcite	0.1405	-1.46×10^{-4}	-2.63×10^{-5}
Aragonite	-0.0129	-9.38×10^{-5}	$+1.61 \times 10^{-5}$
Gypsum	-1.8521	$+1.49 \times 10^{-2}$	$+1.22 \times 10^{-2}$
Anhydrite	-2.313	$+1.54 \times 10^{-2}$	$+3.35 \times 10^{-2}$
Fluorite	-1.6413	$+8.09 \times 10^{-5}$	$+3.50 \times 10^{-5}$
Gibbsite	1.2512	-3.70×10^{-6}	-5.70×10^{-6}
Chalcedony	-0.0635	$+3.71 \times 10^{-4}$	-3.13×10^{-5}
Quartz	0.4723	$+4.17 \times 10^{-5}$	-1.44×10^{-4}
Silica gel.	-0.917	$+3.95 \times 10^{-3}$	$+7.03 \times 10^{-4}$
Dolomite	-0.0334	Not considered	
Microcline	2.867	$+6.87 \times 10^{-6}$	-6.97×10^{-6}

Computations (Table II) show that the water is slightly supersaturated with calcite at ambient temperature of this groundwater. The decrease in porosity resulting from calcite precipitation is only 0.2% and 0.04% at 50°C and 1°C respectively. The water is slightly undersaturated with aragonite at ambient temperature and the decrease in porosity at 50°C is very small (0.1%) and the increase in porosity is insignificant (0.02%) at 1°C. Dolomite is not considered as it will not precipitate or dissolve in the temperature and time ranges considered. The water is undersaturated with gypsum at ambient temperature; the increase in porosity is 44% at 50°C and 36% at 1°C. However, the low sulfate concentration in the water indicates that gypsum is probably not present in the aquifer in significant amounts, and hence no porosity increase is to be expected. The same argument applies to anhydrite. Gibbsite, chalcedony, quartz, and micro-cline are in small quantities either as precipitate or dissolution, and the porosity changes do not exceed 0.3%. Only silica gel shows increase in porosity of 4% at 50°C and 0.7% at 1°C.

Kinetic calculations show that these changes are very slow and changes in porosity in a season of six months are negligible. All the above computations are carried out assuming instantaneous reequilibration between water and minerals. Rates of mineral dissolution and precipitation reported in literature (Plummer, Wigley and Parkhurst, 1978, and Lasaga, 1982) were used to make these calculations and the effects of precipitation and dissolution are found to be insignificant in this example.

CONTROL MEASURES

Geochemical models mentioned above can also be used to evaluate the feasibility of the following control measures that can minimize water-mineral interactions: (1) construction of a storage tank below the ground level. During summer, hot water may be cooled to atmospheric temperature and then injected back into the aquifer. During winter, cold water may be warmed to ground temp-

erature and then injected back into the aquifer. At present this method appears to be feasible; (2) addition of chemicals to neutralize the precipitating or dissolution reactions. If the water chemistry is well established by analysis, it is possible to adjust the pH by adding suitable chemicals; and (3) adjusting the flow rate of water to keep temperature changes to a minimum.

CONCLUSION

A method has been developed to predict mineral precipitation or dissolution in aquifers caused by injecting through a heat pump, water at a temperature different from that of the ambient groundwater. Computations for a dilute groundwater in a limestone aquifer indicate that changes in porosity resulting from these water—mineral interactions are small even when instantaneous reequilibration is assumed. Waters with higher concentrations of solutes may bring about more rapid changes in aquifer porosity. Rates of dissolution and precipitation of minerals are to be used to predict more accurately these changes in porosity with time.

REFERENCES

Civil Engineering (1983). Thermal Storage, Now and Future. ASCE Civil Engineering, Dec., 43-45.

Hem, J.D. and Cropper W.H. (1959). Survey of Ferrous-Ferric Chemical Equilibria and Redox Potentials. U.S. Geological Survey Water Supply-Paper 1459A, 4-6, Washington, D.C.

Kharaka, Y.K. and Barnes I. (1973). SOLMNEQ: Solution-Mineral Equilibrium Computations. U.S. Geological Survey, PB-215899, U.S. Department of Commerce, NTIS, Springfield, VA.

Lasaga, A.C. (1984). Chemical Kinetics of Water-Rock Interactions. Journal of American Geophysical Research (In Press).

Mercer, J.W., Faust, C.R., Miller, W.J. and Pearson, F.J., Jr. (1982). Review of Simulation Techniques for Aquifer Thermal Energy Storage (ATES). Advances in Hydroscience, Vol. 13, 90-93, Academic Press, New York, N. Y.

Parkhurst, D.L., Thorstenson, D.C. and Plummer, L.N. (1982). PHREEQE: A Computer Program for Geochemical Calculations. U.S. Geological Survey, Water Resources Investigations 80-96, May, pp. 1-210.

Plummer, L.N., Wigley, T.M.L. and Parkhurst, D.L. (1978). The Kinetics of Calcite Dissolution in CO$_2$ — Water Systems at 5°C to 60°C and 0.0 to 1.0 atm. CO$_2$. American Journal of Science, Vol. 278, 179-216, Kline Geology Laboratory, Yale University, New Haven, CT.

Reed, D.B. and Reddell D.L. (1980). Heat Transport in Groundwater Systems. Texas Water Resources Institute, Texas A & M University, TR-104, Vol. II, 81-82, College Station, TX.

Utah Water Research Laboratory (1979). Groundwater Heat Pump: An Efficient Way to Heat and Cool Your Home, pp. 12, Utah State University, Logan, UT.

White, D.E., Hem, J.D. and Waring, G.A. (1963). Data of Geochemistry, Chapter F, Chemical Composition of Subsurface Waters. U.S. Geological Survey Professional Paper 440-F, F22, Washington, D. C.

Wollast, R. (1967). Kinetics of the Alteration of K-feldspar in Buffered Solutions at Low Temperature. Geochim. Cosmochim. Acta, 31, pp. 635-648.

Pore size distribution in filtration analyses

Répartition des vides dans les analyses de la filtration

A. MUSSO, Lecturer in Geotechnics, University of Palermo, Italy
F. FEDERICO, Research Fellow, University of Palermo, Italy

SYNOPSIS - With reference to the analysis of filter stability, a theoretical model based on information theory to obtain the pore size distribution of a particulate medium is presented in the paper. The maximum probability of occurrence is provided to the distribution so determined by imposing to the particulate system a condition of maximum entropy, without the introduction of fictitious or oversimplified hypotheses on soil packing. The theoretical pore size distribution curve depends on porosity and, then, it allows to investigate the development of clogging process accounting for the whole range of filter density, from the loosest to the densest state. The physical significance of the piping ratio is explored and the known empirical limit value justified.

INTRODUCTION

Two phenomena can usually reveal the loss of filters efficiency. The first, known as "clogging", refers to the action of retaining fine base particles up to complete filling of filter pores, thus impairing its drainage function to an unacceptable degree. On the other hand, filtering action fails if grains, eroded from the base material at the boundary with filter, are transported by seeping water, thus initiating backward erosion.

In both cases, the physical background of filter stability is to be looked for in the aptitude of filter voids to catch the smaller base particles within a certain length of penetration. The latter check, in turn, calls for the analysis of the diffusion process of particles of some assigned size through voids of aggregates of coarser particles.

Though unsolvable in a deterministic way, the problem is still approachable by considering the geometric hindrance of the movement of base soil grains through voids of the filter (Silveira, 1965).

The methods based on this principle aim mainly at determining the filter pore size distribution by assuming some ideal arrangement of particles and calculating the frequency of pores formed by specified groups of particles. The maximum length of the probable path within the filter of an assigned base particle can then be calculated for a given confidence level.

However, as pointed out by De Mello (1977) and later by Wittmann (1979), these methods suffer of limitations, some of which still unsolved. Among them, the distribution of pores accounting for the true packing of grains needs further research effort. As the maximum density is often assumed in computations, in fact, the existing methods reveal scarce flexibility in accounting for the actual density of filter materials.

In the paper, authors propose a theoretical model based on information theory arguments to find the pore size distribution of particulate systems, taking in due account the porosity.

The proposed approach offers the possibility of obtaining in a straightforward manner the void distribution curve in percentage of the number of pores, thus eliminating the fallacy hidden in the fact that pore size curves constructed on the basis of grain distributions by weight overlook the large number of small particles, which actually are available to build up denser arrangements (De Mello, 1977).

Finally, it is discussed whether and up to what extent the proposed computation model could be used to investigate the physical significance of empirical filter criteria that refer to some values of grain diameters, both of base and filter materials, corresponding to a few percentages by weight of granulometric fractions.

FUNDAMENTALS OF THE THEORETICAL MODEL

The volume of voids contained in a particulate material is usually expressed by the porosity or the void ratio. Even with a constant value of void ratio, however, different arrangements of particles do occur, corresponding to different pore size distributions.

Of course, a "local" description of soil structure, which takes into account location, average size, and shape of all voids is unfeasible; then, to face the problem, it is necessary to adopt some macroscopic variables, that do not imply special hypotheses on soil particles packing but can be related to possible states or configurations of the discrete mass (Gudehus, 1968), (Mogami, 1969).

Owing to extremely high number of particles that are to be considered in the construction of a significant model of the porous medium, the study can be carried out by means of statistical mechanics methods, introducing the concept of "state probability".

In order to apply this line of thought, consider a volume frequency distribution of voids belonging to a particulate medium and let n, V_{min}, V_{max}, be respectively, the porosity of the system, and the minimum and maximum value of the volumes of pores.

The entire interval from V_{min} to V_{max} is divided into Q sub-intervals, each containing N_j pores of volume V_j and of associated frequency f_j defined as:

$$f_j = N_j / N_V \qquad (1)$$

where N_V is the overall number of pores.

It is worth observing that, if the population composing the system is sufficiently numerous, as it is the case, the number N_V of pores can be replaced by the number N_p of particles; moreover, the sum of all volumes $N_j \cdot V_j$ equals the whole volume of pores, the latter depending upon the porosity n of the medium.

The distribution of numbers N_j among the Q sub-intervals V_j must then obey the following "compatibility" conditions:

$$\sum_{j=1}^{Q} N_j = N_p \qquad (2')$$

$$\sum_{j=1}^{Q} N_j V_j = n V_{tot} \qquad (2'')$$

In (2''), V_{tot} represents the total volume (particles plus voids) of the system; while, in (2'), the term N_p can be expressed as a function of V_{tot}, if one observes that the following relation between the number N_i of particles of diameter D_i and the corresponding percentage by weight Δp_i holds:

$$N_i \frac{\pi D_i^3}{6} \gamma_s = (1-n) V_{tot} \gamma_s \Delta p_i \qquad (3)$$

in which γ_s is the specific gravity of grains. From (3) one obtains:

$$N_i = \frac{6 V_{tot}}{\pi} (1-n) \frac{\Delta p_i}{D_i^3} \qquad (4)$$

And summing up over all the N diameters D_i:

$$N_p = \sum_{i=1}^{N} N_i = \frac{6 V_{tot}}{\pi} (1-n) \sum_{i=1}^{N} \frac{\Delta p_i}{D_i^3} \qquad (5)$$

Observe, now, that a given configuration (macro-state) of the system can be obtained in all the different ways (micro-states) in which the number N_j can be associated to volumes V_j. Recalling that there exist N_1 indistinguishable pores of volume V_1, N_2 of volume V_2, ... N_Q of volume V_Q, the number W of all possible micro-states can be obtained from combinatorial analysis as:

$$W = \frac{N_p!}{N_1! \, N_2! \ldots N_Q!} \qquad (6)$$

If the ways of forming a given configuration are all equally probable, as it can be supposed in absence of particular structural features of the porous medium, then the number W of micro-states leading to the considered configuration is proportional to the probability of occurrence of the configuration itself.

The value of such probability is not known in general; however, the degree of uncertainty about the knowledge concerning the state of the material depicted by the distribution $N_j(V_j)$ is expressed, according to the theory of information, as:

$$E = k \ln W \qquad (7)$$

where K is a constant.

The function E plays a role similar to the entropy in classical thermodynamics, hence it is called entropy also in the theory of information.

Looking for a stable configuration of the system, a distribution $N_j(V_j)$ which has the maximum probability of occurrence so as to supply the maximum uncertainty about the micro-states forming the configuration itself, has to be identified.

The latter requirement, in turn, is assured by imposing to the system the condition of maximum entropy.

One has then to find a distribution $N_j(V_j)$ which maximizes the function E expressed by (7) under the constraints dictated by (2') and (2'').

This problem of conditional maximum has been solved by means of Lagrange's multipliers method. Without going further into mathematical details, the distribution of pores can be expressed as follows:

$$N_j = N_p \frac{e^{-\beta V_j}}{\sum_{j=1}^{Q} e^{-\beta V_j}} \qquad (8)$$

in which the well known Maxwell-Boltzmann

distribution law in ricognizable.
The frequency of voids can thus be cast in the form:

$$f_j = \frac{N_j}{N_p} = \frac{e^{-\beta V_j}}{\sum\limits_{j=1}^{Q} e^{-\beta V_j}} \qquad (8')$$

In order to determine the parameter β, letting:

$$\delta(\beta) = \sum_{j=1}^{Q} e^{-\beta V_j} \qquad (9)$$

one can observe that:

$$-\sum_{j=1}^{Q} V_j\, e^{-\beta V_j} = \frac{\partial}{\partial\beta}\left[\sum_{j=1}^{Q} e^{-\beta V_j}\right] = \delta'(\beta) \qquad (10)$$

where $\delta'(\beta)$ indicates the derivative of the function $\delta(\beta)$ with respect to β.
On the other hand, replacing (8) in (2"), one also obtains:

$$\sum_{j=1}^{Q} V_j\, e^{-\beta V_j} = \frac{n V_{tot}}{N_p} \qquad (11)$$

Hence, equating (10) and (11), the following differential equation is obtained:

$$\frac{\delta'(\beta)}{\delta(\beta)} = -\frac{n V_{tot}}{N_p} \qquad (12)$$

The relation (12) holds true for whatever function $V_j(j)$; the latter, however, is conditioned by the necessity of describing the whole range of pore sizes.
After some trials, the following expression has been chosen:

$$V_j = V_{min} + \ell n\, c^{(j-1)} \qquad (13)$$

where $c = \dfrac{1 + \Delta V}{\Delta V}$ and ΔV is a prescribed increment of pore volume.
It is easily verified that the adopted expression for V_j allows the calculation of $\delta(\beta)$ and $\delta'(\beta)$, so that replacing them in (12) the parameter β is finally obtained:

$$\beta = \frac{\ell n\, \dfrac{V_{min} - \overline{V}}{V_{min} - \overline{V} + \ell n\, c}}{\ell n\, c} \qquad (14)$$

having indicated with $\overline{V}$ the term $n V_{tot}/N_p$.
One can observe that β is a function of porosity; moreover, it depends upon the grain size distribution of the medium through the number N_p of particles (see eq. (5)), and upon the range of pore volumes.

COMPARISON WITH EXPERIMENTAL DATA

Very few experimental results are available in technical literature on pore size distribution of granular media.
Some of them have been reported by Kezdi (1968) with reference to various materials, from natural pit gravel to quarried rock.
Test data are presented, in semi-logarithmic plot, as void volume distribution curves (fig. 1), and therefore they are particularly well suited for comparison with theoretical values predicted by the calculation model presented in the preceding section. Experimental results are

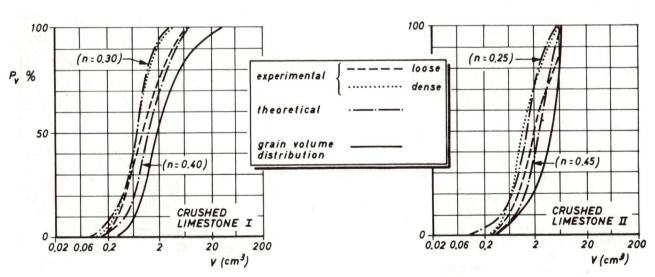

Fig. 1 - Theoretical and experimental volume distribution curves; solid particles and pores.

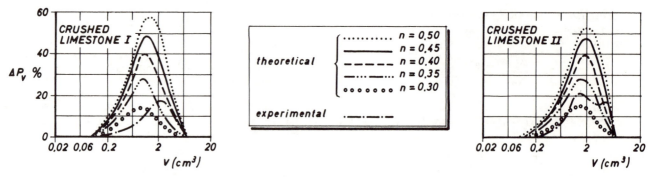

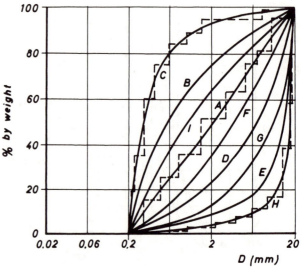

Fig. 2 - Difference among percentages of pore volumes at various porosities.

furnished for the dense and for the loose state as well, although nothing is reported in the original paper by Kezdi about the corresponding porosities.

In order to fit the experimental data by theoretical values, the relative frequency f_j has been transformed into the cumulative one p_v by means of the formula:

$$p_v = \frac{\sum_{i=1}^{j} V_i f_i}{\sum_{i=1}^{Q} V_i f_i} \qquad (15)$$

The theoretical curves, obtained by (8'), (14) and (15), that best fit the experimental data, are also reported in fig. 1. For sake of simplicity only two values of porosity have been considered; one can observe, however, that they are sufficiently representative of the states labelled, respectively, as dense and loose.

On the other hand, with reference to same materials, in fig. 2 are reported the curves representing the differences between the cumulative frequencies calculated for various porosities and the cumulative frequency relative to the porosity $n = 0.25$; in the same figure, curves representing the differences between experimental "dense" and "loose" curves reported in fig. 1, can be compared.

Theoretical curves are regular bell-shaped in the semilogarithmic plot; it can thus be anticipated that there is a range of pore sizes, intermediate between maximum and minimum, for which the maximum reduction occurs in the transition from the dense to the loose state. In fact, the volume of larger voids does not undergo substantial reduction because of the limited number of them; on the other hand, further reduction of smaller voids can hard occur. Experimental results confirm, at least qualitatively, the trend depicted by theoretical curves.

It is also interesting to note that with increasing porosity the influence of large pores on frequency distribution increases so that the peak of bell curves moves progressively toward the high values of pore sizes.

FILTRATION ANALYSIS

An analysis of particulate diffusion processes occurring at the boundary between base material and filter can be started from the obvious consideration that all base particles smaller than the smallest filter void will pass through the filter, while all particles larger than the largest void will not enter the filter; particles of intermediate size will penetrate to varying depth into the filter.

Once the pore size distribution of the filter is known, one has then to compute the probability that an assigned base particle be larger than a certain pore. From a different point of view, it can be questioned how many confrontations between the base particle size and the filter void sizes are needed to find a pore smaller than the grain under consideration.

The value **m** of these proofs in given by (Silveira, 1965):

$$m = \frac{\ln(1-P_0)}{\ln(1-P_v)} \qquad (16)$$

Fig. 3 - Grain size distribution curves.

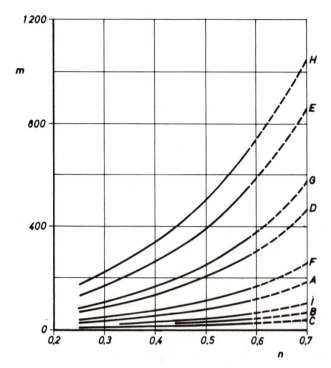

Fig. 4 - **Number of confrontations versus porosity for various grain size distributions.**

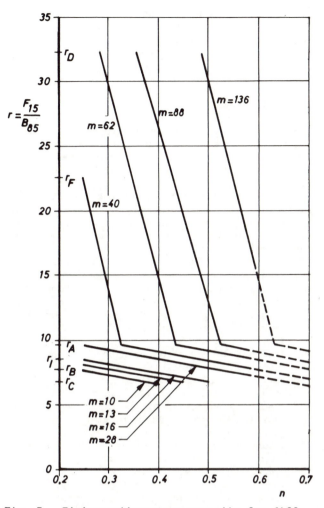

Fig. 5 - **Piping ratio versus porosity for different numbers of confrontations.**

where p_v represents the percentage of pores smaller than the considered base particle and P_o is a confidence level.

The number **m** could further be transformed into the filtration length **S** if the average distance **s** of changing pore size were quantified (Wittmann, 1979). In this case, $S = m \cdot s$.

In order to examine the influence of porosity on the diffusion process, various filter materials, whose grain size distribution curves are reported in fig. 3, have been considered. The determination of number **m** of proofs, for each material, has been carried out with reference to only one base particle, whose volume has been assumed as equal to the smallest pore volume of the filter. The latter volume can be computed as $0,1712\ D_{min}^3$, where D_{min} denotes the minimum diameter of filter grains.

The results of computations, for a confidence level $P_o = 0,9999$ are reported in fig. 4, where the increase of number **m** with increasing porosity shows, at least indirectly, the modification of structural arrangement resulting from change of porosity. Then the question of the influence of porosity on filter efficiency arises.

As it is known, empirical criteria of filter design refer to some ratios determined by experiment. Widely used in practice, the "piping ratio" $r = F_{15}/B_{85}$ which, for the safety of the filter, must not exceed $5 \div 6$.

A preliminary analysis of the physical significance of the piping ratio can be carried out if the size of the base particle considered in the above computations is now intended as just the B_{85} grain size.

In doing so, for each of filter materials reported in fig. 3, the **r** values can be calculated (fig. 5). Moreover, for each **r** value, the **m** values obtained for different porosities are reported in the graph. Linking the points at same **m** value, the curves drawn in fig. 5 are obtained.

It is easily observed that each curve shows a sudden discontinuity at a value $\bar{r}$ of the ratio **r** of the order of 10; for $r < \bar{r}$ (as for grain size curves labelled with A, B, C, I, in fig. 3) the number of confrontations required to arrest the considered base particle varies between 10 and 100, even for high values of porosity. Moreover, the variations of porosity do not cause large variations of the number **m**.

On the contrary, for $r > \bar{r}$, the higher is the piping ratio the higher becomes the number of confrontations and the more it is sensible to variations of porosity. It can thus be concluded that the existence of a critical value of piping ratio (10 in the present preliminary analysis) seems to be justified by the necessity of arresting the B_{85} particles within short distances, so that at the boundary between base material and filter a thin transition zone (sealing) composed of particles belonging to both materials can be formed.

CONCLUDING REMARKS

The fundamental principle governing the filtering action can be found in the geometric hindrance of the movement of particles of the base soil through voids of the filter. Consequently, the available theoretical formulations approach the problem by comparing the base soil particle sizes with sizes of filter pores; hence, the probable length of the path covered by an assigned base grain through filter pores can be calculated.

The method, however, suffers of limitations invalidating its safe applications to filter design. Among them, the packing model adopted in the computation of pore size distribution of the filter may be the source of significant errors.

To elude this shortcoming a theoretical model based on information theory has been built, avoiding the introduction of hypotheses on local arrangements of particles. In this way, the assembly of grains composing the porous medium can be characterized by its state probability; the resulting pore size distribution is known in Statistical Mechanics with reference to other physical problems. The model, however, still needs some refinements in order to be applicable to filter materials characterized by discontinuous grain size distribution.

The agreement of the theoretical results with some available experimental data confirms the suitability of the proposed approach, which offers the possibility of taking into account the porosity of the filter. A preliminary analysis of clogging process occurring in the filter shows that the known empirical piping ratio is susceptible of theoretical justification.

LIST OF MAIN SYMBOLS

B_{85} diameter corresponding to 85% by weight of the base material;

E entropy;

D_i diameter of filter grains;

D_{min} minimum diameter of filter grains;

f_j frequency of pores of volume V_j;

F_{15} diameter corresponding to 15% by weight of the filter material;

K constant of the entropy;

m number of confrontations between the base particle size and the filter void sizes;

n porosity of the filter;

N overall number of granulometric fractions of the filter;

N_i number of particles of diameter D_i;

N_j number of pores of volume V_j;

N_p overall number of particles of the filter;

N_v overall number of pores of the filter;

p_v cumulative frequency of pores;

P_o confidence level;

Q overall number of void fractions;

r piping ratio;

$\bar{r}$ critical value of the piping ratio;

s average distance of changing pore size;

S filtration length;

V_j volume of filter voids;

V_{min} V_{max} minimum and maximum values of the volumes of pores;

V_{tot} total volume of the filter;

W number of micro-states corresponding to a given configuration;

ΔP_i percentage by weight of particles of diameter D_i;

ΔV increment of pore volume.

REFERENCES

De Mello, V.F.B. (1977). Reflections on design decisions of practical significance to embankment dams. Geotechnique, 27, 3.

Gudehus, G. (1968). Gedanken zur Statistischen Bodenmechanik. Der Bauingenieur, 43.

Kezdi, A. (1968). Distribution of grains and voids according to their volume. Proc. of the 3rd Budapest Conf. on Soil Mech. and Found. Engrg..

Mogami, T. (1969). Mechanics of a granular material as a particulated mass. Proc. of the 7th Int. Conf. on Soil Mech. and Found. Engrg., Mexico City.

Silveira, A. (1965). An analysis of the problem of washing through in protective filters. Proc. of the 6th Int. Conf. on Soil Mech. and Found. Engrg., Montreal.

Wittmann, L. (1979). The process of soil filtration - its physics and the approach in engineering practice. Proc. of the 7th Eur. Conf. on Soil Mech. and Found. Engrg., Brighton.

Varying permeability of clayey soils linings

Changement de la perméabilité des écrans argileux

V. M. PAVILONSKY, Laboratory Head, All-Union Research Institute "Vodgeo", Moscow, USSR

SYNOPSIS   At the present time geotechnique faces many complicated problems connected with environmental control. This report deals with one of them, namely, the problem of varying permeability of impermeable clayey linings as a result of long-term seepage of industrial sewage and solution of acids, alkalis, salts. The test results on the samples of 15 clayey soils (mono-mineral clays and polymineral clays and loams) are presented. It is shown that the coefficient of permeability of clayey soils changed (in several cases 100-1000 times) due to the long-term seepage (200-700 days and in individual cases up to 1100 days) of the liquids mentioned above. The reasons of such changes are discussed.

The increase of the research and development work into environmental control problems made it imperative for geotechnique to solve a number of new complex tasks. This report is devoted to the problem of the environmental and ground water protection in the vicinity of ponds for industrial sewages which are complex solutions of inorganic and organic substances (acids, alkalis, salts and so on). Various impermeable systems (bore walls, linings, diaphragms and others) made of clayey soils, polyethylene films, asphaltic concrete are used for decreasing the amount of seepage (and in some cases for full prevention of seepage) from the ponds. The linings of clayey soils are widely used. However it is necessary to bear in mind the following. Under the action of industrial sewages during the period of pond operation the properties of clayey soils can change. The increase of the permeability of soils and thus the decrease of the lining effectiveness are particularly dangerous. Unfortunately the problem of varying clay soil properties under the action of different chemical substances has not been investigated in the field of geotechnique sufficiently well. Therefore it is impossible to estimate theoretically the possibility and the amount of these changes. As a rule this problem is solved experimentally. Such investigation has being carried out for a number of years at VODGEO Institute in connection with the development of impermeable linings of clayey soils for industrial sewage ponds. New special devices were designed and made including permeameters, oedometers and a device for swelling of soils under the action of industrial sewage (1-2). One of characteristic features of the permeameters was the prevention of boundary flow (leakage at the soil-permeameter wall interface). The diameters of the devices differ depending on the kind of tests and the tasks solved. The diameter of permeameters, for example, was from 77 to 310 mm and the diameter of the devices for soils swelling was from 70

to 450 mm. The procedures developed for long-term investigations take into account the conditions under which the linings for industrial sewage ponds operate. To make the test soil sample have similar changes of porosity and other characteristics to the changes in the lining which occur during its maintainance it was necessary to permeate through the sample the same relative volume of liquid as in-situ. This condition was ensured by carrying out tests at high values of hydraulic gradients (30-135). Chemical composition and pH values of the filtrate were determined regularly during the tests. Such control made it possible to study the changes in the soil and in the components which were leached by the flowing liquid. To obtain the grounded data on the lining permeability variation under the action of seeping solution the duration of the tests was sufficiently long (200-700 days and even sometimes up to 1100 days). The tests were carried out with the portions of linings made of various compacted clayey soils (monomineral: bentonite, kaolin, monotermite and polymineral: loams and clays). The properties of the soils are listed in Table I. Used in the test were both the industrial sewages (6 kinds) and the solutions of acids (nitric, sulphuric, acetic, hydrochloric etc), caustic soda and salts met in a number of industrial sewages. Industrial sewages 1-3 contain Ca^{2+} 26-42.5 g/l, Mg^{2+} 23.18-27.48 g/l, Cl^- 86.72-107.5 g/l and SO_4^{2-} 0.5-0.81 g/l. Industrial sewage 4 contains about 70 inorganic and organic substances (dry residue 56 g/l) including sulphuric, nitric and hydrochloric acids (the acidity 13.5 g H_2SO_4 per 1, pH 1). Industrial sewage 5 is the solution of sulphate, chloride and bicarbonate of sodium, calcium, magnesium (dry residue 10-13 g/l, pH 6.4-7.7). At the first stage of the majority of tests (30-100 days) was investigated the seepage of water.

TABLE I

Properties of the Soils

Soil	Density of solid particles, $10^3 kg/m^3$	Particle-size distribution, %			Liquid limit	Plastic limit	Plastici-ty index	Maximal molecular moisture content by Lebedev,%
		0.25-0.05mm	0.05-0.005mm	0.005 mm				
Bentonite	2.73	2.8	2.8	94.4	106	37	69	58.9
Kaolin	2.61	9.2	26.4	64.4	44	32	12	32
Monotermite	2.71	0.2	5.3	94.5	69	35	34	39.1
Clay 6	2.77	26.97	47.25	25.78	48	27	21	18.6
Clay 12	2.70	1.4	42.7	55.9	43	25	18	21.2
Loam 1	2.70	67.2	24.6	8.2	31	16	15	11.2
Loam 3	2.71	62.78	24.81	12.41	31	17	14	12.2
Loam 4	2.77	16.22	71.70	12.08	34	24	10	15.6
Loam 8	2.69	23.7	36.1	40.2	33	19	14	7.3
Loam 9	2.68	39.9	35.7	24.4	34	18	16	12
Loam 10	2.76	9.84	32.78	57.38	38	24	14	16.8
Loam 11	2.79	15.77	47.88	36.35	41	25	16	18.4
Loam 17	2.76	33.27	42.56	24.17	38	25	13	14.86
Loam 18	2.69	59.92	22.64	17.44	31	19	12	11.92
Sandy Loam 3	2.74	52.46	24.81	22.73	19	13	6	8.28

The coefficient of permeability value obtained (K_w) was used as a basis for comparison

with the variation of soil permeability due to the long-term action of solutions. Complex physical, chemical and physical-chemical processes occured during solution transport in soil samples (the change of the composition of exchangeable ions; osmosis and diffusion; the breaking of soil aggregates and releasing smaller fraction of the soil which moved under the action of seepage force and colmotaged large soil pores; the change of the number and size of entrapped air bubbles as a result of change of atmospheric pressure and soil temperature etc). Some of them caused the increase of active porosity and permeability of soil. Some other processes on the other hand decreased the soil permeability. The intensity and the degree of the influence of every process on the soil permeability varied in time. In addition the effect of some of them was compensated by the others. Therefore the variation of permeability of the soil in time changed according to a rather complicated law. The typical curves of the soil coefficient permeability versus time are illustrated in the figure enclosed. In most tests the coefficient of permeability reached its maximum value (K_{max}).

Then it began decreasing till its final value (K_f). In Table II are listed the ratios of these values to the corresponding values of the coefficient of permeability (K_w) obtained

at the first stage of each test. The data in Table II show that the changes of soil coefficient of conductivity due to the long-term permeation of industrial sewages and solutions differed substantially. In some of the tests permeability increased greatly and $K_{max} = (100-1000)K_w$ and in other tests it increased

less and K_{max} was within the range $(1.1-3,2)K_w$.

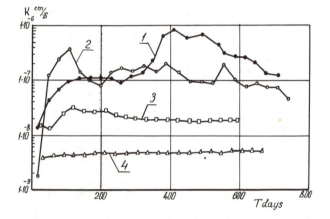

Fig.1 Curves of the coefficient of permeability value vs time $K=f(T)$ according to data obtained during the tests: 1 - with loam 9 and industrial sewage 4; 2 - with loam 4 and 4% NaOH solution; 3 - with clay 6 and 7% HNO_3 solution; 4 - with loam 1 and 6% CH_3COOH solution.

At the same time in a number of tests under the action of industrial sewage 6, acetic acid and caustic soda solutions the permeability decreased and $K_{max}=(0.08-0.9)K_w$, $K_f=(0.01-0.8)K_w$. The analysis of the obtained data

shows that the change of permeability of the portions of linings depended upon a number of factors and first of all on the composition of percolating solution, mineralogical and chemical composition of soil and its properties, dry density and the period of time of solution

TABLE II

Variation of the Soil Coefficient of Permeability
Values as a Result of Long-Term Permeation of
Industrial Sewages and Solutions

Permeant	Soil	K_{max}/K_w	K_ℓ/K_w
Acid solutions			
Industrial sewage 4	Loam 9	up to 215	up to 142
Industrial sewage 6	Sandy loam 3	0.7-1.2	0.02-0.5
Industrial sewage 6	Loam 10	1.2-9.7	0.1-1.8
Industrial sewage 6	Loam 17	0.8-0.9	0.01-0.05
Industrial sewage 6	Loam 18	0.08-0.3	0.02-0.08
Industrial sewage 6	Bentonite	3.4-924	2.9-924
Industrial sewage 6	Kaoline	0.3-1.1	0.07-0.2
7% HNO_3	Loam 1	2.1	1.7
7% HNO_3	Clay 6	1.9-2.3	1.3-1.5
7% HNO_3	Bentonite	7.4-11.9	5.6-7.7
7% HNO_3	Kaoline	2.1	1.8
1% HNO_3	Loam 1	1.8	1.3
0.7% HNO_3	Bentonite	16.3	11.6
0.7% HNO_3	Kaoline	1.6	1.3
5% H_2SO_4	Loam 1	1.4	0.8
5% H_2SO_4	Bentonite	10.3	6.9
5% H_2SO_4	Kaoline	1.3	1.1
3.65% HCl	Bentonite	15.2	10.2
3.65% HCl	Kaoline	5.0	3.5
0.36% HCl	Bentonite	11.8	10.9
0.36% HCl	Kaoline	2.7	1.8
6% CH_3COOH	Loam 1	0.8	0.8
6% CH_3COOH	Bentonite	5.6	3.7
6% CH_3COOH	Kaoline	1.7	1.3
Alkaline solutions			
Industrial sewage 1	Monotermite	1.3-2.2	0.8-1
Industrial sewage 1	Clay 12	up to 91	0.7-23.0
Industrial sewage 1	Kaoline	1.9	0.7
Industrial sewage 2	Loam 8	17-198	1.6-22.3
Industrial sewage 2	Bentonite	181-1000	150-483
Industrial sewage 3	Loam 8	1.6-17.1	1.6-7.4
Industrial sewage 3	Clay 12	2.2	2.2
Industrial sewage 5	Loam 10	0.9-1.9	0.5-0.9
Industrial sewage 5	Loam 11	1.1-1.3	0.8-0.9
4% NaOH	Bantonite	0.5	0.3
4% NaOH	Kaoline	0.9	0.8
4% NaOH	Loam 4	302	15.6
0.4% NaOH	Bentonite	1.4	0.2
0.4% NaOH	Kaoline	1.4	1.1
0.4% NaOH	Loam 4	1.3	0.4
Salts			
5.85% NaCl	Bentonite	2.8	2.0
5.85% NaCl	Kaoline	1.7	1.2
11.1% $CaCl_2$	Bentonite	4.7	2.5
11.1% $CaCl_2$	Kaoline	1.4	1.1

percolation. The test data on bentonite demonstrate the influence of percolation fluid composition upon the permeability. The maximum increase of the coefficient of permeability value (in 181-1000 times) was observed during the tests with industrial sewage 2 and 6. In the tests with nitric, sulphuric and acetic acids the permeability increased smaller and $K_{max} = (5.6-16.3)K_w$. In the tests with chloride of sodium and calcium solutions $K_{max} = (2.8-4.7)$

K_w. The minimum change of bentonite permeability was observed during the seepage of caustic soda solution and $K_{max}=(0.5-1.4)K_w$. The solution concentration also influenced the values of the coefficient of permeability (K_{max} and K_f). For example, when the permeating liquid was 7% HNO_3 the ratio K_{max}/K_w was larger for loam 1 and kaoline and it was smaller for bentonite than in the tests with 0.7% HNO_3. In the tests with permeation of 4% NaOH the value of K_{max}/K_w was larger for loam 4 and smaller for bentonite and kaoline than with the percolation of 0.4% NaOH. The influence of mineralogical and chemical composition and soil properties upon the permeability of the portions of lining is evident for example while comparing the data obtained in the tests with industrial sewage 6. As a result of its long-term action K_{max} for bentonite was greater and for loams 17 and 18 was on the contrary smaller than K_w. With the increase of initial dry density the amount of solution affecting soil decreased resulting in variations of ratios K_{max}/K_w and K_f/K_w. Test results obtained during percolation of industrial sewage 1 through the samples of clay 12 are a good example of it. In the tests with dry soil density equal 1.59 g/cm^3 $K_{max}=10.2$ K_w and in the test with its value equal 1.67 g/cm^3 $K_{max}=3K_w$, the duration of these tests were practically equal. The influence of dry density on permeability is the same even in the case when equal volumes of liquid (in relation to the soil mass) are percolating through the soil. The curves K=f(T) in the figure demonstrate the influence of duration of tests upon the variation of permeability. The influence of long-term percolation of industrial sewages and solutions on other properties of the soils (density, particle-size distribution, Liquid and plastic limits etc) were investigated in the tests.

CONCLUSIONS

1. During the long-term (200-1100 days) percolation of acid and alkaline industrial sewages (complex solutions of inorganic and organic substances) and the solutions of acids, caustic soda and salts resulted in the change of the coefficient of permeability of the portion of lining made of clayey soils. In most tests the coefficient of permeability first increased to its maximum value (K_{max}) and then decreased to its final value (K_f).

2. For soils tested K_{max} and K_f values differed from the value K_w which was obtained during water percolation. Ratios K_{max}/K_w and K_f/K_w depended on a number of factors including the composition of percolating solution, mineralogical and chemical composition of the soil and its properties, dry density and the duration of solution percolation.

3. In most cases the percolation of industrial sewages and solutions through the portions of lining made of monomineral clays (bentonite, kaoline, monotermite) and polymineral loams and clays $K_{max} = (1.1-17.4)K_w$ and only in some cases $K_{max}= (100-1000)K_w$. A few tests showed the decrease of K_{max} and K_f in comparison to K_w.

4. The increase of dry density makes it possible to reduce the influence of long-term percolation of industrial sewages and solutions on the permeability of linings.

REFERENCES

Pavilonsky,V.M. (1973). Swelling Effect on the Coefficient of Permeability Alteration for Compacted Clayey Soils Samples. In: Voprosi filtratsionnih raschetov gidrotechnicheskih sooruzenii. Moscow, Stroyizdat, p.96-110 (in Russian).

Pavilonsky,V.M. (1982). The Swelling vs Time Along the Height of Compacted Clayey Soil Layer. In: Izmeneniya geologicheskoy sredi pod vliyaniem deyatelnosty cheloveka. Moscow, Nauka Publishers, p.107-111 (in Russian).

Control of chemical grout injected in seepage domain

Contrôle de l'injection chimique dans les zones d'infiltration

T. PEREZ, Consulting Engineer, Panama City, Republic of Panama

R. J. KRIZEK, Professor and Chairman of Civil Engineering, Northwestern University, Evanston, Illinois, USA

SYNOPSIS   An extensive series of 79 large-scale laboratory tests have been performed to determine the limiting conditions under which a chemical grout can be injected successfully into a cohesionless soil deposit permeated by water to form a cut-off. Four different chemical grouts and five different soils, ranging from fine sand to pea gravel, were included in the experimental program. The gel times of the grouts extended from a few minutes to more than half an hour, and seepage velocities as high as 60 cm/min were used. The behavior of a given soil-grout system is strongly related to the viscosity of the grout and moderately dependent on the effective grain size of the soil. Both of these properties influence the extent of the dilution that takes place, and dilution, in turn, delays the gelation of the grout and lowers its viscosity, and thereby exerts a dominant effect on the distribution of the grout in the soil mass.

INTRODUCTION

The use of chemical grouting for soil stabilization and water cut-off applications has increased significantly in recent years. However, one problem common to all grouting operations is that of ascertaining the distribution of the grout after being injected into the ground. Even when injections are made into dry granular media, the distributions are sometimes difficult to predict due to the anisotropy and/or heterogeneity of the soil deposit, and this situation becomes increasingly more difficult when the grout is injected into the soil under conditions of groundwater flow. This is because water movement induces dilution in the grout mixture, thus influencing its viscosity and gel time and therefore its final distribution in the soil mass. Also, the grout may dissolve or be eroded, even after gelation, due to the flow of water under a high gradient. Accordingly, the result may range from a satisfactory grouting application to one in which the grout does not gel in the ground; intermediate possibilities include partial or complete elutriation of grout which has gelled. Two of the most important studies along this line, the results of which are generally available, are those by Karol and Swift (1961) and Einstein and Schnitter (1970). However, although these studies do provide a general appreciation of certain specific problems attendant to the injection of chemical grout in a soil deposit permeated by groundwater, they offer very little help in developing any general guidelines for predicting the immediate and short-term performance of a given grout injected in such a regime.

OBJECTIVE

The aim of this study is to provide a reasonable first-order evaluation of the ability of several chemical grouts with differing physical and chemical properties to produce and maintain a water cut-off under varying conditions of groundwater flow. Also examined is the effect of the grain size characteristics of the soil on the final distribution and permanence of one particular grout.

EXPERIMENTAL PROGRAM

The experimental program was performed in two phases. In the first phase four different chemical grouts (three silicate and one acrylate) were injected individually into one particuar soil (Torpedo sand), and in the second phase one particular grout (AC-400) was injected into five different cohesionless soils (four sands and one pea gravel) to assess the effect of grain size and coefficient of uniformity on the immediate and short-term performance of the grout.

Chemical Grouts

Three of the four chemical grouts had sodium silicate as a base and a reagent consisting of a mixture of ethyl acetate and formamide, termed Geloc 3 (Hayward Baker Company), sodium aluminate (Nalco Chemical Company), or an aldehyde called CYSET III (American Cyanamid Company); the remaining grout was an acrylate polymer called AC-400 (Geochemical Company). Gel times in all cases were controlled by varying the concentration of reagent in the grout mix.

Geloc 3 -- The reagents for Geloc 3, ethyl acetate and formamide, are organic compounds; ethyl acetate is used as an accelerator to control the rate of the reaction, and formamide is used to enhance the miscibility of ethyl acetate with water. Upon contact these two compounds react with the water-silicate mixture to form an acid or an acid-salt which causes precipitation of the silicate. The gel time is controlled primarily by varying the concentration of ethyl acetate. The initial viscosity of this grout is about 5 cp, and it increases to 10 cp or higher shortly before gelation.

Sodium Aluminate -- This compound ($Al_2O_3Na_2O$) mixes perfectly with sodium silicate due to the amphoteric nature of aluminum, and it produces a uniform gel of aluminum silicate. The initial viscosity of this grout is about 2 to 3 cp, but it may change quite rapidly with time; shortly before gelation the viscosity may increase to 20 cp for grouts with gel times less than 15 minutes, and 10 cp for grouts with larger gel times.

CYSET III -- This reagent is a clear to slightly yellow solution which belongs to the chemical family of aldehydes (that is, a compound with a C=0 grouping which is capable of coagulating the grout). An accelerator (in this case $CaCl_2$) can be used and the gel time can be changed by varying the proportions of either CYSET III or $CaCl_2$. The viscosity of this grout gradually increases from an initial value of about 2 to 3 cp or less to around 4 to 6 cp shortly before gelation.

AC-400 -- This polymer grout (designed to replace AM-9) is a mixture of acrylate monomers and a small amount of methylene-bis-acrylamide (MBA) crosslinking monomer. When properly catalyzed with triethanolamine (TEA) and ammonium persulfate (AP), which act as

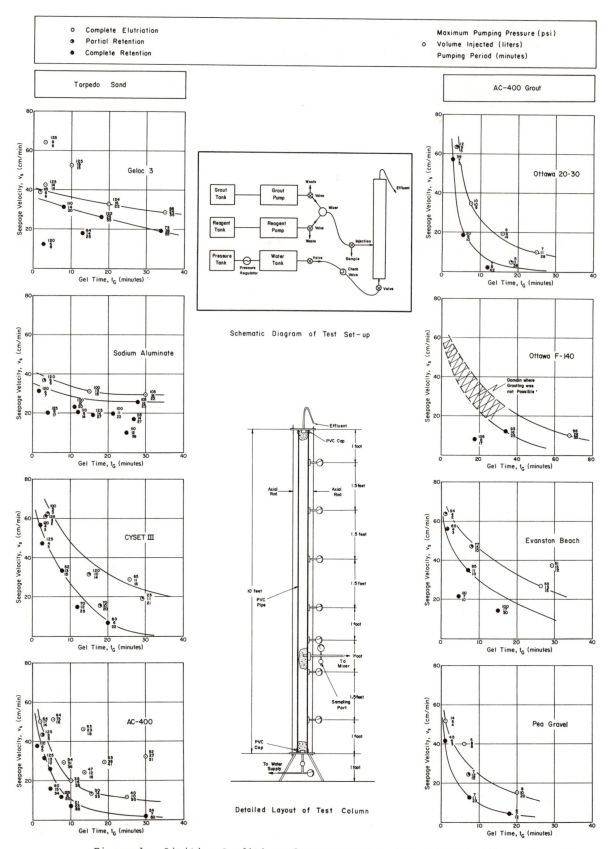

Figure 1. Limiting Conditions for Grout Retention and Elutriation

accelerator and initiator of the reaction, respectively, a virtually impermeable flexible gel is produced from water solutions by the free radical polymerization of the monomers. The viscosity behavior of this grout is quite different from the silicate base grouts in that it remains below 2 cp for at least 90% of its gel time and then suddenly increases.

Soils

Five cohesionless soils (Ottawa 20-30 sand, Ottawa F-140 sand, Torpedo sand, Evanston Beach sand, and pea gravel) were used in this test program. The composition of these soils ranges from predominantly quartz (Ottawa 20-30 and F-140 sands) to soils made up chiefly of fragments of limestone and other rock (pea gravel). The remaining soils (Torpedo and Evanston Beach sands) present a wide spectrum of composition, with quartz as the primary component and other minerals, such as feldspar and mica, included as secondary components. The effective grain size, uniformity coefficient, average void ratio, and coefficient of permeability for all soils are given in Table 1.

Table 1. Characteristics of Sands Tested

Soil	Effective Grain Size (mm)	Coefficient of Uniformity	Average Void Ratio	Coefficient of Permeability (cm/sec)
Torpedo	0.18	3.61	0.41	0.020
Ottawa 20-30	0.56	1.16	0.51	0.22
Ottawa F-140	0.072	1.46	0.57	0.005
Evanston Beach	0.23	1.08	0.57	0.022
Pea Gravel	1.8	2.11	0.58	0.75

Equipment

As illustrated in the center of Figure 1, the test apparatus consisted of a grouting plant (the main feature of which was two double-diaphragm constant-displacement Milroyal pumps), a vertical column (4 inches (102 mm) in diameter and 10 feet (3 m) long) that contained the test specimen, and a water supply system to simulate groundwater flow. The system included appropriate configurations of valves, a mixing chamber, pressure regulator, and gages to control and measure the parameters of interest.

Sample Preparation

Test specimens were prepared by pluviating dry soil into the column through a funnel. After the sand was placed, densification was accomplished by using a standard concrete vibrator attached to the lower third-point of the column for a period of about 4 minutes. In all cases the relative density of the soil was greater than 90%. The column was then capped at the top and reinforced circumferentially and longitudinally.

Test Procedure

The procedure followed in each test consisted of three stages. In the first stage steady-state flow was established through the model, calibration of the pumps was checked, and the gel time of the grout was measured. The grout was injected into the column during the second stage. Although the plan was to inject the grout to refusal (that is, until the allowable pressure (120 psi or 827 kPa) of the pumps had been reached), there were many cases (especially for grouts with long gel times) where a fixed volume (generally from 7 to 15 liters or one to two times the void volume) criterion had to be adopted because refusal was not reached. During injection the flow rate was monitored, pressures were recorded along the column (including the injection pressure), and the pH and gel time of the outflow were measured. In the third stage measurements of the apparent permeability along the column and the pH of the outflow were continued for up to 72 hours, depending on the outcome of the test.

In general, any of four possibilities might result in a given test. First, the seepage velocity may be sufficiently high or gel time sufficiently long that a water seal is never established; in such a case the grout simply exits the end of the column before it has had an opportunity to gel. Second, the coefficient of permeability may decrease several orders of magnitude, almost establishing a water cut-off, and refusal may be achieved, but, under the application of a constant pressure difference across the column, the grout is essentially elutriated after a few hours (several times the gel time of the grout) and the permeability of the resulting homogeneous soil mass approaches its original value. Third, a situation basically the same as the foregoing may be attained, except that the grout is only partially elutriated after a time up to about three days (long in terms of grout gel time, but short in the absolute sense) and a well defined, irregularly shaped grouted region is recovered upon disassembly. And fourth, a water cut-off may be established (that is, no measurable flow), together with refusal, and the application of a pressure difference for up to three days produces no flow. The major objective is to delineate, insofar as possible, the limiting conditions under which complete elutriation and complete retention of the grout take place.

RESULTS AND INTERPRETATION

The experimental relationships that have been established between gel time, t_G, and seepage velocity, v_s, are presented in Figure 1. The gel time was determined from samples collected at the sampling port prior to injection, and the seepage velocity represents the initial value that was measured after a steady-state flow of water had been established; of course, this seepage velocity decreases after the injection of grout commences. These parameters will ultimately determine the final distribution of the grout in the column.

All relationships consist of an upper curve that delineates a lower boundary of the conditions under which no net significant reduction in seepage was achieved (termed complete grout elutriation) and a lower curve which delineates an upper boundary of conditions under which seepage was stopped (termed complete grout retention) for at least three days. In some cases the lower curve also represents the limit of refusal or the boundary identifying the conditions under which the grout gelled while being injected, thus precluding any further grout injection; this is the uppermost refusal boundary that can be established within the geometrical framework of this model. Between these two curves lies a transition zone in which only a partial seepage cut-off occurred. A careful analysis of these families of curves reveals some major differences, which are dependent on the type of grout and the grain size characteristics of the soil. For example, the Geloc 3 and sodium aluminate grouts manifest a rather narrow transition zone that decreases almost linearly as the gel time increases, becoming more-or-less asymptotic to the gel time axis and apparently intersecting the seepage velocity axis. By contrast, the transition zones for the CYSET III and AC-400 grouts widen significantly as the gel time increases, thus making the change from complete retention to complete elutriation more gradual. Furthermore, the boundary curves of the transition zone for these two grouts appear to be asymptotic to both axes.

In general, as depicted in Figure 1 (left), for gel times greater than about 5 minutes, the limiting curves for complete retention of the Geloc 3 and sodium aluminate grouts lie at seepage velocities 3 to 10 times higher than those for the CYSET III and AC-400 grouts. For gel times shorter than about 5 minutes, the difference is relatively small. These differences can be explained in terms of the differences in viscosity and miscibility among the various grouts. The Geloc 3 and sodium aluminate grouts have a higher initial viscosity and lower miscibility than the CYSET III and AC-400 grouts. As a result, when these grouts are injected into the soil, they tend to displace the water instead of mixing with it and less dilution takes place. Since the gelation characteristics of these grouts are not changed substantially due to dilution, their retention in the soil is enhanced, even though prevailing initial seepage velocities may be sufficiently high to anticipate elutriation. At high seepage velocities the Geloc 3 and sodium aluminate grouts are quite sensitive to small changes in seepage velocity; hence, the transition from complete retention to complete elutriation is fairly abrupt. In contrast, the AC-400 and CYSET III grouts are more susceptible to mixing with the water and therefore are less sensitive to small variations in the seepage velocity. This is reflected in a much wider transition zone and a "grout retention" boundary that is located at substantially lower seepage velocities. For cases where no water cut-off was achieved, the gel time of the effluent gradually decreased with pumping time until a minimum was reached (thereby indicating that dilution was minimal), after which it increased dramatically. Using the ratio of the "minimum gel time of the effluent" to the "gel time of the injected grout" as a measure of dilution, the AC-400 grout was found to be clearly the most susceptible to dilution.

The curves for the Geloc 3 and sodium aluminate grouts appear to intersect the seepage velocity axis. There is a strong indication linking this tendency with the susceptibility of these grouts to dissolve and/or erode immediately after gelation. Limited experimental data suggest that, unlike the AC-400 and CYSET III grouts, the Geloc 3 and sodium aluminate grouts are easily dissolved and/or eroded by the action of flowing water, even after periods several times longer than the gel time. This behavior implies that there exists a critical seepage velocity beyond which a long-term water cut-off can not be established; for these two grouts this seepage velocity is around 40cm/min, corresponding to a hydraulic gradient of about 15.

The effect of the grain size characteristics of the soil on the relative position and shape of the seepage velocity versus gel time curves shown in Figure 1 (right) is minor, but this effect becomes somewhat stronger for soils with an effective grain size less than about 0.5mm. All curves resulting from this series of tests (all using AC-400 grout) appear to be asymptotic to both axes and to describe a transition zone that widens significantly as the gel time increases. Perhaps the major effect of grain size characteristics lies in the degree of dilution that takes place. For those tests where refusal was achieved, Figure 2 shows that the ratio of the "injection period to refusal" to the "gel time" becomes larger as the effective grain size increases. This indicates that coarse soils are more conducive to dilution of the grout than fine soils, and this is consistent with the greater tendency for turbulent flow in coarser soils. The inconsistency of Torpedo sand in this general pattern is attributed to the fact that its coefficient of uniformity is larger than that for any of the other soils. For very fine soils, such as Ottawa F-140, the high pressures required to inject the grout at velocities higher than about 15cm/min (corresponding to a hydraulic gradient greater than 20) render grouting in this regime almost impossible.

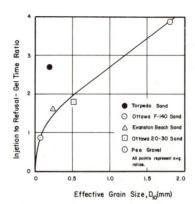

Figure 2. Effect of Grain Size on Dilution

CONCLUSIONS

Data from 79 large-scale one-dimensional laboratory tests have been analyzed to evaluate the effect of water flow on the distribution of various chemical grouts in several different cohesionless soils. Seepage velocity versus gel time curves have been determined experimentally to delineate the limiting conditions of complete retention from those of complete elutriation of the respective grouts, and the enclosed transition zones have been reasonably well defined. Because of their high viscosities (relative to water), two of the silicate grouts manifest narrow transition zones with more-or-less straight line variations as the gel time increases; the curves for these grouts appear to intersect the seepage velocity axis, thereby indicating a critical seepage velocity beyond which no seepage cut-off is possible. This phenomenon appears to be related to the susceptibility of these grouts to be dissolved or eroded after gelation has occurred. By contrast, less viscous and more permanent grouts, such as AC-400 and CYSET III, produced curves that decrease more-or-less exponentially as the gel time increases; these curves seem to be asymptotic to both the seepage velocity axis and the gel time axis, with a more gradual transition from complete retention to complete elutriation, thus indicating a lesser degree of sensitivity to changes in seepage velocity. The grain size characteristics of the soil do not appear to exert a strong influence on the seepage velocity versus gel time curves, except for the fact that, as the effective grain size decreases below about 0.5mm, the curves trend away from the origin, hence making grouting somewhat more difficult. Limited data suggest that dilution of the injected grout tends to increase as the gradation of the soil broadens.

ACKNOWLEDGEMENTS

The advice and suggestions of Dr. Wallace H. Baker of the Hayward Baker Company have been appreciated throughout this project. Also acknowledged is the participation of Philippe Weber and Juan Carlos Villa-Fernandez, who assisted in performing some of the tests and associated calculations.

REFERENCES

Einstein, H. H., and Schnitter, G. (1970), "Selection of Chemical Grout for Mattmark Dam," Journal of the Soil Mechanics and Foundations Division, American Society of Civil Engineers, Volume 96, Number SM6, pp. 2007-2023.

Karol, R. H., and Swift, A. M. (1961), "Symposium on Grouting: Grouting in Flowing Water and Stratified Deposits," Journal of the Soil Mechanics and Foundations Division, American Society of Civil Engineers, Volume 87, Number SM2, pp. 125-145.

Dense smectite clay used as overpack of deeply buried metal canisters with highly radioactive wastes

Argile dense de smectite utilisée comme tropballot pour des boîtes métalliques profondément enterrées avec des déchets extrêmement radio-actifs

R. PUSCH, Dept. Engineering Geology, Lund University of Technology and Natural Sciences, Swedish Geological, Lund, Sweden

SYNOPSIS   The Swedish KBS concept for the disposal of highly radioactive reactor wastes makes use of highly compacted Na bentonite as near-field isolation of canisters emplaced in bore-holes in crystalline rock. The clay is applied in the form of compressed blocks of air-dry bentonite powder which take up water from the rock so that the clay eventually swells to fill the space between the rock and the canisters. The final bulk density of the completely saturated clay will be about 2 t/m^3 which yields a practically impermeable barrier.

The homogeneity of the moistening of the clay and the associated swelling are of fundamental importance for the clay/rock and clay/canister interactions. Recent field experiments serve to illustrate the involved processes.

INTRODUCTION

The Swedish multibarrier concept for the disposition of highly radioactive, unreprocessed spent nuclear fuel, originally termed KBS 2, implies that copper canisters containing radioactive material be surrounded by dense Na bentonite clay (KBS, 1980). The repositories typically consist of tunnel systems at a minimum depth of 500 m in crystalline rock, the canisters being located in deposition holes with about 6 m spacing, drilled from the tunnel floor. A more recent, similar koncept, KBS 3, has formed the basis for fuelling permission for the two latest Swedish reactors.

The clay is applied in the form of well fitting blocks of highly compacted, granulated bentonite powder. They are not water-saturated to start with and take up water from the surrounding rock which makes them swell and form a tight contact with the rock and the canisters. After saturation the clay will ultimately be in equilibrium with the surroundings with respect to the effective stresses as well as to the pore pressure. It then forms a medium with a very low hydraulic conductivity and a low ion diffusivity. In addition to these valuable properties the dense bentonite is also self-healing in the sense that voids or local passages in the clay, caused by possible slight rock or canister displacements, will be sealed by the swelling power of the clay.

Early theoretical predictions based on laboratory experiments suggested that the rate and uniformity of the water uptake by the compacted bentonite from the rock should be largely determined by the distribution and aperture of the joints and fractures exposed in the rock walls of the deposition holes. This has been tested in a large scale field test in Stripa, Sweden, which shows the importance of the joint-sealing capacity of the swelling clay, as well as of the temperature gradient for the water migration.

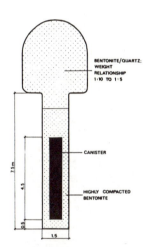

Fig. 1.   Cross section of repository tunnel.

The blocks can be prepared on an industrial scale by applying cold isostatic compaction technique with pressures in the range of 50-110 MPa.

The bentonite used in the experiments referred to is the commercial Volclay MX-80, which has a clay content (<2μm) of approximately 85 % and a montmorillonite content of 80-90 % of this fraction. The specific surface area is about 700 m^2.

WATER UPTAKE AND SWELLING

Mechanisms of hydration

Smectite minerals have a strong affinity to water which is primarily due to hydrogen bonding and van der Waals effects, and to the hydration of adsorbed cations. The latter effect is less important in Li- and Na-saturated smectite than when Ca or Mg occupies the exchange sites. In the latter case, hydration leads to very moderate expansion of a sample that is free to swell. Na smectite takes up water and swells to several times its volume in water of very low salinity.

The bentonite blocks, which suitably have a bulk density of about 2.1 t/m^3 and a water content of 8-14 % depending on the humidity of the air, have a degree of saturation that is of the order of 60 %. Their microstructure is characterized by a domain-type arrangement of the clay platelets, which tends to be increasingly homogeneous in the course of the saturation process (Fig. 2). At a constant dry density of this magnitude the face-to-face grouping is largely preserved in the process, while expansion to a higher water content than about 50 % produces considerable microstructural rearrangement leading to a very open edge-to-face aggregated state after strong swelling. At very low salinities spontaneous dispersion may even take place.

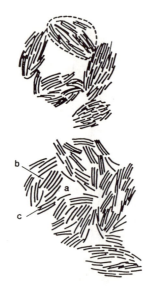

Fig. 2. Microstructure of highly compacted Na bentonite. Upper picture represents the freshly compacted, non-saturated clay. Central picture illustrates the saturated, matured state, while the lower picture represents a strongly expanded clay gel. a is large void ($\geq$10µm), b is small void ($\leq$10µm), c is interlamellar space.

PHYSICAL REACTIONS

Swelling pressure

Since the blocks are confined in the deposition holes the expansion of the clay is very limited, the major swelling being in the vertical direction in which the overlying on site-compacted sand/bentonite backfill can be displaced and compressed. These effects are expected as a consequence of the swelling pressure exerted by the dense bentonite. This pressure, which has been found to be practically independent of the chemical composition and salt concentration of the pore water at higher bulk densities than about 2 t/m^3 in a fully water-saturated state, is approximately 10-50 MPa if the bulk density ranges between 2.00 and 2.15 t/m^3. The corresponding hydraulic conductivity interval at 25-75°C is $5 \cdot 10^{-14}$ to $5 \cdot 10^{-13}$ m/s at hydraulic gradients of 10^3 to 10^4, while the diffusion coefficients of relevant radionuclides is $2 \cdot 10^{-13}$ to $2 \cdot 10^{-11}$ m^2/s (Pusch, 1982). Some of these laboratory-derived relationships, which are also theoretically accounted for, were tested in the large scale field test as shown later in this article.

Uniformity of water uptake

The question of how uniformly water enters the bentonite annulus is of profound importance since a non-uniform wetting may produce a large variation in swelling pressure over the canister surface, leading to bending moments and tensile fractures in the metal. Also, a variation in contact pressure at the clay/rock interface may be produced, by which the heat transfer from the hot canisters to the rock could be insufficient.

Laboratory tests with uniaxial water uptake in confined, cylindrical air-dry bentonite samples have shown that this process can be described as one of diffusion and applying the derived diffusion coefficient ($5 \cdot 10^{-10}$ m^2/s), the rate and distribution of the water uptake was calculated using FEM technique and the assumption that water is available from clearly identified, water-bearing rock joints or fractures (Börgesson, 1982). Fig. 3 illustrates the predicted water content distribution for a particular case.

Thermally induced water migration from the vicinity of the hot canisters towards the confining rock was assumed to be relatively unimportant in the first, preliminary estimation of the uptake and redistribution of pore water in the bentonite. The field test shows, however, that this process is of major importance.

Temperature distribution

Available experimental and literature thermal data yield a maximum canister surface temperature of about 80°C and a temperature gradient of slightly more than 1°C per cm in the radial direction at mid-height of the canisters. Approximately the same temperature distributions are arrived at if the thermal conductivity 0.75 W/m,°C of the freshly compacted non-saturated bentonite is applied as if the actual moisture-dependence of the conductivity is considered. This is explained by the fact that the drop in thermal conductivity in the hot zone close to the canisters is compensated by an increased conductivity in the wetted, peripheral part of the bentonite annulus.

THE STRIPA FIELD TEST

Test arrangement

A large underground test station was estab-

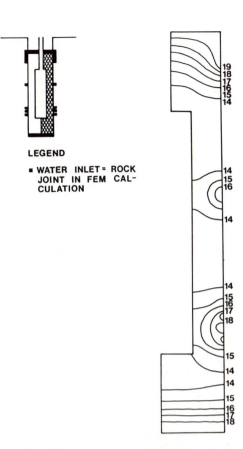

LEGEND

▪ WATER INLET = ROCK JOINT IN FEM CAL-CULATION

Fig. 3. Predicted distribution of the water content for a simple case. Time after onset of water uptake is 64 weeks.

lished in 1976 in an old abandoned iron ore mine at Stripa, about 250 km west of Stockholm. One of the drifts at 360 m depth has been used since 1981 for the international so-called Buffer Mass Test, which is an almost half scale application of the KBS concept (Pusch et al. 1983). The heat production of the canisters is simulated by electrical heating of six 600 to 1800 W-powered metal cylinders with a diameter of 38 cm and a length of 150 cm. The 76 cm diameter "deposition" holes, which have a depth of about 300 cm and 6 m spacing, were made by core drilling in rock with a largely varying degree of fracturing. The six holes therefore represent quite different hydrological conditions that yield a spectrum of water uptake rates in the bentonite, which had an original bulk density of about 2.1 t/m^3 and a water content of 10-13 %. The wettest hole (termed no 2) thus illustrates a saturation state after 3 years that will not be arrived at until 10-20 years in an actual repository where much less fractured rock will be required. The driest hole (no 6), on the other hand, probably yielded a slightly slower saturation than will be met with in practice. Saturation, swelling, and temperature conditions in these two holes will be discussed here with reference to the predictions. The power of the two heaters was 600 W throughout the test period.

Water uptake

The bentonite annuli were equipped with a large number of moisture sensors for continuous determination of the water uptake. This recording and a very comprehensive sampling in connection with the excavation of four holes (no 3-6) after more than 2 years test time, show that two mechanisms dominate:

1. The temperature gradient drives pore water from the vicinity of the "canisters" towards the rock. Thereby, the 1-3 cm peripheral zone becomes fully saturated, swells and forms a tight contact with the rock.

2. Water initially migrates from discrete water-bearing rock joints and fractures but they soon become sealed by penetrating clay if their apertures are wider than about 0.1 mm. Water under pressure in the rock is consequently forced through less wide fractures, which, in turn, tend to be sealed. Ultimately, water seems to migrate through the crystal matrix along fissures and incomplete grain boundaries and this yields a water migration from the rock into the clay which is remarkably uniform over the entire interface.

After more than 2 years test time the degree of water saturation in the "wet", fracture-

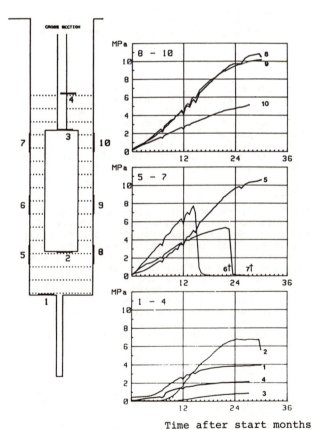

Time after start months

Fig. 4. Computer-plotted swelling pressures in the "wet" heater hole no 2. Cross means failed sensor.

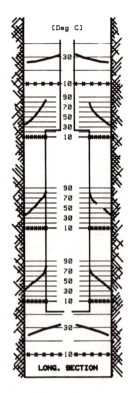

Fig. 5. Computer-plotted temperature distribu-
        tion in the "dry" heater hole no 6. x
        denotes the location of thermocouples.

ses the heat conductivity of the clay. The predicted temperature at the heater surface and
the clay/rock interface, respectively, are in
very good agreement with the recorded temperatures. The conditions in hole no 6 shortly
before the termination of this test after
slightly more than 2 years, is shown in Fig. 5.

CONCLUSIONS

The theoretically derived physical models for
the development of swelling pressures and
temperature fields were nicely confirmed by the
field test. As to the distribution of the water
uptake in the bentonite, the field test unani-
mously shows that it is much more uniform than
the early conservative model predicts. The
rate of water uptake in the practically important case of fracture-poor rock seems to be
slower than predicted by the simple model
based on diffusion from discrete, wider fractures.

REFERENCES

Börgesson, L. (1982). Buffer Mass Test -
    Predictions of the behaviour of the ben-
    tonite-based buffer materials. Stripa
    Project, Internal Report 82-08.

KBS (1980).   Technical Reports No. 80-11, 80-
    13, and 80-16. INIS Clearing House,
    International Atomic Energy Agency,
    Vienna, Austria.

Pusch, R. (1982).   Mineral-water interactions
    and their influence on the physical beha-
    vior of highly compacted Na bentonite.
    Can. Geotech. J., (19) Nov., 381-387).

Pusch, R. (1982).   Buffer Mass Test - Buffer
    Materials. Stripa Project, Internal
    Report 82-06.

rich hole no 2 is about 90 %, as concluded
from the moisture sensor signals, the outer
10 cm of the 19 cm thick bentonite annulus
being completely saturated. At the excavation
and sampling of the "dry", fracture-poor hole
no 6 it was found that only the peripheral
3 cm zone was water-saturated, the water content being slightly higher than 20 %.

Swelling

The high degree of saturation in hole no 2
suggests that the swelling and therefore also
the swelling pressures should be almost fully
developed. With the actual density, the
predicted swelling pressure at the clay/rock
interface is about 10 MPa. As indicated by
Fig. 4 the Gloetzl pressure cells located at
this interface yield almost exactly this pressure. In the dry hole no 6 the saturation of
the thin peripheral zone also produces a
swelling pressure (about 0.5 MPa) but the
deformability of the inner, non-saturated core
prevents the build-up of higher pressures.

Temperature

All the holes were richly equipped with thermocouples through which the development of temperature fields in the clay and the surrounding
rock has been continuously recorded. The heat
distribution in the clay reached an almost
steady state a few months after the test start.
The temperature has then dropped slowly and
slightly due to the water uptake, which increa-

Convection thermique naturelle et forcée en sol saturé

Natural and forced thermal convection in a saturated soil

E. RECORDON, Laboratoire de mécanique des sols, Ecole Polytechnique Fédérale de Lausanne, Suisse
D. BOVET, Laboratoire de mécanique des sols, Ecole Polytechnique Fédérale de Lausanne, Suisse

SYNOPSIS

Un massif de sable de 5 m de diamètre et 3,8 m de hauteur a en son centre un puits crépiné de 80 cm de diamètre, et à sa périphérie une grille thermique froide suivie d'un manteau drainant. De l'eau chaude est injectée dans le puits central et ressort par le manteau drainant, refroidie par la grille. Les isothermes devraient être des cylindres verticaux sans la convection naturelle qui se superpose à la convection forcée du fait de la non-horizontalité des isothermes : celles-ci se trouvent alors évasées vers le haut. On rapporte une observation expérimentale du champ thermique, et sa modélisation par la méthode du complexe topologique; le champ des vitesses est calculé, selon le théorème de Clebsch, comme la superposition d'un champ dérivant d'un potentiel scalaire, et d'un champ dérivant d'un potentiel-vecteur.

Dans la **fosse profonde** de l'ISRF, puits bétonné de 5 m de diamètre et 8 m de hauteur, a été constitué à partir de 1980 un modèle pour l'étude des flux hydrauliques et thermiques couplés dans un massif de sol. Le modèle complet, achevé en 1982, est constitué d'une couche inférieure de 3,8 m de hauteur, relativement perméable($K_D \approx 100 \cdot 10^{-9}$ $[m^3 \cdot kg^{-1} \cdot s]$) dite "zone saturée", et d'un couche supérieure de 3,10 m de hauteur, moins perméable ($K_D \approx 10^{-9}$ $[m^3 \cdot kg^{-1} \cdot s]$) dite "zone non saturée"; les deux couches sont traversées verticalement par un puits central de 80 cm de diamètre, crépiné sur la hauteur de la zone saturée; celle-ci est entourée d'une "grille thermique" formée de tuyaux verticaux dans lesquels circule de l'eau foide, et d'un manteau drainant déversant l'eau injectée par le puits et ayant traversé radialement le massif, dans un trou d'écoulement situé au point bas de la fosse (fig. 1).

La présente communication rend compte d'observations faites en 1981 sur la partie inférieure, soit la zone saturée. Un flux d'eau chaude à 50°C était injecté par le puits central et, traversant le massif, se refroidissait en se rapprochant de la grille thermique; une pompe à chaleur assurait le chauffage de l'eau injectée en même temps que le refroidissement de l'eau circulant dans la grille. L'expérience serait fort banale si la convection forcée ainsi établie n'était pas perturbée par une convection naturelle due au fait que les isothermes étant en première approximation des cylindres verticaux, le gradient de densité de l'eau n'est pas parallèle à la pesanteur. On voit alors les isothermes s'évaser vers le haut : la température sert de traceur au mouvement de l'eau, et indique par la forme des isothermes une ascension d'eau chaude au voisinage du puits, et une descente d'eau froide au voisinage de la grille thermique.

La figure 2 représente les isothermes observées, le régime permanent étant établi, lors d'une injection d'eau chaude à 50°C dans le puits central, la grille thermique imposant une température de sortie d'environ 15°C. Le débit injecté Q était de $0,25 \cdot 10^{-3}$ $[m^3 \cdot s^{-1}]$; la hauteur du massif étant h = 3,8 $[m]$, la vitesse de Darcy en fonction du rayon r est en première approximation

$$v = \frac{Q}{2\pi rh}, \qquad (1)$$

soit $v = 26 \cdot 10^{-6}$ $[m \cdot s^{-1}]$ au voisinage du puits central (r = 0,4 m) et $v = 4,5 \cdot 10^{-6}$ $[m \cdot s^{-1}]$ au voisinage de la grille (r = 2,3 m); ces valeurs supposent l'homogénéité du massif et l'absence de convection naturelle, hypothèses que nous allons précisément examiner pour les rejeter l'une et l'autre.

Supposant tout d'abord qu'il n'y ait pas de convection forcée, occupons-nous seulement de la convection naturelle. L'eau étant dilatable, sa densité ρ est fonction de la température T, et l'on a

$$\rho = \rho_0(1 - \alpha(T - T_0)), \qquad (2)$$

où T_0 est la **température de référence**, ρ_0 la **densité de référence** (valeur de ρ pour T = T_0) et α le **coefficient de dilatation**. Soit $|g| = 9,81$ $[m \cdot s^{-2}]$ la valeur absolue de l'accélération de la pesanteur, nous désignerons par g le vecteur vertical de bas en haut d'intensité $|g|$. Si, la convection forcée étant exclue par hypothèse, nous voulions aussi annuler la convection naturelle, l'équation de l'hydrostatique

$$\text{grad } p = -\rho g \qquad (3)$$

exigerait que

$$\text{rot}(\rho g) = \text{grad } \rho \times g + \rho \text{ rot } g = 0, \qquad (4)$$

c'est-à-dire, en tenant compte de (2) et de rot g = 0 :

$$\text{grad } \rho \times g - \alpha\rho_0 \text{ grad } T \times g = 0. \qquad (5)$$

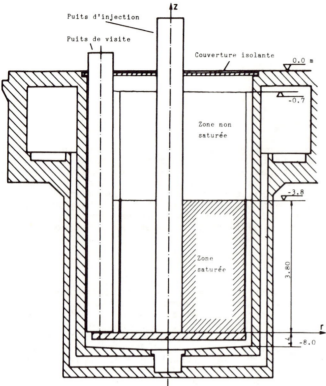

Fig. 1 Fosse profonde de l'ISRF
Coupe verticale

Il faudrait donc que le gradient thermique fût parallèle à g, autrement dit que la température fût répartie en couches horizontales isothermes. Or tel n'est pas nécessairement le cas : lorsqu'une source de chaleur quelconque située dans un massif provoque un gradient thermique, celui-ci n'est en général pas uniformément vertical. Alors les conditions de l'hydrostatique ne sont pas vérifiées, et des forces naissent, imprimant à l'eau un mouvement tendant à rendre les isothermes horizontales. Mais si les sources de chaleur sont maintenues, ce n'est pas l'équilibre qui s'établit, mais un écoulement stationnaire rotationnel, qui est la cause de la convection naturelle de la chaleur.

Revenant au cas général, nous poserons

$$i = - (\text{grad } p + \rho g), \qquad (6)$$

et nommerons le vecteur i la **pente hydraulique**; i n'est en général pas un gradient, et il n'est pas possible d'écrire comme on le fait d'ordinaire i = - grad ϕ, avec ϕ = p + $\rho|g|z$, car on a

$$\omega = \text{rot } i = - \alpha\rho_0 g \times \text{grad } T. \qquad (7)$$

D'après la loi de Darcy, la vitesse de Darcy v est liée à la pente hydraulique par l'équation

$$v = K_D i, \qquad (8)$$

où K_D est le **coefficient de Darcy.** La conservation de l'eau exige dans tout l'intérieur du massif div v = 0; mais sur sa frontière le flux entrant ou sortant peut être considéré comme une densité de sources singulière, et nous écrirons

$$\text{div } v = \zeta, \qquad (9)$$

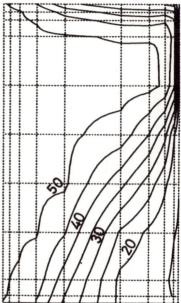

Fig. 2 Isothermes observées dans un plan méridien (Agrandissement de la partie hâchurée de la fig. 1)

étant entendu que ζ est une **distribution** (Schwartz, 1957) nulle à l'intérieur du massif (mais non sur sa frontière).

Cela posé, voici ce qu'affirme le **théorème de Clebsch** (Vogel, 1956) : tout champ vectoriel dans l'espace à trois dimensions peut être représenté comme la somme d'un gradient et d'un rotationnel : la fonction dont on prend le gradient est le **potentiel scalaire,** le vecteur dont on prend le rotationnel est le **potentiel-vecteur.** Dans notre cas, l'écoulement de l'eau dans un massif poreux est décrit par deux champs vectoriels, i et v : mais ils sont liés par l'équation (8), si bien qu'ils ne forment qu'un champ vectoriel indépendant, que nous désignerons par la paire (i,v), pour ne pas privilégier l'un par rapport à l'autre. Nous décomposerons alors le champ total en deux champs partiels :

$$(i,v) = (i',v') + (i'',v''). \qquad (9)$$

Nous ferons dériver le champ (i',v') d'un potentiel scalaire ϕ en posant

$$i' = -\text{grad } \phi, \qquad (10)$$

et en lui imposant la condition

$$\text{div } v' = \zeta; \qquad (11)$$

en combinant les équations (10) et (11), nous obtenons **l'équation de Poisson :**

$$\text{div } (K_D \text{ grad} \phi) = - \zeta. \qquad (12)$$

Nous ferons dériver le champ (i",v") d'un potentiel-vecteur ψ en posant

$$v'' = \text{rot } \psi \qquad (13)$$

et en imposant la condition

$$\text{rot } i'' = \omega; \qquad (14)$$

en combinant les équations (13) et (14), nous obtenons l'équation de Poisson "vectorielle"

$$\text{rot } (\frac{1}{K_D} \text{ rot } \psi) = \omega. \qquad (15)$$

Comme on a évidemment

$$\text{rot } i' = 0 \quad \text{et} \quad \text{div } v'' = 0, \qquad (16)$$

en additionnant (i',v') et (i",v") on obtient un champ total (i,v) satisfaisant les deux conditions

$$\text{div } v = \zeta, \quad \text{rot } i = \omega. \qquad (17)$$

La partie (i',v') du champ des vitesses correspond à la convection **forcée** parce que sa cause (ζ) est imposée à la surface du massif; la partie (i", v") correspond à la convection dite **naturelle** parce que sa cause (ω) prend naissance spontanément à l'intérieur du massif. Cette décomposition est globale : localement, rien ne distingue les deux modes de convection.

Les équations (12) et (15) ne sont que la formulation du **problème hydraulique**; le **problème thermique** est résumé dans l'équation de la propagation convective de la chaleur

$$\text{div}(K_F \text{ grad } T) - \text{div}(\gamma Cv(T-T_0)) - C\dot{T} = -\Gamma, \qquad (18)$$

où K_F est le **coefficient de Fourier**, C la **capacité thermique volumique**, γ le **coefficient de partage** exprimant que la chaleur se répartit dans une certaine proportion entre l'eau interstitielle et le squelette, enfin Γ est la **densité de sources de chaleur**; la fonction inconnue est la température T. On voit que v, solution du problème hydraulique, figure parmi les coefficients du problème thermique; mais en retour T, solution du problème thermique, détermine par l'équation (7) l'un des seconds membres du problème hydraulique. Il y a donc couplage entre les deux problèmes, qui n'en forment·qu'un, le **problème thermo-hydraulique**. Les équations (12), (15) et (18) considérées chacune pour soi, sont linéaires; mais leur connexion en fait un **système non-linéaire**.

Les données du problème thermo-hydraulique sont des conditions de Dirichlet ou de Neumann (éventuellement des conditions mixtes) relatives à la partie "forcée" du champ des vitesses, et au champ des températures : on impose donc aux divers points de la surface du massif soit des flux (d'eau et de chaleur) soit des potentiels hydrauliques et des températures. La résolution en tenant compte de la convection naturelle se fait par itération : on commence par résoudre le problème hydraulique en faisant ω = 0; on porte la valeur trouvée de v dans l'équation (18); en résolvant on trouve une valeur de T qui détermine une valeur généralement non-nulle de ω par l'équation (7); on reprend alors le problème hydraulique et l'on continue... jusqu'à ce que deux solutions consécuti-

ves soient assez proches pour qu'on juge que la méthode a convergé.

Ce calcul a été fait pour analyser le champ de température représenté par la figure 2. On a tenu compte de la symétrie cylindrique pour ramener le problème dans un plan méridien; les équations aux dérivées partielles ont été discrétisées par la méthode du **complexe topologique** (Bovet, 1977), qui a l'avantage de permettre facilement la combinaison d'un potentiel scalaire et d'un potentiel-vecteur; la méthode de résolution était une méthode de relaxation, dite de **Gauss-Seidel**. Les conditions aux limites imposées sont résumées dans le tableau suivant :

Part. de surface Problème	Puits central	Grille thermique	éponte inf.	éponte sup.
Hydraulique	D : $\phi = \phi_1$	D : $\phi = \phi_0$	N : $\zeta = 0$	N : $\zeta = 0$
Thermique	D : T = 50°C	D : T = 15°C	N : $\Gamma = 0$	D : T obs.

Par D ou N nous indiquons respectivement une condition de Dirichlet ou de Neumann; ϕ_1 et ϕ_0 étaient déterminés par tâtonnement afin d'obtenir le débit $Q = 0,25 \cdot 10^{-3}$ $[m^3 \cdot s^{-1}]$. Sur l'éponte supérieure, en contact avec l'atmosphère, les pertes thermiques sont importantes, d'où la forte stratification horizontale des isothermes : renonçant à en analyser le mécanisme, nous avons tout simplement imposé la température observée comme une condition de Dirichlet.

La viscosité de l'eau aussi bien que le coefficient de dilatation dépendent de la température; cependant, pour α, nous nous sommes contentés d'une valeur constante moyenne $\alpha = 0,32 \cdot 10^{-3}$ $[K^{-1}]$. Pour la viscosité η, qui diminue à peu près de moitié entre 15°C et 50°C, nous avons tenu compte de cette variation en admettant que K_D lui est inversement proportionnel, et en prenant

$$K_D(T) = K_D(T_0) \frac{\eta(T_0)}{\eta(T)}, \qquad (19)$$

adoptant pour η(T) la formule donnée par les tables CRC (CRC, 1977-78), p. F51. Cette variation de K_D est en fait une non-linéarité supplémentaire mais qui, si l'on peut dire, "ne coûte presque rien" étant donné le grand nombre d'itérations exigées de toutes façons par la méthode de résolution.

Adoptant pour K_D la valeur de référence uniforme $K_D(15°C) = 100 \cdot 10^{-9}$ $[m^3 \cdot kg^{-1} \cdot s]$, le calcul tenant compte de la convection naturelle nous a donné la répartition de température représentée par les isothermes de la figure 3. On voit que la répartition observée (fig. 2) n'est reproduite que qualitativement.

On s'est alors demandé si une stratification de la perméabilité, faisant de $K_D(T_0)$ une fonction de la cote z, ne contribuait pas aussi à expliquer la répartition observée. La justification de cette hypothèse est d'abord le bon sens : les couches supérieures comprimant les couches inférieures, il est normal que $K_D(T_0)$ diminue avec la profondeur; cette stratifica-

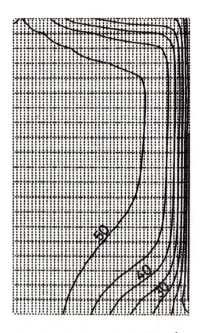 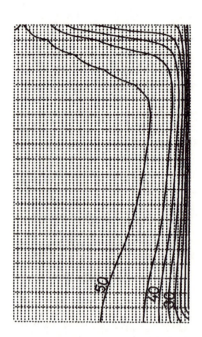 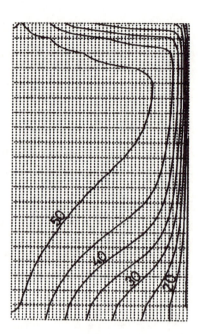

Fig. 3   Isothermes calculées
$\alpha = 0,32 \cdot 10^{-3}$,
$K_D = 100 \cdot 10^{-9}$

Fig. 4   Isothermes calculées
$\alpha = 0$,
$K_D = (40...160) \, 10^{-9}$

Fig. 5   Isothermes calculées
$\alpha = 0,32 \cdot 10^{-3}$,
$K_D = (40...160) \, 10^{-9}$

tion a d'autre part été confirmée par des mesures hydrauliques faites pendant le remplissage progressif du massif : on a constaté une augmentation de la perméabilité à 15°C dans le rapport de 1 à 4 environ entre le fond et la surface. On a alors supposé une variation linéaire de 40 à $160 \cdot 10^{-9}$ $[m^3 \cdot kg^{-1} \cdot s]$ entre le fond et la surface; et pour isoler l'effet de cette stratification de celui de la convection naturelle, on a fait un premier calcul en posant $\alpha = 0$. La figure 4 montre le résultat. Combinant alors les deux effets, en rétablissant $\alpha = 0,32 \cdot 10^{-3}$ $[K^{-1}]$, on a obtenu la figure 5 : la reproduction de la figure expérimentale est bien meilleure.

Le problème que nous venons de traiter est un exemple de "problème inverse", consistant à remonter d'une observation de champ à la détermination des coefficients matériels d'un système : il s'agit de ce que les mathématiciens appellent un problème "mal posé" (Tikhonov et Arsénine, 1976), parce que le nombre des inconnues y excède le nombre des données. Il faut alors suppléer au défaut d'information par des hypothèses plus ou moins arbitraires : la sagacité de l'analyste les choisira les plus "économiques" possibles, c'est-à-dire les plus simples compatibles avec l'inforamtion disponible. Dans notre cas, d'autres modulations de K_D (T_0) nous permettraient d'affiner la correspondance entre l'expérience et sa reproduciton mathématique : nous n'avons voulu montrer que deux étapes dans cette recherche; d'autres peuvent être aisément imaginées. Il y a une conclusion pratique générale à tirer de notre expérience et de notre calcul : c'est que lorsque la pro-

pagation de la chaleur est convective, des inhomogénéités de K_D ordinairement négligées peuvent modifier considérablement la répartition des températures; d'autre part, la convection naturelle modifie elle aussi la répartition des températures; et les effets de chacune de ces deux causes peuvent être du même ordre de grandeur.

Les auteurs tiennent à remercier ici MM. Bernard Corminboeuf, ingénieur-mécanicien, Andréas Nickel, licincié ès sciences naturelles, et Silvano Mariani, physicien diplômé, à qui sont dues la construction et l'exploitation du modèle expérimental, ainsi que la programmation du modèle d'analyse numérique.

REFERENCES

CRC Handbook of Chemistry and Physics, 58th edition Cleveland, CRC press, 1977-1978.

Bovet D.   "La discrétisation des problèmes de la physique mathématique au moyen de complexes topologiques", Z. angew. Math. Phys. 28, pp. 371-374, 1977.

Schwartz L.   Théorie des distributions, T I et II, Paris, Hermann, 1957.

Tikhonov A., Arsénine V.   Méthodes de résolution de problèmes mal posés, Moscou, MIR, 1976.

Vogel Th.   Physique mathématique classique, Paris, A. Colin, 1956.

Session 3C
Geotechnical aspects of environmental control
C. Tailings dams and waste containment structures

Séance 3C
Aspects géotechniques de la réglementation de l'environnement
C. Barrage en déchets et structures pour l'entrepôt de déchets

Estimation of the physical characteristics of deposited tailings in the tailings dam of nonferrous metallurgy

Détermination des caractéristiques physiques des stériles déposés dans les barrages de stériles des métaux non-ferreux

C. B. ABADJIEV, Professor of Civil Engineering, Higher Institute of Civil Engineering, Sofia, Bulgaria

SYNOPSIS: The determination of the physical characteristics of the spigotted tailings are necessary for disigning stable and economical tailings dams. Here a system for estimating and determining these characteristics is presented on the basis of extensive research in several tailings dams in the nonferrous metallurgy, under different spigotting techniques and for different particle sizes of deposited tailings. Methods for determining the separation along the beach of the spigotted material are given, then generalised compression curves as a function of the mean diameters are worked out. Graphs for the shear strength and the permeability as functions of the grain sizes and density are established. By means of characteristics thus obtained for every point of the deposited tailings, one can determine more precisely the flow net, the consolidation and the stability of the tailings dams.

INTRODUCTION

The possibility of constructing high spigotted upstream tailings dams, which are the most economical ones, depends on the physical characteristics of the tailings, deposited in their body in the process of spigotting. To date however, there has not been a convenient, complete and practical methodology for determining these characteristics. This may be one of the reasons for a hurried rejection of this type of construction in so many cases, in favour of other, more expensive constructions. Actually, when correctly constructed, and under the proper management of the spigotting techniques, the deposited tailings can have very good characteristics. Here we present a system for estimating and determining the characteristics of the deposited tailings on the basis of extensive research in several tailings dams in the nonferrous metallurgy, under different spigotting techniques and for different sizes of deposited tailings.

The tailings of the nonferrous metallurgy are milled rock materials of different origin with a maximum diameter of the particles of 0,25 to 0,5 mm. The silt and fine sand fraction are predominant. The fraction with diameter less than 0,074 mm are usually between 60 and 80%, and less than 0,005 mm - between 5 and 20%. The uniformity coefficient $C_u = \dfrac{d_{60}}{d_{10}}$ varies between 6 and 15, but for repreatedly milled tailings it can rize to 50. Although the granulometric curves of the initial and of the settled tailings are similar to the sand-silt, or sand-silt-clay mixtures, they differ essentially from them in mechanical properties, in the origin, in the rectangular form of the particles and the rest of flotation reagents. They have smaller density, bigger angle of internal friction and smaller cohesion than natural materials with the same coarseness.

The initial tailings of the nonferrous metallurgy have such coarseness and granulometry which does not allow the construction of high and stable tailings dams. This is possible only after separation of the tailings in coarseness in the cross section of the tailings dam, placing the coarser particles in the outside zone and the fine material in the inside zone. This separation can be achieved be means of hydrocyclones for the downstream method which is more expensive and by spigotting for the upstream tailings dams. By spigotting, a natural flowing separation of the deposited tailings along the beach is achieved.

The estimation of the physical characteristics of the tailings deposited by spigotting in the entire cross-section of the tailings dam raises the following problems, which must be resolved in the following sequence:

SEPARATION OF THE SPIGOTTED TAILINGS ALONG THE BEACH

When spigotting is going on, the largest particles of the tailings settle at the very beginning of the beach. Moving towards the pond, the deposited particles are getting smaller and finally the finest ones settle in the pond itself. Then a natural flowing separation of the deposited tailings is achieved after the filter principles. The coefficient of permeability, the shear strength, the piping and dynamic stability are also functions of the coarseness and granulometry. For this reason a flowing separation after these properties is achieved as well.

There exist many methods for determination and prognosis of the material separation during the spigotting (Melentiev /1960/, Filahtov and Nikitochkin /1972/, Kisseleva /1976/, Pinalov /1978/ and others). Since the number of the determining factors turns to be more than the known mathematical equations, all these methods use theoretically and experimentally established relations. The latest depend on the specific conditions. In spite of their theoretical and empirical worthiness, these methods are not applicable under all possible conditions. That was the reason which forced us to search for methods and relations, valid under the conditions of our copper and lead flotation plants. Since these relations are worked out on the basis of a wide range of experimental results, one can hope that their validity will be spread out in a wider domain.

First method. This method is applicable for tailings dams, which are already in the phase of

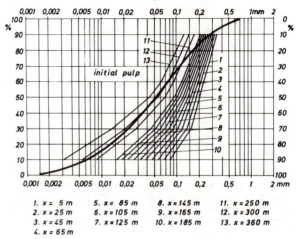

Tailings dam „Malko Tirnovo"
Section 4, April 1979

1. x= 5 m	5. x= 85 m	8. x=145 m	11. x=250 m
2. x=25 m	6. x=105 m	9. x=165 m	12. x=300 m
3. x=45 m	7. x=125 m	10. x=185 m	13. x=360 m
4. x=65 m			

Fig. 3

trial spigotting or in operation. The samples are to be taken along the beach and along the pond, if possible. The granulometric curves have chaotic forms and are crossing each other arbitrarily. Example of the Malko Tirnovo copper tailings dam is shown on Fig. 1. The following step is to draw up the variation of the diameters d_i (d_{10}, d_{30}, d_{50}, d_{60}, d_{90} and $\bar{d}$) along the beach and, if possible, along the pond for the same points of sampling. This is done on Fig. 2 on the basis of the example from Fig. 1. The lines d_i are broken. They can be presented aproximately by flowing curves after the exponential low

$$(1) \qquad d_i(x) = d_{i,o}\, e^{-ax}$$

by means of the method of the least squares. The index zero denotes the respective diameter d_i at x=0 (at the beginning of the beach). The obtained smooth curves $d_i(x)$ are shown on Fig. 2.

Using them one can draw up once again the granulometric curves from Fig. 1, which now do not cross each other and are well situated lines (Fig. 3).

This method can be applied also for the determination of the alteration of the coarseness of the grains settled along the pond. The diameters of the particles at the pond beginning are decreasing very fast, because the coarse grains settle quickly in the water. Then the size of the diameters gets smaller very slowly. The transition of the grain coarseness between the beach and the pond is very abrupt, so in the scale of the tailings dam it can be regarded as a jump. This is illustrated on Fig. 4.

Second method. It explores the analogy with the existing tailings dams. The separation of the tailings in the mean diameter along beach and pond in various experimental conditions on several dams is shown on Fig.4. The conditions are listed on the table of the figure. Obviously the separation is function of the coarseness, of the

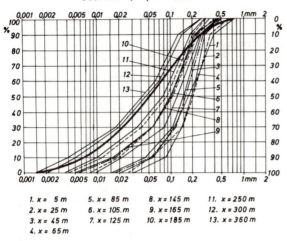

Tailings dam „Malko Tirnovo"
Section 4, April 1979

1. x= 5 m	5. x= 85 m	8. x=145 m	11. x=250 m
2. x=25 m	6. x=105.m	9. x=165 m	12. x=300 m
3. x=45 m	7. x=125 m	10. x=185 m	13. x=360 m
4. x=65 m			

Fig. 1

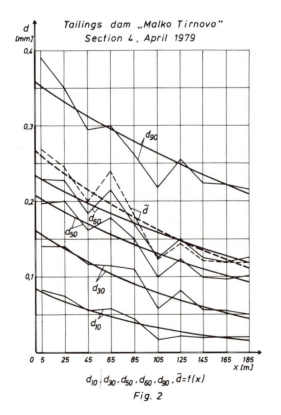

$d_{10}, d_{30}, d_{50}, d_{60}, d_{90}, \bar{d}=f(x)$

Fig. 2

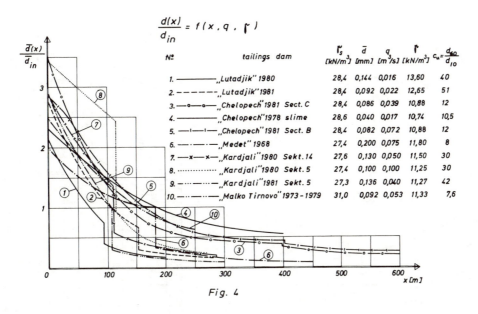

$$\frac{d(x)}{d_{in}} = f(x, q, \gamma)$$

Nº	tailings dam	γ_s [kN/m³]	$\bar{d}$ [mm]	q [m³/s]	γ [kN/m³]	$c_u = \frac{d_{60}}{d_{10}}$
1.	————— „Lutadjik" 1980	28,4	0,144	0,016	13,60	40
2.	—————— „Lutadjik" 1981	28,4	0,092	0,022	12,65	51
3.	—o—o— „Chelopech" 1981 Sect. C	28,4	0,086	0,039	10,88	12
4.	————— „Chelopech" 1978 slime	28,6	0,040	0,017	10,74	10,5
5.	—ı—ı— „Chelopech" 1981 Sect. B	28,4	0,082	0,072	10,88	12
6.	—·—·— „Medet" 1968	27,4	0,200	0,075	11,80	8
7.	—x—x— „Kardjali" 1980 Sekt. 14	27,6	0,130	0,050	11,50	30
8.	·········· „Kardjali" 1980 Sekt. 5	27,4	0,100	0,100	11,25	30
9.	————— „Kardjali" 1981 Sekt. 5	27,3	0,136	0,040	11,27	42
10.	—·—·— „Malko Tirnovo" 1973 – 1979	31,0	0,092	0,053	11,33	7,6

Fig. 4

initial pulp and its coefficient of uniformity of the pulp discharge from one outlet, of the pulp density and the unit weight of the solid particles. In order to avoid the influence of the initial coarseness the results shown on Fig. 4 are divided by the initial mean diameter. Using Fig. 4 and its table we can forecast by analogy the alteration of the mean diameter of the settled material along the beach and the pond.

This method of the analogy is very reliable because it takes in consideration the fundamental technological factors. Figure 4 can be completed continuously with results of new experiments and the reliability of the forecast can be continuously improuved.

The results of these investigations are presented by the mean diameter. This is not quite sufficient, because it is the granulometry which is the representative parameter. The mean diameter and the uniformity coefficient of the tailings of nowadays flotation technology of the nonferrous metallurgy does not vary very much. That is why the mean diameter can be adopted as sufficiently representative parameter.

Third method. The results from Fig. 4 can be described mathematicaly by a full polynominal of second degree of the three variables: the distance x in the range of $0 \leq x \leq 400$ m, the pulp discharge for $0,016 \leq q \leq 0,100$ m³/s and the pulp density for $10,74 \leq \gamma \leq 13,6$ kN/m³:

$$(2) \quad \frac{\bar{d}(x, q, \gamma)}{d_{in}} = -11,065 - 0,0128 \, x + 71,5 \, q + 2,421 \, \gamma -$$

$$- 0,01319 \, x \, q - 63 \cdot 10^{-6} \, x \, \gamma + 8,57 \, q \, \gamma +$$

$$+ 21,14 \cdot 10^{-6} \, x^2 + 295,5 \, q^2 + 0,1034 \, \gamma^2$$

The coarseness of the deposited tailings in each point of the dam can be determined by means of some of these methods.

DENSITY OF THE SPIGOTTED TAILINGS

After the separation of the material after its size and granulometry in the body of the tailings dam is known, we determine its density. On the basis of more than thousand compression tests, generalized compression curves in their functional relation to the mean tailings diameter have been worked out (Fig.5). Using the graphs on Fig.5 and knowing already the coarseness of the deposited tailings, one can determine their density in each point of the dam.

The density, the shear strength and the permeability have been studied successfuly by Fedorov and Dobrovinskaja (1970), Pinalov (1978) and Shulz (1979) for some different conditions.

The tailings of the nonferrous metallurgy usually consolidate very fast. They consolidate in the pond area at depth higher than 40 m even during the exploration period. If the percentage of the fine particles with diameters smaller than 0,005 mm in the initial tailings is more than 20-25% then the consolidation in the pond area continues very long. But that is only in the pond area, and if the spigotting is done properly and the beach is kept long enough, it does not influence the stability of the dam.

SHEAR STRENGTH

As a result of the research, graphs are established for the relationship between the shear strength (angle of internal friction and cohesion) of the deposited tailings and their grain sizes and their density (Fig.6). Since we know already the particle sizes and the density in each point of the dam, we can determine also the shear strength in each point using Fig. 6.

The investigations of our tailings dams have shown, that at the first 50m on the beach, the angle of internal friction is between 30° and 35°. Then it decreases and becomes at 100 m about 25°

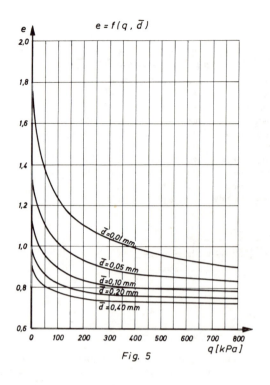

Fig. 5

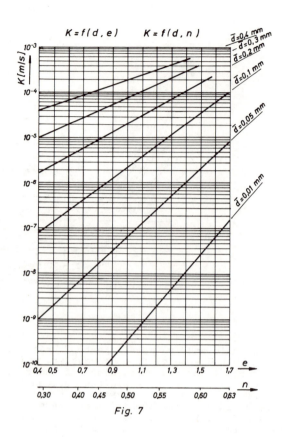

Fig. 7

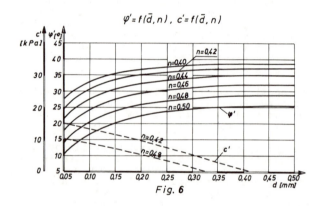

Fig. 6

By means of the physical characteristics thus obtained for any point of the deposited tailings, one can determine more precisely the flow net, the consolidation and the stability of a tailings dam.

REFERENCES

Abadjiev,C.B.(1976) Seepage through Mill Tailings Dams.XII Congress of ICOLD,Q.44,R.18,381-393.

Fedorov,I.S. and Dobrovinskaya,O.H.(1970) Technical Properties and Characteristics of Spigotted Tailings, 151 pp.,Nedra,Moskow (in russian).

Filahtov,A.L. and Nikitochkin,O.G.,(1972) Method of Determination of the Tailings Separation, 62 pp.,NIISP,Gosstroi,Kiev,USSR (in russian).

Kisseleva,M.L.,(1976) Determination of the Material Separation on the Beach of the Spigotted Tailings Dams. Trudy LPI Nr.354,11-15,Leningrad (in russian).

Melentiev,V.A.,(1960) Sand and Gravel Spigotted Dams,163 pp., Energia,Moskow (in russian).

Pinalov,I.V.,(1978) Fine Grained Material Spigotted Tailings Dams. Diss.,MISI,Moskow (in russian).

Shulz,L.V.,(1979) Recommendation for Estimation of the Spigotted Tailings Dams Physic Characteristics, 31 pp.,MECHANOBR,Leningrad (in russian).

-30°, at 200 m about 22°-25° and in the pond itself it is in drained conditions about 20°. The cohesion at the first 50 m of the beach is very small - about 1-2 kN/m². Then it increases till 5 kN/m² at 100 m, till 10-15 kN/m² at 200 m and is higher in the pond area.

PERMEABILITY

On the basis of the experiments on compression together with permeability, the nomogram of Fig. 7 is obtained. It shows the coefficient of permeability as a function of the mean grain diameter and the density. Using this nomogram one can predict the coefficient of permeability and then to investigate the seepage. A thorough study of the seepage through tailings dams is done by Abadjiev (1976).

Improved upstream construction of tailings dam

Construction en amont améliorée d'un barrage de stériles

C. B. ABADJIEV, Professor of Civil Engineering, Higher Institute of Civil Engineering, Sofia, Bulgaria

SYNOPSIS   A new type of construction of a spigotted upstream tailings dam is proposed, designed with a view to improving its stability and thus widening the application of this economical type. The starter dam has a tongue-shaped projecting lower upstream part. This part, or "the tongue", is built of draining material of sufficient strength. The length of the tongue is equal to the distance from the starter dam to the decant pond at the initial stage, and is calculated to ensure the stability of the tailings dam at its maximum height. The tongue's surface has an inclination towards the pond which is not smaller than that of the beach. This ensures the correct spigotting along the tongue and favourable separation of the settled tailings. The decant pond and the slime part shift to the inside, beyond the supporting part, thus increasing stability. The height of the tongue at its verge on the pond is such as to provide a pond sufficiently large to have clear water on the first day of operation. This construction has been applied in the design of a 190 m high tailings dam, which is now under construction.

INTRODUCTION

The spigotted upstream tailings dams (Fig. 1) are the most economical and widely spread ones. Their basic constructions - the starter dam and the decant constructions - are small and are built fastest. That is why, they are to be always preferred, if the necessary conditions for their application are observed: sufficient coarseness of tailings, favourable topographic conditions, and lower seismicity of the region. The upstream tailings dam, however, have a fundamental disadvantage: as is seen on fig. 1, the section of the supporting part, built of coarser tailings at later stages, lie on finer granular material, laid off during the preceding stages, which has smaller strength characteristics, consolidates slowly and is a poor foundation for a higher construction. That is why, this construction is stable only to a limit height (Klohn, 1972). Stability can be achieved with great difficulty when the base incline is great.

The first trend to improve the stability of this type of construction is to make the starter dam higher, which is an expensive solution. The other trend is to build drains at the front of the starter dam (fig. 1). The drains will dry the supporting part by shifting the phreatic curve inside, at the same time aiding slime consolidation. The disadvantige of this kind of solution is, that since the spilway is higher, slime will be deposited over the drain

and, even if it does not clog the drain, it will screen it and considerably reduce its action, if not put it out of operation altogether.

NEW CONSTRUCTION OF AN UPSTREAM TAILINGS DAM

As a better way to improve the stability we propose the construction, shown on fig. 2. The tongue-shaped projecting lower upstream part of the starter dam is built, like the dam itself, of draining material of sufficient strength. Its length is equal to the distance from the starter dam to the decant pond at the initial stage, and is designed in such a way as to ensure the stability of the tailings dam at its maximum height by minimum total cost of the starter dam and the tongue.

The tongue's surface has an inclination towards the pond no smaller than that of the beach, thus ensuring the correct spigotting along the length of the tongue and favourable separation of the settled tailings. The coarser fractions are laid off in the supporting part over the tongue, and the finer material is washed off and carried after the tongue into the pond. This kind of sorting makes it possible to use the good strength of the coarse tailings deposited over the tongue as a substitute for the rock-

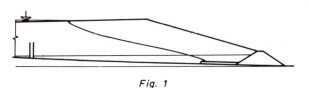

Fig. 1

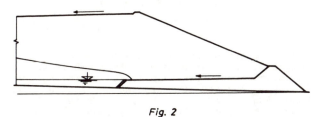

Fig. 2

fill. Such a big portion of the rock-fill is replaced by tailings, as is sufficient to obtain the necessary stability at considerable savings in rock-fill (the area between the unbroken and the dotted lines on fig. 3).

If the available material is not sufficiently permeable, then drainages should be built in the tongue, near the decant pond or over its whole area. In order to achieve good draining of the sides of the tailings dam, drainages should be raised up the slopes of the valley. With the proposed construction, the slime part shifts to the inside, beyond the supporting part, and this increases stability. The slime is in front of the draining tongue, and hence does not screen or clog it. In case there is high water at the time of operation and the decant pond shifts back over the tongue, depositing a layer of fine material there, then after the decant pond has receded, this slime can be washed off and returned to the decant pond by letting a greater discharge via the spigotting outlets.

The height of the tongue at its verge on the decant pond is so great that it can provide such a length of the pond as will be sufficient for decanting the water, and a volume that will provide the time for the necessary degree of decomposition of the reagents used in the floatation, so that the water can be re-circulated on the very first day of operation. The upstream slope of the tongue, bordering on the pond, is screened to hold back water necessary for the plant.

USAGE

This construction has been used for the tailings dam of the Assarel copper floatation plant (fig. 3), begun in 1984. The tailings dam has been designed for more than 10^8 tons, with maximum height of 190 m. The mean diameter of the tailings varies between 0.056 and 0.065 mm, while 70 - 73% are below 0.074 mm. The prototype employs a rockfill starter dam 128 m high (the broken line on fig. 3) which is constructed of the borrowed material from the open mine pit situated at a distance of 11 km, and a 62 m high spigotting supper part.

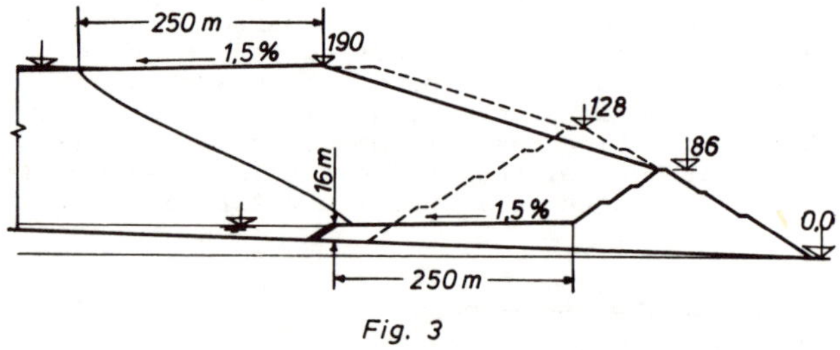

sure the decanting. The upstream slope of the tongue is screened by a polymer film. Its upper surface is covered with 0.30 m of gravel then with geotextile as filter and overloaded by 0.2 m gravel and 0.30 m of rock, to prevent damage caused by the spigotting flow or the sun's rays. Geotextile also insulates the upstream slope of the rock-fill against clogging by the tailings, and vigorous seepage, in case that high water at the initial stage will raise the pond up to the starter dam. Spigotting will be done by a simultaneous release of pulp through some 20 outlets, at 70 - 80 l/s per outlet.

The length of the beach at the initial stage equals the length of the tongue - 250 m, and onwards will continuously increase, becoming nearly 800 m at the top of the starter dam, and over 1000 m when the tailings dam is completed. The decant ponds are of a similar size. With such great lengths and areas of the pond and the beach the 10000 years floods after the first stage (37 m) will submerge only part of the beach, never submerging the whole beach. The seepage and stability tests however have been performed by allowing for great safety a minimum beach of 250 m.

After the final stage of the starter dam, the building of the spigotting part will be done by constructing small secondary dams, using material taken from the open mine pit, 5 m high at the begining and 3 m high after the dam has reached 120 m.

This economical construction saves 8.10^6 m^3 of rock filling, as compared to the prototype of the same degree of stability. It also has a number of advantages concerning the efficiency of draining and the tailings dam consolidation.

REFERENCES

Klohn, E. J. (1972) Design and Construction of Tailings Dams. The Canadian Mining and Metalurgical, April, p. 28 - 44

Fig. 3

The new construction provides for an optimised height of the starter dam of 86 m, while the spigotted super-structure is 104 m. The tongue is 250 m long and 16 m high at its frontal part bordering on the pond. Thus, at its initial stage, the pond is 500 m long, enough to en-

Transport of organic contaminants and geotechnical properties of fine-grained soils

Transport de contaminants organiques et propriétés géotechniques de sols fins

Y. B. ACAR, Assistant Professor of Civil Engineering, Louisiana State University, Baton Rouge, Louisiana, USA
I. OLIVIERI, Research Assistant, Department of Civil Engineering, Louisiana State University, Baton Rouge, Louisiana, USA
S. D. FIELD, Assistant Professor of Civil Engineering, Louisiana State University, Baton Rouge, Louisiana, USA

SYNOPSIS   An evaluation of the transport of acetone and phenol in hydraulic conductivity tests with compacted kaolinite indicated longitudinal dispersion coefficients of the order of 10^{-6} cm^2/sec. It was observed that changes in hydraulic conductivity of compacted kaolinite with organic fluids are strongly affected by the effective stresses. Such changes could qualitatively be estimated from the change in index properties of the soils with a specific contaminant. Index Properties of Na- and Ca-montmorillonite and Georgia kaolinite with various organic contaminants showed that these active clays are highly affected by variations in the dielectric constant of the pore fluid while the pH of the organic contaminant was observed to influence the index properties of Georgia kaolinite.

INTRODUCTION

Among various different methods of waste containment, the most economical is placement in shallow waste disposal facilities where compacted fine-grained soil liners are used to retard the transport of the contaminants. Apart from the inorganic constituents of wastes, a majority consists of organic material and fluids. These contaminants together with the infiltrating water generate the leachates which are then transported through the liner under field gradients.

This study presents the effects of the transport of organic contaminants on geotechnical properties of fine-grained soils as evidenced from hydraulic conductivity tests and index properties of fine-grained soils with organic fluids. The implication of the observed behavior on hazardous waste disposal and contaminant transport are also discussed.

CONTAMINANT TRANSPORT

Expressions representing the movement of chemical species and a fluid in a porous medium may be obtained by the principles of the conservation of mass (Gillham and Cherry, 1982). If the velocity of flow is constant and the diffusion in the solid phase is orders of magnitude less than the one in the bulk solution and the flow is incompressible, isotropic and one-dimensional, and further if the adsorption of chemicals on the clay surfaces dominate the reactions in the medium, conservation of mass requires,

$$R \frac{\partial C}{\partial t} = D_L \frac{\partial^2 C}{\partial x^2} - v_x \frac{\partial C}{\partial x} \qquad (1)$$

where R is the retardation coefficient which denotes the relative velocity of the reaction constituents, v_x, with respect to the bulk flow, v_x, D_L = longitudinal dispersion coefficient, and C = concentration of chemicals. Data from laboratory experiments identify the principal parameters affecting the longitudinal dispersion as,

$$\frac{D_L}{D_o} = \alpha + \beta \, P_e \qquad (2a)$$

$$P_e = \frac{v_x \, d}{D_o} \qquad (2b)$$

where D_o = diffusion in the bulk solution, d = mean pore diameter, α and β are constants. Solution of equation 1 for common boundary conditions in laboratory hydraulic conductivity tests with a contaminant are presented by Hashimoto, et al. (1964).

Assuming that the velocity of flow in fine-grained soils under field gradients range between 10^{-5} to 10^{-8} cm/sec, the mean pore diameter to be 10^{-2} to 10^{-4} cm, and the diffusion coefficients in the bulk solution to be 10^{-5} to 10^{-6} cm^2/sec (Freeze and Cherry, 1979), Peclet numbers for insitu conditions are far less than 1.0. Experimental data suggest that for this range of Peclet number, D_L/D_o ratio ranges between 0.6 to 1.0 (Perkins and Johnston, 1963) implying that longitudinal dispersion is mainly due to the diffusion of the chemical in bulk solution.

EXPERIMENTAL INVESTIGATION

The effect of the transport of organic contaminants on hydraulic conductivity of compacted soils is studied in flexible wall permeameters. The permeameters consisted of a set of triaxial cells where provisions were taken to maintain continuous backpressure (Acar, et al., 1984). The constant head is maintained by marriotte bottles and the gradient is continuously monitored by pressure transducers. All couplings and tubings were made of teflon to avoid adsorption and corrosion. Georgia kaolinite and a Ca-montmorillonite are chosen for permeation studies. Samples are first saturated with 0.01 N $CaSO_4$ solution and permeated with organic fluids. Since index properties of fine-grained soils with a specific molding fluid would give a qualitative indication of possible changes to be expected in their geotechnical properties, a separate study was initiated to investigate the effect of various organic contaminants on the index properties of the clay minerals used in the permeation study. A Na-montmorillonite was also added to this list. Tables I and II present the characteristics of the organic fluids and the clay minerals used in this study.

ANALYSIS OF RESULTS

The analytical or experimental results of equation 1 are often presented as a plot of the change in concentration of the effluent with respect to the input concentration versus the number of pore volumes permeated. Figure 1 presents such a plot for acetone and phenol permeated through kaolinite compacted at the wet of optimum water content. Theore-

tical solution of equation 2 for constant flux boundary conditions is also depicted. The experimental results indicate that the longitudinal dispersion coefficient for acetone and phenol in compacted kaolinite would be in the order of 10^{-6} cm^2/sec. Batch adsorption tests with acetone and phenol did not indicate any significant adsorption of these chemicals on kaolinite implying retardation coefficients of 1.0.

As observed from the theoretical curves in Figure 1, as the rate of flow increases with respect to the longitudinal dispersion coefficient, the transport of the contaminant is mainly controlled by the rate of flow of the bulk solution. An increase in the rate of

TABLE II

Characteristics of Clay Minerals

Characteristic	K	Ca-M	Na-M
Composition (%)			
Kaolinite (K)	96	-	-
Illite	4	1	-
Ca-Mont (Ca-M)	-	99	-
Na-Mont (Na-M)	-	-	100
Index Properties			
Liquid Limit (%)	64	88	425
Plastic Limit (%)	34	54	58
Activity	0.32	2.8	4.5

TABLE I

Characteristics of Organic Fluids

Compound	pH	ε	HC	S
Water	7.0	80.4	-	-
E. Glycol	6.4	38.7	-	-
Nitrobenzene	3.9	35.7	H,T,S,P	1.9
Ethanol		13.1	-	∞
Acetone	6.8	20.7	T	∞
Phenol	3.5	13.1	H,T,S,P	86.3
Aniline	9.9	6.9	T,S	34.0
Xylene	5.6	2.5	T,S	0.2
T. Chloro-ethylene	5.6	2.3	H,T,S,P	0.02
Benzene	5.7	2.3	H,T,S,P	1.77
CCl_4	4.0	2.2	H,T,S,P	0.77
Heptane	5.4	1.9	-	0.03

ε - Dielectric constant (20°C)

HC - Hazard Classification (USEPA, 1977)

H - acute hazardous   P - priority compound

T - toxic   S - section 311 compound

S - Solubility (gm/l) (25°C)

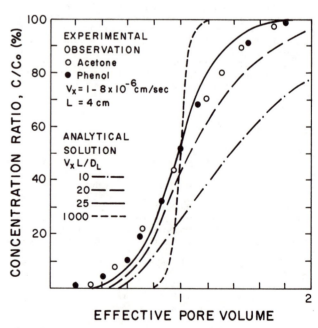

Fig. 1.   Breakthrough of acetone and phenol in compacted kaolinite

flow can be initiated either by increases in the hydraulic gradient or the hydraulic conductivity. Although the field gradients vary within 1-10, it is not uncommon to have 2-3 orders of magnitude change in hydraulic conductivity of fine-grained soils due to fabric changes initiated by the movement of contaminants (Michaels and Lin, 1954). Furthermore, any fabric change will also initiate a volume change and in cases where the soil liner is subjected to differential volume changes, tension cracks might develop which would further increase the rate of flow. Consequently, in order to assess the structural integrity of compacted soil liner, it becomes necessary to estimate the possible fabric changes with a specific leachate.

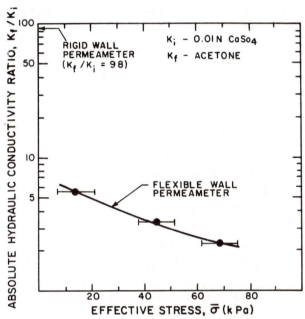

Fig. 2.   The effect of effective stresses and and testing scheme on hydraulic conductivity of compacted kaolinite to pure acetone

Figure 2 presents the change in absolute hydraulic conductivity of compacted kaolinite with pure acetone after saturation with 0.01 N CaSO$_4$ solution. It is observed that effective stresses have a major influence in the changes recorded with flexible wall permeameters. Since samples compacted in rigid wall permeameters are also subjected to effective stresses of unknown magnitude, the dramatic increase in hydraulic conductivity with such a testing scheme was attributed to side leakages due to decreases in the volume of the sample with acetone permeation (Acar, et al., 1984).

Considering the variables that affect the forces of interaction in fine-grained soils, an increase in hydraulic conductivity would imply a decrease in the repulsive forces resulting in a flocculated fabric and vice versa. The liquid limit of a fine-grained soil with a specific leachate could be used as

a qualitative indication of the changes in the thickness of the diffuse double layer or the repulsive forces. The change in the liquid limit of the two smectite minerals with the organic fluids given in Table 1 are presented in Figure 3. In the case of montmorillonites, it is observed that the dielectric constant has a major influence on the index properties. These clays became non-plastic for fluids with dielectric constants of less than 30. Figure 4 indicates that kaolinite does not show the expected trend with dielectric constant. It is observed that different organic fluids induce different responses in index properties of kaolinite. This mineral was non-plastic to acetone and to contaminants with dielectric constants of less than three. Nitrobenzene, phenol and carbontetrachloride with low pH values resulted in high liquid limit values. These variable responses could mainly be attributed to the positive charges at the broken edges of this mineral. In fact, a low pH would tend to dissociate the OH$^-$ groups on the edges of the particles resulting in higher liquid limits (Genevois, 1977). However, it should also be noted that the decrease in index properties of this mineral with organic contaminants, when compared with that of water, is not as drastic as the highly active montmorillonites.

There exists several implications of the observed dramatic decreases in the consistency limits of active clay minerals with the organic contaminants. Presently, soils with high activities are used in order to ascertain the low permeability of the compacted soil liners. Fine-grained soils with high activities are associated with lower water permeabilities (Lambe, 1954). However, the above results indicate that the initial structure of these soils will be more sensitive to post-constructional changes in the pore fluid chemistry. Decreases in the dielectric constant of the pore fluid with the transport of the organic contaminant would depress the thickness of the diffuse double layer resulting in a decrease in the forces of repulsion in the system. As a consequence, there will be a restructuring of the fabric leading to a decrease in volume (Green, et al., 1981), increases in hydraulic conductivity (Michaels and Lin, 1954; Anderson, et al., 1980; Acar, et al., 1984), decrease in compressibility (Sridharan and Rao, 1974), and an increase or decrease in shear strength depending upon the dielectric constant of the medium (Ladd and Martin, 1967; Moore and Mitchell, 1974).

SUMMARY AND CONCLUSIONS

Hydraulic conductivity and index tests presented in this study lead to the following conclusions with regard to the effect of the transport of organic contaminants.

(i)   When acetone and phenol are permeated through kaolinite compacted at the wet of optimum water content, the longitudinal dispersion coefficient is found to be in the order of 10^{-6} cm^2/sec.

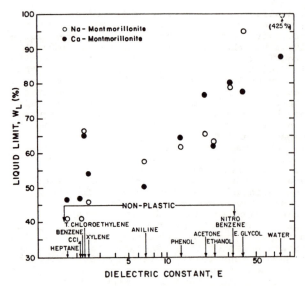

Fig. 3. The effect of dielectric constant on liquid limit of Na- and Ca-montmorillonite

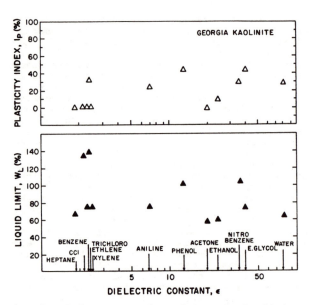

Fig. 4. Index properties of Georgia kaolinite with different organic fluids

(ii)   The testing scheme is a major consideration in assessment of the possible changes in hydraulic conductivity of fine-grained soils with an organic fluid. Changes in absolute hydraulic conductivity are observed to be highly affected by the applied effective stresses.

(iii)   Index properties of active montmorillonitic clays are highly affected by the variations in the dielectric constant of the pore fluid while, kaolinite does

not indicate such a trend. The pH of the solution is observed to be dominant on the index properties of kaolinite.

REFERENCES

Acar, Y.B.,, Hamidon, A., Field, S., Scott, L. (1984). The effect of organic fluids on hydraulic conductivity of compacted kaolinite. ASTM, STP on Impermeable Barriers on Soil and Rock, Denver, CO.

Anderson, D., Brown, K.W., Green, J. (1982). Effect of organic fluids on the permeability of clay soil liners. USEPA Office of Research and Development, MERL No. EPA-600/9-82-002, pp. 178-190.

Freeze, R.A., and Cherry, J.A. (1979). Groundwater. Prentice Hall, Inc., New Jersey, 604 p.

Genevois, R. (1977). Chemical interactions on the compressibility of remolded kaolin. Proceedings of the IX ICSMFE, Vol. 1.

Gillham, R.W., and Cherry, J.A. (1982). Contaminant migration in saturated unconsolidated geologic deposits. Geotechnical Society of America, Special Paper 189, pp. 31-62.

Green, W.J., Lee, G.F., Jones, R.A., Pallt, T. (1983). Interaction of clay soils with water and organic solvents: implications for the disposal of hazardous wastes. Environ. Sci. Tech., Vol. 17, pp. 278-282.

Hashimoto, I., Desphande, K.B., and Thomas, H.C. (1964). Peclet numbers and retardation factors for ion exchange columns. Industrial and Eng. Chem. Fund., Vol. 3, pp. 213-218.

Ladd, C.C., Martin, R.T. (1967). The effects of pore fluid on the undrained strength of kaolinite. MIT Civil Engineering Research Report R67-15.

Lambe, T.W. (1954). The permeability of fine-grained soils. ASTM Special Technical Publication No. 163, pp. 56-67.

Michaels, A.S., and Lin, C.S. (1954). The permeability of kaolinite. Industrial Engineering Chemistry, Vol. 46, pp. 1239-1246.

Moore, C.A., and Mitchell, J.K. (1974). Electromagnetic forces and soil strength. Geotechnique, Vol. 24, No. 4, pp. 627-640.

Perkins, T.K., and Johnston, O.C. (1963). A review of diffusion and dispersion in porous media. Soc. Pet. Eng. Journal, Vol. 3, p. 70.

Sridharan, A., and Rao, V.G. (1973). Mechanisms controlling volume change of saturated clays and the role of effective stress concept. Geotechnique, Vol. 23, No. 3, pp. 359-382.

USEPA (1977). The report to Congress: Waste disposal practices and their effects on groundwater. Office of Water Supply, USEPA Office of Solid Waste Management Programs.

Heat storage in clay – Geotechnical consequences and use of heat drains
Stockage thermique dans les argiles – Conséquences géotechniques et utilisation de drains thermiques

K. ADOLFSSON, Eng., Chalmers University of Technology, Göteborg, Sweden
B. G. RYDELL, M.Sc., Swedish Geotechnical Institute, Linköping, Sweden
G. SÄLLFORS, Tekn. Dr., Chalmers University of Technology, Göteborg, Sweden
M. TIDFORS, M.Sc., Chalmers University of Technology, Göteborg, Sweden

SYNOPSIS   To reduce the dependence of oil for heating, one alternative is to store energy surplus in clay deposits and then use it in the winter time.   The problems associated with heat storage in clay have been studied thoroughly and this paper provides a few examples of test results and observed phenomena from the extensive field and laboratory test programs. Also included is a description of the so-called heat drain which can be used for an effective heat exchange in a clay deposit.

INTRODUCTION

During the last decade, techniques for seasonal heat storage in clay have been developed in Sweden as means of reducing the dependence of oil. Experiences from pilot plants show that technical as well as ecconomic requirements can be fulfilled when storing summer heat for use in the winter.

It is a well known fact that temperature changes influence the geotechnical properties of a clay. Therefore, part of the research has been concentrated on the conditions necessary for the geotechnical consequences of heat storage in clay with respect to land-use planning and existing structures. Studies have also been conducted to improve the effectiveness of the heat exchanger in the ground.

GEOTECHNICAL INVESTIGATIONS IN THE FIELD AND LABORATORY

The changes in the geotechnical properties of a clay due to heating have been thoroughly studied at the Geotechnical Department of Chalmers University of Technology by means of laboratory and field investigations.

Field investigations

The field tests were carried out in the western part of Sweden in a lightly overconsolidated, postglacial clay, approximately 40 m in depth. Profiles of shear strength, sensitivity, water content and bulk density are illustrated in figure 1.

The clay was heated by circulating hot water in heat exchangers consisting of plastic and steel tubes, respectively, installed to a depth of 12 m, in a rectangular pattern with the dimension of 2.0 m x 2.8 m. Equipment necessary for monitoring temperatures, pore pressures and settlements were installed in the clay.

LABORATORY TESTS, U-TUBES-FIELD
TEMPERATURE +7.3 DEGR. C, AVERAGE VALUES

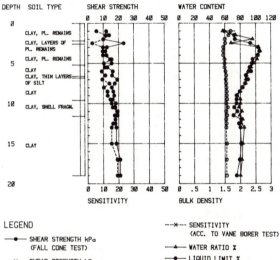

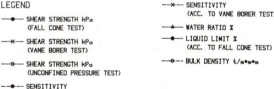

Fig.1   Soil profile for test site at Kungälv, Sweden.

Over a period of 150 days, the average storage temperature increased almost linearly from an initial value of 7°C to a final value of 22°C. This increase in temperature was accompanied by an increase in pore pressures from 5 to 16 kPa, measured at four levels within the storage and at one level below the storage. Examples of tests results are given in figure 2.
Settlements were measured with bellow hose gauges at different depths, and the results

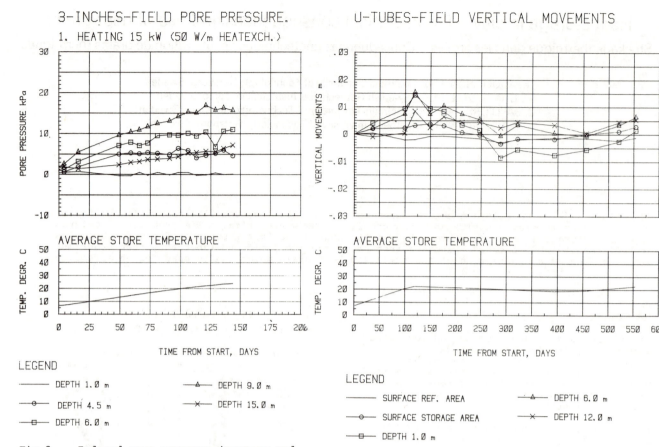

3-INCHES-FIELD PORE PRESSURE.
1. HEATING 15 kW (50 W/m HEATEXCH.)

U-TUBES-FIELD VERTICAL MOVEMENTS

AVERAGE STORE TEMPERATURE

AVERAGE STORE TEMPERATURE

TIME FROM START, DAYS

TIME FROM START, DAYS

LEGEND

—————— DEPTH 1.0 m   —△— DEPTH 9.0 m

—○— DEPTH 4.5 m   —✕— DEPTH 15.0 m

—□— DEPTH 6.0 m

Fig.2   Induced pore pressure increase and
average storage temperature at
different levels measured at the
midpoint between heat exchangers.
In the figure data are given only
for the heating period of 120 days.

LEGEND

—————— SURFACE REF. AREA   —△— DEPTH 6.0 m

—○— SURFACE STORAGE AREA   —✕— DEPTH 12.0 m

—□— DEPTH 1.0 m

Fig.3   Settlements and temperatures.

are given in figure 3. The accuracy of the
measuring system was ± 1 mm.

The observed settlements were generally small
but a certain heave in the soil was observed
during the heating period. The heave seemed
to disappear gradually as the temperature
was kept constant.

Laboratory investigations

Standard geotechnical laboratory tests were
made on field samples taken prior to heating
and at the end of the heating period when
the average storage temperature was 22°C.

Preconsolidation pressures prior to and after
heating have been evaluated from oedometer
tests and are given in figure 4. The scatter
in figure 4 is considerable but a regression
analysis indicates that a reduction of the
preconsolidation pressure may have occurred.
However, in this case the effective overburden pressure in the clay was still less
than the preconsolidation pressure after the
heating, which is why severe settlements,
caused by the heating, were neither expected
nor measured.

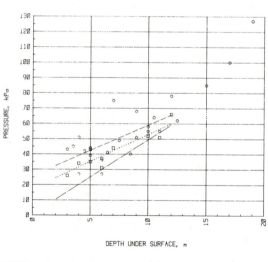

LEGEND

—·—·— REGR.LINE, 7.3 DEGR. C   ○ PRECONS. PR. 7.3 DEGR. C

············ REGR.LINE, 22.8 DEGR. C   □ PRECONS. PR. 22.8 DEGR. C

———— REGR.LINE, EFF. PRESSURE

Fig.4   Preconsolidation in relation to depth.

INFLUENCE OF HEAT STORAGE ON THE GEOTECHNICAL
PROPERTIES OF CLAY

When the temperature in a clay is changed,
the pore pressures will change too since the
water has a greater coefficient of volumetric
expansion than the solids. Also, the water
constitutes a larger part of the clay volume.
A temperature rise (when charging a heat
storage) will cause an increase in pore pressure and a corresponding reduction of the
effective overburden pressure which is analogous, in effect, to the unloading of the
ground. As a consequence, the soil layers
will heave. Cooling of the clay (when discharging a heat storage) will reverse the
process and, possibly, cause consolidation.

The results from field and laboratory tests
show that the apparent preconsolidation pressure decreases when the temperature increases.
The simultaneous increase of pore pressure
will, to some extent, compensate this decrease. While cooling the clay, the pore
water pressure decreases and the simultaneous
increase of the effective overburden pressure
may exceed the reduced preconsolidation pressure. If so, settlements may occur. During
this process normally, or even slightly overconsolidated clays, can experience settlements without any external loading to the
soil.

For seasonal heat storage the temperature
varies cyclically during the year. The long
term settlements will, therefore, depend on
the average temperature and the extreme
variations in the soil during the year.

Presently, it is not known whether the decrease of the apparent preconsolidation
pressure, when heating a clay, is caused by
a disturbance of the soil structure as the
pore pressure changes, or if it is an effect
of the increased creep rates and the increased viscosity of the water as a result
of the higher temperatures. The results
from the tests have not yet been fully
analyzed to give a distinct answer in this
regard.

It has been reported that the heating of a
clay can result in a decrease of shear strength.
The field tests did not indicate this effect.
A possible explanation for this finding is
that the temperature varies cyclicly during
the heat storage process and as such, the shear
strength varies inversely with temperature
changes. Should the clay consolidate, and
permanent settlements occur, the long term
effect will be an increase in shear strength.

HEAT DRAINS

Heat exhangers in clay

The charging and discharging of heat in clay
has so far been accomplished using small, vertical, plastic, U-shaped tubes. Since soft
clay has a low thermal conductivity, the heat
exchangers must be installed close together.
To increase the thermal effectivity, a new
type of heat exchanger, the "heat drain", has
been developed at Chalmers University. This

type of heat exchanger may also help to reduce the problems associated with the changes
in the geotechnical properties of the clay.

Performance of heat drains

The heat drain consists of a conventional
sand drain with a diameter of 180-200 mm
and a supplementary plastic tube in which the
fluid circulates. The plastic tube is U-
shaped and spans the entire length of the
sand drain (figure 5).

The heat drains will be installed by means of
slightly modified equipment used for the
installation of sand drains in Sweden.

A small prototype has been tested in the same
test field as previously discussed and the
results indicate very small changes in pore
pressure to the surroundings while heating
the clay. The thermal effectivity increased
significantly compared with U-tubes in the
clay.

In a prestudy concerning heat storage in clay
for a school and a sports building, a theoretical study of the thermal and geotechnical
function of the heat drain had been performed.
The technique for installing the heat drains,
along with their thermal and geotechnical
function, will be investigated by means of
full-scale testing at this heat storage site.

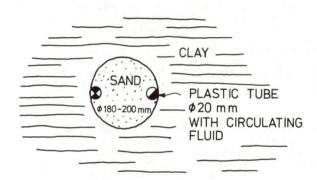

Fig.5   Horizontal cross-section of a heat
         drain.

Thermal function

Since clay has a low thermal conductivity, it
is advantageous to use heat exchangers with
as large contact areas as possible. Also,
since sand has a higher thermal conductivity
than clay, this reduces the heat resistance
closest to the plastic tubes compared with
their counterpart in clay. Furthermore,
sand has a higher hydraulic conductivity
(permeability) which makes convective heat
transport possible in the heat drain.

Calculations, using theoretical models, show
that the heat transfer capacity, at the heat
drain, is 20 to 40% higher when compared
with pipes in clay. The lower value corre-

sponds to no convection and the upper value for full convection and a uniform temperature in the sand column. This will, for the same storage capacity, lead to an increase in the required distance between the heat exchangers or a lowering of the temperature difference between the fluid in the pipes and the clay. This way, lower installation costs can be obtained.

Geotechnical function

Heat drains will give rise to a more rapid water flow within the soil. When charging (heating) the storage, the heat drains facilitate the pore water pressure equalization. Discharging (cooling) of the storage will produce negative pressure in the pores, and if free water is available in the heat drains this water may possibly flow back into the clay and prevent settlements.

Settlements will most likely occur anyhow due to changes in the geotechnical properties when heating and cooling the clay. Further research may lead to a better understanding of the pore water flow during cyclic changes of the temperature and make it possible to predict the settlements.

CONCLUSIONS

Field and laboratory tests on clay, during heat storage, indicate that the pore pressures increase with the temperature. Heaving of the soil was recorded during the heating period. The apparent preconsolidation pressures decrease, somewhat, when heating a clay layer. The long term effects will be that settlements will most likely occur due to the cyclical heating and loading of the clay.

Heat drains, used as heat exchangers in clay, will increase the thermal effectivity and may mitigate some adverse effects as a consequence of changes to the geotechnical properties as a result of cyclic heating and cooling. This will make heat storage in clay more feasible from an exonomic point of view.

REFERENCES

Abrahamsson, T., Adolfsson, K., Palmgren, C., Rydell, B. (1984). Ramunderheat. Heat storage in clay for a school and sports building in Söderköping. (In Swedish). Swedish Council for Building Research, Project No. 830538-2, Stockholm.

Adolfsson, K., Lindblom, U., Rhen, I. (1983). Geotechnical and geological consequences of heating/cooling and freezing/thawing of clay. Proc. Conference on Subsurface Heat Storage, Stockholm.

Campanella, R.G., Mitchell, J.K. (1968). Influence of temperature variations on soil behaviour. Proc. ASCE, Vol. 94 (1068):SM3.

Mitchell, J.K. (1969). Temperature effects on the engineering properties and behaviour of soils. HRI Special Report 103, Washington, DC.

Rydell, B. (ed.) (1983). Geotechnical consequences of heat storage in clay. (In Swedish). Seminar in Linköping. Swedish Geotechnical Institute, Varia 119, Linköping.

Hydrodynamic and mechanical aspects of heat transfer in clay

Aspects hydrodynamiques et mécaniques de la diffusion de la chaleur dans les argiles

A. BURGHIGNOLI, Associate Professor of Soil Mechanics, University of Rome, Italy
P. PAOLIANI, ENEA-DISP, Rome, Italy

SYNOPSIS   The behaviour of natural soils subjected to temperature changes has been extensively studied in past decades particularly with reference to frost and geothermal problems. More recently, the potential use of geologic media as disposals for radioactive wastes has been considered, and thus there is a growing need for specific studies on the behaviour of soils and rocks in contact with heating elements. This paper deals with an experimental and theoretical work on this topic and in particular the variation of temperature, pore-water pressure and displacements produced by heating a clay mass under different boundary conditions. The experimental program was carried out in the laboratory on large blocks of overconsolidated undisturbed clay and on remoulded specimens of normally consolidated clay. Comparisons between the experimental data and the theoretical values obtained by the simple model of diffusion and by the coupled consolidation theory are presented and discussed.

INTRODUCTION

The study of the behaviour of natural soils and rocks subjected to thermal loading has become increasingly important in recent years as a consequence of the large use being made now of nuclear energy which however raises serious problems in relation to the disposal of radioactive wastes.

This problem has been tackled by many countries by selecting appropriate geological sites and studying their mechanical, thermal and hydraulic characteristics. An actual literature has been developed on this topic, but to date, a number of problems still await a solution. At the last Conference on Field Measurements in Geomechanics held in Zurich in 1983, W.Hustrulid, in his lecture on Design of Geomechanical experiments for Radioactive Waste Disposal, said: ".. *experiments to date have sometimes raised more questions than they have answered* " Thus the need for a greater insight into this problem seems urgent.

Within the European Community a common research program on radioactive waste disposal was developed (EEC,1981), each country studying a particular problem: Germany, evaporitic formations; France and England, granite rocks; Belgium and Italy, clayey formations.

This paper deals with some preliminary results of a research on heat transfer in clayey soils. Some selected results of laboratory tests are presented and discussed, attention being focused particularly on the heat diffusion process and on its hydrodynamic and mechanical effects.

EXPERIMENTAL PROGRAM

Two different series of tests - D-tests and C-tests - were used in the experiments. The D-tests were mainly conceived to verify the capability of the mathematical model of simple diffusion to predict the distribution of temperature increments produced in the sample by an electrical heater. These tests were carried out on samples obtained from large blocks from the Trisaia overconsolidated Plio-Pleistocene clay; only temperature changes within the sample were monitored during the tests.

With the C-tests a more complete set of measures were obtained from experiments. Remoulded samples from the Fiumicino Holocene clay were used in the tests; pore pressure changes and deformations related to the heating process were measured. The main geotechnical properties of the clays used in the experiments are reported in Table I.

For the D-tests, 49 cm diameter and 50 cm high cylindrical samples were trimmed from undisturbed blocks of the Trisaia clay. An electrical resistance, closed in a 1.7 cm diam. brass tube filled with silicon oil, was inserted in a hole drilled along the axis of the sample. Temperature measurements were made by J-type thermocouples driven into the sample at various depths and distances from the heater. Thermocouples were also installed in the heater and along the sides of the sample to control the boundary conditions for the diffusion process. In order to minimize the thermal gradients along the axis of the sample and therefore to simplify the interpretation of the experimental data, two discs, 5 cm thick, of polystyrene were placed at both ends.

The D-tests were all carried out in undrained conditions, with the surface coated with paraffin wax. The scheme of the experimental equipment used in such tests is represented in Fig.1.

Electrical powers of 20 and 30 watts were supplied to the heater; this corresponds to 0.75 and 1.12 kW/m^2 respectively. Maximum power was applied instantaneously and kept constant for about 40 hours. Then the power was suddenly removed but temperature readings were taken during the following 20 hours also.

In the C-tests, remoulded specimens of normally consolidated clay were used to obtain more reliable measurements of

Table I - Geotechnical characteristics of the tested clays.

	LL (%)	IP (%)	CF (%)	γ (kN/m^3)	W (%)	S_r	λ	k	K (m/s)	c' (kPa)	φ'
TRISAIA UNDISTURBED CLAY	53	32	45	27.4	26	0.98	0.200	0.020	$4\cdot10^{-11}$	4	23
FIUMICINO REMOULDED CLAY	68	43	42	27.5	59	1	0.243	0.043	$1.6\cdot10^{-10}$	0	25

the excess pore pressure induced by thermal loadings. Moreover, in order to establish well-controlled boundary conditions in terms of stresses and pore pressures, a 4-inch triaxial cell was used. The cell, suitably modified, allows for the insertion of micropiezometers and thermocouples from the pedestal into the sample. The piezometers consist of thin hypodermic needles connected to a strain gauge pressure transducer. All the specimens, 12 cm high, were trimmed from a large remoulded sample consolidated to 40 kPa in a Rowe-type oedometer. The scheme of the equipment is shown in Fig. 2.

The heater was obtained by placing an electric resistance into the loading head of the cell. A porous stone at the base of the specimen allowed drainage of the water; a thermocouple was installed into the heating head, while three other thermocouples were placed to monitor the temperature at the boundaries of the specimen and in the ambient ambient; the specimens were insulated by rubber membranes from the silicon oil, used as cell fluid.

Before the heating phase, each specimen was isotropically consolidated up to p' = 200 kPa. Full saturation of the clay was guaranteed by a back pressure of 300 kPa. After consolidation, an electrical power of 44 watts (5.6 kW/m^2) was instantaneously applied and kept constant for four days. The power was then completely removed but the data recording was continued for two more days.

ANALYSIS OF THE EXPERIMENTAL RESULTS

A typical result of the D-tests is shown in Fig. 3a, where the temperature changes with time for W = 30 watts are reported. A maximum temperature increment of about 30°C was measured with this test. The curves show a sharp temperature change during the first hour of heating and values near the steady state condition after one day. Very similar changes but of opposite sign were observed during the cooling phase after the power break. The radial distribution

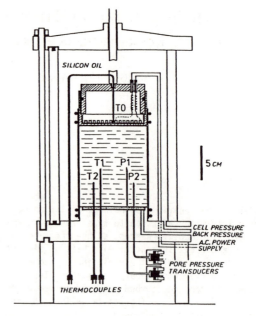

Fig.2 Modified 4-inch triaxial cell used in the C-tests

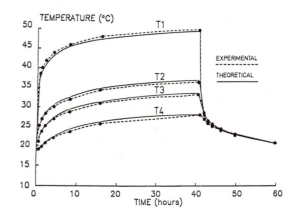

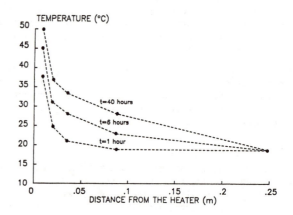

Fig.3 D - Test : Temperature changes with time (a) and their radial distribution (b)

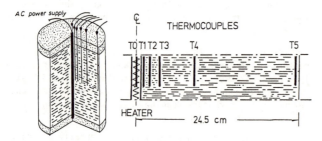

Fig.1 Experimental equipment used in the D-tests

of temperatures at different times during the test is reported in Fig. 3b.

Experimental data have been compared with the results obtained by the diffusion theory. By neglecting the effect of mass transport because of the low permeability of clays, the corresponding equation can be written, using polar coordinates, in the following form:

$$(\lambda T,_r),_r + (\lambda/r)T,_r + q - c\rho T,_t = 0 \qquad (1)$$

where λ : thermal conductivity
         c : specific heat

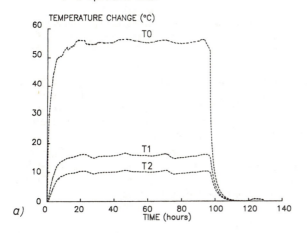

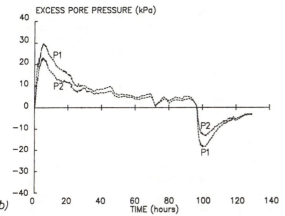

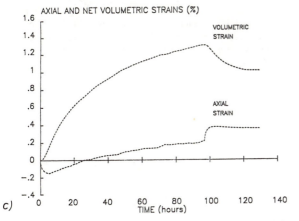

Fig.4   C-Test: Temperature (a), pore pressure (b) and
        strain (c) changes with time

ρ : density
q : internal heat source

Eq. (1) was solved numerically with the appropriate boundary conditions. By a fitting procedure the following values of the thermal characteristics of the Trisaia clay were found:

$$\lambda = 1.6 \frac{W}{m°K} \qquad c\rho = 2 \cdot 10^6 \frac{Ws}{m^3°K}$$

Using the same values a good fit was obtained for the test where W = 20 watts; moreover, they agree with those measured on the same clay by other authors (GERA et al.,1976).

Experimental results of one of the C-tests are shown in Fig.4 where the temperature, pore pressure and strain changes with time are reported for a cycle of thermal loading and unloading.

Temperatures rose very quickly during the first six hours of heating and reached stationary values after about one day. Similar variations were observed during the cooling phase (Fig.4a). Maximum values of about 16°C and 10°C were measured by the thermocouples T1 and T2 respectively, whereas the corresponding temperature change at the heater was about 55°C.

As a consequence of the thermal water expansion, pore pressures increased rapidly in the early stage of the test and maximum changes of 30 and 23 kPa were measured after about six hours by the piezometers P1 and P2 (Fig.4b). Afterwards, the process of hydraulic diffusion prevailed over the thermal effects and dissipation of pore pressure was measured for four more days. A similar behaviour was observed during the cooling phase.

A closer inspection of the temperature and pore pressure curves, shows a correspondence between the change in temperature rate and the maximum pore pressure. This behaviour is probably to be related to a mass transport effect, although only to a small extent.

The diagrams in Figs.4c show the changes with time of the axial and net volumetric strains. The latter do not correspond to the actual volumetric changes of the specimen, as these depend also on thermal expansion. This term refers to the volume of water crossing the pervious boundary of the specimen and therefore it has been used to represent the consolidation effect.

The axial strain changes reflect the variations in pore pressure. After an expansion in the early stage of the test (where maximum expansion coincided with that of the excess pore pressure), a progressive reduction of the specimen height was found during the following days. A further, but sudden, axial reduction occurred after the power break and the final value ε_a = 0.4% was then reached.

Finally, regarding the consolidation effect of the thermal cycle, the maximum net volumetric strain ε_v = 1.3%, and a final value ε_v = 1.0% were measured.

In order to describe, in an analytical form, the hydrodynamic effects of the thermal loading on the clays and the corresponding deformations, a numerical model of coupled consolidation was used. This model is based on the modified Cam-clay constitutive law (BURLAND, 1965) and accounts for temperature effects through equivalent body forces. The governing equations are:

$$c^t_{ijkl}(\dot{\varepsilon}_{kl} + \alpha \dot{T}) + \dot{u}_{,j} = 0$$

$$(K_{ij}(u_{,j}))_{,i} + \varepsilon_v{}_{,t} - [n\alpha_w + (1-n)\alpha_s] T_{,t} = 0$$

where c^t_{ijkl} : stress-strain tensor

K_{ij} : permeability tensor

α : thermal expansivity of soil

α_w : thermal expansivity of water

α_s : thermal expansivity of skeletal material

n : soil porosity

These equations were solved by an F.E.M. technique, and the the results corresponding to the material properties in Table I and the boundary conditions of the present case, are reported in Fig.5.

Although the theoretical results do not exactly match the experimental data, the assumed mathematical model seems to be in excellent qualitative agreement with the observed behaviour.

FINAL REMARKS AND CONCLUSIONS

Although the experimental work is still in an early stage, preliminary conclusions may be drawn.

Heat transfer in clays may be represented, without serious errors, by the simple diffusion theory. This depends main-ly on the low permeability of such soils, which therefore are not influenced by phenomena of mass transport. The field of temperature changes may be thus evaluated without keeping account of the fluid flow.

The mechanical effects of clay heating consist mainly in thermal and consolidation strains. Thermal strains depend on temperature changes, the bulk modulus of the solid skeleton and especially on the thermal expansivity of the fluid phase. Due to the latter effect, these strains are almost recovered when the heat supply is cut off. Consolidation strains depend on the constraint between the solid and liquid phase. Pore pressure rises during the early stage of the heating process until temperature changes develop. Later, when stationary thermal conditions are reached, the hydrodynamic effects prevail and the consolidation process takes place.

A first tentative analytical model of the observed behaviour was developed. The model is based on Cam-clay stress-strain relationships and allows for thermal effects through equivalent body forces. The corresponding equations were numerically solved by the F.E.M.

The comparison between experimental and analytical results shows a good qualitative agreement but further work on this subject is required so as to reach a better quantitative representation of experimental evidence.

ACKNOWLEDGEMENTS

Thanks are expressed to F.Brogi and D.Irti for their precious contribution in preparing the laboratory tests. Dr.P. Ricci is also thanked for his help in the computational analyses.

This research was partially supported by a grant made available by ENEA (Comitato Nazionale per la Ricerca e per lo Sviluppo dell'Energia Nucleare e delle Energie Alternative).

REFERENCES

Burland J.B.(1965) The Yielding and Dilation of Clay . Correspondance,Géotechnique, 15, 211-214.

E.E.C.(1981) . Confinamento geologico dei rifiuti radioattivi nella Comunità Europea. Commissione delle Comunità Europee, Bruxelles-Lussemburgo, 1981.

Gera F., Lenzi G., Sensi L., Cassano G.(1976). Disposal of Long-Lived Radioactive Wastes in Italy. Management of Radioactive Wastes from the Nuclear Fuel Cycle, Vol.2. IAEA, Wien.

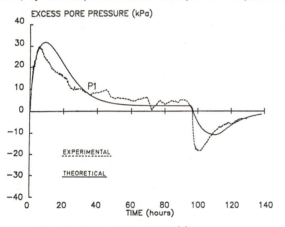

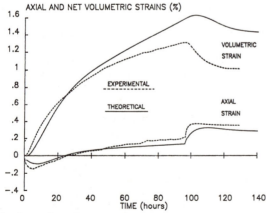

Fig.5 Comparison between theoretical and experimental results for a C-test

Les injections dans le sol et l'environnement

Soil grouting and the environment

D. GOUVENOT, Directeur Technique et Développement, Solétanche Entreprise, Paris, France

RESUME : A une époque où l'on parle beaucoup de protection de l'environnement, il nous a paru intéressant de faire le point sur un domaine assez peu exploré : celui de la protection de l'environnement souterrain. La question est abordée sous deux aspects :
. soit lors de constructions de Génie Civil,
. soit dans le cadre des travaux de protection nécessités par les dangers que présentent les déchets industriels, qu'ils soient radioactifs ou non.

Les rapports entre les travaux spéciaux dans le sol (injections, parois moulées) et l'environnement sont donc traités :
. dans le cadre de la réduction des nuisances, provoquées par les travaux, par la mise au point de matériaux stables et non polluants,
. dans l'emploi des travaux spéciaux pour la protection de l'environnement au voisinage des stockages de déchets.
L'évolution des coulis d'injection est décrite en partant des coulis classiques. Les nouveaux matériaux mis au point permettent de résoudre le grand problème de la pollution souterraine et particulièrement des nappes phréatiques.

INTRODUCTION

Les matériaux injectés classiquement dans le sol présentent à des degrés divers des instabilités pysico-chimiques. Il s'ensuit des risques de pollution de l'environnement. Les coulis les plus stables sont ceux à base de ciment. Les gels de silice destinés à l'injection des matériaux plus fins sont étudiés sous le double aspect de la formulation et de la stabilité dans le temps.

INCIDENCE DES TRAVAUX D'INJECTION SUR L'ENVIRONNEMENT

Rappel des caractéristiques des coulis d'injection classiques

Nous ne parlerons que des coulis de base à savoir :

. les coulis de ciment, utilisés pour les injections des sables grossiers ou des roches,

. les gels de silice nécessaires à l'obtention de bonnes caractéristiques dans les sables fins.

1) Les coulis à base de ciment

Ils résultent du mélange d'eau et de ciment auquel peuvent être joints de l'argile, de la bentonite et certains adjuvants (fluidifiants, retardateurs, accélérateurs, etc...).

En général, les coulis de ciment sont considérés comme non polluants à condition que les adjuvants soient bien adaptés à l'environnement.

En conclusion, le choix d'un ciment pour un coulis d'injection se pose donc plus en terme d'agressivité de l'eau vis-à-vis du ciment que l'inverse.

2) Les gels de silice

Il est connu que les coulis de ciment, contenant des grains en suspension, ont un pouvoir de pénétration limité dans les sols. C'est pourquoi, il est fait appel couramment aux gels de silice, pour traiter les sols fins. Il faut rappeler, très sommairement le principe de ces coulis. Dans un silicate de soude, la silice est en état d'équilibre que de nombreux facteurs peuvent rompre (température, pH, etc...). Classiquement, la transformation du silicate en gel se fait à l'aide de réactifs organiques du type esters, qui en libérant des acides neutralisent la soude du silicate (CARON,1965) (CAMBEFORT, 1967).

Malheureusement, la réaction est rarement complète. De ce fait, des produits chimiques peuvent rester libres et migrer vers les nappes phréatiques. Des précautions peuvent être prises pour limiter ces phénomènes (CAMBEFORT, 1967) (LUONG, GANDAIS, ALLEMAND, 1977), mais des doutes subsistent quant à la stabilité à long terme du gel.

C'est pourquoi de très nombreux procédés ont été proposés pour adapter le mieux possible les gels aux problèmes posés :

a) gels d'étanchéité à résistance réduite mais stables pour améliorer l'imperméabilité du sol. Pour ces coulis l'utilisation de réactifs minéraux est courante.

b) gels à neutralisation améliorée qui réduisent les risques de pollution et d'instabilité sans toutefois les annuler complètement.

De récentes découvertes ont conduit à l'obtention de produits stables et non polluants.

Etude particulière des gels de silice

L'essai classique, mais non normalisé, qui permet d'étudier la stabilité d'un sol injecté consiste à le faire traverser par un courant d'eau (sous gradient élevé voisin de 30) et à doser les produits chimiques entraînés par l'eau à la sortie de l'échantillon : essai de percolation (fig. 1 et 2)

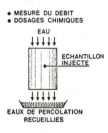

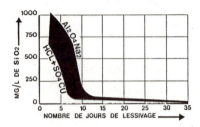

Fig. 1

Schéma d'un essai
de percolation

Fig. 2

Teneur en silice des eaux
de percolation pour
différents gels
en fonction du temps

Il est intéressant de suivre également l'évolution des débits d'eau (ou la perméabilité k) en fonction du temps.

Cette procédure teste la stabilité du produit injecté sous courant d'eau mais est souvent trop sévère pour rendre compte de la pollution chimique.

A cet effet, on réalise des essais de lixiviation au cours desquels un échantillon est placé dans un volume d'eau donné qui est renouvelé toutes les 24 heures.
Les produits chimiques recherchés sont dosés périodiquement.

Deux paramètres importants pour assurer la stabilité des gels ont été mis en évidence :

. la formulation du coulis et le taux de neutralisation (LUONG, GANDAIS, ALLEMAND, 1977),

. la granulométrie du sable injecté (CAMBEFORT, 1967).

Toutefois, en raison des nuisances causées par certains rejets issus des coulis et des difficultés rencontrées pour éviter la synérèse, certains Maîtres d'Oeuvre refusent l'emploi de gels dans les circonstances suivantes :

. recherche d'un traitement dont l'efficacité doit être de longue durée,

. protection absolue de l'environnement et notamment de la nappe phréatique.

Dans ces cas particuliers, les spécialistes peuvent proposer des produits qui présentent encore plus de sécurité par rapport aux gels classiques.

Ce sont ces nouveaux produits que nous allons décrire maintenant.

Les nouveaux coulis non polluants à base de ciment

Récemment, nous avons mis au point des coulis à base de ciment qui présentent les caractéristiques suivantes :

a) aucun rejet de produits dans l'environnement,

b) très bonne résistance aux eaux agressives grâce à une microstructure très compacte et stable.

. La compacité de la microstructure est donnée fig. 3 et comparée à celle d'un coulis de ciment classique. Ces résultats sont obtenus par la porosimétrie au mercure qui permet d'atteindre la répartition des pores de matériaux en fonction de leur dimension géométrique (PELLERIN, 1980).

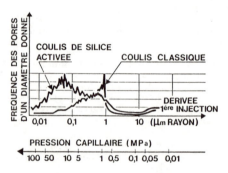

Fig. 3 - Microstructures comparées de deux coulis de ciment par porosimétrie au mercure

La stabilité chimique est bien mise en évidence à l'aide des rayons x car il y a disparition totale de la chaux ainsi que la formation de silicates de chaux hydratés (CSH) bien connue par les chimistes des ciments pour leur insolubilité et leur pérennité.

Les nouveaux coulis de silice

Les nouveaux coulis à base de silice active se composent :

- d'une part d'une liqueur de silice très activée où, contrairement aux silicates de soude alcalins commerciaux qui sont en fait

des suspensions instables de micelles de silice
ultracolloîdale dans la soude, la silice est
dissoute sous forme d'une solution vraie.

- d'un réactif à base de calcium.

A l'inverse des coulis de silice classiques,
la silice activée dissoute associée à son réactif minéral ne conduit pas à un gel, mais à une
structure cristalline reproduisant exactement
celle des ciments.

Les méthodes de détermination des produits
formés ont conduit aux résultats suivants :

. La microscopie électronique à balayage met
  en évidence les cristaux de CSH occupant
  l'espace d'une façon homogène, analogue à
  un ciment base laitier.

. La diffraction X révèle la composition miné-
  ralogique d'un gel de silice, d'un coulis de
  silice et d'un coulis de bentonite-ciment
  servant de référence (fig. 4).

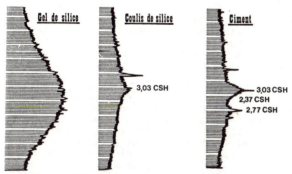

Fig. 4   Diagramme de diffraction X sur :

a) - Un gel de silice classique
b) - Un coulis de silice active de conception
     nouvelle
c) - Un ciment

Dans le premier cas, le diffractogramme apparaît avec une unique bosse arrondie et l'absence totale de pics, traduisant bien la
structure amorphe d'un gel; au contraire dans
le deuxième cas, la bosse arrondie correspondant à la structure gel a disparu, des pics
apparaissent, notamment celui à 3,03 A du
CSH; ce comportement se rapproche bien de
l'allure du troisième diffractogramme du coulis de ciment qui présente également un pic de
CSH à 3,03 A.

3) Conséquences : propriétés des coulis de
silice active

. Absence de pollution : d'après les résultats de
  l'analyse chimique des sous-produits de la
  réaction, le coulis de silice active apparaît
  comme un produit d'injection non polluant.

. Stabilité et pérennité : du fait de la nature
  des produits formés (cristaux totalement
  insolubles de silicates de chaux CSH) et de
  l'absence de sous-produits agressifs (Synérèse),
  le coulis de silice a la stabilité d'un liant
  hydraulique.

Les essais de lixiviation (fig. 5) montre la
très bonne stabilité de ces nouveaux coulis
par rapport aux gels classiques.

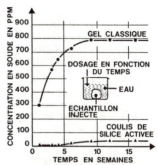

Fig. 5 -   Essais de lixiviation comparés sur
gel classique et coulis de silice
active

Enfin, une propriété très intéressante a été
étudiée à l'Université de Vienne : il s'agit
de la stabilité sous charge constante ou
fluage.

Les essais montrent que les déformations d'un
sable injecté au coulis de silice restent
très limitées par rapport à celles que l'on
obtient traditionnellement avec les gels
de silice classiques.

Dans ce domaine de stockage et d'isolation
de produits polluants, un nouveau progrès
vient d'être réalisé grâce à la mise au
point des coulis sorbeurs, qui représentent
une barrière physico-chimique complémen-
taire de la barrière hydraulique.

Position du problème

Le stockage de déchets ou de matériaux industriels variés peut poser des problèmes de
pollution du milieu avoisinant, en particulier, pour les nappes aquifères en cas de
fuites ou d'infiltrations d'eau.

Une des méthodes désormais classique consiste
à créer autour du lieu de stockage une
barrière étanche soit par injection de coulis bentonite-ciment soit par création d'une
paroi d'étanchéité. Cet écran qui doit
s'ancrer dans un substratum étanche, présente
en général une perméabilité k moyenne de
10^{-6} à 10^{-8} m/s.

Une amélioration importante a été apportée
il y a quelque temps par l'utilisation de
matériaux pouzzolaniques activés (cendres
volantes, pouzzolanes ou autres), qui amé-
liorent la pérennité et diminuent la perméabilité. Celle-ci peut descendre jusqu'à
1.10^{-9} voire 1.10^{-10} m/s.

LA PROTECTION DE L'ENVIRONNEMENT PAR LES
INJECTIONS : LES NOUVEAUX COULIS SORBEURS

Présentation des coulis sorbeurs

Les coulis sorbeurs sont des coulis classiques
à base de liants hydrauliques auxquels l'addition de constituants secondaires confère des
propriétés de sorbtion physico-chimique et
d'autre part, des propriétés purement chimiques
de précipitation des ions indésirables.

1) Etanchéité physique

Les propriétés hydrauliques des liants sont
bien connues. L'hydratation de ces liants conduit à la formation de différents cristaux
hydratés insolubles tels que des silicates et
des aluminates de chaux. Les nouveaux coulis
sorbeurs sont conçus pour présenter la microstructure la plus compacte, donc la plus étanche.

2) Rétention chimique

L'addition dans les coulis de certains réactifs
chimiques, différents suivant la nature des
ions en solution, permet de réduire très fortement la concentration de ces ions nocifs par
formation de composés insolubles.

3) Rétention physico-chimique

La rétention se fait par échange d'ions et par adsorption. Les microstructures très fines utilisées dans ces coulis se prêtent très bien à la
rétention.

Application des coulis sorbeurs

Les applications sont multiples et deux voies
essentielles s'offrent à cette technique :

- obtention des barrières supplémentaires autour des stockages de déchets radioactifs.
  Cette barrière peut être obtenue aussi bien
  dans le sol (injection, écran étanche) que
  dans les containers qui contiennent les
  déchets. les cations à sorber sont en général le césium, le radium, le strontium, etc...

- obtention de barrières physico-chimiques qui
  protègent l'environnement et surtout les
  nappes phréatiques. Les cations à sorber sont
  alors le plomb, le mercure, le chrome, etc...

A partir de ces notions de base les propriétés
naturelles des différents matériaux ont été
exaltées par divers processus :

. défloculation des argiles pour augmenter les
  capacités d'échange,

. addition de matériaux de grande surface spécifique pour accroître les propriétés d'adsorption.

Les réalisations actuelles ont consisté à
remplir des containers en béton chargés de
déchets actifs et à assurer le remplissage de
conduites dans une centrale nucléaire désaffec-
tée.

Le mélange in situ ou dans des malaxeurs de boues
industrielles confère aux déchets liquides :

. résistance (réglable selon les besoins entre
  0,1 et 50 MPa)

. étanchéité (de 10^{-8} à 10^{-12} m/s selon le
  projet)

. fixation irréversible des ions selon les
  procédés décrits ci-dessus

. durabilité.

CONCLUSIONS

Les travaux de construction ont souvent été
réalisés sans grand souci des incidences sur
le milieu environnant. Désormais, cette attitu
de n'est plus de mise et nous pensons que les
efforts entrepris pour protéger le milieu
souterrain font partie de la qualité des constructions.

Ainsi, les coulis d'injection et des parois
moulées peuvent être désormais formulés pour
apporter la perturbation minimale dans le
milieu souterrain notamment vis-à-vis des
nappes phréatiques.

De plus, la question délicate et actuelle de
la protection de l'environnement vis-à-vis
des sotckages de déchets qu'ils soient radioactifs ou non peut trouver une solution par
l'utilisation des coulis sorbeurs.

L'homme ressent de plus en plus la nécessité de protéger son milieu tout en produisant
de plus en plus de déchets d'une très haute
toxicité : les spécialistes doivent poursui-
vre les efforts entrepris. les réalisations
industrielles décrites dans cet article
laissent espérer que des solutions sûres et
durables peuvent être apportées à la lutte
contre la pollution, particulièrement celle
des eaux souterraines si nécessaires à l'hu-
manité.

REFERENCES

CAMBEFORT,H. (1967). Injection des sols, Tome1
        Principes et méthodes. Edition Ey-
        rolles - Paris

CARON, C. (1965). Etude physico-chimique des
        gels. Annales de l'Institut Tech-
        nique du B.T.P. n° 207- 208

LUONG,GANDAIS, ALLEMAND (1977). Comportement
        mécanique des sols injectés aux
        produits chimiques. Annales de
        l'Institut du B.T.P. n° 354

PELLERIN, F.M. (1980). La porosimétrie au
        mercure appliquée à l'étude géo-
        technique des sols et des roches.
        Bulletin de liaison des Labora-
        toires des Ponts et Chaussées n° 106.

Devil's Dingle ash disposal works dam

Le barrage de dépôt de cendres à Devil's Dingle

E. T. HAWS, M.A., F.I.C.E., Partner, Rendel Palmer & Tritton, London, UK
P. L. MARTIN, M.Sc., D.I.C., M.I.C.E., Head of Soil Mechanics Section, Rendel Palmer & Tritton, London, UK
T. H. YU, M.Sc., D.I.C., M.I.C.E., Geotechnical Engineer, Rendel Palmer & Tritton, London, UK

SYNOPSIS   The paper describes the geotechnical aspects of the design, construction and performance of a 66m high earth fill embankment dam at Devils Dingle near Ironbridge, Shropshire, U.K. The dam is located across a steep-sided valley formed in weathered mudstone. Extensive landslipping has occurred in the valley and this necessitated the adoption of residual shear strength parameters in design stability analyses, which in consequence led to a shallow overall downstream slope for the embankment. Observations made of dam and foundation behaviour are compared with expected performance.

INTRODUCTION

The dam is part of a scheme for the disposal of pulverised fuel ash (p.f.a.) from the 1,000 MW Ironbridge 'B' coal-fired power station. The structure, constructed mainly of p.f.a, is built across the lower end of a valley (dingle)(Fig. 1). As an impounding reservoir the dam is subject to the Reservoirs (Safety Provisions) Act 1930. The dam was raised in stages to keep ahead of the ash disposal and, on completion, reached a height of approximately 66m with a crest length of 570m. Some 250,000 tonnes of ash were disposed of per annum and in total approximately 3 million tonnes of ash were placed in the embankment and another 2 million tonnes in the lagoon. Ash arrived at Devils Dingle in two ways. Conditioned ash having a moisture content of about 23% was delivered by truck for use in embankment construction. The remainder of the ash was slurried and delivered to the lagoon by pipeline. Construction of the dam was carried out between 1967 and 1983. The layout of the scheme is shown in Fig. 2.

GEOLOGY AND GEOMORPHOLOGY

The site is mainly underlain by the Hughley Shale of Lower Silurian (Upper Llandovery) age. This is a heavily overconsolidated fissured argillaceous deposit mainly comprising 'mudstone' but with occasional thin bands of calcareous siltstone or sandstone. Following exposure of the deposit during excavation prior to the start of dam construction the lithology and structure were studied (Cocks and Walton, 1968). The position of a normal fault was noted along the eastern stream of Devils Dingle having a throw of at least 18m and smaller scale faulting trending WNW-ESE was also observed. The bedding of the material revealed in the excavation showed a variety of dips, the material having been affected not only by structural disturbance but also landslipping. Dips of up to 12° were noted trending down the west valley.

The site lies in an area which has been affected by both glacial and periglacial conditions which have resulted in deep weathering of the mudstone. As a consequence of the glacial effects and the oversteepening of valley sides due to downcutting of the streams extensive landslipping has occurred in the area. A well documented case is the Jackfield slide near Ironbridge (Henkel and Skempton 1955).

The Devils Dingle site straddles the confluence of two small streams flowing down to the River Severn in valleys having side slopes of up to 40° and bed slopes of about 8° (Fig. 1).

SITE INVESTIGATION

Twenty seven boreholes were sunk in 1964 to investigate the feasibility of developing Devils Dingle for the ash disposal scheme. The boreholes encountered up to 6m of soft to stiff silty clay overlying the weathered Hughley Shale. Based on the borehole information, the results of laboratory tests, site reconnaissance and desk studies it was considered that the site, although far from ideal from geotechnical considerations, could be developed for the proposed ash disposal scheme.

Additional information was obtained on three subsequent occasions. In 1975 undisturbed samples of the weathered mudstone were taken from the borrow area and in 1978 and in 1980 the installation of additional instrumentation provided the opportunity to take further samples for testing. Altogether a total of 40 boreholes were sunk. The maximum depth of borehole into natural ground was 28m.

Laboratory tests were carried out on samples of the weathered mudstone and the results are summarised in Table I together with the design parameters adopted. Because of the evidence for extensive landslipping on the site reversal

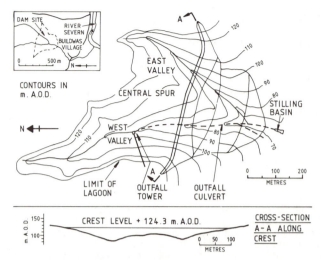

Fig.1 Location and contour plan of the disposal works site

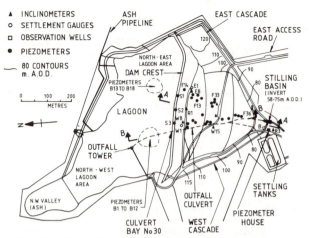

Fig. 2 Plan showing the disposal works

TABLE I

Soil parameters for in-situ weathered mudstone

	Laboratory Test Results (Range)	Design Values
Natural Moisture Content(%)	10 to 34	-
Liquid Limit(%)	32 to 69	-
Plastic Limit(%)	17 to 29	-
Plasticity Index(%)	15 to 40	-
Bulk Density (kg/m^3)	1800 to 2250	-
$\varnothing'$ peak (degrees)	19 to 26	-
$\varnothing'$ residual (degrees)	13.5 to 17.5	14
c' peak (kPa)	0 to 44	-
c' residual (kPa)	0 to 51	0
m_v (kPa)$^{-1}$	7x10^{-5} to 3.4x10^{-4}	9x10^{-5}
c_v (m^2/sec)	3.81x10^{-8} to 2.95x10^{-7}	1.8x10^{-7}

shear box tests were carried out to determine drained residual shear strength parameters and shear strengths on bedding planes.

The design value of drained residual strength assumed initially (1964) was 15°. This was changed to 14° following a review of additional test data obtained during construction.

DESIGN CONSIDERATIONS

The main factors governing the design of the dam were the need to ensure at all stages of construction and lagooning:

o stability of the structure
o adequate height of the embankment to allow uninterrupted disposal of slurried p.f.a.
o safe disposal of the p.f.a. and of the supernatant water from the lagoons without causing environmental pollution.
o maximum use of conditions p.f.a. for the construction of the dam.
o aesthetic acceptability.

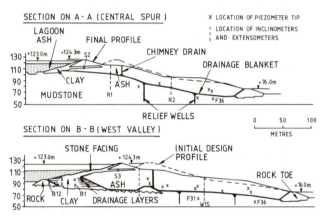

Fig. 3 Sections through dam

The above factors related to the founding conditions for the dam led to the design which is shown in Figs. 2 and 3.

A compacted clay embankment with drainage layers and upslope rockfill berm were required for the initial lagooning prior to the conditioned ash becoming available. The main body of the dam is composed of compacted p.f.a. with a rockfill berm at the downstream toe. The upstream face of the dam above the clay embankment was sealed by a 3.5m thick clay blanket which was protectec from wave erosion by a layer of coarse gravel and rockfill.

A vertical chimney drain was provided downstream of the final crest line of the embankment, connecting with a drainage blanket under the whole of the downstream shoulder. Two rows of 100mm diameter drainage wells were also installed under the downstream shoulder.

The spillway and supernatant water outlet works were combined in the form of a vertical concrete tower of 4.6m diameter. The water discharged into a pipe laid in a 2.5m high culvert under the dam, which led to settling tanks where "floaters" (ie. the buoyant ash fraction) were removed in order to ensure satisfactory quality of water returned to the river.

The site is in close proximity to the village of Buildwas (Fig. 1). For environmental protection temporary ash surfaces were water sprayed against dust blow, and final surfaces were landscaped, soiled and sown.

GEOTECHNICAL DESIGN

Embankment Construction Materials

Test results and design values are given in Table II.

TABLE II

Soil parameters for compacted p.f.a. and clay fill

	P.F.A.		CLAY
	Laboratory Test Results (Range)	Design Values	Design Values
$\emptyset'$ (degrees)	36 to 39	33	20
c' (kPa)	0 to 63	0	10
Bulk density (kg/m^3)	1570 to 1810	1630	2160
Moisture Content (%)	21 to 30		
Specific Gravity	2.57		
Coefficient of Permeability (m/s)	4×10^{-7}		2×10^{-10}
c_v (m^2/sec)	0.88 to 7.1×10^{-7}		1.2×10^{-7}
m_v (kPa)$^{-1}$			1.9×10^{-4}
Opt m.c (%)	21 to 26	21	16
Max dry density (kg/m^3)	1370 to 1440	1400	1800

For construction of the rolled clay embankment the weathered mudstone existing on site was found to be suitable and borrowing upstream increased the volume of the lagoon.

Local limestone was used for the rockfill bunds and drainage zones. Furnace bottom ash (f.b.a.) from the power station, formed the filter between p.f.a. and drainage stone. Gradings of materials are shown in Fig. 4.

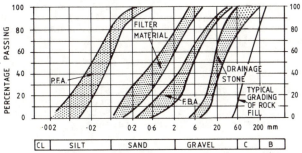

Fig. 4 Gradings of construction materials

Design analyses

The dam was designed against partial drawdown of the lagoon, and against sliding on the foundation or deeper seated instability, both for the whole embankment section and for the downstream part only. The design allowed for earthquake intensities predicted for a 75 to 100 year return period (a=0.05g).

The initial design was reassessed regularly throughout construction taking into account both the additional information obtained from the results of new laboratory testing and also the results of monitoring. Information obtained from boreholes sunk in 1978 and 1980 for additional instrumentation revealed evidence showing a wider extent of pre-existing slip surfaces in the foundation mudstone beneath the dam. Following comprehensive reanalysis of stability using Sarma (1973) and the revised $\emptyset'$ of 14° the embankment profile was subsequently modified with the design final crest being relocated upstream and more p.f.a. placed at the lower part of the embankment. A factor of safety for the critical end of construction condition of 1.3 was demonstrated. For the upstream slope rapid drawdown was the most critical condition. To achieve the design factor of safety of 1.25 a 1 in 3 profile was adopted. The original and revised final embankment profiles are shown in Fig. 3.

Foundation preparation

Excavation was carried out prior to construction to remove unsuitable clay and other material from the site of the dam. Shallow slips which were evident on the valley sides were stabilized by means of trench drains.

INSTRUMENTATION AND MONITORING

The instrumentation consisted of 26 hydraulic piezometers, 16 pneumatic piezometers, 4 standpipe piezometers, 4 observation wells, 7 inclinometers and 2 settlement gauges (magnetic probe borehole extensometers). The instrumentation is shown in Figs. 2 and 3. All instruments were monitored regularly on a monthly basis.

The following were also recorded: daily rainfall; seepage flow weekly; culvert invert levels periodically; tops of inclinometer tubes, positions and levels periodically.

PERFORMANCE

Pore water pressure

Fig. 5 shows typical piezometric levels. At shallow depth in the upstream side of the clay embankment beneath the lagoon piezometric

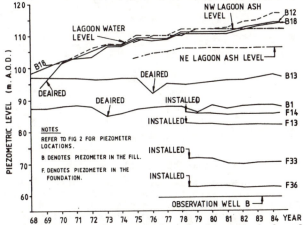

Fig. 5 Lagoon, lagoon ash and piezometric levels

levels closely followed lagoon water levels.
(eg B12 and B18). Water head loss of about 15m
occurs through the upstream clay blanket (eg B13
installed within the clay blanket). All piezometers installed within the p.f.a. embankment
remained dry indicating that the drainage measures performed satisfactorily. The foundation
piezometers indicated that the piezometric level
remained at least 0.9m below the bottom of the
drainage blanket, and there were no excess pore
pressures.

Embankment movement

No untoward movement has been observed.

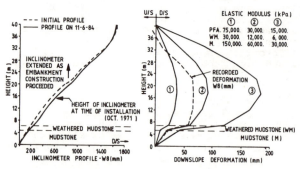

Fig. 6 Recorded and calculated downslope
deformation

The deflection profile at the end of construction for a typical inclinometer (W8) is shown
in Fig. 6 compared with the profile on installation. The total downslope deformation, i.e.
the difference between these profiles, is also
shown together with the results of analyses
made on the basis of an incremental simple
shear elastic model. This indicates deformation moduli (E) for the mudstone and weathered
mudstone of 60,000 and 12,000 kPa, respectively,
and of the order of 50,000 kPa for the p.f.a.,
all within the ranges expected.

Over three years the tops of the inclinometer
tubes were precisely surveyed by the Building
Research Establishment to check whether the
lower parts of the tubes which were installed
to a minimum depth of 7m into mudstone were
stable. The maximum observed movement of the
top of an inclinometer tube was 21mm. The survey results and the concurrent inclinometer
readings confirmed base stability.

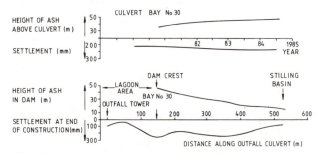

Fig. 7 Settlement of outfall culvert.

Fig. 7 shows culvert settlement at the end of
construction with fill height, and a time plot
for Bay 30, beneath the crest. Under 47m of
fill settlement was 244mm. Back calculation
gives m_v for foundation mudstone of 4×10^{-5} $(kPa)^{-1}$
compared with the design value of 9×10^{-5} $(kPa)^{-1}$.

Seepage

The yearly average seepage flows through the
drainage blanket are shown in Fig. 8 together
with the annual rainfall and lagoon water level.
The total average seepage flow is about 1.6×10^{-5}
m^3/s compared with an estimated flow from the
lagoon into the drainage blanket of 1×10^{-6} m^3/s
(assuming a high permeability for the clay fac-
ing of 10^{-8} m/s). The flow discrepancy is probably mainly due to seepage from the valley
sides. Fig. 8 also shows typical weekly seepage
flows and the corresponding rainfall and lagoon
water levels. Two brine tracer tests of the
drainage blanket showed good hydraulic continuity
and coefficients of permeability of 2×10^{-3} and
4×10^{-2} m/sec.

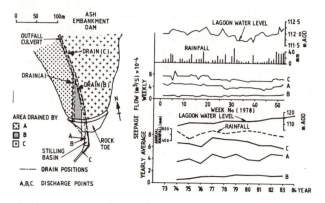

Fig.8 Seepage flow observations

CONCLUSIONS

The dam was constructed successfully on a steeply sloping weak foundation. Design modifications were made in response to monitoring
throughout construction. Discharge measurements
and tests of the blanket drain show its continued effectiveness. F.b.a. is an effective
filter between p.f.a. and drainage stone. Piezometers show substantial head loss through the
clay facing. No excess pore pressures occurred
in the embankment p.f.a. and no seepage downstream of the chimney drain. Excess pore pressures were not recorded in the foundation
mudstone presumably because of the slow rate of
construction. Consequently further settlements
are expected to be small.

ACKNOWLEDGEMENTS

The authors thank the Central Electricity Generating Board for permission to present the paper,
and colleagues within Rendel, Palmer & Tritton,
the designers, for their assistance.

REFERENCES

Cocks, L.R.M., and Walton, G. (1968). A large
temporary exposure in the Lower Silurian of
Shropshire. Geol.Mag.(105), 4, 390-397.

Henkel, D.J., and Skempton, A.W. (1955). A landslide at Jackfield, Shropshire in a heavily
overconsolidated clay. Geotechnique (5),131-137.

Sarma, A.K. (1973). Stability analysis of
embankments and slopes. Geotechnique (23),
423-433.

Engineering and environmental considerations in tailings deposition

Considérations relatives à l'ingénierie et à environnement des résidus

R. W. HENDRY, Associate Dames & Moore Consulting Engineers, Cape Town, South Africa
D. WRIGHT, Metallurgist, Rössing Uranium Mine, South West Africa / Namibia

SYNOPSIS   During the production of uranium at Rössing Mine, 40 000 tonnes of tailings is required to be deposited daily.   An embankment of tailings reaching a height of 56 metres has been
constructed across a gorge.   The stability of the embankment is investigated.   At the same time
alternative methods of tailings deposition are considered and the environmental implications of
tailings deposition and seepage away from the impoundment area are studied.

INTRODUCTION

The Rössing Uranium Mine is situated in the
heart of the Namib Desert, 70 kilometres from
the Atlantic Coast of South West Africa (Namibia).   In terms of material recovered from
the open pit, it is the largest uranium mine
in the world.   Geologically it is unique in
that it is the largest known deposit of uranium
occurring in granite.   Most of the other major
uranium deposits of the world such as those
of the Witwatersrand in South Africa, Blind
River in Canada, Wyoming and New Mexico in
the USA, and the Northern Territory of Australia, occur in sedimentary formations.

SITE DESCRIPTION

Surface

The area around Rössing Uranium Mine consists
mainly of exposed rock with little surface
soil and sparse vegetation.   What vegetation
and surface soils there are, are confined mainly to dry river channels.

Natural drainage in the mine area is provided
by three major gorges each draining from north
to south.   The gorges, Panner Gorge to the
west, Pinnacle Gorge and Dome Gorge to the
east, all drain into the Khan River which runs
just to the south of the mine (Fig 1).   This
discharges approximately 10km to the southwest
into the Swakop River.   A ridge of hills (maximum elevation 707m) running northeast-south-
west forms the eastern flank of the tailings
disposal area.   The embankment presently has
a crest elevation of about 606m and a downstream toe elevation at its lowest point of
534m.

As of May 1984 the area of the free water pond
is $1,09 \times 10^5$ m² with a volume of $6,7 \times 10^5$ m³.
A second dam has been constructed approximately
1km downstream of the tailings dam to collect
water seeping through the toe of the tailings
dam.

Subsurface

The geology of the tailings disposal area con-

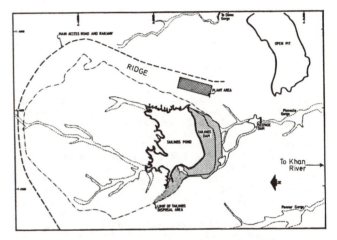

Fig 1   Mine Layout with Embankment Details

sists primarily of two rock types; metamorphic
rocks of the Damara system and pegmatic granit-
ic gneiss known as the Khan formation. Many
pegmatic dykes have intruded both rock types.
The area has undergone intense folding and
fracturing.   Alluvial silty sands and gravels
occur in the valley bottom.   Much of the present tailings impoundment overlies alluvial
deposits.   Investigations have shown that
most of the bedrock is highly fractured. The
main direction of fractures is approximately
northsouth.   Most fractures tend to be of
an 'open' nature and prone to water percolation.

Groundwater

The regional groundwater flow consists of subsurface flow through rock fractures, and through
alluvial soils in the 'dry' river beds, draining the upland areas.   Hence, the flow in
the mine area is mainly confined to southerly
and westerly directions towards the Khan River.
It is likely that this flow has existed for
a considerable period and that surface flow

has only occurred for brief periods following heavy rain. The natural groundwater is of a poor quality having a 'chloride' content often in excess of 6000ppm and can be as high as 14 000 ppm.

The construction of the tailings embankment and water impoundment pond has imposed an increased water pressure head, causing an increase in the hydraulic gradient in the vicinity of the dam. The result of this has been an increased subsurface flow - both in volume flow rate, and in flow velocity.

GENERAL TAILINGS DISPOSAL

The tailings are disposed of by the construction of a tailings dam across Pinnacle Gorge. Initially mine waste was placed in a starter dam across the gorge to an elevation of 560m, and over a length of 900m. This mine waste forms the downstream filter toe of the dam through which the majority of seepage water flows before collection in the seepage dam. Tailings disposal began in mid-1976, and tailings slurry has been deposited to the upstream of the starter dam throughout operations.

The dam has been constructed in benches, each bench 15m wide and 6m above the previous one. The slope between benches is 2:1 horizontal to vertical, and the average overall slope of the downstream face of the embankment is 4,5:1 horizontal to vertical. From the crest of the tailings dam the tailings form a beach sloping from about 8% at the point of discharge to 1 to 2% over the last 100 to 200m of the beach. The curved shape of the beach can be ascribed to gravitational segregation which occurs during sheet flow of the slurry down the beach. The coarser particles settle out rapidly at the top of the beach, and as the slurry becomes finer, the beach flattens out. The finest tailings only drop out when the slurry reaches the free water pond. An hydrograph survey has shown that tailings extend almost right across the pond.

EMBANKMENT INVESTIGATION

Drilling and Sampling

A drilling and sampling programme was carried out on the downstream face of the embankment. Twelve holes were drilled from the level benches of the tailings embankment. Because of the cohesionless nature of the tailings material, a drilling mud was used during the advancement of the holes from collapsing and to facilitate the removal of the casing at the completion of the hole. Because of the coarseness of the tailings, the drilling mud was also required to efficiently wash the tailings to the surface of the hole as the hole was advanced. As it was intended that at the completion of each boring a slotted PVC pipe would be installed in the hole to act as an observation well or piezometer, it was necessary that the drilling mud used during the boring should be of a revert type.

As each boring was advanced through the tailings material, Standard Penetration Tests (SPT's) were carried out at approximately 2m intervals. The relative density of the embankment varied from 'medium dense' to 'dense'.

In addition to SPT's performed in the material, above the phreatic surface an attempt was made to obtain a number of relatively undisturbed samples using Shelby Tubes. A limited amount of success was achieved. The holes were logged throughout their depth. A typical profile of the material encountered in the embankment is depicted in Figure 2.

Samples of the slimes were obtained from the beach on the upstream side of the embankment using Shelby Tubes.

	SPT	CONS.	ANGLE OF FRICTION	DESCRIPTION
	15	Medium dense	41°	Light greyish brown coarse to fine well graded medium dense sand
	20	Medium dense		
	28	Dense	39°	
	30	Dense		
	22	Medium dense	37°	
	30	Dense		
	35	Dense	40°	
	30			Fine poorly graded medium dense sand
				Marble : white to light grey coarse grained highly fractured highly weathered
				Feldspar : highly to moderately weathered

Fig 2 Typical profile of tailings

Rock Coring

Of the 12 holes drilled and sampled, 6 were advanced into the underlying rock. The cores were extracted and logged.

Rock Seepage Tests

In each hole in which rock coring was performed at least one seepage test was carried out using the packer equipment. The major rock types encountered below the embankment included Bonded Gneiss, Marble with Feldspar and Schist, with an average RQD of 35%. The permeability of the rock varied from just above 0cm/sec in the marbles and veldspar to $5,28 \times 10^{-4}$ cm/sec in the marble.

Piezometers

To monitor the phreatic level in the embankment, a system of piezometers was installed in the embankment. Generally the piezometers have been installed on the downstream face of the embankment in rows parallel to the radius of the embankment. Each piezometer or observation well consists of a 50mm Ø PVC sleeve installed in a borehole and slotted over the lower 4 to 6 metres. The lengths of the piezometers vary from 2,8 metres on the lower benches to 44,9 on the higher benches.

Regular measurements are made of the water

level in the piezometers and the effect of depositing in a particular zone of the embankment is monitored in the relevant piezometers. Although there is a lag in time between the commencement of tailings deposition and an increase in the phreatic level, this simple method of monitoring has proved effective. It has been used as a control on the length of time deposition may occur in a particular area before the phreatic level rises sufficiently to cause seepage from the downstream face. The underlying rock surface topography has a pronounced effect on the level of the phreatic line in the embankment. Where high points occur in the rock topography beneath the embankment, the phreatic line is forced upwards and has a tendency to exit higher up the face than is the case in sections of the embankment where the rock lies well below the surface.

No significant or continuous clay lenses were encountered in the embankment where a perched water table might occur. With the increase in embankment height however, as deposition continues, a check on the validity of the observation well or standpipe type piezometers is being carried out by the installation and monitoring of several pneumatic type piezometers.

Laboratory Testing

(i) Gradings and Atterberg Limits

Typical particle size distribution curves from the embankment material and from slimes of the tailings beach are shown on Figure 3.

(ii) Strength Tests

In addition to the SPT's carried out in-situ, consolidated undrained triaxial tests were performed on the Shelby Tube samples obtained from the tailings embankment. The free draining material gave values of internal friction from 37° to 41° with an average value of 38,8.

(iii) Moisture and Density

Density tests were performed on samples of material taken from both the embankment and the beach upstream of the embankment. The density of the material constituting the embankment varied from 1636kg/m³ to 1890kg/m³ with an average of 1788kg/m³. On the beach upstream of the embankment the average density was slightly less at 1769kg/m³. The highest densities encountered were from material furthest from the free water pond and nearest to the tailings embankment.

Above the phreatic line, the moisture content of the embankment material ranged from 9,0% to 14,6% with an average of 12,3%. Below it varied from 22% to 32% with an average of 26%. On the beach the moisture content of the material varied from 2,8% near the top of the beach to 25% near the edge of the free water pond.

(iv) Permeability Tests

Laboratory permeability tests were carried out using the falling head and constant head methods. The permeabilities of typical tailings material measured on samples remoulded to 1800kg/m³ varied from 0,4 x 10⁻⁴ cm/sec to 13 x 10⁻⁴cm/sec with an average of 8 x 10⁻⁴cm/sec. Samples extracted from the slimes layers gave an average permeability of 0,4 x 10⁻⁴cm/sec.

EMBANKMENT STABILITY

The tailings embankment stability analysis was carried out for two general conditions, namely; overall embankment and localised stability of the downstream face of the embankment and embankment toe influenced by seepage. The slope stability analysis was carried out using the modified Bishop's method. Critical failure surfaces were identified. Manual calculations were also performed using the same method of calculation as the computer analyses.

In the computer analyses the phreatic surface was postulated at three different levels. The existing level at the time of calculation and two additional levels, one showing the phreatic surface level as it might be expected some time in the future and the other midway between the expected level and the current level. The minimum factors of safety against slope failure on the downstream face were

1,48   present level
0,42   future level
0,79   intermediate level

The manual calculations were carried out for three cases, for both overall and localised stability:-

(a)   Static drained
(b)   Seepage conditions
(c)   Pseudostatic conditions

The analysis for pseudostatic incorporated a peak horizontal particle velocity co-efficient to simulate seismic shock waves. The

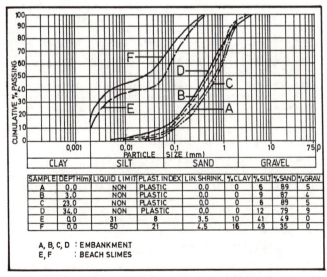

A, B, C, D : EMBANKMENT
E, F : BEACH SLIMES

SAMPLE	DEPTH(m)	LIQUID LIMIT	PLAST. INDEX	LIN. SHRINK.	%CLAY	%SILT	%SAND	%GRAV
A	0,0	NON	PLASTIC	0,0	0	6	89	5
B	3,0	NON	PLASTIC	0,0	0	9	87	4
C	23,0	NON	PLASTIC	0,0	0	6	89	5
D	34,0	NON	PLASTIC	0,0	0	12	79	9
E	0,0	31	8	3,5	10	41	49	0
F	0,0	50	21	4,5	16	49	35	0

Fig 3 Typical particle size distribution curves

co-efficient used was 0,05g, a nominal value assumed to be applicable to the Rössing area. The effect of blasting in the open pit was considered. Because of the distance to the embankment however, the energy, displacement and duration of such an event is considerably less than the acceleration considered in the calculations.

The calculations indicated typical values of safety for the overall embankment for the three cases as follows:
Static Drained condition   FS = 3,61
Seepage condition   FS = 1,64
Pseudostatic condition   FS = 1,45
It was postulated that under present deposition conditions and embankment construction methods with 15m wide benches and slopes between benches of 2:1, future extensions to the embankment would produce an overall factor of safety tending towards a conservative 3,6.

An alternative construction configuration of 5m wide benches with 1,5 to 1 slopes between benches would produce overall embankment factors of safety as follows.

Static Drained condition   FS = 2,01
Pseudostatic condition   FS = 1,75

The analyses indicate that the downstream slope of the overall embankment could be significantly steepened while still maintaining an adequate factor of safety. While the steepening of the slopes of subsequent extensions and reduction of bench width represent potential savings in construction costs, the bench widths are required for roadways and service facilities.

If the water table in the embankment rises to such an extent that seepage emerges from the downstream face of the embankment, slips and sloughing are likely to occur. The localised instability is more a maintenance problem and does not pose a threat to the stability of the overall embankment, provided that deposition in the zone is temporarily halted and a form of waste rock buttress placed in the area of seepage.

Based on a series of manual calculations, a table was drawn up showing the factors of safety of the downstream face for various levels of the phreatic surface within the embankment under normal seepage conditions. (Table 1)

TABLE 1

Water Level	Factors of Safety
Existing	1.48
+0,5	1,24
+1,0	1,1
+1,5	0,88
+2,0	0,79

Embankment Stability Control Measures

Two basic principles were considered for increasing the factor of safety and hence the stability of the downstream slopes of the embankment. The first was to weight the toe of the slope and in so doing prevent any slippages from occurring. The method of gravel buttresses, discussed below, incorporates this principle. The second principle was to prevent seepage from emerging from the face of the slope.

(i) **Gravel Buttress**

A 150mm thick layer of 6-15mm stone aggregate is placed over the slope to be buttressed. On top of this filter layer, crushed stone or minus 450mm mine waste is placed to a thickness of +1,5m at the toe. Thus the seepage is able to pass through the embankment but piping is effectively prevented. In certain circumstances, a geofabric such as Bidim or Terram is placed over the surface of the embankment and mine waste or ripped country rock placed on top of it.

(ii) **Prevent Seepage**

Seepage may be prevented from exiting on the downstream face by lowering the phreatic surface below the downstream face. This may be accomplished by well-pointing interceptor ditches and horizontal drains.

Considering cost of installation, availability of materials and operational management, the most efficient and effective method of stabilising the localised areas of the downstream toe of the embankment was the construction of a weighting zone at the toe of the slope with free draining backfill. The effect of a minimal thickness of properly placed buttressing fill on the stability of the toe is considerable. Stability analyses were carried out in a particular section of embankment with the water table postulated approximately 2m above the toe of the embankment. The resulting factor of safety was 0,61. The analyses were repeated with the gravel buttress in position and a factor of safety of 1,2 was computed.

ALTERNATIVE METHODS OF TAILING DISPOSAL

Disposal from Upstream

This method of tailings disposal was considered in order to reduce the final elevation of the existing tailings embankment and to curtail the further flow of seepage water to the surrounding country rock from the embankment. The method of tailings disposal considered involved discharging the tailings at the upstream end of the watershed. By maintaining the plan position of a single point discharge constant while raising the outfall as required, a cone of tailings would develop with side slopes similar to those of the beach upstream of the embankment. (Figure 4)

Adopting this method of deposition would (1) minimise embankment construction (2) reduce activities related to shifting the slurry pipeline and (3) ensure proper control of the free water pond by causing it to move away from the fractured rock in the west to the less fractured rock in the east.

(1) **Stability of Upstream Cone**

To establish profile data and strength parameters of the proposed prototype cone a survey profile was carried out on a

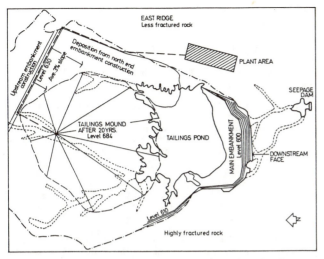

Fig 4 Cone deposition, no raising of embankment

'model' cone constructed on the beach upstream of the existing embankment.

The results of the grading analyses indicated the deposition of the coarsest grind near the top of the cone with the finer material lower down and the finest fraction at the bottom of the slope. Angles of internal friction ranged between 37° and 41°. The density of the tailings material varied from 1630kg/m³ to 1973kg/m³. Moisture content measurements on the same samples ranged from 2,8% to 25%.

In order to calculate the stability of the slope of the cone deposit, certain conservative assumptions were made. The average slope of the cone was taken as 8,5%, the internal angle of friction as 35° and the dry density as 1700kg/m³. It was assumed that the water was seeping from the tailings.

In the analysis the static forces were modified using the previously adopted horizontal acceleration co-efficient of 0,05g. Slope failure was assumed to be in the form of composite slip surfaces.

The results of the analysis indicated that in the worst case the factor of safety with regard to slope failure varied between 5,3 and 5,8.

It was postulated that in the absence of thickening, the overall prototype cone would form more like the beach shape upstream of the embankment, i.e. from 8% to 2% and flatter. Slopes of thickened tailings of saturated sand when subjected to seismic accelerations from 0,03 to 0,1g flatten to 0,3 to 2,0 degrees. The material as discharged would be unthickened and in the event of a seismic shake would be unlikely to flatten further than 2%. The possibility of thickening the tailings was not considered as a viable cost alternative to embankment construction.

(ii) Effect of the Cone Shape

The effect of allowing a cone to form would require close control. Once a certain height was reached the toe of the cone would reach the edge of the free water pond. A further increase in elevation would push the pond towards the embankment. The phreatic line in the embankment would rise and the stability of the embankment would be affected.

(iii) Environmental Implications

The cone would tend to create a topographic high above the plateaus and gorges. The dry tailings on the cone would be susceptible to wind movement and this tendency could be exacerbated by the prominent shape of the cone. In addition, tailings fluid flowing down the face of the cone would tend to pond upstream of the cone. To prevent this fluid from seeping into the surrounding rock in an uncontrolled fashion, consideration was given to draining the fluid back downstream through the tailings mound. Field tests were carried out to study the feasibility of placing Bidim drains through the mound. The Bidim however became blocked with slimes and through flow ceased after 2 or 3 days.

Ring Method of Deposition

The geotechnical and environmental advantages and disadvantages of depositing tailings in a conical mound over the more conventional embankment construction methods have been briefly highlighted above. The most feasible alternative method is one which capitalises on the disadvantages of the conical mound deposition. Such a method would require to maintain as low an embankment profile as possible to prevent environmental intrusion on to the surrounding topography. It would at the same time require to minimise the chances of tailings dust blowing over surrounding areas and prevent as far as possible any ponding upstream behind the deposition. The alternative method selected would also require to ensure that the free water pond is readily controlled in position and size by tailings deposition. An advantage over the conical method would be to permit more flexibility in the deposition system and at the same time adopt an effective system which requires minimum additional training for tailings deposition management. Finally, it is obviously advantageous to operate a system economically favourable and as a criterion preferably more so than rival ones. Owing to the great distance from the plant to the most suitable position for the cone, the cost implications of the two systems considered tended to reflect against the conical method of deposition.

An efficient utilisation of the impoundment area and good pond management would be achieved by aiming to partially enclose the impoundment area. This would be by depositing on the main embankment in the south, by depositing on the west and by depositing from the north. The main embankment would be raised to an elevation of 625m and then by preferential building at a later stage the western embankment would be raised to an elevation of 645m. (Figure 5).

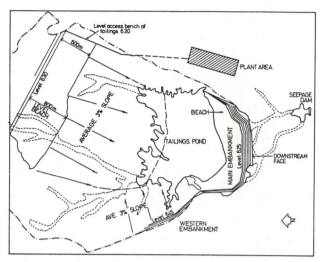

Fig 5 Ring Deposition and Raising Embankment

From the north end of the impoundment area, tailings deposition would raise the embankment ot a maximum height of 635m. Thus the elevations of all sections of the ring embankment would be considerably lower than the cone would have been. The position and elevation of the free water pond, particularly in relation to the main embankment would be controlled by the flexibility of deposition, i.e. from southwest and north.

SEEPAGE AND SEEPAGE CONTROL

It was established that the average permeability of both the calcareous and non-calcareous rock was 3×10^{-4}cm/sec. Seepage occurs through both the embankment and through the foundation rock. Both components are related to the surface area of the free water pond which in turn is a function of the depth. Most of the seepage through the embankment is intercepted in the surface seepage pond. Seepage taking place through the foundation is trapped in gorges downstream of the embankment by means of cutoff trenches. The trenches are excavated through the alluvium in the gorges and taken some 2 metres into rock. Pumps are installed in sumps which are connected to the surface by means of pumping wells. The trenches are backfilled with graded rock forming a filter zone. Water trapped by the trenches is pumped back to the surface seepage dam for recycling.

The hydraulic conductivity of the bedrock is related to the size and spacing of the joints and fractures. Where the bedrock is highly fractured, as is generally the case, or open bedding plans are closely spaced, large seepage losses are expected. Flow into open fractures could occur at a rate several times greater than the 3×10^{-4}cm/sec. However as tailings cover these fractured areas, there is a reduction of maximum flow into the fractures as the

tailings blanket restricts flow into these conduits.

FUTURE EMBANKMENT STABILITY

The embankment stability will in the immediate future be enhanced by the following factors.

(i) 85% of the fresh water to the rodmills is being replaced by the return dam solution and seepage water. The result will be a shrinkage of the free water pond and lowering of the pond surface.

(ii) A seepage trench is being installed along the toe of a zone of the tailings embankment. This will control the potential exit level of the phreatic surface in the zone during and after deposition.

By effectively monitoring and controlling the phreatic level in the embankment and permitting an increase in embankment height, the distance of slurry transportation and hence the costs can be greatly reduced.

PLANNING BY PREDICTION

Making use of the flexibility of the ring method of deposition, together with the continued prediction of phreatic levels in embankment construction is to be effectively controlled by means of a mathematical model. The objectives of the model will be:

(1) To estimate the shape assumed by tailings solids with time and to distinguish, as far as possible, between the relative positions of tailings sands and tailings slimes.

(2) To estimate the position attained by tailings liquid surface, and depths of this liquid measured from the surface, with time.

(3) To evaluate the effects of alternative tailings discharge methods, and locations, upon the shape of tailings solids and position of tailings liquids.

(4) To estimate the effects of wastewater recovery and recycling upon the position of tailings liquids.

(5) To estimate costs of alternative discharge methods and locations as a function of time.

CONCLUSION

To maintain flexibility in deposition, alternative deposition systems within the framework of a particular method must be functional. At the same time, monitoring of embankment stability and seepage is essential for the planning of deposition. To capitalise on the flexibility of a deposition system predictive planning is eminently desirable. The mathematical tailings management model provides a suitable tool for such predictive planning but information is required to be supplied as input to the model on a continuously updated basis. This information includes phreatic level in the embankment, actual and predicted seepage flow, position and elevation of the free water pond and potential embankment stability. The key to the supply of this information is monitoring.

ACKNOWLEDGEMENTS

The authors are grateful to Rössing Uranium Ltd for permission to publish this paper.

REFERENCES

Cedergren H R (1967). Seepage, Drainage and Flow Nets. Wiley Interscience pp 34-45

Dames & Moore (1974). Manual of Technical Practice for Subsurface Investigations

Dames & Moore (1984). Mathematical Model for Uranium Tailings Management

Department of Mines Geological Survey (1979). Seismic History of Southern Africa

Gevers T W and Frommurze (1929). The Geology of North-Western Damaraland in South West Africa. Trans. Geol. Soc., South Africa 32, pp 31-55

Robinsky E I. Thickened Discharge - a New Approach to Tailings Disposal Bulletin. The Canadian Institute of Mining and Metallurgy, December 1975, pp 47-59

Rössing Uranium Mine. Tailings Dam Monthly Reports. Jan 1980 to present

Rössing Uranium Mine (1983). Economic Evaluation of Tailings Deposition

Rössing Uranium Mine (P Vernon) and Rio Tinto Management Services (A Guzman and C O Beale). Hydrotransport 8, 1982. The design and operation of the Rössing tailings pumping system.

Reducing environmental impact of in-pit ash disposal

La réduction de l'effet de l'environnement sur le traitement de cendres dans les puits des mines

A. R. LANDBY, Electricity Supply Commission, Johannesburg, South Africa
G. E. BLIGHT, University of Witwatersrand, Johannesburg, South Africa
I. J. A. BRACKLEY, Steffen, Robertson and Kirsten Inc., Johannesburg, South Africa
A. C. SMITH, Steffen, Robertson and Kirsten Inc., Johannesburg, South Africa

SYNOPSIS   A description is given of an investigation into the stowing of power station ash in the mined-out portions of an open-pit coal mine so as to limit environmental impact. It was decided to place the ash above the restored phreatic surface in the pit thus reducing the transfer of soluble salts to a river bordering the site and to an underlying dolomite aquifer.

INTRODUCTION

A new thermal electricity generating station of 3600 Mega-Watt capacity will be fuelled by coal from an adjacent open pit mine. About 230 million tons of ash are expected to be produced during the forty year life of the station. The disposal of this ash with a loose volume of close to 250 million cubic metres, is obviously a problem with major environmental implications.

Investigations were made for disposal of ash in the following ways :

1. In the pit, with ash positioned at the bottom of the excavation, below the restored water table.

2. In the pit, with the ash positioned at the top of the replaced overburden, above the restored water table, with a relatively thin soil cover.

3. On a surface in an area underlain by andesite lava which was likely to be free of major aquifers.

For the third case above, investigations considered both dry disposal using stackers, supplemented by mobile earth moving equipment and disposal of the ash in slurry form.

The writers, after completing their investigations, recommended the adoption of surface disposal because this method would cause a minimum of underground and surface water pollution and also because they considered it the most cost-effective method of ash disposal at this site.

The owners of the facility, the Electricity Supply Commission, decided, however, to adopt the in-pit dry disposal system with the ash placed in a 20m thick layer located near the surface of the backfilled pit. This location would minimize groundwater pollution from in-pit disposal.

REASONS FOR PREFERRING IN-PIT DISPOSAL

Figure 1 shows the location of the power station, the open-pit mine and the site for surface disposal of the ash. The mine will be located on the inside of a loop in the Vaal River, giving a river frontage of 18km. The site for surface disposal is across the river and some 7km from the Lethabo power station. Directly across the river from the mine is the large industrial and residential town of Vereeniging.

As the Vaal River is the major source of water for the Pretoria-Witwatersrand-Vereeniging complex, a residential and industrial area of some 10 million inhabitants, the possibility of soluble salt transfer from the ash to the river was clearly a most important consideration. Because of the leachable constituents of the ash, there is a threat of salt transfer however the ash is stowed. Surface disposal simplifies salt control, but increases the problems of wind-borne dust and of visual intrusion. Moreover a large area of farmland would be sterilized by the formation of a surface dump. There is also the problem of transporting the ash cross river and overland by pipe-line or conveyor with the accompanying visual intrusion and dangers of spillage along the route.

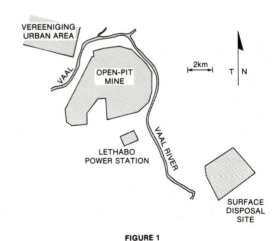

FIGURE 1

Location of possible ash disposal sites.

Perhaps the clinching argument for in-pit disposal arose from the fact that if the ash is not
returned to the pit more of the surface level of
the 2700 ha mined-out area will be below river
level. It would be difficult to prevent the formation of a swampy wasteland unless the backfill
were properly contoured. If the ash is returned
to the pit, however, surface contours can be restored to something approaching the pre-mining
topography.

LEACHABLE CONSTITUENTS OF ASH

The leachable constituents likely to occur in the
ash were assessed by means of a test programme
on ash taken from a number of nearby pulverised
coal-fired power stations. Water was percolated
through specimens of the ash and the leachate
analyzed. The leachate analysis taken for design
purposes was as set out in Table 1.

TABLE 1
"Design" Analysis of Leachate from Power
Station Ash

Component or Parameter	Mean Recorded Value	Permissible Values for Industrial Effluent According to: Regulations under South African Water Act	United States EPA, 40 CFR Part 257
pH	11,5+	5,5-9,5	6,5-8,5
Conductivity	760 mSm^{-1}		
Total Dissolved solids*	1800 mg/ℓ+	increase of 500 mg/ℓ above intake	500 mg/ℓ
Total Alkalinity	1260		
Calcium, Ca	600		
Sodium, Na	62	80 above intake	
Potassium, K	7		
Magnesium, Mg	0,1		
Carbonate, CO$_3$	210		
Hydroxide, OH	275		
Chloride, Cl	75		250
Sulphate, SO$_4$	320+		250
Nitrate, NO$_3$	5		10
Fluoride, F	2+	1,0	1,4
Silica, SiO$_2$	5		
Aluminium, Al	10		
Iron, Fe	0,2		0,3
Manganese, Mn	0,02		0,05
Copper, Cu	0,01	1,0	1,0
Zinc, Zn	0,02	5	5
Cadmium, Cd	0,04+		0,01
Molybdenum, Mo	0,5		
Boron, B	1,1	1,0	
Vanadium, V	0,1		
Arsenic, As	0,03	0,5	0,05
Selenium, Se	0,05+		0,01

* All units below this line are mg/ℓ

This is the average analysis for all the specimens subjected to test and represents the material leached by passing one bed volume of water
through the ash in a permeameter.

The contents of all constituents marked + exceed either South African or United States limits

for industrial effluent. Examination of the
table shows that the leachate did not meet the
requirements for an acceptable industrial effluent
as far as pH, total dissolved solids, sulphate,
fluoride, cadmium and selenium contents were concerned, but was otherwise acceptable.

Tests in which ash/water mixtures were allowed
to stand for up to 10 days before analyzing the
leachate showed that the limiting solubility of
the total dissolved solids was about 1800 mg/ℓ.
Repeated leaching of the same specimen showed
that the leachate analysis remained sensibly
constant even after 10 bed volumes of water had
been passed through the ash. Hence it can be
expected that the leachate will maintain sensibly the same analysis for a long period of time,
after which it should gradually improve in quality, although there is a possibility that the
heavy metals will become more mobile if the pH
decreases sufficiently.

The main problem appears to be the alkalinity of
the leachate and the high sulphate content.
Salination of the Vaal River from mining activities to the north, in the Witwatersrand area consists mainly of low pH sulphates, hence the
highly alkaline leachate from the ash will not
necessarily be detrimental if it finds its way
into the river in small quantities.

STRATIGRAPHY OF OPEN PIT SITE

Figure 2 shows a generalized stratigraphic column
for the site of the open pit. The coal-bearing
Ecca sediments are underlain by two older rock
sequences, an ancient glacial deposit, the Dwyka
tillite and the even older Transvaal dolomite.
It is not certain that the tillite is present
over the whole area of the pit but either the
tillite or the fissured and jointed, sometimes
cavernous and water-bearing dolomite will form
the floor of the mine.

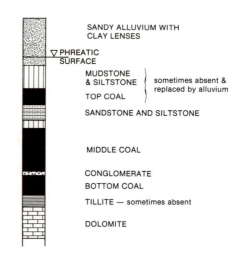

FIGURE 2

Stratigraphic column for site of open pit.

There are three principal coal horizons, with the lower horizons separated by a conglomerate parting that varies in thickness from zero to 3m. The top coal seam is capped by mudstone or siltstone strata that are up to 15m in thickness. However, the meandering of the river has, in places, eroded away both the mudstone and top coal.

The entire mining area is overlain by alluvial deposits of sand, silt and clayey sand, varying in thickness from 4m to 26m, with an average thickness of 15m. The total thickness of coal is up to 40m and averages about 20m. The floor of the open pit will be at an average depth of some 45m below present ground level. Hence once the coal has been removed, and if the ash is not disposed of in the pit, contours of the restored pit surface will be about 10m below present ground level and large areas will be below river level (even allowing for a 33 per cent bulking of the excavated materials).

SURFACE HYDROLOGY AND GEOHYDROLOGY

The mean annual precipitation for the site is 650mm, 85 per cent of which falls in the hot months from October to March. The mean annual evaporation (Symons'pan) is 1570mm, with the maximum evaporation occurring in December and January (185mm) and the minimum in June and July (75mm). The rain falls mostly in short duration storms of high intensity from which there is a large percentage runoff. Most of the runoff from the site of the open pit occurs as sheet flow into the river, although a swampy area collects runoff in the north east corner of the site.

There are two primary aquifers in the area. The sandy alluvium forms an unconfined aquifer with an average saturated thickness of 8m, while the dolomite strata form an underlying confined aquifer. Because of the large macro-permeability of the dolomites and the possibility that they will at least partially form the pit floor, the piezometric surface in this aquifer is of great importance. This surface, established by means of boreholes, is shown in Figure 3. The mean river level is 1420m, a level very similar to the piezometric head in the dolomite.

The phreatic surface in the alluvium is also important as it will affect pre-mining dewatering of the pit over-burden. It also represents an upper limit to the phreatic surface that will be established in the mined-out pit. This phreatic surface is shown in Figure 4.

GROUND WATER IN PIT DURING AND AFTER MINING

During mining, the upper sands will have to be dewatered in the immediate vicinity of the mining face to ensure pit stability. Depending on the permeability of the floor and the presence or absence of a tillite confining layer, inflow will also occur from the dolomites. Once the mining face is far enough away so that it no longer affects the ground water in the backfilled pit, the phreatic surface will re-establish itself.

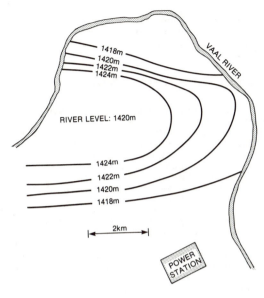

FIGURE 3

Phreatic surface in dolomite aquifer.

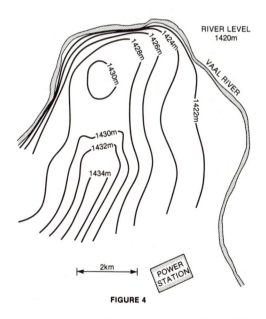

FIGURE 4

Phreatic surface in alluvial aquifer.

Upward seepage from the dolomite, together with lateral seepage from the river will ensure that the re-established phreatic surface is at least at river level. Infiltration of rainfall will tend to raise the phreatic surface above river level.

In the long term, it is unlikely that the present phreatic surface in the alluvium will be exceeded, but the present surface can be taken as an upper limit to the re-established phreatic surface.

PREFERRED ELEVATION FOR STOWING ASH

After being removed from the ash hoppers, it is intended to condition the ash to a moisture content of about 20 per cent in order to minimize dusting as the ash is conveyed from the power station and stowed in the pit. It would clearly be advantageous to stow the ash above the re-established phreatic surface in the mined out pit. The ash would then remain unsaturated, with a reduced permeability and the only leachate generation would come as a result of the limited infiltration through the surface. Studies showed that it will only be possible to stow the ash above the phreatic surface over about two-thirds of the area of the pit and that the thickness of the ash layer will average 12m. The ash layer will be capped by a 2m thick layer of soil and it will be accepted that the remaining one-third of the pit area, or 900 ha will end up at or below the level of the re-established water table. Figure 5 shows the stratigraphic column for the backfilled pit with the ash in the preferred position.

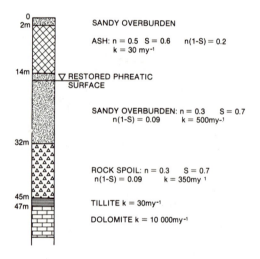

SANDY OVERBURDEN

ASH: n = 0.5 S = 0.6 n(1-S) = 0.2
k = 30 my⁻¹

▽ RESTORED PHREATIC SURFACE

SANDY OVERBURDEN: n = 0.3 S = 0.7
n(1-S) = 0.09 k = 500my⁻¹

ROCK SPOIL: n = 0.3 S = 0.7
n(1-S) = 0.09 k = 350my⁻¹

TILLITE k = 30my⁻¹

DOLOMITE k = 10 000my⁻¹

FIGURE 5

Stratigraphic column for backfilled open pit.

TIME TO RE-ESTABLISH PHREATIC SURFACE

The re-establishment time was calculated from the following water balance for the pit area:

inflow to pit = net infiltration from surface
+ upward seepage through pit floor

+ lateral seepage from river.

where:

Net infiltration from surface = precipitation
- run-off
- evapo-trans-piration
- lateral seepage into river.

As the pit has lateral dimensions of 5 to 6 km and a depth of only 45m, the lateral flow terms are negligible except around the perimeter of the pit.

The rates of rise of the phreatic surface will depend not only on the rate of water inflow, but also on the volume of air-filled pore space in the backfill. Calculations showed that the rate of re-establishment of the phreatic surface will depend greatly on the permeability of the floor of the pit, as the rock spoil and sandy overburden through which the water will rise are likely to be far more permeable than the pit floor, unless the floor consists of highly permeable dolomite.

The calculations showed that the phreatic surface could re-establish itself in as short a time as 1½ years and was unlikely to take more than 15 years. As the life of the pit is 40 years, the phreatic surface will have fully re-established itself over most of the area of the pit by the time mining ceases.

ESTIMATED SALT TRANSFER TO THE DOLOMITE AQUIFER

Infiltration studies showed that annual net infiltration from the surface is unlikely to exceed 10 per cent of the mean annual precipitation, and will be less if trees having a large water extraction capability, e.g. eucalyptus species, are established on the restored pit surface. Hence the surface infiltration is expected to be less than 65mm per annum. As the permeability of the ash is 450 times larger at 30m per annum, the infiltration term will completely control the generation and movement of leachate from the ash. Over most of the 1800 ha covered by the ash, flow will be vertically downward, and initially, before any leachate penetrates the re-established phreatic surface, the air-filled voids in the ash will have to be substantially filled by the infiltration. It is estimated that this process will take about 20 years from the cessation of dumping in any particular area. There is, however, a possibility that if the ash is carelessly placed on a segregated coarse overburden material, the transfer of salt to the pit floor could take place much more rapidly along paths of preferential flow. Thereafter, there will be a slow downward movement of salt-laden water through the sandy overburden and rock-spoil. If the effects of dispersive flow and attenuation by ion exchange with the soil are ignored, the first salt-bearing leachate will enter the dolomite aquifer after another 50 years, i.e. about 30 years after the pit has been abandoned. The steady-state pollution load is expected to be about 0,1 kg per annum per m² of pit area, i.e. a total salt load of 1800T per annum over the 1800 ha pit area.

ESTIMATED SALT TRANSFER TO THE VAAL RIVER

Figure 6 shows the situation along the Vaal
River once an adjacent portion of the pit has
been mined out. Flow of groundwater is expected to occur through the undisturbed alluvium
to the river, once the phreatic surface has re-
established itself. Two-dimensional flow analyses showed that the quantity of flow into the
river will be very dependent on the permeability
of the pit floor. For example, if the floor permeability is 30 my^{-1} flow will be predominantly
downwards into the dolomite, whereas if it is
only 0,3my^{-1}, almost all the flow will be directed towards the river. It is therefore likely
that flow to the river will be highly variable
along the river frontage. This variability will
be enhanced by the known heterogenity of the
alluvium.

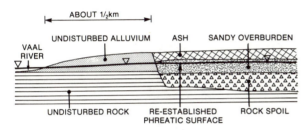

3 TO 1 VERTICAL EXAGGERATION

FIGURE 6

Flow from back-filled pit to river.

The best estimate of the salt load that will
be discharged into the river under steady-state
conditions is between 85 and 170T per annum,
over the 18 km river frontage. Allowing for
dispersion of the flow, it is estimated that salt
will start reaching the river 20 to 30 years
after the first leachate reaches the phreatic
surface, i.e. 40 to 50 years after the cessation
of dumping at a particular point.

Monitoring will be undertaken to check on actual
conditions during the life of the pit and after
its closure.

COMMENT

The above estimated annual salt loads are considered by the authorities to be acceptable in
the light of present pollution loads reaching
the river and ground water in the area. The
present pollution load reaching the river,from
the Witwatersrand to the north, averages
400 000T per annum. Hence, the entire salt
load from the ash represents only 0,05 per cent
of the present pollution load. Existing salt
loads are expected to reduce in future as better
control is gained over pollution from mine waste
deposits in the Witwatersrand area. However,
additional water pollution could have been almost completely eliminated had the surface disposal option been adopted.

ACKNOWLEDGEMENTS

This paper is published by kind permission of
the Electricity Supply Commission of South
Africa.

REFERENCES

Anderson, M (1979). Using models to simulate
the movement of contaminants through
groundwater flow systems. Critical Reviews
in Environmental Control, Vol. 9, No.2.

Chen, C.Y., Bullen, A.G.T. and Elnaggar, H.A.
(1977). Permeability and related properties of coal refuse. Transportation
Research Record, No.640.

Dudas, M.J. (1981). Long term leachability of
selected elements from fly ash.
Environmental Science and Technology,
Vol. 15 No.7.

Freeze, R.A. and Cherry, J.A. (1979).Ground-
water. Prentice-Hall, New Jersey.

Konikow, L.F. (1977). Modelling chloride move-
ment in the alluvial aquifer at the Rocky
Mountain Arsenal. US Geological Survey
Water Supply Paper, 2044.

Ogata, A (1970). Theory of dispersion in granular medium. US Geological Survey Professional Paper 411-1.

Technical properties of waste products from coal combustion
A laboratory study in accordance with soil analysis procedures

Propriétés techniques de déchets provenant de la combustion du charbon
Etude en laboratoire réalisée selon les méthodes usuelles d'analyse des sols

B. MÖLLER, Swedish Geotechnical Institute, Linköping, Sweden
G. NILSON, Swedish Geotechnical Institute, Linköping, Sweden

SUMMARY   This paper presents the results of a laboratory study of the technical properties of different coal combustion waste products. The investigations have involved fly ashes and bottom ashes from pulverized coal combustion, grate firing and oil combustion (only fly ash) and waste products from wet-dry and wet flue gas desulfurization procedures. Properties of fly ash found in the literature are also included for comparison. The laboratory investigations have comprised determination of the main chemical content, microstructure, general parameters, compaction properties, permeability and strength and strain properties.

INTRODUCTION

As an assignment for the Swedish Coal-Health-Environment (KHM) project, the Swedish Geotechnical Institute (SGI) has performed an extensive laboratory investigation on different kinds of waste product from coal combustion.

The main purpose of the investigation has been to determine the strength and permeability properties of the waste products. Knowledge of these parameters is very important in the utilization of the products, which will be different kinds of fill. Furthermore these parameters are essential for the evaluation of a deposit and its environmental effects.

Some 90 t coal per hour are combusted in a pulverized coal combustion plant for the generation of 260 MW of electricity. At an ash content in the coal of 10-15% 9-13.5 t of ash will be produced per hour. Flue gas desulfurization is in operation with the wet-dry method, which increases the amount of waste by 6 t/h. Such a plant will produce 15 to 20 t of waste per hour and, if it operates for 8,000 hours/year, will produce 110,000-160,000 t of waste anually.

For comparison purposes, the results of investigations from three different fly ashes, those of Braehead in Scotland, Skelton Grange in England and Trenton Channel in the USA, are included in this paper.

GENERAL PARAMETERS

The general parameters of different types of waste are presented in Table 1. The grain size distribution for different kinds of coal waste product varies, depending on from where in the processes they are extracted and the type of combustion.

Bottom ashes are coarse material in these contexts, with a relatively high content of grains bigger than 20 mm. Slag pieces of up to 500 mm in diameter are often found.

The grain density (2,130-2,390 kg/m^3) of the ashes indicates porous particles and the formation of scenospheres. By comparison, the grain density of natural soil is 2,700-2,800 kg/m^3. The bottom ashes have an even lower grain density, which means that the pieces of slag have a higher content of confined pores than fly ash.

The grain density of the product of flue gas desulfurization at Wilhelmshafen is relatively high, 2,950 kg/m^3, which seems to be an effect of the content of calcium sulphite.

The specific surface area of fly ashes is important to the strength properties, especially the fact that a higher specific surface area increases the reaction speed, but does not increase the final strength values, Lin (1971). From Table 1 it is clear that no relationship exists between the grain size distribution and the specific surface area.

MAIN CHEMICAL CONTENT AND MICROSTRUCTURE

One of the most essential components for the strength properties of fly ash is the content of SiO_2 + Al_2O_3, free lime and the content of unburnt coal. These are very important for the puzzolanic activity. The values of CaO, presented in Table 2, are the sums of total lime content. Analysis of free lime from Braehead and Skelton Grange fly ashes shows values <0.01% and 0.03% respectively, Sherwood and Ryley (1966). Lack of free lime in fly ash will eliminate the puzzolanity, Lin (1971).

The microstructure of the waste products also plays an important part in the strength properties. The characteristic grain form and the structure of the different kinds of waste product are summarized in Table 3. The fly ashes often contain scenospheres. The content of spherical grains is almost nil in fly ash from grate firing. The bottom ashes often have a very porous structure, which then gives a very low compact density. Grains of bottom ash have a

TABLE 1. Summary of general parameters for different kinds of coal waste product.

	Waste product	Grain density kg/m³	Specific surface area m²/kg	Characteristic grain size µm d_{10}	d_{60}	Uniformity coeff. $C_U = d_{60}/d_{10}$	Classification according to soils system
Fly ash	Asnaes	2280	539	4	- 40	10.0	Sandy silt
	Ingå	2200	298	3	- 20	6.7	" "
	Wilhelmshafen	2210	270	20	- 30	1.5	" "
	Trenton Channel	2360	305	3	- 20	6.7	" "
	Braehead	2240	397	15	- 27	1.8	" "
	Skelton Grange	2130	360	4	- 25	6.2	" "
	Norrköping	2390	-	10	- 125	12.5	Silty sand
	Perstorp	2180	-	30	- 300	10.0	" "
	Uppsala (oil burning)	2750	-	-	-6	-	-
Bottom ash	Asnaes[2]	1910	-	80	- 1600	20.0	Gravey sand, stony
	Wilhelmshafen[1]	2170	-	60	- 500	8.3	Sand
	Norrköping[2]	2025	-	400	- 7000	17.5	Sandy gravel, stony
	Perstorp[2]	2100	-	700	- 8000	11.4	" " "
Flue gas desulfurization product	(wet-dry) Asnaes	2520	1240	(-5)	- (-20)	(4)	Silt
	(wet) Wilhelms-hafen	2950	-	(-3)	- (-12)	(4)	"

[1] Bottom ash from Wilhelmshafen is ground after processing, so it does not contain grains >20 mm.

[2] Grain size distribution is performed on material <20 mm. The bottom ashes often consist of pieces of slag bigger than ~500 m.

vitreous cover, which seems to prevent puzzolanic activity taking place.

The flue gas desulfurization products have a microstructure that is derived from their chemical content. The Wilhelmshafen product is characteristized by crystals of calcium sulphite and calcium sulphate. The calcium oxide dominates in the Asnaes product, and appears as a fluffy, porous and undefinable structure.

TABLE 2. The essential chemical components in different kinds of coal waste product.

	Waste product	SiO_2 %	Al_2O_3 %	CaO %	Content of unburnt coal %
Fly ash	Asnaes	49	26	5.4	3.3
	Ingå	53	23	3.3	3.6
	Wilhelmshafen	53	30	4.0	0.9
	Trenton Channel	47	27	0.9	4.3
	Braehead	53	33	1.0	3.7
	Skelton Grange	49	25	2.3	1.4
	Norrköping	32	15	6.1	25
	Perstorp	30	14	5.9	33
	Uppsala (oil burning)	1.9	0.4	0.8	65
Bottom ash	Asnaes	46	19	5.1	9.4
	Norrköping	45	20	4.3	18
	Perstorp	42	19	6.0	17
	Wilhelmshafen	54	27	5.3	0.7
Flue gas desulfurization products	(wet-dry) Asnaes	17	10	40	
	(wet) Wilhelms-hafen	1.5	0.4	37	

COMPACTION PROPERTIES

The compaction curves are plots of standardized heavy laboratory compaction results. Figure 1 shows i.a. for fly ashes a variation in the maximum dry density, from 0.99 to 1.54 t/m³, at a relatively constant optimum water content of 18 to 21%. The fly ashes from pulverized coal combustion give the highest density. The maximum dry density for a comparable soil is 1.7-1.8 t/m³.

The compaction properties of the bottom ashes were determined using a vibration method to avoid crushing the material. The maximum dry density of Asnaes, Norrköping and Perstorp bottom ashes are 0.67-0.84 t/m³, which is low. However, the heavy compaction method was used for the Wilhelmshafen bottom ash, because this material had been ground to particles smaller than 8 mm. Even here slight crushing is to be expected. By comparison, the dry density of lightweight clinker is 0.35-0.4 t/m³.

The desulfurization products are very unstable at water contents above the optimum, which may lead to difficulties in compaction work, for example. The water saturation limit for both products is about 44%.

STRENGTH PROPERTIES

The strength of compacted fly ashes and flue gas desulfurization products will be affected by variations of their relative density, R_D, curing time and water content before compaction.

These parameters can be changed after the waste product has left the plant. This means that the strength could be increased from one level to another by compaction, the addition of water and

TABLE 3. Summary of grain form, structure and colour of different kinds of coal waste product.

	Waste product	Characteristic grain form and structure	Colour
Fly ash pulverized coal combustion	Asnaes Ingå Wilhelmshafen Trenton Channel Braehead Skelton Grange	Mainly spherical grains, partly scenospheres. Non-spherical grains are occasionally encountered.	Grey
Fly ash grate firing	Norrköping Perstorp	Mainly grains of undefinable form, with a porous and fibrous structure. Spherical grains do exist.	Black
Bottom ash	Asnaes Wilhelmshafen Norrköping Perstorp	Grains of undefinable form, with a vitreous cover, often melt into bigger aggregates. The grains are porous under the vitreous cover.	Black
Flue gas desulfurization products	(wet-dry) Asnaes	Mainly undefinable structure. Porous smaller grains, sometimes connected to form aggregates. In this case, spherical grains from fly ash are present.	Grey
	(wet) Wilhelmshafen	Thin flakes often connected, sometimes like roses in form.	White

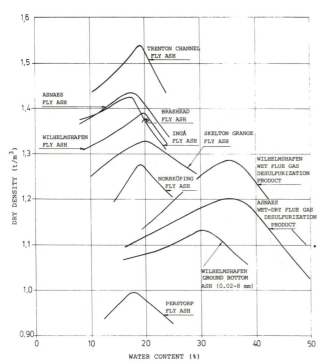

FIG. 1. Compaction properties of different kinds of coal waste product, determined from standardized heavy laboratory compaction tests.

size distribution, content of unburnt coal and grain form.

A statistical calculation has been done on the results of unconfined compression tests performed on fly ash from the Asnaes plant. The compressive strength can be expressed by the relationship shown in equation (1), with a multiple correlation coefficient of 0.93 and a significance of 99.5%.

$$\sigma = a \log (t) + b\, R_D + d \qquad (1)$$

where

σ = compressive strength (kPa)
t = curing time (days)
R_D = degree of compaction
w = water content
a, b, c, d = constants

Statistical calculations have also been done on the compressive strength of the wet-dry gas desulfurization product from Asnaes, where the products are also dependent on the water content equation (2). The relationship has a multiple correlation coefficient of 0.89 and a significance of 99.99%.

$$\sigma = a + b \cdot R_D + c \cdot t + d \cdot w \qquad (2)$$

The constants (a, b, c, d) in the equations (1) and (2) are affected by the content of SiO_2 + Al_2O_3, free lime, specific surface area and the content of unburnt coal, consequently, such parameters are dependent on the combustion technique, operation, coal quality and type of ash separation and handling.

Figure 2 shows the compressive strength related to the curing time for the coal waste products investigated, together with references. The compressive strength was determined at optimum water content and at a degree of compaction of 0.90, with the exception of the reference ashes.

curing. The absolute strength level is determined by the combustion technique, combustion efficiency and composition of the coal. In this context, the technical parameters that can be changed are the chemical composition, grain

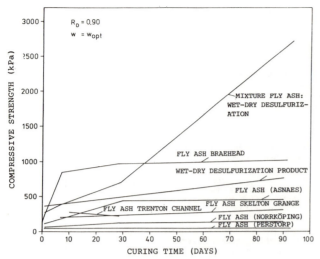

FIG. 2. The compressive strength in relation to the curing time for the waste product.

The strength and its increase with time are very low for the ashes from grate firing at Norrköping and Perstorp, which is an effect of the large amount of unburnt coal and the irregular grain shape. The explanation for this is that the unburnt coal covers the grain surfaces so that they are not available for puzzolanic reaction.

The content of free lime in fly ashes seems to be very important for the puzzolanic reaction. Several investigations such as Sherwood and Ryley (1966) and Sutherland et al (1964), show that free lime has a decided effect on the strength after curing. Sherwood and Ryley report that if the fly ash consists of more than 0.1% free lime (crystalline) the cementing effect will be high.

Triaxial tests on compacted and cured fly ash give an angle of internal friction $\phi' = 40°-45°$, which seems to be independent of the puzzolanic activity. By constrast, the cohesion is related to the value of the cementing effects.

PERMEABILITY

The results of permeability tests are presented in Figure 3, together with figures for the reference ashes.

The permeability will decrease with increasing degree of compaction. There seems to be no relation to curing time in the interval 1-90 days. One exception is the wet-dry desulfurization product which exhibits a slight decline in permeability with curing time.

CONCLUSIONS

This study shows that soil laboratory investigation methods are applicable to coal waste products. The number of tests is larger than in traditional soils because the increase of

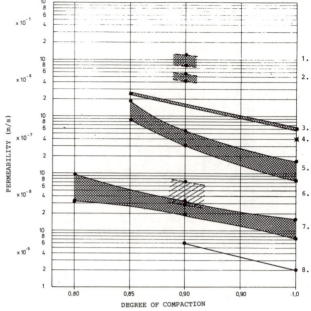

1. Perstorp fly ash
2. Norrköping fly ash
3. Trenton Channel fly ash
4. Braehead fly ash
5. Asnaes fly ash
6. Asnaes fly ash: dry flue gas desulfurization product 1:1, 2:1, 3:1
7. Asnaes wet-dry flue gas desulfurization product
8. Wilhelmshafen wet flue gas desulfurization product

FIG. 3. Permeability related to the degree of compaction for different kinds of coal waste product.

strength with time give one more parameter to consider.

The investigation shows also that the final strength value depends very much on the coal quality and combustion technique, but improvement of strength can be done due to water content, aging and compaction, consequently such parameters which can be changed after the waste product has left the plant.

REFERENCES

Lin, Y. (1972). Compressibility, strength and frost susceptibility of compacted fly ash. Dissertation, University of Michigan, Ann Arbor.
Möller, B. and Nilson, G. (1983). Tekniska egenskaper hos restprodukter från kolförbränning - en laboratoriestudie. SGI rapport nr 21, Linköping.
Sherwood, P.T. and Ryley, M.D. (1966). The use of stabilized pulverized fuel ash in road construction. A laboratory investigation. Road Research Laboratory, Report No 49, Crowthorne.
Sutherland, H.B. and Finlay, T.W. (1964). A laboratory investigation of the age hardening characterictics of pulverized fuel ash (vol. 1). University of Glasgow, Dept. of Civ. Eng., Report No 01038/1.

Stability problems of tailings dams

Problèmes de stabilité des barrages de stériles

V. PERLEA, Senior Research Engineer, Hydraulic Engineering Research Institute, Bucharest, Romania
E. BOTEA, Professor Emeritus, Romania

SYNOPSIS   Tailings dams are hydraulic fills susceptible to liquefy, not only when subjected to earthquakes but due to shear deformation under high confining stresses also.   The liquefaction likelihood in retaining deposit is generally favorized by the grain size distribution without fine particles of the cycloned sand and by the loose state obtained as a result of hydraulic placement without compaction. The paper presents proposed procedures for taking into account in stability analysis of the liquefaction hypothesis, suitable for the specific deposition method.   Stability charts may be useful for safety control of existing tailings dams, when piezometric measurements are available.

INTRODUCTION

Hydraulic transport and placement of tailings is usually the most efficient system for tailings disposal, as the mining operations for recovering valuable materials (copper, zinc, iron, and others) generally use water in large quantities. The resulted hydraulic fill is particularly susceptible to liquefy, so that liquefaction is a phenomenon having to be taken into account in stability analyses.

Liquefaction may be an effect not only of dynamic loadings (earthquake, blasting) but of shear deformations due to static (monotonically increasing) loads. As well, the possibility of liquefaction occurence must be considered even in zones with low seismic activity; this very type of situation is discussed in the following.

The stability analysis procedures must correspond to the chosen construction technique. According to the deposition technique used for resistant wall building, tailings dams can be classified in three main categories: tailings dams built by the upstream method, by the centerline method, and by the downstream method.

A decisive feature of tailings dams is that construction usually takes a long time to be completed, years or even tens of years. On another hand, the engineering properties of tailings can not be well known a priori, and may also modify with time. So, the initial design must periodically be re-examined, as the construction is accomplished; the corresponding stability analyses can accordingly rely on in situ measurements and tests, this fact being especially important for an accurate consideration of seepage action and for a good estimation of in situ density state.

As a result, stability charts for preliminary design, concerning simplified typical cross sections and assumptions, are useful for the stability control during the tailings dam construction. Some graphs, similar to those presented in the following, can be drawn up for important tailings dams, taking into account the actual conditions in the site, the real cross section, and the engineering properties of the tailings.

ENGINEERING PROPERTIES OF TAILINGS

Grain size distribution

Material produced by mill and flotation processing generally falls in the category of fine sand or silty sand; their unit weight of solid particles is usually about 27 - 29 kN/m^3, greater than that of soils in natural deposits.

For carrying out the resistant wall of tailings disposal, the coarse fraction of tailings separated by spigotting or cycloning is used. The coarse fraction leads to more permeable deposits that may easier be drained, and has more favourable strength caracteristics than deposits built up by fine or total tailings. Cyclones can be used for building by any deposition method, but are essential to the downstream and centerline methods of construction. A review of the requirements for tailings dam construction indicates that the fines content (less than o.o74 mm fraction) has usually been restricted to less than about 12%. As by cycloning the water content is substantially decreased, sand with up to 2o - 25 % fines can be used in the embankment constru- ction when on - the dam cycloning technique for sand placement is followed (Mittal and Morgen- stern, 1977).

Figure 1 shows the grain size distribution curves for some typical tailings dams that will be discussed in the following from point of view of their stability. It can be noticed that, in the case of the typical material T, the total tailings is initially liquefiable. After separation, the coarse fraction may be classified as easy liquefiable, that is more vulnerable than

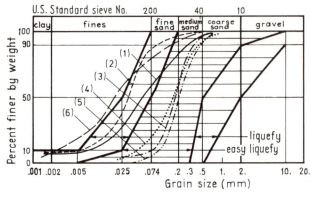

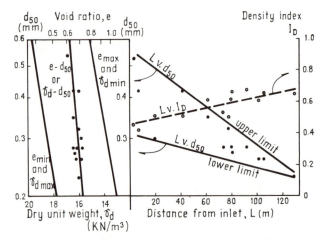

Fig.2 Relationships between Distance from Tailings Discharge Point and Grain Size of Deposited Material and its Density Index (for a given material, relationships in semi-logarithmic plot between 5o-percent diameter and maximum and minimum densities can also be established, as illustrated in the left side graph)

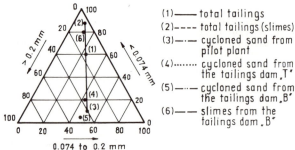

(1) —— total tailings
(2) ---- total tailings (slimes)
(3) —·— cycloned sand from pilot plant
(4) .... cycloned sand from the tailings dam „T"
(5) —··— cycloned sand from the tailings dam „B"
(6) —— slimes from the tailings dam „B"

Fig.1 Grain Size Characteristics of Tailings from: Tarnitza Dam (T); Baia Borsha Dam (B); Pilot Plant for Tarnitza Dam

the total original tailings, according to the criterium presented in Figure 1 (Perlea V. and Perlea M., 1984).

Density properties

The material classified as liquefiable from the grain size distribution point of view may be stabilized against liquefaction by decreasing moisture content under the saturation value or by densifying. So, the degree of compaction is a determining feature for the liquefaction prevention.

Some densifying of the small containment dykes is usually accomplished in the upstream method of construction, but as a rule by means of low efficiency. The greatest part of the resisting wall is placed by sedimentation in water, in a rather loose state, and become denser due to overburden pressure only, as the dam is rising up. In the case of centerline and downstream methods of construction, equipments for spreading are usually used, but compaction achieved in this way is at random and not uniform.

Density state obtained by straight hydraulic placement without any mechanical compaction generally correspond to a relative density of about 2o - 60%, and a mean value of 45 - 50%. Density mainly depends on the grain size of tailings (distribution of fractions, uniformity coefficient, shape of grains), but also on the flow characteristics of the slurry (discharge quantity, concentration in solid particles, discharge velocity, deepness of water flow, drainage conditions). For a given material and in stable deposition conditions, relationships similar to those given in Figure 2 can be derived.

Shear strength

Tailings resulted from the mining industry on low grade ore bodies are generally cohesionless materials with the angle of internal friction $\phi = 25° - 4o°$. The angle of internal friction value primarily depends on the grain size distribution and to a lesser extent on the deposit density. The influence of confining stress level is negligible in the range of 5o to 5oo kPa but becomes sensible when confining stress increases to about 2ooo kPa, representative pressure for the lowest zones of high deposits.

Figure 3,a shows the variation of the angle of internal friction with density for some characteristic materials presented in Figure 1. Curves A and B have been obtained on the same material (4) by direct shear of samples consolidated under normal vertical stresses in the range of 5o to 3oo kPa; the distinction was that specimens corresponding to B-line have previously been subjected to a vertical pressure of 2ooo kPa.

Permeability

The increase in density is favourable as regards the shear strength; on the contrary, it has an unfavourable influence from the permeability point of view. Figure 3,b illustrates the variation with density of the coefficient of permeability determined in laboratory on remoulded specimens, for some tailings materials defined in Figure 1.

By deposition in horizontal strata, the resulting deposit has a marked anisotropy from the permeability point of view; this is much more important for the seepage network than the value of the coefficient of permeability.

As the anisotropy degree directly depends on the chosen deposition method, the variation of ore processing, possible interruption of disposal

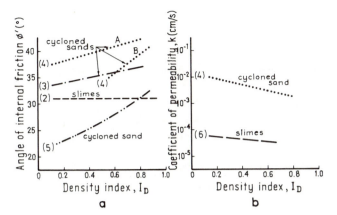

Fig.3   Curves that Illustrate the Influence
         of Density on Some Properties of
         Tailings

site operation, climatic conditions, and so on,
it is impossible to estimate it a priori. As a
result, it is convenient to have in view some
more possible locations of the phreatic line,
having to determine the actual location of this
line by piezometric measurements during operation. Therefore, it becomes possible to establish by the initial design some alarm levels
and some corresponding adequate measures to be
taken for stability ensuring on measurement in
situ basis.

Liquefiability

Loose sands show a tendency to densify when subjected to shear strain (are contractive);   in
drained conditions the densifying just occur,
but when deformation takes place in undrained
conditions, the densifying tendency finds expression in a build-up of pore pressure that can
lead to liquefaction. Critical state, in which a
soil can flow at constant void ratio, is a
function of applied normal stress. The steady -
state line represents the locus of these states
in a normal stress - void ratio diagram (Castro
and Poulos, 1977).

Figure 4,a illustrates the liquefiability of a
loose sand subjected to static load, when its
state corresponds to a point located above the
steady-state line (it is contractive). The pore
pressure build-up by liquefaction is so much
the greater as the point is more distant from
the steady-state line. A dense sand (dilatative)
can not be liquefied but by a cyclic loading.

Clasical shear tests (direct shear, triaxial
compression) with volume control are not accurate enough for steady state determination, as
shear deformations take place in a rather thin
zone as against the total height of the specimen; moreover, it is very likely that volume
changes in the shear deformations zone to be
partially compensated by opposite changes in
adjoining zones. Nevertheless, a simple device
with many shearing surfaces (e.g. 15 on 3o cm,
as illustrated in Figure 5, where volume changes
are of about 0.5 - 1.0 mm for shear strains of
40% at the most) can successfully be used.

In Figure 4,b the steady - state line for a
cycloned sand is compared with oedometric curves
for two initial density states: disposal by
bulldozer spreading, with or without subsequent
compaction. Liquefaction is possible in the case
of uncompacted sand, the danger of liquefaction
having to be taken into account when normal
stresses are high, i.e. in the case of high
deposits only.

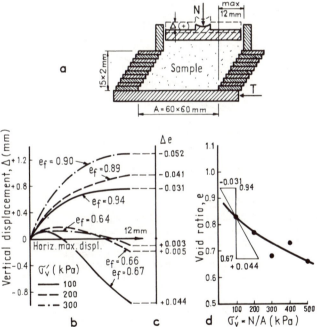

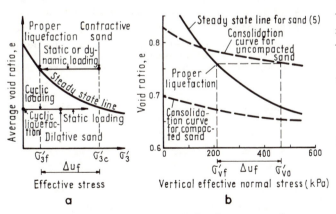

Fig.4   Liquefaction Potential of Saturated
         Sands, Undrained Loaded, Made Evident
         on the State Diagram

Fig.5   Steady State Line Determination:
         a - the multiple shearing surfaces
         device; b - vertical displacement
         versus relative displacement of the
         two horizontal faces of the sample;
         c - void ratio change at the 12 mm
         maximum horizontal displacement;
         d - points defining the steady-state
         line for sand (5), determined by
         linear interpolation

STABILITY OF TAILINGS DAMS

Expression of material strength

Figure 6 presents two typical effective stress paths for loading of a cohesionless material, both in drained and undrained conditions (Bishop, 1971): the pore pressure build-up during shear strain development lead to a more reduced undrained strength as compared to the shear strength mobilizable in drained conditions (τ_r).

When peak undrained shear strength (c_u) is attained, the angle of internal friction (ϕ') is only partially mobilized; at its complete mobilizing, undrained strength ($c_{u\ rez}$) is much more decreased, corresponding to the pore pressure build-up Δu_f. In stability analyses with liquefaction taking into account, it is more convenient to consider the residual strength, $c_{u\ rez}$, as a lower bond of undrained strength, directly or through a fictitious effective angle of internal friction (ϕ'_m) defined by:

$$c_{u\ rez} = (\sigma'_{vo} - \Delta u_f)\tan\phi' = \sigma'_{vo}\tan\phi'_m \qquad (1)$$

$$\tan\phi'_m = (1 - \Delta u_f/\sigma'_{vo})\tan\phi' \qquad (2)$$

where ϕ'_m has been named mobilizable angle of internal friction and has not a physical meaning.

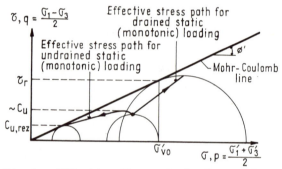

Fig.6   Effective Stress Paths for Sand

Impoundment by upstream method

Upstream method of tailings disposal is the most economical, since it implies the lowest investments both initially and during operation. Raising possibilities are limited however by the need of safety; in zones with relatively high seismicity risk, such impoundments are, as a rule, allowed only to low heights of about 5 - 10 m. Any of chosen deposition techniques (Figure 7) leads to a shell-type retaining wall, its thickness being a function of the disposal methodology.

The coarse material deposited in shell is, from the grain size point of view, more susceptible to liquefy as against the slime in pond, that can be a little cohesive, too. For the shallow stability of the resisting wall a good drainage is essential; this can be provided both by an adequate structure of the starter dam and a drainage system at the soil surface, and, if the

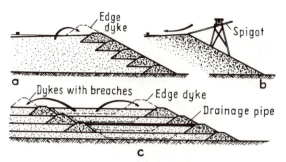

Fig.7   Upstream Method of Construction: a - with compacted dykes; b - by spigotting; c - with double contour dykes

initial drains become out of order, by some drains at several intermediate heights. Even in saturated condition, coarse material at shallow depth may not be liquefied under static loading, as confining stresses are low.

Finer material in the pond, even if unliquefiable, has a lower shear strength, a great capacity of water retaining, eventually remaining a long time in underconsolidated state. However, in normal (good) drainage conditions and usual rates of tailings dam height increasing, it is not expected that excess pore pressure would be of concern for stability (Nelson et al, 1977).

For drawing up design charts, the simplified scheme in Figure 8,a has been considered. The phreatic line has been assumed to be the same as the boundary between the two types of material: fine and coarse; as angles of shearing resistance for the two materials, two pairs of values, more frequently encountered, have been taken into account; pore pressure in every point of slime mass has been considered to correspond to the same piezometric water level as the phreatic line above the point.

Charts can be used both in preliminary design and for the stability checking up of existing tailings dams. So, e.g. in the hypothesis of more resistant materials (Figure 8,b) it results:

- if the shallow stability corresponds to a safety factor $F_1 = 1.5$ (according to the infinite slope method $m = F_1 \cot\phi'_1 = 2.14$), the stability corresponding to deep failure surfaces is ensured with the same safety factor if the beach (confirmed by piezometric measurements) is 0.92 H;

- for a smaller safety factor in the case of deep possible failure, at the same slope, i.e. $m = 2.14$, the needed beach has 0.70 H in width;

- if the slope coefficient is $m = 2.5$ ($F_1 = m / \cot 35° = 1.75$), $F_2 = 1.3$ is ensured if the beach width is 0.62 H, and $F_2 = 1.5$ if B = 0.85 H.

For a better understanding of the usefulness of such charts, Figure 9 explains the procedure followed for their drawing up. If all deposit had been formed by (wet) fine sand, the safety

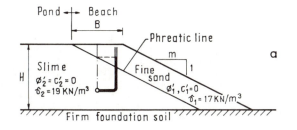

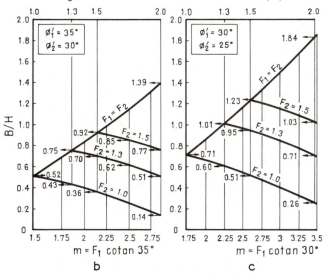

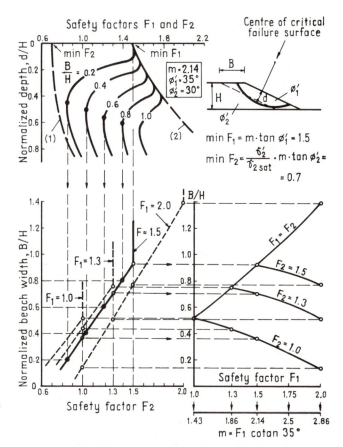

min F_1 = m·tan ϕ_1' = 1.5

min F_2 = $\dfrac{\delta_2'}{\delta_{2\,sat}}$·m·tan ϕ_2' = 0.7

Fig.8 Design Charts for Upstream Method: a - considered cross section; b - graph for materials with more favourable strength properties; c - graph for materials with less favourable strength properties

Fig.9 Procedure for Graphs Drawing up: starting from the initial graph (up, left), passing through the intermediate graph (down, left), to the final graph (down, right)

factor variation with depth of the assumed slip surface would have had the shape of curve (1), with a minimum value for the shallowest surface (1.5 for m = 2.14). If only (saturated) slime had been in deposit, with seepage lines parallel to the slope, the safety factor variation would have corresponded to curve (2), with the minimum value (0.7) according to the stability of a particle on the surface principle also.

The actual variation links the two curves, the positions of inflexion points depending on the beach width (B). The minimum values of safety factors for different B-values served to the plotting, in the left lower part of Figure 9, of a curve (a polygonal path in fact) of variation of minimum safety factor with normalized width of the beach (B/H). In the Figure this plotting is exemplified for a safety factor at the surface of F_1 = 1.5 (i.e. m = 2.14). This curve has been used to obtain the three points corresponding to F_1 = 1.5 (and F_2 = 1.0, 1.3, and 1.5 respectively) in the final graph. Performing calculus for other slopes (m = 1.43; 1.86; 2.86) the other representative points of the graph have been obtained.

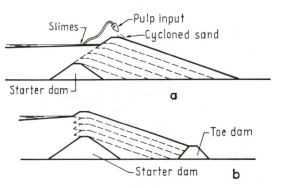

Fig.10 Downstream Disposal of Tailings: a - downstream method; b - center-line method

Inpoundment downstream developed

The downstream deposition of coarser material obtained by cycloning, that theoretically lead to a stable deposit of any height, can be applied in two main variants, as the discharge point from cyclones is successively moved to downstream or on a vertical (Figure 10).

It is generally considered that the downstream method is better than the centerline one from the seismic stability point of view. In practice, the downstream method is seldom adopted, as it requires great quantities of cycloned sand, which makes it possible in very favourable site conditions (narrow valley at the starter dam, but large reservoir). On the other hand, in sensitive seismic areas, the main danger is that of liquefaction; therefore, the better the drainage the safer is the resisting structure. In the case of downstream method the pond edge moves downstream, so that the seepage water is more and more difficultly intercepted by the starter dam or by the other drains provided at the foundation soil level. Our opinion is that, for this reason, the centerline method should be prefered as against the downstream one in any seismic conditions.

Even in the hypothesis of similar draining conditions, stability increase provided by the downstream development is not important. This is illustrated in Figure 11 for an actual case. Stability analysis has been performed by the wedge method and had in view partial liquefaction due to shear strain under high confining stress at the deposit bottom. Determining an average value of the mobilizable angle of internal friction (ϕ'_m, according to equation 2)

led to the conclusion that the given deposit can be designed with 3.5 : 1 slope and the centerline method in the desired safety condition (F $\geqslant$ 1.5). It is expected that relying on field measurements during operation it will be possible to steepen the slope to 3 : 1.

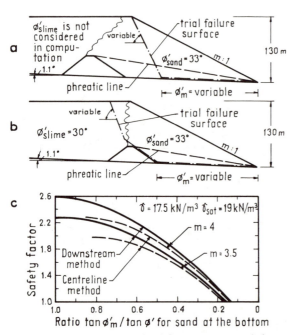

Fig.11 Variation of Safety Factor with Liquefaction Degree at the Deposit Bottom: a - scheme for downstream method; b - scheme for centerline method; c - comparison between results obtained by calculus

CONCLUSIONS

As tailings disposal is not a lucrative activity, the corresponding construction works must be of a minimum cost, in the same time observing safety and environmental preserving requirements. Therefore, it is imperiously necessary to use in the greatest part of the resisting structure just the material to be deposited, that generally is easy liquefiable.

Among the causes that can induce failure of tailings dams, liquefaction is the only one not implying previous signs (cracks, large or sudden settlements, wet spots, alarming rise in phreatic surface). Therefore, it is very important to take liquefaction into account in stability analyses, regardless of the seismicity degree of the zone where the dam is located. There are many well - known failures of tailings dams following liquefaction, with catastrophic consequences due to their suddenness: Barahona - Chile, 1929, El Cobre - Chile, 1965 and Mochikoshi - Japan, 1978, following earthquakes (cyclic liquefaction); Buffalo Creek - U.S.A., 1972, following overtopping; Aberfan - Great Britain, 1964 and Certej - Romania, 1971, during static loading (proper liquefaction).

Proper liquefaction, as the cyclic one, can be taken into account in stability analyses performed by conventional methods (pseudo-statical), by introducing a fictitious parameter, the mobilizable angle of internal friction, ϕ'_m, defined by equation (2).

Charts in Figure 8,b and c, or those similar to them, are useful both for preliminary design and for a rough estimate of the safety of tailings dams in operation, relying on control measurements. In the case of important works it is necessary to periodically verify the safety from the stability point of view, as the dam is raising, using similar graphs developed for the very cross section and the actual strength parameters.

REFERENCES

Bishop, A.W. (1971).Shear strength parameters for undisturbed and remoulded soil specimen. Proc. Roscoe Memorial Symp., 3 - 59, Cambridge Univ.

Castro, G., and Poulos, S.J. (1977). Factors affecting liquefaction and cyclic mobility. ASCE J. Geotechnical Engg Div., 12994, June, 501 - 516.

Mittal, H.K., and Morgenstern, N.R. (1977). Design and performance of tailings dams. Proc. ASCE Conf. on Geotechnical Practice for Disposal of Solid Waste Materials, 475 - 429, Ann Arbor.

Nelson, J.D., Shepherd, T.A., and Charlie, W.A. (1977). Parameters affecting stability of tailings dams. Proc. ASCE Conf. on Geotechnical Practice for Disposal of Solid Waste Materials, 444 - 460, Ann Arbor.

Perlea, V., and Perlea, Maria (1984). Dynamic Stability of Sandy Soils (in Romanian). 336 pp., Ed. Tehnica, Bucharest.

Pollution controls for calcine and gypsum waste disposal

Contrôle de la pollution des déchets de calcin et de gypse

C. E. REA, Lecturer in Civil Engineering, University of Zimbabwe, Harare, Zimbabwe
A. WOODS, Construction Engineer, Zimbabwe Phosphate Industries Ltd, Harare, Zimbabwe

SYNOPSIS   The production of fertilizers from phosphates generates waste products with a high pollution potential. The waste disposal facilities at Zimbabwe Phosphate Industries Ltd were inadequately designed to prevent the contamination of surface and ground water resulting in severe pollution of a tributary to the main river that supplies municipal water to Harare. Extensive remedial control measures were constructed to contain the waste and prevent water pollution. This paper discusses the nature of the chemical wastes, the attenuation capacity of the soils, the design of the pollution control measures and assesses their efficacy in the 2 year period since construction.

INTRODUCTION

The factory for Zimbabwe Phosphate Industries Ltd is situated on the outskirts of the city of Harare, the capital of Zimbabwe. The factory has produced fertilizers since 1958, and the process generates solid and aqueous wastes with a high pollution potential. The location of the factory is adjacent to the Mukuvusi stream which is a tributary to the Hunyani river from which the water supply for Harare is obtained. Severe problems were encountered with highly polluted wastes entering the watercourses and threatening the closure of factory. This paper outlines the nature of the problems, the attenuation capacity of the soils, the methods adopted to control pollution emanating from the wastes, and the effect of the control measures.

The four groups of waste material produced by the factory are gypsum, calcined pyrites, miscellaneous waste and liquid effluent. The location of the principal waste areas are indicated on the airphoto (fig 1). Various measures were adopted to control the pollution from these sources as awareness of the problems grew, but their ineffectiveness and poor operation led to a complete appraisal and remedial design in 1980. The remedial civil works were designed to control the surface water run-off, curtail the groundwater pollution around major waste areas and to reshape disposal facilities thereby enabling correct operation procedures. The works were carried out in the period 1981-1982 and there are indications that the remedial measures are taking effect since construction.

GEOLOGY OF THE SITE

The factory area is situated in an area of massive basement granites with a major dolerite dyke crossing the eastern side of the area as shown on figure 1. The topography is typical "Castle kopje" granite remnants of the African erosion surface in a gently undulating land-

scape in which shallow "vleis" have been formed.

A detailed site investigation was carried out in order to define the soil profiles, rock stratigraphy and the engineering characteristics of the various materials. Test pits (62 No) were excavated to define the subsurface geology and hydrogeologic characteristics of the near surface soils. Percussion boreholes (16 No) were drilled to define the geology and depth of weathering.

The findings of the investigation revealed that there were two major categories of soil profile which are summarised in figure 2. Profile 1 covers most of the area but is prevalent in the vleis and has a characteristic clayey horizon. Profile 2 is similar except that the clayey horizon is absent which enhances vertical drainage from infiltration. In some areas the clayey horizon displays relict joints which are filled by the overlying silty sand but can be open, thus increasing the overall permeability of the clayey horizon by virtue of the secondary flow. This clayey horizon progressively grades down into less decomposed granite with reducing permeability as the frequency of relict joints decreases. Permeability tests were conducted which indicated a low coefficient of permeability $k = 5 \times 10^{-9}$m/sec. The overlying silty sand horizon which is a transported material was tested giving an average value of $k = 5 \times 10^{-6}$m/sec. It was observed from the test pits that there was usually a "perched" water table within the silty sand of the soil profile type 1.

The drilling results showed that the bedrock topography is extremely irregular which is typical of the "Castle kopje" geomorphology. The Hatfield dyke consists of dolerite and the trace is indicated on figure 1. The dyke appears to be discontinuous through the granites at the surface and does not appear to be a major conduit of groundwater.

Figure 1 : Air photo of factory and waste disposal areas before remedial measures (1977)

HYDROGEOCHEMISTRY OF THE POLLUTANTS

The remedial design philosophy is based upon dealing with the mechanisms associated with the pollution which have been identified as:

- the availability of a solute transport mechanism
- the quantity of water associated with the mechanism
- low pH conditions.

The gypsum tailings liquid is a major source of pollutants having a high total dissolved solids (T.D.S.) comprised mainly of calcium sulphate, fluoride, phosphate and silica combined with a very low pH in the range 1,3-1,5 which is due

to the free sulphuric acid. The solubility of calcium sulphate depends upon its solubility in water, the presence of other ions dissolved in the water and the pH. Solute reactions are the dominant controlling process for the high concentrations of calcium sulphate and control measures should include the reduction of water volume as well as neutralisation, thereby reducing the calcium concentrations in the water.

Phosphate concentrations in natural waters are usually very low suggesting strong natural control reactions restricting the solubility of phosphorous. Hem (1970) suggests that adsorption on metal oxides or ferric hydroxide,

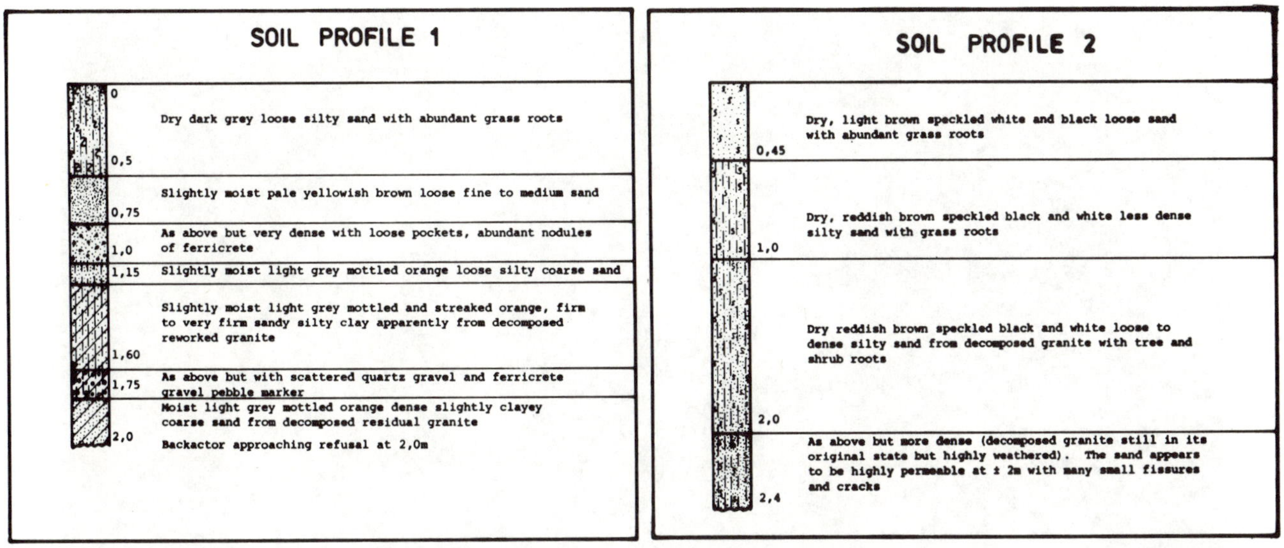

Figure 2 : Typical soil profiles

coupled with removal by aquatic vegetation, will effectively fix phosphate ions in natural waters. It is also evident that the ferric ion has low solubility in neutral conditions which will enhance the precipitation of phosphorous as iron phosphate if the pH is raised.

Fluoride and silica solubility are strongly related at low pH levels forming fluosilicate complexions, SiF_6 (Sillen and Martell, 1964).

This accounts for the high levels of both these ions in the gypsum tailings liquid and removal is best effected by neutralisation reactions to reduce the availability of a solute transport mechanism.

Calcined pyrites are produced as burnt waste ore in the production of sulphuric acid for the fertilizers. When the calcine is dumped and subsequently leached by rainfall the chief pollutants are sulphate, iron and hydrogen ions which reduce the pH thereby increasing the potential for solution reactions to take place. The preventative measures to arrest the production of leachate from the calcine dumps should be directed towards reducing the infiltration and migration of groundwater from the dump thus minimising the quantity of water associated with the transport mechanism.

CHEMICAL ATTENUATION CAPACITY OF THE SOILS

Chemical attenuation is the general term for the chemical processes, such as ion fixation, redox reactions, pH reactions by which natural materials change the chemical properties of a permeant fluid. The site investigation of the area showed two basic lithological soil profiles:

Profile 1 : a sand and silty sand overlying a clayey sand horizon
Profile 2 : a sand and silty sand overlying an irregular weathered granite bedrock.

The two attenuating media consist of the sand/silty sand and the clayey sand through which the polluting fluids must permeate to contribute to the groundwater regime. Samples of these in-situ soils were tested to assess the bulk capacity to attenuate the gypsum tailings liquid.

Sand was found to have little effect in modifying the chemistry of the gypsum tailings permeant. The sulphate levels increased due to removal of sulphates from the clay fraction by solution in the low pH conditions.

In contrast to the sand the clayey soil displayed attenuation capacity for calcium, fluoride, phosphate and T.D.S. to 30% of the original level even with the sulphate content increasing due to the low pH conditions. The attenuation process also reduced the permeability of the samples indicating a decrease in pore sizes due to physical or chemical reaction by the permeant fluid.

POLLUTION PREVENTION AND CONTROL

The whole area shown in figure 1 was divided into five separate zones for the purpose of pollution control on the basis of the rainfall catchment area, groundwater flow direction and the relative position of the pollution source. Each area indicated on figure 1 is discussed with comment on the effectiveness of the remedial works subsequent to construction in 1981/82.

(1) Epworth vlei and gypsum dam

The contamination of the watercourse forming Epworth vlei in the south of the area was caused by seepage of groundwater and polluted surface runoff from the gypsum dam. The cause of groundwater pollution was due to inadequate design of the impervious clay lining underneath the original dam and omission of an impervious liner under subsequent extensions of the dam allowing ingress of heavily contaminated gypsum tailings liquid into the groundwater regime at the headwaters of the vlei. Inadequate management of the dam and return water system contributed to the surface pollution which denuded

Figure 3 : Reshaped Gypsum Dam (1982)

the vegetation and also infiltrated into the groundwater system.

The site investigation revealed that the typical vlei soil profile (fig 2) exists under most of the dam, i.e. a silty sand horizon overlying a clayey sand horizon which infers that the contaminated groundwater should be restricted to being perched on the relatively impervious clayey horizon. Remedial measures were directed at reducing the pollution of the vlei area by means of an interceptor drain to collect contaminated seepage from the dam and pumping to a lined holding dam (fig 3) where it could be stored prior to treatment. Difficulties were encountered with loose collapsing material and

huge granite boulders representing core stones within the soil profile which is typical of "Castle kopje" granite geomorphology. The interceptor drain was the type shown in figure 4 comprising a 19mm crushed stone enwrapped with geotextile and open-jointed earthenware pipes on the invert of the drain leading to a sump which was founded at 8 metres depth. The system operates very efficiently with up to 12 m³/hr of intercepted contaminated groundwater being recovered. It is expected that the long-term effect of the pumping will produce a drawdown of the phreatic surface south of the drain causing a reversal of groundwater flow in the contaminated area, which together with the attenuation capacity of the clayey soil will retard the development of the pollution plume in Epworth vlei. An electrical resistivity survey has been carried out to map the pollution plume south of the gypsum dam. The area of very low apparent resistivity is associated with seepage of undiluted gypsum tailings liquid emerging from the southern toe of the dam. The iso-resistivity lines indicate the progression of the pollution plume towards the interceptor drain. The plume has been intercepted by the drain and the attenuation of the pollutant level in the groundwater regime is monitored.

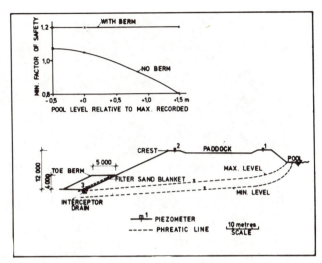

Figure 5 : Gypsum Dam Stability - West Side

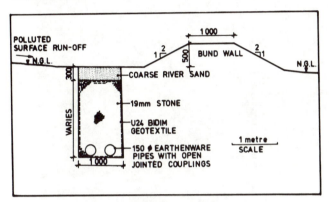

Figure 4 : Section of Interceptor Drain

The gypsum dam had been managed in a haphazard manner endangering the stability and causing the spread of gypsum waste into the environment. The dam was completely reshaped into the one main dam and two sales dams. A management system was instituted to raise the perimeter paddock walls in an orderly manner to prevent the pool from approaching the crest of the dam (fig 3). After commissioning the reshaped main dam a series of tension cracks developed at the crest and in the paddocks together with a series of progressive toe failures on both the east and west sides of the dam. Piezometers were installed to measure the phreatic surface and it was observed that a seepage line was apparent on both sides at the toe. This condition was caused by impeded vertical drainage through the underlying massive granites and no provision for filter drains under the slopes of the dam to intercept the phreatic surface. A stability analysis was carried out which showed that the elevated phreatic surface was causing instability in the dam. A toe berm with a drainage system was installed which trapped the seepage line and reinstated the stability of the dam as shown in figure 5. A sensitivity analysis was computed on the elevation of the phreatic surface to design the size of toe berm. With the addition of a berm, the stability of the slope is insensitive to small phreatic surface variations because the most critical failure surfaces are shallow and do not intercept the phreatic surface.

A clean water trench was constructed around the north, east and south-west sides of the dam to divert stormwater run-off from the area surroun -ding the dam. A large holding pond was constructed on the south side of the dam to facilitate safe storage of contaminated water until treatment or evaporation takes place.

(2) Central "clean water" area

There are no major pollution sources in this area which forms the main catchment divide. In order to prevent pollution of waters falling on this area it was necessary to construct two clean water trenches to divert the stormwater away from the major developments.

(3) Eastern vlei

The main source of pollution in this area is the old dis-used S.E. calcine dump. The remedial works consisted of isolating the calcine deposit by constructing a dump on which all the waste was deposited. The dump was shaped in preparation for establishment of vegetation cover to minimise infiltration.

(4) Western and North-Western area

This area is the most complex area for pollution control as there has been much indiscriminate dumping of calcine waste with two major dumps in the north-west corner of the site and the main dump to the south-west of the factory. Pollution of the groundwater system occurs beneath the major calcine dumps and migrates northward to the Mukuvusi stream. The remedial measures for the N.W. calcine dump are shown on figure 6 consisting mainly of an interceptor drain along the north and west boundary of the dump. These drains lead to a sump from which polluted leachate is returned to the factory for treatment. The surface water effluent discharge from the dump area is also collected by a berm which allows seepage into the interceptor drain as shown in figure 4. Provision is made for stormwater which has sufficient dilution to be discharged directly into the stream. It was anticipated that the iron in the leachate would precipitate in the drain forming a gel which would limit the serviceability of the drain in the long term. Some tests were performed on the geotextile to research this phenomenum. Provision was made for introducing a form of backwashing or flushing by means of manholes along the length of the drain. The gel could then be loosened by agitation from the backwash pressure and collected in the sump for

Figure 6 : N.W. Calcine Dump - Pollution Control Measures (1982)

removal to the factory area for treatment.

An electrical resistivity survey was carried out to trace the pollution plume as shown by the iso-resistivity lines on figure 6. There are two distinct plumes arising from the main portions of the dump and the direction of migration is controlled by bedrock topography. The extent of severe groundwater pollution from this dump is limited to approximately 50 metres north of the dump. The migration has been retarded by the reduction of hydraulic gradient due to the interceptor drain and the drawdown of the plume is clearly taking effect as indicated by the iso-resistivity lines.

The main calcine dump was also poorly managed which led to the spread of calcine in the area causing unnecessary surface water pollution. The remedial measures for control were to reshape the dump to enable satisfactory management and form toe catchment paddocks to contain polluted surface run-off.

(5) Factory

The main sources of pollution in this area

were due to both the direct run-off of storm-water via open drains which flow northwards to the Mukuvusi stream, and the club car park which is constructed using calcine being situated adjacent to the stream. The remedial control measures consisted mainly of limiting discharge of effluent through the open drains and removal of the calcine car park. The liquid effluent is now considered to be polluted and is returned to the water treatment plant.

The water treatment plant was of inadequate capacity and with the increased load there was ineffective control of the treatment. A pilot treatment plant is under construction to research the correct treatment methodology before a larger plant of $50m^3/hr$ capacity is constructed in the second phase of the project. This will alleviate the disposal problems associated with the safe discharge of the return water from the various parts of the factory and the new remedial pollution control measures.

CONCLUSION

The remedial measures to control water pollution at Zimbabwe Phosphate Industries Ltd are successful with clear evidence of improvements around the major sources of pollutants. The Epworth vlei area is much improved with grass and trees now being re-established successfully in the areas denuded by polluted surface water run-off. Groundwater emanating from the gypsum dam and N.W. calcine dump is intercepted and returned to the water treatment plant retarding the development of pollution plumes in the vicinity of these rehabilitated disposal facilities. The pollution plumes are being monitored to assess the attenuation in the direction of the water courses. A water treatment plant is being designed to deal with the increased volume of liquid effluent. The rehabilitated disposal facilities are now operated correctly and monitored to ensure stability and control.

ACKNOWLEDGMENTS

Mr J Mills, General Manager of Zimbabwe Phosphate Industries Ltd and Dr O K H Steffen, Managing Director of Steffen Robertson and Kirsten Incorporated, are gratefully acknowledged in the provision of information and enthusiastic support.

REFERENCES

Hem, J.D. (1970). Study and interpretation of the chemical characteristics of natural water. USGS Water Supply Paper, 1974, pp.364.

Sillen, L.G. and Mantell, A.E. (1964). Stability constants of metal-ion complexes. Chem. Soc. (London), Spec Pub. 17, pp. 754.

Steffen Robertson and Kirsten Inc. (1980). Reports on site investigation, water balance and pollution control, chemical attenuation and slope stability for Zimbabwe Phosphate Industries Ltd. S859.

Faurie, J.N. (1982). The use of the resistivity method to evaluate groundwater pollution in southern Africa. Groundwater '82, University of the Witwatersrand, Johannesburg. pp.72.

Dynamic properties and behavior of copper tailings

Propriétés dynamiques et fonctionnement de déchets de cuivre

L. F. ROJAS-GONZÁLEZ, Research Assistant, Department of Civil Engineering, University of Pittsburgh, PA, USA
H. A. BEN-KHAYAL, Research Assistant, Department of Civil Engineering, University of Pittsburgh, PA, USA
K. H. LEWIS, Associate Professor, Department of Civil Engineering, University of Pittsburgh, PA, USA

SYNOPSIS   The shear modulus and damping ratio of three samples of dry and saturated copper tailings with different gradation characteristics were determined with the use of a Hardin Resonant Column Apparatus. The general dynamic behavior of tailings with respect to content of fines, initial void ratio, confining pressure, and percent shear strain is discussed. The results are compared with averages published for sand, and average curves and useful relationships are presented for tailings.

INTRODUCTION

During the mining and refining of copper, huge quantities of waste in the form of copper tailings are generated as a by-product. As a consequence, the safe storing of copper tailings is an item of major concern. Today, one of the most widely used processes, called cycloning, involves the separation of a significant portion of the fine grained material from the coarse, and the use of the latter for the construction of a dam to retain the former. In order to be able to analyse and design such impoundments safely in areas where seismic activity is common, one must make use of the dynamic properties of tailings. However, the dynamic characteristics of these materials are not well understood. The work covered in this paper deals with the evaluation of two dynamic parameters, shear modulus and damping ratio, under low shear strain levels using the Hardin Resonant Column device, and general findings of the dynamic behavior of copper tailings.

In the past several years, significant advances in the analysis of problems involving the dynamic loading of soils have been made and the study of soil dynamics has attained remarkable growth and importance. Some investigators such as Whitman and Richart (1967) have addressed problems related to foundation vibrations whereas others such as Seed (1967) have concentrated on the effects of earthquakes and the elements of protective construction. However, as Richart, Hall and Woods (1970) have pointed out, "the process of obtaining representative values for the critical soil properties is probably the most difficult part of the design study," and this is still true today. In the design of earthen impoundments subject to dynamic forces under symmetrical cyclic loading conditions but involving no residual soil displacements, the shear modulus and the damping ratio are the most important soil properties. The shear modulus, G, is the slope of the line joining the extremities of the cyclic stress-strain loop in Figure 1, and G_{max} is defined as the shear modulus at zero percent shear strain or for all practical purposes at very low percent strain amplitudes ($\gamma \approx 3 \times 10^{-4}$%). The damping ratio, D, is the area of the above loop divided by 4π times the triangular area shown in Figure 1.

Efforts to experimentally evaluate the dynamic properties of soil using laboratory equipment and establish empirical relationships date back to the work of Casagrande and

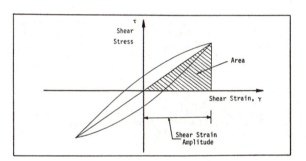

Figure 1.   Definition of Shear Modulus and Damping Ratio.

Shannon (1948) on the effect of bomb explosions on the stability of the Panama Canal. Since that time, various dynamic testing devices such as the cyclic triaxial apparatus, oscillatory simple shear test apparatus, M.I.T. apparatus for rapidly loaded triaxial tests, and resonant column apparatus, have been used to determine the dynamic characteristics of soil. In addition, investigators such as Hardin and Black (1968), Hardin and Drnevich (1970), Roesler (1979), and Yu and Richart (1984) have presented useful empirical relationships. Hardin and Black have expressed the shear modulus at zero shear strain as a function of void ratio and mean principal effective stress, whereas Roesler has incorporated the individual components of the confining pressures, and Yu and Richart have accounted for the effects of stress ratio. The following general form of these expressions as discussed by Seed and Idriss (1970) may also be used for the shear modulus:

$$G = 1000 \, K_2 \, (\bar{\sigma}_o)^{0.5} \qquad (1)$$

in which $\bar{\sigma}_o$ is the mean principal effective stress and K_2 is a parameter which accounts for the influence of void ratio and shear strain amplitude. On the other hand, Hardin and Drnevich defined a hyperbolic strain function, γ_H, as follows:

$$\gamma_H = (\gamma/\gamma_r)\left[1 + a \, \exp\{-b(\gamma/\gamma_r)\}\right] \qquad (2)$$

in which

$$\gamma_r(\%) = (\tau_{max}/G_{max})100 \qquad (3)$$

and

$$\tau_{max} = \{(\frac{1+K_o}{2}\,\bar\sigma_v\sin\bar\phi + \bar c\cos\bar\phi)^2 - (\frac{1-K_o}{2}\,\bar\sigma_v)^2\}^{0.5} \qquad (4)$$

where K_o = coefficient of earth pressure at rest.

$\bar\sigma_v$ = effective vertical stress.

$\bar c, \bar\phi$ = static effective strength parameters.

and were able to derive the following unique expressions for both sand and clay:

$$G/G_{max} = 1/(1+\gamma_H) \qquad (5)$$

$$D/D_{max} = \gamma_H/(1+\gamma_H) \qquad (6)$$

LABORATORY TESTING PROGRAM

During the testing program, three different samples were tested using a "free-fixed end" Hardin Resonant Column Apparatus. One sample, designated tailings-A, was made of copper tailings as they came from the mine, another sample, labeled tailings-C, comprised of tailings that had undergone cycloning, and the third sample, called tailings-W, was manufactured in the laboratory by washing away all of the fines (particles smaller than 0.074 mm) from a sample of tailings-C. The general characteristics of the three samples which geotechnically range from clean fine sand to fine silty sand are given in Figure 2.

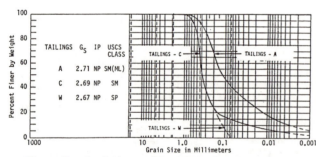

Figure 2. Gradation and Basic Physical Properties of Tailings.

In total, 51 dynamic tests were performed on samples of the material at void ratios representing approximately 50%, 70% and 90% relative densities. Twenty seven tests were performed on air dried samples using effective confining pressures of 147.11, 294.21 and 490.35 kPa, and 24 tests were conducted on saturated samples using effective confining pressures of 147.11, 294.21 and 441.32 kPa. After the dynamic tests were completed, triaxial compression tests were performed on the samples. In the former tests, the number of cycles ranged from 5,000 to over 100,000 cycles and the shear strain ranged from approximately 5×10^{-4} to $3 \times 10^{-2}\%$, whereas in the latter, the maximum deviator stress occurred on the average at about 8% axial strain. In the case of the dynamic tests, the percent shear strain levels were so low that no appreciable volume change or development of excess pore pressure took place.

LABORATORY TESTS RESULTS

The results given below represent data obtained by Rojas-González (1982) and Ben-Khayal (1983), as well as that compiled by Salgado (1983). Where the results for dry and saturated samples are close, they are represented by the same symbol in the figures. In order to generate comparisons with published results, parameters and forms of equations presented by previous investigators have been used where possible. Since the range of the number of cycles used did not appreciably influence the tests' results, it was not considered as a factor in the laboratory testing program.

Shear Modulus

The variation of the normalized shear modulus, G/G_{max}, with the average percent shear strain is shown in Figure 3.

As expected, G/G_{max} for the copper tailings cited decreases in a non-linear fashion as percent shear strain increases and exhibits the general pattern of behavior presented by Seed and Idriss (1970). However, most of the data plots above the graph which represents the average for sands. As shown in Figure 3, the results for tailings-A yield the best agreement with the average for sands, whereas those for tailings-W give the worst.

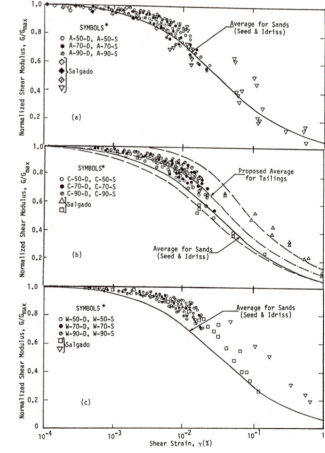

* A-50-D = Tailings A, 50% relative density, dry.
Figure 3. Variation of Normalized Shear Modulus with Percent Shear Strain.

In other words, the data presented tend to approach the average given for sands as the percentage of silty fines increases. Also, the saturated samples gave values which were generally lower than those for the dry samples. At this time, no explanation has been found for the above behavior of tailings with silty fines but it is believed to be a function of gradation, grain characteristics and structure of the soil. In any case, the proposed average curve presented in Figure 3(b) appears to be a better representation for copper tailings than the average curve given for sands.

Again as expected, G_{max} increases with increasing effective confining pressure and decreasing void ratio. However, if the data is presented as shown in Figure 4, in a form similar to that discussed by Seed and Idriss (1970), the average values for $\bar{K}$ (which is really a function of $\bar{\sigma}_o$) are shown to be for the most part below those for clean sands. Further comparison between the data presented and that for clean sands indicates fair agreement for clean tailings but generally poor agreement for tailings with silty fines. Based on the data presented, the proposed curve given in Figure 4 is thought to be more representative for cycloned tailings.

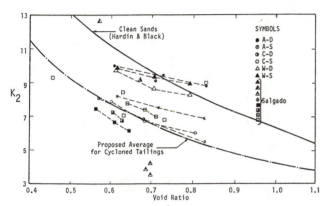

Figure 4. Variation of K_2 with Void Ratio

On the other hand, if the data is replotted according to Hardin and Drnevich (1970), values for parameters a and b may be obtained for dry and saturated samples, and their relation with void ratio and mean effective principal stress determined as shown in Table I.

TABLE I. Expressions for Parameters Related to G/G_{max}

Samples	a	b
A-DRY	$0.7+(3.8e-1.2)\exp(-3.7/\bar{\sigma}_o)$	$12.4\exp(-0.8/\bar{\sigma}_o)$
A-SAT	$0.5+2.9\exp(-0.6/\bar{\sigma}_o)$	$13.5\exp(-2.3/\bar{\sigma}_o)$
C-DRY	$(8.7e-4.5)\exp(-1/\bar{\sigma}_o)$	$11.5\exp(-1.5/\bar{\sigma}_o)$
C-SAT	$0.5+(7e-3)\exp(-0.75/\bar{\sigma}_o)$	$14.9\exp(-3/\bar{\sigma}_o)$
W-DRY	$-0.5+(10.5e-2.6)\exp(-5/\bar{\sigma}_o)$	$0.14+67\exp(-4.5/\bar{\sigma}_o)$
W-SAT	$0.5+(11.8-13.2e)\exp(-4/\bar{\sigma}_o)$	$0.14+16\exp(-4/\bar{\sigma}_o)$

$\bar{\sigma}_o$ in kg/cm^2

Figure 5 indicates that the functional relationships developed for a and b yield results that are in good agreement with the hyperbolic curve presented by Hardin and Drnevich. This means that if the maximum shear stress can be obtained from Equation 4, the reference shear strain may be found from Equation 3 using a value of G_{max} from Figure 4, the hyperbolic strain may be

obtained from Equation 2, and the shear modulus determined from Equation 5. Figure 6 furnishes the relationship between $\bar{\phi}$ and e for the tailings samples considered, and thus affords the evaluation of the maximum shear stress and ultimately the determination of G once the void ratio is known.

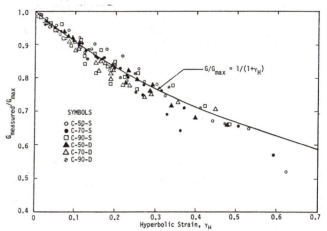

Figure 5. $G_{measured}/G_{max}$ vs. $G_{calculated}/G_{max}$.

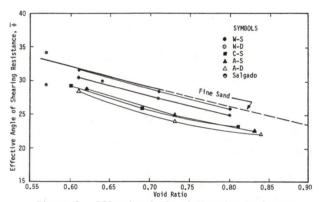

Figure 6. Effective Angle of Shearing Resistance vs. Void Ratio.

Damping Ratio

With regard to the damping ratio, the data also follows the general pattern of behavior previously established for natural soils. As shown in Figure 7, the damping ratio, D, increases as the average percent shear strain increases, but most of the data presented falls below the curve representing the average for sands and this is especially true at shear strains greater than approximately 0.001%. For all values of percent shear strain considered, the saturated samples gave slightly higher values of D. At high percent shear strain, the damping ratio is extrapolated to be in the relatively low range of approximately 18%. As with the shear modulus, the agreement with the average for sands is fairly good for tailings-A but relatively poor for tailings-C and W, and it is believed that the proposed curve in Figure 7(b) is a better representation for copper tailings than the average curve presented for sands.

As was the case for the normalized shear modulus, expressions given in Table II were developed for parameters a and b, and values of D/D_{max} were plotted versus hyper-

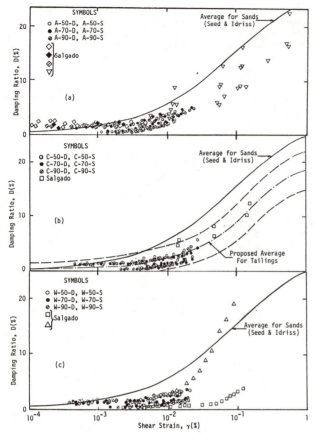

Figure 7. Damping Ratio vs. Shear Strain.

bolic strain for all three samples. However, only the results for cycloned tailings are shown in Figure 8. Once again, the data obtained is shown to fit the hyperbolic relationship presented by Hardin and Drnevich.

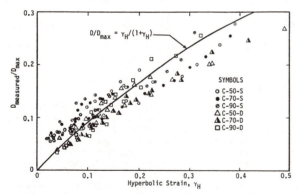

Figure 8. $D_{measured}/D_{max}$ vs. $D_{calculated}/D_{max}$.

TABLE II. Expressions for Parameters Related to D/D_{max}.

Samples	a	b
A-DRY	$0.5+0.2\bar{\sigma}_o-0.4e$	$9+6\bar{\sigma}_o-18e$
A-SAT	$2+0.5\bar{\sigma}_o-0.4e$	$18.5+8.7\bar{\sigma}_o-28e$
C-DRY	$2.4+0.2\bar{\sigma}_o-2.7e$	$32+2.6\bar{\sigma}_o-49e$
C-SAT	$6+0.4\bar{\sigma}_o-3.8e$	$12+11\bar{\sigma}_o-25.8e$
W-DRY	$6.2+0.5\bar{\sigma}_o-8e$	$81.5+4.3\bar{\sigma}_o-110e$
W-SAT	$9+0.7\bar{\sigma}_o-7.7e$	$10+14.9\bar{\sigma}_o-27e$

$\bar{\sigma}_o = kg/cm^2$

CONCLUSIONS

Based on the data presented, the following conclusions may be drawn regarding the shear modulus and damping ratio of copper tailings:

(1) Copper tailings follow the general pattern of behavior previously established for natural soils such as sand. However, when compared to sand, the tailings exhibit (on the average) lower G_{max}, higher normalized shear moduli and lower damping ratios for the same percent shear strain.

(2) Clean tailings do not always yield the best agreement with clean sands and the average for sands. Thus, it appears that gradation and possibly grain characteristics and soil structure do influence the shear modulus and damping ratio.

(3) There was not much difference in behavior between the dry and saturated samples. In general, the saturated samples gave lower values for the normalized shear modulus and higher values for the damping ratio.

(4) Curves and functional relationships have been presented for use in evaluating the shear modulus and damping ratio of tailings.

REFERENCES

Ben-Khayal, H. A. (1983). Shear Modulus and Damping Ratio for Saturated Samples of Copper Tailings. M.S. Graduate Project, University of Pittsburgh, Pittsburgh, PA.

Casagrande, A., and Shannon, W. L. (1948). Soft Rocks Under Transient Loading. Harvard Soil Mechanics Series, No. 31, Boston, MA.

Hardin, B. O., and Black, W. L. (1968). Vibration Modulus of Normally Consolidated Clay. JSMFD, ASCE, vol. 94, SM2, 353-369.

Hardin, B. O., and Drnevich, V. P. (1970). Shear Modulus and Damping in Soils: II. Design Equations and Curves. Technical Report UKY 27-70-CE 3, Lexington, KY.

Richart, F. E., Jr., Hall, J. R., and Woods, R. D. (1970). Vibrations of Soils and Foundations, 414 pp., Prentice-Hall, NJ.

Roesler, S. K. (1979). Anisotropic Shear Modulus due to Stress Anisotropy. JGED, ASCE, vol. 105, GT7, 871-880.

Rojas-González, L. F. (1982). Shear Modulus and Damping Ratio of Copper Tailings. M.S. Graduate Project, University of Pittsburgh, Pittsburgh, PA.

Salgado, S. (1983). Dynamic Behavior of Tailing Sands (compilation of published data, in spanish) C.E. Thesis, Universidad de Concepción, Concepcion, Chile.

Seed, H. B. (1967). Slope Stability During Earthquakes. JSMFD, ASCE, vol. 93, SM4, 299-323.

Seed, H. B., and Idriss, I. M. (1970). Soil Moduli and Damping Factors for Dynamic Response Analysis. Report No. 70-10, E.E.R.C., Berkeley, CA.

Whitman, R. V., and Richart, F. E., Jr. (1967). Design Procedures for Dynamically Loaded Foundations. JSMFD, ASCE, vol. 93, SM6, 169-193.

Yu, B. P., and Richart, F. E., Jr. (1984). Stress Ratio Effects on Shear Modulus of Dry Dands. JGED, ASCE, vol. 110, 331-345.

Pollutant migration through clay soils

Migration des pollutants à travers les sols argileux

R. K. ROWE, Faculty of Engineering Science, University of Western Ontario, London, Ontario, Canada
C. J. CAERS, Faculty of Engineering Science, University of Western Ontario, London, Ontario, Canada
J. R. BOOKER, University of Sydney, Sydney, Australia
V. E. CROOKS, Faculty of Engineering Science, University of Western Ontario, London, Ontario, Canada

SYNOPSIS   A new and very simple method of calculating contaminant migration profiles through soils is illustrated by comparing observed and predicted migration profiles both in laboratory model tests and in the field. This technique permits consideration of a changing concentration in the leachate due to mass transport into the soil, diffusion, advection and sorption within the soil, as well as the effects of the presence of a permeable strata beneath the clay. Using this method of analysis, both the diffusion/dispersion coefficient and the distribution coefficient can be deduced for a particular contaminant from a single laboratory model test as described in the paper.

INTRODUCTION

The movement of contaminants from waste disposal sites into the general groundwater system may be inhibited by a liner which can take the form of a natural insitu clay soil or a compacted clay borrow. Since the liner will often be underlain by a relatively permeable soil, it should be designed to limit the concentration of contaminant in the pore fluid of this underlying strata. However, design of an appropriate liner will usually require some calculation of the contaminant concentration profile and in particular, an estimate of the maximum contaminant concentration in the groundwater will be needed.

In this paper, the use of a new and very simple method for calculating concentration profiles will be illustrated for situations where the clay liner and underlying strata are of finite thickness. Consideration will first be given to the use of this technique for backfiguring soil parameters from laboratory column tests. Potential problems arising from the use of an effective diffusion coefficient will then be illustrated and a procedure for determining both the dispersion and sorption parameters from one test will be described. Finally, the use of the technique in the back analysis of field results will be demonstrated.

THE ANALYSIS AND PROGRAM POLLUTE

The movement of contaminants from waste disposal sites (e.g. landfills) into the surrounding soil is often governed by the one-dimensional dispersion-advection equation viz.

$$\frac{\partial c}{\partial t} = D \frac{\partial^2 c}{\partial z^2} - v \frac{\partial c}{\partial z} - \frac{K\rho}{n} \frac{\partial c}{\partial t} \qquad (1)$$

where c = concentration of contaminant at depth z at time t;

D = coefficient of hydrodynamic dispersion for the contaminant;
v = average linearized seepage velocity;
n = effective porosity of the soil;
K = distribution (sorption) coefficient;
ρ = bulk density of soil
t = real time.

The dispersion coefficient D is usually determined from back-calculations of earlier field tests or from laboratory model tests and includes the effect of tortuosity. The interpretation of field migration and laboratory model tests involves finding the solution to equation 1. The parameter K is usually determined from separate batch tests (e.g. Hajek and Ames, 1968).

For most cases involving mass transport through clay liners, the advective (superficial, Darcy) velocity $v_a = nv$ will be relatively small and the coefficient D will primarily reflect diffusion rather than dispersion effects. The adsorption term is assumed to be linear. This is the approach adopted by many previous workers (e.g. see Gillham and Cherry, 1982) and although sorption may not be precisely linear, the use of a suitable linear relationship determined over the appropriate concentration range may be expected to provide reasonable and conservative results.

For many landfills with a clay liner, it can be assumed that the pollutant species of interest has a maximum concentration, c_o, shortly after construction (time zero) and that this concentration will then decrease with time as material is transported into the soil. The total mass of any particular species of pollutant available for migration from the landfill is directly related to the concentration of that species within the leachate and to the total volume of leachate. The concentration can be measured. The volume of contaminant is more difficult to determine but may be estimated from the porosity of the landfill material and the time average height of the water table within the landfill. The height of leachate H_f represents the volume of leachate divided by the area of the landfill. An examination of a limited number of landfills would suggest that H_f is likely to range from 0.5 - 10 m, with values of 1-5 m being most probable.

If the clayey liner (which may be natural or manmade) is underlain at some finite depth H by a far more permeable stratum with water flow in the horizontal direction with a superficial (discharge, Darcy) velocity v_b, then solute will be transported away from the landfill at a rate dependent on the velocity, porosity and geometric dimensions of this layer. The concentration in this permeable layer will tend to zero as the base velocity tends to infinity, however in many cases the velocity will be relatively small and there will be a change in concentration with time in this stratum. An efficient technique for solving equation 1 for these boundary conditions has been described by Rowe and Booker (1984a,b).

The strategy of this solution consists of taking the Laplace Transform of the governing equation and boundary conditions, finding an analytical solution in transformed space and then inverting the transform numerically using an algorithm developed by Talbot (1979). This solution has been implemented in the computer program POLLUTE (Rowe and Booker, 1983) which solves the one-dimensional dispersion-advection equation for a layered deposit of finite depth. The program has the following capabilities and features:

- the deposit may be subdivided into individual layers where each layer may have different parameters (e.g., D, v, n, ρ and K);
- the effect of geochemical reactions on a non-conservative ion may be considered (i.e., sorption or desorption of the contaminant from the clay surface);
- provision is made for depletion of the contaminant in the landfill with time (i.e., the concentration of contaminant in the landfill can be automatically reduced as contaminant is transported into the soil. The case where the landfill concentration remains constant represents a limiting situation);
- the deposit may be underlain by either a relatively permeable or an impermeable base strata (e.g., a thin sand layer which is permeable relative to the clayey deposit or intact sound rock which is impermeable relative to the clayey deposit);
- provision is made for horizontal flow within any permeable stratum beneath the less permeable barrier;
- the maximum concentration of contaminant in a permeable base stratum can be automatically determined;
- the program requires minimal data preparation and generally provides accurate results for relatively little computational effort.

Unlike finite element and finite difference formulations, POLLUTE does not involve a "time marching" procedure. Thus, the concentration of contaminant can be directly determined at any specified time without calculating the concentration of earlier times.

BACKFIGURING A DISPERSION COEFFICIENT FROM MODEL TESTS

One of the most commonly reported techniques for estimating the dispersion coefficient for any particular contaminant consists of the use of laboratory models in which the contaminant migrates through the soil of interest under controlled conditions. Contaminant concentration profiles in the soil are measured and a dispersion coefficient is obtained by using various values of D and fitting the theoretical profile to the observed results. This approach provides the most practical solution to determining a value of D, particularly when an analysis is available (e.g. POLLUTE) which allows accurate modelling of the boundary conditions in the experiment. To illustrate the suitability of POLLUTE for modelling even quite complicated boundary conditions, the program was used to re-analyze the laboratory model test results performed at The University of Western Ontario (Crooks and Quigley, 1984).

Crooks and Quigley reported the results of two model tests involving the migration of sodium chloride (NaCl) through a silty clay. The clay was compacted in the models to a thickness of 15 cm at a moisture content of 21%. The compacted unit weight of the soil was 19 kN/m^3 at a porosity of 0.38. The soil was maintained at the laboratory ambient temperature (19-23°C). In model I, a head of 3.7 m at the top of the soil column gave rise to a superficial velocity of 0.022 m/a. Model II was similar except that the head of 1.0 m gives a superficial velocity of 0.0056 m/a. An important detail in the model design was the 0.6 cm thick porous (porosity 0.43) polyethylene plate at the bottom of the column which served to collect fluid exiting from the soil and allowed this fluid to be collected from an outlet pipe (see Fig. 1). Soil was taken from the models at different depths and times (see Crooks and Quigley, 1984 for details) and was analyzed to determine the concentrations of Na^+ and Cl^- in the pore fluid.

Typical results for Chloride and Sodium migration through the silty clay in Model I are presented in Figs. 1 and 2. A preliminary analysis of this data using the analytical solution of Ogata (1970) for a halfspace with a uniform surface concentration was reported by Crooks and Quigley (1984) and gave values for the diffusion coefficient D of 0.031 m^2/a for Chloride and 0.011 m^2/a for Sodium. It was recognized that the Ogata solution did not accurately simulate the actual test conditions and considerable judgement was required to obtain reasonable values of D. Consequently, the test data was re-analyzed using the far more general solution to 1-D migration problems (Rowe and Booker, 1984) together with some additional data concerning the actual test conditions which could be used in conjunction with program POLLUTE.

POLLUTE permitted the modelling of the 0.6 cm thick polyethylene plate as a permeable base stratum (n_b = 0.43) with an outflow velocity dictated by flow continuity requirements. It also permitted a consideration of changes in leachate concentration in the source reservoirs due to

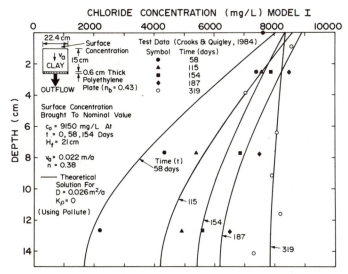

Fig. 1 Backfiguring the Dispersion Coefficient From the Results of a Laboratory Model Test

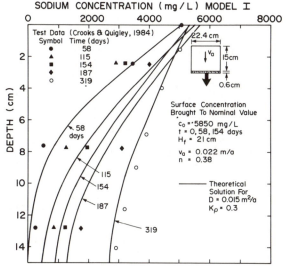

Fig. 2 Backfiguring D and Kρ From the Results of a Laboratory Model Test

salt migration into the clay. It should be noted that maintaining a constant surface concentration (as required if the data is analyzed using Ogata's solution) involves practical difficulties at the model scale when the volume of leachate is relatively small. These difficulties arise from the fact that significant mass transport into the soil will occur and consequently the source concentration will drop. Maintaining a uniform concentration would require frequent replacement of the leachate however this results in undesirable fluctuations in the flow through the soil. In practice, a compromise must be met between allowing some drop in concentration and avoiding too frequent replacement of leachate.

In the model tests under discussion, the initial Sodium and Chloride concentrations were 5850 mg/L and 9150 mg/L respectively (Stage 1). After 58 days, the concentrations of Sodium and Chloride in the reservoir were measured to be 15% (Na⁺) and 17% (Cl⁻) lower than the initial leachate values (presumably due to significant mass transport into the clay). At this point, the model reservoir was drained and refilled with leachate at the initial concentration (Stage 2). This procedure was repeated again at 154 days after the start of the test (Stage 3).

The three stage sequence described above was directly simulated using the program POLLUTE. The dispersion coefficient D (and in the case of Sodium, the dimensionless sorption parameter Kρ) were adjusted to provide the "best fit" to the experimental data. The parameters giving the "best fit" are summarized in Table I and the theoretical concentration profiles are compared with the observed data for model I in Figs. 1 and 2 for Chloride and Sodium respectively. The agreement between the observed and predicted profiles is quite good. It should be noted that the Ogata solution will not provide a good fit to the data over the entire depth for any of these times and, furthermore, any value of D which gives a fair fit at any time will give a poor fit at the other times. This is simply because the

TABLE I

Paramaters From Model Tests
(T ≃ 20°C)

Species	Model Test	v_a (m/a)	D (m²/a)	Kρ	D (7°C)* (m²/a)
Cl⁻	I	0.022	0.026	0.0	.019
	II	0.0056	0.018	0.0	.013
Na⁺	I	0.022	0.015	0.3	.011
	II	0.0056	0.013	0.3	.0095

* Corrected for estimated field temperature (i.e. $D_{7°C} = 0.73 D_{20°C}$; see Crooks and Quigley, 1984).

boundary conditions in the model test are too far removed from those assumed in developing the Ogata solution.

These results (and comparable agreement obtained for model II tests) serve to demonstrate that the proposed theory, and the program POLLUTE, can adequately model dispersive (diffusive)-advective transport in clay subject to quite complex boundary conditions.

USE OF AN EFFECTIVE DIFFUSION COEFFICIENT

Equation 1 may be rewritten as

$$\frac{\partial c}{\partial t} = D^* \frac{\partial^2 c}{\partial z^2} - v^* \frac{\partial c}{\partial z} \qquad (2)$$

where $D^* = \dfrac{D}{1 + \dfrac{K\rho}{n}}$ is an effective diffusion coefficient; and

$$v^* = \frac{v}{1 + \frac{K\rho}{n}} \text{ is an effective velocity.}$$

This representation of the diffusion/dispersion-advective process in terms of only two effective parameters (D*, v*) may be quite useful for situations where the advective velocity is small and the boundary concentrations are maintained at specified values. However, even in the laboratory, it is not always easy to maintain these boundary concentrations while in the field many situations will arise where the concentration in the leachate and any underlying aquifer will vary with time as mass is transported into or out of the clay liner. These cases where the boundary concentrations are flux controlled can be modelled using the theory proposed by Rowe and Booker (1984) and program POLLUTE however in doing so care is needed to avoid potential errors which can arise from the inappropriate use of an effective diffusion coefficient and effective velocity.

To illustrate the effect of the boundary conditions on the results obtained using actual and effective parameters, consideration was given to a hypothetical "laboratory test" as indicated in Fig. 3. Supposing that the soil has D = 0.01 m^2/a, Kρ = 10, n = 0.4 and v_a = 0.02 m/a, an analysis was performed assuming a height of leachate H_f of 15 cm. The results shown in Fig. 3 indicate that there is a substantial difference between the results obtained using the actual and the corresponding "effective" parameters. This difference arises because the use of only the effective parameters gives incorrect fluxes at the boundaries. (The same conclusion would be reached even if v_a were zero.)

To illustrate the practical implications of the use of "effective" parameters D* and v*, consider a 200 m long landfill resting on a 2 m thick clay barrier which in turn is underlain by a 1 m thick sand layer. Assuming that the advective velocity in the clay and sand are 0.02 m/a and 5 m/a respectively, Fig. 4 shows the variation in the base concentrations with time predicted using "actual" parameters D = 0.01 m^2/a, n = 0.4, Kρ = 10 and the corresponding effective parameters D* and v*. It is apparent from Fig. 4 that the analysis performed using only the effective parameters D* and v* is both incorrect and unconservative. Because of potential problems inherent in the use of effective parameters, it is recommended that the use of these parameters be avoided in any analysis where the boundary conditions are flux controlled.

SUGGESTED PROCEDURE FOR DETERMINATION OF PARAMETERS FROM LABORATORY MODEL TESTS

As previously noted, there are some practical difficulties associated with maintaining a constant concentration of contaminant within a source fluid in model tests. This difficulty can be avoided by adopting a simple test where the source concentration is initially specified and then allowed to drop due to mass transport into the soil. This situation is readily analyzed using POLLUTE and in fact the marked different effects of D and Kρ which are apparent under these circumstances can be used to permit the determination of both D and Kρ from the one test. For example, Fig. 5 shows a single column which consists of 0.1 m of source fluid (leach-

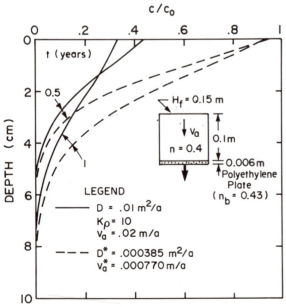

Fig. 3   Effect of Using "Effective" Parameters D*, v* Upon Predicted Concentration Profiles in a Hypothetical Model Test

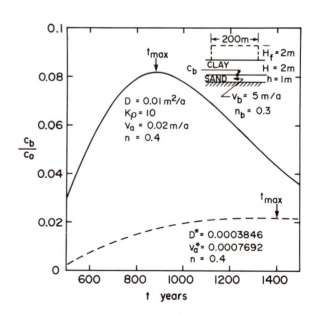

Fig. 4   Effect of Using "Effective" Parameters D*, v* Upon Base Concentration c_b

ate), overlying 0.1 m of clay overlying 0.006 m of polyethylene porous plate. At the start of the test, the species of interest in the leach-ate has a concentration c_o. Diffusion/advection is then allowed to reduce the concentration within the leachate (and this reduction with time should be monitored). The effluent exiting from the base plate should also be collected and the concentration of species in this effluent monitored. The test should be terminated at some time t (the actual time is not critical provided that there has been time for signifi-cant diffusion into the clay sample) and the concentration profile in the soil determined. Knowing the advective velocity v_a, the initial concentration c_o, the height of leachate H_f and the time t, theoretical profiles can be deter-mined for different values of D and $K\rho$. The values of D and $K\rho$ are adjusted until a reason-able fit of the experimental profile is ob-tained.* The validity of these best fit para-meters can then be checked by comparing the predicted and observed variation in concentra-tion within the leachate and effluent. To il-lustrate the sensitivity of the procedure, Fig. 5 shows the concentration profiles obtained at three times for $D = 0.01$ m^2/a and $K\rho = 0$ and 0.25 and it can be seen that even a relatively low level of sorption ($K\rho = 0.25$) can have an appre-ciable effect on the concentration profile and hence can be readily detected. The results shown in Fig. 5 were obtained for a relatively small height of leachate H_f (0.1 m) and advec-tion velocity (0.003 m/a).† Even for much larger values of H_f and v_a, the effect of small values of $K\rho$ is readily apparent and consequently both D and $K\rho$ may be deduced.

APPLICATION TO FIELD SITUATIONS

The concentration profile beneath the Confedera-tion Road landfill near Sarnia, Ontario has been extensively studied in recent years (Goodall and Quigley, 1977; Crooks and Quigley, 1984). Fig. 6 shows the observed Chloride profile at two locations beneath the Confederation Road land-fill 12 years after completion. The concentra-tion of Chloride in the leachate at these two locations is 1700 mg/L and 3000 mg/L at Bore-holes 101 and 102 respectively. An inspection of the measured concentrations in the silty clay beneath the landfill indicates a substantial drop in concentration compared to the leachate values over a very small distance. These results would suggest that something special is happening at the interface between leachate and the general mass of clay (similar results were obtained for the Sodium ions). There are several ways of ex-plaining this behaviour (e.g. see Crooks and Quigley, 1984; Quigley et al., 1984) and the various mechanisms will be discussed in detail in a forthcoming publication. In this paper, we wish to show that the large drop in concentra-tion from the leachate values to those measured a short distance below the refuse-clay interface can be modelled by postulating a thin interface layer of thickness H_I with an apparent disper-sion coefficient D_I. Analyses were performed varying the ratio D_I/H_I and the dispersion co-efficient in the clay to obtain a fit with the data at BH102. The best fit was obtained for a value of $D_I/H_I = 0.02$ m/a and $D = 0.018$ m^2/a. The dispersion coefficient in the clay is con-sistent with that obtained from model tests on the same clay once an adjustment is made for the difference in temperature in the laboratory and field (see Table I).

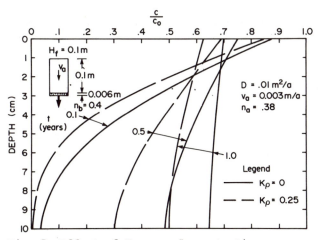

Fig. 5   Effect of $K\rho$ on a Concentration
         Profile for $H_f = 0.1$ m

---

* An initial estimate of D can be obtained by first determining the value of D for a non-reactive reference species (e.g. Chloride) and then multiplying this value by the ratio of the diffusion coefficient of the species of interest in pure water to the diffusion coefficient of the reference species in pure water.

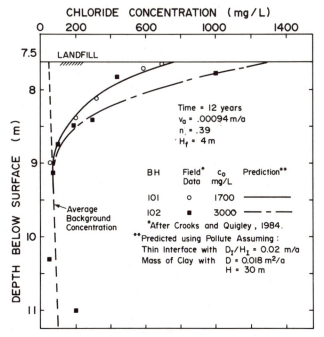

Fig. 6   Measured Porewater Chloride Concen-
         tration and Calculated Profiles -
         Sarnia Landfill

These parameters were then used to predict the concentration profile at BH101 and the resulting predictions shown in Fig. 6 are in very good agreement with the observed concentration profile. The consistency of the results at two locations suggests that some form of interface effect is occurring at the landfill which was not evident in the model tests on the same clay (see Figs. 1 and 2*). The mechanisms responsible for this interface are currently under investigation at The University of Western Ontario and will be discussed in detail in a subsequent publication.

In the design of landfills, it would be conservative to neglect the effects of any interface layer which may be formed. However, the possible presence of such a layer should be considered when attempting to backfigure parameters from laboratory tests. The "leachate" in laboratory tests (by Crooks and Quigley) described earlier, did not contain any metals suitable for forming precipitates at the interface or bacteria which could multiply and cause clogging, however it is possible that a true leachate which is chemically very complex and possibly bacterially active may well result in an interface effect. If present, this interface effect should be modelled when backfiguring D and $K\rho$ from the model tests and only the values determined away from the interface should be used in design of landfills. Failure to allow for possible interface effects in model tests could give rise to an artifically low dispersion coefficient and/or an artificially high value of sorption coefficient $K\rho$.

CONCLUSION

A new and simple method of calculating concentration profiles in laboratory column tests and in field applications has been shown to provide good agreement with observed behaviour. This technique has then been used to demonstrate the potential dangers which may arise from the use of an effective diffusion (dispersion) coefficient. Finally, a procedure for determining parameters from laboratory column tests has been proposed. This procedure readily permits the determination of both the dispersion (diffusion) coefficient and the sorption potential (in terms of the distribution coefficient K) for a given species of contaminant.

ACKNOWLEDGEMENT

The work described in this paper was supported by NSERC grant Nos. A1007 and G0921. The authors gratefully acknowledge the value of discussions with Dr. R.M. Quigley.

REFERENCES

Crooks, V.E. and Quigley, R.M. (1984). Saline Leachate Migration Through Clay: A Comparative Laboratory and Field Investigation. Canadian Geotechnical Journal, 21(2), 349-362.

* As previously noted, the modest drop in concentration in the model tests is the result of a drop in concentration within the leachate. This mechanism cannot explain the large concentration drop observed in the field.

Gillham, R.W. and Cherry, J.A. (1982). Predictability of Solute Transport in Diffusion-Controlled Hydrogeologic Regimes. Proc. Symp. on Low Level Waste Disposal: Facility Design, Construction and Operating Practices, Nuclear Regulatory Commission, Washington, D.C.

Goodall, D.E. and Quigley, R.M. (1977). Pollutant Migration From Two Sanitary Landfill Sites Near Sarnia, Ontario. Canadian Geotechnical Journal, 14, 223-236.

Hajek, B.F. and Ames, L.L. (1968). Trace Strontium and Cesium Equilibrium Distribution Coefficients: Batch and Column Determinations. Battelle Pacific Northwest Laboratories, Richland WA.

Ogata, A. (1970). Theory of Dispersion in a Granular Medium. U.S. Geological Survey Professional Paper 411-I.

Quigley, R.M., Crooks, V.E. and Yanful, E.(1984). Contaminant Migration Through Clay Below a Domestic Waste Landfill Site, Sarnia, Ontario, Canada. Int. Symp. on Groundwater Resources, Utilization and Contaminant Hydrogeology, Montreal, May.

Rowe, R.K. and Booker, J.R. (1983). Program POLLUTE - 1D Pollutant Migration Analysis Program. SACDA, Faculty of Engineering Science, The University of Western Ontario, London, Ont.

Rowe, R.K. and Booker, J.R. (1984a). 1-D Pollutant Migration in Soils of Finite Depth. Journal of Geotechnical Engineering, ASCE (in press).

Rowe, R.K. and Booker, J.R. (1984b). The Analysis of Pollutant Migration in a Non-Homogeneous Soil. Geotechnique (in press).

Talbot, A. (1979). The Accurate Numerical Integration of Laplace Transforms. J. Inst. Maths. Applics. 23, 97-120.

Geomechanical interaction in a nuclear waste disposal vault

Interaction géomécanique dans un dépôt souterrain des déchets nucléaires

A. P. S. SELVADURAI, Professor of Civil Engineering and Chairman, Department of Civil Engineering, Carleton University, Ottawa, Ontario, Canada

R. S. LOPEZ, Section Head, Vault Sealing, Fuel Waste Technology Branch, AECL Whiteshell Nuclear Research Establishment, Pinawa, Manitoba, Canada

G. A. HARTLEY, Associate Professor and Associate Dean of Engineering, Department of Civil Engineering, Carleton University, Ottawa, Ontario, Canada

SYNOPSIS

This paper examines the geomechanical interactions that take place in a borehole of a thermally inactive nuclear waste disposal vault during fluid-induced separation at the buffer rock mass interface. The buffer considered is a clay or clay-sand mixture which can exhibit either linear or non-linear material properties. Numerical methods, such as boundary-element and finite-element techniques, are employed to study this interaction problem. Results presented in the paper indicate the manner in which fluid pressures which act at the buffer rock mass interface are transmitted to the buffer waste-container interface.

INTRODUCTION

The Canadian research and development program for nuclear fuel waste disposal can be divided into three major areas of study: 1) immobilization of used fuel and fuel-recycle waste, 2) disposal of the immobilized waste, which involves geochemical and geotechnical research, and 3) environmental and safety assessment. The program is concentrating on the concept of immobilizing nuclear fuel waste in cylindrical metal containers for subsequent disposal in an underground vault, excavated at a depth of 500 to 1000 m in plutonic rock of the Canadian Shield (Rummery and Rosinger, 1982).

The current design concept is a single-level vault, approximately 1700 m by 3600 m, consisting of 822 rooms arranged in 16 rectangular arrays. The rooms would be 195 m long, 7.5 m wide and 5.0 to 6.2 m high (Acres Consulting Services Limited 1980a and 1980b). Based on current forecasts of growth of electrical energy demand, a vault would start operation early in the 21st century, and would have an operating life of approximately 50 years before being permanently sealed.

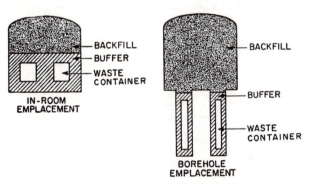

Figure 1: Schematic Waste Container Emplacement Configurations (Bird and Cameron, 1982)

Used fuel or immobilized fuel-recycle waste would be placed in metallic containers for final disposal. Several container designs with different aspect ratios are being considered (Cameron, 1982). Relatively short, broad containers could be placed within the rooms, whereas long, narrow containers could be placed in boreholes drilled into the room floors (Figure 1). In both cases the containers would be surrounded by a clay or a clay/sand mixture of a very low permeability, called the "buffer", that would support the container and protect it from corroding chemicals in the groundwater (Bird and Cameron, 1982).

VAULT SEALING

The fuel waste containers could fail gradually by corrosion or mechanical damage, some hundreds of years following emplacement. Once a container is breached the waste form will slowly start to dissolve by the action of groundwater in the pores of the surrounding buffer.

Isolation from the biosphere of radioactive isotopes (radionuclides), released by dissolution of the waste form is effected by a system of multiple barriers, each one engineered to a high degree of integrity (Nuttall et al., 1982). These barriers are: 1) the buffer, 2) the backfill in the rooms, drifts and shafts, and 3) the seals and plugs for the shafts and site exploration boreholes. These engineered barriers supplement the natural barrier provided by the host rock, and are shown schematically in Figure 2.

The buffer separates the fuel waste containers from the host rock, and is a combined physical and chemical barrier, designed to:

a) minimize groundwater access to the container,

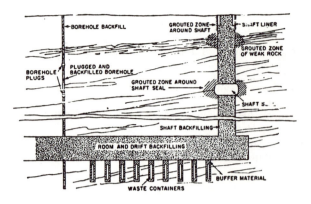

Figure 2: Engineered Barriers and Components of the Vault Sealing Program (Lopez et al., 1984)

b) dissipate radiogenic heat from the containers,
c) provide mechanical support for the container, and
d) retard the migration of radionuclides from failed containers by providing a low-permeability, low-diffusivity and high-sorption medium.

The backfill is primarily a physical barrier, whose main functions are to prevent groundwater ducting through vault drifts, dissipate heat, and minimize deformation of the host rock.

Shaft and drift seals will be required to isolate backfilled emplacement rooms from other areas of the vault, and to seal selected zones of service shafts to prevent them from becoming preferential paths for groundwater flow. In addition, local regions of high fracture density in the shafts and drifts will require grouting to decrease their permeability. Plugs must be designed to achieve the permanent closure of boreholes drilled during site investigations so that they do not become preferential paths for water flow and release of radionuclides.

FACTORS AFFECTING THE THEORETICAL MODELLING OF BUFFER-CONTAINER-ROCK MASS INTERACTION

Current design concepts for the waste disposal facility regard the flooding of the disposal vault as inevitable (Cameron, 1982). It is assumed that full hydrostatic pressures of the order of 10 MPa could be developed at a depth of 1000 m in the disposal vault during its anticipated lifetime. At present there is no estimate of the time required for the generation of the full hydrostatic pressure in the disposal vault. This time-scale is influenced by a number of factors, including the groundwater flow characteristics in existing fissures of the rock mass, alteration in the fluid conductivity patterns of existing fissures due to the creation of the vault, the creation of new fissures due to stress relief or thermal effects and thermomechanical influences on the fluid flow characteristics. In the absence of specific

data on the fluid influx rate, it is prudent to assume that the full hydrostatic head could obtain at the location of the waste disposal facility at its completion. The Geomechanics Research Programme at Carleton University has examined several aspects of the interaction between the container, buffer and rock mass, caused by the influx of water into the waste disposal vault. The modelling focusses on the situation in which the container-buffer-rock mass system may be regarded as being thermally inactive; that is, the condition of the buffer material is such that there is no interaction between the generated heat and the incoming fluid. Such a situation can occur at the end of construction of the facility when insufficient time has elapsed for the occurrence of either steady-state or transient heat conduction. In the modelling, it is assumed that water can enter the buffer and backfill regions through natural fissures or fissures that may be created by stress relief of the surrounding rock mass (Figure 3). The theoretical studies focus on the mechanical processes that would occur in the container-buffer-rock mass system by virtue of fluid pressures transmitted via cracks in the rock mass.

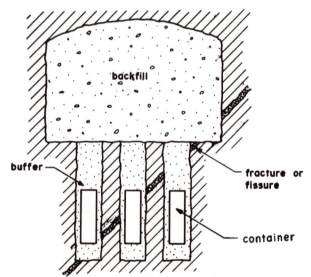

Figure 3: Possible interaction between a fracture plane and the waste disposal vault (Selvadurai, 1984a)

Several processes can occur due to the influx of water into the buffer region. For example, in the initial stages of water influx, the fluid pressures could cause separation between the relatively impermeable buffer and the rock mass, leading to the lateral or axial displacement of the container (Figure 4). Alternatively, the water could enter the buffer region via cracks or fissures which may develop by processes similar to hydraulic fracturing or thermally-induced desiccation effects (see e.g., Radhakrishna, 1984) (Figure 5). Finally, an intact buffer system which is subjected to prolonged fluid pressures, similar to that illustrated in Figure 4, could experience swelling. The fluid-induced mechanical processes that can be encountered in a container-buffer-rock mass system are varied and quite intricate.

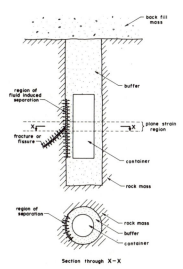

Figure 4: Fluid-induced separation at the buffer-rock mass interface - plane strain configuration.

For this reason it is prudent to examine a variety of possible loading situations. Such analyses should provide assessments of the displacements of the waste container and the stresses that are induced at the buffer-container interface by virtue of fluid-induced or swelling-induced pressures.

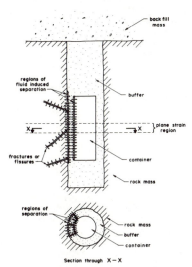

Figure 5: Fluid Pressures in a desiccation-induced cracked zone in the buffer material - plane strain configuration.

FLUID-INDUCED SEPARATION AT THE BUFFER-ROCK MASS INTERFACE

The theoretical studies by Selvadurai (1984a, 1984b) investigated the fluid-induced inter-action between the container-buffer-rock mass system in the absence of any swelling phenomena. Either the presence or the development of fissures in the rock mass will subject the buffer-container system to fluid pressures that

are naturally present in the rock mass. These fluid pressures can act at arbitrary locations of the buffer rock mass interface and induce separation at the respective locations. Considering the geometry of the buffer-container system and the possible location and orientation of the zones of separation it is evident that the state of deformation in the system is generally three-dimensional (Figure 3). The analysis of such a three-dimensional, container-buffer-rock mass region which incorporates several cells of the emplacement room will be the subject of future investigations. In this paper attention is restricted to the situation in which fluid-induced separation takes place over a wide region of the buffer-rock mass interface. The extent and location of the separation zone is assumed to be such that an approximate state of plane strain deformation exists over a section of the waste container (Figure 4). The plane strain model of the container-buffer-rock mass interaction essentially yields a plausible upper bound loading configuration for the estimation of the displacements of the container and the pressures that are generated at the buffer container interface. To complete the modelling of the problem it is necessary to examine the performance and mechanical characteristics of the individual components in the disposal facility.

The Rock Mass

In these studies the rock mass is treated essentially as a rigid medium. The stiffness and strength characteristics of the rock mass are expected to be considerably higher than those of the buffer region. It is also assumed that the fractures or fissures which transport the groundwater into the vault region do not experience any relative displacement, either along or normal to the plane of the fracture. In essence, the rock mass is modelled as an intact region and the fractures are merely artifices to transmit the fluid pressures. Also, attention will be restricted to a single cell of the vault configuration and the influence of neighbouring cells (or voids) will be neglected

The Waste Container

The waste container is modelled as a rigid cylinder. During the container-buffer-rock mass interaction, the cylinder experiences a rigid-body translation. The boundary between the container and the buffer can exhibit a variety of interface characteristics, ranging from completely smooth to completely bonded conditions, with Coulomb friction or finite friction occupying intermediate positions. The exact mechanical characteristics of the container-buffer interface cannot be described with certainty. The frictional characteristics of a buffer-container interface system are currently under experimental investigation. In a series of experiments the frictional characteristics of candidate container materials such as Inconel 625, titanium and copper, in contact with various buffer compositions (i.e. various mixtures of bentonite clay and sand compacted to a specified density), were investigated. Preliminary results indicate that for a pure bentonite/(dry)-copper interface, the interface friction angle is of the order of 20-23° for maximum normal stresses of the order of 200 kN/m². In the present investigation the interface between the container and the buffer was assumed to exhibit bonded conditions. The analytical studies can be extended to include interface characteristics which model more closely the actual conditions of any experimental arrangement.

The Buffer Region

The mechanical behaviour of the buffer, as well as any multiphase geological material, can be influenced by a variety of factors, which include (a) grain size, grain shape, size distribution, surface texture, clay mineralogy and the mechanical properties of the individual soil particles, (b) the configuration of the soil structure or the soil fabric, including physico-chemical and mechanical bonding, (c) the intergranular stresses, stress history, current stress state and loading rates, and (d) the presence of soil moisture, degree of saturation, permeability and drainage charcteristics of the various phases. The above factors generally pertain to soils which display marked non-linear, irreversible and time-dependent phenomena and to soil masses which exhibit anisotropic and non-homogeneous material properties. It is evident that any attempt to solve the container-buffer-rock mass interaction problem, or any other type of soil-structure interaction problem, by taking into account all such material characteristics, will be a complex task. Firstly, the correct mathematical forms of the stress-strain-time relationships should be postulated and, secondly, all of the material constants, material functions, or material functionals (i.e. history-dependent material functions) which govern these formulations need to be accurately determined from laboratory or in-situ tests. Therefore, to make any progress in the analytical treatment of soil-structure interaction problems such as the container-buffer-rock mass interaction discussed here, it is necessary to idealize the mechanical behaviour of the buffer mass by taking into account specific aspects of its mechanical response. For example, in the simplest time-independent mechanical model, the buffer is assumed to be an isotropic elastic continuum. Linear elastic soil models, by definition, ignore elastic-plastic or irreversible phenomena. In general, all soils exhibit irreversible phenomena even when they are subjected to stress levels well within the working stress range. Within the working stress range, however, reversible deformations are assumed to dominate. In such circumstances it is possible to carry out the linear elastic analysis of a soil-structure interaction problem using reduced values of the material properties (e.g. linear elastic moduli, Poisson's ratios, etc.) to account for the existence of irreversible effects. Such analyses represent useful first approximations for the treatment of soil-structure interaction problems.

In certain situations, the buffer materials can be subjected to load levels at which significant yield or failure zones may develop. In these circumstances it is necessary to take into account the effects of irreversible deformations. Currently, there are a multitude of mathematical models that can be used to describe the mechanical behaviour of soils which exhibit both

reversible and irreversible time-independent phenomena. Current developments in soil plasticity are quite extensive and no attempt will be made to provide an exhaustive coverage of the subject (see, e.g., Gudehus, 1977; Desai and Christian, 1977; Chen and Saleeb, 1982; Pande et al., 1983; Selvadurai, 1985). Every soil model that has been proposed for the examination of non-linear phenomena in soils has its respective advantages and disadvantages. For example, the more fundamental elastic-ideal plastic approach has a well-developed mathematical basis. With accurate yield criteria and flow rules (associative and non-associative) these elastoplastic models can account for fundamental processes, such as dilatancy and collapse of the soil fabric. These models are, however, incapable of duplicating very accurately non-linear stress-strain phenomena in the pre-and post-yield ranges. The non-linear soil models, such as the incremental stress-strain relationships, are capable of duplicating more accurately features of non-linear stress-strain phenomena. Certain incremental soil models, are, however, limited in their mathematical foundation and are incapable of duplicating dilatancy and strain-softening phenomena, and effects of non-coincidence of principal stress increments and principal strain increments at near-failure loads. Despite these limitations the incremental models have been used quite extensively for the analysis of many complex soil-structure interaction problems in geotechnical engineering. The accurate constitutive modelling of the buffer behaviour in the inelastic range can be achieved only upon completion of an extensive program of testing. Such testing should include the determination of non-linear stress-strain relationships, volume change characteristics and strength criteria for specific buffer compositions at the anticipated levels of external loading. In this paper both linear elastic and incrementally non-linear stress-strain relationships of the hyperbolic type have been used to examine the container-buffer-rock mass interaction during fluid-induced separation.

NUMERICAL RESULTS

The modelling of the container-buffer-rock mass interaction is restricted to the situation in which fluid-induced separation causes a state of plane strain in the central region of the waste containers. The linear elastic analysis is performed by employing a boundary-element formulation of the problem. Details of the boundary-element analysis of problems in linear elasticity are given by Brebbia (1978) and Banerjee and Butterfield (1981). The interface between the rock mass and the buffer is assumed to be smooth and the interface between the buffer and the container is assumed to be bonded. The extent of fluid-induced separation at the buffer-rock mass interface is an unknown parameter in the calculation. In a complete analysis of this interaction problem an iterative technique should be used to determine the extent of the separation zone. In the present paper the extent of the separation zone is prescribed; this gives a useful upper bound for the displacements of the container and the normal stresses generated at the buffer-container interface. The fluid pressures in the separated zone are assumed to be either constant or of a non-linear harmonic type. Figure 6 illustrates a typical result for the rigid displacement of the container due to fluid-induced separation at the interface. Similar results for the contact stresses developed at the buffer-container interface are given in Figure 7. In the particular instance where fluid induced separation takes place over the entire buffer-rock mass interface radial symmetry exists and the solution of the linear elastic problem can be obtained in exact closed form. The radial stress (σ_i) induced at the buffer-container interface is given by

$$\frac{\sigma_i}{p_0} = \frac{2(1-\nu)}{\{1+(a_0/b_0)^2 (1-2\nu)\}} \qquad (1)$$

where P_0 is the fluid pressure in the separation region, ν is Poisson's ratio for the buffer material, a_0 is the inner radius of the annular buffer region and b_0 is the outer radius of the buffer region.

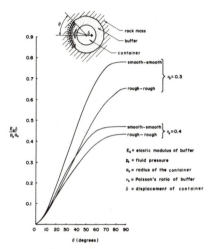

Figure 6: Displacements of the rigid container due to uniform fluid pressure in the separation zone - results of the boundary-element analysis $[p(\phi) = p_0]$.

The non-linear incremental finite-element technique first proposed by Duncan and Chang (1970) and later refined by Duncan et al. (1980) has been used in the non-linear finite-element analysis of the buffer-container-rock mass interaction. Comprehensive accounts of the analysis, which utilizes the FEADAM non-linear finite-element code and the associated hyperbolic stress-strain formulations, are summarized in the reports by Duncan et al. (1980) and Selvadurai (1984b). Also, in the non-linear analysis the region of fluid-induced separation at the buffer-rock mass interface is prescribed and the fluid-pressure in the separation zone is assumed to be constant. All other interfaces (i.e. the non-separated zone of the buffer-rock mass interface and the buffer-container interface) are assumed to be bonded.

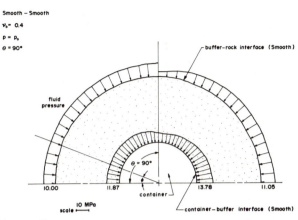

Figure 7: Normal stresses at the container-buffer and buffer-rock mass interface.

The non-linear analysis has been carried out for the following groups of material parameters: (i) cohesion c = 0, 0.1, 0.2 MPa; (ii) angle of internal friction ϕ = 0, 20, 40°; (iii) for the purpose of normalizing the results the initial elastic modulus E_{ib} is set equal to 100 MPa; (iv) Poisson's ratio at zero deviator stress is taken to be 0.3 and 0.4; (v) the failure ratio R_f is set equal to 0.9; (vi) the factors m and n which characterize the modulus exponent are such that m = n = 0, 0.25 and 0.50; (vii) the initial stress state in the plane strain region is such that the total horizontal stress is 0.10 MPa.

The finite-element model of the buffer-container-rock mass system is shown in Figure 8. Figure 9 illustrates a typical variation of the normalized container displacement ($E_{ib}\delta / p_0 a_0$), with the extent of the separation zone as defined by θ. The normal contact stresses that are developed at the buffer-container and buffer-rock mass interfaces are shown in Figure 10. In the limiting case when there is complete separation at the buffer-rock mass interface, the interaction problem exhibits a state of axial symmetry. Selvadurai (1984c) has developed an analytical solution to this problem for the particular case where the buffer material exhibits an ideal elastic-plastic response characterized by a Tresca-type yield condition (i.e. c ≠ 0 ; ϕ = 0). A Hencky-type deformation theory is used to describe the total strain-stress relationships. The stress developed at the buffer-container interface is given by

$$\frac{\sigma_i}{p_0} = 1+ \frac{1}{\beta}\{1 - \left(\frac{a_0}{b_0}\right)^2 \left(\frac{c_0}{a_0}\right)^2\}+ \frac{2}{\beta} \log_e \left(\frac{c_0}{a_0}\right)$$

where $\beta = p_0/c$ and c_0 is the radius of the elastic-plastic interface, which is determined from the characteristic equation

$$(1-2\nu)[\{\left(\frac{c_0}{a_0}\right)^2 - 1\}\{\beta+1- \left(\frac{a_0}{b_0}\right)^2 \left(\frac{c_0}{a_0}\right)^2\} -2 \log_e \left(\frac{c_0}{a_0}\right)]$$

$$= \left(\frac{c_0}{a_0}\right)^2 (1+\nu)[(1-2\nu)\beta - 1 - (1-2\nu) \left(\frac{a_0}{b_0}\right)^2 \left(\frac{c_0}{a_0}\right)^2]$$

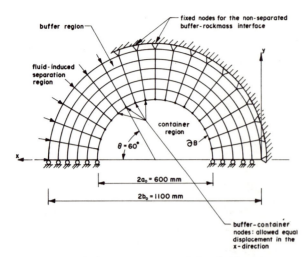

Figure 8: Finite-element model of the container-buffer-rock mass system.

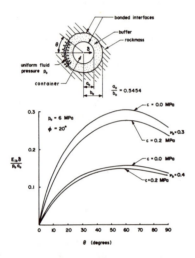

Figure 9: Displacements of the rigid container due to a uniform fluid
pressure of 6 MPa in the separatio.
region.

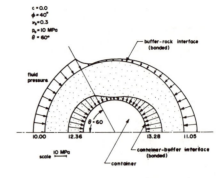

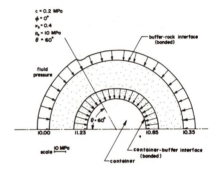

Figure 10: Normal interface stress

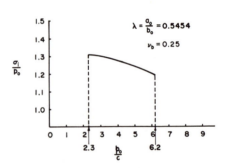

Figure 11: Normal contact stress (σ_i) at the
container-buffer interface due to
uniform pressurization of the
buffer-rock mass interface - analytical results (Selvadurai, 1984c)

Figure 11 illustrates the manner in which the
normal stress at the container-buffer interface
is influenced by the extent of plastic yielding
in the buffer region. The value of $\beta = 2.3$
corresponds to the situation where plastic yield
is initiated at $r = a_o$ and the value of $\beta = 6.2$
corresponds to the situation where the entire
buffer region undergoes plastic yield.

CONCLUSIONS

In this paper a theoretical model for solving
the problem of fluid-induced separation at the
buffer-rock mass interface of a borehole in a
nuclear waste disposal vault has been described.
The fluid-induced separation is a plausible
loading of the buffer region where full hydro-

static pressures at the vault level are transmitted via fractures or fissures to the buffer-
rock mass interface. Furthermore, such
separation can be enhanced by higher permeability (compared with the buffer material) at
the interface. During such a separation process the container can experience non-symmetric
lateral movements. Also, the stresses in the
separation zone are amplified at the buffer-
container interface. Such effects are reduced
in situations where the buffer materials
exhibit non-linear stress-strain phenomena.
Currently available non-linear finite-element
codes can be successfully applied to study
this type of time- and temperature-independent
buffer-container-rock mass interaction problem.

ACKNOWLEDGEMENTS

This work was carried out with the support of Atomic Energy of Canada Limited.

REFERENCES

Acres Consulting Services Limited and Associates. (1980a). "A Disposal Centre for Immobilized Nuclear Waste: Conceptual Design Study. Atomic Energy of Canada Limited Report, AECL-6416.

Acres Consulting Services Limited and Associates. (1980b). "A Disposal Centre for Irradiated Nuclear Fuel: Conceptual Design Study. Atomic Energy of Canada Limited Report, AECL-6415.

Banerjee, P.K. and Butterfield, R. (1981). Boundary Element Methods in Engineering Science, McGraw-Hill, New York

Brebbia, C.A. (1978). The Boundary Element Method for Engineers, Pentech Press, London.

Bird, G.W. and Cameron, D.J. (1982). Vault Sealing Research for the Canadian Nuclear Fuel Waste Management Program. Atomic Energy of Canada Limited Technical Record*, TR-145.

Cameron, D.J. (1982). Fuel Isolation Research for the Canadian Nuclear Fuel Waste Management Program. Atomic Energy of Canada Limited Report, AECL-6834.

Chen, W.F. and Saleeb, A.F. (1982). Constitutive Equations for Engineering Materials: Volume I Elasticity and Modelling, John Wiley, New York.

Desai, C.S. and Christian, J.T. (Editors). (1977). Numerical Methods in Geotechnical Engineering, McGraw-Hill, New York.

Duncan, J.M. and Chang, C.Y. (1970). Nonlinear Analysis of Stress and Strain in Soils", Journal of the Soil Mechanics and Foundation Engineering Division, Proceedings ASCE, Vol. 96, pp. 1629-1653.

Duncan, J.M., Wong, K.S. and Ozawa, Y. (1980). FEADAM: A Computer Program for Finite Element Analysis of Dams, University of California, Berkeley, Report UCB/GT 80-02.

Gudehus, G. (Editor). (1977). Finite Elements in Geomechanics, John Wiley, New York.

Lopez, R.S., Cheung, S.C.H., and Dixon, D.A. (1984). The Canadian Program for Sealing Underground Nuclear Fuel Waste Vaults. Canadian Geotechnical Journal (in press). Also issued as AECL-8311.

Nuttall, K., Cameron, D.J., and Sargent, F.P. (1982). The Canadian Engineered Barriers

Program. Proceedings International Conference on Radioactive Waste Management, Winnipeg. Canadian Nuclear Society, Toronto, pp. 46-53.

Pande, G.N. and Zienkiewicz, O.C. (Eds.) (1982). Soil Mechanics - Transient and Cyclic Loads; Constitutive relations and numerical treatment, John Wiley, New York.

Radhakrishna, H.S. (1984). Thermal Properties of Clay-Based Buffer Materials for a Nuclear Fuel Waste Disposal Vault, Atomic Energy of Canada Limited Report, AECL-7805.

Rosinger, E.L.J. and Dixon, R.S. (1982). Fourth Annual Report of the Canadian Nuclear Fuel Waste Management Program. Atomic Energy of Canada Limited Report, AECL-7793.

Rummery, T.E. and Rosinger, E.L.J. (1982). The Canadian Nuclear Fuel Waste Management Program. Proceedings International Conference on Radioactive Waste Management, Winnipeg, Canadian Nuclear Society, Toronto, pp. 6-15.

Selvadurai, A.P.S. (1984a). Theoretical Modelling of Container-Buffer-Rock mass Interaction in a Nuclear Fuel Waste Disposal Vault During Water Uptake, Atomic Energy of Canada Limited, Technical Record*(in preparation).

Selvadurai, A.P.S. (1984b). Influence of Nonlinear Buffer Material Response on the Container-Buffer-Rock mass Interaction in a Nuclear Fuel Waste Disposal Vault During Water Uptake, Atomic Energy of Canada Limited, Technical Record* (in preparation).

Selvadurai, A.P.S. (1984c). On the Elastic-Plastic Response of Cylindrical and Spherical Composite Regions, Department of Civil Engineering, Carleton University, (Unpublished).

Selvadurai, A.P.S. (1985). Soil-Structure Interaction, Chapter 46 in Ground Engineers Reference Book (F.G. Bell, Editor), Butterworths, London.

---

* Technical Records are unrestricted, unpublished reports available from SDDO, Atomic Energy of Canada Limited, Chalk River, Ontario K0J 1J0.

Isolation of abandoned uranium tailings

Isolement de stériles miniers d'uranium abandonnés

G. R. THIERS, Principal Engineer, Earth Sciences Division, International Engineering Company, Inc.,
San Francisco, California, USA
E. S. SMITH, Chief Engineer, Earth Sciences Division, International Engineering Company, Inc.,
San Francisco, California, USA

SYNOPSIS   The radioactivity in tailings from processing of uranium ores can enter the environment in two forms: 1) Radon gas, the product of decay of uranium and radium; 2) Water-born contaminants, carried into the ground-water by leaching. A typical approach to controlling the escape of radon is to provide a cover of compacted moist soil. This cover can also help in the control of leaching, though total isolation using a compacted soil underliner may be required.

This paper discusses the radiological and chemical aspects of tailings isolation, including the following key aspects of design of an isolation system: (1) Reduction of the rate of radon exhalation (radon flux) by specifying a computed thickness of cover, 2) analysis and control of leaching and contaminant migration, 3) design of riprap for cover protection, and 4) certification of long-term durability of the cover protection material.

INTRODUCTION

Uranium tailings are produced when uranium ore is crushed and subjected to extraction processes, including acid leaching, ion exchange, precipitation, etc. The products resulting from these separation processes are uranium, which is of course the useful product, and tailings, which are discarded. A typical uranium tailings deposit is shown in Figure 1. Even though most of the uranium is removed from the ore, the extraction processes do not capture 100 percent, and the amounts left in the tailings are enough to make them radioactive to a level requiring special consideration.

Modern tailings management techniques include careful isolation, which minimizes the threat to humans and the environment. However, tailings deposits, formed before the dangers to people were fully realized, were often not so rigorously controlled. The steps needed to isolate tailings deposited under these conditions are the subject of this paper.

The health threat from uranium tailings is generally not the direct radiation, which is minor, but the gas, radon, which is given off as the uranium, and other radioactive elements present, decay. The radon not only gives off radiation at a harmful rate, but can be inhaled into the lungs, where it can decay into lead and remain in the body in this form until death. In addition, leaching of radioactive elements out of the tailings into the ground water can cause migration of these elements offsite, resulting in exhalation of radon at other locations.

Non-radioactive metals (lead, nickel, copper, arsenic, etc.) are often present in the tailings at toxic levels, posing an additional threat to the ground water. Finally the sealed site must be made secure against breaching, erosion or disturbance by human, animal or natural forces, which might accelerate radon emission, leaching, or actual transport of tailings to offsite locations.

Figure 1. Typical Abandoned Uranium Tailings Deposit (Photo provided by DOE UMTRA Project Office, Albuquerque)

The basic unit of radiation is the curie, Ci, defined as 3.7×10^{10} disintegrations per second. This unit appears in uranium tailings studies in the following three ways:

1. The concentration of radioactivity in radon in a given volume of the atmosphere is given in curies (or more commonly picocuries) per liter. (One picocurie = 1 pCi = 10^{-9} curies.)

2. The rate at which radon leaves a unit area of tailings surface (radon flux) is given in picocuries per square meter per second (pCi/m²/sec).

3. The concentration of a given radioactive element (radium, thorium, or uranium) in a unit mass of tailings is given in picocuries per gram (pCi/gm.).

The radiological and chemical standards to be met in isolation of uranium tailings in the United States were developed by the Environmental Protection Agency (EPA, 1983). Two alternative sets of standards are acceptable to EPA:

1. Remove all material contaminated to concentration levels exceeding 5 picocuries per gram (pCi/gm) in the top 15 cm of soil and exceeding 15 pCi/gm for any 15 cm thickness at greater depths. This brings the site to a condition allowing unlimited public access; or

2. Seal the site in a manner satisfying the following requirements. (In this case, except for maintenance activities, the site must be secured to prevent future access.)

a. Average concentrations of radon at the site boundary do not exceed 0.5 pCi/1, or average radon flux from the site surface does not exceed 20 pCi/m²/sec.

b. Ground-water aquifers are protected or restored to a level determined on a case-by-case basis taking into account relevant State and Federal Water Quality Criteria, considerations described in EPA's hazardous waste management system (47 FR 32274, July 26, 1982), feasibility, cost, and the future value of the aquifers.

The elapsed time for uranium, radium, etc., to decay to safe levels of radioactivity exceeds 10,000 years. Because the practicality of designing structures to last one thousand years can be questioned, EPA standards stipulate a minmum design life of 200 years and, where practical, a design life of 1,000 years (EPA, 1983).

PREDICTION AND CONTROL OF RADON FLUX

Measurement of the distribution of radioactive materials in an abandoned tailings deposit is illustrated by the work of Baker, et. al. (1984), at the Canonsburg, Pennsylvania site. (See Mason and Ball, 1984, for overview of this work.) At Canonsburg, surface gamma-ray exposure rate measurements were obtained (giving radon flux rates), surface soil samples were taken and analyzed (giving concentrations of radioactive contaminants), and borings were drilled and logged (giving gamma-ray exposure rates with depth). Radioactive material at varying concentrations, ranging as high as 1,000 pCi/gm, was found to be distributed heterogeneously throughout the site.

It was determined that a practical approach to tailings isolation would be to collect material having contamination concentrations exceeding 100 pCi/gm in a single location, minimizing the area requiring the thickest seal. (U.S. Department of Energy, 1983). Before receiving the tailings the area would be lined with clay to form the bottom of an encapsulation cell and to restrict leaching. Therefore, contour maps showing the thickness of material exceeding 100 pCi/gm were prepared for use in planning the excavation and designing the encapsulation cell (Fig. 2).

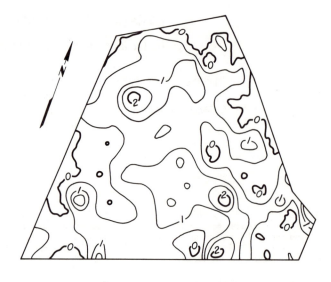

SCALE 100 0 100 200 300 METERS

CONTOUR INTERVAL = 0.5 METER

Figure 2.   Thickness Contours for Typical Deposit of Contaminated Material - Radiation Level 100 pCi/gm (After Baker, et. al, 1984)

Figure 2, showing the irregularity of distribution of the contaminated material, was used to estimate the volume of material to be excavated. Contour maps showing the elevation of the lower boundary of the material contaminated to levels exceeding 100 pCi/gm, were also prepared to define the limits of required excavation.

Control of radon flux from tailings is generally achieved by providing a cover of compacted moist soil, which becomes the radon barrier. The resulting reduction in flux depends on the thickness of the soil cover and the residual moisture content of the soil, expressed in terms of degree of saturation. The flux can be estimated using a procedure developed by Rogers and Nielson (1981), which is used by the designer to determine the soil layer thickness required to avoid exceedence of the allowable limit of 20 pCi/m²/sec. The soil layer is protected from erosion and desiccation by overlying layers of riprap and vegetated topsoil. The residual moisture content for a given design will depend on the corresponding long-term water balance. A typical cover cross-section is shown in Figure 3.

PREDICTION AND CONTROL OF GROUND-WATER CONTAMINATION

Even tightly compacted clay will have a permeability coefficient greater than zero, so that for significant rates of precipitation, infiltration through the radon barrier can occur. The rate of precipitation, infiltration through the radon barrier, and through the radon barrier into the tailings, can be predicted using the computer program HELP developed by Walski, et. al. (undated). This program, Hydrologic Evaluation of Landfill Performance, models the effects of monthly precipitation on a layered system, accounting for the permeability and slope of each layer. The program

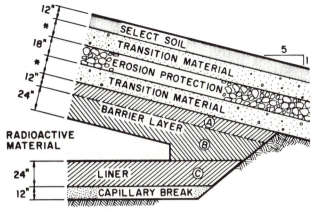

Figure 3.   Cross-Section for Typical Encapsulation
            Cell (After Thiers, et. al., 1984)

predicts runoff at the upper surface of each layer,
infiltration into and through each layer, and evapotranspiration. Based on an assumed permeability of
10^{-7} cm/sec., infiltration through the radon barrier
at Canonsburg will be at the rate of 1.2 inches per
year, for the local annual rainfall of 38 inches/year.
(U.S.D.O.E., 1983.)

A low permeability liner placed between the tailings
and the underlying soil restricts upward inflow from
any temporary rise in ground-water level. (The tailings
should be located above the long-term ground-water
level.) The liner is designed to permit seepage of
precipitation infiltration through the tailings and
lining without ponding.

The change in ground-water level expected as a result
of installation of an isolation system can be predicted
using the Illinois State Water Survey finite difference
hydrodynamic flow mode (Prickett and Lonnquist, 1971).
Contaminant travel from tailings to the water table has
been modeled by Gilbert, et. al. (1983). Studies have
shown that the time required for uranium at Canonsburg
to be leached from the tailings to the water table may
be as much as 2,000 years (Brinkman, 1983).

Lateral migration of contaminants within the ground
water can be predicted using the Prakash (1982) equations. In the ideal design, the concentration in the
ground water is diluted to acceptable levels before
exiting the site. (This is the case at the Canonsburg
site, Brinkman, 1984.) If necessary, the soil cover
thickness can be increased, or the soil permeability
decreased by adding bentonite, to conform to water
quality requirements.

SIZING OF RIPRAP TO PREVENT RILL GROWTH IN A LAYERED
SYSTEM

A schematic cross-section of a typical tailings pile
cover is shown in Figure 3. The design storm for the
1000-year life is generally taken to be the probable
maximum precipitation-PMP (U.S. Nuclear Regulatory
Commission, 1983). The resulting runoff will form
rills in topsoil which may extend downwards to the
underlying riprap. In one approach (Bone and Schruben,
1983), rill spacing and the resulting drainage area

contributing to a given rill are determined using rill
patterns observed by Mosley (U.S. Nuclear Regulatory
Commission , 1983). A typical rill pattern is shown in
Figure 4.

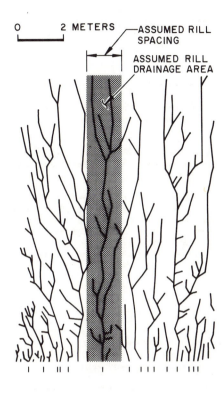

Figure 4.   Typical Rill Development on Plane
            Surface (After USNRC, 1983)

Applying the design storm to the drainage area contributing to a given rill, it is possible to compute the
peak flow to be carried by the rill. It is then
assumed that a trapezoidal rill cross-section will be
formed, with the bottom width equal to two times D_{50},
the mean size of the riprap. The rock size to prevent
further down-cutting can then be determined using
methods presented by the U.S. Department of Transportation (1975). D_{50} values of 10 to 12 inches were
required at Canonsburg, which has a relatively high
rainfall and a 5H to 1V cover slope (Bone and Schruben,
1983).

CERTIFICATION OF ROCK DURABILITY FOR 1,000-YEAR DESIGN
LIFE

Prediction of riprap durability for a design life of
200 years using testing procedures currently available
(hardness, sulfate soundness, freeze-thaw, etc.) is not
possible (Lindsey, et. al., 1982). Until predictions
using present test methods become more reliable, it
will be necessary to use historical data as the primary
evidence of durability for protection of uranium tailings covers. In this approach, fresh surfaces of a
rock in question that have been exposed for long
periods of time are examined for signs of weathering,
and data obtained in this fashion form the main basis
for certification.

For example, in the Canonsburg, Pennsylvania area, rock from a particular formation has served in building foundations and as paving stone for periods of approximately 100 years. The weathering during this period has been negligible, forming at the most a 1/32-inch thick layer of discoloration, with no change in stone size. Based on the available evidence, this formation has been designated an approved source of riprap for encapsulation cell protection at Canonsburg.

SUMMARY

Uranium tailings pose two threats:

1. Radon gas, given off as the radioactive constituents decay, can enter human lungs and cause radiation damage.

2. Radioactive elements and other heavy metals can be leached into the ground-water, producing toxic effects locally and off-site.

Contaminated material can be removed from the tailings site or encapsulated in an envelope of compacted moist soil. Encapsulation will meet EPA requirements by reducing radon concentrations at the site boundary and radon flux from the site surface, and controlling contaminant migration to the ground water. Encapsulation design must consider four key aspects:

1. Prediction and control of radon flux.

2. Prediction and control of ground-water contamination.

3. Protection of the radon barrier.

4. Certification of long-term design.

Radon flux is the rate at which radon is given off at the surface of the tailings deposit. Procedures for predicting this rate are discussed. It can be controlled by covering the tailings with compacted moist soil. The same procedures can be used to design the soil cover.

Contaminants can be leached to the ground water by downward seepage of infiltration, lateral seepage of ground water, or a rise and fall of ground water. The compacted soil cover can control infiltration; separating the tailings and the ground water can be accomplished by relocating the tailings, lowering the ground-water table, or extending the soil cover around and below the tailings, forming a soil envelope.

The soil cover, which forms a radon barrier, must be protected from erosion. This is currently accomplished using riprap, covered by topsoil. Design of riprap to resist the probable maximum precipitation is discussed. Isolation systems for uranium tailings are to be designed for a 1,000-year life if practical, with a minimum design life of 200 years. Given the reliability of available testing procedures for prediction of riprap durability, the use of the historical data approach is recommended for certification of riprap for a 200-year life.

REFERENCES

Baker, K. R., Mohr, D. E. and Hillman, R. L. (1984). "Radiological Aspects - Canonsburg, Pennsylvania UMTRA Site", Proc. 6th Annual Symposium on Management of Uranium Mill Tailings, Low-Level Waste and Hazardous Waste, Fort Collins, Colorado.

Bone, M. J. and Schruben, T. J. (1984). "Long-Term Stability - Canonsburg, Pennsylvania UMTRA Site", Proc. 6th Annual Symposium on Management of Uranium Mill Tailings, Low-Level Waste and Hazardous Waste, Fort Collins, Colorado.

Brinkman, J. E. (1984). "Ground Water - Canonsburg, Pennsylvania UMTRA Site", Proc. 6th Annual Symposium on Management of Uranium Mill Tailings, Low-Level Waste and Hazardous Waste, Fort Collins, Colorado.

EPA (1983). "Standards for Remedial Actions at Inactive Uranium Processing Sites", U.S. Environmental Protection Agency, Federal Register, Vol. 48, No. 3, Washington, D.C.

Gilbert, F., Chee, P. C., Knight, M. J., Peterson, J. M., Roberts, C. J., Robinson, J. E., Tsai, S. Y. H., and Yuan, Y. (1983). "Pathways, Analysis and Radiation Dose Estimates for Radioactive Residues at Formerly Utilized MED/AEC Sites", ORO-832. U.S. Department of Energy, Washington, D.C.

Lindsey, C. G., Long, L. W. and Begej, C. W., (1982). "Long-Term Survivability of Riprap for Armoring Uranium Mill Tailings and Covers: A Literature Review", U.S. Nuclear Regulatory Commission Report No. NUREG/CR-2642.

Mason, W. C. and Ball, D. M. (1984). "Overview - Canonsburg, Pennsylvania UMTRA Site", Proc. 6th Annual Symposium on Management of Uranium Mill Tailings, Low-Level Waste and Hazardous Waste, Fort Collins, Colorado.

Prakash, A. (1982). "Ground-Water Contamination Due to Vanishing and Finite-Size Continuous Sources", ASCE Journal of the Hydraulics Division (108) No. HY4.

Prickett, T. and Lonnquist, G. (1971). "Selected Digital Computer Techniques for Ground-Water Resource Evaluation", Illinois State Water Survey Bulletin 55, Champaign, Illinois.

Thiers, G. R., Guros, F. B., and Smith, E. S., (1984). "UMTRA Project: Canonsburg Final Design", Proc. 6th Annual Symposium on Management of Uranium Mill Tailings, Low-Level Waste and Hazardous Waste, Fort Collins, Colorado.

Rogers, V. C. and Nielson, K. K. (1981). "A Handbook for the Determination of Radon Attenuation Through Cover Materials", U.S. Department of Energy Report No. NUREG/CR-2340, RAE 18-1, Albuquerque, New Mexico.

U. S. Department of Energy (1983). "Remedial Action Plan for Stabilization of the Inactive Uranium Mill Tailings Site at Canonsburg, Pennsylvania", Report No. UMTRA-DOE/AL-140, Albuquerque, New Mexico.

U.S. Department of Transportation (1975). "Design of Stable Channels With Flexible Linings", Hydraulic Circular No. 15.

U.S. Nuclear Regulatory Commission (1983). "Design Considerations for Long-Term Stabilization of Uranium Mill Tailings Impoundments", prepared by Colorado State University, Fort Collins, Colorado.

Walski, T. M., Morgan, J. M., Gibson, A. C., and Schroeder, P. R. (undated). "User Guide for the Hydrologic Evaluation of Landfill Performance (HELP) Model", Municipal Environmental Research Laboratory, EPA, Cincinnati, Ohio.

Silt content and dynamic behavior of tailing sands

Contenue de silt et comportement dynamique de déchets

J. H. TRONCOSO, Professor of Civil Engineering, Pontificia Universidad Católica de Chile, Chile
R. VERDUGO, Research Assistant, Pontificia Universidad Católica de Chile, Chile

SYNOPSIS   Design of tailing dams in seismic countries requires considering the problems of excessive deformation and liquefaction in order to assure environmental protection. The dynamic behavior of silty sands, used in the construction of tailing dams, is analyzed to determine the influence of silt content. Triaxial tests of sands with different silt contents are reported, showing the variation of the shear modulus with strain and of the cyclic strength with the duration of the dynamic loading events.

INTRODUCTION

Dynamic behavior of tailing sands is largely controlled by the percentage of silts which form their fine content. Thus, experience has shown that a tailing dam built with sands with a low percentage of silts is more resistant to earthquake loadings than the same structure built with sands with higher silt contents. Because tailings produced by most mining processes are mainly composed by silts, resulting from fine grinding, it is necessary to mechanically separate coarse and fine fractions in order to obtain acceptable materials for tailing dams. This separation is generally expensive and it may require centrifugal cycloning to treat the complete slurry and to produce required low silt content sands as underflow product. The cost of this process rapidly increases as the acceptable percentage of fines decreases.

Therefore, the question of how high a silt content may be considered acceptable for the stability of tailing dams is of great importance in the economy of tailing disposal systems. This paper presents a contribution to this subject through the analysis of the influence of silt in the dynamic properties of tailing sands.

SEISMIC BEHAVIOR OF TAILING DAMS

Several tailing dams have failed during earthquakes, in recent years. Heavy losses in human lives and the destruction of valuable agricultural lands have resulted from catastrophic flow slides attributed to liquefaction failures of tailing materials. The consequences of these destructive failures have prompted the adoption of strong legal restrictions to construction of tailing dams resulting in substancial increases in cost and, sometimes, in the need to design more expensive conventional earth dams to contain the tailings, instead of traditional hydraulic fill structures. This problem of tailing disposal shall become more and more complex in future years as the increase in mining operations shall require more and larger tailing dams and as the growth of population shall reduce the availability of low risk dam sites.

Frequent problems associated with seismic failures of tailing dams have been related to substancial losses of shear strength induced by cyclic loadings in loose lenses of fine silty sands. The strength reduction is a consequence of pore water pressure increase during or inmediately after occurrence of an earthquake of strong magnitude and long duration. Cyclic decrease of shear strength in a lense of silty sand may induce slope stability failures or displacements in parts of a tailing dam, which even if limited to a small volume, do cause decrease of confinement and consequent increase in liquefaction potential of adjacent soils. Thus, a progressive failure is induced which worsens itself until complete failure may occur.

Progress of a liquefaction and slope stability failure process stops when pore water pressure dissipates to the extent necessary to bring shear strenth back to values larger than acting stresses. The rate of pressure dissipation depends upon the permeability of the soils and here, again, silt content is an important variable since smaller fine contents should contribute to faster decrease of water pressures.

RESEARCH PROGRAM

To analyze the influence of silt content in the dynamic behavior of tailing sands, a laboratory testing program was performed. Tested tailing soils were obtained, from a copper mine located in Central Chile, and prepared to form compacted specimens for static and cyclic triaxial tests. These soils were fine sands, SP, and silty sands, SM, with 0.42 mm maximum diameter. X-ray microscope photographs have shown solid particles to be very irregular and angular in shape (Troncoso, 1982). Fine fraction contained up to 18 percent colloidal particles.

After complete separation of fine and coarse fractions, in 74 micron-mesh, homogeneous mixtures of sands and silts were prepared to contain 0, 5, 10, 15, 22 and 30 percent fines.

Properties of the different silty sands were measured to define index and mechanical characteristics. In particular, properties of the soil structure were determined in static triaxial tests through the analyses of stress-strain curves and shear strength parameters.

Dynamic behavior of these soils was determined by cyclic triaxial testing. First, series of tests were performed to define hysteretic loops of stress-strain and dynamic shear modulus as a function of strain. Second, shear strength and liquefaction tests were performed to monitorize pore pressure build-up and strain history, and to determine stress ratios required to induce cyclic failure as a function of duration of the loading event. Equipment used for these dynamic tests was a Seiken triaxial compression press which characteristics have been described elsewhere (Verdugo, 1983).

PROPERTIES OF SOIL STRUCTURE

Static mechanical properties of the silty sands are herein discussed on the basis of series of test results obtained with different silt contents and with same initial void ratio comparable to those representative of specimens tested in dynamic tests. Static shear strength of tested silty sands, as measured in consolidated drained triaxial tests, is due to frictional resistance between highly angular particles. Therefore, effect of silt content is well represented by results of a series of triaxial tests as shown in Fig. 1. Internal friction angle, $\emptyset$, determined by the slope of the envelope of shear strength as a function of effective stress, σ_0', decreases as silt content increases. These results, which correspond to soils compacted to same void ratio equal to 0.9, show that $\emptyset$ decreases from 44° to 39° as silt content increases from 0 to 30 percent. Volumetric deformation measurements of tailing silty sands, under same confining pressure, show strong dilative tendency for these soils. Measurements recorded for 147 kPa confining pressure, indicate that, at maximum deviator stress, dilatancy of silty

sands decreases, from 2.2 to 0.3 percent, as silt content increases, from 0 to 30 percent. Compressibility of silty sands, represented by initial tangent modulus, increases very significantly as fine content increases from 0 to 15 percent and further increases for 22 and 30 percent.

Critical state lines were determined in monotonic triaxial compression tests to analyze the influence of silt content on the relationships between volume change and confining pressure. Critical void ratio, as defined by Casagrande (1979), was found to range between 1.15 and 1.05, for clean tailing sand, and to decrease to a range between 1.0 and 0.8, for silty sands with 15 percent silt, for same range of confining pressures between 10 and 588 kPa. Therefore, silt content decreases the void ratio that marks the boundary between compressional and dilatational behavior. The silt content has then an unfavorable influence upon volume change characteristic under shear stresses. This fact will be reflected in the dynamic behavior of these soils as will be analyzed in next section.

CYCLIC STRENGTH AND DYNAMIC SHEAR MODULUS

The effects of dynamic loading on tailing sands have been measured in series of cyclic triaxial tests devoted to determine curves of shear modulus as function of shear strain and curves of cyclic strength as function of number of cycles. In both types of tests silt content was the main parameter. Compacted soil specimens were consolidated and tested with a combination of deviator stress, σ_d, and consolidation stress, σ_0', such that cyclic stress ratio varied between $+\sigma_d/2\sigma_0'$ and $-\sigma_d/2\sigma_0'$. Relevant test results are summarized in Figs. 2 to 4.

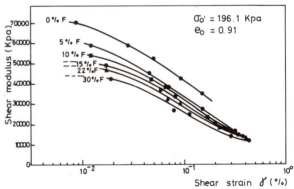

FIG. 2 SHEAR MODULUS AS A FUNCTION OF STRAIN

Curves in Fig. 2 show that shear modulus decreases in a significant amount, as shear strain increases, for all tested silty sands. In effect, under 196 kPa effective confining stress, and for 0.91 initial void ratio, modulus decrease rate is about 40 percent, as shear strain increases from 10^{-2} to 10^{-1} percent. It is also noticeable that, for any given strain value, shear modulus decreases as silt content increases. These results confirm that deformability of tailing sands increases with silt content and with magnitude of strain. Therefore, it should be

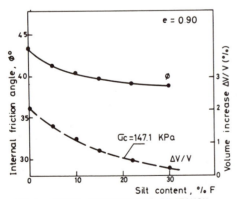

FIG. 1 SHEAR STRENGTH AND DILATANCY OF TAILING SANDS.

expected that, when these soils become saturated, their behavior under cyclic loading should be strongly influenced by their capabilities to deform.

This assumption is indeed confirmed by results of cyclic strength and liquefaction tests. For instance, as it is observed in Fig. 3, for same pore water pressure increase, much larger axial deformations are obtained in tailing soils with greater silt content. This is so because, as shear modulus, G, is proportional to effective stress, or:

$$G = K(\sigma_0 - u_W)^{1/2} \qquad (1)$$

where:
K = coefficient dependent on silt content, strain level and density
σ_0 = confining stress
u_W = pore water pressure

any increase in the pore water pressure results in a decrease in shear modulus, which in turn leads to a further increase in pore pressure. This fact, compounded with the lower permeabilities of siltier sands, results in that, if the number of repetitions of loadings is sufficiently large, liquefaction failure should occur, and it should occur in a smaller number of cycles in tailing sands with higher silt contents.

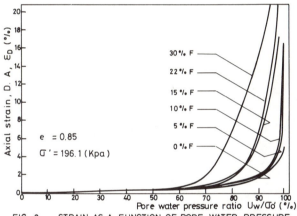

FIG. 3   STRAIN AS A FUNCTION OF PORE WATER PRESSURE INCREASE FOR TAILING SANDS WITH DIFFERENT SILT CONTENT.

In fact, noticeable differences are appreciated in the cyclic strength, or stress ratio required to reach a state of liquefaction, of tailings with different silt contents. For instance, under same initial confining stress and void ratio, curves in Fig. 4 show that cyclic strength may be larger by a factor of 2.7, if silt content is reduced from 30 to 0 percent. A moderate reduction in silt content from 30 to 15 percent may improve cyclic strength by 50 percent.

The duration of the cyclic loading event similarly affected all tested soils in the sense that significative reductions of strength occurred as number of cycles increased.

Therefore, silt content is a very important variable in cyclic strength and in cyclic deformability of tailing sands. This is so because of the mechanical characteristics of progressive decrease of strength and of liquefaction phenomena.

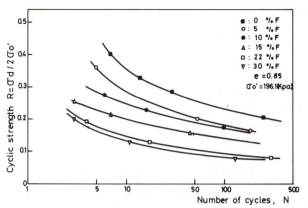

FIG. 4   CYCLIC STRENGTH OF TAILING SANDS WITH DIFFERENT SILT CONTENT.

The important influence of silt content in cyclic behavior of tailing sands may be further attributed to significative changes in the fabric and structure of these soils as particles of fine non-cohesive silts fill in the voids of otherwise stronger angular sands and, therefore, increase their tendency to fail in shear during dynamic loading events.

The effects of these changes are much more important in cyclic behavior than in static conditions, as it may be noticed from comparison of Figs. 1 and 4, because the advantages of dilatational capabilities do not have time to materialize when repeated short-period cycles of loading and low permeabilities preclude fast dissipation of the net increments in pore water pressures.

CONCLUSIONS

Tailing soils, which result from fine grinding and flotation process of rock minerals, such as copper mineral tailings, are composed of angular particles with sharp edges and irregular shapes. These particles form structures characterized by strong resistance to shear deformation because of interlocking between particles. Large energies are required to overcome this resistance and to cause relative displacements of the particles. This is demonstrated by large internal friction angles and by strong tendencies to dilate under shear.

Inclusion of silt particles, much smaller in size than sand particles, reduces the strength of resulting silty sands. This may be due to an effect of silt particles filling in irregular voids of larger sand grains and thus decreasing favorable interlocking effects. Then, angle of internal friction, tendency to dilate and moduli of compressibility are reduced as silt content is increased.

Cyclic strength of tailing sands is significantly and unfavorably affected by silt content. Thus, it has been shown that even a moderate increase in percentage of fines may cause substantial increase in the susceptability of the soils to suffer liquefaction failure. The reasons are larger compressibilities and smaller permeabilities of sands with higher silt contents.

Test results summarized in preceding sections show that larger stress ratios and greater number of repetitions of loadings are required to cause cyclic failure of clean sands as compared with silty sands. These results indicate that while a deposit of clean tailing sand should be able to stand without failure a strong earthquake, equivalent to a given acceleration level in a certain number of repetitions, a similar deposit of silty sands should fail with a much weaker event, equivalent to accelerations only one-half or one-third as large, or for a same acceleration with only a small fraction of the duration of the strong event.

The differences in the behavior of silty sands with different silt contents is important for practical purposes. Changes seem to be more noticeable in the lower range, such as between 0 and 15 percent, and 15 and 22 percent, than between 22 and 30 percent. Therefore, depending upon seismicity of an area where tailing dams are to be built, it is worthwhile to invest in necessary cycloning efforts required to lower silt content. However, since small differences may result in significantly different seismic behavior, the precise allowable percentage of silts should be determined by an adequate program of dynamic tests.

ACKNOWLEDGMENTS

The authors are indebted to the Dirección de Investigación of the Pontificia Universidad Católica de Chile which sponsored project DIUC 38/81, about "Variation of Dynamic Properties of Sands Under Earthquake Loadings", and made possible the performance of the experimental part of this work.

REFERENCES

Casagrande, A. (1976) "Liquefaction and Cyclic Deformation of Sands. A Critical Review", Harvard Soil Mechanics Series N° 88.

Troncoso, J.H. (1982) "Variación del Módulo de Corte de Arenas ante Cargas Sísmicas", Proceedings, First Chilean Conference on Geotechnical Engineering, 67-83, Santiago.

Troncoso, J.H. (1983) "Seismic Pore Water Pressures in Tailing Dams", Proceedings, Seventh Panamerican Conference on Soil Mechanics and Foundation Engineering, 641-655, Vancouver.

Verdugo, R. (1983) "Influencia del Porcentaje de Finos en la Resistencia Cíclica de Arenas de Relaves". Thesis presented to the School of Engineering, Catholic University of Chile, in partial fullfillment for the degreee of Civil Engineer.

Field consolidation of thin layers of dredged material

Tassements de couches de faible épaisseur formés par des matériaux dragués

C. VALORE, Researcher in Geotechnical Engineering, University of Palermo; Lecturer in Earth Retaining Structures,
University of Calabria, Italy
I. A. GIGLIO, Civil Engineer

SUMMARY - Preliminary results of a research programme on the geotechnical behaviour of thin layers of organic hydrauli- cally deposited dredged material are reported and discussed. The paper focuses on the spatial variability of the proper- ties of soils and on the singularities of the pattern of settlements. The layers present intricate,yet non-random, va- riations in geotechnical properties. The initial heterogeneities, mainly controlled by the flow regime of the slurry wi- thin the containment area, govern the progress of consolidation, in so far as they entail selective evaporation, de- siccation and crack formation processes, which are strongly coupled. The related one-dimensional moving boundary problem might be solved by a step-by-step procedure, the most important single factor to be accounted for being the formation of desiccation cracks. Deterministic prediction of settlements of the layer appears, however, overwhelmingly difficult.

1 - INTRODUCTION

Fine-grained organic dredged materials are frequently deposited within diked disposal areas, in order to control unfavourable effects on the physical environment. The per- formance of the impoundment basins and of the containment structures are governed by sedimentation, seepage, con- solidation, diffusion, evapotranspiration processes. The analysis of these is complicated by initial heterogenei- ties and by variations - in space and with time - of the properties of the material and of boundary conditions.
While classical consolidation models fail to describe ade- quately the behaviour of the layer, recent studies point to the feasibility of reliable predictions, provided the layer is homogeneous and that unidimensional deformation conditions apply (Salem & Krizek, 1976). When the layers are heterogeneous, the prediction of the progress of settlements still proves to be uncertain.
A research programme on the mechanical behaviour of thin layers of organic dredged materials, hydraulically deposi- ted within confined basins was recently started in conne- ction with dredging of the bottom of Pergusa Lake. The study is directed toward investigating the spatial varia- bility of geotechnical properties of soils after deposi- tion, the progress of settlement, the feasibility of modelling the actual consolidation process, the diffusion of slurry particles into the containment dikes. Concurren- tly, assessment of the effectiveness of probability-based subsoil exploration of deposits built-up by oriented processes is being investigated. Some of the data and observations as yet collected on the soil formation and on the field consolidation processes are outlined and discussed in the paper, that is primarily concerned with the identification of main factors which determine actual behaviour.

2 - ENVIRONMENT, FOUNDATION SOILS, CONTAINMENT STRUCTURES

Pergusa Lake, in Sicily, was once renowned for the redden- ing of its waters. Some years ago, it reached an eutrophic condition, associated - among other events - with the overgrowth of sea-weeds. The lake is fed by a

small watershed; no stream flows into it; the outflow is prevented by a calcarenitic relief which develops round the basin. The volume of the lake is about 2×10^6 m^3.
Soils below lake bottom consist of recent organic sandy silts and of sands down to depths ranging from 10 to 15 m. Decay of sea-weeds adds more and more to the organic content of the upper layers. Recent soils are underlain by a clay formation which is conch-shaped at the top. The lake beach is formed by loose sands interbedded with soft silt lenses. The permeability coefficient of the sands ranges from 10^{-3} to 10^{-5} cm/sec. Among the measures taken to give the lake normal biological conditions, removal by dredging of a layer, 1 to 3 m thick, of organic sediments from the lake bottom was included. Land disposal of dredgings at considerable distances, though feasible, was disregarded on account of the limited volume of the lake, which might have turned dry in consequence of heavy water removal. It was, on the contrary, necessary to return, as soon as possible, into the lake the waters subtracted during dredging. For this purpose, six sedimentation and accumulation basins were built on the lake beach, fig. 1. The basins were enclosed by embankment dikes, formed with very soft calcarenitic rocks, that after compaction were almost completely reduced to a fine-medium sand. Seepage through the dikes and filtration was required for the intended functions of the basins.
The permeability coefficient of the uncontaminated mate- rial forming the dikes, as backfigured from field data, is about 3×10^{-4} cm/sec. Maximum height of dikes is 2.5 m. The basins were connected in series, three by three, at crest level, by small overflow weirs, fig. 1.

3 - SEDIMENT FORMATION

Dredged sediments were pumped in slurry form into basins, through an inlet pipe, 0.3 m diam. and 500 m long. At in- let head, the solid fraction, ranging from 3 to 6% by weight, was completely disgregated with the exception of some well rounded "boulders" formed by indurated hard sandy silt.
The discharge of slurry into the basins was carried out

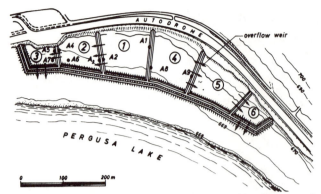

Fig. 1 - Plan of diked disposal area; A1, A2, .. settlement beacons.

discontinuosly, 5 days per week and 12 hours per working day. The discharge took place into a basin at a time, until the containment area was filled up to dikes crest level. The average slurry discharge rate was 350 m³/h. The configuration of the upper surface of the layer being formed during filling in basins 1 and 2 was periodically surveyed. Collected data point out that the top surface of accumulated sediments is never horizontal, and that the rate of sediment formation varies markedly with space and time. Rates of layer thickening vary likewise. Monthly accretion rates range from 0.1 to 5.4 cm/day, yearly rates from 0.2 to 0.7 cm/day; their spatial distribution show no simple pattern, although it is not random. In fact, it depends upon the flow regime, which is, in turn, influenced by former configuration of the top of the layer. Streams departing from the discharge point were detected by observing the paths of small polystyrene balls and were found to be winding up and meandering within the basin. Higher accretion rates were distributed near the paths of the "streams". Flow velocities never exceeded 1 m/min.
The accretion rates could not have been predicted on the

basis of results of "tube" sedimentation-consolidation tests carried out under one dimensional vertical seepage conditions. Results of such a test are shown in fig. 2. The tube, 2 m in diam. and 2 m high, was filled with slurry recovered at the inlet pipe head. Test duration was 175 days. Immediately after filling, sand-sized particles settled to the bottom; during next 30 minutes, flocculation and sedimentation took place. Curve B in fig. 2 shows that sediment formation was complete after 50 hours and selfweight and seepage induced consolidation started. After 200 h gas bubbles were observed; after 1000 h sea-weeds grew on the surface of the sediment. After 700 h from test beginning, consolidation did not progress, although the sand filter was not clogged, as confirmed by curva A in fig. 2 and by direct inspection at the end of the test. This standstill is probably due to gas generation, and to the high degrees of freedom of each particle within the particulate system. Due to the very high void ratio, the interaction of particles is so limited that intergranular stresses are vanishingly low and the effective stress state is not uniquely determined. This "indeterminacy" is confirmed by the experiments of Been and Sills (Been & Sills, 1981).
At the end of the test, the water content of the sedimented materials was found to vary linearly from 136% at bottom up to 466% at the top; corresponding void ratios ranged from 3.4 to 11.2.
Actual sediment formation within the basins was much more rapid, due to boundary conditions very different from those of the tube test, to the effect of drag forces associated with the movement of the slurry, to heterogeneities and to desiccation during interruptions of filling. To get an indication of the overall influence of the above processes - considering that selfweight and seepage induced effective stresses in the test cylinder were not less than in the field - it suffices to mention that 1.05×10^6 m³ of slurry was discharged into basins 1 and 2 in the period between April 1980 and July 1981, and that the volume of accumulated sediments during the same time interval amounted to 30,178 m³ whereas it would have been 70,000 m³ should the results of the test apply.

4 - SPATIAL VARIABILITY IN GEOTECHNICAL PROPERTIES OF ACCUMULATED MATERIALS

Hydraulic deposition of sediments implies selective sorting of the particles in function of their grain-size and specific gravity, the rate of discharge, the flow velocities and the composition of the slurry. Once the slurry has been discharged in the basin, the coarser particles settle near and around the inlet zone, silt particles are carried farther away from the discharge point, the fines reach the dikes or the overflow weirs. The process, in reality, is not so paradigmatically regular, especially when the discharge rates and the flow velocities within the disposal area are low. Under such circumstances, "currents" and streams do not conform to fixed stable patterns. As a consequence, the distribution of geotechnical properties of dredged materials is not easily identifiable. However, it may be hardly assumed that the soil properties vary randomly, since the formation process, though irregular, is definitely oriented. Accordingly, geotechnical properties must show definite patterns. The operational definition of these for engineering purposes is, of course, related to the size of

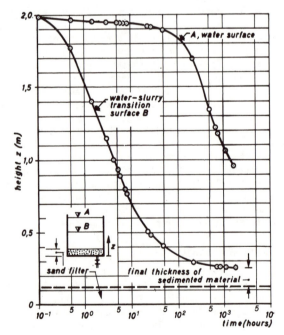

Fig. 2 - Results of tube sedimentation-consolidation test.

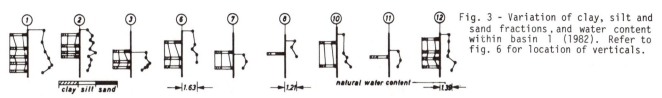

the geotechnical system to be dealt with.

Available data, while not yet sufficient to precisely describe the macrostructural arrangement of the layers and the spatial distribution of geotechnical properties, do point to conspicous heterogeneities and to a marked influence of the deposition mode. Heterogeneities - original and induced by the consolidation process - are reflected by the peculiarities of the distribution of settlements. Some of available data are reported below.

Index properties

The range of **grain-size distribution** is rather large. Soil fractions vary as follows: sand 0 - 0.50; silt 0.18 - 0.57; clay 0.18 - 0.43. Clay, silt and sand fractions within basin 1 are shown in fig. 3. Particle-size distribution varies appreciably with depth, and from vertical to vertical. Sand fraction is larger in correspondence and near the discharge point, farther from this variations of granulometric composition along a single vertical are much less sharp. Apart from this general trend, differences between verticals located a few meters from each other are relevant. Direct inspection of excavation walls, in the central part of basin 1, put into evidence sand lenses and laminations that do not appear to be located at random nor equifrequently distributed.

Organic matter content (OMC), ranges from 0.1 to 0.7; maximum relative frequence corresponds to OMC values between 0.4 and 0.5. Distribution of OMC within basin 4 is shown in fig. 4.

Specific gravity range from 21 to 26 kN/m^3; lower values are associated with higher organic matter content. **Unit weight** of saturated material ranges from 11 to 14 kN/m^3.

Void ratio values depend on depth and on the time after filling completion. Typical values are 3.3 - 4.1 near the top, and 2.1 - 2.4 in the vicinity of the bottom. Since the range of specific gravity of solids is narrow and the degree of saturation is almost always 1, the distribution of void ratios is conformable to that of water content, shown in fig. 4.

Water content profiles are shown in figures 3 and 4. Water contents are very high, spatial variations being relevant. In general higher water contents are related to higher organic contents; however, no clear correlation is apparent probably because consolidation is still in progress and has reached different stages within the basin. The materials can be classified as organic silts of high compressibility. The **liquid limit** ranges from 0.48 to 0.93

the **plasticity index** from 0.10 to 0.24.

Compressibility

Volume change behaviour under low applied stresses was investigated by means of oedometer tests on samples recovered, from basin 1, six months after filling completion. Each load increment was maintained about one month. Typical data are summarized in table I. It must be noted that e - log σ'_v curves are nearly linear.

Shear strength

Laboratory vane tests were performed on samples from basin 1; c_u values are overestimated due to compression of the material during sampling and range from 6.7 to 22.5 kN/m^2. A detailed in situ vane test programme has been recently initiated. Preliminary results confirm that c_u values are very low, except for the desiccated crust.

Penetration resistance

To uncover details of the constitution of the layers, and obtain a simple - yet effective - description of the spatial variability of mechanical characteristics, 26 penetration tests were carried out within basin 4, 22 months after completion of filling. A special, light, hand operated, penetrometer consisting essentially of a conical point of standard dimensions and shape (angle: 60°; area: 10 cm^2) and of a hammer dropping apparatus was used. The hammer weight is 102 kN; the height of fall was established in 10 cm, after preliminary investigations, which proved that a height of 20 cm would be ineffective for the detection of variations. Usual penetration tests would yield a "flattened" picture of the deposit.

Uncorrected results are shown in fig. 4. Penetration induced by a single blow of the hammer is reported, instead of the number of blows necessary to obtain a fixed length of penetration. The diagrams in fig. 4 clearly point out that:
- the variations along each vertical are relevant even when the layer is thin;
- the difference in penetration resistance is enormous within the basin; it is, moreover, very marked from one vertical to the adjacent, compare for example verticals S9 and S10, section b-b in fig. 4;
- the penetration logs accurately depict the pattern of consolidation progress at each location within the basin, and are in good agreement with the water content distribution;
- bottom and upper drainage appears to be more effective than drainage toward the containment dikes. In fact, penetration resistances are lower along S4, S1, S15, S14, S13, S21, S25, S11 and S26 than along inner verticals, irrespective of their distances from the containment structures;
- the penetration resistance distribution along each vertical strongly correlates to the presence of ridges and troughs on the upper surface of the layer:

Table I - Typical data on compressibility of dredged material, from basin 1, sampled six months after completion of filling.

sample	w_n initial	e_0	γ_{sat} (kN/m^3)	γ_s (kN/m^3)	σ'_v (kN/m^2)	E' (kN/m^2)	C_c	C_α	C_v (cm^2/sec)
8 g	1.03	2.62	12.0	21.6	58.8	324	075	0.013	–
11 a	1.05	2.91	12.4	23.6	98.1	294	1.15	0.014	$2.5 \cdot 10^{-4}$
102 b	1.38	3.45	13.1	24.5	73.6	608	1.04	0.006	$1.7 \cdot 10^{-4}$
103	1.82	4.18	12.4	22.6	76.5	324	1.60	0.007	$1.0 \cdot 10^{-6}$

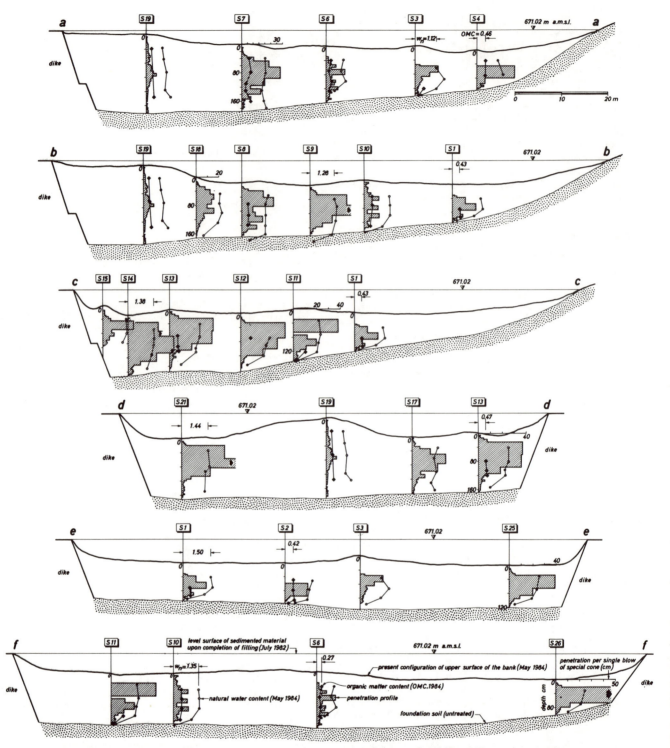

Fig. 4 - Penetration resistance within basin 4, 22 months after completion of filling. The arrow signals free penetration of the cone under the weight of the rod. Settlement profiles, water and organic contents are also shown.

resistance is higher in correspondence of the ridges and very low below the troughs, compare verticals S9 and S10. S10 corresponds to a ridge and S9, about 10 m apart, is below a trough; despite the fact that the surface settlements do not differ appreciably, that the initial thickness of the layer was the same, penetration

resistances are strikingly different; in the central part along S9 the cone freely penetrated under the weight of the rod.
The recorded penetration resistances reflect the influence of many factors. It is, however, readily apparent from fig. 4 that effects depending upon deposition modalities

Table II - Ratio surface settlement/initial thickness of the layer in function of time elapsed from filling completion.
t: days; **t** = 0, June 1981. Initial thickness in cm: **A3**: 56; **A4**: 68; **A6**: 214; **A7** 135. For location of settlement beacons refer to fig. 1.

time t beacon	25	30	45	126	540	1,082
A 3	0.11	0.20	0.25	0.39	—	—
A 4	0.13	—	0.26	0.48	—	—
A 6	0.06	0.07	0.09	0.16	0.44	0.53
A 7	0.14	0.22	0.33	0.36	—	—

play a remarkable - direct and indirect - role. This conclusion is supported by the pattern of settlement distribution of the upper surface of the layer.

5 - FIELD SETTLEMENTS

Settlements of the upper surface of the layers were measured, after the completion of filling, by means of settlement beacons, placed prior to the initiation of filling. Only six of the installed beacons survived long enough to allow assessment of the progress of settlement. Data are summarized in table II. Beacons Al to A4 were placed on the shells of dikes; A6 and A7 rested on the bottom of basins at a distance of about 10 m from the bunds. Referring to the time interval 0 - 126 days, for which it is possible to compare the deformational behaviour, it may be noted that strains and strain rates are very large everywhere. Strains increase almost linearly with time near the dikes (beacons Al - A4) in the first 45 days; then the strain rates slow down. The behaviour along A7 is similar to that of Al - A4 in the first period; afterwards, the progress of settlement rapidly slows down. The settlement in A6 progresses almost linearly with time up to 540 days, with an average strain rate of 8×10^{-4} /day. The observed behaviour cannot be traced back solely to selfweight and seepage induced consolidation. On the contrary, it largely results from desiccation processes which start soon after completion of filling and are activated and sustained by high evaporation rates. In this regard, it should be reported that monthly average values of temperatures of the air range from 5.5° C (January) to 25° C (July) and that during daylight, in summer period, temperature is higher than 35° C. Desiccation entails the formation of a network of cracks, which in turn increase the rate of evaporation of soils. Cracks were observed to develop firstly near the dikes and in the spots where the

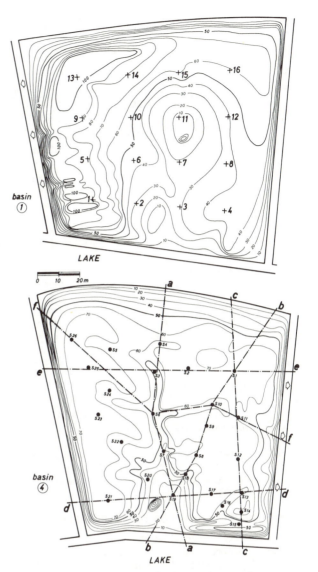

Fig. 6 - Basin 1 and 4 - Settlement contours of upper surface of the layer, May 1984 - Settlements in cm.

upper part of the layer was formed by clayey silts. Cracks formed in a few days near the edges of the dikes and after about 20 days within the basins. Spacing, depth and opening of cracks decreased from the dikes toward the central part of basins. Where the sand fraction was relatively high, cracks either did not develop, or were spaced more than 1 m, whilst where silts prevailed the spacing was about 0.2 m, fig. 5. The presence of sand fractions from 15 to 20% considerably delayed the development of cracks. The depth of cracks is likewise conditioned. The progress of settlement with time is correlated to the above processes. Along vertical Al - A4, cracks develop rapidly due to the vicinity of a draining boundary, and to limited thickness of layers. In A7 the influence of the dikes is not appreciable, but the development of cracks is rapid as the material predominantly consist of clayey silts: as a result the settlement rate is similar to that observed in Al - A4 in the first period; at the onset of winter season the rate slows down.

Fig. 5 - Differential settlements in correspondence and in the vicinity of a ridge, basin 6. Crack spacing in the ridge is larger than in the adjacent zone.

Table III - Volume reduction of accumulated material after completion of filling. V: initial volume; A: area of basin; ΔV: volume reduction up to May 1984; ΔV_c: volume of open cracks; w_m: average settlement over the basin.

basin	V (m^3)	A (m^2)	ΔV (m^3)	ΔV_c (m^3)	t (months)	$\frac{\Delta V}{V}$	w_m (m)
1	19,490	11,812	5,506	2,953	36	0.30	0.50
2	10,688	7,125	6,413	1,781	32	0.60	0.90
3	16,875	11,250	6,122	2,812	22	0.36	0.54
4	13,672	10,937	6,016	2,734	18	0.44	0.55

The behaviour recorded in A6 is, again, related to desiccation and to crack progress: cracks develop later and slowly due to material composition and to the presence of heterogeneities. The effects of these factors on the distribution of settlements within the single basin are strikingly evidenced by settlement profiles, fig. 4, and by settlement contours shown in fig. 6. In all basins, the upper surface of the layer is characterised by ridges and troughs; differential settlements over short distances are marked and sometimes sharp. Ridges and troughs are not randomly distributed; their location can be traced back to the flow pattern during deposition. This oriented process determines the initial spatial variability of the geotechnical system and controls the pattern of cracks and their propagation rate. Induced heterogeneities are associated with the above processes, which are coupled.

Data on volume reduction, after hydraulic deposition, are summarised in table III. Average settlement over each basin range from 0.5 to 0.9 m; the rate of volumetric strain varies from 0.019 to 0.024 per month.

Volume decrease, in reality, is larger due to the presence of open cracks. The horizontal area of these is estimated to be, in May 1984, about 50% of the basin area; their average depth amounts to about 0.5 m; associated volume decrease is reported in table III.

6 - FEASIBILITY OF MODELLING THE CONSOLIDATION PROCESS

The possibility of modelling the actual process is currently being explored. Two distinct problems may be envisaged. The first refers to one-dimensional consolidation of thin layered banks of soil; the second to the prediction of the behaviour of the deposit within each disposal area. The first, moving boundary, problem, may be solved by a step-by-step procedure, taking account of field indications. The major difficulty appears to be the interdependence of the many different involved processes. The most relevant factors - as yet overlooked by researcher in this field - to account for are the growth of cracks, their widening and deepening.

Steps toward modelization should include consideration of accretion history of the layer, consolidation induced by selfweight and by seepage forces, large strains, induced heterogeneities, evaporation, crack growth and propagation. It is also to note that the effects of capillarity actions, which would slow or hinder downward movement of water, may be greatly reduced at the onset of cracks. Each single aspect of the process may be handled by known theories (Gibson et al., 1967 and 1981; Gardner, 1961). The second problem, i.e. deterministic modelization of the process taking place within the single basin, is overwhelmingly difficult, if not impossible. Statistical and probabilistic treatment must be resorted to. Usual methods

of analysis fail, however, to account for the non-random nature of spatial variations in physical and mechanical properties of the layer and for the selective pattern of desiccation and crack formation and may well lead to unsafe prediction of the expected range of differential settlements and distortions.

7 - CONCLUDING REMARKS

Results of preliminary investigations point out that the hydraulic deposition of dredged materials within containment basins give rise to marked spatial variations in the physical and mechanical properties of accumulated soils. The initial state of the layer is marked by intricate but non-random heterogeneities, which are controlled to a great extent by the flow regime of slurry within the basin. Initial heterogeneities govern the progress of consolidation in so far as they entail selective evaporation, desiccation and crack formation. Induced heterogeneities further enhance differential settlements. Due mainly to desiccation and to the development of closely spaced cracks, which continously alter the upper boundary conditions, field progress of settlement is faster than could be predicted by classical consolidation models. It is suggested that modelling of local behaviour of the layer, under one-dimensional deformation conditions, is feasible provided coupled effects of the various involved processes be accounted for. In this regard growth and propagation of cracks appear to be the most important factors. Deterministic prediction of the settlements of the whole layer is reputed overwhelmingly complex. Statistical or probabilistic treatment of this latter problem requires to account for the non-random nature of the deposition and subsequent processes.

Although the field experiments referred to cannot be taken as representative of natural deposition and deformational processes, field observations give some insight into the origin of variabilities in the geotechnical properties of recent natural soil deposits.

REFERENCES

Been K. and Sills G.C. (1981) - Self-weight consolidation of soft soils: an experimental and theoretical study. Geotechnique, 31, 519 - 535.

Gardner W.R. (1961) - Soil suction and water movement. Proc. Conf. on Pore Pressure and Suction in Soils. 137 - 140 - Butterworths, London.

Gibson R.E., England G.L. and Hussey M.J.L. (1967) - The theory of one-dimensional consolidation of saturated clays, I. Finite non-linear consolidation of thin homogeneous layers. Geotechnique, 17, 261 - 273.

Gibson R.E., Schiffman R.L. and Kargill K.W. (1981) - The theory of one-dimensional consolidation of saturated clays, II. Finite non-linear consolidation of thick homogeneous layers. Can. Geot. Jl., 18, 280 - 293.

Salem A.M. and Krizek R.J. (1976) - Stress-Deformation-Time Behaviour of Dredgings. Jl. Geot. Eng. Div., A.S.C.E., GT2, Feb. 1976, 139 - 157.

ACKNOWLEDGMENTS

Senior author is grateful to Prof. R. Jappelli for his suggestions and review of the paper. Thanks are due to Consorzio di Bonifica Borgo Cascino, Enna, and to Dr. A. Risita for permission to conduct the field investigations.

Compressibility of neutralized phosphogypsum

Compressibilité du phosphogypse neutralisé

B. P. WRENCH, Steffen, Robertson and Kirsten, Johannesburg, South Africa
G. E. BLIGHT, University of Witwatersrand, Johannesburg, South Africa

SYNOPSIS   Phosphogypsum tailings is a by product of the fertilizer industry. A large tailings impoundment has been formed of phosphogypsum neutralized by the addition of lime. This paper describes a field and laboratory study to determine the compressibility parameters of the material. The tests show the phosphogypsum to be highly compressible and to display considerable secondary compression.

INTRODUCTION

In 1984 a phosphoric acid plant was established at Richards Bay on the east coast of Natal, South Africa. The town has developed rapidly because of the recent construction of a deep water harbour. Further harbour related and industrial development is planned which must take account of extensive mangrove marshes around the harbour. Reclamation of large areas of swamp has already been accomplished by the use of hydraulic fill recovered during dredging for the harbour. Further development of the marsh lands is however being delayed by a shortage of fill materials.

The phosphoric acid factory is located close to the harbour and potential sites for the tailings impoundment were therefore limited. A site was chosen for the impoundment in a low lying marsh on the northern boundary of the harbour. The site is underlain by up to 30m of interbedded soft clays and sands. Following evaluation of the environmental impact of the facility it was decided to neutralize the phosphogypsum at the factory by the addition of lime prior to its placement on the impoundment. The impoundment is constructed by the upstream method of construction.

The owners of the land were anxious to evaluate the suitability of the neutralized phosphogypsum as a light weight landfill to reclaim the site for possible future development. A study was conducted to investigate the geotechnical properties of the phosphogypsum with particular reference to the load deformation characteristics. A test site was established on the surface of the impoundment and the compaction, hydraulic conductivity, compressibility and shear strength characteristics evaluated both in the field and in the laboratory. This paper presents the results of the tests to determine the compressibility characteristics of the neutralized phosphogypsum.

MATERIAL PROPERTIES

Phosphoric acid is produced at the factory by treating phosphatic ore with sulphuric acid to yield orthophosphoric acid, calcium sulphate and hydrofluoric acid. The orthophosphoric acid is removed by filtration and the remaining products form the phosphogypsum tailings. Over 95% by weight of this product is dihydrate phosphogypsum ($Ca\ SO_4.2H_2O$) and the remaining constituents comprise hydrofluosilicic acid, phosphoric acid and complex fluorine based products. The waste is strongly acidic and presents potential problems for disposal, both in the primary handling of the material and in subsequent secondary or resultant effects. The problems associated with disposal of phosphogypsum waste have been discussed by Wissa & Fuleihan (1980) and Smith & Wrench (1984). At Richards Bay, lime is added to neutralize the tailings and the pH of the product is controlled to between 7,0 and 8,0.

The shape of the dihydrate calcium sulphate crystals is controlled in the factory. These are plank shaped with an average length to width ratio of between 5 and 9. When placed hydraulically the crystals are sorted such that the long axis of the crystals is nearly always horizonal. Electron microscope photomicrographs have been used to investigate the structure of the tailings.

Figure 1: Photomicrograph of neutralized phosphogypsum

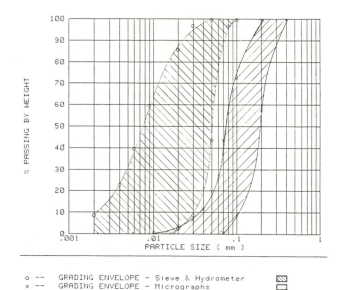

o -- GRADING ENVELOPE - Sieve & Hydrometer
x -- GRADING ENVELOPE - Micrographs

Figure 2: Grading envelopes for Richards Bay phosphogypsum

An example of a photomicrograph of the phosphogypsum from the factory is presented in Figure 1.

Tests on acid phosphogypsum (Blight 1969, Vick 1977) have shown that the product is highly compressible and displays appreciable secondary compression. Experience from the construction of acid phosphogypsum impoundments has shown that the material consolidates rapidly. Similar characteristics were observed on the neutralized phosphogypsum impoundment.

From tests carried out by the authors it is apparent that conventional grading and hydrometer tests give grading envelopes that are too fine. An alternative method of establishing the particle size distribution for the tailings was therefore developed using the photomicrographs. Grading envelopes for the neutralized phosphogypsum from Richards Bay obtained by this method and by conventional sieve and hydrometer methods are presented in Figure 2.

The specific gravity of the phosphogypsum varies between 2,27 and 2,40 depending on the percentage of other minerals and waste products in the tailings. The in situ dry density of the surface phosphogypsum on the impoundment varies from 700 to 900kg/m³ and the initial void ratio between 1,60 and 2,30.

Field and laboratory tests have shown the horizontal permeability of the surface phosphogypsum to vary between 300 to 2000 m/year, and vertical permeability varying between 30 to 100 m/year. During consolidation the vertical permeability reduces with reducing void ratio.

Gypsum is soluble in fresh and sea water. Solubility increases for higher total dissolved solids in the water and saturation is obtained at a concentration of approximately 0.3 percent by weight.

TESTING PROGRAMME

The consolidation properties of neutralized phosphogypsum were investigated by field and laboratory testing. The test programme comprised short and long term consolidation tests in the laboratory and long term static plate bearing tests on the surface of the impoundment. Details of the tests are presented below.

Laboratory Testing

Twenty one consolidation tests were carried out in the laboratory on undisturbed block samples of phosphogypsum recovered from the impoundment. All samples were tested vertically i.e. with the crystals orientated perpendicular to the applied load. Tests were carried out on 75mm diameter samples and conventional one dimensional consolidation test equipment was used.

Both the primary and secondary compression characteristics were measured. A suite of ten tests were carried out with incremental loading from 10kPa to 1600kPa. Load durations varying from 12hrs to 7 days were used. Secondary compression effects were measured in eleven tests where compression under constant load was measured for up to 100 days. Typical curves of void ratio versus pressure and void ratio versus time are presented in Figure 3. Tests were carried out on both unsaturated and saturated materials.

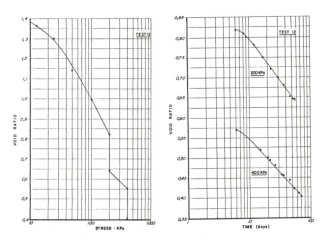

Figure 3: Typical laboratory consolidation results

Field Testing

In situ testing was carried out on the impoundment at a paddock underlain by approximately 6 metres of phosphogypsum. As part of the test programme in situ compaction of the paddock was undertaken using a light roller. On completion of this work a 150mm layer of ash was placed and compacted over part of the compacted area. The compressibility of the phosphogypsum at the test paddock was measured using three identical loading frames. The frames were square with rigid steel plates of equal area located at each corner. Two of these plates were square with sides 500mm long and two were rectangular measuring 350 by 820mm. The frames were constructed on the test paddock and the plates were embedded 20mm into the phosphogypsum. The first frame was located wholly on the uncompacted phosphogypsum, the second on compacted phosphogypsum and the third on ash overlying the compacted phosphogypsum. Settlement sensors were installed at four plates to record settlements at various depths below the plates. The sensors comprised steel rods fixed

in prebored holes in the phosphogypsum at depths of 250, 500 and 1000mm vertically below the plates. A photograph of one of the frames is presented in Figure 4.

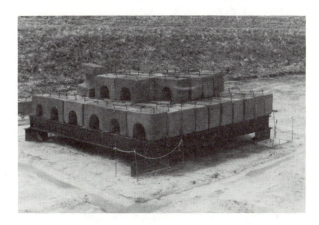

Figure 4: Photograph of Loading Frame

Load was applied by kentledge comprising concrete blocks. An initial loading of 48kPa was applied to the plates and settlements of each plate were measured at regular intervals for 268 days. These measurements were made using an optical level mounted on a stable plinth buried into the phosphogypsum. A second load increment was then applied to the frames. Different load increment ratios were applied to each frame resulting in plate bearing pressures of 64, 72 & 96kPa respectively. The resulting additional settlements were measured for a further 886 days. Plots of settlement versus time for one of the plates founded on the uncompacted phosphogypsum and the corresponding settlement sensor readings are given in Figure 5.

COMPRESSION PARAMETERS

The study has provided both primary and secondary compression characteristics of the neutralized phosphogypsum.

The void ratio versus log pressure curves show that the neutralized phosphogypsum has similar consolidation characteristics to normally consolidated clays. Values of the coefficient of consolidation (c_v) and compression index (C_c) were computed from the test results. These coefficients describe the primary compression of the phosphogypsum. The time settlement curves obtained

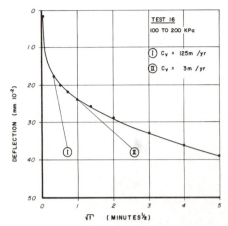

Figure 5: Settlement record for one plate

versus square root of time were prepared. Analysis of these plots was difficult since a straight line portion of the curve was not obtained in the early stages of consolidation. A typical plot is presented in Figure 6 and shows very large initial displacements followed by a conventional decay curve. It is probable that primary consolidation of phosphogypsum is not only controlled by dissipation of excess pore water pressures but also includes short term elasto-plastic deformation of the crystals themselves.

Analysis made using secants from the start of the consolidation curve show c_v ranging between 30 to 200 m^2/year. Using tangents over the linear range of the curves yields values from 1 to 3 m^2/year. These may be compared with values of c_v of 1000m^2/year obtained by Blight (1969) for acid phosphogypsum and greater than $6.10^5 m^2$/year obtained by Morasky et al (1980).

in the laboratory are similar to the Type III curves defined by Leonards and Girault (1961). Primary consolidation occured rapidly and the subsequent secondary compression was large. It is known that for Type III curves the Terzaghi consolidation equation does not adequately describe the rate of pore water pressure dissipation. The results of eighteen time settlement measurements were used to evaluate c_v for the phosphogypsum samples. The log time method proposed by Casagrande (1938) was found to be inappropriate since the rate of displacement did not reduce with increasing time thereby making it impossible to identify the end of the primary consolidation phase. The square root of time method proposed by Taylor (1948) was then used. Plots of sample deformation

Compression indexes were calculated from the consolidometer loading curves. In common with normally consolidated clays these show peak values of C_c near the "critical" pressure (Mesri and Godlewski 1977). Typical plots of C_c versus effective applied pressure are presented in Figure 7. Maximum values of C_c from the tests vary from 0,7 to 1,4. It was expected that C_c would increase for the longer load durations. This trend was not always evident and the variations are probably due to differences in initial density and void ratio of the test samples.

Secondary compression parameters were calculated from both the laboratory consolidation tests and the field plate tests. The secondary compression index ($C_\alpha = \Delta e / \Delta \log t$) and secondary compression ratio ($S_\alpha = [\Delta s/So]/\Delta \log t$) were computed from the results as applicable.

Laboratory tests on clays reported by Mesri & Godlewski (1977) show that C_α is not constant for a given material but reaches a peak at the critical pressure. A similar trend was observed for the laboratory tests results on phosphogypsum. C_α values of 0,07 were recorded at a consolidating pressure of 25kPa increasing to a maximum of between 0,18 and 0,22 at an effective pressure of 400kPa. These peak values correspond to secondary compression ratios of 0,07 to 0,14.

Secondary compression ratios were calculated for the plate loading tests. The ratios were similar for the plates founded on the compacted and uncompacted phospho-

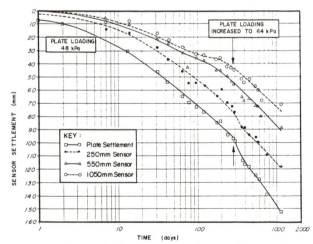

Figure 6: Typical laboratory time-settlement plot

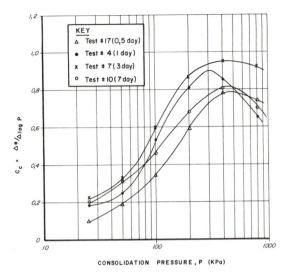

Figure 7: C_C vs Consolidation pressure

is approximately constant for most normally consolidated clays and peats. Analyses of many test results showed the ratio to lie within a range of 0,025 to 0,10 with the higher values corresponding to organic soils. The ratio did not exceed 0,1 for all of the natural soils considered. The results of the laboratory tests show the ratio to vary within the range 0,15 to 0,20 for neutralized phosphogypsum. This result reflects the great importance of secondary compression in the consolidation of phosphogypsum.

Electron micrographs were made of phosphogypsum samples at the end of the long duration load tests in the laboratory. A typical micrograph is presented in Figure 9. It is of interest to note the presence of much additional fine phosphogypsum. The origin of this material is uncertain but probably results from partial breakage of crystals and secondary crystallisation.

gypsum and values of $S\alpha$ ranging from 0,06 to 0,07 were obtained for the 48kPa loading. The ratio increased for the second load increment to 0,08 and 0,12 for the plates loaded to 64 and 96kPa respectively. These values are similar to those obtained from the laboratory consolidation tests. A plot of secondary compression ratios computed for the laboratory and field tests against consolidation pressure is shown in Figure 8. Mesri and Godlewski (1977) have shown that the ratio $C\alpha/C_C$

Figure 9: Photomicrograph of phosphogypsum after laboratory consolidation

CONCLUSIONS

The tests show that the neutralized phosphogypsum is highly compressible and displays appreciable secondary compression. The mechanism of secondary compression in the material is not understood but is probably greatly influenced by creep of the long calcium sulphate crystals. The angularity of the crystals also probably results in high inter-crystal contact stresses.

The tests results have been used to derive consolidation

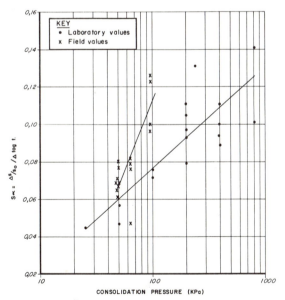

Figure 8: Secondary Compression ratios vs consolidation pressure

models of the neutralized phosphogypsum at the impoundment. These models are of the form both of a family
of void ratio pressure curves as proposed by Bjerrum
(1967) and of a rheological model based on the theory
presented by Gibson and Lo (1961).

REFERENCES

Bjerrum L (1967) "Engineering Geology of Normally Consolidated Marine Clays as Related to Settlement of Buildings"
Geotechnique, Vol 17 pp 2 - 36.

Blight, G E (1969) "Waste Gypsum as an Embankment Material",
Proc. 7th Int Conf SM & FI, Mexico pp 39 - 43.

Casagrande A (1938) "Notes of Soil Mechanics" Harvard
University (unpublished).

Gibson & Lo (1961) "A Theory of Consolidation for Soils
Exhibiting Secondary Compression". Norges Geoteckniske
Institutt, Publication no 41.

Leonards G A & Girault P (1961) "A Study of the One
Dimensional Consolidation Test" Proc. 5th Int. Conf
SM and FE Vol 1 pp 213 - 218.

Morrasky T, Ingra T, Larrimore L, Garlanger J (1980)
"Evaluation of Gyspum Waste Disposal by Stacking" Proc. Symp
on Flue Gas Desulfurization, Houston, Energy/Environment
Agencies Report.

Mesri G and Godlewski P (1977) "Time and Stress Compressibility Interrelationship" Journal of the Soil Mechanics
& Foundations Division, ASCE Vol 103, No GT5 pp 417
- 430.

Smith A and Wrench B (1984) "Aspects of Environmental
Control of Phosphogypsum Waste Disposal" 8th Regional
Conf. for Africa, Int. Soc SM & FE, Harare 1984.

Taylor (1948) "Fundamentals of Soil Mechanics" Wiley,
New York.

Vick S (1977) "Rehabilitation of a gypsum tailings
embankment", Solid Waste Materials 1977 pp 697 - 714.

Wissa A and Fuleihan (1980) "Control of Groundwater
Contamination from Phosphogypsum Disposal Sites" Proc. Int
Symp on Phosphogypsum, Floride Inst of Phosphate Research
1980 pp 482 - 539.

Session 4A
Piles and other deep foundations
A. Pile foundation design methods

Séance 4A
Pieux et autres fondations profondes
A. Méthodes de calcul de fondation sur pieux

Nonlinear analysis of piles in rock

Analyse non-linéaire des pieux en roche

J. M. AMIR, Consulting Engineer, Tel-Aviv, Israel

SYNOPSIS

The behavior of shear piles in rock is analyzed by the spring model method, assuming an exponential relationship between sidewall shear and displacement. The resulting nonlinear differential equation, in terms of dimensionless force, may be solved by iterative finite differences. The load-settlement curves and axial force distribution obtained from this solution show good agreement with field measurements.

INTRODUCTION

Since the early seventies, drilled cast-in-situ piles have become the most important foundation method in the rocky regions of Israel. The main reason for this is that piling, especially in jointed and karstic rock, has obvious economical advantages over shallow footings (Amir 1983). The rapid advance in construction techniques has, however, left analytical techniques behind. In order to achieve safer and more economical design, engineers need better understanding of the way these piles function. The paper presented here proposes a new analytical approach in this direction.

SIDEWALL SHEAR MODELLING

Piles in rock (with the exception of short, large-diameter sockets) derive their capacity mainly from sidewall shear. The problem, therefore, is reduced to modelling the behavior of the pile in shear. Basically, there are three analytical techniques which can be used to model the load-deformation behavior of piles:

a) The spring model (Scott 1981)
b) The half-space model (Mattes & Poulos 1969)
c) The finite element method (Pells & Turner 1979).

The spring model was chosen for this work because of its relative simplicity, and because the extra computational effort involved with the other (more accurate) methods can only be justified if reliable material parameters are available. Unfortunately, rock testing techniques have not yet matured to this stage.

In its simplest form, the spring model is linear, and may be characterized by a single spring element. Although it can represent the behavior of piles under relatively small loads, this single-parameter model can simulate neither work-hardening nor yield.

The elasto-plastic model, which consists of a spring and a friction element connected in series, does represent yield phenomena. Still, it lacks continuity and is grossly in error in the working range of the pile, which is of most interest to the engineer.

Multi-element elasto-plastic models, consisting of a series of springs and friction elements, have none of the above shortcomings. Generally, the stress-displacement curves for such models are in the shape of broken lines. In the special case where both spring constants and friction values decrease in a geometrical progression (Fig. 1), the slopes of the successive sections also form a descending geometrical progression. In the limit, if an infinite number of elements is taken, a smooth curve, obeying Eq. (1), results:

$$\ln (\tau') = a - n.s \qquad (1)$$

where τ is the sidewall shear stress, s the displacement and both a and n are constants. Rearranging and integrating, Eq. (1) becomes:

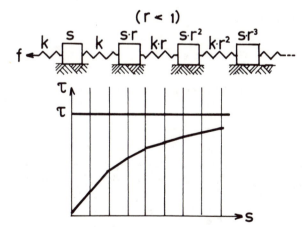

Fig. 1 - Multi-element elasto-plastic model

$$\tau = K - \frac{e^a}{n} e^{-ns} \qquad (2)$$

Since $\tau = 0$ when $s = 0$, the integration constant K is equal to e^a/n, therefore:

$$\tau = m(1-e^{-ns}) \qquad (3)$$

where m, the yield shear stress, is equal to $e^{a/n}$. This exponential expression has the required attributes of strain-hardening, continuity and eventual yield, still using only two parameters. Eq. (3) is identical to the expression suggested by Scott (1981), and to the load-settlement function for complete piles given by van der Veen (1953). By differentiating at the origin, it can be verified that mn is the corresponding tangent modulus.

For the linearly elastic case, it can be shown (Appendix I), that the pile modulus (the ratio of mean sidewall shear to pile settlement) is practically independent of the pile diameter. It was therefore assumed that, for given site conditions, the spring parameters m and n are constant.

Unfortunately, there is little published data regarding shear tests between concrete and rock. Results of such tests, reported by Pells et al. (1980) and Williams & Pells (1981), show that the exponential dependence of shear stress on displacement is basically correct.

LOAD-SETTLEMENT BEHAVIOR

Under an applied axial load Q, the pile deforms with depth z according to the function $s = s(z)$. For a pile section with a length Δl and circumference C, the axial force changes from F to $F + \Delta F$, and the equilibrium condition gives:

$$F' = \frac{dF}{dz} = \tau \cdot C \qquad (4)$$

substituting the value of τ from Eq. (3), one gets:

$$F' = C \cdot m(1 - e^{-ns}) \qquad (5)$$

differentiating,

$$F'' = C\,m\,n\,e^{-ns} \cdot s' \qquad (6)$$

Hooke's law for the same pile section yields:

$$s' = \frac{ds}{dz} = \frac{F}{E\,A} \qquad (7)$$

where E and A are the modulus of elasticity and the cross-sectional area of the pile, respectively. Substituting in (6):

$$F'' = C\,m\,n\,e^{-ns} \cdot \frac{F}{E\,A} \qquad (8)$$

Combining (5) and (8) yields:

$$F'' + \frac{n}{E.A} FF' - \frac{n.C.m}{E.A} F = 0 \qquad (9)$$

Equation (9) may be normalized by the following substitutions:

$$\emptyset = F/Q \qquad (10)$$

and

$$\zeta = \lambda \cdot z \qquad (11)$$

so that Eq.(9) becomes:

$$\emptyset'' + \frac{n\,Q}{\lambda\,E\,A} \emptyset.\emptyset' - \frac{C\,m\,n}{\lambda^2\,E\,A} \emptyset = 0 \qquad (12)$$

the derivatives being with respect to the dimensionless depth ζ. To simplify Eq. (12), it is convenient to make the following substitutions:

$$\lambda = \frac{n.Q}{E.A} \qquad (13)$$

and

$$k = \frac{m.C.E.A}{Q^2.n} \qquad (14)$$

thus:

$$\emptyset'' + \emptyset.\emptyset' - k.\emptyset = 0 \qquad (15)$$

Eq. (15) is a non-linear differential equation in terms of the dimensionless force $\emptyset$. This is a convenient form, since in practice the boundary values are also known in terms of force: At the top ($\zeta = 0$) $F=Q$, so $\emptyset$ is equal to unity. As for the bottom ($\zeta = \lambda l$), it was demonstrated (Mattes & Poulos 1969) that for normal slenderness ratios the proportion of the force reaching the bottom does not exceed a few percent. For shear piles in rock, in which debris is allowed to collect at the bottom, assuming zero force ($\emptyset = 0$) at the end will usually be quite appropriate. For extremely long piles, it may be more accurate to assume that the point of zero axial force is higher up, but this does not introduce any additional difficulty.

Eq. (15) has no closed-form analytical solution, and a conventional finite difference formulation produces non-linear algebraic equations which are difficult to solve. To overcome this difficulty, a fictitious section was added on top of the pile, and an arbitrary value of $\emptyset$ assumed at the top of this fictitious section. Using central differences then produced an algorithm that yielded the value of $\emptyset$ at the next node. This procedure was repeated until the value of $\emptyset$ at the bottom has been obtained. Depending upon the sign of this, the value of $\emptyset$ at the top of the fictitious section was iteratively adjusted until a value of $\emptyset$ close enough to zero was reached at the bottom.

Once the distribution of forces along the pile is known, the corresponding distribution of sidewall shear stresses is easily obtained, enabling the calculation of settlements from Eq. (3). An important precaution, though, is not to base the settlement calculation on the shear stress on the top section of the pile: At the top, the shear stress can be very close to the yield stress m, and this can introduce a large numerical error. Instead, the settlement was computed from the shear at the bottom. The shortening of the pile, calculated by integrating s' from Eq. (7), was then added to give the settlement of the top.

By the procedure described above, The load-settlement behavior for piles of different diameters and lengths be predicted, as well as the distribution of axial force for any given load.

DERIVATION OF THE m AND n PARAMETERS

The m and n parameters in Eq. (3) can be derived from laboratory shear tests between concrete and representative rock samples, or preferrably from field tests performed on short sockets with a uniform stress distribution. In rock consisting of different strata, m and n should be evaluated for each layer separately.

In homogeneous rock, m and n may also be derived by back-calculation from the results of a pile test. Given such results, the yield load (and hence the yield shear stress m) can be evaluated by any of the many available methods (Fellenius 1980). The second parameter (n) can be back-calculated for any point on the load-settlement curve by a trial and error technique which may be conveniently programmed on a computer. Since each point will produce a somewhat different n, the final n value can be chosen by the least squares method to provide the best fit. The fit can be further improved by final adjustment of the m parameter.

A typical example of back-calculation of spring parameters from load test results is given in Fig. 2. The pile, 300 mm in diameter and 1.2 m long, was drilled in chert and loaded by the embedded piston method (Amir 1983a). The computed load-settlement curve, corresponding to the back-calculated values of m = 2050 KPa and n = 900 m^{-1}, is shown in Fig. 2 together with the points obtained from the test.

COMPARISON WITH EXPERIMENTAL DATA

Caissons in Mica Schist - Philadelphia

A high-rise building in Philadelphia was underpinned on instrumented caissons socketed deep into sound mica schist (Koutsoftas 1981). Since the sockets were designed with a very high factor of safety, the load-settlement curves were essentially linear. Using the yield stress m quoted by the author (1500 KPa), a value of n = 2900 m^{-1} was back-calculated from the load-settlement curve given for a 610 mm diameter socket. The load distribution along the pile was then computed for two different loads, comparing well with the measured values (Fig.3).

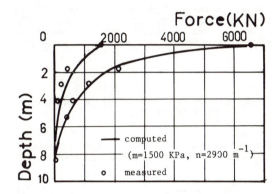

Fig. 3 - Axial force distribution along socket in mica schist

Piles in Mudstone - Melbourne

Four instrumented test piles were installed in moderately weathered mudstone and tested by Williams et al. (1980). Test pile No. M10 (diameter 660 mm, length 7.8 m) settled 3.6 mm under a load of 7660 KN. Based on the back-calculated parameters (m = 900 KPa and n = 2900 m^{-1}), the load distribution along pile M10 was calculated for an applied load of 7660 KN. Again the results (Fig. 4) show a marked resemblance to the measured values.

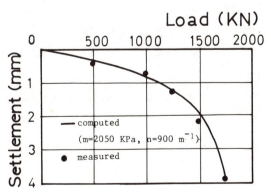

Fig. 2 - Load-settlement curve for pile in chert

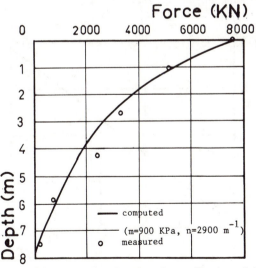

Fig.4 - Axial force distribution along pile in mudstone

CONCLUSIONS

a. The dependence of sidewall shear on displacement may be represented by an exponential function, with the yield stress m and the tangent modulus mn as parameters.

b. Using this function leads to a nonlinear differential equation in terms of force, describing the complete behavior of shear piles in rock.

c. The parameters m and n may be obtained directly from shear tests, either in the field or in the laboratory. In uniform rock, m and n may also be back-calculated from the results of pile load tests.

d. Using the parameters thus obtained, the prediction of load distribution along the pile becomes rather straightforward, and the results show good resemblance to in-situ distributions measured in a variety of rocks.

APPENDIX I – INFLUENCE OF THE DIAMETER ON THE SETTLEMENT OF PILES

According to Mattes & Poulos (1969), the settlement of piles in a linearly elastic half-space is given by:

$$s = \frac{Q}{l\, E_R}\, I_\rho \qquad (16)$$

where I_ρ is an influence factor and E_R the rock mass modulus. For modulus ratios K which are typical of rock, the I_ρ values published by Mattes & Poulos are roughly in direct proportion to the slenderness ratio l/D (Fig. 5). Therefore, I_ρ may be approximately substituted by:

$$I_\rho = B\, \frac{l}{D} \qquad (17)$$

where $B = B(K)$ is constant for a given modulus ratio. Substituting in Eq. (16) results:

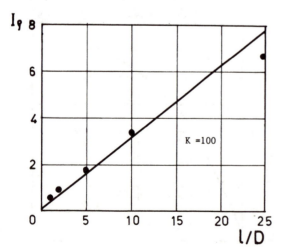

Fig. 5 - Influence factor I_ρ vs. slenderness ratio l/D

$$s = \frac{Q}{l}\, \frac{B}{E_R}\, \frac{l}{D} = \frac{\pi B \bar{F}\, l}{E_R} \qquad (18)$$

where $\bar{F}$ is the mean sidewall shear. The pile modulus M_p is, therefore:

$$M_p = \frac{\bar{F}}{s} = \frac{E_R}{\pi B\, l} \qquad (19)$$

From Eq. (19) it emerges that, at least as a first approximation, the pile modulus is independent of the pile diameter D.

REFERENCES

Amir, J.M. (1983). Piling in rock - construction aspects. Proc 7th Asian Reg Conf SMFE, (1), 231-234, Haifa

Amir, J.M. (1983a). Interpretation of load tests on piles in rock. Proc 7th Asian Reg Conf SMFE, (1), 235-238, Haifa

Fellenius, B.H.(1980). The analysis of results from routine pile tests. Ground Engineering. Vol 13 No.6, September

Koutsoftas, D.C. (1981). Caissons socketed in sound mica schist. J Geotech Div ASCE, Vol 107 No. GT6, June

Mattes, N.S. & Poulos, H.G. (1969). Settlement of single compressible piles. J SMFD ASCE, Vol 95 No. SM1, January

Pells, P.J.N. & Turner, R.M. (1979). Elastic solutions for the design and analysis of rock socketed piles. Can Geotech J Vol 16 No 3, 481-487

Pells, P.J.N., Rowe, R.K. & Turner, R.M.(1980). An experimental investigation into side shear for socketed piles in sandstone. Proc Intl Conf on Struc Found on Rock, Vol 1, 291 - 302

Scott, R.F. (1981). Foundation analysis. Prentice-Hall, 284-296

van der Veen, C.(1953). The bearing capacity of a pile. Proc 3rd Intl Conf SMFE, Vol.2,84-90, Zurich

Williams, A.F. & Pells, P.J.N.(1981). Side resistance of rock sockets in sandstone, mudstone and shale. Can Geotech J Vol 18 No. 4, 502-513

Williams, A.F., Donald, I.B. & Chiu, H.K. (1980). The design of socketed piles in weak rock. Proc Intl Conf on Struc Found on Rock, Vol 1, 317-325

Shaft adhesion on bored and cast-in-situ piles

Frottement latéral sur des pieux forés

W. F. ANDERSON, Lecturer, Department of Civil and Structural Engineering, University of Sheffield, UK
K. Y. YONG, Lecturer, Department of Civil Engineering, National University of Singapore
J. I. SULAIMAN, Research Student, Department of Civil and Structural Engineering, University of Sheffield, UK

SYNOPSIS   Laboratory scale tests at realistic stress levels have simulated various methods of construction of bored and cast-in-situ piles in normally and overconsolidated clays.   After construction pile elements have been load tested.   Stress changes have been monitored at all stages. Results indicate that the shaft adhesion may be predicted using an effective stress method by assuming K_o conditions exist and that adhesion is governed by the drained residual angle of shearing resistance of the clay, as measured in a ring shear test.

INTRODUCTION

The unit shaft adhesion, τ_s, acting on a pile in a cohesive soil is generally estimated using a total stress adhesion factor, α, but a more fundamental approach suggested by Chandler (1968) is to consider the problem in terms of effective stress. Assuming zero effective cohesion, the unit shaft adhesion on a pile element may be expressed as

$$\tau_s = K_s \, \sigma_v' \, \tan\delta \qquad (1)$$

where K_s is an earth pressure coefficient, σ_v' is the effective vertical stress at the pile element depth and δ is the angle of shearing resistance acting when full shaft adhesion is mobilised. Burland (1973) pointed out that during pile installation the effective horizontal stress will be altered from the 'at rest' (K_o) condition, and having reanalysed previously published load test data he showed that assuming a K_o condition and δ equal to ϕ', the peak angle of shearing resistance, equation (1) led to an upper bound prediction of shaft adhesion.

Recent effective stress studies (e.g. Kraft 1982) have concentrated on driven piles because of the potential economies in the offshore industry. Installation effects for bored and cast-in-situ piles are different from those for driven piles in that negative pore pressures are set up due to stress relief, as opposed to positive pore pressures generated by pile driving. Also, considerably less soil remoulding occurs during pile installation.

To assess the effects of using different bored pile construction techniques on the horizontal effective stresses and mobilised shaft adhesion, a major laboratory scale study has been carried out.

TEST EQUIPMENT AND PROCEDURES

Since only shaft adhesion was being studied an element of a pile, with a base void to eliminate end bearing, was simulated as shown in Fig.1.

Normally and overconsolidated beds of high plasticity clay (kaolin, $w_\ell = 72\%$, $w_\rho = 36\%$) and intermediate plasticity clay (pottery clay, $w_\ell = 40\%$, $w_\rho = 23\%$) were prepared by consolidating slurries along a known stress path. Whilst maintaining a vertical pressure to simulate the stresses at depth, a hole was augered in the clay, the base void and instrumentation inserted, and the hole filled with microconcrete. The concrete was pressurised to simulate the stress applied to the soil by a head of fresh concrete and left to cure. Some series of tests were carried out with unsupported boreholes, whilst other series were carried out using different casing techniques to support the hole during concreting. The concrete was allowed to cure for at least seven days before a slow maintained load

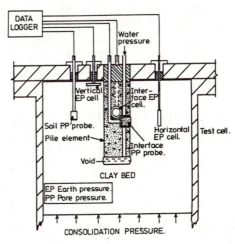

Fig. 1 Soil and pile element instrumentation

test was carried out on the pile element, failure being defined as the load at which continuous settlement of the pile element occurred after application of a small load increment. The unit shaft adhesion, τ_s, was found by dividing the failure load by the measured pile surface area.

Total stress cells and miniature pore pressure transducers both in the clay bed and at the pile/soil interface (Fig.1) allowed the vertical and horizontal effective stresses to be monitored during all stages of the construction, curing and load testing. Fuller details of the equipment and test techniques have been given by Anderson et al (1984).

TEST RESULTS

Fig.2 shows typical total horizontal stress, pore water pressure and effective horizontal stress changes monitored with time. At the end of consolidation (point A), the horizontal effective stresses gave K_O values which were very close to the values predicted by the Jaky equation for normally consolidated soils and the Wroth (1975) equations for overconsolidated soils (Table 1). On boring there was a reduction of total horizontal stress to zero. Because of cavitation effects it was impossible to monitor large negative pore water pressures so it was assumed that the instantaneous reduction of pore water pressure at the borehole surface equalled the change in total stress (B). After placing of the concrete (C) it was pressurised (D) and with time the stresses increased so that at thirty days more than 90% of the initial 'at rest' effective stress had been recovered. Moisture migration studies during the curing period indicated some increase in the clay water content close to the pile soon after concrete casting, but with time the water content reverted to its original value or slightly below it. Earth pressure measurements and moisture migration studies in long term tests indicated that the 'at rest' condition was re-established about 2 to 3 months after construction.

Most loading tests were carried out 7 days after casting, by which time K_s had recovered to about 90% of the K_O value (Fig. 3). As the overconsolidation ratio increased there was a tendency for smaller reductions in horiztonal effective stress to occur during construction, and hence the 7 day K_s values were closer to the K_O values. All casing methods were found to reduce stress relief during construction and slightly higher earth pressures were measured at 7 days.

A major problem in bored pile construction can be deterioration of the soil due to delay between boring and concreting. A series of tests were carried out in which the holes were left open for 30 minutes, 12 hours and 24 hours before concreting. It was found that increasing effective stress relief occurs with increasing delay, the relief reducing as the overconsolidation ratio increased. However, it would also appear that the greater the stress reduction during construction, the greater the percentage recovery during the first 7 days of curing.

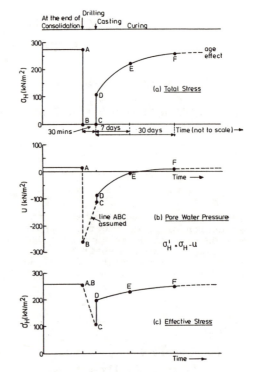

Fig. 2 Stress changes with time.

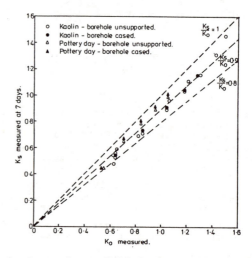

Fig. 3 Comparison of '7 day' K_s and K_O values.

Fig. 4 shows the measured K_s value at 7 days for different delay times and the effects can be clearly seen. It is probable that K_O values will eventually be re-established even if there has been considerable delay between boring and concreting, but to achieve a pile capable of taking the full load as soon as possible after concreting, construction delays should be avoided or casing used.

From the measured shaft adhesion and effective horizontal stress it was possible to use equation (1) to find δ.

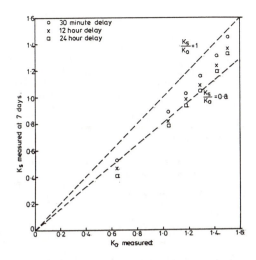

Fig. 4 Effects of delay on K_s values.

Results of a number of series of tests are summarised in Table I. Deduced values are considerably lower than ϕ' (23° for kaolin, 27° for pottery clay), and approach the values of the residual angle of shearing resistance found from ring shear tests on clay subjected to the same stress history as the clay beds, as shown in Table I.

DISCUSSION

Field observations on bored piles (e.g. O'Neill and Reese, 1972) and microfabric studies on laboratory specimens in which a pile element had been inserted in the soil with minimum fabric disturbance (Chandler and Martins, 1982) have shown that shearing occurs in a thin zone within the clay close to the pile shaft. The slow application of load in the current tests, the thin shear zone and the fact that no excess pore water pressures were recorded during shearing indicates failure under drained conditions.

Meyerhof (1983) stated that size effects are unlikely to influence shaft adhesion in bored piles. In this study three different diameters of pile element (25mm, 38mm, 50mm) were tested and unit shaft adhesion varied by only 6%. Maximum adhesion was achieved for all sizes of pile at settlements of about 1% of the pile diameter. This relatively small movement necessary to mobilise full shaft adhesion agrees with numerous field studies on bored piles e.g. O'Neill and Reese (1972), O'Riordan (1982).

The similarity between deduced values of the angle of shearing resistance, δ, and the residual angles, ϕ'_r, from the ring shear tests (Table I) would suggest that only residual shearing resistance is being mobilised. During the augering process a thin annulus of soil at the borehole surface will be sheared to large strains by the rotating auger. Lupini et al (1981) have reported that once an orientated shear surface is formed in clay it is then a permanent feature of the soil and is unaffected by subsequent stress history. Furthermore Chandler (1977) showed that only a small displacement may be required to establish the new residual state on a presheared surface, although in the current situation the direction of shear on pile loading is perpendicular to that during augering. The small settlements necessary to mobilise full shaft adhesion would support the view that the soil is presheared during augering and relatively small movements are sufficient to mobilise the residual strength of the clay.

Table I shows that when there is minimum delay between boring and concreting δ values are slightly higher than residual values, but with delay in construction they are found to be almost equal to ϕ'_r. Values of δ deduced from casing tests were found to be lower than the ϕ'_r values. There was some evidence in these tests that shearing occurred on the smoother pile/soil interface rather than in the soil, and ring shear tests in which the normal rough top platen was replaced by a smooth concrete one gave values of ϕ'_r very similar to those found in the pile tests.

TABLE I

TEST RESULTS

Soil Type	OCR	K_O Predicted (Wroth) 1975	K_O Measured	Mobilised angle of shaft adhesion, δ^O no casing, delay time 30 min	12 hr	24 hr	Casing for support	ϕ'^O_r ring shear
Kaolin	1	0.66	0.64	14.4	–	–	13.0	13.0
	2	0.83	0.85	13.5	–	–	11.6	12.3
	3	0.99	1.04	12.7	12.3	12.0	11.0	12.1
	4	1.16	1.18	12.4	11.7	11.6	10.5	11.4
	5	1.26	1.29	12.1	11.7	11.6	10.3	11.3
	6	1.37	1.42	11.9	11.5	11.3	–	11.1
	7	1.46	1.50	11.7	11.4	11.3	–	11.0
Pottery clay	1	0.54	0.54	23.1	–	–	21.7	21.8
	2	0.68	0.71	22.5	–	–	20.5	21.8
	3	0.82	0.84	22.3	–	–	20.2	21.7
	4	0.96	0.95	22.2	–	–	19.9	21.7
	5	1.10	1.05	22.2	–	–	19.8	21.7

Also of interest is the trend for both δ and ϕ_r' to be stress history dependent, particularly for the high plasticity kaolin. Lupini et al (1981) in their residual stress study also found some evidence of stress history dependency.

Reanalysis of published data in terms of effective stress for shaft adhesion on bored piles is difficult because of lack of detailed information and the difficulty of separating end bearing from shaft adhesion. However, Searle (1979) reexamined some of the original case histories which were used for the establishment of the total stress adhesion factor, α. Using a residual angle of shearing resistance for London clay, he found very good agreement between his predictions and measured shaft adhesion. O'Riordan (1982) in a detailed study on a single instrumented test pile assumed a residual angle of shearing resistance for the Woolwich and Reading clay and backfigured values of K_s which were found to be very close to K_o values for the deposit.

Useful data from load tests on piles formed with voids in blue London clay (Fearnside & Cooke, 1978) have been reanalysed. Assuming K_o values for London clay given by Chandler (1968) and ground water level at the top of the London clay, values of δ for five augered piles were found to range from 7° to 11° (mean value 8°), and for two holes formed by a bucket values were 11.3^O and 11.5^O. Lupini et al (1981) quote a ring shear residual value of 9.4^O for blue London clay.

CONCLUSIONS

1) The horizontal effective stress which reduces due to boring is almost fully recovered with time. However, delay between boring and concreting increases the time required for recovery. Stress relief effects reduce as overconsolidation ratio increases.

2) Due to augering shear planes may be created in the clay adjacent to the interface and subsequently only small movements are required to mobilise the residual shearing resistance of the soil.

3) Use of casing during construction reduces stress relief but may also reduce the mobilised angle of shearing resistance.

4) An assessment of the unit shaft adhesion likely to be mobilised on a bored and cast in-situ pile can be made using equation (1). Values of K_o may be predicted, or preferably measured in-situ using a self boring pressuremeter (Wroth 1975). The value of δ should be found from a ring shear test on a sample subjected to the same stress history as the deposit.

5) Scale effects on shaft adhesion appear minimal and reanalysis of some published case histories confirms the above method, but further detailed instrumented field studies are required.

REFERENCES

Anderson, W.F., Yong, K.Y. and Sulaiman, J.A., (1984) Laboratory testing of bored and cast-in-situ microconcrete piles to study shaft adhesion. Proc. I.Struct.E/B.R.E. Seminar on Design of Concrete Structures- The Use of Model Analysis, Watford, U.K.

Burland, J.B., (1973). Shaft friction of piles in clay: a simple fundamental approach. Ground Engineering (16), 2, 30-42.

Chandler, R.J. (1968). The shaft friction of piles in cohesive soils in terms of effective stress. Civil Engineering and Public Works Review (63), 48-51.

Chandler, R.J. (1977). Back analysis techniques for slope stabilization works: a case record. Geotechnique (27), 4, 479-495.

Chandler, R.J. and Martins, J.P. (1982). An experimental study of skin friction around piles in clay. Geotechnique (32), 2, 119-132.

Fearnside, G.R. and Cooke, R.W. (1978). The skin friction of bored piles formed in clay under bentonite. CIRIA Report 72, London.

Kraft, L.M. (1982). Effective stress capacity model for piles in clay. ASCE J.Geot.Engng. (108), GT 11, 1387-1404.

Lupini, J.F., Skinner, A.E. and Vaughan, P.R. (1981). The drained residual strength of coehsive soils. Geotechnique (31), 2, 181-213.

Meyerhof, G.G. (1983). Scale effects of ultimate pile capacity. ASCE J.Geot. Engng (109), GT6, 797-806.

O'Neill, M.W. and Reese, L.C. (1972). Behaviour of bored piles in Beaumont clay. ASCE J. Soil Mech. and Fdn. Div. (98), SM2, 195-213.

O'Riordan, N.J. (1982). The mobilisation of shaft adhesion down a bored and cast-in-situ pile in the Woolwich and Reading beds. Ground Engineering (15), 3, 12-26.

Searle, I.W. (1979). The design of bored piles in overconsolidated clays using effective stresses. Proc.Conf. on Recent Developments in the Design and Construction of Piles, Instn Civil Engineers, London, 265-274.

Wroth, C.P. (1975). In-situ measurement of initial stresses and deformation characteristics. Proc. ASCE Spec. Conf. on In-situ Measurement of Soil Properties, Raleigh, (2), 181-230.

Experimental study of bearing capacity of cast-in-situ hollow piles

Recherches expérimentales de capacité portante des pilotis vides

B. V. BAKHOLDIN, Cand. Techn. Sci., NIIOSP, Moscow, USSR
V. I. BERMAN, Cand. Techn. Sci., VNIIGS, Kiev, USSR

SYNOPSIS   The paper gives the results and analysis of field test studies of bearing capacity of bore hollow cast-in-situ piles, underreamed and smooth, subjected to compression or pull-out loads.   Comparison is made with similar data for solid piles.

In the USSR bore hollow cast-in-situ piles produced by vibro-compaction technique are used. The bearing capacity of such piles was studied at the test-sites.

The piles of 12 m in length incorporated cavity of 530 mm dia at its upper part and of 430 mm dia at its lower part.

Diameter of the piles was 800 mm while their lengths ranged from 11 to 16 m. Some bore cast shell-piles were underreamed with 1.2 - 1.6 m dia bulbs.

Conventional piles were also erected and tested nearby at the site along with the shell-piles with the same outer dimensions as the latter ones(Fig.1).

The piles were erected in stable soils without casing. They cut through loess soils and penetrated stiff clays 2-4 m deep (Table I). To measure forces along the shaft length string transducers were welded on the reinforcement cage to feed data to a special remote periodometer on the form of electric frequences.

The load acting on the tip and on the bulb was registered by soil contact string sensors whose operation is based on the change of the natural frequency of the string resonator under the load. Not less than 2 sensors were installed on the tip and 3 sensors were installed on the bulb. The settlements of the pile heads were measured by 2 deflectometers with the accuracy of 0.01 mm.

The piles were tested by loads increasing stepwise. There were 15 steps for compression on 10 steps for pull-out tests. Each subsequent step was applied after the settlements stabilized i.e. achieved 0.1 mm settlement increase per 30 min. in compression and 0.1 mm per 120 min. in pull-out. Some tests

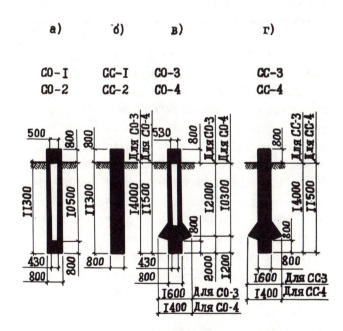

Fig. 1 Identification of Tested Piles

a),b)- shell-piles and solid piles without bulbs

c),d)- shell-piles and solid piles with bulbs

TABLE I

Item to be measured	Kind of soil	
	Loess-sandy loam	Clay
Natural water content, w	0.09	0,21
Natural water content at the plastic limit, w_p	0.18	0.23
Natural water content at the liquid limit, w_L	0.23	0.40
Liquidity index, I_L	-1.80	-0.10
Water content ratio, S_r	0.27	0.87
Specific weight of soil, γ, kN/m³	15.80	19.50
Specific weight of dry soil, γ_d, kN/m³	14.50	15.90
Void ratio, e	0.84	0.71
Deformation modulus, E, MPa	30.0	25.0
Angle of internal friction, φ, degree	18	21
Cohesion, c, MPa	0.01	0.11

negligibly along the lower third, friction along the upper portion achieves maximum rather quickly while the middle portion exhibits the most intensive change of friction (Fig. 3).

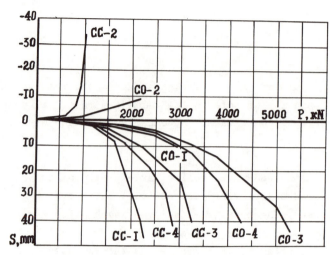

Fig. 2　Settlement-Compression Load
Curves for CO-1, CO-3, CO-4,
CC-1, CC-3, CC-4 Piles and
Upheave-Pullout Load Curves
for CO-2 and CC-2

were stopped due to the repture of reinforcement of an anchor or of a tested pile.
The analysis of consolidated load settlement graphs of cast bore shell-piles both with and without bulbs and cast bore solid piles of the same geometry subjected to compression (Fig. 2) showed that the bearing capacity of hollow piles produced by vibro-compaction of concrete is 1.3-1.5 times higher than that of the piles produced by conventional technique from the liquid concrete mix.
This difference is even more pronounced for pull-out tests. This fact shows that the greater bearing capacity of cast bore shell-piles without bulbs results from the increased resistance along the shaft.
The analysis of friction distribution (f) along the shaft length (e) in pull-out (P) tests yields the fact that friction changes

E.g., when the pull-out force grows twofold friction along the middle portion of the shaft increases 3-6 fold.
Theoretical values of friction are represented on the graph by the dotted curve. Side friction (F) in compression (P) tests grows more continuously and is proportional to the applied load until the lower tip is activated then their growth rate lowers (Fig. 4).
The tip of the piles without bulbs endures great loads only after the side friction achieves 60-80% of its maximum value. Notably, even for short piles (l/d=1/14) the tip resistance amounts only to 30% of the total strength of solid piles and 20% of the cast bore shell-piles. This high side friction results from the fact that the piles cut through dry loess soils at all the test-sites.
The lower tip (bulb and heel) of underreamed piles is activated more intensively than that

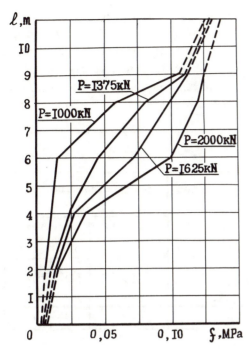

Fig. 3   Friction Distribution Along
the Shaft of CO-2 Pile Versus
Various Pull-out Loads

of smooth piles while the interaction of resistances at the tip and at the shaft becomes more complicated; the greater is the load applied to the tip the less is the side friction growth which even alternates its direction and then stabilizes. The tip load is the sum of loads applied to the bulb and to the heel.
The bulb is activated much earlier. The pressure applied by the bulb to the soil depends on its diameter to a low extent.
Table II displays data on distribution of loads between the bulb and the heel for piles CO-3 and CO-4 and variation of pressures under them versus pile load growth.
The heel is intensively activated when the load achieves 2/3 of the pile strength. Although the area of the heel is 2-3 fold less than that of the bulb, the load endured by the heel is greater than that endured by the bulb when the pile achieves its ultimate state. This fact demonstrates the low specific effeciency of the bulb. The shares of loads endured by the shaft anf by the tip of the shell-pile with

TABLE II

Pile load, kN	Pressure under bulb, MPa		Load on bulb, kN		Pressure under heel, MPa		Load on heel kN	
	for CO-4	for CO-3	for CO-4	for CO-3	for CO-4	for CO-3	for CO-4	for CO-3
500	0.023	–	24	–	–	–	–	–
1000	0.050	–	52	–	0.032	–	16	–
1500	0.083	–	86	–	0.037	–	19	–
1750	0.108	–	112	–	0.038	–	29	–
2000	0.167	0.043	173	64	0.097	–	49	–
2250	0.240	–	249	–	0.127	–	64	–
2500	0.297	0.200	308	350	0.130	0.015	65	7.5
2750	0.373	–	387	–	0.163	–	82	–
3000	0.464	0.510	481	765	0.462	0.200	232	100
3250	0.581	0.585	602	878	0.880	0.340	442	170
3500	0.651	0.660	675	990	1.630	1.050	820	525
3750	0.682	0.730	707	1100	1.925	1.730	968	871
4000	0.730	0.795	757	1193	2.170	2.400	1092	1200
4250	0.768	0.835	796	1253	2.300	2.815	1157	1408
4500	–	0.870	–	1305	–	3.140	–	1570

1.5 d bulb relate as 1.3:1, they are almost equal to each other for 1.75 d bulb and relate as 1:1.5 for 2.0 d bulb.

To investigate the geometry of the pile shafts and the quality of concrete the soil around 32 piles was excavated down to 6-8 m depth and then the piles were cut off. The measurements showed that the technique of piling did not affect their outer diameters while the concrete-soil adhesion for shell-piles was much higher than that of solid cast bore piles. The concrete moulded by vibro-compaction had denser structure than that of solid piles. The thickness of the shell-pile shaft varied less than 15% in the same cross-section and amounted to 17 cm in the middle portion of the pile.

Thus the strength of soil around cast bore piles without bulbs as compared to that of identical solid piles cast from liquid concrete mix is greater due, mainly, to the side friction increase that results from better concrete-soil adhesion as well as from vibro-compaction of soil mass during casting.

The increase of soil bearing capacity of underreamed cast bore piles is also linked up with side friction growth. This, however, is strongly connected with vibro-compaction of concrete in the bulb and of the soil paste in the heel which is not compacted to such an extent when the shaft is filled with liquid concrete mix.

Table III displays the specific bearing capacity values of various shell-piles and solid piles per 1 m³ of concrete as well as the efficiency which is equal to the ratio of specific bearing capacity of the shell-pile to that of the solid pile.

TABLE III

Kind of piles	Specific bearing capacity value, kN/m³			
	Pile without bulb	Underreamed pile with the bulb dia equal to		
		1.5d	1.75d	2d
Shell-pile	890	844	816	786
Solid pile	318	361	365	351
Efficiency	2.80	2.34	2.24	2.24

The studies has shown that the efficiency of consumption of concrete in the cast bore shell-pile both with and without bulbs is more than 2 fold higher as compared with that of the solid piles made of liquid concrete mix.

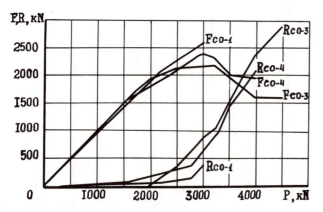

Fig. 4   Side (F) and Heel (R) Resistance
          Versus Loads Applied to the Pile (P)

Dynamic pile tests – German practice

Tests dynamiques du pieu en Allemagne

H. G. BALTHAUS, Inst. für Grundbau und Bodenmechanik, TU Braunschweig, FRG
H. MESECK, Inst. für Grundbau und Bodenmechanik, TU Braunschweig, FRG
J. SEITZ, Bilfinger + Berger AG, Mannheim, FRG

SYNOPSIS   Dynamic pile testing has been introduced to Civil Engineering practice in the early 1970's. Since then it has steadily been improved and applied to a variety of pile types. The different methods applied to driven and bored piles for integrity and bearing capacity testing in Germany shall be discussed in this paper.

1. INTRODUCTION

After the start of dynamic pile testing in the U.S.A. about 20 years ago, first dynamic bearing capacity tests on piles were carried out in Germany in the late 70's. Today various pile types, like driven and bored piles, caissons, and auger drilled piles are tested both for bearing capacity and integrity.

For integrity testing usually the low-strain method with measurement of acceleration at the pile top is applied. Judgement on integrity is then done from velocity-time records that can be derived from the measured accelerations by analog or digital integration.

For bearing capacity testing the method according to Goble & Ass. with subsequent CASE- and CAPWAP-evaluation is widely used. Dynamic pile testing in this field aims to support or replace static load testing.

2. MEASURING SYSTEMS FOR DYNAMIC PILE TESTS

Since the introduction of dynamic pile tests about 10 years ago a number of systems for measuring and data processing have been developed. Two of these systems have been widely used in Germany and shall be described here.

The first system is centered around the Pile Driving Analyser (PDA) that was introduced by Goble & Rausche Ass. in Cleveland as a result of a decade of research work in stress-wave measurements and pile driving analysis (Likins, 1984). Fig. 1 shows the arrangement for measuring and monitoring pile bearing capacity during driving. For this purpose pairs of specially designed strain gages and piezoelectric accelerometers are bolted rigidly to the pile, about two pile diameters below the top.

The values of strain and acceleration measured during a hammer blow on the pile are transferred to the Pile Driving Analyser (PDA) for data processing and display of test results on an oscilloscope or strip chart. A tape recorder is used for analog data storage of successive hammer blows.

In the described arrangement the PDA works as a micro processor-equipped, partly digital device for data evaluation and A/D-conversion and as a transient memory for data to be transferred to a computer for further calculations.

The measuring system shown in Fig. 2 essentially works the same way as the previous one, except that data processing is exclusively done in a digital way after digitized data from the transient recorder have been transferred to the microcomputer that acts as a central processor unit for A/D-conversion, computations, plotting and printing of results, and permanent data storage on magnetic discs.

Both the described measuring systems are predominantly used on site for CASE-method evaluation of bearing capacity during driving. Also the systems are normally utilized as A/D-converter for post-driving analysis of data stored on magnetic tape. This analysis may include more elaborate CASE- or CAPWAP- data processing. These analyses will be described in the next chapter.

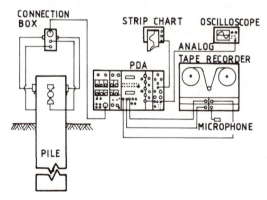

Fig. 1: Measuring system with Pile Driving Analyser (PDA)

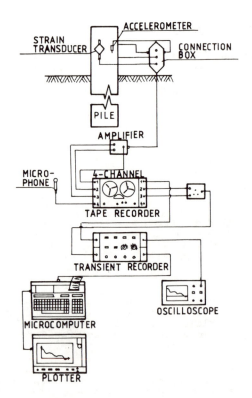

Fig. 2: Measuring system for digital data processing

3. EVALUATION OF BEARING CAPACITY

3.1 METHODS OF ANALYSIS

Different methods for the evaluation of pile bearing capacity have been developped and are in wide use today.

A first group of approaches is based on purely analytical solutions for the one-dimensional wave propagation problem in a pile (Goble/Rausche, 1976 and Klingmueller, 1984). The solution algorithms can be based on the Finite Difference, Finite Element or Characteristics Methods. Application of computer programs incorporating one of these solution mechanisms involves two

main problems: realistic numerical modelling of the driving impact of the hammer and static and dynamic soil-pile interaction.

Since only a limited degree of accuracy can be reached for both tasks, solely analytical approaches have so far been limited to pile drivability preestimates and parameter studies.

As a result of this limited quantitative capability new methods have been introduced that utilize force and acceleration measurements during driving and thus by-pass the problem of numerical hammer description. These methods are the well established CASE- and CAPWAP- analyses (Goble et al., 1975 and 1970).

A detailed description of these methods shall not be given here. A table of the characteristic features of different analytical methods is given in Fig. 3.

3.2 DRIVEN PILES

For driven piles dynamic pile tests for the determination of bearing capacity are now generally accepted in the FRG.

The necessary measurements and evaluations are carried out on a routine basis by a number of firms. Increasingly, dynamic pile tests are also used for the optimisation of driving systems. Today, dynamic pile tests offer an economic way of quality control for driven pile foundations. They allow us to test a larger number of piles in a short period of time.

All prefabricated piles made of wood, reinforced concrete, prestressed concrete or steel can be tested. Welding joints, couplings and welded on reinforcing steel or side wings impose no limitations on dynamic testing.

Dynamic pile tests are usually carried out first during driving. If possible, the piles are redriven a few days later and tested dynamically again. Preliminary CASE-evaluations are done on site. Final reports are prepared in the office. Fig. 4 shows a typical example for on-site CASE-results.

The development of bearing capacity during driving can be monitored if dynamic pile measurements are carried out continuously during the driving process. By such measurements a graph of bearing

Method	Measured Quantities	Estimated Quantities	Computed Results	Ref.
WEAP	none	Hammer properties Magnitude and Distribution of soil resistance	Bearing graphs: Resistance vs. blow count, Various mechanical quantities vs. time or location	Goble/Rausche 1976
FEM	none	as for WEAP or with arbitrary load function	as for WEAP	Klingmueller 1984
CASE	$F(t)$, $v(t)$	CASE-damping value	Dynamic and static pile resistance	Goble et al. 1970
CAPWAP	$F(t)$, $v(t)$	Initial estimate of magnitude of soil resistance	Dynamic and static pile resistance vs. displacement, Final magnitude and distribution of soil resistance	Goble et al. 1975

Fig. 3: Characteristic features of methods for pile driving analysis

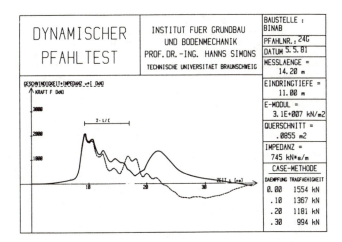

Fig. 4: Example for on-site CASE-evaluation
of a dynamic pile test

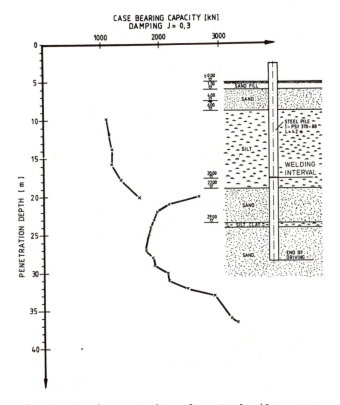

Fig. 5: Bearing capacity of a steel pile versus
depth of penetration

capacity versus depth of pile penetration is obtained. Fig. 5 shows an example for a 42 m long steel pile that was monitored during driving between 20 m and 34 m of penetration. At 20 m driving was halted for welding of a follower joint. Final penetration was reached at 34 m.

Fig. 5 clearly shows how the pile gained bearing capacity during the welding interval. Upon the continuation of driving a typical loss of bear-

ing capacity occurred. As the pile penetrated into the dense sand layer at a depth of 30 m bearing capacity increased considerably.

The example shows how dynamic pile tests during driving can be used to determine the required pile length and depth of penetration.

The CAPWAP-method allows a separation of total bearing capacity in portions due to mantle resistance and tip resistance. Static load-settlement behavior can also be estimated.

To check CAPWAP-results the Institute for Foundation Engineering and Soil Mechanics at Braunschweig University equipped driven piles on a number of sites with strain gages and tested the piles statically and dynamically.

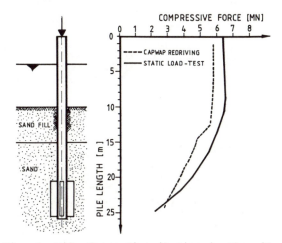

Fig. 6: Pile force distribution in the pile
(load transfer)

Fig. 6 shows an example for good agreement between a measured static pile force distribution and a computed one that is based on dynamic measurements and subsequent CAPWAP-evaluation. Equally good agreement is achieved for the load-settlement curves.

Bearing capacities determined from dynamic pile tests are usually in good accordance with static load test results. An average deviation of ± 10 % is common. The damping behavior of cohesive soils and time-dependence of bearing capacity are problems to which further research efforts should be devoted.

3.3 BORED PILES AND CAISSONS

Different from driven piles, for bored piles a bearing capacity determination during construction is not possible. Capacity determinations can only be done on the basis of empirical data or by static test loading.

Since 1980 Bilfinger + Berger AG, Mannheim, has been working on the practical development of methods for dynamic testing of large bored piles.

In a research and development program the fundamentals of theory and measuring techniques have been evaluated. A set-up suitable for testing large bored piles up to 2 m in diameter has been developed (Klingmueller/Seitz, 1984).

For bearing capacity testing of bored piles, data interpretation by the simple model of the CASE-method has proven a valuable tool for quick on-site checking of measurement results and for comparing the behavior of different piles. Difficulties can be expected if, due to the construction process, material and geometric properties of the pile are not known well enough.

Measuring and test evaluation is done according to the methods described in chapter 3.1. For the conversion of strains into forces Youngs modulus is determined by horizontal travel-time-measurement, by integrity testing, or with a rebound hammer (German Standard, DIN 1048). Due to large variations in elastic properties of in-situ piles this approach has to be followed.

In contrast to a static test, where loads of up to 20 MN have to be provided, a dynamic pile test is less complicated and more economical. At the same expenses a larger number of piles on a given site can be tested.

A set-up for impact loading is shown in Fig. 7. The main components are: drop weight (5-10 to), release mechanism, anvil with load distribution plate and guide pipe for the drop weight. No additional measures for the pile are required.

For testing a drop height is chosen according to admissable settlements and compressive and tension stresses. The maximum height is about 2.5 m for a 10 to - weight.

Two to three impact tests are sufficient for a pile. Impact loading should lead to permanent settlements corresponding to a mobilised resistance force as high as possible. For bored piles of large diameter dynamic as well as static testing usually cannot reach ultimate bearing capacity.

Fig. 8 shows dynamic test results as force and velocity curves for a non-cohesive soil. Typical for the used testing set-up is the triangular force-time-history of duration 5 - 10 ms.

After testing of more than 20 piles (Seitz/Klingmueller, 1984) a correlation between permanent set at the pile top and effective impact energy delivered into the pile (ENTHRU) has been found. With effective impact energies up to 50 kNm and a drop weight of 15 % to 54 % of the pile weight, settlements of up to 6 mm have been reached for piles up to 1.2 m in diameter and 20 m in length. For these permanent settlements it can be assumed that most of the skin resistance along the pile shaft has been mobilised.

The definition of a limit load for bored piles can be based on different criteria. Dynamic and static resistance from CASE-evaluation with an empirical damping value fall between common failure and limit load definitions (Seitz, 1984).

Investigations by Seitz/Klingmueller (1984) avoid usage of an empirical damping factor or calculating skin friction according to the CASE-method since this analytical approach is based on assumptions that are not generally applicable to bored piles.

Instead computation of skin friction distribution and bearing capacity analysis were done by the CAPWAP-method. Fig. 8 shows results of a CAPWAP-analysis for a pile of 24 m length.

As for static load tests on large bored piles dynamic impact loading in many cases cannot reach a limit load. Therefore it is useful to calculate stiffness moduli for each dynamic test and compare them to the static stiffness modulus (Fig. 10).

Fig. 7: Set-up for impact loading of large bored piles

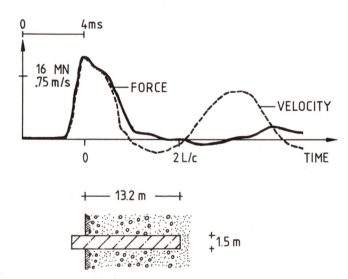

Fig. 8: Dynamic test results for a bored pile

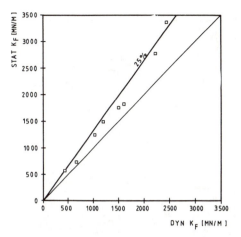

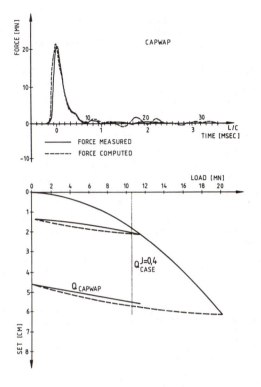

Fig. 9: CAPWAP-results for a bored pile

Fig. 10: Correlation of static and dynamic test results

Static stiffness moduli were derived from the reloading branch of the load-settlement-curve after the second unloading. Dynamic tests were done after the static test.

As can be seen from Fig. 10, dynamic stiffness moduli were smaller than static ones for all soil types. Mobilised skin friction from dynamic tests amounted to up to 90 % of the estimated skin friction under working load.

Even for more complex systems, like pile-column constructions, the suggested method has been successfully applied (Seitz/Klingmueller, 1984).

Due to reflections at the change in cross-section between column and pile, mobilised soil resistances usually remain low.

Dynamic pile tests have proven a valuable tool for estimating the bearing capacity of large bored piles and optimising pile size and distribution for large foundation jobs.

4. INTEGRITY TESTS

The measurement systems described in Ch. 2 can also be used for integrity testing.

If measurements are carried out during driving, the integrity test is termed "high strain" test. Thus any dynamic pile test for bearing capacity determination can also be used as high strain integraty test. A continuous monitoring of the integrity of the pile and possible connection joints is possible.

If the pile top is only hit with a light hammer and an acceleration-time-history is recorded at the pile top surface, the test is called "low-strain" test.

With this fast and economical method all piles on a site can be tested for integrity in a short period of time. Fig. 11 gives two examples for results of "low strain" integrity tests. Measured accelerations were integrated digitally to obtain the shown velocities.

Low strain integrity tests can generally be used for all kinds of driven and bored piles. Certain limitations are imposed by the pile length due to the small energy delivered into the pile. Only for low values of skin friction piles longer than 20 m can be tested.

5. RESEARCH PROJECTS

A number of research projects concerning dynamic impact testing of driven and in-situ bored piles have been initiated during the last 5 years in Germany.

A group of three research projects, supported by the "Deutsche Forschungsgemeinschaft (DFG)" and the Government of Lower Saxony, investigates all aspects of driven pile behavior (comparability of statically and dynamically determined bearing capacities, influences of pile type and soil characteristics, pile integrity). All three projects are carried out by the Institute of Foundation Engineering and Soil Mechanics at Braunschweig University.

Another research grant was given by the Volkswagenwerk-Foundation to this institute for a systematic investigation of the influence of soil density, pile roughness and driving energy on dynamic and static pile bearing capacity by means of model tests on a small scale (2 m lang) model pile, equipped with a number of accelerometers and strain gages.

This research particularly aims to study the influence of soil characteristics on pile tip resistance. The relation between dynamic pile resistance and displacement, velocity, and ac-

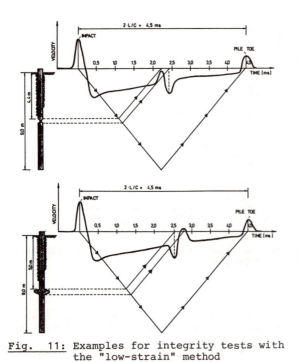

Fig. 11: Examples for integrity tests with the "low-strain" method

celeration at the pile tip is investigated (Balthaus/Fruechtenicht, 1984).

Another research project that investigates the applicability of dynamic impact tests for large bored piles is supported by the West German Government and carried out by the companies of Bilfinger + Berger AG and Philipp Holzmann AG. The Institute for Foundation Engineering and Soil Mechanics, Braunschweig University is involved as a subcontractor to the companies.

The research program involves testing of numerous bored piles and detailed soil investigations (Seitz/Klingmueller, 1984)

It has been shown (Ch. 3.3) that the fundamental requirements for dynamic testing of large bored piles have been fulfilled. Testing set-ups are now available that can mobilise large portions of the soil resistance. Working loads can generally be exceeded.

6. NATIONAL STANDARDS

Since 1980 a subcommittee of the DGEG is working on a national standard concerning the recommended procedures for measurement and data processing in dynamic pile testing. A first draft of the proposed standard was published in 1984.

7. OUTLOOK

The paper has given a summarised view of West German practice in dynamic pile testing of both driven and bored piles. Special emphasis was placed on testing methods for the evaluation of bearing capacity of large bored piles.

Due to the continuation of present research projects that involve both testing of construc-

tion as well as model piles further improvements in bearing capacity and integrity testing of driven and bored piles can be expected.

8. REFERENCES

Balthaus, H.; Fruechtenicht, H. (1984),"Model Tests for Evaluation of Static Bearing Capacity of Piles from Dynamic Measurements", 2nd Int. Conf. on the Appl. of Stress-Wave Theory on Piles, Stockholm.

Bredenberg, H. (1984), 2nd Int. Conf. on the Appl. of Stress-Wave Theory on Piles, Stockholm.

Goble, G.G.; Likins, G.E. and Rausche, F. (1975), "Bearing Capacity of Piles from Dynamic Measurements", Case Western Reserve Univ., Cleveland.

Goble, G.G. and Rausche, F. (1976), "Wave Equation Analysis of Pile Driving" , US Dept. of Transportation,Washington.

Goble, G.G.; Rausche, F. and Moses, F. (1970), "Dynamic Studies on the Bearing Capacity of Piles" Case Western Reserve Univ., Cleveland.

Klingmueller, O. (1984), "Computational Tools for Dynamic Pile Testing", 2nd Int. Conf. on the Appl. of Stress-Wave Theory on Piles, Stockholm.

Likins, G.E. (1984), "Field Measurements and the Pile Driving Analyser" 2nd Int. Conf. on the Appl. of Stress-Wave Theory on Piles, Stockholm.

Seitz, J. (1984), "Dynamic Testing of Large Bored Piles in Non-Cohesive Soils" 2nd Int. Conf. on the Appl. of Stress-Wave Theory on Piles, Stockholm.

Seitz, J.; Klingmueller, O. (1984) "Dynamische Tragfähigkeiten an Bohrpfählen" Vorträge der Deutschen Baugrundtagung 1984, Deutsche Gesellschaft für Erd- und Grundbau, Essen.

Back analysis of test piles driven into estuarine sands

Analyse rétrospective des pieux d'essai pilotés dans des sables d'estuaire

A. J. BARRETT, Steffen, Robertson and Kirsten Inc., Johannesburg, South Africa
B. P. WRENCH, Steffen, Robertson and Kirsten Inc., Johannesburg, South Africa
J. D. LEGGE, Steffen, Robertson and Kirsten Inc., Johannesburg, South Africa

SYNOPSIS

Precast concrete piles were driven at Richards Bay, to support a large bridge. The piles were driven through surface clays to found in a medium dense and dense estuarine sand. Back analysis of preliminary pile tests showed that both static and dynamic computer models gave good indications of production pile behaviour. The availability of this information during construction proved invaluable for controlling installation of production piles.

INTRODUCTION

This paper describes a case history where piled foundations have been used to support part of a road bridge in Richards Bay Harbour, South Africa. The piles are precast concrete sections, driven into sands where they carry most of the working load in side friction. In particular this paper addresses the prediction of pile capacity from driving performance and in situ testing. The project was approached on a design and construct basis. The authors formed part of the client team and the analyses described here were carried out to check the design and ensure satisfactory performance. In addition as future development is expected in this area, the back analyses described not only provide valuable information regarding the behaviour of the soils in general, but will be directly applicable to future projects.

The proposed bridge is 850m long and crosses a canal and railway tracks. It comprises 20m long simply supported bridge decks and typical pier loads are 15000kN. The structure is designed to be settlement tolerant.

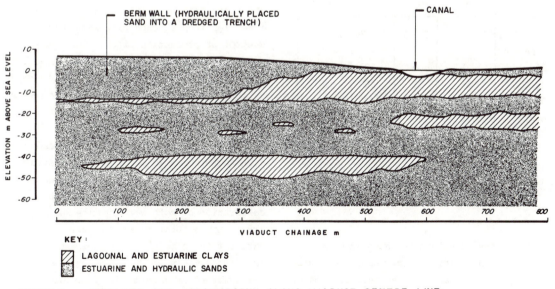

FIGURE 1   IDEALISED SOIL STRATIGRAPHY ALONG VIADUCT CENTRE LINE

INVESTIGATION, SITE GEOLOGY AND FOUNDATION CONCEPT.

The investigation was carried out using both rotary drilling techniques and piezometer cone-penetration tests. This showed very soft and soft lagoonal clays to 13,5m depth over medium dense and dense estuarine sands which became very dense with depth. The estuarine sands contain inter bedded clay horizons. Below 40m, a stiff lagoonal clay was encountered over half of the site. These soils were generally proved to 50m depth and in one borehole to 75m depth indicating that part or all of the viaduct is located over a deeply incised channel in the Cretaceous mudrocks that underlie the harbour area. The soil stratigraphy indicated by this investigation is shown in Figure 1.

Average geotechnical properties for the clays and sands at the site are presented in Table I & II respectively.

CLAY HORIZON	C_v m^2/yr	Cc	Pc/Po	Average	
				e_0	γd kg/m^3
Upper Lagoonal	0,36 – 3,4	0,75	1,0	2,3	8,0
Middle Estuarine	3,5	0,4	–	–	–
Lower Lagoonal	1 – 5	0,5*	1,4	1,13	1240

TABLE 1: ENGINEERING PARAMETERS FOR CLAY HORIZONS

SAND HORIZON	Av SPT "N"	Av qc (MPa)	Ø	E (MPa)
Hydraulic Fill	10 – 25	5 – 10	30° – 36°	10 – 20
Estuarine sand				
15 – 20m	15	5	32°	15
20 – 25m	26	11	35°	22
25 – 30m	38	20+	37°	30 – 35
30 – 40m	44	20+	38°	30 – 25
40 – 60m	67	–	38°	45

TABLE 2: IN SITU TESTING RESULTS AND ENGINEERING PARAMETERS FOR SAND HORIZONS

On the basis of the stratigraphy shown in Figure 1 it was recommended that part of the viaduct be founded on friction piles driven into the estuarine sands. The problems foreseen for piling were as follows:

- downdrag forces on piles as a result of consolidation of the near surface clays due to recently placed fill.

- variable SPT "N" values in the estuarine sands indicating the presence of medium dense and very dense pockets in a generally dense soil horizon;

- the presence of a compressible lower lagoonal clay horizon.

The bridge piled foundations were put to tender on a "design and construct" basis. The design selected from tender submissions comprised the use of 350mm square precast concrete piles driven to a set in the dense estuarine sands at depths ranging from 30m to 38m. The piles were raked outwards at 1 in 6 to avoid concentrations of load into the underlying compressible clay horizon.

QUALITY ASSURANCE DURING PILE DRIVING

The selection of suitable driving control criteria for predominantly friction piles posed a problem due to the variation in density in the sand founding horizon. A conservative approach using a small set would result in many piles being overdriven into the underlying compressible clay horizon. Alternatively too large a set would result in reduced pile capacity, requiring more piles and increased piling costs.

Two preliminary test piles were driven to criteria that included a set and minimum driving resistance over the final 2 metres. The pile test results were satisfactory and these driving criteria and the results of borehole investigations at each pier were used as a basis for control of production piles. Despite these measures a small number of piles did not achieve the criteria before reaching the maximum allowable depth imposed by the underlying clay horizon. A pile test was carried out to failure on one of these piles.

It was realised that a rapid method of correlating the driving resistance of piles to their load carrying capacity was needed. Back analysis of the behaviour of the test piles under both dynamic and static conditions enabled calibration of both wave equation and static axial load transfer computer models. Correlation of the input data for these models with piezometer cone penetration resistance values and pile driving records has increased the confidence with which pile behaviour can be predicted at the bridge site and at other locations.

COMPUTER MODELLING OF STATIC AXIAL LOAD RESPONSE

The axial load transfer from the piles to the surrounding soils was modelled using a modified version of the programme described by Bowles (1974). The pile is represented using a finite element model. The deformation behaviour of the pile, pile-soil shear transfer and end bearing resistance are required as input parameters. The load response curve for the pile can then be generated by performing the analysis for a number of different loading conditions.

The selection of representative input parameters for the programme from results of in situ testing requires some discussion. Many correlations of side friction and cone resistance, SPT 'N' value and laboratory test results are published. Some of these are briefly discussed below:

Correlations with cone resistance

The peak skin friction that is mobilized along a pile shaft segment (f_s) is usually related to cone resistance (q_c) by a relationship of the following form:

$$fs = q_c/a \qquad \text{where } a = \text{constant} \qquad (1)$$

Published values for "a" vary between 20 and 400, depending on the nature of the soil and compressive or tensile pile loads (Beringen et al, Meyerhof, Tong et al, Mohan et al)

Correlations with SPT 'N' values

The SPT 'N' value is usually related to peak skin friction by a relationship of the form

$$f_s = N/b \qquad \text{where } b = \text{constant} \qquad (2)$$

Published values for b are usually of the order of 50 to 60 (Meyerhof).

Although many correlations of side friction with laboratory test results are published, these were not used in the analysis described here.

Modelling of pile load settlement behaviour requires a knowledge of the mobilization of skin friction with pile movement. Vijayvergiva has published the following correlation for driven and bored piles in both clay and sand (Beringen, et al)

$$f = fmax \left(2\sqrt{Z/Zc} - Z/Zc \right) \qquad (3)$$

where f = unit friction mobilized along a pile segment at movement Z.

$fmax$ = peak unit friction

Zc = critical movement of a pile segment at which fmax is mobilised.

Berigen shows that the value of Zc is difficult to define, but in general appears to be in the range 5 to 13mm.

In the analysis described here, the mobilization of end bearing is modelled by a linear function. It was assumed that the maximum unit end bearing is mobilized over a distance of 5% to 7% of the equivalent pile diameter. The maximum end bearing was estimated using two methods as follows:

i) $$q_1 = 50 \, N_q \tan \phi \qquad (4)$$

where q_1 is the limiting effective stress at pile point at failure (after Meyerhof)

ii) q_u = 2.5N for silts (5a)

4N for sands (5b)

6N for gravels (5c)

where q_u = ultimate point resistance

N = SPT 'N' value

BACK ANALSIS OF PILE TEST RESULTS

The results of the pile tests performed before production piling started were used to back analyse the static load transfer at the site and the dynamic driving characteristics of the piles.

STATIC LOAD TRANSFER

Of the in situ testing carried out at the site, the electrical piezometer cone penetration testing gives the highest quality results. The equipment is described by Jones (1982), and the test provides a continuous record of cone resistance and pore water pressure response with depth thus enabling accurate determination of boundaries between different soil horizons. Where possible therefore, results of electrical cone testing were used to estimate peak skin friction values. This was not possible in the dense sand at the base of the piles as the cone refused on this horizon. In these areas, qc values were estimated by comparing the SPT values for the upper and lower horizons.

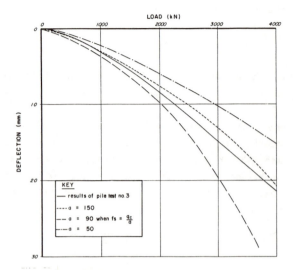

FIGURE 2: COMPARISON OF PREDICTED AND MEASURED LOAD SETTLEMENT CURVES

Analyses were carried out using different values of the constant "a" (Eqn 1) and an average value for the estimated point resistance. Results of these analyses carried out for the soil profile recorded at Test Pile 3 are presented in Figure 2. The sensitivity of the results to assumed point resistance is shown in Figure 3. In carrying out the above analysis, it was assumed

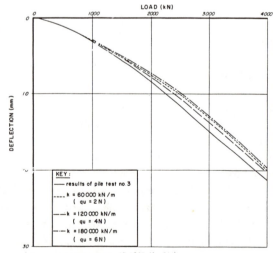

FIGURE 3: SENSITIVITY OF MODEL OUTPUT TO PILE POINT SPRING CONSTANT

that skin friction is mobilized over a distance of 8mm. The sensitivity of the results to this assumption is examined in Figure 4.

These analyses show that the peak skin friction could be estimated using the relationship

$$f_s = q_c / 90$$

DYNAMIC ANALYSIS

Following back analysis of the static load test results, dynamic analysis were carried out using the wave equation method.

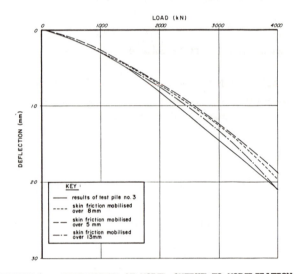

FIGURE 4: SENSITIVITY OF MODEL OUTPUT TO MOBILIZATION DISTANCE FOR SKIN FRICTION

The computer programme used is described by Wiseman and Zeitlin (1983). The soil/pile friction and end bearing parameters from the static back analysis were used as initial input parameters. The ultimate end bearing value was then adjusted to obtain the measured set in the dynamic analysis output. Further analyses were carried out using reduced friction values to estimate the pile capacity for different values of set. In carrying out these analyses, it was assumed that the ultimate end bearing capacity of the pile remains constant after driving whereas the friction values increase due to "freeze". Analyses were also carried out on the same basis using increased and decreased end bearing values. Results of these analysis are presented in Figure 5.

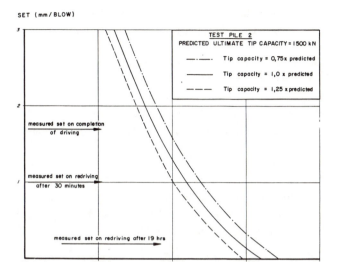

FIGURE 5: SENSITIVITY OF WAVE EQUATION ANALYSIS TO
TIP CAPACITY

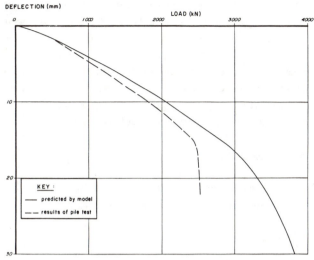

FIGURE 6: RESULTS OF PILE TEST CONDUCTED ON "SOFT BOTTOM"
PILE

Test pile no 2 was redriven at various times after initial driving. The improvement of pile capacity with time as predicted by the wave equation method on the basis of observed sets is also shown on Figure 5.

COMPARISON OF PREDICTIONS AND PERFORMANCE

Some piles at various locations across the site did not achieved the desired set. Driving was however stopped to prevent the piles from founding too close to the underlying clay. A third pile test was therefore scheduled on one of these "soft bottom" piles to check the load carrying capacity. A static analysis was carried out using input information from a nearby cone penetration test. The looser sand pocket was not present at this test site, however, and the static analysis was expected to overpredict the pile capacity. The predicted and measured load deflection curves are presented in Figure 6. Dynamic analyses were then performed and a set/capacity curve generated as described above. The pile load capacity at completion of driving was estimated from this curve on the basis of the measured set. This was then uprated to take account of freeze by the same ratio observed for Test Pile 2. The actual pile failure load was found to be in agreement with that predicted by this method to within 10%.

CONCLUSIONS

A case history has been described in which precast piles were driven into estuarine sands. Back analyses of

preliminary pile test results has shown that both the static and dynamic analyses computer models give a good indication of pile behaviour when calibrated using pile test information. The availability of this information during construction provided invaluable pile driving control data.

Back analysis of the static load testing of the piles indicates that the peak skin friction achieved may be estimated from cone resistance as follows

$$f_s = q_c/90$$

The analysis is not sensitive to the distance over which the peak friction is mobilised. It was found that the piles tested in this project carry load predominantly by shaft friction. The prediction of pile performance is therefore not very sensitive to the assumed mobilization of end resistance.

Pile capacity can be predicted within reasonable accuracy on the basis of the driving record using the wave equation method. The programme used in this project is suitable for adaption to microcomputers and can therefore be easily available on site. Although the correlation between predicted and measured pile capacity agreed to within 10% here, this is considered to be good fortune rather than sophistication. On the basis of published information, correlations to within more than 30% cannot be consistently expected.

Comparison of calculated and observed pile behaviour have been made for 3 test piles. The good agreement achieved in these comparisons confirms the applicability of the models. The interactive use of the computer models and site measurements for individual piles at construction stage not only provides a rational basis for decisions regarding pile driving control criteria, but may offer significant cost savings.

ACKNOWLEDGEMENTS

The permission of the South African Transport Services to publish this paper is gratefully acknowledged.

REFERENCES

1   Meyerhof G G (1975) Bearing Capacity and Settlement of Pile Foundations. J Geotech Div, Proc ASCE, Vol 102, No GT5, March 1976.

2   Beringen F L, Windle D and van Hooydonk W R (1979). Results of loading tests on driven piles in sand. Recent Developments in the design and construction of piles. ICE, London.

3   Mohan D, Jain G S and Kumar V (1963) Load bearing capacity of piles. Geotechnique, Vol 13, No 1.

4   Bartomoley A A, Yushkov B S, Doroshkevitch N M, Leshin G M, Khanin R E, Kolesnik G S, and Mulyukoy E 1 (1982) Pile Foundation Settlements. Proc Tenth Int Conf SMFE, Stockholm.

5   Tong Y X, Chen Q H and Chen X L (1982). Pile Foundations in Soft Soils. Proc Tenth Int Conf SMFE, Stockholm.

6   Broms N (1982). Pile Foundations - General report (preliminary) Proc Tenth Int Conf SMPE, Stockholm.

7   Cheeks J R (1979) Analytical Methods to predict Pile Capacities. Behaviour of Deep Foundations, ASTM STP 670 Raymond Lundgren Ed. American Society for Testing and Materials.

8   Bowles J E. (1982) Foundation Analysis and Design. Third Edition, Mc Graw Hill Book Company.

9   Bowles J E (1974) Analytical and Computer Methods in Foundation Engineering, Mc Graw Hill Book Company.

10   Peck R B, Hanson W E and Thornburn T H (1974) Foundation Engineering. John Wiley and Sons Inc.

11   Chellis R D (1961) Pile Foundations. Mc Graw Hill Book Company.

12   Poulos H G and Davis E H (1980) Pile Foundation Analysis and Design. The University of Sydney, John Wiley and Sons Inc.

13   Wiseman G and Zeitlin J G (1983) Wave Equation Analysis of Pile Driving using Personal Computers and Programmable Calculators. Technicon Israel Institute of Technology, Haifa.

14   Jones G A and Rust E: Piezometer Penetration Testing CUPT. Proceedings of the Second European Symposium on Penetration Testing. Amsterdam May 1982.

A pressuremeter method for laterally loaded piles

Méthode pressiométrique pour pieux chargés latéralement

J. L. BRIAUD, Associate Professor, Civil Engineering Department, Texas A&M University, College Station, Texas, USA
T. D. SMITH, Assistant Professor, Division of Engineering and Applied Science, Portland State University, Portland, Oregon, USA
L. M. TUCKER, Research Associate, Civil Engineering Department, Texas A&M University, College Station, Texas, USA

SYNOPSIS   A method is presented to predict the behavior of piles subjected to monotonic lateral loads on the basis of the results of pressuremeter tests performed in prebored holes. The method is used to predict the pile head response of 17 laterally loaded piles including driven and bored piles ranging from 0.32m to 1.37m in diameter and from 3m to 21m in length. The predictions are compared with the load test results.

BASIC MODEL

The F-y/Q-y Mechanism

A laterally loaded pile derives most of its resistance from frontal resistance Q and from friction resistance F at the pile soil interface (Fig. 1).

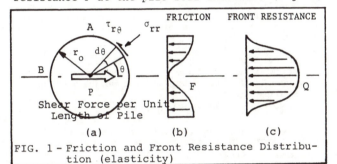

FIG. 1 - Friction and Front Resistance Distribution (elasticity)

Q and F have units of force per unit length. On any elemental area of soil pile interface, a shear stress $\tau_{r\theta}$ and a normal stress σ_{rr} exist (Fig. 1). The elementary force per unit pile length dF due to the component of $\tau_{r\theta}$ in the direction of the shear force P (Fig. 1) is:

$$dF = \tau_{r\theta} \, r_o \, \sin\theta \, d\theta \qquad (1)$$

where r_o is the radius of the pile and θ is the angle between the direction of the lateral load and the direction of σ_{rr}.

$$F = \int_{-\frac{\pi}{2}}^{\frac{\pi}{2}} \tau_{r\theta} \, \sin\theta \, d\theta \qquad (2)$$

Similarly, the elementary forces due to σ_{rr} are:

$$dQ = \sigma_{rr} \, r_o \, \cos\theta \, d\theta \qquad (3)$$

$$\text{and } Q = \int_{-\frac{\pi}{2}}^{\frac{\pi}{2}} \sigma_{rr} \, r_o \, \cos\theta \, d\theta \qquad (4)$$

No friction nor frontal resistance is considered to exist in the back of the pile (ABC on Fig. 1). Baguelin et al. (1977) gave the expression of σ_{rr} and $\tau_{r\theta}$ for a linear elastic soil:

$$\sigma_{rr} = \sigma_{rr(max)} \cos\theta, \text{ with } \sigma_{rr(max)} = \frac{P}{2\pi r_o} \qquad (5)$$

$$\tau_{r\theta} = \tau_{r\theta(max)} \sin\theta, \text{ with } \tau_{r\theta(max)} = \frac{P}{2\pi r_o} \qquad (6)$$

Use of Eqs. 1-6 leads to:

$$Q = \sigma_{rr(max)} \times 2r_o \times \frac{\pi}{4} \qquad (7)$$

$$\text{and } F = \tau_{r\theta(max)} \times 2r_o \times \frac{\pi}{4} \qquad (8)$$

The total soil resistance P to the lateral movement of the pile element y is the addition of the front resistance Q and the friction resistance F. As a result, the P-y curve is the addition of the Q-y curve and the F-y curve.

Experimental Evidence

Fig. 2 gives an example of existence of the two components. A 0.90m dia. bored pile was loaded laterally in a stiff clay with an undrained shear strength from unconfined compression tests averaging 100 kPa (Kash et al., 1977). Pressure cells were installed on the shaft as shown on Fig. 2 in order to record the front pressure. The shaft was loaded and the resulting load-deflection curve is shown on Fig. 2. At a horizontal load of 47.3

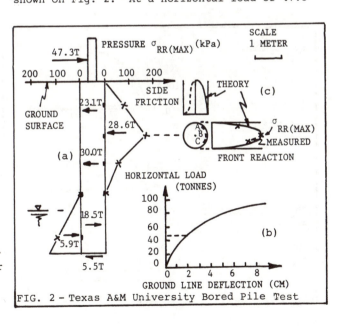

FIG. 2 - Texas A&M University Bored Pile Test

tonnes applied at 0.75m above the ground line, the soil resistance due to front reaction was calculated from the pressure cell readings by using Eq. 7 and calculating the area under the diagram of $\sigma_{rr(max)}$ versus depth. Considering front resistance only, horizontal and moment equilibrium cannot be obtained. The soil resistance due to friction was calculated by using the following equation for F:

$$F = \tau_{r\theta(max)} \times 2r_o \times 1 \qquad (9)$$

Eq. 9 allows for enough friction to exist in the back of the pile (dotted line on Fig. 2c) to raise the shape factor $\pi/4$ in Eq. 8 to one in Eq. 9. It was further assumed that $\tau_{r\theta(max)}$ was equal to one half of the unconfined compression strength, in other words, that at that point in the test the full friction resistance was mobilized. After including the friction forces (Fig. 2) corresponding to the full shear strength of the stiff clay, both horizontal and moment equilibrium are approximately satisfied. Other similar case histories have been published that confirm the existence of friction and front resistance (Briaud, et al., 1983). This example tends to indicate two points: 1. the friction resistance is an important part of the total resistance, 2. the friction resistance is fully mobilized before the front resistance because it takes less displacement to mobilize friction than point resistance. Hence, a soil model which distinguishes between friction and front resistance is a proper model.

The Q-y Curve and the Pressuremeter Curve
The theoretical distribution of the elementary forces dQ was found to match the measurements recorded on three pressure cells (A,B,C on Fig. 2) on the shaft of the load test. This validated the use of Eq. 7 provided $\sigma_{rr(max)}$ could be obtained. Pressuremeter tests were performed in a prebored hole and the pressuremeter curves were compared with the response of the pressure cells which measured $\sigma_{rr(max)}$ on the shaft. Fig. 3(b) shows the comparison between pressure cell responses at the front of the pile and the pressuremeter response. For the load cells, P is the cell pressure ($\sigma_{rr(max)}$) and y/R is the lateral movement of the cell y divided by the pile radius R. Fig.3(b) shows

very good agreement between pressure cells and pressuremeter response (Smith, 1983). This tends to prove that the curve obtained from a pressuremeter test performed in a prebored hole simulates well the reaction of the front pressure cell for a bored pile. In the proposed method the front resistance model will be obtained as follows:

$$Q(front) = p(pmt) \times B(pile) \times S(Q) \qquad (10)$$

where
Q(front) = the soil resistance due to front reaction (in force/unit length of pile)
p(pmt) = the net pressuremeter pressure
B(pile) = the pile width or diameter
S(Q) = the shape factor = 1.0 for sq. piles
    = $\pi/4$ for rnd. piles

$$y(pile) = y(pmt) \times \frac{R(pile)}{R(pmt)} \qquad (11)$$

where
y(pile) = the lateral deflection of the pile
R(pile) = pile radius
y(pmt) = increase in radius of the soil cavity in the pressuremeter test
R(pmt) = initial radius of the soil cavity in the pressuremeter test

If the pile is driven into the soil and fully displaces it, one would expect that the resulting Q-y curve would be different from the one for a bored pile in the same soil. In the case of a bored pile preboring the hole for the pressuremeter seems to be appropriate; in the case of a closed end driven pile it may be more appropriate to drive the pressuremeter in place. Alternatively the hole can be bored, the pressuremeter expanded a first time to simulate the driving of the pile and then expanded a second time. The Q-y curve for the driven pile can be derived from the reload portion of the pressuremeter curve.

The F-y Curve and the Pressuremeter Curve
Based on the previous theoretical and experimental considerations the friction on the sides of the pile according to the proposed method is:

$$F(side) = \tau(soil) \times B(pile) \times S(F) \qquad (12)$$

where F(side) = the soil resistance due to friction resistance
    B(pile) = the pile width or diameter
    S(F) = the shape factor = 2 for sq. piles
                            1 for rnd. piles
$\tau(soil)$ = the maximum soil shear stress at the soil-pile interface

It has been shown that a shear stress-strain curve can be obtained from the selfboring pressuremeter curve by a theoretical method called the subtangent method (Baguelin et al., 1978). Applying the subtangent method to the curve of a pressuremeter test performed in a prebored hole (preboring pressuremeter test) leads to shear moduli which are too low and peak shear strength which are too high. However, appling the subtangent method to the reload curve from a preboring pressuremeter test (Fig. 3) leads to shear moduli comparable to selfboring shear moduli. As a result, in the proposed approach, the reload portion of the preboring pressuremeter curve is used to obtain the $\tau(soil)$ versus y(pmt)/R(pmt) curve (Fig. 3).

CRITICAL DEPTH: SOIL-STRUCTURE INTERACTION

The Phenomenon

When a pile is loaded laterally to failure, there is a zone just below the ground surface where the lateral soil resistance is reduced. This zone of reduced lateral resistance extends to the critical depth, D_c. Above D_c the absence of constraint caused by the stress free ground surface influ-

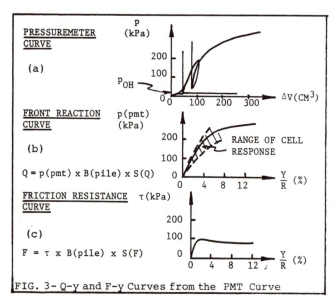

FIG. 3- Q-y and F-y Curves from the PMT Curve

ences the lateral soil resistance. Below D_c, that influence is negligible and the lateral soil resistance is called the deep soil resistance. The basic model described in previous sections refers to the deep soil resistance. Above D_c the shallow soil resistance is obtained by multiplying the deep resistance by a reduction factor. The evaluation of D_c and of the reduction factor is described in this section. The variation of soil resistance along a laterally loaded pile can be approximated by the solid line CBA on Fig. 4. The horizontal pile displacement y increases from

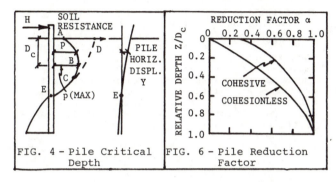

FIG. 4 - Pile Critical Depth   FIG. 6 - Pile Reduction Factor

point E to the ground surface. If there were no weakening influence due to the close proximity of the stress free ground surface, the variation of resistance in a soil of constant strength with depth would be as shown by the dotted line CD. Instead, the soil resistance distribution follows CBA with a maximum resistance $P_{(max)}$, at the critical depth D_c. Within D_c the soil resistance p is less than $P_{(max)}$ and the ratio $p/P_{(max)}$ is the reduction factor α.

Pile Critical Depth and Reduction Factor
The critical depth D_c is a soil structure interaction phenomenon. The closed form solution of the interaction problem in linear elasticity makes use of the key interaction parameter:

$$\ell_o = \sqrt[4]{\frac{4EI}{E_{sh}}} \qquad (13)$$

where ℓ_o is the pile transfer length, E is the modulus of the pile material, I is the moment of inertia of the pile cross-section perpendicular to the plane of bending and E_{sh} is the modulus of subgrade reaction of the soil. The following interaction parameter called relative rigidity was defined for this study:

$$RR = \frac{1}{B} \sqrt[4]{\frac{EI}{P_L^*}} \qquad (14)$$

where B is the pile diameter and P_L^* is the pressuremeter net limit pressure within the critical depth. The correlation of Fig. 5 is a plot of the relative critical depth D_c/B versus soil-pile relative rigidity RR for 10 piles. The data show that, in the same soil, piles of different rigidity generate different relative critical depth (Caisson and H pile in the silt of Plancoet) and that the same pile generates different relative critical depths in different soils (same pipe pile at Sabine and at Lake Austin). Within the critical depth D_c, the reduction factor is defined as $p/P_{(max)}$ (Fig. 5). Fig. 6 shows the recommended values for the variation of α within the critical depth D_c. These recommendations are

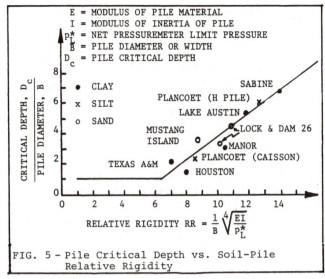

FIG. 5 - Pile Critical Depth vs. Soil-Pile Relative Rigidity

based on experimental data collected for 4 piles in clay and 2 piles in sand.

Pressuremeter Critical Depth and Reduction Factor
The critical depth phenomenon exists also for the pressuremeter. Baguelin et al. (1978) state that the pressuremeter seems to be below its critical depth Z_c if it is at least one meter deep in clay and two meters deep in sand. This would correspond to critical depths Z_c equal to 30 and 60 pressuremeter radii in clay and sand, respectively, for the conventional 35mm radius probes. The statement made by Baguelin et al. (1978) seems to refer to the limit pressure. A finite element study was performed to investigate the pressuremeter critical depth problem at small strain levels (Smith, 1983). The results of that study combined with the above statement lead to the recommendations shown on Fig. 7 for the pressuremeter critical depth and reduction factor β.

SUMMARY OF THE PROPOSED METHOD

More details and background on this method can be found in Briaud et al. (1984) and Smith (1983). The following is a summary:
1. Perform pressuremeter tests in a prebored hole at the site with close spacing near the surface and down to a depth of approximately 20 pile diameters.
2. Correct the pressuremeter curves for membrane resistance, system compressibility and

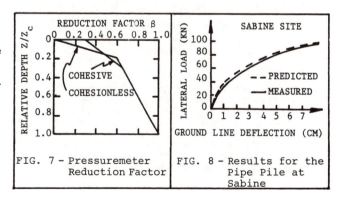

FIG. 7 - Pressuremeter Reduction Factor   FIG. 8 - Results for the Pipe Pile at Sabine

pressuremeter critical depth effect by using the factor β.
3. Obtain the front reaction curves (Q-y) by using Eqs. 10 and 11 together with the pressuremeter curves of step 2 as shown on Fig. 3 for bored piles. For driven piles use the reload pressuremeter curves.
4. For any test within the pile critical depth apply the proper α reduction factor to obtain the true Q-y curves.
5. Obtain the friction resistance curves (F-y) by applying the subtangent method to the reload pressuremeter curves and then by using Eqs. 11 and 12.
6. Obtain the P-y curves by adding at each depth the Q-y curve to the F-y curve.
7. Run the finite difference program to obtain the pile response.

COMPARISON OF MEASURED AND PREDICTED BEHAVIOR

The proposed method was used to predict the lateral load versus ground line deflection of 17 piles ranging from 0.32m to 1.37m in diameter and from 3m to 21m in length. These piles were loaded with time to failure varying from a few hours to a few days. Fig. 8 shows a case where a very good prediction was obtained. The results of the other comparisons between the predictions and the load test results are shown in Table 1. The comparisons were made by

SITE	PILE TYPE	PILE DIAM. (m)	EMBED. LENGTH (m)	PRED. LOAD MEAS. LOAD (at 2%*)	PRED. LOAD MEAS. LOAD (at 10%*)	SOIL TYPE
LACKLAND	BORED	0.457	10.5	1.14	1.37	CLAY
DELTA	BORED	0.610	3.0	1.36	----	CLAY
BAYTOWN	BORED	0.610	11.9	1.13	1.24	CLAY
VIRGINIA	BORED	1.370	3.51	1.21	----	CLAY
CAROLINA	BORED	1.370	4.54	0.59	----	SAND
IOWA	BORED	1.370	4.57	0.58	0.75	CLAY
TEXAS A&M '77	BORED	0.915	6.10	0.87	1.00	CLAY
TEXAS A&M '78	BORED	0.76	4.57	0.60	0.87	CLAY
TEXAS A&M '79	BORED	0.76	4.57	0.71	1.06	CLAY
HOUSTON	BORED	0.762	13.0	1.08	----	CLAY
MUSTANG ISLAND	DRIVEN	0.610	21.0	0.95	----	SAND
LAKE AUSTIN	DRIVEN	0.324	12.2	2.00	1.16	CLAY
SABINE	DRIVEN	0.324	12.2	1.15	1.02	CLAY
LA BAULE 1	DRIVEN	0.609	6.0	1.11	1.04	CLAY
LA BAULE 2	DRIVEN	0.609	6.0	1.00	0.93	CLAY
PLANCOET CAISSON	JACKED	0.95	4.40	0.80	----	SILT
PLANCOET H	DRIVEN	0.357	6.10	1.15	0.92	SILT

TABLE 1: COMPARISON OF PREDICTED AND MEASURED BEHAVIOR

* AT GROUND LINE DEFLECTION EQUAL TO 2% OR 10% OF PILE DIAM.

comparing predicted and measured loads (Q_p and Q_m respectively) at two displacement levels: 2% of the pile diameter and 10% of the pile diameter. For the 2% displacement comparison, the average of the ratio Q_p/Q_m was 1.030 and the standard deviation 0.337. For the 10% displacement comparison, the average of the ratio Q_p/Q_m was 1.003 and the standard deviation 0.190.

CONCLUSION

A pressuremeter method to predict the behavior of laterally loaded piles is described. The soil resistance model is the addition of a friction model and a front resistance model. It is shown on one case history that the pressuremeter curve gives the front resistance model directly and that the friction model can be obtained from the pressuremeter curve. The

critical depth effect for the pile is handled through a soil structure interaction approach; the critical depth effect for the pressuremeter is also included. The method is used to predict the behavior of 17 piles. The predictions are compared to the results of load tests. These comparisons allow to quantify the accuracy of the load predictions by a coefficient of variation of 33% at a pile head deflection equal to 2% of the pile diameter and of 16% at a pile head deflection equal to 10% of the pile diameter.

ACKNOWLEDGMENTS

The first two years of the research were funded by the National Science Foundation under a joint University Industry Cooperation Grant No. CME 8006727. McClelland Engineers were the industry counterpart in that Cooperation. The pile load test results were provided by: Exxon Chemical Americas, GAI Consultants, Laboratoire Central des Ponts et Chaussees, Los Angeles Department of Water and Power, Shell Development Company, Texas State Department of Highways and Public Transportation, and U.S. Army Engineers Waterways Experiment Station. Mr. Tim Braswell of Texas A&M University provided valuable help in running the computer program to obtain the predicted behavior of the piles.

REFERENCES

Baguelin, F., Frank, R., and Said, Y., "Theoretical Study of Lateral Reaction Mechanism of Piles," Geotechnique, Vol. XXVII, No. 3, September 1977.

Baguelin, F., Jezequel, J.F., Shields, D.H., "The Pressuremeter and Foundation Engineering," Trans Tech Publications, Rockport, Mass., 1978.

Briaud, J.L., Smith, T.D., Meyer, B.J., "Pressuremeter Gives Elementary Model for Laterally Loaded Piles," Proceedings of the International Symposium on In Situ Testing of Soil and Rock, Paris, May 1983.

Briaud, J.L., Tucker, L.M., Smith, T.D., "Pressuremeter Design of Laterally Loaded Piles," Research Report, No. 340-3, Texas Transportation Institute, Texas A&M University, February 1984.

Kash, V.R., Coyle, H.M., Bartoskewitz, R.E., Sarver, W.G., "Lateral Load Test on a Drilled Shaft in Clay," Research Report No. 211-1, Texas Transportation Institute, Texas A&M University, 1977.

Smith, T.D., "Pressuremeter Design Method for Single Piles Subjected to Static Lateral Load," Ph.D. dissertation, Texas A&M University, August 1983.

Coefficients de sécurité liés au calcul des pieux

Safety factors in piling design

M. BUSTAMANTE, Docteur-Ingénieur, Laboratoire central des Ponts et Chaussées, Paris, France
L. GIANESELLI, Technicien, Laboratoire central des Ponts et Chaussées, Paris, France

RESUME   L'observation du comportement d'un grand nombre de pieux d'essais, mais aussi le suivi de pieux sous charges réelles, intégrés à des ouvrages de franchissement, a conduit à s'interroger sur le bien-fondé des valeurs des coefficients de sécurité imposés jusqu'à maintenant lors du dimensionnement des fondations profondes par les règlements actuels. Il est apparu, au vu des données expérimentales, qu'il semblait opportun de proposer un premier système de coefficients utilisé pour le calcul de Q_N, mieux calé et justifié expérimentalement que les systèmes existants. On a été également conduit à élaborer un second système dont l'originalité réside dans le fait qu'il permet de coupler les différentes combinaisons de charges avec les différentes charges caractéristiques du pieu (nominale Q_N, de fluage Q_C, limite Q_L). En introduction, on rapporte brièvement les valeurs des coefficients de sécurité pris en compte lors du calcul des pieux dans une vingtaine de pays.

INTRODUCTION

Les auteurs ont pu réaliser en 1982, auprès de palistes de 22 pays (Belgique, Brésil, Chine, Grande-Bretagne, Grèce, Israël, Italie, Japon, Pologne, RFA, Suède, URSS, USA, etc.) une enquête portant sur les valeurs des coefficients de sécurité adoptés lors du calcul de la charge nominale Q_N (ou charge admissible) des pieux verticaux isolés, sollicités statiquement. L'examen des réponses a montré :

- que bon nombre de pays ne possèdent aucun texte réglementant les valeurs des coefficients de sécurité laissés alors à l'appréciation du projeteur,

- que certains pays préféraient adopter un coefficient unique F_G dont on frappe la charge limite globale calculée : $Q_N = Q_L/F_G$

- d'autres pays, dont la France, optent pour 2 coefficients distincts, F_P et F_S, à appliquer respectivement à la résistance de pointe limite calculée (Q_L^P) et le frottement latéral limite calculé (Q_L^S) suivant le schéma : $Q_N = Q_L^P/F_P + Q_L^S/F_S$. Dans ce dernier cas, en fonction du type de structure, de la nature des pieux ou de la possibilité de réaliser des essais de chargement en vraie grandeur, les valeurs s'échelonnent de 1,7 à 6,0 pour F_P, et de 1,5 à 3 pour F_S. En France, les deux textes qui réglementent les valeurs des coefficients tant pour le bâtiment, DTU 13.2 [1], que pour les ouvrages d'art, FOND. 72 [2], imposent $F_P = 3$ et $F_S = 2$ pour les pieux battus et forés.

La disparité des approches (opposition d'un coefficient global F_G à des coefficients partiels F_P et F_S) ou pour une même option, les différences sensibles de valeurs entre coefficients, ont incité à entreprendre une étude spécifique du problème. Une telle étude s'imposait d'autant plus que les auteurs du présent article, ayant élaboré une méthode de calcul de la portance, basée sur l'exploitation des essais pressiométriques (sonde Ménard) ou pénétrométriques statiques (CPT), il semblait opportun de l'associer à un système original de coefficients de sécurité, moins sommaire que celui en vigueur et, si possible, mieux calé et justifié expérimentalement. On rappellera qu'élaborée exclusivement à partir de données recueillies après interprétation de nombreux essais de chargement en vraie grandeur sur pieux instrumentés, cette méthode de calcul, décrite par ailleurs [3] [4] [5], permet de calculer la charge limite Q_L, ou plus précisément les composantes Q_L^P et Q_L^S de cette dernière. Les Figures 1 et 2 donnent une idée de sa validité en comparant les charges réellement mesurées $\overline{Q}_L$ et calculées pour des pieux forés et battus.

L'étude a finalement abouti à proposer deux systèmes de coefficients de sécurité interdépendants et constituant un tout avec la méthode de calcul élaborée.

Le premier système de coefficients permet, partant de la charge limite calculée Q_L, de chiffrer la charge nominale Q_N du pieu et la charge critique de fluage Q_C dont l'intérêt et les propriétés seront mis en évidence par la suite. Le second système de coefficients permet, lui, de coupler différentes combinaisons de charges avec les différentes charges caractéristiques du pieu, aussi bien calculées d'ailleurs que réelles (déduites de l'essai de chargement), à savoir Q_N, Q_C et Q_L.

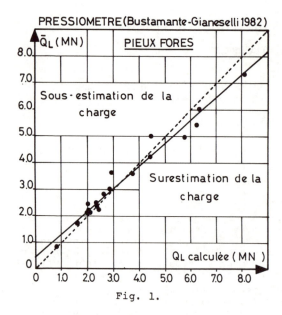

Fig. 1.

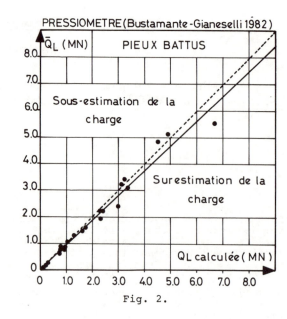

Fig. 2.

CHARGES CARACTERISTIQUES DE L'ESSAI EN VRAIE GRANDEUR.

IMPORTANCE DE LA CHARGE CRITIQUE DE FLUAGE Q_C

Pour la majorité des essais de pieux en vraie grandeur, indépendamment du type de pieu, battu ou foré, et de la nature ou compacité des sols d'encastrement, la relation expérimentale Q_o-y_o qui traduit l'enfoncement de la tête (y_o) en fonction de la charge appliquée en tête (Q_o), a l'une des allures illustrées par la Figure 3. On peut distinguer sur chacune des relations indiquées (a, b, c) deux charges caractéristiques : $\bar{Q}_L$ et Q_C. La première, $\bar{Q}_L$, est bien connue sous l'appellation de charge limite réelle, par opposition à la charge limite calculée que l'on désignera par Q_L. La charge $\bar{Q}_L$ est repérable d'autant plus facilement que la verticalité de Q_o-y_o est prononcée. Lorsque cette verticalité est moins évidente, on considère que $\bar{Q}_L$ correspond à des enfoncements de la pointe au moins égaux au 1/10è du diamètre ou des vitesses d'enfoncement de la tête de l'ordre de 1 à 5 mm/mn sous charge constante. La seconde charge caractéristique est la charge critique de fluage Q_C, qui peut être assez difficile à situer sur la relation Q_o-y_o au premier abord, bien que correspondant à un changement de pente généralement net. Il est préférable toutefois de la déterminer dans tous les cas par la méthode graphique proposée par Cambefort-Chadeisson [6] et rappelée dans plusieurs textes à caractère réglementaire [7]. On a vérifié pour un total de 74 pieux :

- que Q_C peut être toujours déterminé sans ambiguité (à l'exception des pieux pour lesquels la part de frottement latéral restait inférieure à 10 % de l'effort total) pour tous les types de sols et la totalité des

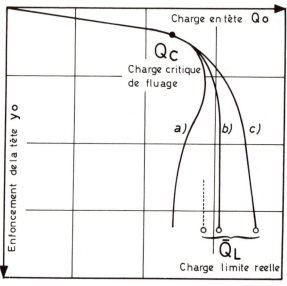

Fig. 3.

techniques de mise en oeuvre de pieux,

- que Q_C restait pratiquement indépendant de la durée des paliers d'application de la charge en tête, pour peu que ceux-ci restent dans des limites acceptables.

Hormis ces propriétés déjà soulignées, et dont les conséquences sont évidentes pour le praticien chargé de réaliser un essai de chargement, on a pu établir que Q_C constitue un seuil critique annonçant le début des grands enfoncements.

Cela s'explique par des taux de mobilisation des composantes de la portance déjà élevée sous la charge Q_C. C'est ainsi que lorsque l'on atteint cette dernière :

- le taux moyen de mobilisation du frottement latéral limite Q_L^S est de l'ordre de 77 % pour les pieux forés et 85 % pour les pieux battus,

- le taux de mobilisation moyen de la résistance de pointe limite Q_L^P varie de 52 % pour les pieux forés à 63 % pour les pieux battus.

On a pu aussi vérifier que les marges moyennes de sécurité séparant Q_C de Q_L, exprimées par le rapport $\bar{Q}_L/Q_C$ valent :

. 1,40 pour l'ensemble des pieux étudiés,
. 1,34 pour les pieux battus,
. 1,45 pour les pieux forés.

L'ensemble des propriétés que présente la charge Q_C fait bien de cette dernière une charge caractéristique, au même titre que $\bar{Q}_L$. Il est donc intéressant de savoir la calculer pour la prendre comme seuil de référence dans un système de coefficients de sécurité.

VALEURS DES COEFFICIENTS DE SECURITE POUR LE CALCUL DE Q_N et Q_C

Disposant d'une méthode de calcul permettant d'évaluer avec une approximation satisfaisante les composantes Q_L^P et Q_L^S de la charge limite Q_L, on s'est attaché à chiffrer les valeurs des coefficients F_{PC} et F_{SC} afin de pouvoir calculer directement Q_C dont on a montré la signification et l'importance plus haut, soit :

$$Q_C = \frac{Q_L^P}{F_{PC}} + \frac{Q_L^S}{F_{SC}}$$

Une étude comparative des valeurs mesurées et calculées, effectuée séparément pour des pieux battus et forés, a conduit aux couples de valeurs ci-après (Figures 4 et 5) :

. $F_{SC} = F_{PC} = 1,5$ pour les pieux battus,

. $F_{SC} = 1,5$ et $F_{PC} = 2,0$ pour les pieux forés.

On a vérifié, pour plus de 70 pieux, que la prise en compte de ces couples de coefficients donnait les rapports Q_L/Q_N suivants :

. 1,97   tous pieux confondus,
. 1,87   pour les pieux battus,
. 2,08   pour les pieux forés.

Ces valeurs ne sont rien d'autre que les valeurs de coefficients globaux F_G que garantit l'adoption des valeurs F_{PN} et F_{SN} proposées.

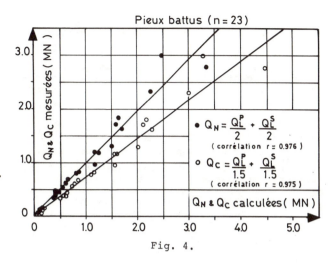

Fig. 4.

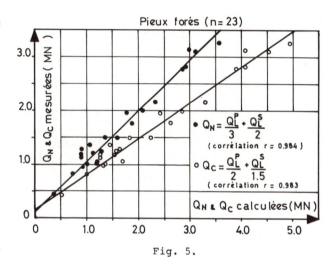

Fig. 5.

COMBINAISONS D'ACTION

Le comportement du pieu sous charge statique étant bien connu, et le calcul offrant la possibilité de chiffrer les seuils caractéristiques de la portance (Q_N, Q_C, Q_L), on peut établir un lien, par le biais d'un nouveau jeu de coefficients spécifiques, avec les différentes combinaisons d'action agissant sur la structure.

Les directives ou documents réglementaires de certains pays, notamment la France, introduisent aujourd'hui pour le bâtiment et les ouvrages d'art des notions d'états limites qui correspondent à des régimes de sollicitations définis en intensité et degré d'occurence. On distingue ainsi :

- les états limites ultimes (ELU), lesquels, sans correspondre nécessairement à des ruptures, peuvent induire de grandes déformations irréversibles entraînant la mise hors

service de l'ensemble ou partie de la
structure et impliquent des réparations,

- les états limites de service (ELS) ou d'utilisation, qui ne peuvent pas, en principe, occasionner de déformations irréversibles, ou même amener une mise hors service
temporaire.

On désignera respectivement les sollicitations
liées à chacun de ces états par Q_{max} (pour ELU)
et Q_{min} (pour ELS). On distinguera aussi pour
chacun de ces états des combinaisons d'action
caractéristiques qui sont les suivantes :

(a) Combinaison fondamentale induisant à
l'ouvrage une sollicitation d'intensité
$Q_{max,o}$ dont le degré d'occurence est
rarissime (1000 ans) ;

(b) Combinaison accidentelle, laquelle implique des sollicitations difficilement pré-
visibles et d'intensité $Q_{max,1}$ extrêmement
élevées (par exemple : chocs et séismes) ;

(c) Combinaison rare, d'intensité $Q_{min,o}$ pouvant se produire tous les 50 ou 200 ans,
c'est-à-dire, à coup sûr, au moins une
fois au cours de la durée de l'ouvrage ;

(d) Combinaison quasi-permanente $Q_{min,1}$
qui correspond aux conditions d'exploitation habituelles des ouvrages sous trafic
relativement intense (par exemple, cas
des ouvrages d'art d'une grande métropole
soumis au trafic des heures de pointe).

Si l'on se reporte à présent à une relation type
Q_o-y_o sur laquelle figurent les 3 charges caractéristiques de la portance (très proches, en
fait, des charges mesurées $\bar{Q}_N$, $\bar{Q}_C$ et $\bar{Q}_L$, compte
tenu de la représentativité de la méthode de
calcul proposée par les auteurs), à savoir :
Q_N, Q_C et Q_L, on peut faire correspondre à chaque régime de sollicitations, ELS ou ELU, un
domaine bien particulier des enfoncements
(Figure 6). La frontière entre ceux-ci passant
par Q_C, on départage ainsi un premier domaine
caractérisé par les très faibles enfoncements :
n'excédant pas en moyenne le 1 % du diamètre,
comme le montre l'examen des nombreuses mesures.
Le second domaine est réservé aux grands enfoncements, croissant d'autant plus vite que l'on
s'éloigne de Q_C. On peut ensuite distinguer au
sein d'un même domaine des plages correspondant
aux différentes combinaisons d'action. On établit
ainsi un couplage réel entre les combinaisons
d'action et les différents stades de la portance
du pieu. Enfin, moyennant l'adoption de coefficients réducteurs bien définis, on a la possibilité, pour une combinaison d'actions imposée,
de limiter la charge calculée Q par des seuils
caractéristiques. Ces coefficients réducteurs,
équivalents de coefficients de sécurité, peuvent
prendre les valeurs ci-après, suivant les combinaisons :

- quasi-permanente : $Q < 0,7\ Q_C$

- rare : $Q < Q_C$

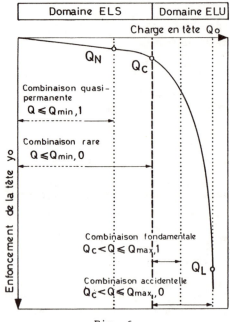

Fig. 6.

- fondamentale (ELU) : $Q < 0,85\ Q_L$

- accidentelle (ELU) : $Q < Q_L$

Les valeurs proposées constituent des valeurs de
principe. Il est possible d'envisager de légères
fluctuations, de l'ordre de 10 % par exemple, de
part et d'autre des bornes proposées. Cela peut
être le cas, par exemple, lorsque sur un projet
donné, on dispose de la possibilité de réaliser
des essais de chargements en vraie grandeur.
Dans de pareilles circonstances, on peut envisager de réduire les marges de sécurité pour
certaines combinaisons d'action.

REFERENCES

[1] DTU 13.2 - Fondations profondes, sept. 1963.

[2] Document FOND. 72, Fondations courantes d'ou-
    vrages d'art. LCPC-SETRA, févr. 1972.

[3] Bustamante, M. et Gianeselli, L. (1981).
    Prévision de la capacité portante des
    pieux isolés sous charge verticale. Règles
    pressiométriques et pénétrométriques.
    Bull. Liaison LPC, N° 113, mai-juin.

[4] Bustamante, M. et Gianeselli, L., Pile Bea-
    ring capacity prediction by means of
    static penetrometer CPT. Proceedings of
    II ES, Amsterdam, 1982.

[5] Bustamante, M. et Gianeselli, L., Réajuste-
    ment des paramètres de calcul des pieux.
    Xè Cong. int. Méc. Sols, Stockholm, juin
    1981.

[6] Cambefort et Chadeisson. Critère pour l'éva-
    luation de la force portante d'un pieu.
    Vè Conf. int. Méc. Sols, Londres, 1961.

[7] Axial Pile Loading Test, Part. 1 : Static
    loading. ISSMFE (1983).

Pile damage due to soil heave

Dommage aux pieux à cause de soulèvement de sol

F. K. CHIN, Jurutera Consultant (SEA) Sdn. Bhd., Kuala Lumpur, Malaysia

SYNOPSIS   This paper outlines the behaviour at two sites of displacement piles driven into a two-layered soil profile consisting of a top layer of soft marine clay overlying stiff residual soils. At the first site, because the piles were structurally sound and were embedded in the stiffer residual soils, pile heave was small. Pile bearing capacities were not affected by heave. At the second site, due to structurally inadequate joints, soil heave separated each pile into two lengths with a vertical gap of more than 75mm between them. This bifurcation could be identified from the load-settlement plot of the load test results. Redriving of the damaged piles with the object of closing the gap caused by soil heave was shown to be unreliable and not completely effective.

When a displacement pile is driven into a saturated cohesive soil, the soil displaced during the driving process is partly heaved up at the ground surface and partly displaced laterally from around the pile shaft. At a certain depth below the ground surface due to the overburden pressure, vertical heave ceases to prevail and only lateral displacements take place. It has been reported (BROMS, 1981) that measurements have indicated that heave within a pile group corresponds to 30 to 60% of the total volume of the piles. About half of the total volume appears as heave outside the pile group. Consequently the driving of a pile would cause adjacent piles that have already been installed to rise.

MACALLUM STREET GHAUT DEVELOPMENT

This site was identified for high rise development which included a number of blocks of 24 floors. In this site the residual soils consisting of stiff fine to coarse sandy clay formed by the insitu weathering of granite were overlain by a layer of marine clay which varied from 10 to 13 metres in thickness. For a number of years municipal refuse had been dumped on this site and covered over periodically with thin layers of imported soil. Since the thick layer of soft alluvium would demand the use of large displacement piles in order to prevent buckling, the effects of soil and pile heave were included in the engineering feasibility study.

Three test piles of various lengths were driven at each of three test pits. In each test pit the three reinforced concrete piles of cross-section 406mm by 406mm were driven with their centres forming the vertices of an equilateral triangle of side 1.37 metres. The spacing of the piles was therefore less than the pile perimeter (1.624 metres) which was the minimum spacing for friction piles as required under CP 2004:1975. The purpose of driving these test piles at a closer spacing than normal was to generate a more severe condition for heave.

Test Pit No. 1

In the case of Test Pit No. 1, Pile A1 with a penetration of 24.4m was the first pile driven. Pile B1 and then Pile C1 were driven to a penetration of 25.0m and 24.4m respectively.

On the completion of the driving of Piles B1 and C1, Pile A1 was found to rise 3mm. After all the three piles were load tested, they registered significant settlements and

Test Pit No. 1   TABLE I

REDUCED LEVEL OF PILE TOP (METRES)			DATE	TIME (HRS)	REMARKS
A1	B1	C1			
4.371			17.4.76	14.45	On completion of driving Pile A1
4.374	4.361	4.361	23.4.76	14.15	On completion of driving Piles B1&C1
4.358	4.331	4.346	7.5.76	11.50	
4.361	4.325	4.343	18.6.76	08.15	

Test Pit No. 2

REDUCED LEVEL OF PILE TOP (METRES)			DATE	TIME (HRS)	REMARKS
A2	B2	C2			
		4.885	6.4.76	15.05	On completion of driving of Pile C2
4.846		4.885	7.4.76	21.35	On completion of driving of Pile A2
4.849		4.888	7.4.76	16.00	On completion of driving of Pile B2
	4.885		2.5.76	12.25	
4.843	4.882	4.885	24.5.76	15.45	On completion of load testing of Piles A2, B2 & C2
4.846	4.879	4.885	19.6.76	20.20	

Test Pit No. 3

REDUCED LEVEL OF PILE TOP (METRES)			DATE	TIME (HRS)	REMARKS
A3	B3	C3			
		4.173	31.3.76	14.30	On completion of driving of Pile C3
		4.179	1.4.76	17.55	On completion of driving of Piles B3 and A3
4.118		4.182	2.4.76	16.00	
4.112		4.176	5.4.76	16.00	
4.115	4.179	4.179	7.4.76	16.10	
4.109	4.060	4.170	7.5.76	11.55	On completion of load testing of Piles A3, B3 & C3
4.106	4.054	4.166	18.6.76	08.15	

Piles B1 and C1 continued to settle even after the load testing was completed and the kentledge removed. (TABLE I)

Test Pit No. 2

Pile C2 was the first pile driven in this test pit, followed by Pile A2 and then Pile B2. Their respective depths of penetration were 35.9m, 24.1m and 30.6m. Immediately after the other two piles were driven, Pile C2 which had the longest length of embedment of which about 22 metres were in the stiff residual soil, was found to have heaved 3mm. After the load testing of all the 3 piles in this group, this pile was found to have settled 3mm.

Test Pit No. 3

In this test pit, the driving of Pile C3 to an embedded length of 35.6m was completed on 31st March 1976 followed by Pile A3 and Pile B3 on 1st April to depths of penetration of 24.1m and 38.7m respectively. Immediately after the last two piles were driven, Pile C3 was found to have heaved 6mm and by a further 3mm after a lapse of about 22 hours. Three days later it settled 6mm, then rose 3mm after two days and settled again 9mm after the completion of the load testing of all the 3 piles in the group. It continued to settle after that and registered a reduced level of 4.166m on 18th June 1976 which was 16mm below the observed peak level.

The observations on the nine test piles would indicate that the driving of displacement piles had caused adjacent piles already installed to heave. The magnitudes of heave were, however, small mainly because of the long embedment and anchorage of the piles in the stiffer residual sandy clays which were underneath the marine clay. The high strains resulting from the large radial displacements led to considerable re-orientation of the clay particles and produced high excess pore pressures. The resultant high hydrostatic gradients triggered off a process of consolidation at a significantly high rate resulting (a) in the rapid recovery of the loss in pile capacities of 212.3, 221.7 and 206.2 tonnes respectively as computed from the stability plots (CHIN, 1978). The adhesion which was observed to occur when a short pause

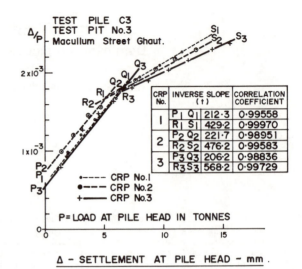

FIGURE 2: Test Pile C3: Stability plots for 3 CRP tests.

in driving resulted in a considerable increase in driving resistance. This increase, however was observed to be transient because the driving resistance rapidly decreased to approximately the original values soon after pile driving was resumed, and (b) in the pile settlements which were observed to occur immediately after the peak heave had taken place.

Despite the heave and subsequent settlements, the piles were observed to have high values of ultimate shaft friction and end bearing capacities when they were load tested about a month after they were installed. For example, in the case of Pile C3 which registered the greatest heave, the three consecutive cycles of Constant Rate of Penetration tests yielded estimated ultimate shaft frictional estimated ultimate end bearing capacities viz 216.9. 254.5 and 362.0 tonnes respectively, showed significant increases with each subsequent CRP test (Fig. 1 and 2).

BAYAN BAHRU DEVELOPMENT

Reinforced concrete piles of similar size as those used in the Macallum Street Ghaut Development were used at Bayan Bahru. At this site, the soil formations also consisted of a thick layer of marine clay (12 to 15.5m thick) overlying stiff residual sandy clays formed by the insitu

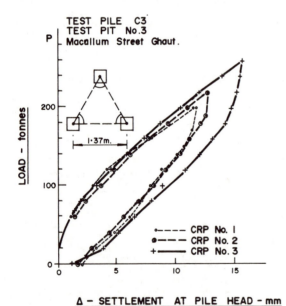

FIGURE 1: Test Pile C3: Load-settlement relationship for 3 CRP tests.

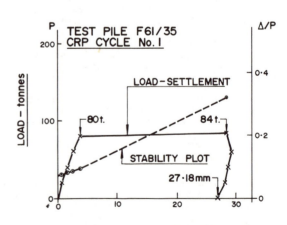

FIGURE 3: Test Pile F61/35: Load-settlement relationship for CRP test No. 1

weathering of granite. On the top of the marine clay was a layer of loose sandy clay of about a metre thick. When the engineers of this project load tested some of the piles, unusually large settlements and permanent sets were registered. Some of the test piles with embedded lengths of more than 30m had plunging failures at test loads of as low as 80 tonnes. The behaviour of test pile F61/35 was a typical example.

Test Pile F61/35

This pile had been driven to an embedment of 31.36m. When the first length of 12.18m was pitched and after penetrating the surface layer of about a metre in depth on two blows with a K32 hammer, this length of pile penetrated a further 4m into the marine clay on its own weight.

At the first CRP test, the settlement registered at the pile head increased rapidly after a test load of 80 tonnes and the pile continued to settle without any appreciable increase in load. A total settlement of 28.91mm was registered when the test load reached 84 tonnes. On releasing the entire test load, there was a permanent set of 27.18mm. The five points representing the observed test results (Fig. 3) defined a reasonably straight line with a product moment correlation factor of 0.99743 for the stability plot of Δ/p against an abscissa of Δ, where Δ was the settlement corresponding to a load of p at the pile head. The inverse slope gave a value of 89.3 tonnes

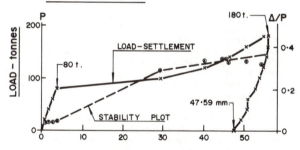

FIGURE 4: Test Pile F61/35: Load-settlement relationship for CRP test No. 2

as the ultimate shaft friction. There was no indication of end bearing capacity. This was too low an ultimate shaft friction for a pile with a penetration of 31.36 metres into the soil formation concerned. In the case of test Pile C3 in the Macallum Site with an embedment of 35.06m the ultimate shaft friction was more than 200 tonnes.

At the second CRP test, the jacking was continued after the "plunging failure". After a total settlement of about 30mm significant increase in load was observed. The testing was continued until the test load reached 180 tonnes (Fig. 4). On release of the load to zero, there was a permanent set of 47.59mm.

At the third cycle of CRP test, the plunging settlement with little apparent increase in load observed in the first and second CRP tests did not occur (Fig. 5). At a test load of 180 tonnes, the settlement at the pile head was 12.20mm as compared to 54.99mm at this load in the second CRP test. On release of the entire test load, the permanent set was also reduced considerably to 3.416mm.

At the fourth cycle of CRP test, the plunging settlement was also absent (Fig. 6). When the test load reached the value of 180 tonnes, the settlement at the pile head was 11.93mm and the permanent set on the release of the entire test load was 2.45mm.

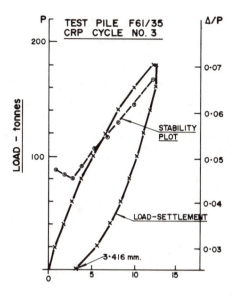

FIGURE 5: Test Pile F61/35: Load-settlement relationship for CRP test No. 3

From the above observations, it was clear that before this pile was load tested, it had consisted of two separate lengths with a vertical gap between them. As a result of a structurally inadequate joint, the heaving of the soil had lifted up the top length of this pile from its bottom length by about 27.18 + 47.59 = 74.77mm. It was only after the continued jacking in the CRP tests No. 1 and 2 that this vertical gap was substantially reduced. This pile had two joints, one at 7.0m and the other at 19.18m below the ground surface. As a 7.0m embedment in the marine clay and surface layer would not provide an ultimate shaft frictional capacity of 89.3 tonnes, it was the lower joint that had failed.

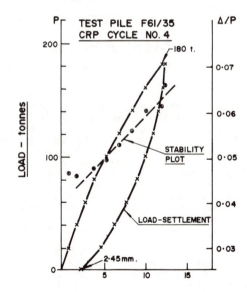

FIGURE 6: Test Pile F61/35: Load-settlement relationship for CRP test No. 4

Six other piles were load tested and as all the results revealed a similar bifurcation, all the seven hundred piles that had already been driven were suspect.

As a remedial measure, the contractor redrove some of the piles with the purpose of closing the gap which separated each pile. Using a K25 diesel hammer, the redriving of each pile was stopped when a set less than 12.5mm for the last 10 blows was attained. Of the first lot of 154 piles which were thus redriven, 31 penetrated less than 50mm, 32 penetrated between 50 and 75mm and 91 had a penetration of more than 75mm. One of these redriven piles, F62/168, which registered a penetration of 4.54mm at the last 10 blows, was load tested.

Test On Redriven Pile F62/168

Figure 7 gives the load-settlement plots of the first two cycles of the CRP tests. There was an improvement in that a load of about 160 tonnes was attained before plunging

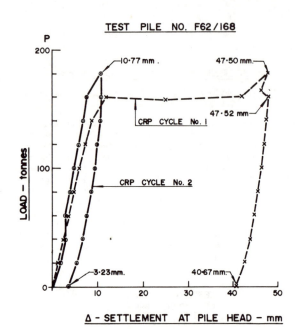

FIGURE 7: Load-settlement relationship of redriven pile.

failure commenced. The plunging failure continued over a settlement of about 30mm before there was further increase of load to 180 tonnes. The residual settlement on releasing the entire load was 40.67mm which was rather large and unacceptable. As in the tests of the piles before redriving, there was no plunging failure at the second cycle of the CRP test. At a test load of 180 tonnes, the settlement at the pile head was 10.77mm and the residual settlement was also considerably reduced to 3.23mm. On the third cycle of the CRP test, the settlement at the pile head was further reduced to 10.05mm at a test load of 180 tonnes and the residual settlement was 2.57mm.

The redriving was therefore not completely effective as a load capacity of only 160 tonnes was generated and this was 20 tonnes below the specified test load. Plunging failure still prevailed and there was no means by which any relative lateral displacements between the two ends of the bifurcation could be determined. It was also not possible to assess the extent of the structural damage sustained at these two ends of the bifurcation.

A comparison of the behaviour of the piles in the two sites would point to the importance of providing not only pile shafts but also pile joints which are structurally adequate to cater for the tensile forces generated by soil heave in the case of piles driven into stiff residual soils underlying marine clay.

Splicing of piles by welding together the two abutting steel plates using a fillet weld was shown to be inadequate in the Bayan Bahru site. Reflection waves and heave forces impose tensile stresses on the fillet weld. It is bad design practice to subject fillet welds to tensile stresses. Fillet welds should only be used in shear (CHIN, 1982). The hard driving which develops when the pile begins to penetrate into the stiffer residual soils tends to deform the steel plate at the pile head. Consequently it will not bear over its entire surface area against the plane surface of the abutting plate on the top length of pile that is added on.

Conclusions

The results of this study would indicate that:

(a) when displacement piles are driven into stiff residual soils which are overlain by a thick layer of saturated marine clay, the piles will heave,

(b) the upward displacement will be small if the pile is structurally adequate. The small upward displacement is followed rapidly by a small settlement. These pile displacements have little effect on ultimate shaft frictional capacity,

(c) Soil heave will cause a structurally inadequate pile to separate into two or more lengths. Such damage will seriously reduce pile bearing capacity. Redriving to close the vertical gap which is formed when the upper length of pile is lifted upwards by soil heave from the lower length of the damage pile is unreliable and cannot re-establish original pile bearing capacity and

(d) the design of piles to be founded in such a two-layered soil formation should provide for the tensile forces generated by the driving process and by soil heave.

REFERENCES

BROMS, B.B. (1981). Precast Piling Practice, Thomas Telford Ltd., London.

CHIN, F.K. (1978). Diagnosis of pile condition, Guest Lecture; Fifth Southeast Asian Conf. on Soil Engr., Geotechnical Engr. pp 85-104.

CHIN, F.K. (1982). The behaviour of piles in loose sands, Proc. Seventh Southeast Asian Geotechnical Conf. Hongkong, Vol. 1 pp. 106-118.

Uncertainties in the design of driven piles in sands

Incertitudes au calcul des pieux battus dans les sables

S. G. CHRISTOULAS, Soils Division, Ministry of Public Works, Athens, Greece

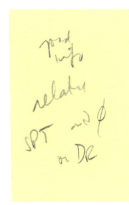

SYNOPSIS   The aim of this paper is to show the uncertainties involved in the design of driven piles in sands.   Some comments on the factors affecting the bearing capacity are given and the scatter of the results by the participation of each factor is evaluated.

INTRODUCTION

It is well known, that the bearing capacity of driven piles in sands depends on many factors. It is also known that, at the present time, exist several design methods and several means of soil investigation.   Thus, the problem of the convenient choice for the soil investigation in connection with the convenient method for estimate the bearing capacity is very important. So, the design path gives the most reliable result when the above choices are justified by a pile load test.   However, the pile load test is a rather difficult and time consuming job and particularly for small works is not always justified.   So, it is useful to know the mean and method possibilities thereby being able to evaluate the design uncertainties.

METHODS OF BEARING CAPACITY ESTIMATION

The ultimate load of a single pile in sand may be estimated by using the static formulae or by using different theoretical or empirical interpretation models of in situ tests.

On the basis of the classical expression of static formulae, the ultimate load of a single pile in sand is given by the relation:

$$P_u = \int_0^L C \cdot \sigma_v \cdot K_s \cdot tan\varphi_\alpha \cdot dz + A_b(\sigma_{vb} \cdot N_q + 0.5 \cdot \gamma \cdot d \cdot N_\gamma) - W(1)$$

where, the first term on the above formula is the ultimate shaft friction between pile and soil, P_{su}, the second term is the ultimate base resistance, P_{bu}, and the third one is the weight of the pile.
More precisely in the above expression:
L is the length of pile shaft.
C is the pile perimeter.
σ_v is the normal stress between pile and soil.
K_s is the coefficient of lateral pressure frequently related with the vertical stress σ_n with the relation $\sigma_n = K_s \cdot \sigma_v$.
φ_α is the angle of friction between pile and soil.

A_b is the area of pile base.
σ_{vb} is the vertical stress in soil at the level of pile base.
γ is the unit weight of the soil.
d is the pile diameter.
N_q, N_γ are the bearing capacity factors, primarily functions of the angle of internal friction φ of the soil.   For the short term ultimate load, φ and γ correspond to the undrained conditions and σ_v, σ_{vb} are total stresses.

On the basis of in situ tests, the interpretation models are referred to the Standard penetration test (SPT), to the relative density (D_r), to the Cone penetration test (CPT) or to the pressuremeter test.

According to the results of SPT, the ultimate load of a single pile in sand may be determined by the empirical formula

$$P_u = 4N \cdot A_b + \frac{\bar{N}}{50} \cdot As \qquad (2)$$

as suggested by Meyerhof (Cassan, 1978), where:
P_u is the ultimate load of the pile in tons.
N is the average number of blows of SPT at the point level.
$\bar{N}$ is the average number of blows of SPT along the pile shaft.
A_b is the area of pile base in sqft.
A_s is the area of pile shaft in sqft.

According to the results of the relative density D_r, the ultimate load of a single pile in sand may be determined by the empirical formula (Vesic, 1970).

$$P_u = 4.10^{2,4D_r^3} \cdot A_b + 0,08 \cdot 10^{1,5D_r^4} \cdot A_s \qquad (3)$$

where,
P_u is the ultimate load of pile in tons.
A_b is the area of pile base in sqft.
A_s is the area of pile shaft in sqft.

According to the results of CPT and pressure-meter test, the ultimate load may be determined by several theoretical and empirical formulae.

FACTORS AFFECTING THE PILE BEHAVIOUR

The behaviour of driven piles under given load conditions has not yet fully understood. It is affected by several factors and among them, they can be referred the follow one's:

- The pile installation method, the type of construction material and its surface finish in contact with the soil.
- The influence of driving in the mechanical properties of sand.
- The unit shaft friction distribution with depth.
- The use of different empirical relationships for the determination of the mechanical properties of soil.

The above factors are commented on more precisely in what follows.

Pile installation method etc.

The pile installation method may have an important influence on its behaviour. It is obvious that the bearing capacity of the pile is affected by the tip dimensions and its construction procedure. On the other hand, the construction procedure of the tip may affect the magnitude of the shaft friction, particularly in the case where this tip has a greater diameter than the shaft. An other important point for the pile behaviour is the water content of the sand in connection with its surface roughness. According to different shear tests carried out in the past (Potyondy, 1961), the angle of friction between pile and soil shows a large variation. Thus e.g. for dry sand, smooth surface finish of the concrete, $\varphi_\alpha/\varphi=0.76$, while for rough interface, $\varphi_\alpha/\varphi=0.98$. The corresponding values for saturated sand are respectively 0.80 and 0.90.

Driving influence

It is generally acknowledged that, when a pile is driven into sand, this sand is compacted. Therefore, it can be assumed, that the mechanical properties of the sand and more precisely its angle of internal friction is increased resulting in an increase in the pile bearing capacity. According to tests on model piles (Kezdi, 1960) it is shown that, during the driving of a pile, soil lines parallel to the pile axis remain parallel during their displacement. For a cylindrical concrete pile, the sand grains displace radially into a zone represented by an imaginary cylinder co-axial with the pile and with a radius α-fold larger than the pile radius. Suppose that the initial angle of internal friction is φ, e_o is the initial void ratio, φ_f is the average angle of internal friction after the sand compaction due to driving into the above zone of influence and e is the corresponding void ratio, then

$$\varphi_f > \varphi, \quad e = e_o - \Delta_e$$

where Δ_e is the average decrease in the void ratio into this zone. On the basis of many tests carried out in the past it is known that, etanφ, is constant and normally ranges between 0.45÷0.55.

It can be written

$$e_o \cdot \tan\varphi = 0.45 \div 0.55 \qquad (4)$$

$$(e_o - \Delta_e)\tan\varphi_f = 0.45 \div 0.55 \qquad (5)$$

The average decrease in the void ratio is given (Kezdi, 1960) by the equation

$$\Delta_e = \frac{1 + e_o}{\alpha^2} \qquad (6)$$

where, α, is the radius ratio of the imaginary cylinder and the pile. This equation gives a special expression for the average unit strain of the sand into the above zone. The solution of the above system of equations (4) and (5) gives:

$$\tan\varphi_f = \frac{0.45 \div 0.55}{\dfrac{0.45 \div 0.55}{\tan\varphi} - \dfrac{1 + \dfrac{0.45 \div 0.55}{\tan\varphi}}{\alpha^2}} \qquad (7)$$

For, α, equal to 5, 7.5, 10 and respectively for φ, equal to 20°, 30° and 40°, the table I gives the change of the angle φ due to pile driving.

TABLE I

α	Const.	$\varphi=20°/\varphi_f$	$\varphi=30°/\varphi_f$	$\varphi=40°/\varphi_f$
5	0.45	21°.4	32°.4	43°.4
	0.55	21°.3	32°.2	43°
7.5	0.45	20°.6	31°	41°.5
	0.55	20°.6	30°.9	41°.3
10	0.45	20°.3	30°.5	40°.8
	0.55	20°.3	30°.5	40°.7

Unit shaft friction distribution with depth

The most conventional methods for the estimation of pile bearing capacity in sands assume, that, the stresses σ_v and σ_{vb} correspond to overburden pressures. Namely, the unit shaft friction and point resistance increase linearly with depth. From previous research, it is well known that the above considerations are not common with reality. This research has shown that the unit shaft friction and point resistance increase linearly with depth only until a critical depth, which depends on the pile diameter, and ranges between 10÷20d. After a critical depth the unit shaft friction seems to remain constant.

Empirical correlations for the determination of the mechanical properties of soil

For the application of the methods concerning the bearing capacity of piles it is necessary to know the mechanical properties of the soil. But the static formulae require the knowledge of the angle of internal friction although such measurements do not exist. Thus, indirect values based on empirical correlations are used. These correlations are usually very attractive for the engineer because they overcome rather simply the existing problems.   But, the risk of using these correlations must not be disregarded. Their use leads some times to considerable errors because these relationships have been established and are therefore valid only for particular sand formations and field conditions. Consequently, the following comments on these correlations are necessary, particularly those concerning correlations between the angle of internal friction, number of blows of SPT and relative density.

Relationships between N and φ

There are several direct relationships between SPT and φ.   In figure 1 the limits of some empirical relationships are plotted, according to Osaki, Dunham, Peck et al. (Cassan, 1978).

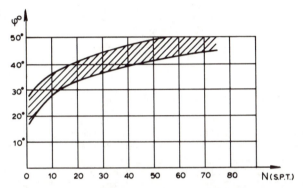

Fig.1   Relationship between N and φ

An important scatter on the values of the above relationships can be observed.   Also, it must be noted that, at the present time, more sophisticated relationships exist between N and φ as a function of overburden pressure.

Relationships between D_r and φ

There are several direct relationships between the relative density D_r and the angle of internal friction.   In figure 2 the limits of some empirical relationships are plotted according to Meyerhof, Parry (1977) and Schmertmann (1975).

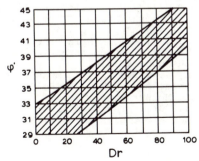

Fig.2   Relationship between D_r and φ

An important scatter on the values of the above relationships can be observed. Also, it must be noted that, at the present time, more sophisticated relationships exist between D_r and φ as a function of overburden pressure.

Relationships between N and D_r

Using the above relationships between N-φ and N-D_r an other relationship between N and D_r can be established.   It is also possible the use of the well known Terzaghi-Peck relationship (Cassan, 1978).

NUMERICAL CONSIDERATIONS

In the table II some numerical considerations of bearing capacity are given for various pile lengths and diameters and for various mechanical properties of soil.

The angle of internal friction is indirectly estimated using the N-φ (Peck et.al.) formula. The relative density is indirectly estimated using the empirical relation of Terzaghi-Peck. The pile bearing capacity is calculated using the equation 1, with

$$K_s=0.5\tan^2\left(45°+\frac{\varphi}{2}\right)$$

$$\varphi_\alpha=0.8\varphi$$

$$\gamma=18KN/m^3$$

(8)

N_q=Terzaghi coefficient of bearing capacity

The bearing capacity, on the basis of SPT results, is estimated using the equation 2. The bearing capacity, on the basis of the relative density results, is estimated using the equation 3.   Using the above design principles the bearing capacity is estimated for a case of pile load tests (Gregersen et al., 1973).   So, the table III is constructed in relation with the load test results.   From the results of these tables the scatter in the different design paths is obvious.

GENERAL COMMENTS AND CONCLUSIONS

It is clear that the estimation method of the angle of internal friction affects its magnitude. For a range of 4° of the angle of internal friction (e.g. φ=34°-38°) it may be said:

(i)   The influence of the pile installation method is important in the bearing capacity estimation. The bearing capacity is affected by the moisture content and its surface finish.   So, a scatter of the order of 50% for the total shaft friction can be evaluated for different ways of installation.

(ii)   The increase of the angle of internal friction due to the driving influence and consequently in the bearing capacity is important, especially in the case of high values of φ.   Into the influence zone,

TABLE II

N_{SPT}, φ, D_r	L/d $10^m/0.30^m$ P_{su} KN	L/d $10^m/0.30^m$ P_{bu} KN	L/d $10^m/0.40^m$ P_{su} KN	L/d $10^m/0.40^m$ P_{bu} KN	L/d $10^m/0.50^m$ P_{su} KN	L/d $10^m/0.50^m$ P_{bu} KN	L/d $15^m/0.30^m$ P_{su} KN	L/d $15^m/0.30^m$ P_{bu} KN	L/d $15^m/0.40^m$ P_{su} KN	L/d $15^m/0.40^m$ P_{bu} KN	L/d $15^m/0.50^m$ P_{su} KN	L/d $15^m/0.50^m$ P_{bu} KN	L/d $20^m/0.30^m$ P_{su} KN	L/d $20^m/0.30^m$ P_{bu} KN	L/d $20^m/0.40^m$ P_{su} KN	L/d $20^m/0.40^m$ P_{bu} KN	L/d $20^m/0.50^m$ P_{su} KN	L/d $20^m/0.50^m$ P_{bu} KN
N=1 $\varphi=27°$ $D_r=0.03$	20 447 80	30 256 30	27 596 106	53 452 53	33 745 133	83 707 83	30 1005 120	30 382 30	40 1340 159	53 678 53	50 1675 199	83 1061 83	40 1787 159	30 509 30	53 2382 212	53 905 53	66 2978 266	83 1414 83
N=5 $\varphi=29°$ $D_r=0.23$	100 524 81	149 331 32	133 699 107	266 588 57	166 873 134	415 919 89	150 1179 121	149 496 32	199 1572 161	266 882 57	249 1965 202	415 1378 89	199 2096 161	149 662 32	265 2795 215	266 1176 57	332 3493 269	415 1838 89
N=10 $\varphi=30°$ $D_r=0.40$	199 566 87	298 369 43	265 755 116	531 656 76	332 944 145	829 1025 118	299 1274 130	298 553 43	398 1699 173	531 984 76	497 2123 217	829 1537 118	398 2265 173	298 738 43	530 3020 231	531 1312 76	663 3775 289	829 2050 118
N=15 $\varphi=32°$ $D_r=0.44$	299 660 90	447 445 48	398 880 119	797 792 85	498 1100 149	1244 1237 133	449 1485 134	447 668 48	597 1980 179	797 1188 85	746 2475 224	1244 1856 133	597 2640 179	447 891 48	795 3520 239	797 1583 85	995 4400 299	1244 2474 133

TABLE III

Bearing Capacity	Pile A P_{su} KN	Pile A P_{bu} KN	Pile A P_u KN	Pile D/A P_{su} KN	Pile D/A P_{bu} KN	Pile D/A P_u KN
By Load Test	206	59	265	373	108	481
By SPT	45	26	71	30	52	82
As a function of φ	148	99	247	631	218	849
As a function of D_r	59	27	86	118	26	144

Note: For the pile A : L=8^m, d=0.28^m, $\gamma' \cong 10 KN/m^3$
$N_{SPT}=1$ for the point
$N_{SPT}=3$ for the shaft
For the pile D/A: L=16^m, d=0.28^m, $\gamma' \cong 10 KN/m^3$
$N_{SPT}=2$ for the point and shaft

An indirect estimation of the angle of internal friction by SPT or D_r leads sometimes in over-estimating or underestimating the bearing capacity by a factor which may exceed 10. Finally, because the bearing capacity factor N_q is an exponential function of the angle of internal friction it is easy to understand that a change from 34° to 38° may influence the point resistance by about ±70%.

ACKNOWLEDGEMENTS

The author wishes to thank Mr. Gerochristodoulou and Mrs. Tsepa for their valuable help in the preparation of figures, tables and typing.

REFERENCES

Cassan, M. (1978). Les essais in situ en Mécanique des Sols. Eyrolles, Paris.
Gregersen, A.S. (1973). Load tests on friction piles in loose sand. 8th ICSMFE, Vol.2.1 pp.109-117.
Kezdi, A. (1960). Contributions to the bearing capacity of piles. Acta Technica.
Parry, R.H.G. (1977). Estimating bearing capacity in sand from SPT values. ASCE, GT9, Vol.103, Sept. pp.1014-1019.
Potyondy, J.G. (1961). Skin friction between various soils and construction materials, Geotechnique, Vol.11.
Schmertmann, J. (1975). The Measurement of in situ shear strength. ASCE, Sp. Conf. of in situ Measurements, Vol.2.
Vesic, A. (1970). Tests on instrumented piles Ogeechee River site. ASCE, SM2, pp.561-584.

of 7,5α, the shaft friction increase is about 5%.

Obviously, this increase is higher when considering the increase due to the installation of the other piles of the group.

The non-linear distribution of shaft friction with depth affects the bearing capacity of piles especially in the case of L/d>20.

The use of some empirical relationships and methods leads to a great scatter of results.

Load tests and load transfer on short bored piles

Essais de chargement et transfert de charge en pieux forés

A. J. COSTA NUNES, Professor of Engineering, Universidade Federal, Rio de Janeiro; President, Tecnosolo S.A., Brazil
S. GOLOMBEK, Consulting Engineer, Director, Consultrix Ltda., Brazil
M. OKAY, Senior Foundation Engineer, Paulo Abib Engenharia S.A., Brazil
J. C. TÁVORA PINHO, Geotechnical Engineer, Paulo Abib Engenharia S.A., Brazil
M. BICHARA, Civil Engineer, Petrobrás Mineração S.A., PETROMISA, Brazil

SYNOPSIS   This paper deals with the behaviour of short reinforced concrete bored piles, in holes drilled with bentonite slurry, through the interbedded shales and limestones corresponding to the Taquari member of the Riachuelo formation, a Cretaceous shallow-marine deposit, which makes up the sub-surface material at the Potassio Sergipe Project of Petrobrás Mineração S.A.-PETROMISA.

To obtain the actual load transfer profile from piles inserted in the aforementioned ground, two vertical compression tests on piles instrumented with strain-gages and tell-tales were performed.

The measured Friction and Point resistances are presented and correlated, at each test pile, to the sub-surface geological column as indicated by two previous percussion and rotary borings, performed at the same locations.

The test results showed the prevalence of the Friction (F) over the Point (P) resistance even for short piles, although the F/P ratio increased significantly with pile length.

INTRODUCTION

A pile foundation was mandatory for the industrial structures that compound the Potassio Sergipe Project.   In order to optimize pile length and to evaluate pile behaviour, a few non-destructive vertical compression pile load tests, with settlement readings confined to pile head, were initially performed.   The data obtained, however, were unsatisfactory for a true knowledge of the load transfer characteristics along the pile.   It was decided, then, to instrument two pilot piles by means of strain-gages and tell-tales, and load test them up to rupture, or up to 11000 kN, whichever came first.   Both were 0.80m diameter piles; the shorter was 8.05m long and the other 14.00m long (see figures 1a and 1b).   The load was applied by two 7000kN-capacity hydraulic jacks pushing against a steel reaction frame fastened deeply into the ground, by eigtheen 900kN-capacity tiebacks.

GEOTECHNICAL AND ELASTIC CHARACTERISTICS

The sub-surface materials fall into three classes geotechnically:

1st) The topmost fine-grained fill (whose SPT index varies between 5 and 8 at the 8.05m pile location, and between 11 and 14 at the 14.00m pile location) and the weathered portions of limy and shaly beds (whose SPT varies between 11 and 14).

2nd) The shale beds, varying from laminated to massive, with an average Young's Modulus of 25 x 10^5 kPa and a Poisson's ratio of 0,25.

3rd) The limestone beds, varying from

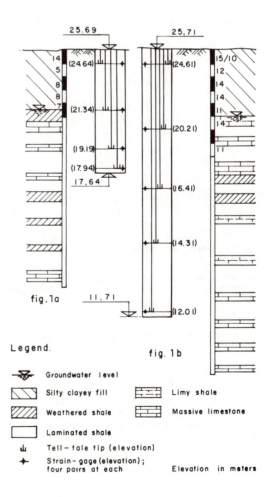

fig.1a

fig. 1b

Legend.

⩗ Groundwater level

▨ Silty clayey fill   ▤ Limy shale

▨ Weathered shale   ▦ Massive limestone

▢ Laminated shale

⊥ Tell-tale tip (elevation)

✛ Strain-gage (elevation);
four pairs at each

Elevation in meters

brecciated to massive, with an average Young's Modulus of 85×10^5 kPa and a Poisson's ratio of 0,20.

The fill and the weathered materials invariably occupied the top of the geologic column at each pile; the limestone and shale beds occur erratically at bottom. Thicknesswise, the laminated shale prevails, as can be seen from figures 1a and 1b.

LOAD TEST PROCEDURES

Figure 2a indicates the load frame assembly which was used for both tests and figure 2b indicates the reference beams set-up for dial-gages readings.

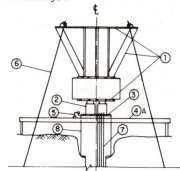

fig. 2a Load frame assembly cross-section

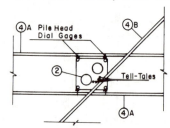

fig. 2b Reference beams set-up

Legend.

①	Steel Reaction Frame	⑤	Dial Gages
②	Hydraulic Jacks	⑥	Tiebacks
③	Steel Plates	⑦	Tell-Tales
④A	Reference Beams	⑧	Pile Cap
④B	Master Reference Beam		

The two jacks were activated simultaneously by an electric pump; the whole system was calibrated previously at a Technical Institution and a certificate was issued.

The pile head displacements were monitored by 4 dial-gages with an accuracy of 10^{-2} mm.

A thermometer was attached to the pile head for temperature monitoring.

Final load for the 8.05m long pile was 10125kN; for the 14.00m long pile was 11000kN. The pile's settlements were of 6.44mm and 10.34mm respectively.

Tell-tale rods were 1" in diameter rebars placed in 2 1/2" galvanized steel casings with a lid at

the bottom, previously fastenned to the pile's reinforcement.

Strain-gages were Kyowa's KFC-10-C1-11, installed by pairs so as to have one "active" and one "dummy" for temperature compensation. Strain readings were done in a Peekel B-105 Strainmeter, whose sensitivity is 10^{-6}.

TEST RESULTS AND INTERPRETATION

The pile's reinforced concrete had an Young's Modulus of 3.43×10^7 kPa; once confined into the ground, its Elastic Modulus would depend upon the compressive stress level, since the pile becomes mobilized by a three-axial stress condition.

To determine the proper Elastic Moduli for stress computation at each strain-gage level, the following continuity equation was used at the boundary level between the free pile and the confined pile:

$$E_O \cdot \varepsilon_O = E_C \cdot \varepsilon_C$$

where: $E_O = 3.43 \times 10^7$ kPa
ε_O = strain pile's head (applied stress/E_O)
E_C = confined Elastic Modulus
ε_C = strain obtained from the pile's strain-gage profile by projecting it orthogonally to the boundary level (see figures 3a and 3b).

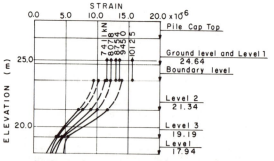

fig. 3a Measured Strain x Depth (8.05m long pile)

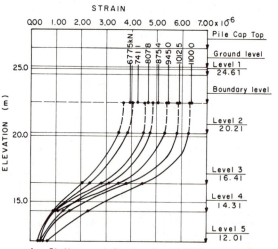

fig. 3b Measured Strain x Depth (14.00m long pile)

The ratio $\varepsilon_o/\varepsilon_c$ was then computed at each load stage and also the E_c values, as shown by the following table of results:

TABLE I

Confined Elastic Moduli E_c

LOAD (kN)	14.00m long Pile		8.05m long Pile	
	$\varepsilon_o / \varepsilon_c$	E_c	$\varepsilon_o / \varepsilon_c$	E_c
6 775	1.06	3.64	—	—
7 411	1.06	3.64	1.21	4.15
8 078	1.03	3.53	1.20	4.12
8 754	1.05	3.60	1.15	3.84
9 450	1.01	3.46	1.11	3.81
10 125	1.01	3.46	1.12	3.84
11 000	1.01	3.46	—	—

E_c values in 10^7 kPa

Then the compressive stresses (σ_z) were computed at each level using the relationship

$$\sigma_z = E_c \times \varepsilon_z$$

where: ε_z is the measured strain, yielding the following results:

TABLE II

Compressive Stress σ_z

LOAD (kN)	8.05m long Pile Elevation (m)				14.00m long Pile Elevation (m)				
	24.64	21.34	19.19	17.94	24.61	20.21	16.41	14.31	12.01
6 775	—	—	—	—	134.9	128.1	76.8	33.1	10.6
7 411	147.5	110.7	58.1	33.4	147.5	140.9	86.6	34.9	11.3
8 078	160.8	123.9	60.4	44.5	160.8	158.1	102.0	35.3	13.4
8 754	174.2	142.3	68.6	46.0	174.2	169.9	113.0	49.3	16.2
9.450	188.0	157.8	72.9	53.2	188.0	184.4	122.8	39.4	—
10 125	201.5	171.8	78.0	63.7	201.5	201.4	133.9	55.7	13.1
11 000	—	—	—	—	218.9	216.3	156.0	80.3	23.5

σ_z values in 10^2 kPa

Once known the σ_z values, the average friction stress (τ) for each interval between instrumented levels were computed. These values were the following:

TABLE III

Average Friction Stress τ

LOAD (kN)	8.05m long Pile			14.00m long Pile			
	24.64/21.34	21.34/19.19	19.19/17.94	24.61/20.21	20.21/16.14	16.41/14.31	14.31/12.01
6 775	—	—	—	0.58	2.70	4.16	1.96
7 411	3.41	4.89	3.95	0.58	2.86	4.92	2.05
8 078	3.42	5.91	2.54	0.24	2.95	6.35	1.90
8 754	2.95	6.36	3.62	0.38	2.99	6.07	2.88
9 450	2.30	7.90	3.15	0.31	3.24	7.94	—
10 125	2.75	8.73	1.49	0.10	3.58	7.45	3.70
11 000	—	—	—	0.23	3.17	7.21	4.94

τ values in 10^2 kPa

From the aforementioned results it becomes possible to compute the amount of applied load that turned partially into Friction load and partially into Point load:

TABLE IV

Friction and Point Loads

APPLIED LOAD	8.05m long Pile			14.00m long Pile		
	FRICTION	POINT	F/P	FRICTION	POINT	F/P
6 775	—	—	—	6 245	530	11.78
7 411	5 733	1 678	3.42	6 841	570	12.00
8 078	5 842	2 236	2.61	7 408	670	11.06
8 754	6 443	2 311	2.79	7 944	810	9.81
9 450	6 777	2 673	2.54	—	—	—
10 125	6 674	3 451	1.93	9 475	650	14,58
11 000	—	—	—	9 820	1 180	8,32

Loads in kN

The 8.05m pile displacement results from the tell-tales measurements are presented in figure 4a.

The 14.00m pile displacement results from the tell-tales measurements are presented in figure 4b.

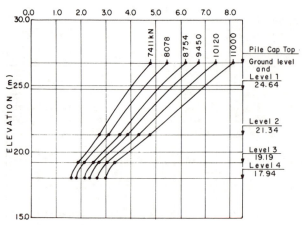

fig. 4a Measured total displacement x Depth (8.05m long pile)

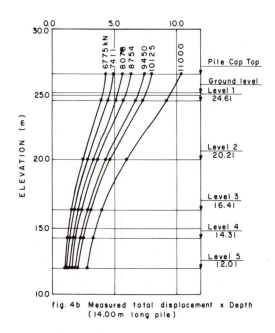

fig. 4b Measured total displacement x Depth (14.00m long pile)

CONCLUSIONS

The tell-tale monitoring allowed for a check on the strain-gage data; it also provided a knowledge of the true piles displacements at their tips.

The Friction load (F)predominated over the Point load (P) for both piles; their ratio (F/P)however

was substantially higher for the 14.00 m pile in comparison with the shorter one.

The load transfer characteristics for the shorter pile (8.05m) and for the longer pile (14.00m) were about equal in their stress levels - as can be verified by the σ and τ values-since both are restricted by the same sub-surface materials.

ACKNOWLEDGEMENTS

The authors are much obliged to Petrobrás Mineração S.A.-PETROMISA, in particular to its Vice-President, Dr. José Edilson de Melo Távora, and to Paulo Abib Engenharia S.A., for having allowed the presentation of this paper, as well as to Prof. C.E. de M. Fernandes for his valuable cooperation in compiling the load tests results.

REFERENCES

COSTA NUNES, A.J.da and M.Fernandes, C.E.de (1981)-Computed friction in a pile's rock-socket. Proc. 10th. Int.Conf.Soil Mech. Found.Engg., (2), 677-680, Stockholm.

COSTA NUNES, A.J.da and M.FERNANDES, C.E.de (1982)-Aspects related to the interpretation of load test results in instrumented piles (in portuguese). Proc. 7th. Brazilian Conf. Soil Mech.Found.Engg., (3), 201-209, Recife, Brazil.

FJELLERUP,F.E. (1981)-Load tests on large bored piles in sand. Proc. 10th. Int.Conf.Soil Mech.Found.Engg., (2), 713-716, Stockholm.

MASSAD,F.; NIYAMA, S. and ROCHA, R. (1981)-Vertical load tests on instrumented root-piles. Proc. 10th. Int.Conf.Soil Mech. Found.Engg., (2), 771-776. Stockholm.

ROSENBERG, P. and JOURNEAUX, N.L. (1976) -Friction and end bearing tests on bedrock for high capacity socket design. Canadian Geotechnical Journal, vol. 13, nº 3,August.

End bearing capacity of pile foundations by means of characteristics

Force portante à la base des pieux avec la méthode des caractéristiques

P. DE SIMONE, Istituto di Tecnica delle Fondazioni, Facoltà d'Ingegneria, Napoli, Italy
G. SAPIO, Istituto di Tecnica delle Fondazioni, Facoltà d'Ingegneria, Napoli, Italy

SYNOPSIS   Following an approximate approach suggested by Vesic (1963) and Berezantzev et al. (1963), the punching failure mechanism occurring below the base of a pile is simulated by classical plasticity theory through a reduced extent of the slip volume.
Values of the bearing capacity coefficient Nq are obtained by the method of characteristics in axial symmetry; the reduction of slip volume is obtained by considering a variation between 0 and $\pi/2$ of the angle ω formed by the limit surface and the horizontal plane through pile base.
In addition, the effect of base roughness, self weight and distribution and inclination of the overburden pressure is also analysed.
The results obtained are compared with previous findings, and some conclusions are drawn.

INTRODUCTION

As shown by Vesic (1964) the failure mechanism below the base of a pile cannot be but a punching failure, even in very dense soils. Accordingly, the end bearing capacity of piles should be evaluated by means of an elastic-plastic model, accounting for soil deformations before failure.
In order to avoid the difficulties involved by this model, two simplified approaches have been suggested.
The first one (Vesic, 1963; Berezantzev et al., 1963) makes use of the rigid-plastic model of classical plasticity, but reducing the extent of the slip volume. The second one (Skempton et al., 1953; Vesic, 1977) resorts to the theory of the expansion of a spherical cavity in an elastic-plastic medium.
In this paper the end bearing capacity of a pile is evaluated by means of characteristics following the first approach, and a reduction of the extent of the slip volume is obtained by considering a variation between 0 and $\pi/2$ of the angle ω formed by the limit surface and the horizontal plane through pile base (fig. 1).
In addition, the effect of: i) base roughness; ii) self weight and iii) distribution and inclination of the pressure q acting on the limit surface, is also analysed.
The results obtained are compared with previous findings and some conclusions are drawn.

$$\frac{\partial \sigma_r}{\partial r} + \frac{\partial \tau_{rz}}{\partial z} + \frac{\sigma_r - \sigma_\vartheta}{r} = 0 \qquad (1a)$$

$$\frac{\partial \tau_{zr}}{\partial r} + \frac{\partial \sigma_z}{\partial z} + \frac{\tau_{zr}}{r} = \gamma \qquad (1b)$$

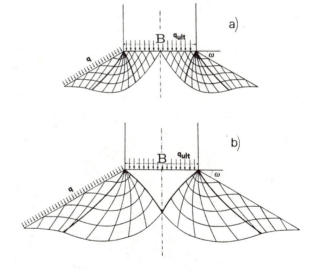

Fig. 1. Failure volume under pile point: a) smooth base; b) rough base.

GOVERNING EQUATIONS

The axially symmetric problem of a Mohr-Coulomb medium is governed by the equilibrium equations:

and the yield condition:

$$\sqrt{\left(\frac{\sigma_r - \sigma_z}{2}\right)^2 + \tau_{rz}^2} = \frac{\sigma_r + \sigma_z}{2}\sin\varphi + c\cos\varphi \qquad (2)$$

Consideration of the Haar-Von Karman (1909) hypo
thesis:

$$\sigma_\theta = \sigma_3 \qquad (3)$$

makes the problem a statically determined one.
It can be solved by the method of characteristics,
since it is of the hyperbolic type (Cox et al.,
1961).
As it is well known, the cohesion may be accoun
ted by Caquot's corresponding states theorem,
leading to the expression:

$$N_c = (N_q - 1) \cot \varphi \qquad (4)$$

Accordingly, only a cohesionless medium (c = 0;
$\varphi \neq 0$; $\gamma \neq 0$) needs be considered.
The stress state at a point may be defined by
means of the angle ϑ formed by the direction of
the major principal stress σ_1 and the horizontal r-axis, and of the Sokolovskii (1965) stress
parameter χ defined as.

$$\chi = \frac{\cot \varphi}{2} \ln \frac{p}{p_r} \qquad (5)$$

in which p is the mean stress and p_r a reference
stress. The governing equations (1) to (3), rewritten in terms of χ and ϑ, with respect to
the characteristic curves α and β:

$$\frac{dy}{dx} = \tan(-\vartheta \mp \varepsilon) \qquad (6)$$

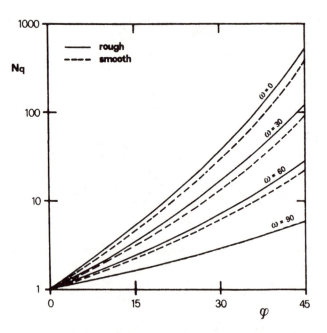

Fig. 2. Bearing capacity factor N_q for rough and
smooth base.

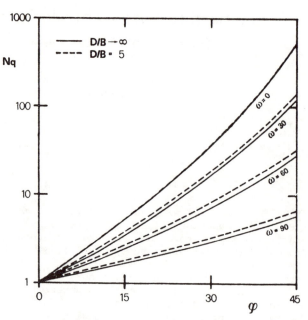

Fig. 3. Bearing capacity factor Nq for D/B→∞
and D/B = 5

become:

$$\frac{\partial \chi}{\partial s_\alpha} + \frac{\partial \vartheta}{\partial s_\alpha} = -\frac{\sin \varepsilon \cos \vartheta}{r} - \frac{\gamma \cos(-\vartheta + \varepsilon)}{2 p_r \sin \varphi} \exp(-2\chi \tan \varphi) \quad (7a)$$

$$\frac{\partial \chi}{\partial s_\beta} - \frac{\partial \vartheta}{\partial s_\beta} = -\frac{\sin \varepsilon \cos \vartheta}{r} + \frac{\gamma \cos(\vartheta + \varepsilon)}{2 p_r \sin \varphi} \exp(-2\chi \tan \varphi) \quad (7b)$$

where s_α and s_β are curvilinear abscissae along the characteristic curves α and β, and
$\varepsilon = \pi/4 - \varphi/2$.

NUMERICAL SOLUTION

Following Cox et al. (1961), eqs.(6) and (7) have
been solved numerically by finite differences.
A parametric study has been carried out, considering the influence of: i) the angle ω varying
between 0 and $\pi/2$; ii) the base roughness; iii)
the self weight and iv) the distribution and inclination of the pressure q acting on the limit
surface.

In the case of smooth base (fig. 1a) all the three failure zones occur, namely the passive or
Cauchy zone, the intermediate one or Prandtl fan,
and the active or mixed one, and the failure mechanism is of the Hill type. For the rough base
(fig. 1b) only the first two zones occur; a rigid wedge forms below the base and the failure
mechanism is of the Prandtl type.

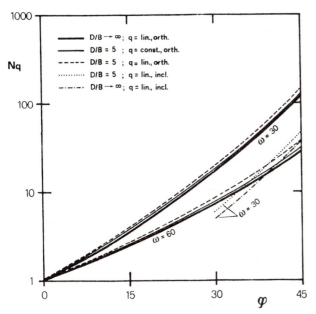

Fig. 4. Bearing capacity factor N_q for different
overburden pressure conditions.

The bearing capacity factor Nq is defined by the
relation:

$$q_{ult} = N_q \cdot q \qquad (8)$$

where q_{ult} is the end bearing capacity of the pile.
Values of Nq for rough and smooth pile base are
plotted in fig. 2 against φ, for $0 \leq \omega \leq \pi/2$.
The effect of the self weight, generally neglected in piles end bearing capacity calculations,
is shown in fig. 3 (rough base) where Nq is plotted for D/B→ ∞ (weightless medium) and D/B = 5,
being D and B respectively depth and diameter of
the pile base.
Finally, the influence of different hypotheses
about the inclination and distribution of q is
depicted in fig. 4. The pressure acting on the
limit surface has been considered either constant or linearly increasing with depth, and either
orthogonal to the limit surface or vertical, and
hence inclined to the normal of an angle ω. In
the latter instance, of course, only the cases
with $\varphi > \omega$ are possible.

ANALYSIS OF THE RESULTS

Figs. 2 and 3 shown that Nq decreases considerably as the angle ω increases from 0 to $\pi/2$.
This had to be expected, since the increase of
stress from the value at the limit surface (q) to
the value at the pile base (q_{ult}) depends on the
rotation of the principal stress within the Prandtl fan, and hence on the opening of such fan.
The same effect occurs in plane strain, where the

coefficient Nq has the expression:

$$N_q = \frac{1+\sin\varphi}{1-\sin\varphi} \exp(2\psi \tan\varphi) \qquad (9)$$

the angle ψ being the opening of Prandtl fan.
Consideration of base roughness implies a significant increase of Nq (fig. 2), while it is well
known that for the plane strain case it affects
only N_γ. The influence of roughness increases
with increasing φ and decreasing ω; for $\omega = \pi/2$;
the influence vanishes. It is believed that the
case of smooth base has no practical interest;
accordingly, further results are shown for the
only case of rough base.
The effect of self weight (fig. 3) seems unimportant, thus substantiating the usual practice of
disregarding it.
Finally, the effect of the distribution of the
overburden pressure q (fig. 4) seems to be unimportant when q is normal to the limit surface,
and significant when q is vertical, i.e. inclined of ω to the normal. The decrease of Nq with
increasing inclination of q may be explained with the above considerations on the opening of
Prandtl fan; the inclination of q, indeed, makes
the angle ϑ on the limit surface increase, thus
reducing the width of the Prandtl fan.

COMPARISON WITH PREVIOUS FINDINGS

In order to compare the present results with those obtained by other Authors, the values of Nq
by Vesic (1963, 1977) and by Berezantzev et al.
(1961, 1963) are plotted in fig. 5 together with

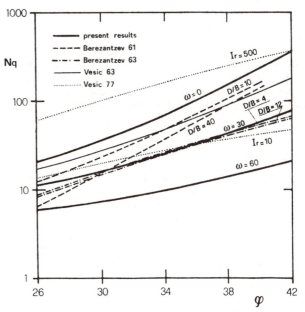

Fig. 5. Comparison between present Nq values and
previous ones.

those calculated by the writers for rough base, q normal to the limit surface and D/B→∞ (self weight = 0).

It is to remember that Vesic (1963) and Berezan tzev et al. (1963) adopt a reduced opening of Prandtl fan, equal respectively to 1.9 φ and to (π/4+ φ). Berezantzev et al. (1961) assume ω = 0, and Vesic (1977) makes use of the spherical cavity expansion theory. It is also to note that Vesic (1977) introduces a coefficient N_σ that is related to Nq by the expression:

$$N_\sigma = N_q \frac{3}{1+2K_0} \qquad (10)$$

To the writers' knowledge, the results by Berezantzev et al. (1961) are widely used in practice and believed to provide the best fit with experimental evidence for medium diameter piles (B=40÷60cm). The results by Berezantzev et al. (1963) were proposed for caissons and are sometimes adopted for large diameter bored piles, since they account for the reduction in end bearing capacity with increasing pile diameter.

Fig. 5 shows that the values of Nq obtained by the writers with ω= 30° fit rather well Berezantzev et al. (1963) ones. To fit Berezantzev et al. (1961) values, values of ω decreasing from 30° to 10° with increasing φ should be considered. This trend could be interpreted as a reduction of the local failure effect with the increase of φ.

CONCLUSIONS

The procedure proposed in the present paper is to account for the punching character of pile base failure through a reduced extent of the slip volume; this approach, first suggested by Vesic (1963), allows a unified treatment of both medium and large diameter piles.

The results obtained fit those by Berezantzev et al., provided suitable values are assigned to the angle ω. For large diameter bored piles a value ω= 30° seems to apply; for medium diameter piles a value of ω decreasing from 30° to 10° with increasing φ should be used.

REFERENCES

Berezantzev, V.G. Khristoforov, V.S. Golubkov, V.N. (1961). Load bearing capacity and deformation of piled foundations. Proc. 5th ICSMFE, 2, 11-15, Paris.

Berezantzev, V.G., Medkov, E.I., Yaroshenko, V.A., Tyulenyev, Y.A., Sidorov, N.N. (1963). Investigations of sand beds of shell foundations. Proc. 2nd Asian RCSMFE, 1, 251-256, Tokyo.

Cox, A.D., Eason, G., Hopkins, H.G. (1961). Axially symmetric plastic deformations in soils. Phil. Trans. Royal Soc. London, Series A, 254, 1-45.

Cox, A.D. (1962). Axially-Symmetric plastic deformation in soils-II. Indentation of ponderable soils. Int. J. Mech. Sci., 4, 371-380.

Haar, A., Von Karman, T. (1909). Zur Theorie der Spannungszustände in plastichen und sandartigen Medien. Nachr. Ges. Wiss. Göttingen, Math. Phys. Kl. 204-218.

Skempton, A.W., Yassin, A.A., Gibson, R.E.(1953). Theorie de la force portante des pieux. Annales ITBTP 6, 63-64, 285-290.

Skolovskii, V.V. (1965). Statics of granular media, 270 pp., Pergamon Press, Oxford.

Veisc, A.B. (1963). Bearing capacity of deep foundations in sand.Highway Res. Record, 39, 112-153.

Vesic, A.S. (1964). Investigations of bearing capacity of piles in sand. Conf. on Deep Found., 1, 197-224, Mexico.

Vesic, A.S. (1977). Design of pile foundations. Transp. Res, Board, 42.

Performance of timber piles in interbedded sands and clays

Performance des pieux en brois dans les sables et argiles

M. C. ERVIN, Principal Engineer, Coffey & Partners Pty Ltd, Melbourne, Australia
P. J. N. PELLS, Principal Engineer, Coffey & Partners Pty Ltd, Sydney, Australia

SYNOPSIS   Potentially aggressive groundwater conditions precluded use of conventional concrete cast-in-situ piles to support twin haul road bridges. Treated hardwood timber piles were adopted, and a programme of test piling carried out. The testing indicated conventional static analysis for piles in interbedded sands and clays would have been conservative. A Class A prediction of pile performance, which ignored the influence of layering, satisfactorily predicted the observed behaviour.

INTRODUCTION

Development of an open cut coal mine at Ulan in western New South Wales, Australia, was commenced in 1981, providing a considerable expansion to an existing underground operation. At the southern boundary of the proposed mine, the Permian Age coal measure rocks have been eroded and the area infilled by Tertiary Age deposits, consisting of interbedded sands and clays. Prior to development of the mine, it was necessary to divert the Goulburn River to the south of its existing course through the proposed mine area, via a 7km long diversion channel up to 12 metres deep through these Tertiary deposits.

Twin haul road bridges, to accommodate 170 tonne pay load haul trucks, were constructed over this diversion channel. The 40m long adjacent bridges were of two spans, with design abutment and pier loads of 10MN and 20MN respectively. The bridge decks are continuous and simply supported with horizontal loads transmitted directly into abutment headwalls. Differential settlement between abutments and pier of up to 25mm was acceptable.

A driven pile foundation system was considered to be appropriate for the structure, and given the high loads to be accommodated, maximizing the allowable pile loads was important in order to reduce the group size. Prediction of pile capacity with confidence was made difficult due to the interlayered soil strata, and a programme of test piling was agreed upon. Driven cast-in-situ piles were favoured at first, however, a routine check on the potential aggressiveness of the groundwater indicated severe corrosion potential towards both steel and concrete. As a result, treated hardwood timber piles were adopted. After test loading four piles, a confident prediction of performance was obtained, with the resulting foundation system being considerably less expensive than the original concrete pile proposal.

INVESTIGATION PROGRAMME

An extensive drilling, sampling and testing programme had been completed to allow design of the river diversion channel, thus allowing a good geological model of anticipated conditions to be established. Three additional boreholes were drilled at the actual bridge

site, as shown on Fig. 1. A typical borehole log is presented as Fig. 2, together with a summary of test data obtained from both the bridges and diversion investigations. Three separate aquifers were encountered, as shown. The use of mud drilling below 8m depth precluded measurement of the piezometric level in each of the lower sand layers, but upon completion of the drilling the mud was "killed" and the level shown recorded after bailing the borehole.

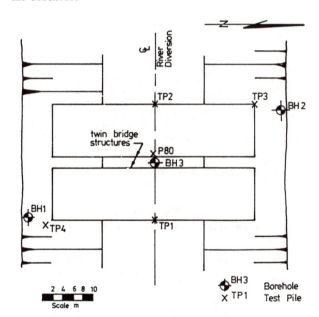

Fig. 1   Site Plan

Reasonable continuity of sub-horizontal layers corresponding to the two distinct material types shown in Fig. 2 was found to exist. As shown by the Standard Penetration Test "N" values, the sand varied considerably in density both between and within the layers. The sands within the aquifers are generally fine to coarse grained and contain only a trace of fines. The high plasticity clays varied in undrained shear strength from layer to layer, and were highly fissured. Some concern existed as to possible softening of these clays after the stress relief due to the diversion channel excavation, especially given the sub-artesian pressures which exist within the aquifers confined by these clays.

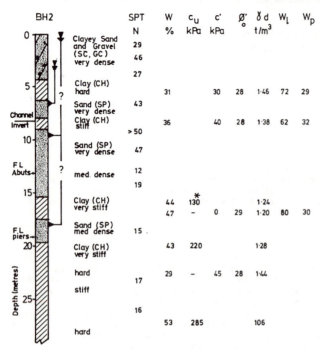

FL = Founding level
* Saturated and consolidated with σ_3 = 75 kPa

Fig. 2   Borehole Data

A sample of the groundwater was taken from the top aquifer prior to adoption of mud drilling, and of the groundwater recovered after bailing the borehole at completion of the drilling. These samples were submitted for analysis for potential aggressiveness to concrete and steel. The testing indicated a high level of aggressiveness, and it was therefore resolved to carry out additional testing on further more rigorously obtained samples. The testing on these samples, summarised below, confirmed the potential aggressiveness with low pH values and unacceptable levels of free CO_2.

TABLE I

Results of Chemical Analyses

Depth m	pH	Cl' mg/ℓ	SO_4" mg/ℓ	Free CO_2 mg/ℓ
7	5.25	1650	320	83
14	4.65	350	30	176
19	3.35	570	70	195

FOUNDATION DESIGN

Initial recommendations were for 500mm dia driven cast-in-situ piles, approximately 9 metres long. Estimation of allowable pile capacity required a rationalization of the influence of the two major soil types and of their layering. It is suggested by Meyerhof (1976) that a pile tip situated within 10 diameters of a weaker stratum is influenced by that stratum (Fig. 3). To maximize pile capacity at the site it was advantageous to found within the medium dense to dense sand layers, thus making use of the higher capacity offered by granular materials. The founding layers considered for the abutment and pier piles are only 6m and 2m thick respectively, corresponding to 12 and 4 pile diameters (if no base-enlargement). Hence using the Meyerhof criterion the adjacent clay layers dominate. For example, the allowable base resistance in the clay after excavation was considered to be 475kPa, compared to 1600kPa in medium dense sand at 9 metres depth (water table at surface). Applying the Meyerhof criterion, piles founding mid-depth on the upper founding layer may be proportioned for about 1100kPa base resistance, and in the lower layer negligible influence of the sand is allowed. Clearly in the upper layer overdriving would result in a reduction in allowable base capacity.

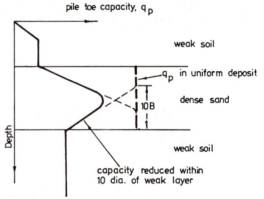

Fig. 3   Influence of weak layer
(after Meyerhof, 1976)

Using this approach an allowable pile capacity of 650kN was decided upon. It was recognised this was well below the structural capacity of a 500 dia pile, and it was recommended that test piling be considered with a view to improving the allowable pile capacity.

Construction methods which would allow use of concrete cast-in-situ piles in these aggressive conditions were considered, but due to uncertainty and cost were rejected. As a result creosote treated hardwood timber piles were subsequently accepted as the most appropriate piling system for the site.

The axial structural capacity of 280mm toe Australian hardwood piles corresponding to Strength Group S4 or better (SAA Timber Engineering Code, 1975) is 780kN. Clearly such piles had sufficient structural integrity but due to their smaller diameter their calculated static capacity was considerably less, despite the increased shaft resistance due to the pile taper (8mm per metre). The adoption of test piling to allow pile performance to be optimized was therefore considered essential.

TEST PILING

Four test piles were driven at the site, at the locations shown on Fig. 1. Due to industrial trouble it became necessary to drive the piles using a Delmag D12 diesel hammer, with a ram mass of 1.25 tonnes and a rated energy of 30.5kNm. It was initially proposed to use a drop hammer. Preboring was carried out through the upper cemented materials at the abutment pile locations.

Driving of TP1 was stopped at anticipated Contract level

(Fig. 4) at which stage its allowable capacity using the Hiley Formula and a F.O.S. = 3 was 530kN. It was also apparent that its capacity was still increasing. An additional pile was therefore pitched and driven (Pile P80) to assess driving resistance below Contract level. It was found (Fig. 4) that driving resistance improved up to 1.8m below Contract level, before decreasing significantly as the influence of the clay layer began to dominate. TP1 was then redriven, a further 1.5 metres, with a corresponding increase in dynamic capacity up to 610kN.

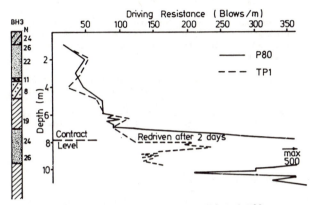

Fig. 4   Driving resistance – TP1 and P80

The remaining three piles were driven to a set corresponding to an allowable pile capacity of at least 650kN, the desired pile capacity.

The influence of the two soil types on driving resistance (and therefore capacity) is apparent in Fig. 4, particularly for P80 which was driven within a few metres of Bore 3. Only marginal increase in capacity results from driving through the clay, but once the underlying sand is penetrated the resistance increases dramatically. Heavy driving continues until the sand is penetrated when the resistance suddenly decreases.

It is interesting to note that the sand layer is about 9 pile toe diameters thick, yet its influence is almost immediate and continues to within a few centimetres of the clay layer. The subsequent increase again in resistance within the clay layer is judged to be an increase in shaft resistance corresponding to the taper effect within the sand layer.

Load testing was carried out using four 13m long 600 dia grout injected piles as reaction. Loading was carried out in increments, with time-displacement records kept at each increment. An unloading cycle was carried out at 650kN. TP1 failed by gross (40mm) deflection at 1175kN after behaving essentially elastically at earlier increments. The remaining three piles exhibited less dramatic behaviour, accepting between 1300kN and 1675kN for permanent pile head deflections of 4mm to 7mm. At the maximum applied loads, however, onset of signifncant settlement had occurred. Figs. 5 and 6 present load-deflection behaviour of TP1 and TP3. Table II presents the results of the test loading.

As noted, driving records were maintained to allow the dynamic capacity of the piles to be determined, therefore providing a basis for acceptance of the subsequent proto-type piles. The dynamic capacity was determined using both the Hiley and Janbu formulae (refer Poulos & Davis, 1980). As shown in Table III below, the Janbu formula predicted the measured ultimate capacity within 12%,

compared to 55% for Hiley. The Janbu formula has the added practical advantage of not requiring a graphical record of temporary compression and set to be obtained.

TABLE II
Results of Test Piling

Pile No	Maximum Load kN	Deflection at 650kN mm	Residual Deflection after test mm
TP1	1175	4.6	37.8
TP2	1300	3.9	4.0
TP3	1675	3.5	6.9
TP4	1450	3.6	5.5

TABLE III
Predicted Dynamic Capacity of Piles

Pile No	Ultimate Load (kN)		
	Load Test	Hiley	Janbu
TP1	1180	1830	1240
TP2	1450 est	1980	1515
TP3	1675	2020	1475
TP4	1450	1960	1355

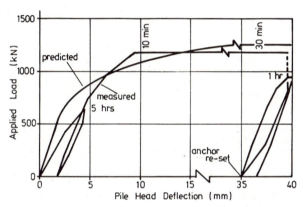

Fig. 5   Predicted and Actual Performance – TP1

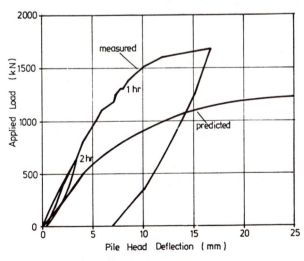

Fig. 6   Predicted and Actual Performance – TP3

PREDICTION OF PILE PERFORMANCE

Some months after completion of this project the data were used in a Class A prediction exercise. Various engineers, including the second author of this paper, were provided with the site investigation data and pile installation details. Predictions had to be made of the static pile load performance of the four test piles. The following is a brief description of the approach adopted by the second author of this paper.

* Formulate a simplified geotechnical model at each location assuming that clayey sands would behave as sands, and that localised lower density or weaker horizons would be bridged by the pile and hence would have little effect.

* Determine ultimate side shear values in sands and clays. The method presented by Nordlund (1965) was used for the sand layers but with a check against the data presented by Tomlinson (1977 - Fig. 4.19). Adhesion values for the clay horizons were taken from Tomlinson (Fig. 4.7).

* Determine ultimate end bearing component assuming 9 c_u for clay and the end bearing values of Berezantsev (1961) for sand.

* Calculate the elastic settlement of the pile using the method of Mattes (1972) as given in Poulos and Davis (1980), assuming that the effective short term modulus would be that of a very dense sand (E=200MPa) and that the load-settlement curve would be elastic up to 40% of ultimate load.

* Assume that ultimate capacity would be obtained at a displacement of 10% of the nominal pile diameter. The predicted load-displacement curves were then produced by linking the elastic portion with the ultimate load using curves obtained from previous pile load tests in sand.

In carrying out these analyses no account was taken of the interaction between the sand and clay layers as suggested by Meyerhof (1976). It was considered that, unless the base of the pile was within $1\frac{1}{2}$ diameters of an underlying soft layer, there would be no significant effect.

Table IV gives the predicted ultimate loads and the displacements at 650kN. These can be compared with the measures values given in Table II. Figures 5 and 6 compare the predicted load-displacement curves for TP1 and TP3 with the measured data.

TABLE IV

Pile No	Predicted Ultimate Load kN	Predicted Deflections at 650kN	
		mm	% of measured
TP1	1250	2.0	44
TP2	1600	2.0	51
TP3	1200	5.5	166
TP4	1500	4.4	122

The predictions were generally quite satisfactory with the worst being TP3 where the predicted ultimate capacity was about 70% of the measured value.

CONCLUSIONS

1. The value of a comprehensive test piling programme was clearly demonstrated for this project, with adopted design pile capacities considerably exceeding those which would have been adopted from static analysis. Considerable cost savings over the original foundation scheme resulted, highlighting the advantages over concrete and steel which can be offered by timber piles if the structural capacity of timber is utilized. The structure has been in service for some two years and is performing satisfactorily.

2. Based on the observed performance of the test piles, particularly during driving, it appears that the Meyerhof criteria regarding the influence of adjacent weak strata is conservative.

3. The approach presented by Nordlund (1965) for calculating side shear values for tapered piles in sand provided a satisfactory basis for predicting the behaviour of these timber piles.

4. The adhesion factors given by Tomlinson, and adopted in the prediction, are higher than presented in many texts and codes. Adoption of such factors for prediction purposes appears to have been satisfactory, although in static analysis without supporting test pile data caution would be required.

ACKNOWLEDGEMENTS

The data in this paper was obtained for Ulan Coal Mines Limited, who are gratefully acknowledged for permitting it to be presented here.

REFERENCES

Beresantsev, V G, et al (1961). Load Bearing Capacity and Deformation of Piled Foundations. Proc. 5th Int. Conf. SMFE, Paris (2), 1-35.

Mattes, N S (1972). The analysis of settlement of Piles and Pile Groups in Clay Soils. PhD Thesis, University of Sydney, Australia.

Meyerhof, G G (1976). Bearing capacity and Settlement of Pile Foundations. Jnl Geot. Eng. Div., ASCE, Vol 102, No GT3, 195-228.

Nordlund, R L (1965). Bearing Capacity of Piles in Cohesionless Soils. Jnl S.M.F.D., ASCE, No SM3, 1-35.

Poulos, H G and Davis, E H (1980). Pile Foundation Analysis and Design. John Wiley & Sons Inc. 397 pp.

Standards Association of Australia (1975). Timber Engineering Code.

Tomlinson, M J (1977). Pile Design and Construction Practice. Cement and Concrete Association, 413 pp.

A calculating model of cap-pile-soil interaction

Un modèle de calculation de longrine-pieu-sol

GUO-DONG FENG, Professor, Wuhan Institute of Hydraulic and Electric Engineering, Hubei, China
ZU-DE LIU, Professor, Wuhan Institute of Hydraulic and Electric Engineering, Hubei, China
SHAO-KENG HUANG, Lecturer, Quangxi University, Nanning, China

SYNOPSIS   It was found in model tests by authors that there are "Weakening", "Barrier" and "Strengthening" effects acting on a cap-pile-soil system. This was also proved afterward by large scale in-situ tests of pile groups in a district near the Yellow River. The importance of settlement to the cap-pile-soil interaction is emphasized. A calculating model is proposed for estimating the bearing capacity and settlement of pile foundations.

INTRODUCTION

The importance of cap-pile-soil interaction has attracted foundation engineers' attention for quite some time, but in pile foundation design "block failure" concept still dominates   in practice. The aim of this paper is to search for a calculating model reflecting the behaviour of interaction and applicable to engineering practice.

It is learned that the cap-pile-soil interaction which is caused by the relative displacement among cap, pile and soil includes the following main aspects: (1) The pile cap induces a "weakening effect" which restricts the mobilization of the side resistance in upper sections of piles. (2) The pile group induces a "barrier effect" which constrains the soil inside the piles to be squeezed out sideward. (3) In soils with internal friction the stress induced by the cap increases the soil bearing capacity at pile tip and also increases the normal stress and frictional resistance between piles and soil. It is called "strengthening effect". Under different geological conditions, the role of each of these effects is different.

The development of pile-soil relative displacement is characterized by:
(1) To a certain depth the displacement between pile and soil is limited by the pile cap pressure. Therefore the load transfer from pile sides to soil around is developing from tip to top.
(2) The study of interaction usually has more practical meaning for short friction pile groups in which the elastic compression of pile is insignificant.
(3) Pile-soil relative displacement occurs only when piles are placed apart far enough (e.g.>3d) or the soil is rather soft.
(4) Under certain loading, the pile-soil relative displacement △S below depth z may already reaches or exceeds the $(\triangle S)_{f_{max}}$ which is the displacement required for mobilizing ultimate side resistance of piles. Therefore the amount of load transferd by pile shaft is limited. Below z, the side resistance becomes constant or gradually decreases (in soils of strain softening) (see Fig. 1).

(5) The average amount of relative displacement in the whole pile length lies between two values, the pile top settlement S_0 and zero. The former shows the soil inside piles does not settle. The latter indicates the piles and soil act as a unit. The case happened in reality lies in between these two.

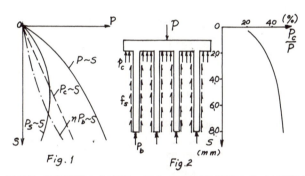

Fig. 1   Fig. 2

BASIC STARTING POINTS FOR ESTABLISHING A CALCULATING MODEL

(1) The allocation of load is (Fig. 2)

$$P = P_C + nP_b + n\pi d \sum_{1}^{n} l_i f_{si} \qquad (1)$$

where P_C-total pressure on the cap bottom, $P_C = A_C p_C$; A_C-effective area of cap (pile section deducted); p_C-stress on the cap bottom; P_b-end resistance of pile; n-number of piles; l_i-length of the i section of pile; f_{si}-side resistance on i section; d-pile diameter.
(2) The stress-strain characteristics in pile itself and in pile-soil boundary are very complicated spatial problem. Attention is only paid here to the approximate stress state in the points on the pile-soil boundary in order to be able to take more factors into account and makes the calculation simple.
(3) Based upon the following physical phenomena, an approximate method of load transfer analysis is proposed.
   a. The mobilization of side resistance accords with load transfer theory. The relation between (△S) and f_s can be expressed as:

$$f_S = F_1 (\triangle S) \qquad (2)$$

b. The final settlement of soil between piles should satisfy both the deformation induced by the cap and the mobilization of certain amount of side resistance.

c. For rigid pile, the settlement at any depth S_{pz} are equal to that of pile top S_G. For compressible pile, the compression δ_{sz} of pile section above depth z should be considered.

d. Since the displacement of any section of piles in a pile group $(S_{pz}-\delta_{sz})$ and the settlement of soil between piles (S_z) both are known, then the pile-soil relative displacement equals $(\triangle S)_z = (S_{pz}-\delta_{sz}) - S_z$, $(\triangle S)_z$ may be used to derive the side resistance f_S at point z (see Fig. 3).

e. With known subsurface condition, the relation between the settlement of pile tip $S_{pb}-\delta_{sb}$ (δ_{sb}-compression of whole pile length) and P_b can be expressed by a known function which will be discussed later.

f. Pile foundation settlement will induces stresses on the boundary between piles and soil correspondingly. The resultant of vertical components of these stresses should balance the loading on pile foundation.

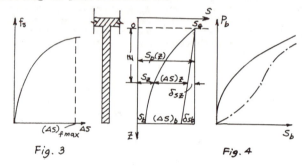

Fig. 3   Fig. 4

FUNDAMENTAL FORMULA FOR LOAD TRANSFER ANALYSIS

(1) The formula for the allocation of load Eq. (1) can be rewritten as:

$$P = nP_b + p_c + n\pi d l \bar{f}_s \qquad (3)$$

(2) All terms of Eq. (3) are functions of the settlement of pile top S_G, as following:

a. Considering the influences of installation of piles, soil conditions and the geometry of piles, the relation between the end resistance P_b and the settlement of pile tip S_b can be expressed by a cubic equation. (Fig. 4)

$$P_b = a_0 + a_1 S_b + a_2 S_b^2 + a_3 S_b^3 \qquad (4)$$

where a_0, a_1, a_2, a_3-coefficients derived from the result of loading test of piles installed by same method. They can also be determined by deep seated loading plate or pressuremeter test. For rigid pile, $S_b=S_G$, for compressible pile, $S_b = S_G-\delta_{sb}$. (Fig. 4).

Considering the strengthening effect acting on the end resistance by the pile cap pressure, concept of stress dispersion may be introduced to evaluate the increment of overburden pressure at pile tip $\triangle\delta_x$ which increases P_b to P_b^1, thereby, $P_b^1=KP_b$. K-coefficient of strengthening (K>1.0).

In general case, K value in sand is a linear function of the overburden pressure, then:

$$P_b^1 = KP_b = (\frac{\gamma l+\triangle\delta_z}{\gamma l})P_b \qquad (5)$$

where γ-effective unit weight of soil. If the ground consists of c-ϕ soil, P_b can be increased by the q value in the N_q term in the bearing capacity formula of deep foundation. If the soil at pile tip is soft, Terzaghi formula should be used. In case of friction pile installed in homogeneous soil, the calculation method based on the mechanism of expansion of cavities in infinite soil mass may then be used.

b. From model tests it is learnt that due to the barrier effect, $p_c \sim S_G$ shows linear relation. i.e.

$$p_c = CS_G \text{ and } P_c = A_c CS_G \qquad (6)$$

same notations used as Eq. (1). Coefficient C can be determined as follows: for cohesive soil, use the tangent slope of the P-S curve of plate load test; for cohesionless soil, use Terzaghi-Peck empirical formula derived from the result of plate load test with size effect considered. As for layered foundation, C can be calculated by layerwise summation method.

c. The relation between $\triangle S$ and $\bar{f}_s$ may be as follows: for certain conditions of soil and pile material, the required $(\triangle S)_{fmax}$ is comparatively constant and small (<10mm for sand and < 4mm for clay). When $(\triangle S)<(\triangle S)_{fmax}$, the load transfer function of $f_s \sim (\triangle S)$ can be expressed as:

$$f_{sz} = F_1(\triangle S)_z \qquad (7)$$

then the total side resistance P_s is given by

$$P_s = \pi d \sum_{i=1}^{n}\int_o^l (f_{sz})_i dz = \pi d \sum_{i=1}^{n}\int_o^l F_i(\triangle S)_{zi} dz \qquad (8)$$

Where $(\triangle S)_{zi}$-the pile-soil relative displacement of any points in the pile length of i pile. If $(\triangle S)_{zi}$ equals to the difference between pile top settlement S_G and the soil settlement S_z obtained by Boussinesq's equation (or even minus the compression of the pile δ_{sz}), then integrate $F_1(\triangle S)_{zi}$ over l to find P_s.

In considering the strengthening effect of the pile cap pressure on the end resistance f_s, Boussinesq's theory also can be used to calculate the horizontal stress increment in soil.

$$(\triangle\delta_x)z = (K_x)z \cdot p_c \qquad (9)$$

where K_x-coefficient of horizontal additional stress. By integrating Boussinesq's formula, the increment of f_s induced by $\triangle\delta_x$ is written as:

$$\triangle f_{sz} = (\triangle\delta_x)z \, F_1 (\triangle S)_z / tg\delta \qquad (10)$$

where δ-the friction angle between soil and pile, then integrate it over l and remained procedures as those above mentioned.

The basic formulas proposed only point out some comprehensive calculating principles. Detailed investigation for a concrete method of calculation is out of the scope of this paper.

CONCLUSIONS

It may be concluded that the theory of load transfer is applicable to analysing the bearing capacity and settlement of pile foundations with cap-pile-soil interaction under consideration. With such a model, portions of load carried by the cap, the pile shaft and the pile tip can be evaluated and also the P-S curve of a pile foundation can be predicted.

Foundation on creep piles: Design parameters, graphical presentation by computer of resultant force systems as well as an analysis of test pile results

Fondation sur pieux sous charge de fluage: Paramètres de calcul, présentation grafique des résultats par ordinateur et analyse d'un essai in-situ

A. FREDRIKSSON, Ph.D., ADG Grundteknik AB, Stockholm, Sweden
R. ROSÉN, Civil Engineer, ADG Grundteknik AB, Stockholm, Sweden

SYNOPSIS According to a new principle for design of building foundations in soft cohesive soils, devoloped in Sweden, the building is founded on a piled raft. The use of this design principle is discussed in this report. A case record from design of foundations for dwelling houses using this design principle is also presented.

INTRODUCTION

The pile foundation on conventional friction piles is designed to carry the total load of the building with a safety factor against pile failure of about 3.

According to a new principle of design, developed in Sweden (Hansbo et. al.,1973 and Hansbo and Källström, 1983), the building is founded on a piled raft. The total load of the building is assumed to be carried partly by the piles and partly by direct contact pressure at the raft/soil interface, as shown in Fig. 1. The design load of the piles is equal to the "creep load", meaning the pile load that causes a state of creep failure. The piles are designed so that the load in excess of the preconsolidation pressure of the clay is assumed to be carried by the piles and the rest by contact pressure.

In cases where the average net load increase exceeds the preconsolidation pressure of the clay, the object of creep piling is to reduce consolidation settlements. This is achieved by the fact that the stress increment exceeding the preconsolidation pressure of the clay is transferred to greater depths. Moreover the piles can be distributed in such a way that the differential settlement of the building is minimized.

CALCULATION OF SETTLEMENTS

To be able to calculate the final settlements in any point at the base of a building, not only the compression properties of the soil, but also the stiffness of the building, including the foundation, must be known. If the superstructure is statically indeterminated, differential settlements will cause a redistribution of support reactions and section forces in the superstructure. This redistribution in its turn will affect the settlements.

A correct consideration of the soil-structure interaction requires very extensive calculations. In order to make such calculations computer programs have been developed to take soil-structure interaction into consideration. The superstructure is modelled by finite element methods and the calculation of the settlements in the soil is based on the oedometer modulus, (Beigler, 1976). The vertical stress increase within the soil from contact pressure is calculated according to Boussinesq stress distribution. The vertical stress increase from the load on the creep piles is determined using Geddes (1966) integration of the Mindlin equation for a pile with linear variation of skin friction.

In order to get consistency between distribution of contact pressure, distribution of settlements and the deformations of the building, an iterative method is used in the computer program.

CASE RECORD

The foundations of dwelling houses, in the blocks Sigurd and Edda, in the town Uppsala, have been designed by the authors, according to the new principle of design. In Fig. 2 is shown a plan over the block Sigurd. The buildings have 3 - 6 storeyes and a basement. The houses are constructed of cast in-situ concrete.

The subsoil at the site of the buildings consists of soft clay underlain by silt and sand.

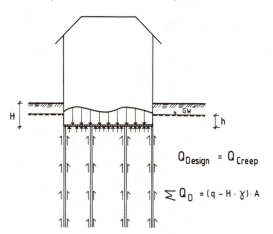

$$Q_{Design} = Q_{Creep}$$

$$\sum Q_D = (q - H \cdot \gamma) \cdot A$$

FIG. 1. New design principle for foundation on friction creep piles.

TABLE I.

Pile	Dimension
B1	18 m wood + 10 m concrete 0.27 * 0.27 m
B2	32 m concrete 0.27 * 0.27 m
B3	35 m concrete 0.27 * 0.27 m
B4	18 m wood + 10 m concrete 0.27 * 0.27 m
B5	32 m concrete 0.27 * 0.27 m
B6	35 m concrete 0.27 * 0.27 m

TABLE II.

Results from load tests.

Pile	$Q_{Failure}$, kN	Q_{Creep}, kN	Q_C/Q_F
B1	560	490	0.88
B2	550	480	0.87
B3	670	560	0.84
B4	570	510	0.89
B5	460	390	0.85
B6	630	530	0.84
		Mean	0.86

The thickness of the clay layer is about 40 m. The rock is about 100 m below the ground surface. Typical soil characteristics are presented in Fig. 3.

Determination of preconsolidation pressure and deformation characteristic of the clay.

The preconsolidation pressure has been determined in the laboratory by using oedometer tests with a constant rate of strain (CRS-test). The Modulus and permeability evaluated from a CRS-test are showned in Fig. 4. In the same figure is also showned the used variation of Modulus with the effective overburden pressure. This variation is expressed by four parameters, namely M_L, a, $\bar{\sigma}_L$ and m, according to Larsson and Sällfors, 1981. The variation of preconsolidation pressure with depth is showned in Fig.5. The variation of the modulus parameters with depth is showned in Fig. 6. In the figure is also marked the design values used for building G.

Load tests on friction piles.

In order to investigate the most economic pile type for the buildings in block Sigurd were 6 test piles loaded to failure. Three different

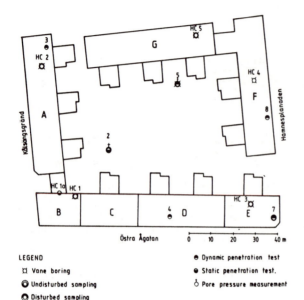

LEGEND

⌗ Vane boring
◎ Undisturbed sampling
◉ Disturbed sampling
⊕ Dynamic penetration test
● Static penetration test.
◊ Pore pressure measurement

FIG. 2. Plan over the block Sigurd.

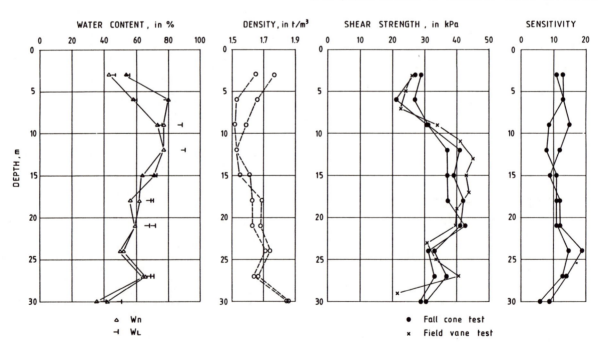

△ Wn
⊣ WL
● Fall cone test
× Field vane test

FIG. 3. Geotechnical characteristics of the subsoil at Sigurd.

pile types were tested, se table I. The piles
were tested 112 days after pile driving. The
piles were loaded stepwise and, in each step,
a load of about 1/10 of the estimated failure
load was applied. In each step, the load was
kept constant for 18 minutes and the creep displacement during the loadstep was measured.
The results from all load tests are summarized
in table II. The relationship between the creep
load and the failure load is about 0.86. This
is consistent with other experiences, see
Bengtsson and Hansbo, 1979.

In Table III and IV the calculated failure
loads based on shear strength determined by the
field vane test are compared with the observed
failure loads. As can be seen, the relationship
between the calculated and observed load is
0.89 for the wood piles and only 0.49 for the
concrete piles.

TABLE III.

Pile	$Q_{Failure}$, kN	Q_{Vane} , kN	Q_F / Q_V
B1	434	471	0.92
B4	444	516	0.86
		Mean	0.89

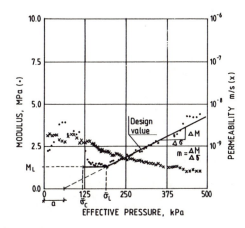

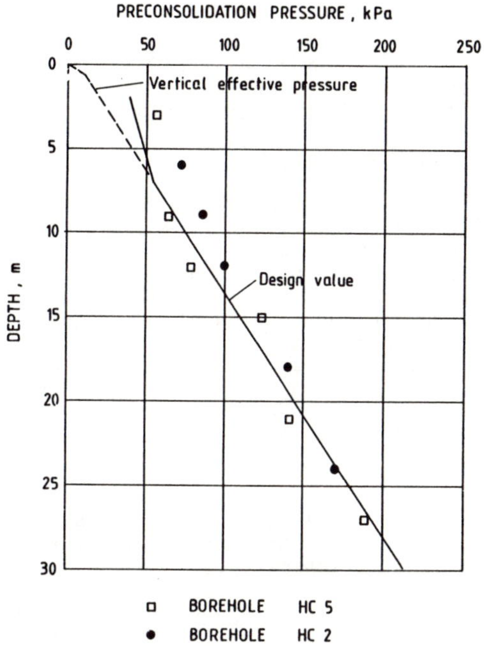

FIG. 4. Modulus and permeability evaluated from
CRS-test.

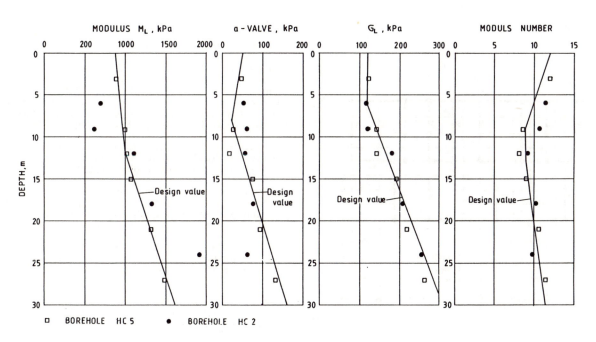

FIG. 5. Variation of preconsolidation pressure
with depth.

□ BOREHOLE HC 5
● BOREHOLE HC 2

□ BOREHOLE HC 5   ● BOREHOLE HC 2

FIG. 6. Variation of settlement characteristics with depth.

TABLE IV.

Pile	$Q_{Failure}$, kN	Q_{Vane}, kN	Q_F / Q_V
B2	550	1176	0.47
B3	670	1289	0.52
B5	460	1176	0.39
B6	630	1289	0.49
		Mean	0.49

The choosen piles for the foundations consists of 18 m long wooden piles, spliced with 7 m long concrete piles. The creep failure load was estimated to 420 kN for this type of pile.

Calculated settlements.

In Fig. 7 is shown the computer model for the building G. In the figure is also marked the positions of the creep piles. The calculated settlements after 50 years are shown in Fig. 8. The consolidation settlements have been calculated under the assumption of onedimensional flow of the pore water. Calculated settlements, contact pressure , section forces in walls and plate were presented in diagrams by a computer. This made the design process easier and the results more accessible.

CONCLUSION.

The following conclusions have been drawned from using the new design principle for foundations on friction piles.

- The new principle of foundation design has turned out to be a cost-effective alternative to conventional friction piles.

- The number of piles can be reduced.

- Cheap wooden piles can be used.

- The bearing capacity of the piles is better utilized.

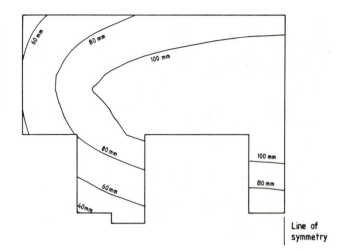

FIG. 8. Calculated settlements after 50 years.

- The differential settlements can be minimized using creep piles.

- Differential settlements between the building and the surrounding soil is also minimized.

- The time for construction of the foundations is reduced.

ACKNOWLEDGEMENT.

The foundations of the buildings in the presented case record were designed by order of A-projektering, Västerås, Sweden, when the authors were employed at J&W (AB Jacobson & Widmark, Lidingö, Sweden). The authors wish to express appreciation to J&W and A-projektering AB for the possibility of using the design material for this paper.

REFERENCES.

Beigler, S-E, 1976. Soil-structure interaction under static loading. Department of Geotechnical Engineering, CTH, Gothenburg, Sweden.

Bengtsson, P.E. and Hansbo, S, 1979. Settlement and bearing capacity of friction piles in soft highly plastic clay. Proceeding of the Nordic Geotechnical Meeting, Helsingfors, 1979.

Geddes, J.D., 1966. Stresses in foundation soils due to vertical subsurface loading. Geotechnique Vol. 16 no. 13, sept., pp 231-255.

Hansbo, S., Hofmann, E. and Mosesson J., 1973. Östra Nordstaden, Gothenburg. Experiences concerning a difficult problem and its unorthodox solution. Proc. VIII ICSMFE, Vol.2.2, Moscow.

Hansbo, S. and Källström, R., 1983. Creep piles - a costeffective alternative to conventional friction piles. Väg- och vattenbyggaren 7-8, 1983, Stockholm, Sweden.

Larsson, R. and Sällfors, G.. Beräkning av sättningar i lera. Väg- och vattenbyggaren 3, 1981, Stockholm, Sweden.

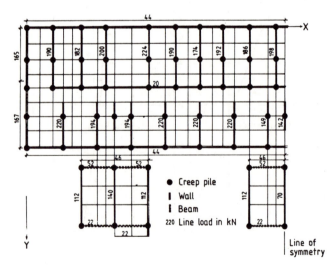

FIG. 7. Computer model for building G.

Failure analysis of pile foundations

Analyse de l'état limite des fondations sur pieux

BENT HANSEN, Professor of Soil Mechanics, Technical University of Denmark

SYNOPSIS   The design of pile foundations by specifying a safety against ultimate failure using the theory of plasticity is permitted in the Danish Code of Practice.   This paper outlines the general principles of calculation and describes the method which was used for checking the safety of some of the piers of the Faroe Bridge.   In these piers the piles are able to transmit moments and transversal forces to the foundation.   The calculation method is based on statically admissible lower bound solutions,   and it utilizes the optimization technique of the Simplex method from Linear Programming.

INTRODUCTION

Pile groups supporting bridge piers must be able to take eccentric and horizontal loads. They must therefore include batter piles, and the determination of the loads on the individual piles for any given load case on the pier foundation is a general three-dimensional equilibrium problem, in which all six equilibrium equations must be satisfied.

A calculation method for such pile groups was first formulated by Nøkkentved (1924), who assumed linearly elastic piles which are able to take only axial forces. Schiel (1960) introduced a systematic notation to facilitate calculations in practice and to take into account piles which are rigidly fixed in the foundation and laterally supported by the soil. On this basis a pile group may be calculated by the theory of elasticity, the design criterion being that the design axial pile force, or bending moment, or transversal force, must not be exceeded in any pile.

In Danish design practice (DIF, 1984) the design criterion is ultimate failure under the theory of plasticity of the entire pile group. By this theory the individual piles are assumed to yield when design stresses are reached,   and ultimate failure will not occur until so many piles have yielded that the foundation has become a mechanism.   The safety factors involved may be adjusted so that the number of piles required in a given group is much the same by the two calculation methods, but calculations by the theory of plasticity are simpler, especially during design when piles with given design strengths are to be arranged so that the resulting group can take a given total load.

Design and calculation procedures for pile groups by the theory of plasticity, assuming only axial loads in the piles, was formulated by Hansen (1959). This assumption is reasonable for precast concrete piles with widths up to 0.40 m. For larger piles, e.g. 0.70 m steel

tubes, the moments and transversal forces will frequently be important for the bearing capacity of the pile group. Since no generally applicable method existed to take these effects into account by the theory of plasticity, such pile groups are usually still calculated by the theory of elasticity, however.

In 1981 a new calculation procedure was developed which utilizes the technique of Linear Programming to find statically admissible lower bound solutions to the bearing capacity problem of pile groups, also when the piles are rigidly fixed in the foundation and laterally supported by the soil. This method was used to check some of the piers of the Faroe Bridge against ultimate failure for the most critical load cases.

THEORY OF PLASTICITY

In calculations by the theory of plasticity all strains in the piles and in the soil are plastic. Therefore, the corresponding stresses are yield stresses resulting from design values of axial pile forces, pile moments, and transversal forces, and from lateral earth pressures in ultimate failure. The usual upper and lower bound theorems for kinematically and statically admissible approximate solutions, respectively, can be shown to apply.

Upper bound solutions

A kinematically admissible solution for a given pile group acted upon by a given total load can be defined by specifying the 6 rigid body movement components (3 translations and 3 rotations) for the foundation block. This determines the axial and lateral movements of the piles, the development of yield hinges etc. As the corresponding resistances are known, the work equation can be used to determine the factor of safety on the total load above the safeties which have been applied on the individual load components and resistances.

Such a solution is known to be an upper bound solution. Thus, the correct solution according to the theory of plasticity may be found by seeking the rigid body movement which determines the minimum value of the total factor of safety.

This defines a calculation method which is useful e.g. for plane pile foundations where the possible rigid body movements to investigate are either translations perpendicular to some pile rows or rotations about intersection lines between pile row planes. The method is less useful for three-dimensional pile groups because of the large number of possible rigid body movement states. The seeking of a minimum solution is difficult by hand, and it is not simple to program for a computer.

Consequently, computer calculations of ultimate failure in pile groups are frequently done by assuming the total factor of safety to increase monotonously from zero, taking the pile group from the initial elastic state through intermediate elastic-plastic states until ultimate failure is reached. This leads to a unique solution, but the work of computation is considerable.

Lower bound solutions

A statically admissible solution is defined by a set of axial loads, moments, and transversal forces in the piles which are in equilibrium with the given total load multiplied by a factor of safety, and which do not exceed the failure conditions anywhere in the piles or the soil. Such a solution is known to be a lower bound solution, i.e. the correct solution according to the theory of plasticity corresponds to the set of pile forces which permits the maximum factor of safety to be multiplied on the total load.

This defines a calculation method which is useful for design. As the forces between piles and foundation can be fixed at known design values, the problem of arranging a pile group so that it can take a known total load is reduced to the problem of arranging known forces so that they in an efficient way, e.g. using the least possible number, balance the given load.

Efficient calculation procedures have been developed to design by this method e.g. doubly symmetrical pile groups acted upon by doubly symmetrical load cases. The method has not been used on the bearing capacity problem for given pile groups until it was realized that the determination of the set of pile forces which corresponds to the maximum factor of safety can be considered as a problem in Linear Programming.

LINEAR PROGRAMMING

In order to formulate the determination of an optimal lower bound solution as a linear programming problem it is necessary to write the equilibrium equations as linear equations in a number of variables, each of which takes values between known bounds. The total factor of safety, F, for which a maximum is sought, is one of the variables. The others are pile force components.

Pile force components

There are 6 unknown force components per pile. However, disregarding the twisting moments, as it is usually done for bridge piers, there are only 3 quantities which take values between known bounds: The axial force, the resulting moment at the pile top, and either the resulting transversal force at the top or a maximum moment in the pile at some depth below the top. Therefore, in order to linearize the problem the following approximation is made: The transversal force and the moments are for each pile assumed to act in the same plane. The directions of these planes are chosen initially and are kept constant during the optimization of F.

The axial force in pile no. r, P_r, is positive as pressure. Its bounds are determined by the resistances Q_r^c in compression and Q_r^t in pull:

$$-Q_r^t \le P_r \le Q_r^c \qquad (1)$$

The simplest case for the transversal force T_r, the moment at the pile top, M_r, and the maximum moment, M_r^1, in the pile is shown in Fig. 1 for a vertical pile. It is assumed in this case that the pile is fixed at the depth d below the pile top, and that it has no lateral earth support above this depth.

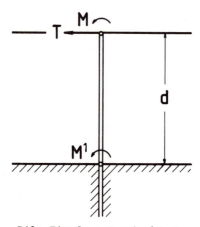

Fig. 1   Pile Fixed at Depth d below Pile Top

If d is small, M_r and T_r may be taken as the unknown quantities with the yield moment, Y_r, and the shearing resistance, S_r, respectively, determining the bounds:

$$-Y_r \leq M_r \leq Y_r \qquad (2)$$

$$-S_r \leq T_r \leq S_r \qquad (3)$$

For sufficiently large values of d, however, the bending moment M_r^1 in the pile becomes more critical than T_r. The unknowns must then be chosen as M_r and M_r^1 with the bounds (2) and:

$$-Y_r \leq M_r^1 \leq Y_r \qquad (4)$$

respectively. In the equilibrium equations it is used that:

$$T_r = \frac{M_r^1 - M_r}{d} \qquad (5)$$

Fig. 2 shows a pile in homogeneous soil. In ultimate failure the upper part of the pile above a yield hinge will be deflected laterally, and the soil resistance at failure, p (kN/m), will be developed along this part.

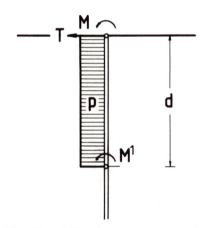

Fig. 2   Pile in Homogeneous Soil

The yield hinge will clearly develop at the depth:

$$d = \frac{T_r}{p} \qquad (6)$$

and the moment at this depth is:

$$M_r^1 = M_r + \frac{1}{2} T_r d \qquad (7)$$

The bounds (2) and (4) are valid, but T_r is seen not to be a linear function of the two moments. It is, however, on the safe side to use an approximate value of d, determined by:

$$d^2 = \frac{Y_r}{p} \qquad (8)$$

together with (5).

Equilibrium equations

If the pile group consists of n piles, the equilibrium conditions can be written as 6 equations with $m = 3n+1$ unknown quantities. With the usual tensor notation:

$$a_{ki} X_k = B_i \qquad (9)$$

The first n variables, X_k, are the axial pile forces, P_r, and the next n variables are the moments, M_r. The third group of n variables are either the transversal forces, T_r (for stiffly supported piles), or the bending moments, M_r^1. The last variable, no. m, is the safety factor F. The coefficients to F are the 6 components (with opposite signs) of the total load on the foundation:

$$a_{mi} = -R_i \qquad (10)$$

The other coefficients, a_{ki}, are found from the geometry of the pile group, the chosen direction angles, θ_r, for the planes in which T_r and M_r are assumed to act, and, if M_r^1 are unknowns, also from (5) and possibly (8). The 6 quantities B_i are initially zero.

The problem is now to find a set of values X_k which satisfies (9) and also the conditions (1) - (4), which may be written on the general form:

$$L_k \leq X_k \leq U_k \qquad (11)$$

and which minimizes the function:

$$f = r_k X_k \qquad (12)$$

Initially, all coefficients r_k are zero except r_m which is -1. In (11) L_m is zero and U_m is infinite.

Calculation procedure

The description of an efficient calculation procedure to solve this problem, the so-called Simplex method, may be found in a number of textbooks on Linear Programming, e.g. Luenberger (1973). This procedure may be outlined as follows:

1.   The optimization is obtained by an iteration process, each step going from one so-called basic feasible solution to another. A basic feasible solution is a set X_k which satisfies (9) and (11), all variables except 6, the basic variables, taking a bound value, L_k or U_k.

2.   During the calculations the variables X_k are replaced by the transformed variables X_k^e, e being an indicator which takes the values +1 or -1. The trans-

formed variables are defined by:

$$X_k^{+1} = X_k - L_k$$

and   (13)

$$X_k^{-1} = U_k - X_k$$

Thus, only the basic variables X_k^e take values different from zero. X_m^e (i.e. F) will always be one of the basic variables. For this, the indicator e is always +1.

3.   The basic feasible solutions are represented by transformations of the equation system (9) and (12): By row operations the coefficients a_{ki} are transformed so that they in each equation (9) are unity for one of the basic variables and zero for the others. In this way the transformed right hand sides B_i indicate the values of the pertinent basic variables X_k^e, the indicator e showing which of the expressions (13) is valid. By row operations, using the equations (9), the coefficients r_k in equation (12) are also transformed so that they are zero for all 6 basic variables.

4.   It can easily be seen that in the transformed equation system the coefficients different from zero and unity can be interpreted as:

$$r_k = df/dX_k^e = -dF/dX_k^e \qquad (14)$$

and

$$a_{ki} = -dX_b^e/dX_k^e \qquad (15)$$

where b indicates the basic variable which is represented by equation no. i. In the Simplex method (14) is used to decide in each step which of the non-basic variables to increase, and (15) is then used to find the size of the increment, depending on which of the following happens for the smallest increment:

a. One of the basic variables, X_b^e, decreases to zero, i.e. becomes non-basic.

b. Another variable X_b^e increases to its upper bound, $U_b - L_b$. It also becomes non-basic, but the sign of e should be changed.

c. The non-basic variable, X_k^e, increases to its upper bound. The sign of e should be changed.

5.   In cases b. and c. the variable transformation according to (13) implied by the changed sign of e is performed. In cases a. and b., where X_k^e now becomes a basic variable, a row operation is then performed, so that the equation system represents the new basic feasible solution. When all values of r_k have be-

come positive, no further increase of F is possible, and the optimal solution (for the chosen values of θ_k) has been found.

6.   An initial basic feasible solution may be found by assuming initially $F = 0$ and all indicators $e = +1$. The equilibrium equations (9) are satisfied by introducing 6 formal variables Y_j which are the initial basic variables. By an optimization process similar to the above the values of these variables are brought to their lower bounds, which are zero.

If necessary, the calculation may be repeated with another choice for the direction angles θ_r, seeking in this way to optimize the final value of F.

Final solution

The final transformed equation system (9) and (12) indicates the value of F and also, using (5) and (13), all pile force components. A useful further information is obtained by the fact that, according to (14) the individual coefficients r_k indicate the changes in F caused by changes in the design values for the pile foundation. Thus, if all values of Q_r^c are equal, the sum of all coefficients r_k, for which k indicates an axial pile force at the upper bound, Q^c, will indicate the sensitivity dF/dQ^c. In a similar way dF/dQ^t, dF/dY and, when applicable, dF/dS may be determined.

CALCULATION OF BRIDGE PIER

As an example the pile group supporting the pier called FF 10 for the Faroe Bridge is shown in Fig. 3. The piles are driven as closed steel tubes with 0.71 m diameter into limestone. For

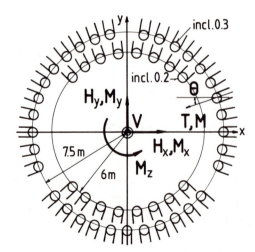

Fig. 3   Pile Group for Faroe Bridge Pier FF 10

all 50 piles are assumed the design values (for normal load cases):

$$Q^c = 4.5 \quad \text{MN}$$

$$Q^t = 0.88 \quad \text{MN} \qquad (16)$$

and

$$Y = 1.0 \quad \text{MNm}$$

The design soil resistance at failure $p = 0.5$ MN/m was estimated. However, the application of (8) and (5) would in this case give unacceptably high values of T_r. Consequently, (3) was used, assuming $S = 0.2$ MN. As an alternative on the safe side the use of (4) and (5) with a formal value $d = 10$ m was also investigated.

The design load case B 093 has the following components:

$$R_1 = V = 158.80 \quad \text{MN}$$

$$R_2 = H_x = 0.36 \quad \text{MN}$$

$$R_3 = H_y = 0.00 \quad \text{MN}$$

$$\qquad (17)$$

$$R_4 = M_x = 35.03 \quad \text{MNm}$$

$$R_5 = M_y = 19.14 \quad \text{MNm}$$

and

$$R_6 = M_z = -0.48 \quad \text{MNm}$$

The same value of θ_r is assumed for all piles. Initially $\theta = 15$ deg was chosen as the mean of the values suggested by the horizontal loads H_x, H_y and the moments M_x, M_y. By repeating the calculations for varying values of θ it was found, however, that $\theta = 36$ deg gives the maximum value of F. The results of the calculations, which were performed on a personal computer, HP 85, are summarized in Table I.

TABLE I

Calculation Results

Assumption	θ deg	F	dF/dQ^c	dF/dQ^t	dF/dY	dF/dS
$Y = 0$	–	0.633	0.118	0.118	–	–
Y , S	15	1.245	0.269	0.000	0.008	0.138
Y , S	36	1.370	0.298	0.000	0.020	0.048
Y , d	15	1.243	0.269	0.000	0.333	–
Y , d	36	1.361	0.298	0.000	0.020	–

As design values of loads and strengths are used, $F \geq 1$ is required. This requirement is not satisfied if the piles cannot transmit moments or transversal forces to the foundation (in this calculation $M_z = 0$ as it cannot then be taken by the pile group).

The pile group was designed by the theory of elasticity with a value of F close to unity. This calculation shows a margin of safety against ultimate failure of at least 30 per cent (this is also valid for the other load cases). This margin does not seem to depend strongly on the value of Y, provided only that Y is greater than zero. In this load case no pile is at its pulling resistance, so $dF/dQ^t = 0$. In load cases with higher horizontal loads this ratio may increase, but it never exceeds the value 0.03.

CONCLUSIONS

When design against ultimate failure of the pile foundation is permitted, as opposed to design against failure in the most critically loaded pile, efficient calculation methods may be obtained by utilizing statically admissible lower bound solutions from the theory of plasticity.

Such methods have been used to arrange pile groups so that they are able to take given total loads. In this paper it is shown that by using the computation technique of Linear Programming they can also be used to find the safety of a given pile group acted upon by a given total load.

REFERENCES

DIF   (Dansk Ingeniørforening) (1984). Norm for Fundering. DS 415, pp. 1-67. Teknisk Forlag, København. (English Translation: Code of Practice for Foundation Engineering).

Hansen, B. (1959). Limit Design of Pile Foundations. Bygningsstatiske Meddelelser, XXX nr. 2, pp. 1-86.

Luenberger, D.G. (1973). Introduction to Linear and Non-Linear Programming, pp.1-356. Addison-Wesley Publishing Company, Reading.

Nøkkentved, C. (1924). Beregning af pæleværker, Diss., pp. 1-248, København

Schiel, F. (1960). Statik der Pfahlwerke, pp. 1-148, Springer-Verlag, Berlin.

Bearing capacity of cast-in-place piles

Capacité portante des pieux moulés dans le sol

T. HORIUCHI, Professor, Department of Architecture, Meijo University, Nagoya, Japan

SYNOPSIS   On the basis of one hundred and eleven in-situ load tests of cast-in-place piles, factors influencing bearing capacity were statistically analyzed. Among many factors, pile diameter and pile length were identified to be the most predominant. The comparison was made between measured and calculated bearing capacity over wide range of these two factors, and the applicability of a present bearing capacity formula of cast-in-place piles was clarified when they were used in engineering practice.

INTRODUCTION

In determining bearing capacity of cast-in-place piles, all the design criteria authorized in Japan recommend in-situ load test rather than the direct use of bearing capacity calculation formula. In most cases of engineering practice, however, the prediction of the bearing capacity is made only in accordance with a calculation formula because of the limitation of both construction cost and construction period. In case of applying a calculation formula to design, however, high amount of uncertainty must be expected in the results of computation. In-situ and laboratory soil tests are, for instance, inevitably associated with certain amount of testing errors. Even in the design formula some errors are also expected because of theoretical assumptions for simplification of real soil behavior. The calibration of these errors should be made by the comparison of computed values with actually measured bearing capacity in in-situ load tests. However, a straight comparison between measured and computed bearing capacity of piles tends to show a large variance and does not always reveal good correlation. This is because there are many factors which influence bearing capacity of piles, such as pile diameter, pile length, N-values and soil quality of bearing stratum, penetration length of pile point bearing stratum, and so on. The comparison between measured and computed bearing capacity should, therefore, be characterized by those factors, and the applicability as well as the limitation of a design formula of bearing apacity of piles should also be described in terms of the ranges of those factors.

FACTORS INFLUENCING THE BEARING CAPACITY OF CASE-IN-PLACE PILES

The samples for in-situ load test of cast-in-place piles used in this analysis were collected widely in great number for many years, and hundred and eleven cases with high reliability (85 cases with earth drill piles and 26 cases with Benoto piles) were selected from them. Although there exist various factors influencing the magnitude of bearing capacity of cast-in-place piles, in the present paper the following are studied: pile diameter D, pile length L, N-values at pile point, mean N-values $\overline{N}$ averaged over 5D length measured from 1D deep below pile point to 4D above the point, and penetrated length of the pile into bearing stratum L'; The effect of these factors are statistically analyzed through examining measured bearing capacity obtained from field load tests. The results are shown in Figs. 1-5, in which measured bearing capacities of earth drill piles are distinguished from those of Benoto piles. In these figures Rm denote measured bearing

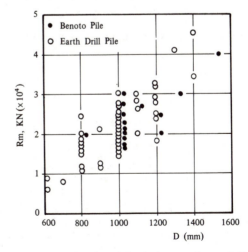

Fig.1 Relationship between Rm and D

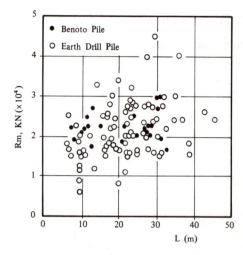

Fig.2 Relationship between Rm and L

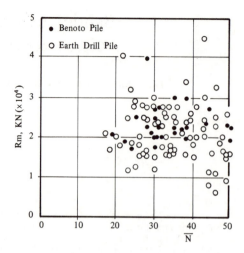

Fig.4 Relationship between Rm and N̄

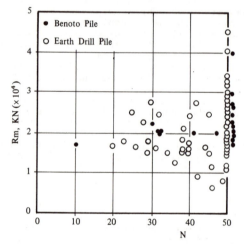

Fig.3 Relationship between Rm and N

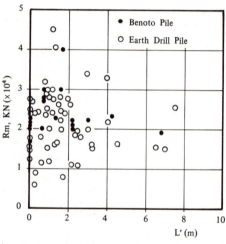

Fig.5 Relationship between Rm and L'

Capacity, the definition of which follows either Rm = 1/2 Qy or Rm = 1/3 Qu where Qy and Qu are yield load and ultimate load, respectively, Since it was very few to observe ultimate load Qu in field test, all the Rm's in these figures followed the former definition except two cases. These figures show a high correlation between the Rm and the pile diameter D, but the other factors L, N, N̄ and L' are difficult to find a good correlation with bearing capacity Rm. Furthermore, followings are drawn from Figs. 1-5: (i) the considerably narrow rang of bearing capacity can be found for each pile diameter, and (ii) there is no significant difference in

bearing capacity between earth drill piles and Benoto piles.

A DESIGN FORMULA OF CAST-IN-PLACE PILES NOW IN USE IN JAPAN

The applicability of the design formula for cast-in-place piles recommended by Architectural Institute of Japan is examined there through the comparison with insitu measurement. The calculation of the bearing capacity of cast-in-place piles is made by the following equation (the AIJ, Design Criteria for Calculating the Foundation Construction, 1976):

$$Rc = \frac{1}{3}\left\{15\overline{N}Ap + \left(\frac{NsLs}{5} + 2NcLc\right)\right\}\psi - W \quad \ldots(1)$$

Where Rc: Allowable bearing capacity for long age loading (kN)
$\overline{N}$: The mean N-values given in the former section, which should not exceed 50
Ap: Total section area of pile point (m²)
Ns: A mean N-value measured in a sandy stratum whithin a ground, which also should not exceed 50
Ls: Pile length penetrated into the sandy stratum
Nc: A mean N-value obtained in a clayey stratum within a ground, which should take the value between 0.5 ~ 4
Lc: Pile length penetrated into the clayey stratum (m)
ψ : Pile perimeter (m), and
W : Dead load of cast-in-place concrete pile (kN)

Fig. 6 shows the correlation between measured bearing capacity Rm and calculated capacity Rc, in which the distribution is also made between earth drill piles and Benoto piles. Although a large scatter is seen in this figure, it is possible to find a positive correlation between Rm and Rc, which may be why Eq. (1) is employed widely in engineering problems. However, in order to get better performance than Fig. 6 implies, the comparison between Rm and Rc should be made more in details considering the effects of some factors such as pile diameter D and pile length L which have been observed to be influential on a measured bearing capacity. Fig. 7 shows the frequency distribution of Rm and Rc at each pile diameter. The pile diameters were classified into five groups: 600 ~ 700mm, 800 ~ 900mm, 1000mm, 1100 ~ 1200mm, and 1300 ~ 1500mm. In this figure the frequency n, the mean value μ, the standard deviation S and the coefficient

of variation V of both Rm and Rc are also tabulated for each class of pile diameter. From this figure and the table, it can be seen that the distribution of Rc lies leftward compared with the distribution of Rm when pile diameter D is less than 1000mm, and vice versa when D > 1000mm. In other words, Eq. (1) tends to give the prediction of bearing capacity on a safe side when D ≦ 1000mm while on a risky side when D > 1000mm. This tendency can be seen more clearly taking the influence of pile length on a bearing capacity into consideration.

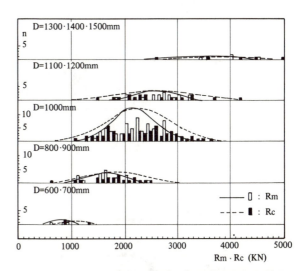

D (mm)	n	Rm			Rc		
		μ	S	V	μ	S	V
600 ~ 700	3	77	12	0.156	99	22	0.222
800 ~ 900	21	163	35	0.215	185	58	0.314
1000	64	216	40	0.185	227	62	0.273
1100 ~ 1200	18	264	39	0.148	259	71	0.274
1300 ~ 1500	5	379	53	0.140	391	84	0.214

Fig. 7 Distribution of Rm and Rc for Each Pile Diameter D

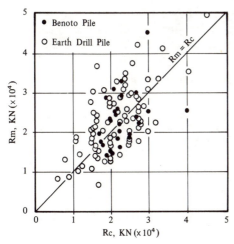

Fig.6 Relationship between Rm and Rc

In the following analysis the pile lengths are classified into four groups: less than 10m, 10 ~ 20m, 20 ~ 30m, and more than 30m. Shown in Figs. 8 (a)-(d) is the comparison between Rm and Rc made in each group. From these figures it should be noted that the threshold pile diameter which was found to be 1000mm based on Fig. 7 will be dependent of pile length. Figs. 8 (a) and (b) show that if pile length is less than 20m Rc tends to be smaller than Rm even when pile diameter D is greater than 1000mm as far as D is less than 1200mm. On the other hand, if pile length is greater than 20m Rc tends to become larger than Rm as far as pile diameter D is greater than 800mm. Thus, it has been found that there exist two kinds of threshold values, one is D ≃ 800 ~ 1200mm and the other is L = 20 m. The bearing capacity computation formula Eq. (1) tends to give "under estimates" (i.e. the prediction on a safe side) below these threshold values, and vice varsa above the thresholds.

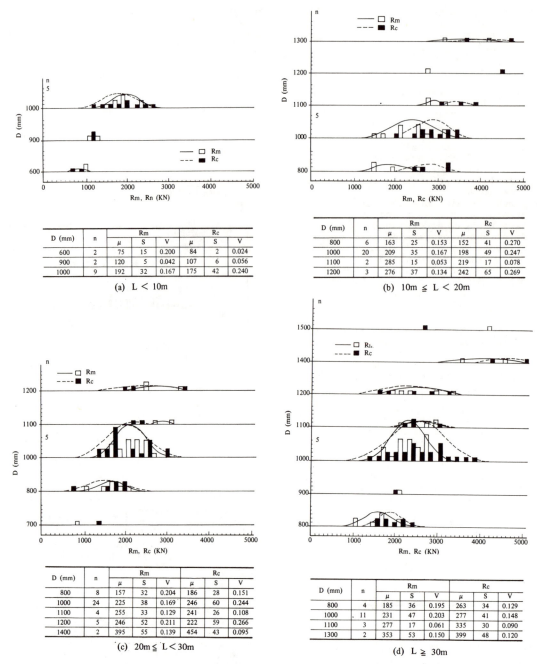

D (mm)	n	Rm			Rc		
		μ	S	V	μ	S	V
600	2	75	15	0.200	84	2	0.024
900	2	120	5	0.042	107	6	0.056
1000	9	192	32	0.167	175	42	0.240

(a) L < 10m

D (mm)	n	Rm			Rc		
		μ	S	V	μ	S	V
800	6	163	25	0.153	152	41	0.270
1000	20	209	35	0.167	198	49	0.247
1100	2	285	15	0.053	219	17	0.078
1200	3	276	37	0.134	242	65	0.269

(b) 10m ≦ L < 20m

D (mm)	n	Rm			Rc		
		μ	S	V	μ	S	V
800	8	157	32	0.204	186	28	0.151
1000	24	225	38	0.169	246	60	0.244
1100	4	255	33	0.129	241	26	0.108
1200	5	246	52	0.211	222	59	0.266
1400	2	395	55	0.139	454	43	0.095

(c) 20m ≦ L < 30m

D (mm)	n	Rm			Rc		
		μ	S	V	μ	S	V
800	4	185	36	0.195	263	34	0.129
1000	11	231	47	0.203	277	41	0.148
1100	3	277	17	0.061	335	30	0.090
1300	2	353	53	0.150	399	48	0.120

(d) L ≧ 30m

Fig.8 Distribution of Rm and Rc for Each Pile Length L

CONCLUSION

Through examining case records of in-situ measurements of bearing capacity of cast-in-place piles and analysing those data by the design formula widely used in Japan, followings are considered to be drawn:

1)   Pile diameter D and pile length L and the most predominat factors which influence the in-situ bearing capacity of cast-in-place piles.
2)   D ≃ 800 ∿ 1200mm and/or L = 20m will be a threshold value when prediction is made on in-situ value by using the bearing capacity calculation formula, that is, the formula gives under or over estimates around these threshold values.

REFERENCE

AIJ (1976): Design criteria for calculating the foundation construction.

Failure mechanisms of foundations in soft rock

Mécanismes de rupture des fondations dans roche molle

I. W. JOHNSTON, Senior Lecturer, Department of Civil Engineering, Monash University, Melbourne, Australia
S. K. CHOI, Postgraduate Student, Department of Civil Engineering, Monash University, Melbourne, Australia

SYNOPSIS   The failure mechanisms involved in the development of the load capacity of model end bearing piles in a synthetic rock are examined by two different techniques. The mechanisms are related to the shape of the load-displacement curve and failure is found to be dominated by the formation of a radial tensile crack.

INTRODUCTION

For some years, the authors and their colleagues have been following a programme of research which has examined the engineering behaviour of soft rocks. While a major component of this work has concerned the application of numerical and analytical techniques to predict foundation performance, it is vitally important that these techniques are relevant to the characteristics of soft rocks and correctly model the mechanisms involved. In order to obtain an appreciation of these mechanisms and the factors which influence them, a series of model foundation loading tests were conducted in the laboratory on a synthetic soft rock, with specific reference to the end bearing component of socketed piles. This paper describes the techniques used to study the mechanisms and presents a summary of the observations made.

PREPARATION OF TEST SPECIMENS

The soft rock which was of primary interest to the authors was the Melbourne mudstone. However, for a variety of reasons, not least of which were the inherent variability of the natural rock and the unpredictable presence of defects, tests conducted on blocks of mudstone were not capable of revealing information of sufficient detail or reliability. It was necessary therefore to develop a synthetic rock which was homogeneous, isotropic and of reproducible properties. This synthetic rock, which is known as Johnstone, is manufactured from a mixture of mudstone powder of predefined grain size distribution, cement, water and set accelerator. The mixture is placed in a mould and compressed under relatively high stresses. Once excess porewater pressures have dissipated, the compression load is removed, the specimen extruded and then allowed to cure for several weeks in a high humidity environment. A major factor influencing the end product is the compression stress applied during preparation. The greater this stress, the lower the voids ratio and hence the less weathered is the

mudstone modelled. In this manner it was possible to produce cylinders of Johnstone of 300 mm diameter and of 200 mm height with water contents ranging between about 10% and 20%. These water contents produced Johnstone of uniaxial compressive strength, σ_c', of between about 7 MPa and 2 MPa, corresponding to Melbourne mudstone of between the moderately weathered and highly weathered classification. A comprehensive account of the rationale and methods of Johnstone production, its properties and its close relationship to the naturally occurring Melbourne mudstone may be found in Choi (1984).

TEST EQUIPMENT AND METHODS

Two approaches were used to study the load-displacement mechanisms of model end bearing piles in Johnstone. Full details of the techniques and results, and their implications on the overall research programme may be found in Choi (1984).

(a) Sectioning of test specimens.

The 300 mm diameter by 200 mm high specimens of Johnstone were confined by steel cylinders placed tightly around their perimeter. The wall thicknesses of these steel cylinders were selected so that the confining stiffness was equivalent to an infinite continuum of rock material around the specimen. The resultant specimen was mounted on the base platen of a universal testing machine. The model piles were represented by steel dowels of 5 mm, 10 mm and 25 mm diameter, and the bottom end of these dowels were flat, and perpendicular to their longitudinal axes. The top end of each dowel was screwed into the upper loading platen of the test frame. A range of test conditions were examined and these involved the 3 sizes of model pile, Johnstone of a number of water contents between 10% and 20%, and a variety of different embedment length to diameter ratios, L/D, of between 0 and 10. Where the embedment ratio was greater than zero, a hole of marginally larger diameter was first drilled to the required depth. For all tests, special care was taken to ensure that the base of each model pile was in perfect contact with the rock. Each test was conducted under a constant rate of penetration of 0.04% of diameter per minute so that full drainage occurred, and all rock specimens were fully saturated. For each test, the load-displacement curves were monitored and some 82 individual tests were conducted.

Since the principal aim of these investigations was to identify failure mechanisms, the specimens of Johnstone were not necessarily loaded to failure but were loaded to predefined points on the load-displacement curves as indicated in Fig. 1. These four points are identified as follows:

Point 1 - at the end of linear elastic deformation.
Point 2 - a little before major yielding.
Point 3 - a little after major yielding.
Point 4 - at failure.

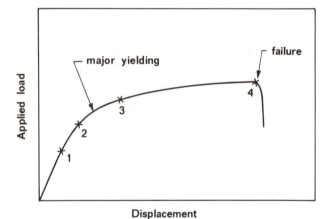

Fig. 1 Typical load-displacement curve.

At one of these preselected points, the test was terminated and the specimen removed from the loading frame. The specimen was then carefully and progressively sectioned to permit the identification of any affected zone.

(b) Use of stereo-photogrammetric techniques.

By application of the above sectioning technique, it was only possible to examine the resulting mechanisms for one point on the load-displacement curve for each model test. Even when sectioned, it was sometimes quite difficult to clearly define the various zones of influence. Therefore, in order to obtain more detailed and progressive information, a stereo-photogrammetric technique was also applied. The basic principle involved a test sectioned through a diameter so that the development of failure could be continuously observed. However, it was important that representative confinement was also applied and that the results so obtained would not be influenced by the test technique. The equipment used in these tests is shown as a general view in Fig. 2 and as a front view in Fig. 3. It should be noted that the photograph of Fig. 2 does not contain a test specimen. The essential features of this equipment included a vertical steel plate with a narrow, thick

perspex window. The steel plate and the window were stiffened by horizontal I-beams and individual I-beams could be removed to reveal a small area of specific interest at the base of the model pile. Behind the steel plate and window, a semi-cylindrical specimen of Johnstone was held tightly in position by a semi-cylinder of steel which modelled the infinite continuum as before. The model pile consisted of a semi-cylindrical steel dowel of 25 mm diameter which, when the test rig was mounted in the universal testing machine, could be forced into the Johnstone specimen flush with the perspex window. Apart from the shape of the specimens, all other conditions of testing were the same as those tests discussed previously.

Fig. 2 General view of equipment for use with stereo-photogrammetric techniques

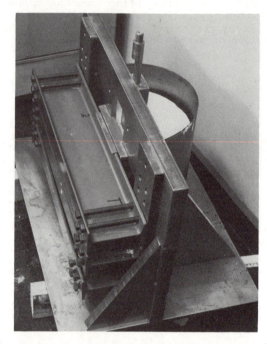

Fig. 3 Front view of equipment for use with stereo-photogrammetric techniques

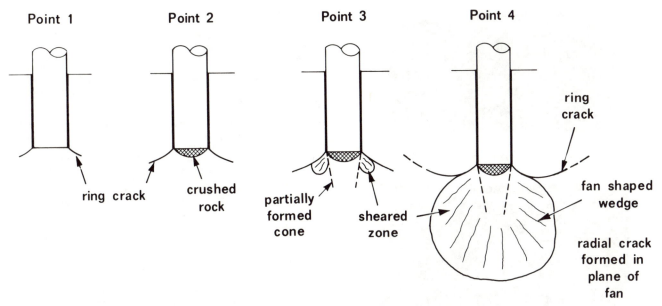

Fig. 4 Failure mechanisms observed for L/D ± 0

As the model semi-cylindrical pile was loaded, a series of photographs were taken from the front of the equipment, similar to Fig. 3, but only of the area of immediate concern around the base of the model pile. The stereo-photogrammetric technique is described in some detail by, for example, Butterfield et al. (1970). However, in principle, the technique is similar to the production of contour maps by aerial photography. In the aerial contouring technique, the camera moves over the static land mass to produce pairs of stereo photographs. In the technqiue used for the model piles, the camera is stationary but the model pile and surrounding Johnstone are displaced. Therefore by observing pairs of successive photographs, taken at various stages on the load-displacement curve, through a stereo viewer, a three-dimensional image emerges with the height of each point proportional to the amount of displacement. By studying these many successive photographs in stereo vision, it was possible to quantify displacements and therefore identify the various mechanisms involved as the model pile was loaded to failure.

SUMMARY OF OBSERVATIONS

The mechanisms observed in the two different test techniques were very similar and indeed, tests conducted by the two methods produced virtually identical applied base stress - normalised displacement (ρ/D) curves for the same model pile diameter, Johnstone water content and L/D ratio. For the range of test conditions examined (intact soft rock, 2 MPa < σ_c' < 7 MPa; model pile diameter, 5 mm < D < 25 mm; embedment ratio, 0 < L/D < 10), the mechanisms were very similar. Only minor differences appeared to occur between tests of L/D = 0 and L/D > 0.

Figure 4 shows the general development of mechanisms for tests conducted at L/D > 0, in relation to the points identified on the load-displacement curve of Fig. 1. For L/D > 0, it would appear that during the early stages of loading corresponding to point 1, a small ring crack developed from the edges of the model piles. As the load was increased, the load-displacement curve became distinctly non-linear and just before major yielding, as identified by point 2, the ring crack had propagated further. Also by this point, a zone of crushed Johnstone had developed under the pile base. At point 3, just after major yielding as indicated by the maximum curvature of the load-displacement curve, a partially formed cone was developed with a zone of apparently sheared Johnstone existing between the cone and the previously formed ring crack. As the applied load was increased further towards failure at point 4, the model piles penetrated the Johnstone at a much reduced value of loading rate and the sheared Johnstone outside the partially formed cone increased rapidly in extent to form a fan shaped wedge. At the same time, the ring crack propagated further and tended to develop back towards the upper surface of the specimen. At point 4, failure occurred by the development of a radial crack in the plane of the fully developed fan shaped wedge.

For L/D = 0, the minor differences from the above were that the ring crack did not appear to develop until about point 3 on the load-displacement curve, and the development of the radial crack was often immediately preceded by surface chips, formed by the Johnstone above the ring crack, rising from the Johnstone surface. Figure 5 shows a view of a model test of L/D = 0 once failure was reached when surface chips were not produced. The specimen was split open in the manner shown by the

Fig. 5   Failure Mechanism for model test of
L/D = 0.

Fig. 6   Surface chips and radial crack for
model test of L/D = 0.

radial crack produced at failure.   Figure 6
shows the surface of a model pile test of
L/D = 0 with surface chips evident as well as
the dominating radial crack.

It must be emphasised that the formation of the
radial crack at failure was not brought about
by inappropriate specimen confinement.   This
opinion was arrived at as a result of a number
of tests, not reported herein, in which
specimen confinement was carefully examined
(Choi, 1984).   Indeed, the mechanisms discussed
above seem to be in reasonable agreement with
the observations of Williams (1980) on full
scale in-situ end bearing pile tests conducted
in the Melbourne mudstone.   These observations
include the appearance of radial cracks at
failure, although at the time, the significance
of these cracks was not fully appreciated.

CONCLUSIONS

On the basis of model tests conducted on a
synthetic rock very similar in characteristics
to the naturally occuring weathered Melbourne
mudstone, it would appear that the mechanisms
leading to end bearing failure are relatively
complex.   The load-displacement curves showed
an early deviation from linear elastic
behaviour as a result of crushing immediately
below the pile base.   The region of major
yielding appears to correspond to the development of a partially formed cone beneath the

base and the commencement of the formation of a
fan shaped wedge.   As failure is approached,
the fan shaped wedge extends rapidly until at
failure, its wedging action causes the
development of a radial tensile crack in the
plane of the fan.   It would appear that this
radial crack is the primary cause of failure,
although for L/D = 0, this crack is sometimes
preceded by the formation of surface chips.

On the basis of the evidence presented, the end
bearing capacity of a pile in soft or weak rock
may be controlled by the tensile strength of
the founding material.   It follows, therefore,
that the influence of the tensile strength of
the founding rock must be given due recognition
when applying numerical or analytical methods
to the prediction of foundation performance.

REFERENCES

Butterfield, R., Harkness, R.M. and
    Andrawes, K.Z. (1970).   A stereo-
    photogrammetric method for measuring
    displacement fields.   Geotechnique, Vol. 20,
    No. 3, pp. 308-314.

Choi, S.K. (1984).   The bearing capacity of
    foundations in weak rock, Ph.D. Thesis, Dept.
    of Civil Engng., Monash University.

Williams, A.F. (1980).   The design and
    performance of piles socketed into weak rock.
    Ph.D. Thesis, Dept. of Civil Engng.,
    Monash University.

Axial static capacity of steel model piles in overconsolidated clay

Capacité axiale statique de pieux modelés en acier dans argile surconsolidée

KJELL KARLSRUD, Norwegian Geotechnical Institute, Norway
TORGEIR HAUGEN, Norwegian Geotechnical Institute, Norway

SYNOPSIS

An instrumented 5 m long steel pipe pile with diameter 15 cm was repeatedly installed in overconsolidated clay and load tested, mostly in tension. Measured effective stresses against the pile surface after pile installation and reconsolidation were significantly smaller than predicted from available theoretical models. The measured limit skin friction agreed closely with the shear strength properties of remoulded, reconsolidated clay, consolidated to the same effective stresses as measured against the pile surface, but was very different from what could be predicted using existing semi-empirical procedures on the basis of shear strength properties of intact clay. The properties of laboratory remoulded, reconsolidated clay also agreed closely with the properties of the clay found next to the pile wall.

INTRODUCTION

The Norwegian Geotechnical Institute has over the past 4 years (1980-84) carried out an extensive pile load testing program with a 5 m long closed ended pile with diameter of 15.3 cm. The pile was instrumented with 6 levels of strain gauges and 4 levels of earth and pore pressure gauges (Fig. 1), in addition to a displacement transducer and a load cell on top of the pile. The instruments were mainly of the vibrating-wire type.

An advanced data logging system has allowed continuous monitoring of the pile performance during pile installation, reconsolidation and pile loading.

The main scope of the pile load tests was to study the performance of the pile under a variety of static and cyclic loading conditions

with main emphasis on tension loading to model pile anchors for tension leg type offshore platforms. The pile is rather stiff, and was ment to model the performance of a pile segment rather than a long flexible offshore pile.

The test program included 16 individual pile installations and pile load tests with the instrumented pile in an overconsolidated clay deposit. In addition 11 tests were carried out with a non-instrumented pile of the same dimensions. This paper summarizes only the soil/pile interaction during pile installation, reconsolidation and static monotonic pile loading.

The main emphasis is put on relating the observed limit skin friction to measured effective stresses against the pile surface and shear strength characteristics of the remoulded, reconsolidated clay close to the pile wall. For further details it is referred to the two summary reports by Karlsrud and Haugen (1983, 1984).

SOIL CONDITIONS

The load tests were carried out in overconsolidated clay at the Haga test site, outside Oslo. At this site the NGI has previously carried out static and cyclic plate load tests (Andersen and Stenhamar, 1982). A soil profile is shown in Fig. 2.

The clay is very homogeneous down to about 4.5 m depth with natural water content of w = 38% and plasticity index of I_p = 15%. From 4.5 m to 5.5 m depth there is a more plastic clay layer with w = 55-60% and I_p = 35-40%. Below 5.5 m the water content decreases and the clay becomes more silty, with transition to a sand layer at approximate 8 m depth. The in-situ undrained vane shear strength is typically 43 kN/m² from 1 to 4.5 m depth and 45-55 kN/m² in the plastic clay. The results of static undrained laboratory triaxial and direct simple shear tests (Fig. 2) clearly expose the anisotropic nature of the un-

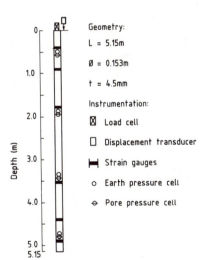

Geometry:

L = 5.15m

Ø = 0.153m

t = 4.5mm

Instrumentation:

Ⓧ   Load cell

▢   Displacement transducer

⊢⊣   Strain gauges

o   Earth pressure cell

⊕   Pore pressure cell

Fig. 1. Pile geometry and instrumentation

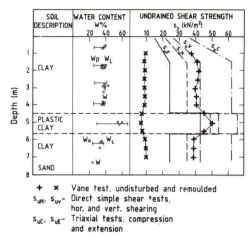

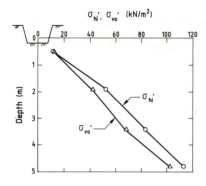

Fig. 2   General soil profile

Fig. 4   Effective stresses after reconsolidation

drained shear strength. The laboratory tests otherwise suggest a friction angle of $\varphi = 33.5^{\circ}$ and cohesion $c = 0$. Compared to to-days average in-situ vertical effective overburden pressure the vertical preconsolidation pressure, as determined by oedometer tests, give an overconsolidation ratio (OCR) decreasing rapidly with depth from OCR = 17 at 1 m to OCR close to 3 at 5 m depth. The overconsolidation is caused by chemical weathering and by a 6 m excavation of the test site area.

PILE INSTALLATION EFFECTS

The time needed to jack down a pile was around 60-80 minutes. Figure 3 shows the average total earth pressure and pore pressure along the pile immediately after pile installation and also the equilibrium pressures after full reconsolidation (t = 7 days).

The most important observations from the pile installation can be summarized as follows:

- The horizontal effective stresses along the pile surface during penetration is close to zero, which emphasize that a severe remoulding of the clay around the pile takes place.

- The total earth pressure along the pile surface decreases significantly during reconsolidation.

- The effective stress ratio after reconsolidation, $\sigma_{hi}'/\sigma_{vo}'$ is on average 1.2, see Fig. 4 (σ_{hi}' = horizontal, and σ_{vo}' = in-situ vertical effective stress). This ratio is somewhat larger than the estimated original K_o'-values

which decrease from 1.2 at 2 m to 0.8 at 5 m depth.

Trenching and sampling close to one of the test piles was performed to study the effects of pile installation on the properties of the clay adjacent to the pile wall. Block samples were carefully cut out at about 2.5 m depth from the zone within 30 cm distance of the pile surface. Routine type of tests were carried out as well as X-ray and microfabric studies.

On the basis of the measured index properties and observed distortion of the originally horizontal clay layering, as illustrated in Fig. 5 below, one can identify three different zones around the pile:

Zone A:
A ~1.5 cm thick zone closest to the pile surface has been completely remoulded and has then been reconsolidated to a much lower water content than the original intact clay. The reduction of water content is as high as 13% corresponding to a relative volume change of around 16-17%. The lower water content is reflected in fall cone shear strength values which are higher than those of intact clay.

Zone B:
This zone appears to have been subjected to more of a pure shear distortion. The water content

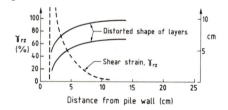

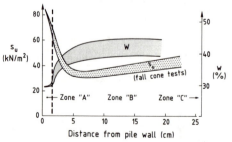

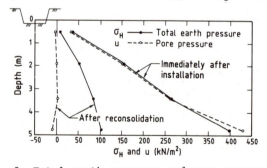

Fig. 3   Total earth pressure and pore pressure distributions

Fig. 5   Measured index properties and observed clay layering close to a pile

change decreases from around 5-10% against zone A to about zero at 10-15 cm distance from the pile surface.

Zone C:
In the zone from about 15-20 cm from the pile surface there are apparently no effect of pile installation on water content and the vertical soil particle displacement is insignificant.

The microfabric of intact undisturbed clay was clearly horizontally oriented while the clay from the distorted zone showed a preferred inclining orientation of the microfabric. On the other hand, in the clay closest to the pile surface (zone A described above) the original particle configuration was broken down. The lower water content in that clay reflects a denser microfabric, which also could be seen from the microscope study.

The most commonly used theoretical pile installation models are based on cylindrical cavity expansion theory (e.g. Randolph et al., 1979), where the soil particle displacements are assumed to occur only in the radial direction. The observations referred to above suggest that this approach is too simple. Although the available cylindrical cavity expansion and reconsolidation models predict reasonably well the earth and pore pressures immediately after the pile installation (Karlsrud and Haugen, 1983, 1984) they fail completely to predict the large reduction in total horizontal stress during reconsolidation. These theories actually predicted $\sigma_{hi}'/\sigma_{vo}'$ of the order of 2.0 to 3.0 in stead of 1.2 as observed (Fig. 4).

STATIC PILE CAPACITY AND SKIN FRICTION

The static pile tests were load-controlled tests with an average rate of loading of 3.3 kN/min. A stepwise loading procedure consisted of 2 steps of 10 kN, 3 steps of 5 kN and then small steps of 2.5 kN until failure or a certain pile top displacement was reached. Figure 6 shows a typical load-displacement response at pile top. It is characterized by increasing creep displacement as the load level increases. Failure was defined at 3 mm of pile top displacement.

Figure 7 shows the initial static capacity in relation to the time elapsed between pile installation and loading. The ultimate static

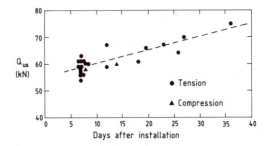

Fig. 7 Initial static pile capacity in relation to time of reconsolidation

pile capacity generally increases with time of reconsolidation (from t = 7 to 35 days). The increase corresponds to 3.5 kN or 5.9% per week. There was no corresponding increase in the horizontal effective stress in the same time period. Thus, the increase in capacity is probably associated with "bonding" of the clay minerals rather than any increase in effective stress. Such a "bonding" effect or gain in strength as well as in preconsolidation pressure and stiffness is also observed in the field and in the laboratory for clays undergoing volumetric creep under constant effective stresses. Notice also from Fig. 7 that the two compression tests show about the same capacity as the tension tests.

The 6 levels of strain gauges along the instrumented pile provided data on the magnitude and distribution of skin friction. Figure 8 shows the average ultimate skin friction at failure in the initial static tests.

Several methods have been developed to predict the static capacity of piles in clay. The limiting skin friction may be expressed as a function of the in-situ undrained shear strength of the soil, $\tau_s = \alpha \cdot s_u$. The α-factor has been empirically determined by backcalculating the results of pile load tests in different clays (e.g. API, RP2A, 1982). Alternatively, it has been argued that the ultimate skin friction should be related to the state of effective stresses along the pile. In this "effective stress" approach, the skin friction has been expressed as some fraction, β, of a usually well defined effective vertical stress, $\tau_s = \beta \cdot \sigma_{vo}'$ (Burland, 1973 and Meyerhof, 1976). Though many different approaches have been made to estimate the β-factor, the basic elements are the pile/clay friction angle and the effective

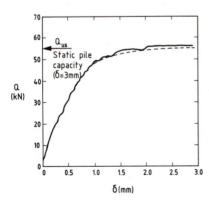

Fig. 6 Typical load-displacement response at pile top

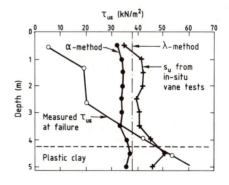

Fig. 8 Measured and predicted ultimate skin friction

stress ratio. A combined solution, the so-called λ-method (Vijayvergiya and Focht, 1972), includes the average values of the in-situ undrained shear strength and the vertical effective stress, $\tau_s = \lambda(\bar\sigma_{vo}' + 2\,\bar{s}_u)$. The α- and λ-method were applied to the present pile and the results are shown in Fig. 8. These empirical models do not predict the actually measured skin friction distributions. Regarding the "effective stress" approach, the different existing β-expressions give very different results. An estimate of the horizontal effective stresses and how the stresses change during pile loading must also be considered to make a reasonable prediction.

The most serious attempt to relate limit skin friction to effective stresses so far was started by Kirby and Wroth (1977) and later developed through the ESAAC project (Kraft, Esrig and Murphy, 1980). Because the developed models are based on the cylindrical expansion and reconsolidation models briefly discussed above, they can not predict correctly the behaviour of these piles. The Critical State Theory also fails to predict the stress-strain behaviour of the remoulded, reconsolidated clay next to the pile wall as described in the next section.

Some of the test series included several static tests on the same pile but with different times of reconsolidation in between the tests. Such tests clearly expressed the effect of previous loading on present capacity (preshearing effects). This is illustrated by the results of one specific test series (4 tests) on the non-instrumented pile. In Fig. 9 the static capacities from these tests are plotted as a function of time after pile installation and clearly show the effect of preshearing.

Similar results were also obtained from other test series. In terms of the effect of static preshearing on static pile load capacity the results can be summarized as follows:

1) One to six days of reconsolidation between a first and second static test caused an increase of static capacity of about 25%. The same increase was noted for the piles which were subjected to 15-20 hrs. of sustained loading between the first and second test.

2) Several static tests with reconsolidation in between each test caused an increase of static capacity to as much as 63% above the initial static capacity (see example referred to in Fig. 9).

This substantial increase in capacity can not be explained by the general increase in pile capacity with time after pile installation (Fig. 7 and 9).

Some of these repeated static tests were performed on the instrumented pile, which provided data on how the preshearing effect is reflected by the shear stresses, pore pressures and horizontal effective stresses measured along the pile. Figure 10 shows an example of distributions of shear stress and horizontal effective stress at the maximum load in the first and second static tests.

The increase of load capacity and skin friction was 22% in this specific case. This increase can only partly be explained by an observed increase of horizontal effective stresses (Fig. 10). The mobilized "effective friction ratio" at maximum load (slightly below the failure load) as given by τ_s/σ_h' also increased from on average 0.50 to 0.60 due to preshearing.

It is believed that the results of many previous repeated pile load tests reported in the literature have errorously been explained by pure consolidation effects, whereas it may be more of a preshearing effect.

LABORATORY TESTS TO MODEL PILE/CLAY INTERFACE FRICTION

The study on the clay next to the pile and the results of measurements during pile installation and reconsolidation had strongly emphasized the importance of pile installation effects to clay properties, stress conditions and eventually the pile/clay interface friction during the subsequent loading. On this basis a special laboratory test program was included in this research project and consisted of:

• shear box tests and direct simple shear tests on completely remoulded and reconsolidated clay. A steel end plate, of the same quality as the pile, was used to model the pile surface,

• shear box tests and direct simple shear tests on undisturbed clay samples and

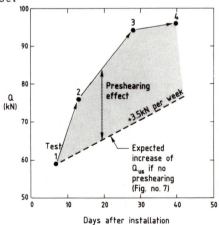

Fig. 9 Influence of static preshearing on static pile capacity

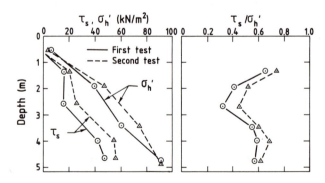

Fig. 10 Shear stress and horizontal effective stress distributions at maximum load

• tests on remoulded, reconsolidated clay in standard direct simple shear apparatus without the special steel end plate

To simulate the remoulding of clay due to pile installation, clay samples were smeared out on a glass plate and built into the shear box apparatus. The samples were consolidated to stresses equal to the average horizontal effective stresses as measured against the pile surface after pile installation and reconsolidation (Fig. 4).

The clay properties achieved after the reconsolidation in the laboratory were compared to the measured values on the block samples from 2.5 m depth. A water content reduction of around 7% was measured on samples reconsolidated to the stress level as measured at this depth. This is somewhat less than the observed 8 to 13% reduction in water content next to the pile surface. However, the pile had been subjected to several static and cyclic tests to failure before the block samples were taken out. This had probably caused further reduction of water content. Thus, after all there is encouragingly good agreement between the consolidation behaviour of the laboratory remoulded clay and remoulded clay next to the pile surface.

The remoulded clay was either tested directly in the shear box apparatus, or it was only consolidated and then built out of the shear box and rebuilt into the direct simple shear apparatus. Figure 11 shows that the shear strength, τ_f, of the remoulded, reconsolidated clay during the first loading is 0.33 times the normal consolidation stress, σ_c' ($\tau_f = 0.33 \cdot \sigma_c'$). On this basis and the measured effective stress against the pile surface just prior to loading one has arrived at the computed ultimate skin friction, $\tau_{us} = 0.33 \cdot \sigma_{hi}'$, in Fig. 12. The computed limit skin friction is on average 20% lower than the measured limit skin friction, but the distributions are in close agreement. The 20% difference may be explained by the fact that the tangential to normal effective stress ratio at onset of undrained shearing is close to $K_o' = 0.5$ in the laboratory samples, which is lower than the corresponding effective stress ratio of $\sigma_{vo}'/\sigma_{hi}' = 1.0/1.2 = 0.83$ against the pile

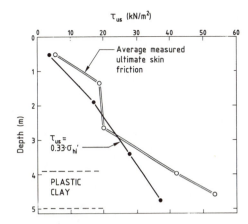

Fig. 12 Measured ultimate skin friction and computed skin friction based on laboratory tests on remoulded, reconsolidated clay

surface. The undrained simple shear strength of remoulded, reconsolidated clay is larger than the shear strength of intact normally consolidated clay (determined on samples consolidated beyond the preconsolidation pressure). For an overconsolidation ratio (OCR) of 1.0 undrained simple shear tests on intact clay give $s_{uV} = 0.28 \cdot \sigma_c'$ and $s_{uH} = 0.20 \cdot \sigma_c'$ for respectively vertically and horizontally trimmed specimens.

The preshearing effect was also studied in the laboratory, both by static tests on undisturbed (intact clay) and on samples which had been remoulded and reconsolidated. Two static tests were generally carried out with one day of reconsolidation in between. The tests on undisturbed clay did not show any increase in shear strength from the first to the second test. However, the laboratory tests carried out on remoulded, reconsolidated clay show a substantial preshearing effect (Fig. 11). The second tests gave a shear strength of $\tau_f = 0.48 \cdot \sigma_c'$, or 45% larger than the first tests, thus confirming the preshearing effects in the pile tests. The simple shear tests showed that this increase in shear strength relative to the first tests was caused by a more dilatant behaviour during the second tests. The same tendency was observed in the pile tests (ref. Karlsrud and Haugen, 1984). Thus, the preshearing effect on the piles is closely related to change in behaviour of the remoulded, reconsolidated clay next to the pile wall.

On the basis of the laboratory tests, it may be concluded that there are no indications that the steel/clay interface represents a "plane of weakness" where failure takes place. The failure, both in the shear box and the direct simple shear tests, seemed to take place within the clay.

CONCLUSIONS

The fairly close agreement between the laboratory tests on the remoulded, reconsolidated clay and the pile load tests suggests that shear tests on remoulded and reconsolidated clay may be a promising approach to the prediction of ultimate skin friction. However, this calls for a reliable prediction of the state of effective stress along the pile after installation and reconsolidation. None of the presently available

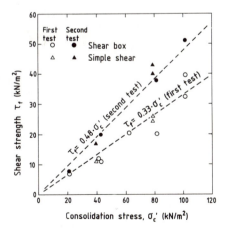

Fig. 11 Shear strength of remoulded, reconsolidated clay versus normal consolidation stress

theoretical models can predict correctly the effective stresses observed during pile installation and reconsolidation. Thus, further developments of models for computing effective stresses after reconsolidation is required for the development of a realistic model for predicting skin friction on the basis of the properties of remoulded, reconsolidated clay.

ACKNOWLEDGEMENTS

The pile research project performed at the Norwegian Geotechnical Institute was financed by twelve industry sponsors:

. Amoco Norway Oil Company
. Chevron Oil Field Research Company
. Conoco Norway Inc.
. Esso Exploration and Production Norway Inc.
. Gulf Research and Development Company
. Marathon Oil Company
. Mobil Research and Development Corp. Offshore Eng.
. Phillips Petroleum Company
. A/S Norske Shell
. Texaco Exploration Norway A/S
. United Kingdom, Department of Energy

The project was also supported by the Royal Norwegian Council for Scientific and Industrial Research (NTNF).

The Norwegian Geotechnical Institute greatly appreciates the financial support given as well as the technical guidance and comments provided by the sponsor representatives.

Many colleagues at NGI also contributed greatly to the work presented herein. Special credit goes to F.Myrvoll, P.Norum, K.Solheim, R.Johnsrud and C.Madshus. NGI's director K.Høeg has provided continuous support and guidance throughout the project.

REFERENCES

American Petroleum Institute, Dallas, (1982)
Planning, designing and constructing fixed offshore platforms.
API. Recommended practice, RP 2A, 13th edition.

Andersen, K.H. and P.Stenhamar (1982)
Static plate loading tests on overconsolidated clay. American Society of Civil Engineers. Proceedings, Vol. 108, No. GT 7, pp. 918-934.

Karlsrud, K. and Haugen, T. (1983)
Cyclic loading of piles and pile anchors - field model tests. Final report. Summary and evaluation of test results.
Norwegian Geotechnical Institute. Report 40010-28.

Karlsrud, K. and Haugen, T. (1984)
Cyclic loading of piles and pile anchors - field model tests - Phase II. Final report. Summary and evaluation of test results and computational models.
Norwegian Geotechnical Institute. Report 40018-11.

Kirby, R.C. and C.P.Wroth (1977)
Application of critical state soil mechanics to the prediction of axial capacity for driven piles in clay.
Offshore Technology Congress, 9. Houston 1977. Proceedings, Vol. 3, pp. 483-494.

Kraft, L.M., M.I.Esrig and B.S.Murphy (1980)
Amoco effective stress axial capacity co-operative program.
ESACC projcect summary report.
Prepared for Amoco Production Co.

Meyerhof, G.G. (1976)
Bearing capacity and settlement of pile foundations; the 11th Terzaghi Lecture.
American Society of Civil Engineers. Proceedings, Vol. 102, No. GT 3, pp. 195-228.

Randolph, M.F., J.P.Carter and C.P.Wroth (1979)
Driven piles in clay - the effects of installation and subsequent consolidation.
Geotechnique, Vol. 29, No. 4, pp. 361-393.

Vijayvergiya, V.N. and J.A.Focht (1972)
A new way to predict capacity of piles in clay.
Offshore Technology Conference, 4. Houston 1972. Preprints, Vol. 2, pp. 865-874.

Downdrag on a three-pile group of pipe piles

Frottement négatif d'un groupe de trois pieux cylindriques

G. H. KEENAN, Soils Engineer, New Brunswick Department of Transportation, Fredericton, NB, Canada
M. BOZOZUK, Research Officer, Division of Building Research, National Research Council Canada, Ottawa, Canada

SYNOPSIS   The development of downdrag load on a group of three piles spaced at four pile diameters was observed for 6½ years. The 32 m long, 324 mm diameter piles were driven through a granular test embankment into a deep deposit of compressible clayey silt. There was no group effect on the development of load. The maximum was 1000 kN in 1½ years, and 900 kN after 6½ years due to changes in embankment loading. The distribution of downdrag loads on the piles for various conditions of vertical effective stress in the soil was adequately estimated with effective stress equations using K_o obtained from a field pullout test and the coefficient of friction between the soil and pile from laboratory tests. The pullout failure load was equivalent to the downdrag and positive skin friction load.

INTRODUCTION

A new bridge over the Saint John River, in Fredericton, was supported on steel end-bearing piles driven through compressible silts into a dense gravel formation. A high approach embankment was required, which could generate large downdrag loads. To obtain design parameters for the piles, the New Brunswick Department of Transportation and the Division of Building Research, National Research Council Canada implemented a field study in 1977 on seven full-scale steel pipe and "H" test piles driven through a granular test fill. Axial compression and pullout tests performed on two end-bearing and two friction piles, were reported by Bozozuk et al. (1979). The three-pile group was used to observe the long-term development of negative skin-friction load.

The axial distribution of downdrag loads calculated from measured pile compressions related to different pore water pressures and vertical effective stresses in the soil is presented. Pile load distributions estimated from effective stress equations using soil parameters obtained from field pullout tests and laboratory soil-pile friction tests are also shown.

TEST EMBANKMENT

The granular test fill was constructed to a height of 11 m in two stages (Figure 1). Stage 1 was raised to an elevation of +3.0 m, providing a good base for installing field instrumentation, and Stage 2 to +9.0 m, providing a surface area of 25 by 40 m. It was constructed with sand fill, with an average measured in-place density of 1825 kg/m³.

From 26 August to 19 October, 1977, dredged

sand fill (S) was placed over a large area around the test embankment (Figure 1). The average measured in-place density was 1800 kg/m³. A granular surcharge was stock-piled to +16.5 m just south of the test piles from 8 December, 1977 to 18 April, 1979, when the south approach ramp to the bridge was constructed to +14.5 m. The maximum range of river levels was +8.0 m to +0.8 m.

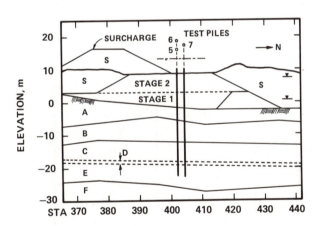

S- DREDGED SAND FILL

Fig. 1   Section through test embankment showing test piles, dredged sand fill and subsoil formations

SUBSOILS

The soil profile consisted of six major horizontal soil formations (A to F on

Figure 1). Layer A (4 m thick) was heterogeneous compressible soft organic silt and sand with some pebbles and wood. Undisturbed soil samples could not be obtained, but it was assumed to have a density of 1680 kg/m³. The standard penetration test gave N = 5.

Layer B was a grey layered clayey silt about 6.5 m thick. The natural water content (W) varied from 23 to 38%, the liquid limit (W_L) was 29% and the plasticity index (I_p) was 9%. Grain size analysis indicated 40% clay and 60% silt sizes. The average density (γ_m) was 1840 kg/m³. In situ vane shear strengths varied from 30 to 50 kPa, and N = 13.

Layer C was a 5.5-metre thick grey-brown layered clayey silt consisting of 45% clay and 55% silt. Water content was 29 to 37%, W_L about 34% and I_p was 12%. In situ vane shear strengths varied from 60 to 90 kPa, N = 14 and γ_m was 1840 kg/m³.

Measured preconsolidation pressures (σ_p') (Figure 2a) show that the formations are highly overconsolidated. Pressures of 375 kPa will not be exceeded by embankment loading.

Layer D was varved brown clay and silt, 1 m thick.

Layer E was a 7-metre thick layered brown clayey silt with W of 35 to 45%, W_L about 40% and I_p of 20%. It was more clayey, with 64% clay size and 36% silt size. The average γ_m was 1840 kg/m³. In situ vane shear strengths varied from 90 to 120 kPa, and N = 10. The four test piles terminated in this formation.

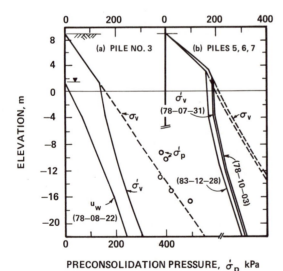

Fig. 2 Distribution of vertical stresses in soil around test piles

Layer F was dense gravel with sand and stones, with N = 64. The end-bearing bridge foundation piles were driven into this formation.

TEST PILES

All pipe piles were 32 m long, 324 mm outside diameter with 7.92 mm wall thickness and weighed 61.74 kg/m. The bottoms were closed with flat steel plates of area 0.0864 m². The layout of the three-pile group is shown on Figure 1. The piles formed a triangle with a centre-to-centre spacing of 1295 mm (four pile diameters). They were located 7.5 m east of the control pile, No. 3 which was identical to Nos. 5, 6 and 7.

Piles 5, 6 and 7 were installed on 18 July and No. 3 on 19 July, 1977 to their design elevation in layer E (Figure 1).

Eight telltales were equally spaced around the circumference of each pile to measure axial deformations. Because they were welded continuously to the piles, they added steel and increased the contact area with the soil. The first telltale extended to the base of the test embankment and the remainder were distributed about equally along the remaining length of the pile. (Summary given in Table I.)

TABLE I. Engineering details of instrumented steel pipe piles

Elevation (m)	Contact perimeter (m)	Total steel area (mm²)
+9.6 to -4.6	1373	9583
-4.6 to -10.6	1284	9154
-10.6 to -16.7	1195	8724
-16.7 to -22.4	1106	8294

[1]Elevation of embankment near test piles +8.8 m.
[2]Length of telltales: 11.3, 14.2, 17.4, 20.2, 23.3, 26.3, 29.3, 32.0 m.

SETTLEMENT

Test Embankment

Most of the test embankment was constructed in the river. Settlement platforms (Series M) were installed on the original ground surface and (Series SA) to greater depths before Stage 1 was completed. The observed settlements at elevations -1.5 and -6.6 m are given for various times in Table II.

After 18 months the settlement at elevation -1.5 m was 187 mm, and 92 mm at -6.6 m. This showed that half of the settlement occurred in layer A, and half in the underlying formations. Unfortunately further observations were not possible because the gauges were damaged.

TABLE II.   Settlement below embankment near
            test piles (mm)

Date	M1 (Elevation -1.5 m)	SA1 (Elevation -6.6 m)	Remarks
77-02-28	0	0	No fill
77-04-30	76	33	Fill at +9.0 m
77-07-18	89	40	Piles 5, 6, 7 driven
77-10-26	103	46	Pullout, Pile 3
77-12-31	143	58	Surcharge at +16.5 m
78-03-31	159	74	Surcharge at +16.5 m
78-08-15	187	92	Last survey

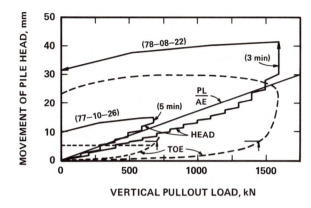

Fig. 3   Pullout tests, pile No. 3

Test Piles

Piles 5, 6 and 7 settled about 80 mm over a
period of 6½ years. Settlements at various
intermediate times are shown with those for
pile 3 on Table III.

TABLE III.   Settlement of test piles measured
             on pile head

Date	Elapsed time (days)	Settlement (mm) No. 3	No. 5	No. 6	No. 7
77-10-14	88	12	12	12	12.5
77-10-26	100	-	13	14	13.5
77-11-28	133	*13	18	20	19
78-07-31	378	*25.5	31	32.5	31.5
78-08-15	393	-	32	33	32
78-10-03	441	*27	34.5	36	35
79-10-04	807	-	52	59	59.5
81-12-18	1614	-	-	75.5	77
82-10-18	1918	-	77	76	-
83-12-28	2354	-	79.5	76	-

*Cumulative settlement adjusted for measured
 displacements caused by pullout tests.

From 18 July to 26 October, 1977, the piles
settled 13 mm and the test embankment 14 mm.
On 15 August, 1978, piles 5, 6 and 7 had
settled 32 to 33 mm, compared to the 98 mm
measured at -1.5m. At -6.6 m, however, the
relative movements between the pile and the
soil were much less. Pile 3 settled about the
same as the piles in the group.

PULLOUT TESTS

The pile was pulled with a 500 tonne hydraulic
jack positioned on a calibrated load cell on
top of a reaction beam (Bozozuk et al. 1979).
Loads were applied in increments of 89 kPa
every ten minutes until the pile failed, and
then unloaded in three increments. Each load
was maintained for nine minutes, allowing one
minute for changing loads.

Pullout tests were performed on 26 October,
1977, and 22 August, 1978. The in situ pore
water pressures during the first test were
about 45 kPa more than during the second. The
load deformation curves shown on Figure 3
reflected the effective stress conditions in
the soil at these times. The maximum applied
load during the first test was 675 kN. It was
maintained for only five minutes because the
pullout had reached 15 mm and the pile was
literally moving out of the ground. In the
second test, the maximum was 1595 kN. It was
maintained for only three minutes.

Movements of the toe determined from telltale
measurements are also shown on Figure 3. They
plotted considerably below the elastic
compression line defined by $\frac{PL}{AE}$. Upon unloading, the toe of the pile was displaced 5 mm
after the first test and 23 mm after the
second.

Failure Load

Davisson's (1972) failure criteria for
standard pile tests consists of two parts: the
elastic compression and the allowable movement
of the toe (s). The movement at the toe is
determined from

$$s = 3.81 + \frac{B}{120} \qquad (1)$$

where B = pile diameter, mm, giving
s = 6.5 mm for the test piles.

Since the toe movements were measured, the
above criterion was used to define the failure
loads in Figure 3. The toe movement in the
first test was only 5.5 mm, so the curve was
extrapolated to 6.5 mm using the measured
deformation from the previous increment as a
guide. The resultant failure loads for the two
tests were 700 and 1440 kN, respectively, which
includes the weight of the pile (20 kN).

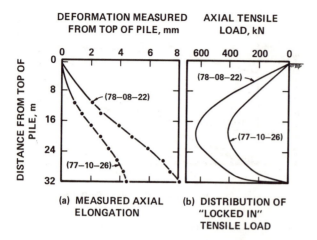

(a) MEASURED AXIAL
ELONGATION

(b) DISTRIBUTION OF
"LOCKED IN"
TENSILE LOAD

Fig. 4 Distribution of pile deformation and
locked-in tensile load, pile No. 3,
upon unloading after pullout to
failure

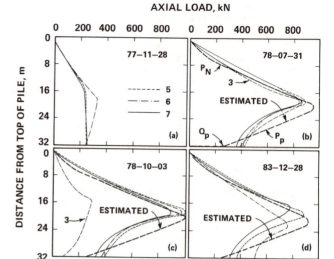

Fig. 5 Observed and estimated downdrag loads
for group of three steel pipe piles

Locked-in Tension Load

Upon unloading, the test pile was stretched
4.5 mm after the first test and 8 mm after the
second. The measured elongations after
complete unloading, shown on Figure 4(a), were
caused by soil:pile friction, which prevented
the pile from regaining its original length.

The axial tensile loads determined from the
deformations are shown on Figure 4(b). The
maximum loads were 410 kPa for the first test
and 640 kPa for the second.

PILE LOAD DISTRIBUTION

Pile compressions for the three-pile group were
observed for 6½ years. Several significant
changes in embankment geometry resulted from
placing and moving granular fill as the south
approaches to the bridge were formed, and in
pore water pressures, which affected the
downdrag loads. Four particular times were
selected to illustrate development of negative
skin friction load and response to changes in
vertical effective stress in the soil.

Observed Changes in Loads

The pile compressions were converted into
axial pile loads, (Figure 5) using the data in
Table I.

On 28 November, 1977, 133 days after
installation, the excess pore pressures were
still very high, and the test piles had settled
18 to 20 mm (Table III). The distribution of
axial pile load due to downdrag is shown on
Figure 5(a). The loads increased linearly and
rapidly to a depth of 14 m for piles 5 and 7
and 18 m for pile 6. Below these depths the
load increased very slowly for piles 5 and 7
and decreased for pile 6. The shape of the
curves indicates that negative skin friction
loads were under development and were easily

resisted by positive skin friction and end
bearing.

On 31 July, 1978, pile settlements had
increased to 31 mm compared to about 95 mm for
the base of the fill in the same time period.
Downdrag loads in piles 5, 6 and 7 had
increased to 890, 840 and 860 kN, respectively,
18-19 m from the top of the piles (Figure 5b).
The downdrag load of 860 kN in pile 3 was
comparable, and it developed in 278 days since
the first pullout test. The increases were due
to the higher effective vertical soil stress
around the piles (Figure 2b), due to the addition of the surcharge load to elevation +16.5 m
and to lower pore water pressures in the soil.
The load distribution curve for pile 3 is close
to that for the three piles in the group.

On 3 October, 1978, the water level in the
river was at its lowest elevation, the excess
pore water pressures had almost dissipated and
pile settlements had reached 35 mm. Under the
increased vertical effective stresses in the
soil (Figure 2b), downdrag loads reached peak
values of 1000, 970 and 890 kN, respectively,
in piles 5, 6 and 7 (Figure 5c). The maximum
load in pile 3 was 290 kN, which was generated
in the 41 days since the second pullout test.

On 28 December, 1983, 6½ years after
installation, the bridge had been in operation
for over two years. Pile settlements were
about 80 mm and had stabilized in the last
year. Vertical effective stresses were also
lower (Figure 2b), due to removal of the surcharge and construction of the approach road.
Long-term downdrag loads on piles 5, 6 and 7
were reduced to 890, 760 and 790 kN,
respectively.

Relation Between Pullout and Downdrag Loads

A long pile preloaded axially by downdrag in
a consolidating soil formation can be compared
to a prestressed column. Downdrag (P_N) is in

equilibrium with the negative skin friction forces dragging the pile down and resisted by positive skin friction plus end bearing for the effective stress conditions at the time. A 49-metre-long steel pipe pile in a consolidating marine clay easily supported an applied axial load equal to the maximum downdrag for a week without movement (Bozozuk, 1981). During the same experiment it was demonstrated that the axial load could be increased to about $2 P_N$ (corrected for end bearing) before the pile failed. The applied load could be increased to $2 P_N$ (assuming no end bearing) if positive skin friction was mobilized for the full length of the pile. This would occur if the relative movements between the pile and soil above the neutral point were reversed.

Pulling a pile out of the ground would mobilize skin friction resistance along its embedded depth. The pullout should therefore be related to mobilized downdrag load. Figure 5(b) shows a single pile prestressed by downdrag in equilibrium with the effective stress conditions in the soil. The total skin friction (P_s) in the pile is the sum of negative and positive friction loads:

$$P_s = P_N + P_P \qquad (2)$$

Since the positive skin friction load $P_P = P_N - Q_P$ (end bearing),

$$P_s = 2 P_N - Q_P \qquad (3)$$

On 22 August, 1978, pile 3 was pulled a second time. The failure load, minus the weight of the pile, was 1420 kN. Although the effective stresses in the ground at the time were not the same as for piles 5, 6 and 7 on 31 July and 3 October 1978, they were close enough (Figure 2b) to check the hypothesis.

On 31 July, 1978 (Figure 5b), P_s for test piles 3, 5, 6 and 7 using equation (3) was, respectively, 1355, 1360, 1270 and 1360 kN (average of 1340 kN). On 3 October, 1978 (Figure 5c), for piles 5, 6 and 7, P_s was 1600, 1570 and 1470 kN, respectively (average of 1550 kN). The averaged loads compared very well with the measured 1420 kN, the difference being entirely due to different vertical effective stresses in the soil.

The relation could be improved if the end-bearing loads were better known. The measured compression at the bottom 2.7-metre length of each pile in Figures 5(b) and 5(c) is due to a combination of end bearing and positive skin friction loads.

Estimated Distribution of Skin Friction Load

If the vertical effective stresses around a pile driven into a consolidating saturated soil are known, the cumulative negative skin friction load generated in the pile down to the neutral point (D) can be determined from Bozozuk (1972):

$$P_N = \sum_{i=1}^{n_D} C_i \, \Delta L_i \, K_O \, \sigma'_{vi} \tan \delta'_i \qquad (4)$$

where C_i = perimeter between pile and soil,

ΔL_i = incremental length of pile,

K_O = relation between horizontal and vertical effective stress in the soil,

σ'_{vi} = average vertical effective stress around ΔL_i,

δ'_i = effective friction angle between the soil and the surface of the pile ($\tan \delta'_i = M \tan \phi'$ where ϕ' = effective friction angle of the soil, and M depends upon type of soil and pile surface).

Similarly the cumulative positive skin friction load mobilized in the pile from the toe (L) up to the neutral point (D) is given by:

$$P_P = \sum_{i=n_L}^{n_{D+1}} C_i \, \Delta L_i \, K_O \, \sigma'_{vi} \tan \delta'_i \qquad (5)$$

The exact location of the neutral point need not be known beforehand. Extending both calculated curves for P_N and P_P until they intersect automatically establishes D.

When the end-bearing load at the toe (Q_P) is substantial enough to carry a fair proportion of the downdrag load, it must be evaluated as it identifies the start of the P_P curve (Figure 5b).

Vesić (1977) suggested that Q_P be estimated from the Standard Penetration Test from $Q_P = A \cdot q_p$, where A is the end area of the pile and

$$q_p = \beta \, \bar{N} \text{ tsf (USA)} \qquad (6)$$

$\bar{N} = N$ when $N < 15$
and $\beta = 2$ for saturated clays
$= 4$ for saturated sands.

Because the test piles were in the ground for long periods of time, a value of 3 as opposed to 2 (Bozozuk et al. 1979) was chosen for the calculations. Using $N = 10$ for soil layer E, and $A = 8.64 \times 10^{-2}$ m^2 (0.93 ft^2) gave $Q_P = 248$ kN, which was 50% greater than the 165 kN ($\beta = 2$) used in the 1979 analysis.

All terms in equations (4) and (5) must be evaluated to determine the distribution of skin friction load along the pile. The increment of pile length (ΔL_i) was selected according to length of telltale, pile geometry (Table I) and the soil profile. C_i was also obtained from the table. The average vertical effective stress (σ'_{vi}) opposite ΔL_i was obtained from the appropriate effective stress curves on Figure 2. Two very important unknowns were δ'_i and K_O.

The coefficient of friction between the soil and the pile (δ') was obtained from laboratory tests in which a steel cylinder was rotated inside a soil mass under various effective contact pressures (Bozozuk et al. 1979). The test results for the fine sand fill gave $\delta' = 29.6°$, $\phi' = 33°$, M = 0.88. For the clayey silt, three tests gave δ' of 24, 25 and 27.5°, averaging 25.5°, $\phi' = 31°$ and M = 0.78.

K_O was evaluated from the pullout test performed 22 August, 1978 . Since the contact area changed with depth because of the attached telltales, a weighted average C = 1273 mm was used for the pile. Similarly, because of the different soil formations, a weighted average $\delta' = 26.8°$ was obtained for the soil. Using the effective vertical stresses plotted on Figure 2(a), and the above values of C and δ' in equation (4) gave an operational K_O of 0.478. This value was assumed to apply to both the sand fill and the underlying clayey silts.

Knowing C, δ' and K_O, the distribution of skin friction loads for the various effective stress conditions given on Figure 2(b) was calculated using equations (4) and (5). The estimated load distributions for 31 July, 1978, 3 October, 1978, and 28 December, 1983, are shown on Figures 5(b, c and d) respectively. The estimated downdrag loads (P_N) compared very well with the observed curves for most of the piles in the group. Below the neutral point, the comparison of the positive friction loads was not as good. This was attributed to poorer measurements of the end-bearing load acting on the foot of the pile. Furthermore, the estimated end-bearing load (Q_p) from $\beta = 3$ rather than from $\beta = 2$ was too high. Using $\beta = 2$ reduces Q_p to 165 kPa, which shifts the estimated positive skin friction curve about 85 kPa to the origin. The correlation between the estimated and observed distribution of P_p is considerably improved. Nevertheless the estimated load distributions were considered quite good. It appeared that there was no group effect on the development of downdrag load.

CONCLUSIONS

1. Observed downdrag loads acting on a group of three full-scale pipe piles spaced at four pile diameters showed that they performed as single piles.

2. The magnitude and distribution of downdrag loads on pipe piles in compressible clayey silts are directly related to the vertical effective stresses in the surrounding soil and to soil settlement relative to the piles.

3. The tensile load locked in a pile by soil friction following pullout to failure is directly related to the vertical effective stress and can be appreciable.

4. The pullout failure load can be defined by applying Davisson's criteria to pile toe movement measured during a load test.

5. The pullout failure load is equal to the combined negative and positive skin friction loads generated in the pile for the effective stress conditions at the time of test.

6. The pullout load test can be used to obtain an operational K_O for a soil profile under an embankment load, provided the coefficient of friction between the pile and soil is known.

7. The distribution of skin friction loads on the test piles was reasonably estimated for various conditions of vertical effective stress using effective stress equations.

ACKNOWLEDGEMENTS

This paper was based on a cooperative study between the New Brunswick Department of Transportation and the Division of Building Research of the National Research Council Canada. It is published with the approval of the Deputy Minister of the Department and of the Director of the Division.

REFERENCES

Bozozuk, M. (1972) Downdrag measurements on a 160-ft floating pipe test pile in marine clay. Can. Geo. J. (9), 2, 127-136.
Bozozuk, M. (1981) Bearing capacity of pile preloaded by downdrag. Proc. 10th ICSMFE, Vol. 2, 631-636, Stockholm.
Bozozuk, M., Keenan, G.H., and Pheeney, P.E. (1979) Analysis of load tests on instrumented steel test piles in compressible silty soil. ASTM, STP 670, 153-180.
Davisson, M.T. (1972) High capacity piles. Proc. A.S.C.E. Lecture Series, Innovations in Foundation Construction, Illinois Section; also in Foundation Engineering, 2nd Ed. 514 pp., Wiley, New York, 1974.
Vesic, A.S. (1977) Design of pile foundations. National Cooperative Highway Research Program Synthesis of Highway Practice No. 42, Transportation Research Board, National Research Council, Washington, D.C.

Behavior of a pile under horizontal cyclic loading

Comportement d'un pieu sous chargement horizontal cyclique

H. KISHIDA, Professor of Geotechnical Engineering, Graduate School, Tokyo Institute of Technology, Yokohama, Japan
Y. SUZUKI, Research Engineer, Kajima Corporation, Tokyo, Japan
S. NAKAI, Research Engineer, Shimizu Construction Company, Tokyo, Japan

SYNOPSIS   Model pile tests are carried out to investigate the behavior of a pile under horizontal cyclic loading. The new subgrade reaction model is proposed on the basis of model tests. The analyses using this model are compared with the field test results of piles.

INTRODUCTION

In a previous paper (Nakai & Kishida : 1982) the behavior of a pile under horizontal load was discussed considering the non-linear behavior of soil and pile shaft. Properties of soil near a pile is changed by movements of pile. Gap between soil and a pile occurs in some cases.

In order to study this problem, the new subgrade reaction model was proposed on the basis of model pile test results. The results of field test of a pile under horizontal cyclic loading are summarized and analyzed by the proposed model.

MODEL TEST

Model tests were carried out to investigate the behavior of a pile under horizontal cyclic loading. The model pile is an acrylic resin pipe being 2cm in diameter and 40cm in length. The thin lead sheet is attached inside the pile shaft so that the deflection of the pile can be taken in the X-ray picture.

Two kinds of tests were made, one for the dry dense sand of relative density of 95% and the other for Kawasaki clay. The clay was remolded and reconsolidated so that the plasticity index

was 27.2% and the value of undrained shear strength was 9.8KPa. These soils were placed in the test box being the 40cm in length, 20cm in width and 40cm in depth. The pile and the lead shot were placed in the soils, and the horizontal cyclic load was applied at the top of the pile. The X-ray pictures were taken during the tests, and movements of the soils and the pile were observed by shadows of the lead shot and the pile shaft in the X-ray film.

The relationships between load and displacement at the top of the pile are shown in Fig.1(a) and Fig.1(b). The test result in the sand(Fig.1(a)) indicate that the hysteresis curves under cyclic loadings show about the same shape, and that the area enclosed by the curve increases with the increment of load. The test result in the clay(Fig.1(b)), however, indicates the different shape of the hysteresis curves compared with the test result in the sand, and the areas enclosed by the curves are much smaller than the ones in the sand.

Movements of the sand and the pile in Fig.2(a) show that the sand in front of the pile is compacted due to movements of the pile, and that the sand in back of the pile moves down to the pile shaft decreasing its density. No gap between the sand and the pile was observed. The sand near the pile shaft is compacted during horizontal cyclic loading. When the partially saturated sand has the apparent cohesion, the

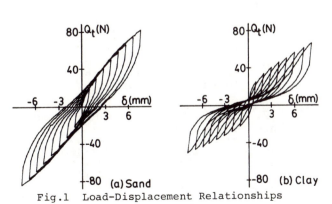

Fig.1 Load-Displacement Relationships

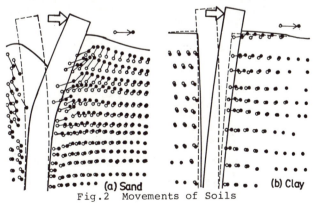

Fig.2 Movements of Soils

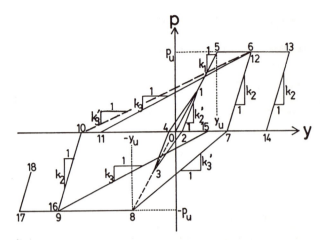

Fig.3 Proposed Subgrade Reaction Model

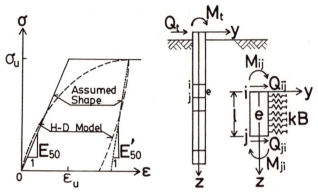

Fig.4 Relation between   Fig.5 Analytical Model
       E_{50} and E_{50}'

sand may have the critical height due to the apparent cohesion. In this case, gap between the sand and the pile occurs, and such phenomena can be observed in field tests. Movements of the clay and the pile in Fig.2(b) show that the gap between the clay and the pile was clearly observed in back of the pile. The height of the gap is a part of the critical height due to cohesion. The clay in front of the pile is remolded and decreases its strength significantly.

The difference of the hysteresis curves between the dry sand and the saturated clay is mainly due to the change of soil properties near the pile and also due to the presence of the gap between the soil and the pile shaft.

THE RELATIONSHIP BETWEEN SUBGRADE REACTION AND DISPLACEMENT UNDER HORIZONTAL CYCLIC LOADING

Based on the model test results, the authors propose a new subgrade reaction model as can be seen in Fig.3, which considers the change of soil properties and the gap between the soil and the pile under horizontal cyclic loading. The explanation of the proposed model is as follows.

(1) P_u in Fig.3 is the ultimate horizontal soil resistance calculated by theory of plasticity (Nakai & Kishida : 1982)
(2) The slope of the line $\overline{05}$ is the initial subgrade reaction coefficient (k_1) given by the following equation.

$$k_1 B = 1.3 \frac{E_s}{1-\nu_s^2} \sqrt[12]{\frac{E_s B^4}{E_p I_p}} \qquad (1)$$

   E_s, E_p : elastic coefficients of soil and pile
   ν_s : Poisson's ratio of soil
   I_p : moment of inertia of pile
   B : diameter of pile
   k_1 : subgrade reaction coefficient

(3) When the value of the subgrade reaction reaches the ultimate value (P_u), the displacement increases following the line $\overline{56}$.

(4) The slope of the reverse line (k_2 at $\overline{67}$) is determined by Hardin-Drnevich model of soil. The ratio of E_{50}' to E_{50} is approximately 1.33. By substituting E_{50}' instead of E_{50} into Eq.(1), the approximate value of k_2 is expressed as follows.(Fig.4)

$$k_2 \fallingdotseq 1.4 k_1 \qquad (2)$$

(5) When the subgrade reaction is less than the ultimate value, the slope of the reverse line $\overline{12}$ is dependent on the value of the displacement, and is expressed as follows,

$$k_2' = k_1 + (k_2 - k_1) y/y_u \qquad (3)$$
   y_u : the value of the displacement at P_u

(6) When the value of displacement y is smaller than y_u, the hysteresis curve($\overline{12}$, $\overline{23}$, $\overline{34}$ or $\overline{41}$) is easily determined by putting the point 1 and 3 at equal distance from the point 0.

(7) When the value of displacement y is greater than y_u, the slope of the reverse line $\overline{67}$ is k_2 until the value of the subgrade reaction reaches zero. When the subgrade reaction is less than zero, that means the pile is moved to the opposite direction, the reverse line $\overline{78}$ is determined to pass the negative maximum displacement point 8 recorded in the preceding loadings. The slope of the reverse line is determined by the following expression.

$$k_3' = P_u/(Ymax - Ymin - P_u/k_2) \qquad (4)$$

   Ymax : Maximum displacement recorded in the preceding loadings in positive direction (6 in Fig.3)
   Ymin : Maximum displcement in negative direction recorded in the preceding loadings (8 in Fig.3)

(8) The elastic modulus of the alluvial soil in Tokyo area decreases its value to about one third of the initial value due to disturbance of soil. The decrease of subgrade reaction due to disturbance of soil is evaluated by decreasing the value of E to one third of the initial one in Eq.(1). The effect of disturbance is expressed as follows,

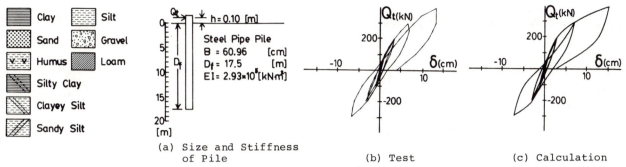

Fig.6 Symbols of Soils

(a) Size and Stiffness of Pile

(b) Test

(c) Calculation

Fig.7 Test at Shiki (Open-Ended Steel Pipe Pile)

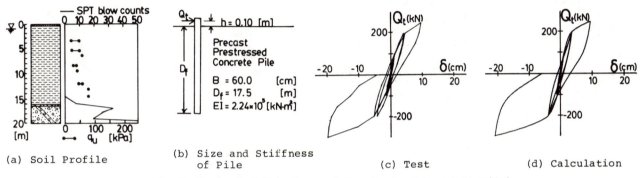

(a) Soil Profile

(b) Size and Stiffness of Pile

(c) Test

(d) Calculation

Fig.8 Test at Shiki (Precast Prestressed Concrete Pile)

$$k_3 \fallingdotseq 0.3k_1 \qquad (5)$$

(9) The case that k_3' is equal to or greater than k_3 means that no gap occurs between the soil and the pile. In this case, the slope of the reverse line is equal to k_3' as shown $\overline{78}$ in Fig.3.

(10) The minimum value of subgrade coefficient is k_3. The case that calculated k_3' (the broken line $\overline{10\,12}$ in Fig.3) is smaller than k_3 ($\overline{11\,12}$) has no physical meaning. The real phnomenon is the line $\overline{10\,11\,12}$. The line $\overline{10\,11}$ means the gap and no subgrade reaction occurs. The slope of the line $\overline{11\,12}$ is k_3. The point 12 is the maximum displacement in the preceding loadings. Thus, the line $\overline{10\,11\,12}$ is obtained.

The successive load-displacement relationships can be determined by the aforementioned procedures.

METHOD OF ANALYSIS

The method of analysis is based on the subgrade reaction theory appling the proposed model under horizontal cyclic loading. The pile is divided into small elements as shown in Fig.5. The deformation of the element is expressed in the form of series.

The relationship between deformation and the nodal force in each element can be calculated by Rayleigh-Ritz method. The nodal force is obtained by minimizing potential energy of the pile-soil system satisfying compatibility condition of displacements and equilibrium of forces at the boundary of each elements. The detailed method of this subgrade reaction theory

that can include the non-linear characteristics of both soil and pile is published previously (Nakai & Kishida : 1982).

COMPARISON BETWEEN CALCULATED AND FIELD TEST RESULTS

Full scale pile loading tests were carried out at four construction sites to compare the test results with calculated ones by the proposed theory. The symbols of soils are shown in Fig.6. The open-ended steel pipe pile and the precast prestressed concrete pile tests were carried out at Shiki in Saitama. The soil is mostly clay and its profile is shown in Fig.8(a). The test and calculated results of the open-ended steel pipe piles are shown in Fig.7. The test and calculated results of the precast prestressed concrete pile are shown in Fig.8. In Figs.7~11, Q_t means the horizontal load and δ means the horizontal displacement at the top of the pile.

The test on the open-ended steel pipe pile is also carried out at Ishikari in Hokkaido. The soil profile, size and stiffness of pile, the test and calculated results are shown in Fig.9.

The tests on the steel cased concrete pile is carried out at Ichikawa in Chiba. The soil profile, size and stiffness of pile, the test and calculated results are shown in Fig.10. The test on the bored concrete pile is also carried out at Sendai in Miyagi. The soil profile, size and stiffness of pile, the test and calculated results are shown in Fig.11. All the tests except at Sendai were carried out under the condition of the pile top being free to rotate.

In the tests of steel pipe piles shown in Fig.7

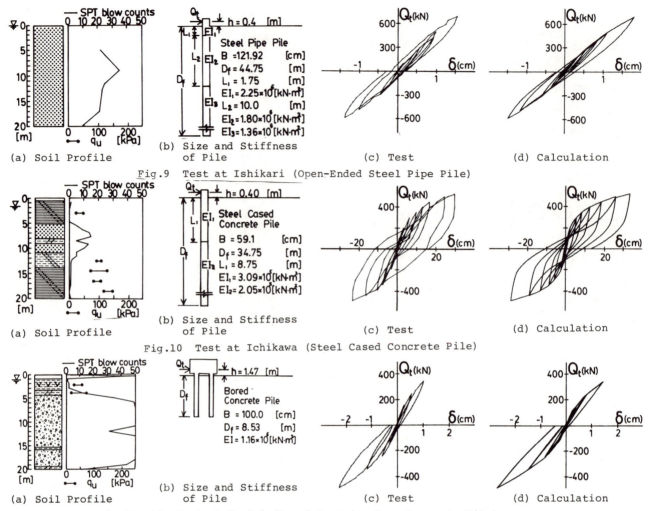

(a) Soil Profile

(b) Size and Stiffness of Pile

(c) Test

(d) Calculation

Fig.9   Test at Ishikari (Open-Ended Steel Pipe Pile)

(a) Soil Profile

(b) Size and Stiffness of Pile

(c) Test

(d) Calculation

Fig.10   Test at Ichikawa (Steel Cased Concrete Pile)

(a) Soil Profile

(b) Size and Stiffness of Pile

(c) Test

(d) Calculation

Fig.11   Test at Sendai (Bored Cast-in-place Concrete Pile)

and Fig.9, the calculated results show fairly good agreement with the test results. In the tests of the precast prestressed concrete and the steel cased concrete piles shown in Fig.8 and Fig.10, the concrete in the pile shaft develops cracks due to large deformation of the pile shaft. Though the non-linear properties of concrete is included in the proposed method, it is difficult to obtain the accurate behavior of concrete in the pile shaft. The difference between the calculated and test results is mostly due to the change of pile stiffness under large deformation of the pile shaft.

In the test of the bored concrete pile, the top of two piles are connected by the reinforced concrete pile cap so that the top of the piles are restrained from rotating. Though the change of stiffness of the reinforced concrete pile shaft is difficult to estimate, the calculated result shows fairly good agreement with the test result. It is due to the reason that the deformation of the pile shaft is rather smaller than the case of Fig.8 and Fig.10.

CONCLUSIONS

The behavior of a pile under horizontal cyclic loading can be explained by the subgrade reaction theory using the proposed model.

The effect of change of soil properties near a pile shaft and the gap between soil and pile are important factors to be considered when a pile is subjected to horizontal cyclic loading.

ACKNOWLEDGMENTS

The tests at Shiki was carried out by Kajima Corporation. The test at Ishikari was carried out by Shimizu Construction Company. The test at Ichikawa was carried out by The Zenitaka Corporation. The test at Sendai was carried out by Nippon Telegraph and Telephone Public Corporation. The authors are grateful for their kind arrangements to prepare the test results. The authors would like to thank Mr. Mano for preparing the figures.

REFERENCE

Nakai, S. and Kishida, H.(1982). Nonlinear Analysis of a Laterally Loaded Pile. Proc. 4th Int. Conf. Numerical Methods in Geomechanics, 835-842, Edmonton.

Behaviour of bored and auger piles in normally consolidated soils

Comportement de divers types de pieux forés

J. KRUIZINGA, Delft Soil Mechanics Laboratory, Netherlands
H. A. M. NELISSEN, Delft Soil Mechanics Laboratory, Netherlands

SUMMARY

Based on the results of pile tests and CPT's design formulas for the load settlement curves of bored piles could be established. These formulas seem to be also valid for the design of the load settlement curves of auger piles. The results of pile-load tests on bored and auger piles are shown in this paper.
Further investigation on the influence of several parameters and the validity of this design method for other pile types is still going on.

1. INTRODUCTION

Due to the soil conditions in the Netherlands, i.e. normally consolidated fine to medium fine pleistocene sand overlain by soft clay and peat layers, driven precast-concrete piles is by far the most economic and most applied piling system. The ultimate bearing capacity of this type of displacement pile, as well as the load settlement behaviour, is calculated from Dutch Cone Penetration Tests (DCPT's) since 30 years and has proved to be very reliable |lit. 1|. However, during the last decade non-displacement piles like large diameter bored piles and auger piles are also applied, in particular in case of high pile loadings and too heavy pile driving (noise, vibrations). As a standard site investigation programme always consists of DCPT's, it would be very much appreciated if for these types of non-displacement piles design rules could be developed based on DCPT's. Therefore - 3 bored piles with 0,6 m diameter and 1 bored pile with 1,2 m diameter constructed with a bucket under bentonite, without casing, have been testloaded stepwise; after every step 4 cycles of loading-unloading have been applied. During the tests the pile head and pile toe settlement have been measured, while built-in Telemac cells at several levels allowed for determination of skin friction and base resistance as a function of the pile displacements. As non-displacement piles might cause a reduction of the initial in-situ stresses in the soil, DCPT's before and after pile construction have been carried out. With respect to the 6 auger piles, constructed without bentonite, only the pile head settlement has been measured as a function of the applied load, according to the usual test procedure in the Netherlands.

2. BORED PILES

2.1. Base Resistance

The ultimate base resistance p_{ult} turned out to be much lower than that of an equivalent driven pile and also lower than according to the expressions of Caquot-Kerisel, Brinch Hansen, a.o., which obviously is a result of the way of installation. A reasonable agreement could be obtained if with respect to the Dutch design rule for driven piles, making use of DCPT-results, a reduction factor of a = 0,5 is applied. So, the ultimate base of a bored pile in normally consolidated sand is about 50% of the base resistance of an equivalent driven pile calculated according to the Dutch method. Also the relation pile settlement and base resistance is different from driven piles: the base resistance p_{base} of a bored pile

in sand slowly developes as a function of the displacement. The expressions

$$s_{head} = \alpha \, \log \frac{a \cdot p_{ult}}{a \cdot p_{ult} - p_{base}} \ cm$$

with α = 15 (cm) seems to be reasonable fitting of the load-settlement curve.
For N.C.-sands it is doubtful if a $\cdot p_{ult}$ exceeds a value of 5000 - 6000 kN/m².

2.2. Skin Friction

In sand the average ultimate skin friction $\overline{\tau}_{ult}$ is in between 0,6% and 0,7% of the mean measured cone resistance $\overline{q}_c$. It seems to be wise not to exceed a value $\overline{\tau}_{ult}$ = 90 - 100 kN/m². The development of the skin friction of the displacement is more rapidly than the base resistance. The expression

$$\tau = \tau_{ult}(\beta1 + \beta2 \, \log \frac{100 \, s_{head}}{D}) \ for \ \frac{s_{head}}{D} > 0,2\%$$

with $\beta1 = \beta2 = 0,5$

is an attempt to describe the behaviour of the test piles. The influence of the diameter D and also the β-factors are subject to further research.
Compared with case-in-situ concrete displacement piles the ultimate skin friction is lower, what can be explained from the installation method, causing a reduction with 30 - 50% in measured local friction values after pile installation.
Figures 1A, 1B, 1C show the results evaluated from a test loading on a bored pile Ø 0,6 m.

2.3. Design Fromulas for Load-Settlement Curves

From the above-mentioned pile load tests the following design rules for bored piles have been derived:

base resistance: $s_H = 15 \, \log \dfrac{0,5* \, p_{ult}}{0,5* \, p_{ult} - p_{base}}$

skin friction : $\tau/\tau_{ult} = 0,5(1 + \log \dfrac{100* \, s_H}{D})$

with : $\tau_{ult} = 6 \,^o/oo * \overline{q}_c$

It will be clear that with respect to the ultimate base resistance and skin friction different safety factors have to be applied.

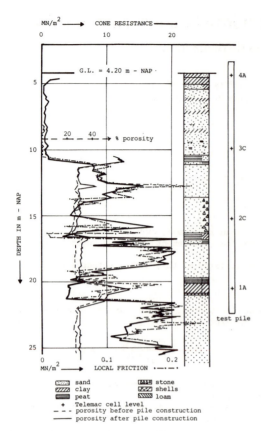

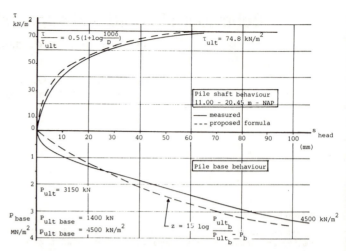

Fig. 1C Pile Test

The allowable pile load depends on the allowable deformations which depends on the type of structure.
Deformations of about 1,5 to 2% of the pile diameter can be quite acceptable which means with respect to the expression in § 2.2 that about 65% of the average ultimate skin friction has been mobilised and about 20% of the ultimate base resistance.

2.4. Case Studies

Based on the fore-mentioned equations some major projects have been designed. During and after construction load and displacement measurements have been carried out for some projects.
The results of two cases are presented here, where also the design load-settlement curves have been plotted.
It can be seen from these graphs, that the design curves are on the safe-side (fig. 2).

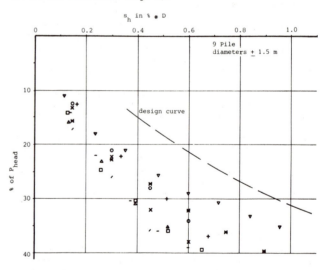

Fig. 2 - Case I: Design Curve and Measured Pile Settlements

Near the village Heerde, in the north of the Netherlands, the new highway No. 50 crosses a local road at a 23° angle, resulting into a viaduct consisting of 3 supports (besides the abutments). Each support consists of one bored pile of 3,26 x 2,20 m² with a working load of about 20000 kN (case 2). After constructing the viaduct on the initial

Fig. 1A Static Penetration Test 01

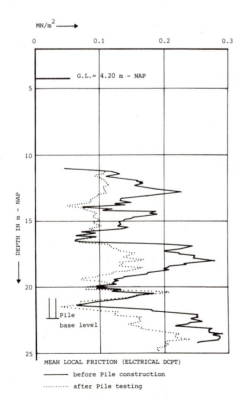

MEAN LOCAL FRICTION (ELCTRICAL DCPT)

—— before Pile construction

.... after Pile testing

Fig. 1B Mean Local Friction (electric DCPT)

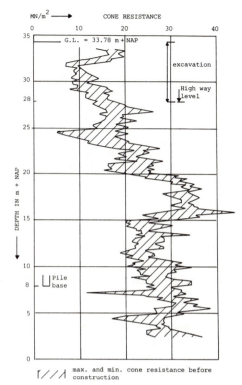

Fig. 3A

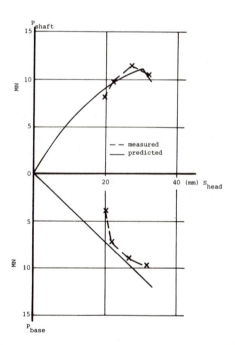

Fig. 3B

groundlevel the highway crossing was made by excavating the soil beneath the concrete structure. It was decided by the Ministry of Public Works to provide the middle bored pile with measuring device at several levels to monitor the strains during the construction stages of the viaduct. Prior to construction the following design

rules were applied: skin friction $\tau = 0,5 \ \tau_{ult} (1+\log \frac{100 \ s_H}{D})$ with $\tau_{ult} = 90 \ kN/m^2$;

base resistance $p_{base} = K \cdot s_H$ with the coefficient of pile subgrade reaction $K = 50 \ MN/m^3$ for $p_{base} < 1,5 \ MN/m^2$.

This is more or less equal to the first part of the expression mentioned in § 2.1.

The predicted and derived values from the measurements for skin friction and base resistance are shown in fig. 3b, together with the cone resistance of the sandy subsoil (fig. 3a). It can be concluded that only in the beginning more settlement has occurred, but that the other values are reasonably well predicted.

3. AUGER PILES

These piles are cast-in-situ by screwing in an auger provided with an injection pipe in the centre of the auger. When the required depth has been reached, the auger is pulled, simultaneously injecting the grout. The soil at least equal to the pile volume is removed during the installation of the pile. The effects of scraping and pulling result into some reduction of the surrounding initial stresses. Therefore, this pile is more or less similar to the bored pile. The bearing capacity of the auger pile consists of base resistance and friction between the pile shaft and the sand.

3.1. Pile Tests

Six pile tests have been analysed and the load settlement curves have been investigated in terms of the formulas derived for bored piles, only with adapted coefficients.

base resistance: $s_{head} = \alpha \ \log \frac{a \cdot p_{ult}}{a \cdot p_{ult} - p_{base}}$

skin friction : $\tau/\tau_{ult} = \beta \ (1 + \log \frac{100 \ s_H}{D})$

In fig. 4 a review of the soil conditions (based on DCPT's and borings) at the test locations is given. Of all test piles the load-pilehead-settlement curves are available.

3.2. Analysis of the Pile Tests

The analysis is based on the assumption that the development of the skin friction as a function of the pile settlement is equal to the bored pile. This assumption has been verified for pile nr. 1. For some reasons, dealing with the execution of these piles, there can be assumed that the bearing capacity of pile nr. 1 mainly consists of skin friction.

$\tau/\tau_{ult} = 0,5 \ (1 + \log \frac{100 \ s_{head}}{D})$

$\tau_{ult} = 6 \ ^o/oo * \bar{q}_c$ (fine medium sands)

It can be concluded that these assumptions are valid for test pile 1 (fig. 5).

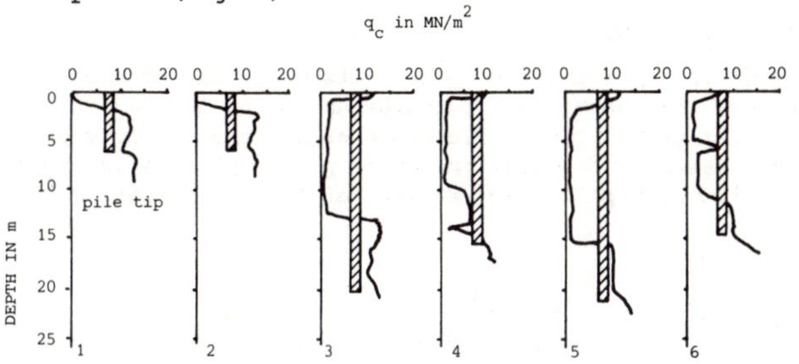

q_c in MN/m^2

Fig. 4 Soil Conditions at Test Locations

The bearing capacities of the other test piles consist partly of base resistance. For these piles there has been assumed that the development of the friction is also according the above-mentioned bored-pile formula.

At all test locations the pile <u>head</u> loads and settlements have been measured. The bearing capacity of the piles has been separated in pile base and skin resistance.

The ultimate friction can be determined more accurately by measuring the local friction (q_f) by establishing the ratio q_f/q_c for each type of sand.

In table 3.2 the a and α factors are summarized:

$$s_h = \alpha \log \frac{a \cdot P_{ult}}{a \cdot P_{ult} - P_{base}}$$

pile nr.	a	α
2	0,7	5
3	0,67	6,7
4	0,61	3,5
5	0,60	-
6	0,54	6-9

3.3. Design Formulas for Load-Settlement Curves

Based on the analysis of the six pile tests the following design formulas are proposed:

pile base : $s_{head} = 8 \log \dfrac{0,67 * P_{ult}}{0,67\, P_{ult} - P_{base}}$ |cm|

skin friction: $\tau/\tau_{ult} = 0,5(1 + \log \dfrac{100\, s_{head}}{D})$

for: $\tau_{ult} = 6\ ^o/oo * \bar{q}_c$

The test piles have been recalculated with these formulas. The results are shown in fig. 6.

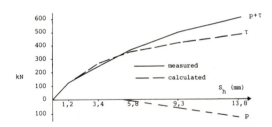

Fig. 5 Test Pile I

The allowable pile load depends on the allowable deformation of the pile head. Deformations of about 1,5% of the pile diameter mean that about 65% of the average ultimate skin friction has been mobilized and about 25% of the base resistance.

4. CONCLUSIONS

Based on the results of pile tests on bored and auger piles, load-settlement formulas have been derived.
The influence of the pile diameter and the validity of the presented formulas for other pile types (including displacement piles) are subject of further research.

SYMBOLS:

$s_h = \alpha \log \dfrac{a \cdot P_{ult}}{a \cdot P_{ult} - P_{base}}$

s_h = settlement of the pile head

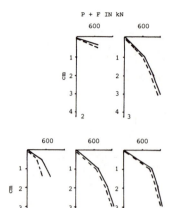

Fig. 6 Measured and Calculated Values of the Test Piles

P_{ult} = ultimate bearing capacity of the base according to the Dutch method

P_{base} = working base load

a, α = coefficients

$\tau = \tau_{ult}\ \beta(1 + \log \dfrac{100\, s_h}{D})$

τ = skin friction at working load

τ_{ult} = ultimate skin friction

D = pile diameter

β = coefficient

REFERENCES

1. Heijnen, W.J., 1974, Penetration Testing in the Netherlands. ESOPT I, vol I, pp. 79-83.
2. Kruizinga, J., 1975, Analysis of test results of bored piles in the Netherlands. LGM-Mededelingen XVII no. 2 (in Dutch).
3. Kooperen, C.H. Van, 1976, Measurements of the settlements of bored piles in Dutch soft soil. 6th European Conf. SMFE, Vienna, Vol. 1.2.

Bearing capacity and settlement of shaped piles in permafrost

Capacité portante et tassement des pieux crénelés et tronconiques dans le pergélisol

B. LADANYI, Professor of Civil Engineering, Northern Engineering Centre, Ecole Polytechnique, Montreal, Canada
A. GUICHAOUA, Graduate Student, Northern Engineering Centre, Ecole Polytechnique, Montreal, Canada

SYNOPSIS   Although in frozen soils most piles act as "friction piles", relying very little on end-bearing, not much attention has been concentrated up to now on the problem of improving their shaft resistance, e.g., by providing corrugations or giving a slight taper to their shaft. Realizing that a systematic study of such shaped piles would be useful, an experimental investigation was undertaken, including a large number of load-and rate-controlled tests on three types of model piles: smooth and corrugated straight-shafted piles, and smooth tapered piles, installed in frozen sand. This paper presents the principal test results, their analysis, and the comparison with theoretical predictions.

INTRODUCTION

With very few exceptions, most of the piles installed in permafrost have a regular cylindrical or square cross-section, their shaft is straight, and their surface is usually relatively smooth. It is well known that, under service loads, most of the load on such piles is carried by adfreeze bond, while the end bearing is small and is often neglected in the design. Many careful studies on the adfreeze bond (Parameswaran, 1978, 1979; Weaver and Morgenstern, 1981a,b) have shown that, under similar conditions, its intensity is affected by the pile material (being the highest for untreated wood, and the lowest for painted steel), and by the method of installation (i.e., whether the pile is driven, drill-driven, or installed in a slurried hole and refrozen). The adfreeze bond is usually assumed in the design to be a fraction of the time- and temperature-dependent frozen soil cohesion. One aspect, common to all straight-shafted piles, is that adfreeze bond fails in a brittle manner, leading to a high loss of pile capacity after failure. (Crory, 1963; Parameswaran, 1978).

In unfrozen soils, shaped piles have been used for many years for increasing their bearing capacity. Several types of such piles are now available commercially, and some design methods have been proposed (e.g., Nordlund, 1963).

In frozen soils, a quite extensive use of in-situ-corrugated straight-shafted piles has been made recently during the construction of the Alyeska Pipeline. However, although some reports on their full-scale performance have been published, showing their clear advantages (Black and Thomas, 1978; Thomas and Luscher, 1980; Luscher et al., 1983), the behaviour of such piles in frozen soils has not yet been systematically investigated and no practical design method has yet been proposed. The effect of corrugations on pulling capacity of anchors embedded in frozen sand was recently studied by Andersland and Alwahhab (1982), who made a

series of model scale pulling tests on steel rods containing one or several lugs on their shaft. The effect of lugs, similar to corrugations, was found to considerably increase the pulling capacity of the rods. In addition, Weaver and Morgenstern (1981a) have studied the effect of the material roughness and the type of frozen soil on adfreeze strength in direct shear.

In order to get a better understanding of the behaviour of shaped piles embedded in frozen soil, an experimental study was undertaken in the laboratories of the Northern Engineering Centre of Ecole Polytechnique (Guichaoua, 1984). The study included a large number of both load- and settlement-rate-controlled tests on three types of model piles: smooth and corrugated straight-shafted piles, and smooth tapered piles. Like in practice, the piles were installed in oversized holes in frozen sand, surrounded by a compacted sand-water slurry, and let to freeze at -5°C. There was no pile-soil contact at the pile end.

In order to find a proper design method for the two types of piles, two theories were considered. The first one was an adaptation of the Johnston and Ladanyi (1972) rod anchors theory, which assumes that a longitudinal shear distortion occurs in the soil around the pile, without shear failure at the pile-soil interface. The second theory, in turn, was based on the fact that a vertical displacement of a tapered piles produces a lateral expansion of the hole in which the pile is embedded, which enabled to relate the settlement rate of the pile with the rate of expansion of a cylindrical hole, following a solution by Ladanyi and Johnston (1973).

The paper presents and analyzes the principal test results obtained, and discusses the prediction of pile behaviour according to the two proposed theories.

TEST EQUIPMENT

All the tests were performed in a cold room where the temperature was controlled with an accuracy of ±1°C. In general, the temperature within the samples remained sensibly constant at -5°C. All load-controlled tests were carried out in cylindrical blocks of frozen sand, contained in a steel tank 762 mm in diam. and 460 mm high. The bottom of the tank was supplied with several water entry tubes to assure a proper sand saturation. In order to avoid the lateral pressure generation during freezing, the inside wall of the tank was covered with a layer of foamed plastic.

The rate-controlled tests, in turn, were carried out in cylindrical blocks of frozen sand 300 mm in diameter and 300 mm high, which were placed in an ordinary 50 kN soil mechanics testing machine, located in the cold room.

TEST MATERIAL

The sand used in the tests was the same as in a previous study described by Ladanyi and Eckardt (1983). Its grain size distribution was about 90% between 0.1 and 1.0 mm, with less than 2% below 0.1 mm, and less than 1% above 2mm, giving a coefficient of uniformity of about 3.0. The maximum and minimum dry densities of the sand were 1810 and 1510 kg/m^3, respectively. Triaxial tests on the dry sand gave peak shear strength angles of 45° at the maximum density and 39° at a density of 1680 kg/m^3.

SAMPLE PREPARATION

The sand is first compacted in the tank with a vibratory compactor and is then saturated from below with distilled de-aerated water. During subsequent freezing, and during the tests, the sand temperature is measured with a set of thermistors embedded at 3 different levels in the sample. About 160 hours were necessary for a sample to freeze and attain a constant temperature of -5°C.

In permafrost practice, the piles are usually installed in predrilled holes with their diameter 50% larger than that of the pile. They are then surrounded by a compacted sand-water slurry and frozen-in. A similar method was used for installing the model piles in this investigation. However, the holes were not drilled, but were obtained by placing either steel tubes with 5 cm diameter (Tests 1 to 12, Table I) or plastic tubes with 6 cm diameter (Tests 14 to 26, Table II), in the sand before freezing. The tubes were silicone-lubricated and wrapped in a thin plastic sheet, to enable their easy retraction.

The piles, with a diameter of 2 to 3 cm, were put in the holes, their ends resting on a cushion of foamed plastic. The sand-water slurry prepared at optimum density, was then placed around the piles, compacted manually and saturated. Before placing, the slurry was cooled to below 4°C.

LOADING AND DISPLACEMENT CONTROL

In load-controlled tests, 8 piles were installed in each sand block, so that their distance from the lateral surface or from another pile was not smaller than 15 cm. The loads were applied and held constant up to over 300 hours by using Bellofram pneumatic jacks. In rate-controlled tests, Table III, only one pile was tested in each block. The available rates of penetration were 0.030, 0.061, and 0.300 mm/min. In the tests, the loads were controlled by load cells, and the displacements by DCDT Transducers with 25 mm range, so that all the data, including the temperature, were recorded on a data acquisition system, and plotted subsequently.

TYPES OF PILES

The three types of piles used in the tests, were: smooth, corrugated and tapered piles. All the piles were machined from high strength aluminium. The smooth straight-shafted piles had the diameter of 2 cm and were 21 to 23 cm long. The corrugated piles had the shape of a screw with a thread sloping down at 10° angle. The thread had a triangular shape with 12.7 mm long base and an ascending angle of 10°. This gave in the longitudinal section of the pile indentations 12.7 mm long and ascending at 10° in the direction of the pile movement. The sizes of the corrugated piles are given in Table I.

All the tapered piles had a taper angle of α = 2.1°. They were about 20.3 cm long and their maximum and minimum diameter was about 3.5 and 2.0 cm, respectively. Data about their embedded lengths and diameters are given in Tables II and III.

TABLE I

Results of load-controlled creep tests with straight-shafted piles

Test No.	Slurry w %	Length L cm	Aver. Diam. D_m cm	Aver. Shear Stress τ kPa	Min. Settl. Rate $\dot{s}$ 10^{-3} mm/h	Total Creep Time h
(A) Smooth piles						
2	16.0	16.2	2.0	43.8	0.05	186
10	15.2	14.8	2.0	62.4	0.08	120
12	15.2	15.4	2.0	69.0	0.43	170
7	16.0	14.1	2.0	75.7	—[1]	0.02
4	16.0	15.7	2.0	90.6	—[1]	0.11
(B) Corrugated piles						
1	16.0	16.1	2.23	118.6	0.21	186
6	16.0	16.3	2.20	147.9	0.15	250
5	16.0	15.3	2.22	190.9	0.25	250
3	16.0	18.2	2.09	224.9	4.31	67
8	15.2	17.2	2.23	263.6	132.50[2]	60
11	15.2	15.1	2.22	277.0	2.70	170

[1] Instantaneous failure
[2] Low slurry compaction

TABLE II

Results of load-controlled creep tests
with tapered piles

Test No.	Slurry w %	Embedded Length L cm	Diameter D cm	d cm	Load Q kN	Aver. Shear Stress τ kPa	Settl. Rate Ṡ* 10⁻³mm/h	Total Creep Time h
14	17.6	15.0	3.08	1.98	3.12	262	0.84	191
15	17.6	13.6	3.00	2.00	4.01	376	5.88	191
16	17.6	14.2	3.07	2.03	2.90	255	0.49	335
17	17.6	13.4	3.03	2.02	3.39	321	0.24	335
18	17.6	14.3	3.03	1.98	1.78	159	0.09	263
19	17.6	12.6	2.98	2.05	8.92	897	22.00	263
20	17.8	10.4	2.74	1.98	2.68	348	6.95	263
21	17.8	13.1	2.89	1.93	2.90	292	9.87	263
22	17.8	10.4	2.74	1.98	2.45	318	2.23	266
23	17.8	10.8	2.90	2.03	8.92	978	1.94	266
24	17.8	14.8	3.08	2.00	2.01	173	3.28	236
25	17.8	9.6	2.73	2.02	7.58	1045	4.53	236
26	17.8	11.9	2.93	2.05	5.60	600	5.12	240

*at 120 hours

TABLE III

Results of rate-controlled tests

Test No.	Slurry w %	Length L cm	Aver. Diam. D_m cm	Settl. rate Ṡ mm/h	Aver. peak Shear Stress τ kPa
(A) Smooth Piles					
IX	18.3	11.81	2.0	1.80	853
III	15.7	15.58	2.0	3.66	429
VI	15.7	15.48	2.0	18.30	438
(B) Corrugated piles					
VIII	18.3	12.34	2.23	1.80	1790
II	15.7	14.04	2.20	3.66	1380
V	15.7	13.23	2.09	18.30	2010
(C) Tapered piles (α = 2.1°)					
VII	18.3	14.41	2.55	1.80	(1460)*
I	17.5	16.96	2.64	3.66	(716)*
IV	15.7	13.26	2.51	18.30	(2040)*

* Steadily increasing after 2 cm settlement.

TEST RESULTS

Altogether 33 pile tests were carried out, 24 of which
were constant load creep tests, and 9 constant settlement
rate tests. Tables I, II and III present the main data
and some results of the tests. For each test, the tables
give the water content of the slurry and the embedded
length and the diameter of the pile. Further, for creep
tests, Tables I and II give the value of the applied average shear stress τ (and the total load Q in Table II),
the resulting minimum settlement rate, and the total creep
time. For rate controlled tests, Table III gives the value of the applied settlement rate and the resulting average peak shear stress τ.

Figures 1 to 4 show some typical results obtained in the
experiments. Figure 1 shows creep curves of a corrugated
and a tapered pile obtained under similar conditions. A
smooth pile would have failed nearly instantaneously under this load. The curves show a long primary creep portion, with some apparent tendency to steady state after
about 100 hours. However, when the results of some most
typical pile creep tests are plotted in a log-log plot,
Fig. 2, after subtracting the instantaneous response, one
gets rather the impression that the settlement of all the
piles tended not to a steady state, but to a stationary
creep with an attenuating trend. A similar conclusion
was made by Weaver and Morgenstern (1981b) for piles in
"ice-poor" soils, and by Luscher et al. (1983) on the basis of full scale tests on corrugated piles in Alaska.

This kind of creep test results can be processed in two
different ways: First, one can concentrate only on the
steady-state portion, or the minimum creep rate, neglecting the attenuating character of the curves. When the
quasi-steady-state creep rates so obtained are plotted
against the applied stresses in a log-log plot for a series of pile creep tests, it is usually found that the
rate sensitivity of the shear strength along the shaft is
rather low, i.e., the exponent of stress n in the creep
equation Eq. (2) shown further is high. Figure 3 shows
one such plot obtained from the present results with
smooth and corrugated piles, containing also the results
of rate-controlled tests. It will be seen that the lines
drawn through the test points give the values of the expo-
nents n of about n = 4 and 5, respectively. It is also
found that the bearing capacity of corrugated piles is
from 2 to 3.5 times higher than that of smooth piles at
the same settlement rate. The above values of n compare
well with those found by Parameswaran (1978, 1979) (n =
4.5 for steel) under similar test conditions. However,
as stated by Ladanyi (1972), and Johnston and Ladanyi
(1972), this kind of plotting has a practical value only
if used in connection with the determined pseudo-instan-
taneous displacements, which include all the preceding
elastic and primary creep strains. But, even then, the
assumption of steady-state creep settlement of a pile usually leads to excessive settlement rate predictions and
over-conservative design.

Another alternative is clearly to draw conclusions from
the log-log plot of creep curves, as in Fig. 2. As shown
in the following, these curves can be approximated by a
more general creep equation, such as Eq. (2). Only very
long term full-scale tests could tell which of the two methods will be able to give more correct long-term predictions.

Finally, in Fig. 4 the observed behaviour of the three
kinds of piles is compared at two different rates of settlement. Their response is seen to be drastically different. The smooth piles failed at low stress in a brittle
manner, loosing all their strength after a displacement
of about 2 mm. The shaft resistance of corrugated piles
continued to climb up to about 2 MPa, reaching its peak
at about 5 mm, and decreasing slowly towards the residual,
which after 12 mm displacement remained still at 50% of the
peak strength. The tapered piles showed typically a small
first peak at about 0.6 mm displacement, indicating the
loss of adhesion as in a smooth pile test, but after this,
their resistance continued to rise steadily without any
sign of strength loss.

From a practical point of view, these test results show a
clear-advantage of using corrugated piles in permafrost,
rather than smooth piles, which follows also from the
Alyeska Pipeline experience (Thomas and Luscher, 1980;
Luscher et al, 1983). The reason is that corrugated piles
show generally a non-brittle behaviour, using most of the
natural soil shear strength. With a proper margin of

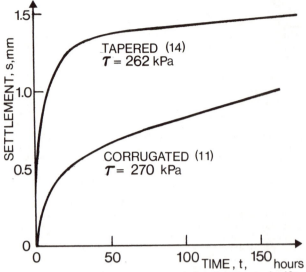

Fig. 1. Creep curves of a corrugated and a tapered pile under similar test conditions.

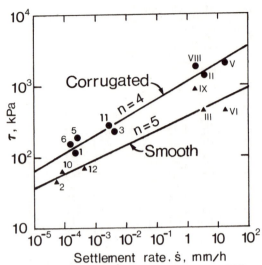

Fig. 3. Minimum creep rates vs. applied shear stress for smooth and corrugated piles.

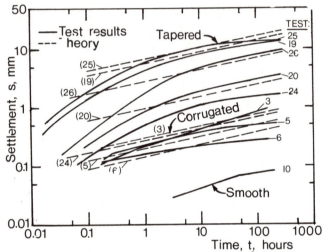

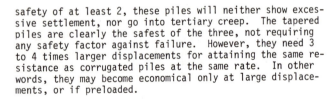

Fig. 2. Typical creep curves of smooth (10) corrugated (19-25), and tapered (3-6) piles, compared with the theory.

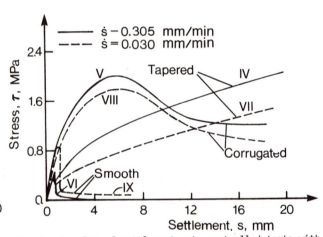

Fig. 4. Results of settlement-rate-controlled tests with three types of piles and at two different rates.

safety of at least 2, these piles will neither show excessive settlement, nor go into tertiary creep. The tapered piles are clearly the safest of the three, not requiring any safety factor against failure. However, they need 3 to 4 times larger displacements for attaining the same resistance as corrugated piles at the same rate. In other words, they may become economical only at large displacements, or if preloaded.

THEORY

Under an increase in stress, containing a substantial deviatoric component, an ice-saturated frozen soil will show an instantaneous response, both elastic and plastic, followed by creep, sometimes combined with consolidation. The creep is initially of a primary type, followed by a short steady-state portion, eventually accelerating to-

wards failure, under favorable boundary conditions. It is usually assumed in frozen soil mechanics that total strain ε, resulting from a deviatoric stress increment, is composed of an instantaneous strain, ε_{inst} and a delayed strain, ε_{creep}

$$\varepsilon = \varepsilon_{inst} + \varepsilon_{creep} \tag{1}$$

Because of the relatively high rigidity of an ice-saturated frozen soil at short term loads, the instanteneous portion of the strain is much smaller than the creep portion, which keeps increasing with time. As this paper is mainly concerned with assessing the long-term behaviour of piles, attention will be concentrated only on creep strains. Besides, for an instantaneous elastic-plastic frozen soil response, the pile design methods developed in unfrozen soil mechanics remain valid.

A convenient form of a creep law for frozen soil, proposed

by Ladanyi (1972), and extended to include the primary creep by Ladanyi and Johnston (1974), can be written as

$$\varepsilon_e = (\sigma_e/\sigma_{c\theta})^n A F_t \qquad (2)$$

where subscript e denotes the von Mises equivalent stress and strain, $n \geqslant 1$ is the creep exponent for stress, and F_t is a time function. In this paper the power law of time $F_t = t^b$ with $b \leqslant 1$ was adopted as the time function, in which case: $A = (\dot{\varepsilon}_c/b)^b$, and $\sigma_{c\theta}$ denotes the reference stress at the arbitrary reference strain rate $\dot{\varepsilon}_c$, obtained from a test made at temperature θ (θ is the number of degrees C below 0°C). In the two last-mentioned papers, it is also shown how $\sigma_{c\theta}$ can be made to incorporate the effects of temperature and normal pressure on creep. This power-law type of time function has been adopted in this paper.

Straight-shafted piles

As shown by Johnston and Ladanyi (1972), as long as there is no slip between the pile and the soil, the pile settlement s due to shear stresses only is equal to the cumulative shear deformation of the frozen soil at the contact with the pile. For a soil obeying the creep law of Eq. (2) with $F_t = t^b$, the pile settlement is given by

$$s = 3^{(n+1)/2}\left[D_m/2(n-1)\right] (\tau/\sigma_{c\theta})^n (\dot{\varepsilon}_c t/b)^b \qquad (3)$$

where s is the settlement, D_m is the average pile diameter, τ is the average shear stress at the pile-soil interface, and the other parameters are defined as in Fig. 2. The range of validity of Eq. (3) depends on the roughness of the pile surface. For very rough grouted-rod anchors, described by Johnston and Ladanyi (1972), the slip started after a displacement of 2 to 3 cm. In this study, the slip occurred for smooth piles at 0.4 to 0.8 mm and for the corrugated ones at about 5 mm.

In the present study, the piles had no end resistance. In reality, the end resistance will be mobilized proportionally to the pile settlement and settlement rate, as described in Ladanyi and Johnston (1974) and Ladanyi (1983).

Tapered piles

When a tapered pile, as in Fig. 5, is pushed into the soil, its shaft resistance originates from the mobilized adhe-

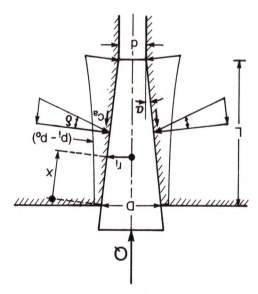

Fig. 5. Notation used in the theory of tapered piles.

sion and friction along the shaft-soil interface, similarly as in the case of a straight-shafted pile. The main aspect by which it differs from the latter is that the lateral normal stress is not only a function of the state of stress in the ground but it also depends on the pile displacement. This stress provides a resistance to pile penetration, even if the pile is perfectly smooth. As the pile settles, it enlarges the hole in the ground, which mobilizes the lateral earth pressure proportionally to the ratio of the lateral displacement over the initial hole radius. As this ratio, at any given pile settlement, increases with depth, the lateral soil reaction will follow the same trend, as observed also in unfrozen soils (Bakholdin and Igon'kin, 1978).

In the following, a solution of this problem is proposed, taking into account the particular creep properties of frozen soils. Using the notations of Fig. 5, the total load Q that can be applied to a tapered pile with no end-resistance can be expressed as

$$Q = 2\pi (I + II + III) \qquad (4)$$

where I is due to the adhesion, c_a:

$$I = \int_0^{L/\cos\alpha} c_a \cos\alpha \, r_i dx \qquad (5)$$

II is due to the friction resulting from the friction coefficient $\tan\delta$ and the natural total ground stress p_0, assumed to act normally to the shaft surface:

$$II = \int_0^{L/\cos\alpha} p_0 (\sin\alpha + \tan\delta \cos\alpha) r_i dx \qquad (6)$$

Considering that

$$r_i = D/2 - x \sin\alpha \qquad (7)$$

and assuming for the average values of p_0, c_a and δ to be constant along the shaft, these two integrals can be easily evaluated, to become

$$I = c_a L (D + d)/4 \qquad (8)$$

and

$$II = p_0(\tan\alpha + \tan\delta)(D + d)/4 \qquad (9)$$

The third integral has the form

$$III = \int_0^{L/\cos\alpha} (p_i - p_0)(\sin\alpha + \tan\delta \cos\alpha) r_i dx \qquad (10)$$

where $(p_i - p_0)$ is the net frozen ground reaction mobilized by the hole expansion.

As shown in some earlier papers, (Ladanyi and Johnston, 1973), Ladanyi, 1976), for a frozen soil obeying the creep law of Eq. (2), this reaction is related to the radial hole expansion u_i by

$$p_i - p_0 = C(u_i/r_i)^{1/n} \qquad (11)$$

where

$$C = \sigma_{c\theta}(n/\sqrt{3})\left[(2/\sqrt{3})(b/\dot{\varepsilon}_c)^b\right]^{1/n} t^{-b/n} \qquad (12)$$

Substituting Eq. (11) into Eq. (10) and taking into account that r_i is given by Eq. (7), while u_i is related to the pile settlement s by

$$u_i = s \tan\alpha \qquad (13)$$

Eq. (10) can be integrated to give:

$$III = C \frac{1 + \tan\delta/\tan\alpha}{2 - 1/n} \left(\frac{D}{2}\right)^2 \left(\frac{1 - d/D}{L}\right)^{1/n} \cdot$$
$$\cdot \left[1 - (d/D)^{2-1/n}\right] s^{1/n} \qquad (14)$$

Observing Eq. (12), it will be seen that the portion of the load Q due to hole extension

$$III \equiv \bar{Q} = \frac{Q}{2\pi} - (I + II) \qquad (15)$$

is proportional to $(s/t^b)^{1/n}$, or inversely, that the pile settlement s is proportional to $(\bar{Q}^n t^b)$. On the other hand, expressing from Eq. (14):

$$s = K \bar{Q}^n t^b \qquad (16)$$

where K contains all the other terms in Eqs. (12) and (14), one finds for the settlement rate

$$\dot{s} = ds/dt = b K \bar{Q}^n t^{b-1} \qquad (17)$$

from which the time can be eliminated to give

$$\bar{Q} = (\dot{s}/b)^{b/n} {}_s(1-b)/n {}_K^{-1/n} \qquad (18)$$

Eq. (18) shows that, for a constant settlement rate, the value of $\bar{Q}$ is proportional to the settlement s to the power of $(1-b)/n$.

It is interesting to note that, when the same considerations are made in connection with a tapered pile embedded in an elastic, laterally infinite, medium, Eq. (11) becomes

$$p_i - p_o = 2G u_i/r_i \qquad (19)$$

where $G = E/2(1+\nu)$ is the shear modulus of the medium. One gets then instead of Eq. (14)

$$III_{el} = \bar{Q}_{el} = G\frac{(D-d)^2}{2L}(1 + \frac{\tan\delta}{\tan\alpha})s_{el} \qquad (20)$$

from which the instanteneous settlement s_{el} of a tapered pile due to hole expansion can be evaluated.

Note that Eq. (4) with all the three sources of shaft resistance included, covers all the cases from a straight-shafted cylindrical pile to a conical pile with d = 0.

COMPARISON WITH OBSERVATIONS

When creep curves obtained from a set of step-loaded creep tests approximately linearize in a log time-log displacement plot, the preceding theoretical considerations show that their slope should give the value of the exponent b, while the value of the exponent n can be obtained from the displacement vs applied stress relationship at any given time, similarly as shown by Ladanyi and Johnston (1973) for pressuremeter creep tests. In addition, when a load-settlement curve at a constant penetration rate is plotted in a log-log plot, according to Eq. (18), its slope should give the value of the ratio $(1-b)/n$.

Using all these available sources of information, it was found that the results of the performed creep tests with corrugated piles (Fig. 2) could fairly well be approximated by Eq. (3), provided one takes: n = 1.6, b = 0.2 and $\sigma_{c\theta}$ = 3500 kPa at $\dot{\varepsilon}_c = 10^{-5}min^{-1}$. These low values of n and b are close to those found by others for dense frozen sand (Weaver and Morgenstern, 1981b), and they fall within the limits established by Ladanyi and Eckardt (1983) on the basis of pressuremeter tests performed in the same frozen sand. However, as in this study, they also found that the creep curves did not linearize in the log-log plot but had an attenuating character, with the value of the exponent b decreasing with time and increasing with the applied shear stress. Clearly, in such a situation the assumption of a time function of the form t^b with b = const. is not the most appropriate one and other alternative forms should be considered in future.

This remark is still more valid for the creep curves in Fig. 2 obtained from the tests with tapered piles. In that case, the curvature is continuous, and a time function of t^b type can give only a crude approximation of the results. Attention was therefore concentrated only on the last portion of the curves, where their slope is about b ≈ 0.2, and their distance corresponds to n ≈ 1.6. These values imply that in the rate-controlled tests the load-settlement curves plotted in a log-log plot should have the slope of $(1-b)/n$ = 0.500, which corresponds quite well with the experimental results.

However, in order to be able to use Eq. (14) for comparison, some additional information on adfreeze strength parameters c_a and $\tan\delta$ was needed. The information on the bond of frozen sand to the smooth aluminium surface was drawn from two sources (Guichaoua, 1984): First, from the results of loading tests on smooth piles, and second, from special torque tests performed with tapered piles. The maximum and residual bond strengths found from the former were, $c_{a,max}$ = 400-800 kPa and $c_{a,res}$ = 50 to 100 kPa, while, $c_{a,max}$ = 140 kPa and, $c_{a,res}$ = 30 - 50 kPa were found from the torque tests.

As for the friction coefficient $\tan\delta$ between the metal and the frozen sand, it is most likely that it was not much smaller than in an unfrozen sand of the same density. According to some published data (Yoshimi and Kishida, 1981), the friction coefficient for the sand against aluminium varies from about 0.26 to 0.50, depending on the roughness.

The values of the two bond parameters adopted in the calculation of the behaviour of tapered piles according to Eq. (14) were: c_a = 50 kPa and δ = 20° ($\tan\delta$ = 0.364). With these basic data on creep and strength parameters, Eq. (14) was used for approximating the last portions of the observed creep curves. This was found to be successful only if the value of $\sigma_{c\theta}$ = 13 MPa was adopted in the calculation. This value of $\sigma_{c\theta}$, back calculated from the test results, is much higher than expected, and it is also over 3 times higher than that back calculated from corrugated pile tests. Two possible explanations are offered for this high $\sigma_{c\theta}$ value: First, in a dense sand, the value of $\sigma_{c\theta}$ is higher, because it contains a frictional term (Ladanyi, 1972, Eq. 81), and second, a freezing prestress might have been created around the piles due to the confined freezing of slurry (Ladanyi, 1982). The two effects would affect particularly the tapered piles, which rely on the soil reaction generated by hole expansion.

CONCLUSIONS

This experimental study and theoretical considerations lead to the following conclusions concerning the behaviour of three different types of friction piles, installed in frozen sand in slurried holes.
(1) Smooth, straight-shafted piles fail in a brittle manner at low shear stress and low settlement. They loose nearly all of their strength after the peak.
(2) Corrugated piles fail in a semi-brittle manner, retaining about 50% of their peak strength at large displacements. At any given penetration rate, their peak strength is from 2 to 3.5 times higher than that of smooth piles. They are the most efficient of the three.
(3) Smooth-tapered piles behave in a hardening manner, gaining strength continuously with increasing displacement. However, for attaining the same strength as corrugated piles, they need 3 to 4 times larger displacements. They are the safest of the three.
(4) Theoretical predictions according to two different

theories appear promising but further work is needed for finding a more appropriate time function in the creep equation for frozen sand in this kind of loading.

ACKNOWLEDGEMENTS

This work was financially supported by the grant A-1801 of the Natural Sciences and Engineering Research Council of Canada.

REFERENCES

Andersland, O.B. and Alwahhab, M.R.M. (1982). Bond and slip of steel bars in frozen sand. Proc. 3rd Int. Symp. on Ground Freezing, Hanover, NH, pp. 27-34.

Bakholdin, B.V. and Igon'kin, J.T. (1978). Investigation of the bearing capacity of pyramidal piles. Transl. from Osnov., Fund. i Mekh. Gruntov, No. 3, 1978, Plenum Publ. Corp.

Black, W.T. and Thomas, H.P. (1978). Prototype pile tests in permafrost soils. In "Pipelines in adverse environments", ASCE, New York, pp. 372-383.

Crory, F.E. (1963). Pile foundations in permafrost. Proc. Int. Conf. on Permafrost, Lafayette, IN., U.S.N.A.S., Publ. 1287, pp. 467-476.

Guichaoua, A. (1984). Capacité portante des pieux tronconiques et crénélés. Mémoire M.Sc.A., Ecole Polytechnique, Univ. de Montréal, 111 p.

Johnston, G.H. and Ladanyi, B. (1972). Field tests of grouted rod anchors in permafrost. Canad. Geotech. J., 9, pp. 176-194.

Ladanyi, B. (1972). An engineering theory of creep of frozen soils. Canad. Geotech. J., 9, pp. 63-80.

Ladanyi, B. (1976). Bearing capacity of strip footings in frozen soils. Canad. Geotech. J., 13, pp. 95-110.

Ladanyi, B. (1982). Ground pressure development on artificially frozen soil cylinder in shaft sinking. In "Amici et Alumni", E.E. DeBeer Spec. Vol., Brussels, Belgium, pp. 187-194.

Ladanyi, B. (1983). Shallow foundations on frozen soil: Creep settlement. ASCE J. of Geotech. Engrg., 109, No. 11, pp. 1434-1448.

Ladanyi, B. and Eckardt, H. (1983). Dilatometer testing in thick cylinders of frozen sand. Proc. 4th Int. Permafrost Conf., Fairbanks, Alaska, Nat. Acad. Press, Washington, DC, I, pp. 677-682.

Ladanyi, B. and Johnston, G.H. (1973). Evaluation of insitu creep properties of frozen soils with the pressuremeter. Proc. 2nd Int. Permafrost Conf., Yakutsk, USSR, North Amer. Contrib. Vol., pp. 310-318.

Ladanyi, B. and Johnston, G.H. (1974). Behavior of circular footings and plate anchors embedded in permafrost. Canad. Geotech. J., 11, pp. 53-553.

Luscher, U., Black, W.T. and McPhail, J.F. (1983). Results of load tests on temperature-controlled piles in permafrost. Proc. 4th Int. Permafrost Conf. Fairbanks, Alaska, Nat. Acad. Press, Washington, DC, I, pp. 756-761.

Nordlund, R.L. (1963). Bearing capacity of piles in cohesionless soils. ASCE J. of Soil Mech. & Found. Div., 89, No. SM3, pp. 1-35.

Parameswaran, V.R. (1978). Adfreeze strength of frozen sand to model piles. Canad. Geotech. J., 15, pp. 494-500.

Parameswaran, V.R. (1979). Creep of model piles in frozen soils. Canad. Geotech. J., 16, pp. 69-77.

Thomas, H.P. and Luscher, U. (1980). Improvement of bearing capacity of pipe piles by corrugations. In "Building under Cold Climates and on Permafrost", Papers from the Joint US-USSR Seminar, Leningrad, 1979. CRREL Spec. Rep. 1980, pp. 229-234.

Weaver, J.S. and Morgenstern, N.R. (1981a). Simple shear creep tests on frozen soils. Canad. Geotech. J., 18, pp. 217-229.

Weaver, J.S. and Morgenstern, N.R. (1981b). Pile design in permafrost. Canad. Geotech. J., 18, pp. 357-370.

Yoshimi, Y. and Kishida, T. (1981). Friction between sand and metal surface. Proc. 10th I.C.S.M.F.E., Stockholm, Sweden, I, pp. 831-834.

The behaviour of a pile-raft foundation in weak rock

Le comportement d'un fondation sur pieux-radieur dans roche faible

C. F. LEUNG, Department of Civil Engineering, National University of Singapore, Singapore
R. RADHAKRISHNAN, Engineering Division, Port of Singapore Authority, Singapore

SUMMARY   This paper describes behaviour of a pile-raft foundation for a 42-story Office Complex constructed in weak rock. Observations from geotechnical instruments installed in the foundation system are presented for the initial stages of superstructure construction. At the end of monitoring period reported here, when seventeen of the forty-two floors had been completed, it appears that the piles had taken up approximately 60% of the structural load whereas the raft supported the remaining 40%. Settlement of raft was found to be negligible.

INTRODUCTION

The paper presents results obtained from field instrumentation of a pile-raft foundation. The foundation was constructed to support a 42-storey tower block of a modern office complex constructed by the Port of Singapore Authority. 203 large diameter bored cast in place piles were installed to support the 2m thick raft. Geotechnical instruments were installed in the foundation to monitor their performance throughout the construction period. The instruments included vibrating wire strain gauges, piezometers, settlemonitors and earth pressure cells. Details of the layout of instruments are shown in Fig 1.

SUBSURFACE CONDITION

The surface condition at the site of the tower block consisted of weathered sedimentary rock. In over 20 boreholes carried out at the project site, the Rock Quality Designation (RQD) values in the highly fractured and weathered siltstone formations were observed to vary from 10% to 50%. The siltstone formations were more fractured at shallower depths than at depths 10 to 15m below the base of the raft. The pile toes therefore may be assumed to rest on more intact rock.

In-situ Plate loading tests carried out on a 380mm diameter plate at about the raft base level gave settlements less than 10mm at a maximum load of 4 MN/m^2.

Pressuremeter tests in boreholes within the siltstone formations could be performed only upto a maximum pressure of 2.5 MN/m^2 due to limitations in available equipment. With the exception of one test, all the other tests (Total of 12 tests in 3 boreholes) had to be terminated before reaching the plastic phase. The pressuremeter modulus computed from the available test data are therefore approximate. The computed values of pressuremeter modulus varied from about 100 MN/m^2 at about the base of the raft to about 4000 MN/m^2 at a depth of 10m below the raft.

INSTRUMENTATION OBSERVATIONS

Construction of the superstructure is still in progress at the time of writing. Instrumentation readings observed for a period of over one year from the time of foundation construction in end 1982 till Dec 1983 are presented in this paper. Only selected instrument results are reported here.

25 bored piles were instrumented with vibrating wire strain gauges along their shafts. Three of these piles were load tested to twice the working load and were observed to satisfy the load-settlement criteria assumed in the foundation design.

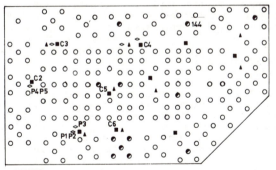

LEGEND
- ● INSTRUMENTED PILES
- ■ TOTAL PRESSURE CELL
- ◇ PIEZOMETER
- ▲ SETTLEMENT GAUGE

Fig. 1 Instrument layout plan

Fig 2 shows the load distribution and shaft resistance distribution of a typical instrumented pile (pile 144) at various stages of construction. Data obtained from pile load test during foundation construction are included for comparison.

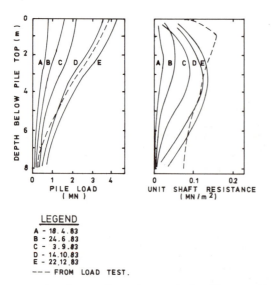

Fig. 2 Behaviour of Instrumented Pile No 144

At the raft-soil interface, 10 contact pressure cells were installed to monitor the load transferred from raft to soil. Typical raft contact pressures observed are presented in Fig 3. Irregularities in the readings between September and November 1982 are attributed to disturbances during concreting of the raft.

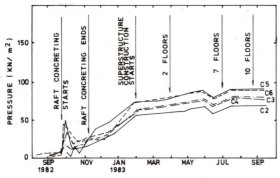

Fig. 3 Pressure Cell Measurements

Altogether nine settlemonitors were installed to monitor the settlement of the raft. Three settlemonitors were found to be malfunctioning after some time. Again large fluctuation in the settlement readings were observed during the raft concreting period after which the readings began to stabilize. It is noted

that the settlements so far have been very small. The maximum settlement recorded was 3.5mm. The maximum differential settlement recorded was also 3.5mm.

Piezometers were installed at 11 locations below the raft to monitor the variation of pore water pressure behaviour during the construction period. Typical variation of pore water pressures with time at different depths is illustrated in Fig 4.

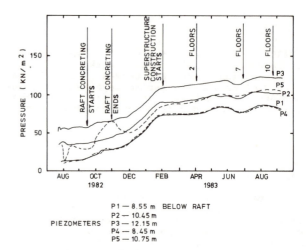

Fig. 4 Piezometer Measurements

ANALYSIS

Pile-Soil Interaction
The well established 'transfer function' approach (Vesic, 1970) was employed in the analysis of pile-soil interaction. The pile load distribution curves were generated from measured strain data using the least squares regression method suggested by O'Neill and Reese (1972). From Fig 2 it may be noted that the load transferred to the pile base was about 18% when the pile load was 4.2 MN. Load test carried out on the same pile soon after pile installation showed that only about 4% of the applied load was transferred to pile base under an applied load of 5 MN. Ladanyi (1977) suggested that such phenomena could be due to the creep of rock and concrete along the socket with time, thus increasing the pile toe loads gradually over a period of time.

Fig 2 also shows that a large proportion of shaft resistance was contributed by the siltstone around the mid-length of the pile. Again the pattern was markedly different from that observed from the earlier pile load test. In general, the pile under maintained load test showed a higher shaft resistance especially in the upper half of the pile compared with that under long term structural load. This could possibly be due to the presence of the raft inhibiting mobilization of shaft resistance near the pile top. Using three dimensional finite element analysis of vertically loaded pile groups in a homogeneous linearly elastic medium, Ottaviani (1975) has shown that the reduction in friction over the upper part of the shaft is associated with an increase in friction near the bottom of the shaft together with a substantial increase in pile toe loads.

Raft-soil Interaction

Because of the limited number of pressure cells employed in the instrumentation, certain assumptions had to be made to estimate the total load borne by the raft. It was assumed that raft pressure varied evenly and radially outwards from the point of highest pressure. Pressure contours were plotted by interpolating linearly the values of earth pressure from the known position of the earth pressure cells as shown in Fig 5. A simplification made was that the raft pressure distribution was unaffected by the presence of piles.

As expected, the raft pressure was highest at the centre of the raft during the period of observation. Area occupied by the pile was not considered in the computation of raft loads. Fig 6 shows the increase in pile and raft load during the period of observation reported herein. It is assumed that the piles only began to take up load in February 1983 when the construction of superstructure started. It is apparent that most of the building load was taken up by the raft during the initial period of construction. The total raft load was computed to be about 140MN in February 1983. Later on it increased to about 190MN in September 1983. The raft seems to have ceased to take up any additional load since then. Although only a relatively small amount of building load was taken up by the piles during the initial construction stage, it appears that the piles started to support more and more load at later stages of construction. At the end of the period of observation, it was noted that about 60% of the building load was carried by the piles and the balance load by the raft. The observation appears to be similar to that reported by Hooper (1979). It is felt that it is still too early to confirm that the foundation will continue to behave the same way.

Pore-water pressure

A rapid increase in pore-water pressure was observed (Fig 4) from Nov 1982 to Jan-Feb 1983 after which the rate of increase was slower with minor fluctuations. The initial rapid increase was perhaps due to the rise in the ground water level which had been lowered during the foundation construction.

CONCLUSIONS

Foundation instrumentation observations of a pile-raft system during the initial construction period of the superstructure has been described. Analysis of instrument observations during this period show the following:

1. The load transfer characterisitics of piles under long term structural load differed from those observed under

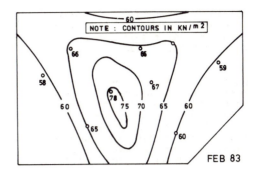

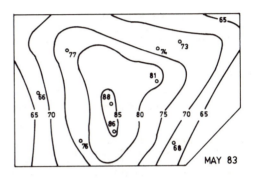

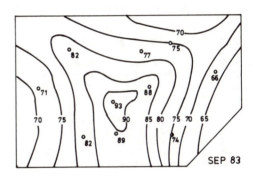

Fig 5   Raft Contact Pressures

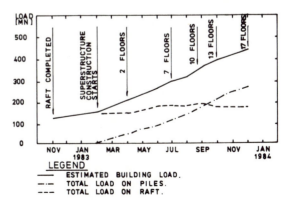

Fig 6   Estimated and Observed Loads

maintained load tests. Pile toe load observed during construction were found to be significantly higher than that obtained from earlier pile load tests.

2. During the early stages of construction, most of the structural load was taken up by the raft. As the construction of the superstructure progressed, the piles started to take up more load and at the end of the monitoring period reported here, it appears that the piles carried about 60% of the structural load.

ACKNOWLEDGEMENT

The authors wish to acknowledge the fruitful discussions they had with Mr B. Tijmann, Senior Design Engineer, Slope Indicator Co, USA.

REFERENCES

Hooper, J.A., (1979). Review of Behaviour of Piled raft Foundations, CIRIA Report 83.

Ladanyi, B. (1977). Friction and End Bearing Tests on Bed Rock for High Capacity Socket Design, Discussion, Canadian Geotechnical Journal, (14), 153 - 155.

O' Neill, M.W. and Reese, L.C. (1972). Behaviour of Bored Piles in Beaumant Clay. ASCE. J. Soil Mech. and Fdn. Div., 8741, Feb, 195 - 213.

Ottaviani, M. (1975). Three-dimensional Finite Element Analysis of Vertically Loaded Pile Groups. Geotechnique (25), 2, 159 - 174.

Vesic. A.S. (1970). Load Transfer in Piles Soil Systems. Proc. Conf. on Design and Installation of Piles Foundations and Cellular Structures, 47 - 74. Lehigh Univ., Pennsylvania.

Cap-pile-soil interaction of bored pile groups

L'interaction semelle-pieu-sol des pieux groupés

J. L. LIU, Senior Engineer, Institute of Soil and Foundation, China Academy of Building Research, Beijing, China
Z. L. YUAN, Assistant Engineer, Institute of Soil and Foundation, China Academy of Building Research, Beijing, China
K. P. ZHANG, Assistant Engineer, Institute of Soil and Foundation, China Academy of Building Research, Beijing, China

SYNOPSIS   This paper analysed some results of systematic field tests on bored pile group in the non-dense sandy soil and found that cap-pile-soil interaction, under certain conditions, effects "settlement-hardening" and "settlement-softening" in the side resistance of piles; the pile cap brings "weakening effect" to the side resistance and "strengthening effect" to the point resistance. No matter the pile spacing is large or small and the cap located is touched ground or separated from ground,"block failure" does not occur. On the base of these, a method, in which the cap-pile-soil interaction is considered, for calculating vertical ultimate bearing capacity of a pile group has been proposed.

INTRODUCTION

Concerning the behaviour and the bearing capacity of pile groups under vertical load, lots of model tests and theoretical studies have been done up to now, but the cap-pile-soil interaction of pile groups in different soils and its effects on the behaviour and the capacity are still a problem that is worth studying.

The systematic field tests on bored pile group have been carried out. The experimental site is located at the embankment of Yellow River near Jinan. The soil conditions in the depth of two times length of testing pile are the uniform silty sand with lightly cohesive. Its fraction are: $0.1\sim0.25mm$-$20\sim40\%$; $0.05\sim0.1mm$-$35\sim50\%$; $0.005\sim0.05mm$-$20\sim30\%$; $<0.005mm$-$2\sim8\%$; its void ratio $e=0.85\sim0.95$; its degree of saturation $Sr=40\sim50\%$; the water table is 8m below the ground level. This experiment on bored pile group included seven series: (1) various pile diameter ($d=125\sim330mm$); (2) various pile length ($L=8\sim23d$); (3) various pile spacing ($Sa=2\sim6d$); (4) various pile numbers ($n=2\sim16$) and various arrangements(square, rectangle and single range); (5) various positions of pile cap located (high-rise cap-separating from ground; low-set cap-touching ground); (6) long-term loading and (7) immersion tests. It contains 51 series of pile groups and 23 series of single pile and totally 330 piles were tested. The plan of tests is shown in Fig. 1. Vibrating wire pressure cells were installed for measuring the soil reaction beneath the cap and the pile bottom, reinforcement stress gauges for the load transfer along pile shaft, and deep settlement marks for the vertical displacement of soil of inside and outside of pile group.Loading was applied gradationally by hydraulic jacks. This paper only presents and analyses some results of this experiment.

THE EFFECT OF CAP-PILE-SOIL INTERACTION ON SIDE RESISTANCE AND POINT RESISTANCE

"Settlement-hardening" and "settlement-softening" of side resistance

The testing results for pile groups with different length and low-set cap as shown in Fig.2a indicate that the side resistance of the group varying with the settlement are obviously different from that of the single pile. The peak of the average side resistance of single pile is evident, and appears at rather small settlement. For pile groups if the pile length $L\geq1.5 Bc$ (Bc= width of cap), after the $\bar{f}s$ mobilizes to the value corresponding to that of single pile, still increases with the settlement. Such a phenomenon is called "settlement-hardening". If $L< Bc$ (as shown by the curve of $L=8d< Bc=9d$ in Fig. 2a), after $\bar{f}s$ reaching its peak value, then it decreases with settlement. Such a phenomenon is called "settlement-softening".

Test results indicate that the behaviour of "settlement-hardening" is closely relative to the pile spacing (Fig. 2b). Under a high-rise cap hardening is the most obvious when pile spacing equals to 3d. As the spacing increases to 6d the $\bar{f}s$-s curve tends to coincide that of single pile, i.e. no more "settlement-hardening" occurs.

"settlement-hardening" is the results caused by pile-soil interaction. If the pile spacing is proper, the soil among the piles is being sheared and compressed under the lateral confinement of piles and causes additional normal stress (represented by $\Delta\sigma'_h$) acting on the pile shaft, and then the side resistance increases with the settlement. The increment Δfs can be simply expressed as below:

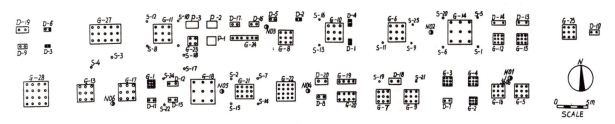

Fig. 1. Plan of tests

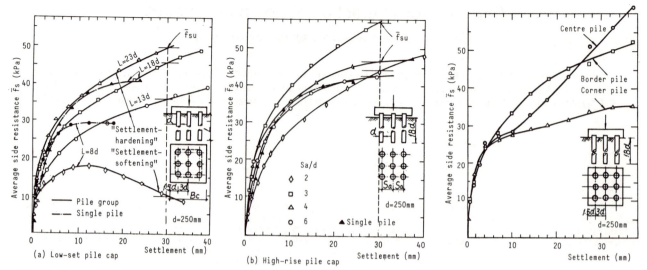

Fig.2 Average side resistance versus settlement of groups and single piles

Fig.3 Average side resistance versus settlement of piles in different locations

$$\Delta f_s = \Delta \sigma'_h \cdot tg \delta \qquad (1)$$

Where δ = angle of friction between soil and pile shaft. The results of analysis according to the principle of superposition in elasticity, the side resistance of centre pile is the smallest (1980, Poulos and Davis). However, the measured results as shown in Fig.3 indicates that the side resistance of centre pile is lower at initial, and then increases with the settlement and exceeds that of corner and border pile at last. This is the illustration that the different conditions of lateral deformation confined causes different influence to "settlement-hardening".

In the same soil, the "settlement-softening" of the side resistance for a pile group with too short length occurs. This seems because the compression zone formed by the soil reaction beneath the pile cap expands to the part below the pile bottom as load increasing. Thus, the pile length of a group should generally not be shorter than 1.5 times width of the cap.

"Weakening effect" on side resistance by pile cap

Results of tests indicate that the average ultimate side resistance of the group with low-set cap is obviously smaller than corresponding that of the high-rise cap as shown in Fig.4a. This explains that the cap causes "weakening effect" in the side resistance. This effect decreases as the ratio of L/B_c increases (Fig.4a). When $L/B_c \geq 1.5$, although the side resistance of the group is weakened by the pile cap, it is still larger than that of single pile because of "settlement-hardening" effect. When $L/B_c < 1$, the side resistance of the group is not only weakened by the cap, but "settlement-softening" effect also exists. Therefore $\bar{f}_{su}$ (The value corresponding the ultimate load not the peak value) drops down to about $1/3$ $\bar{f}_{su1}$ of single pile.

"Strengthening effect" on point resistance by pile cap

As shown in Fig.5, the ultimate point resistance $\bar{q}_{pu}$ of the group with low-set cap is obviously larger than that of the high-rise cap and single pile. It indicates that the cap causes "strengthening effect" on the point resistance. This effect decreases with the increasing of L/B_c (Fig.5a) and increases with the increasing of pile spacing (Fig.5b). Under too small spacing ($Sa \leq 2d$), no such effect is observed. Test results also indicate (Fig.5b) that the point resistance is the largest under

Fig. 4 Variation of average ultimate side resistance $\bar{f}_{su}$ of groups and single piles

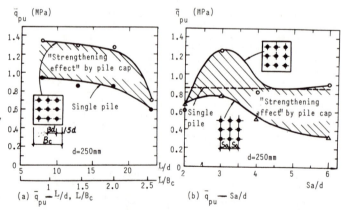

Fig. 5 Variation of average ultimate point resistance $\bar{q}_{pu}$ of groups and single piles

the spacing 3d; but on the contrary, the point resistance becomes less if the spacing is increased. These phenomena explain that the point resistance of the group is decreased due to stress overlapped by neighbor piles; on the other hand, it is increased due to the effect of resistance of opposite direction deformation from the soil below neighbor pile bottom. Under suitable pile spacing (e.g. Sa=3d), the effect of latter is larger than the former.

TYPE OF FAILURE AND CALCULATION OF ULTIMATE CAPACITY OF GROUP

The traditional view about the type of failure of group with small pile spacing is that piles and soil form a block as substantial foundation to bear and deform and fail so called "block failure". It is proved by following results of our test that such assumption cannot conform to the bored pile group in sandy soil.

Type of failure deduced by pile-soil deformation

There are following characteristics measured for vertical displacement of the soil among the piles as shown in Fig. 6. (i) Regardless of small or large pile spacing and the position of the cap, the relative displacements between pile and soil increase with the load inerease, and its distribution along the pile shaft is not uniform. The latter means not only shear deformation but also compression deformation both occur in the soil located among piles. (ii) The scope of a quarter of length of pile near its bottom in which the relative displacements are the largest for all along pile shaft, and thus form an "active zone" of pile-soil deformation. (iii) The soil of surrounding pile at the bottom level no swell is observed throughout but settle with load increase.

Above-mentioned characteristics of pile-soil deformation inside the group indicate: even to the group with small pile spacing, the relative displacement between piles and soil inside the group also occur and thus cause that the side resistance of each pile may be mobilized gradually with the settlement. Regardless of the pile spacing and the position of cap located, piles and soil don't act as a block, and the type of failure all belong to the "non-block failure".

Type of failure of group deduced by soil reaction beneath pile cap

Based on the "block failure" view which is without relative deformation between piles and soil inside the group (i.e. $\varepsilon_p = \varepsilon_s$), the average soil reaction beneath pile

cap of inside the group can be induced as follows:

$$\bar{\sigma}_c^{in} = \frac{P - P_c^{ex}}{n \cdot A_p \cdot \frac{E_p}{E_s} + A_c^{in}} \qquad (2)$$

where, P = applied load; P_c^{ex} = measured total soil reaction along external edge of cap; n = number of piles; A_p = cross area of single pile at top; E_p, E_s = modulus of pile and soil respectively; A_c^{in} = net area enclosed by piles beneath cap (see Fig.2). The assumption of "block failure" and measured value for two groups with n=3, Sa=2d, 3d are shown in Tab. 1.

Tab. 1.

pile spacing Sa	2d (Pu = 1982 kN)			3d (Pu = 2511 kN)		
load P (kN)	319	1560	2090	411	1952	2600
$\bar{\sigma}_c^{in}$ by Eq.(2)	0.21	1.08	1.45	0.35	1.48	1.96
(kPa) measured	6.67	28.6	35.7	2.35	19.8	39.1

Note: $E_p = 2.3 \times 10^7$ kPa; $E_s = 8.8 \times 10^3$ kPa.

Tab. 1. indicates that the measured soil reaction beneath cap are 8~20 times greater than calculated one based on "block failure". These explain that the piles and soil inside the group do not form a unit to work from begining to end and neither have "block failure".

Calculation on ultimate capacity of group

Since "block failure" does not occur to the bored pile group in sandy soil, then it is obviously unreasonable to calculate the ultimate bearing capacity by the method of traditional "equivanlent pier" model. Comparison between the calculated value and measured value is made for 33 series pile group. It is found that the calculated side resistance is less 20~60% than measured, and the calculated point resistance is greater several or several ten times than measured. Therefore, it is proposed that the "non-block failure" calculating model, which the cap-pile-soil interaction is considered, for bored pile group with large or small pile spacing and high-rise or low-set pile cap in sandy soil. The side resistance efficiency η_s and point resistance efficiency η_p of a group are introduced

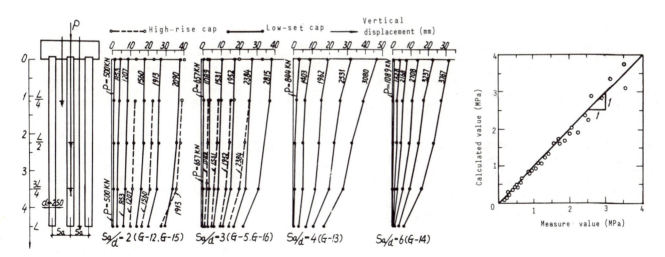

Fig. 6. Vertical displacement of interval soil in the group with different pile spacing

Fig. 7. Comparision between calculated and measured ultimate capacity of group

as follows:

$$\eta_s = \frac{\text{Average ultimate side resistance of pile group } \bar{f}_{su}}{\text{Average ultimate side resistance of single pile } \bar{f}_{su1}} \quad (3)$$

$$\eta_p = \frac{\text{Average ultimate point resistance of pile group } \bar{q}_{pu}}{\text{Average ultimate point resistance of single pile } \bar{q}_{pu1}} \quad (4)$$

From the results of above analysis on the cap-pile-soil interaction, η_s and η_p may be expressed as follows:

$$\eta_s = Gs \cdot Cs \quad (5)$$

$$\eta_p = Gp \cdot Cp \quad (6)$$

Where, Gs,Gp = coefficient considering effect of pile-soil interaction on side resistance and on point resistance respectively; Cs, Cp = coefficient considering effect of cap-pile-soil interaction on side resistance and on point resistance respectively(for high-rise cap, Cs=Cp=1,) as follows:

$$Gs = \frac{\alpha}{L_n(e + 1 - \frac{r+m}{2m})} \quad (7)$$

$$Gp = \frac{8}{(\frac{Sa}{d} - 3)^2 + 9} \quad (8)$$

$$Cs = 1 + 0.1\frac{Sa}{d} - 0.9\frac{Bc}{L} \quad (9)$$

$$Cp = 1 + 0.2\frac{Sa}{d} \cdot \frac{Bc}{L} \quad (10)$$

Where, e = base of nutural logarithm; r,m = number of ranges and number of piles in each range respectively; and r≤m;
$Bc = \sqrt{\text{length of cap } a \times \text{width of cap } b}$, when a/b≥9, take Bc=3d; if calculated Cs over 1, then take 1 for it;
α = dimensionless coefficient as follows:

Sa/d	2	3	4	5	6
α	1.1	1.3	1.2	1.1	1.0

The expression of calculating ultimate bearing capacity of the pile group as follows:

$$Pu = Psu + Ppu + Pc$$
$$= \eta_s \cdot n \cdot Qsu1 + \eta_p \cdot n \cdot Qpu1 + Pc \quad (11)$$

Where, Psu, Ppu, Pc = total side resistance, total point resistance and total cap's soil reaction of pile group respectively; Pc may be calculated by experimental method (1984, Liu, Jin-Li, ect); for high-rise cap, Pc=0; Qsu1, Qpu1 = total side resistance and total point resistance of single pile respectively; $Qsu1 = \pi \cdot d \cdot L \cdot \bar{f}_{su1}$; $Qpu = \frac{\pi}{4} d^2 \cdot \bar{q}_{pu1}$; n = number of piles in a group.

Comparison of calculated and measured value

Comparison between the calculated [by Eq.(5) and (6)] and measured value of side resistance efficiency and point resistance efficiency is shown in Tab.2., and the comparison of the calculated [by Eq.(11)] and measured ultimate bearing capacity of the pile group is also made and shown in Fig. 7. Both of them indecate that two sides are closer.

CONCLUSION

For the bored pile groups with proper pile spacing in non-dense sandy soil, due to pile-soil interaction the

Tab. 2

No.	L/d	Sa/d	n	η_s Measured	η_s Calculated	η_p Measured	η_p Calculated	η_G Measured
G-5	18	3	3x3	1.16	1.06	1.49	1.17	1.51
G-6	18	3	3x3	/	/	/	/	1.33
G-7	8	3	3x3	0.36	0.36	1.44	1.51	1.64
G-8	13	3	3x3	1.09	0.86	1.51	1.27	1.69
G-9	23	3	3x3	1.16	1.19	1.12	1.11	1.15
G-11	14	3	3x3	/	/	/	/	1.25
G-12	18	2	3x3	0.98	0.94	0.70	0.93	1.21
G-13	18	4	3x3	1.11	1.02	0.93	1.19	1.46
G-14	18	6	3x3	0.82	0.85	1.06	0.88	2.23
G-15	18	2	3x3	1.13	1.10	0.81	0.80	1.05
G-16	18	3	3x3	1.42	1.30	0.91	0.89	1.36
G-17	18	4	3x3	1.16	1.20	0.60	0.80	1.03
G-18	18	6	3x3	1.06	1.0	0.37	0.44	0.88
G-19	18	3	1x4	1.11	1.15	1.19	1.08	1.49
G-20	18	3	2x4	0.88	1.04	1.51	1.15	1.40
G-21	18	3	3x4	0.85	0.97	0.77	1.21	
G-22	18	3	4x4	1.03	0.91	1.45	1.42	1.19
G-23	18	3	2x2	1.20	1.30	1.22	1.08	1.60
G-24	18	3	1x6	1.11	1.06	0.92	1.12	1.41

Note: (i) Pile diameter of No. G-6, G-11 are 330mm and the rest are 250mm.
(ii) Pile cap located for No. G-15 G-18 are high-rise and the rest are low-set.
(iii) Pile group efficiency η_G includes action of pile cap for low-set cap.

"settlement-hardening" occur to the side resistance and then it exceeds that of the single pile. This is the essential reason which leads the group effeciency over 1. But when the pile length is too short (near or smaller than the width of cap) and the cap is touched ground, due to cap-pile-soil interaction, the "settlement-softening" may occur to the side resistance. The "weakening effect" on the side resistance and the "strengthening effect" on the point resistance are acted by the pile cap Linear-elastic stress superposition analysis seems not applicable to groups in sandy soil, and "block failure" does not occur regardless of large or small pile spacing and high-rise or low-set pile cap. The "equivalent pier" model adopted for calculating ultimate bearing capacity of the group lead to a large deviation from the practice. According to the method of the "non-black failure" model proposed in this paper, the calculation which takes cap-pile-soil interaction into consideration is in accordance with practice.

ACKNOWLEDGEMENT: The test data described here were some results of the systematic field tests on bored pile group performed by joint effort of Shandong Bureau of Irrigation Committee of Yellow River and Institute of Soil and Foundation of China Academy of Building Research. The authors wish to express their hearty thanks to the joint experimental unit and to the whole members who took part in tests.

REFFRENCE

Poulos, G.H., Davis, E.H. (1980): Pile Foundation Analysis and Design; P.109-142. New York.
Liu, Jin-li; Yuan, Zhen-long and Zhang, Kuo-ping (1984): Distribution of Pile Cap's Reaction; Research Report on Bored Pile Group, ; Report of Building Research; China Academy of Building Research, Beijing.

In situ cast piles: Shape as a result of soil reaction

Pieux moulés dans le sol: Influence de la réaction du sol sur la forme

H. J. LUGER, Research Engineer, Delft Soil Mechanics Laboratory, Delft, Netherlands

SYNOPSIS   Two groups of in-situ cast piles are considered: The soil-displacing and the soil-removing group. Assuming a Mohr-Coulomb type of elasto-plastic soil behaviour analytical formulae are presented which describe the interaction between the soil and the pile during construction. These formulae can be used to prescribe grout pressures and predict resulting pile diameters. Actual measurements and predictions which compare reasonably well are presented for soil-displacing piles.

INTRODUCTION

In the application of in-situ cast concrete piles sometimes problems may arise with respect to the resulting pile diameter. If this diameter turns out too big because the grout pushes aside the soil an unacceptable overconsumption of grout may be the consequence. In other cases the soil rebound may cause such a reduction of the pile diameter that the pile with the used concrete quality must be considered unfit to carry the design load.
It will be self-evident that, apart from the actual soil parameters, the loading history of the soil around the pile is also very important: Depending on the construction method, soil-displacing or soil-removing, the radial stresses around the pile will be higher or lower.

In the following paper it will be pointed out how one may arrive at a quantitative prediction of the diameter of some types of in-situ cast piles. To that end the cavity-expansion theory is used. This theory considers a medium with an internal void, and describes the interaction between pressurechanges in the void and the deformations of the medium. For an easy application of this theory some assumptions are made.
One of these is the assumption that all displacements in the soil are perpendicular to the (vertical) pile-axis and that a cylindrical symmetry may be assumed. This type of problem is a classic one in mechanics, with solutions for an elastic medium already presented by Lamé (1852). Later the theory was applied to the pressuremeter by Ménard (1957) and when this instrument became more popular the amount of publications grew steadily. Baguelin, Jézéquel and Shields (1978) give a state of the art review and references for further study.

Due to the assumption of displacements perpendicular to the pile-axis bored and screwed piles seem more appropiate to consider than driven piles. After all, in case of bored and screwed piles a mainly horizontal-radial displacement field is expected in the soil, whereas driving will cause more vertical displacements.

Since most problems with respect to in-situ cast piles which came to our attention concerned piles in soft or medium soft clays we will restrict ourselves to this type of material. Very frequently the piles carry their loads through layers of clay to the bearing stratum, and the restriction to clay means no drastic reduction of the applicability of the following analysis.

In addition we will only consider undrained loading conditions. It is assumed that during the relatively short fabrication process no volumechanges of the soil take place and that the transition from elastic to plastic deformation is governed by one parameter only, the undrained cohesion c_u.

THE SOIL-DISPLACING PILE

Here we consider a type of pile where the cavity for the pile is formed by means of a tube with a disengagable conical screw-head at the end. When the point reaches the desired depth the tube is filled with grout. Thereupon the tube is pulled out, leaving the screw-head and the grout in the soil.

The soil is characterized by its undrained shear strength c_u, its elastic shear-modulus G, and σ_h, the initial horizontal soil stress. The creation of a cylindrical hole in the soil, which must act as a mould for the yet plastic concrete, is finished at time $t=t_1$.
The radius r of the hole is then equal to r_1.
A zone where the soil is in yielding state and deforms plastic is formed around the hole. Because the cavity expanded from zero radius to radius r_1 the strain is infinite. Therefore the radial stress (or pressure) p_1 on the cavity-wall will be equal to the so-called "limit-pressure" for infinite expansion. This limit pressure is the highest pressure in a cylindrical cavity in the soil which can be supported by that soil. For an elasto-plastic cohesive material this limit pressure is (Bishop, Hill and Mott, 1945):

$$p_1 = p_\ell = \sigma_h + c_u \cdot (1 + \ln(\frac{G}{c_u})) \qquad (1)$$

When the tube is pulled out the grout pressure will act on the cavity wall. This pressure will almost always be lower than the limit pressure. If the grout pressure is higher than the limit pressure the cavity will continue to expand until the grout pressure decreases or until adjacent stronger strata take part of the load.
One would sooner expect that the grout pressure is too low, either permanently or temporarily. Its result can be a pile diameter which is too small.

If the pressure p in the cavity is lowered after time t_1 the cavity radius r will decrease due to elastic rebound of the surrounding soil. For time $t_1 < t < t_2$ the following relation between the pressure p in the hole and the radius r of the hole is found:

$$p = \sigma_h + c_u \cdot (1 + \ln(\frac{G}{c_u} \cdot \frac{r_1^2}{r^2})) + G \cdot (1 - \frac{r_1^2}{r^2}) \qquad (2)$$

At time $t = t_2$, when the pressure p equals p_2 a plastic zone will start to develop around the cavity, much like the plastic zone which was created during the expansion of the cavity. This pressure p_2 is given by:

$$p_2 = \sigma_h + c_u \cdot (-1 + \ln(\frac{G}{c_u} + 2)) \qquad (3)$$

Since in most cases the shear-modulus G is much higher than the undrained cohesion c_u one finds that p_2 is approximated by:

$$p_2 \cong p_\ell - 2c_u = p_1 - 2c_u \qquad (4)$$

At time $t = t_2$ the radius r_2 of the hole will be:

$$r_2 = r_1 \cdot (1 + \frac{2c_u}{G})^{-\frac{1}{2}} \qquad (5)$$

After time $t = t_2$, when the pressure is decreasing below p_2 and the radius of the hole decreases below r_2 we find for the relation between radius r and pressure p:

$$p = \sigma_h + c_u \cdot (-1 + \ln(\frac{4c_u}{G} \cdot \frac{r_1^2 \cdot r^2}{(r_1^2 - r^2)^2})) \qquad (6)$$

If, for whatever reason, the grout pressure in the hole falls even temporarily too far, this can have serious consequences for the resulting pile diameter. The reason for this lies in the fact that when the pressure in the hole increases again the soil deforms elastic at first and behaves rather stiff. If the minimum pressure at time $t = t_3$ equals p_3 one finds the corresponding radius r_3 using eq.(6). When the pressure increases again the relation between radius and pressure is given by:

$$p = \sigma_h - c_u + c_u \cdot \ln(\frac{4c_u}{G} \cdot \frac{r_1^2 \cdot r^2}{(r_1^2 - r_3^2)^2}) + G \cdot (1 - \frac{r_3^2}{r^2}) \qquad \ldots (7)$$

This expression is valid until p reaches the value p_4 and a new plastic zone around the hole starts forming. This transition pressure p_4 follows from:

$$p_4 = \sigma_h + c_u + c_u \cdot \ln(\frac{4 \cdot c_u}{G - 2c_u} \cdot \frac{r_1^2 \cdot r_3^2}{(r_1^2 - r_3^2)^2}) \qquad (8)$$

And is approximately:

$$p_4 \cong p_3 + 2 \cdot c_u \qquad (9)$$

If the pressure continues to increase beyond p_4, the relation between radius r and pressure p for $r < r_1$ and $p < p_\ell = p_1$ can be written as:

$$p = \sigma_h + c_u + c_u \cdot \ln(\frac{G}{c_u} \cdot \frac{r_1^2 \cdot (r^2 - r_3^2)^2}{r^2 \cdot (r_1^2 - r_3^2)^2}) \qquad (10)$$

SOIL-REMOVING PILES

We refer to piles which are cast in-situ in a cavity which is formed by (partly) removing the soil.
This is often done by means of a machine-driven auger. Ideally this auger is screwed down to the desired depth without removing much soil. However, in most cases the actual rate of descent of the auger is less than the product of its pitch and rotation velocity, and soil will be removed accordingly.

Here the volume V_e of the auger itself per unit of its length is equal to $\pi \cdot r_e^2$. Therefore r_e might be called the equivalent auger radius. The maximum radius of the auger is r_m, which is also the radius of the hole formed when pulling the auger from a not rebounding soil.
A volume of soil, V_r, is removed per unit length of the hole during the descent of the auger. We define r_r by:

$$r_r = (V_r / \pi)^{\frac{1}{2}} \qquad (11)$$

It is assumed that enough soil is removed to let:

$$r_r^2 > \frac{c_u}{G} \cdot r_m^2 + r_e^2 \qquad (12)$$

This will almost always be true. The radial soil stress at r_m, the initial concrete-soil interface, is:

$$\sigma_r(r_m) = \sigma_h - c_u + c_u \cdot \ln(\frac{c_u}{G} \cdot \frac{r_m^2}{r_r^2 - r_e^2}) \qquad (13)$$

The level of the grout pressure may vary. It largely depends on the way the grout is inserted in the hole. This can be done through the hollow axis of the auger, while grout pressure is maintained during the upward movement of the auger. It is also possible to fill the hole with bentonite slurry during the extraction of the auger. Concrete is then injected at the bottom of the hole, expelling the slurry from the hole.
If the (grout or bentonite) pressure is lower than $\sigma_r(r_m)$ as given by equation (13), the cavity radius r will decrease according to:

$$p = \sigma_h - c_u + c_u \cdot \ln(\frac{c_u}{G} \cdot \frac{r^2}{(r_r^2 - r_e^2 + r_m^2 - r^2)}) \qquad (14)$$

Say the minimum pressure is p_1 at time $t = t_1$ and that for $t > t_1$ the pressure rises again, for instance when the bentonite slurry is replaced by the concrete. In that case the cavity expands, at first completely elastic as given by:

$$p = \sigma_h - c_u + c_u \cdot \ln(\frac{c_u}{G} \cdot \frac{r^2}{(r_r^2 - r_e^2 + r_m^2 - r^2)}) + G \cdot (1 - \frac{r_1^2}{r^2}) \qquad \ldots (15)$$

A plastic zone starts developing at $t = t_2$, when $p = p_2$:

$$p_2 = \sigma_h + c_u + c_u \cdot \ln\left(\frac{c_u}{G - 2c_u} \cdot \frac{r_1^2}{r_r^2 - r_e^2 + r_m^2 - r_1^2}\right) \quad (16)$$

Then for time $t > t_2$ the relation between pressure and radius is given by:

$$p = \sigma_h + c_u + c_u \cdot \ln\left(\frac{G}{4c_u} \cdot \frac{(r^2 - r_1^2)^2}{(r_r^2 - r_e^2 + r_m^2 - r_1^2) \cdot r^2}\right) \quad (17)$$

At time $t = t_3$ the plastic zone reaches the material which remained elastic during the previous unloading process. Pressure p_3 is given by:

$$p_3 = \sigma_h + c_u + c_u \cdot \ln\left(\frac{G}{c_u} \cdot \frac{2(r_r^2 - r_e^2 + r_m^2) - r_1^2}{(r_r^2 - r_e^2 + r_m^2) - r_1^2}\right) \quad (18)$$

For pressures higher than p_3 the relation between radius and pressure becomes:

$$p = \sigma_h + c_u + c_u \cdot \ln\left(\frac{G}{c_u} \cdot \frac{(r_e^2 - r_r^2 + r^2 - r_m^2)}{r^2}\right) \quad (19)$$

From equation (13) until now a sequence was followed which started with a bentonite or grout pressure lower than σ_r at r_m as given by eq. (13). However, if p is larger than that value, the hole starts expanding elastic according to:

$$p = \sigma_h - c_u + c_u \cdot \ln\left(\frac{c_u}{G} \cdot \frac{r^2}{r_r^2 - r_e^2}\right) + G \cdot \left(1 - \frac{r_m^2}{r^2}\right) \quad (20)$$

Because the process described now differs from the one described by eqs. (14)-(19) we start a new time sequence, beginning with t_1, when a plastic zone starts developing around the pile. The pressure is then:

$$p_1 = \sigma_h + c_u + c_u \cdot \ln\left(\frac{c_u}{G - 2c_u} \cdot \frac{r_m^2}{r_r^2 - r_e^2}\right) \quad (21)$$

For time $t > t_1$ the relation between p and r is:

$$p = \sigma_h + c_u + c_u \cdot \ln\left(\frac{G}{4c_u} \cdot \frac{(r^2 - r_m^2)^2}{(r_r^2 - r_e^2) \cdot r^2}\right) \quad (22)$$

Then, if p is equal to p_2 defined by:

$$p_2 = \sigma_h + c_u + c_u \cdot \ln\left(\frac{G}{c_u} \cdot \frac{r_r^2 - r_e^2}{2 \cdot (r_r^2 - r_e^2) + r_m^2}\right) \quad (23)$$

the plastic zone extends exactly as far as it did during the creation of the hole. (During the unloading phase). For time $t > t_2$, when p increases beyond p_2, the relation between pressure and pile radius is given by:

$$p = \sigma_h + c_u + c_u \cdot \ln\left(\frac{G}{c_u} \cdot \frac{(r_e^2 - r_r^2 + r^2 - r_m^2)}{r^2}\right) \quad (24)$$

Equation (24) is equal to equation (19), as it should be. It can easily be verified that for r approaching infinity the pressure approaches to p_ℓ, the limit pressure as is given by equation (1).

EXAMPLE OF CALCULATIONS

Consider a soil with undrained shear strength $c_u = 25$ kPa, shear-modulus G = 5000 kPa at a depth of ten metres where the initial horizontal soil stress $\sigma_h = 150$ kPa.

At that depth we may expect a hydrostatic grout pressure p = 200 kPa.
Using equation (1) we find for the limit pressure:

$$p_\ell = 307.5 \text{ kPa}$$

Installation of two different pile types can be analysed as follows:

A soil-displacing pile with tube radius $r_1 = 0.4$ m.
Using eq. (3) we find the grout pressure below which a plastic zone starts forming:

$$p_2 = 257.7 \text{ kPa} \cong p_\ell - 2c_u = 257.5 \text{ kPa}$$

With equation (6) we solve r = 0.3937 m for p = 200 kPa. The pile radius decreased only 1.6 %.
If, due to a procedure error, the grout pressure is only 50 kPa at first, to be increased to 200 kPa later on, we find r = 0.2928 m when p = 50 kPa. (Eq. (6)).
Because p = 200 kPa > 50 kPa + $2 \cdot c_u \cong p_4$ (equation (9)) equation (10) must be applied to find r = 0.3011 m for p = 200 kPa.
The procedure error caused a radius decrease of 24.7 % !

A soil-removing pile made with an auger with an outer radius $r_m = 0.4$ m. If the auger-volume $V_e = 0.0154$ m^3/m, then the equivalent auger radius $r_e = 0.07$ m.
Suppose we remove a soil volume $V_r = 0.3884$ m^3/m, then $r_r = 0.3516$ m.
Using eq. (13) one finds a radial stress $\sigma_r(r_m)$ of 5.6 kPa
Therefore the soil is almost completely unloaded.
In order to find out which equation must be applied to find the radius of the pile we first evaluate equation (21), which gives:

$$p_1 = 50.25 \text{ kPa}$$

and equation (23) which gives:

$$p_2 = 277.25 \text{ kPa}$$

Because the expected pressure p = 200 kPa lies between p_1 and p_2 equation (22) must be solved to find r = 0.4422 m when p = 200 kPa. This radius is 10.6 % larger than the maximum auger radius r_m.

If for some reason the grout pressure rises to 250 kPa the radius r increases to r = 0.5238 m. (eq. (22)). Even when the pressure decreases again to p = 200 kPa the rebound is mainly elastic and r will be about 0.5212 m. (using equation (5)). The resulting pile radius is now even 30.3 % larger than r_m!

PRACTICAL APPLICATION

In the summer of 1983 the Delft Soil Mechanics Laboratory had the opportunity to do some pressuremetertests and field vane tests close to a site where diameter-reductions of soil-displacing piles were experienced. Also some undisturbed samples were obtained and tested in the laboratory. Two piles had been made with different grout levels in the tube during the pulling of the tube. After completion these piles had been partly excavated to measure their diameters. The reported values are listed in table I.

- TABLE I -

Pile	:	A	B
Groutlevel (depth in metres below ground level)	:	0.00	2.50
Diameter (in metres) - from 2.5 to 3.5 m depth	:	0.47	0.34
at 3.8 m depth	:	0.47	0.38
at 4.5 m depth	:	0.47	0.41

The pressuremetertests where used to determine c_u and G. Assuming that K_o equals $(1 - \sin\phi')$ and using the laboratory tests on the undisturbed samples to determine the angle of internal friction ϕ' the initial horizontal soil stress was estimated with:

$$\sigma_h = (1 - \sin\phi').\sigma_v' + u \qquad (25)$$

Here u represents the estimated hydrostatic porewater-pressure at the considered depth. The specific mass of the fluid grout was approximately 1900 kg/m^3. The outer (maximum) radius of the tube r_1 was 0.235 m.

At two levels, where pressuremeter data were available, a prediction for the diameter could be calculated. The results are listed in table II.

- TABLE II -

depth (m)	c_u (kPa)	G (kPa)	σ_h (kPa)	pile A p (kPa)	2.r (m)	pile B p (kPa)	2.r (m)
3.3	40	471	50	62.7	0.404	15.2	0.359
4.3	31	444	60	81.7	0.420	34.2	0.370

The predictions for pile B compare very well with the reported values. For pile A no diameter reduction was reported, whereas a reduction of nearly 14 % was predicted. Lacking control over the accuracy of the maintained groutpressures and the diameter-measurements, as well as the assumptions and simplifications in the theory which may cause deviations from reality make it impossible to provide an exact verification.

CONCLUSIONS

A theory is presented which describes diameter changes of cylindrical cavities, especially for cases where the loading path is reversed. The theory can be applied to in situ cast piles if one is aware of some restrictions:
- A simple constitutive model is used. (No influence of remoulding, no softening)
- Undrained loading with absence of volumechanges is assumed.

Despite these restrictions the theory describes some of the phenomena around in-situ cast piles quite well and is certainly able to indicate the large influence of some-times small procedure errors on the resulting pile. A first comparison between measured and predicted values was promising.

LITERATURE

Baguelin, F., Jézéquel, J.F., Shields, D.H. (1978). The pressuremeter and foundation engineering, 1st ed., 617 pp., Trans Tech Publications, Clausthal, Germany.

Bishop, R.F., Hill, R., Mott, N.F. (1945). The theory of indentation and hardness tests, Proc.Phys.Soc.London, Vol. 57, No. 321, Part 3, p 147 - 159.

Lamé, G. (1852). Leçons sur la théorie mathématique d'élasticité des corps solides, Bachelier, Paris.

Ménard, L. (1957). Mesure in situ des propriétés physiques des sols. Annales des Ponts et Chaussées, Paris, Vol 14 p 357 - 377.

Setting sheet piles with driving aids

Forcer par battage des palplanches par des moyens d'auxiliaire

B. K. MAYER, Bundesanstalt für Wasserbau, Karlsruhe, FRG
B. KREUTZ, Bundesanstalt für Wasserbau, Karlsruhe, FRG
H. SCHULZ, Bundesanstalt für Wasserbau, Karlsruhe, FRG

SYNOPSIS   In connnection with the widening of the Mittelland Canal in the FRG for 1350-to-ships sheet pile walls must be built to protect the embankments at several sections. In some of these sections the ground is not or near- ly not drivable, so some kinds of driving aid have to be used. On different sites, different kinds of driving aids were tested and employed, e.g. high pressure water injections, predrilling of holes, and blasting with the newly developed RSB-method.

For driving sheet piles in slopes of overconsolidated clays, which have a rather low factor of safety, the diesel hammer with the aid of jetting water showed to be suitable. The basic soil mechanic properties should not be changed unfavorably by the injections. In rock-like soils or in rock the RSB-method proved to be adequate. The effect of this method was examined optically by test pits and by large-scale ultrasonic measurements, with the pulse tramsmission method. The examination served to find out the width of the shattered zone made drivable by blasting. The examinations showed that in most cases it is possible to produce a slot of 0,4 m to 0,8 m width of loosened material, suitable for driving. Outside of this slot the ground remained in its original conditions.

INTRODUCTION

To win the necessary width for navigation of 1350-to ships the Mittelland Canal has to be lined by steel sheet pile walls along several distances. A view of the lining can be seen on fig. 1. In many sections the ground con- sists of soils, which are nearly not drivable or it consists of overconsolidated clays, in which sheet pile walls can only be driven with some driving aid.

From the known driving aids

- soft drilling, loosening blasting, jetting water and jet cutting as well as blasting with the RSB-method

jetting water and RSB-method were used at some sites. The paper describes some experiences and gives some results of measurements.

Fig. 1: View on Mittelland Canal

SITE 1

Beneath a top layer of 1.0 to 1.5 m thickness the ground at this site consists of a highly overconsolidated clay with a distinct jointing. In the clay potato stones of different sizes are embedded. The properties of the soil are given by the following values:

$$\gamma_s = 27,3 \text{ kN/m}^3 \qquad \gamma = 20 \text{ kN/m}^3$$

$$e = 0,55 - 0,65 \qquad w = 19 - 22 \text{ \%}$$
$$I_c = 0,86 - 1,03 \qquad E_s = 19 - 32 \text{ MN/m}^2$$
$$\varphi' = 20^o \qquad c' = 5 \text{ kPa}$$

Fig. 2: View at site 1, test driving

The existing embankment, fig. 2, is, according to slip circle analysis, near limit equilibrium, so vibrations during earth works had to be limited to a minimum and soil properties must not be changed unfavourably. Therefore a test driving was necessary to find the best method for execution.

Results of test drivings:

1. driving without aid:

driving plant:	diesel hammer D 30 - 02
sheet piles:	Larssen 25, St SPS, length 16,5 m
results:	from a depth of 4 m: blows per 100 mm 55 to 140, total number of blows Q = 2844 to 4482

2. soft drilling and driving: (in this case bore holes were pre-drilled and filled with sand)

   driving plant: diesel hammer D 30 - 02

sheet piles: Larssen 25, St SPS, length 16,5 m
results: until a depth of 5 m easier than with
method 1, total number of blows
Q = 787 to 2239

3. driving with jetting water:

driving plant: diesel hammer D 30 -02
sheet piles: Larssen 25, St SPS, length 16,5 m
driving of pairs and triple piles
results: 44 blows per 100 mm as a maximum,
total number of blows Q = 508 to 687

4. vibrating with jetting water:

driving plant: vibrator MS-504
sheet piles: Larssen 25, St SPS, length 16,5 m
results: with 5 jets penetration time 600 sec
(average value), with 2 jets penetration time 1309 sec (average value)

Fig. 4: Sheet with lance and jets for jetting water

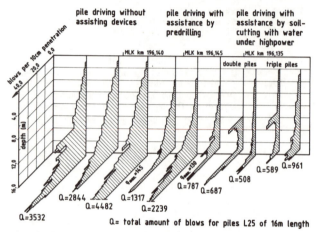

Fig. 3: Records of test drivings, blows per 100 mm

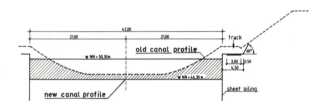

Fig. 5: Cross section at site 2

The jetting water was conducted with 2 to 5 lances, which were tacked at the piles and had jets with a diameter of 0,3 mm. The water pressure was chosen 500 bar, no additives were used. The output of the high-pressure pump was 60 l/min. Because of the disadvantageous vibrating-effect onto the safety of the cutting slope this method had to be given up.

Method 3 was executed, but with only 2 jets on each pair of sheet piles.

Examinations of samples from core drillings after use of jetting water showed with normal soilmechanical testing no negative effects on the strength of the ground. Therefore it can be assumed, that water only flows along bedding planes, joints and fissures and does not penetrate very deep into the rock fragments or will be expelled again by consolidation.

SITE 2

At this site, located from km 120,3 to km 121,5, at both banks steel sheet pile walls had to be driven and afterwards the canal was excavated by dredging as shown in fig. 5.

The ground was given ba y shale from the lower cretaceous period in which layers of geodes werde found.

The inclination of the layers is very small an reaches amounts between 6° an 10° towards SSE. The first system of joints strikes NNE/SSW and dips towards ESE with an angle of 80° to 85°, the second set of joints runs from SE to NW and is inclined towards NE with an angle od 80°. The degree of seperation of the joints varies between k = 0,27 and 0,5 and that for the bedding planes between

k = 0,8 and 0,9. Further parameters have been found out:

γ = 20 KN/m³   w = 0,06
φ_u = 28°   from an in-situ test on
c_u = 165 KN/m²   1 x 1 x 1 m-sample
φ' = 21°   direct shear test with
c' = 17 KN/m²   remoulded soil

For optimization of driving works the following test drivings have been performed:

- setting of pairs of sheet piles, type Larssen III and Larssen 32 with diesel hammer D 20 and D 30
- setting of pairs of sheet piles as before, but with the aid of the RSB (Rosenstock shock blasting)-method (Dadson, 1983).

The results of the test drivings with four pairs of sheet piles are given below:

- without blasting:
two pairs of Larssen 32, depth of penetration 6,0 m, diesel hammer D 22, average value of blows per 100 mm: q = 25 and q = 36, total number of blows Q = 1530 and Q = 2160.

- with blasting:
details as before, blows per 100 mm: q = 12 and q = 13, total number of blows: Q = 756 and Q = 794.

Based on this tests sheet piles Larssen 32, St SPS with the aid of the RSB-method were chosen for execution.

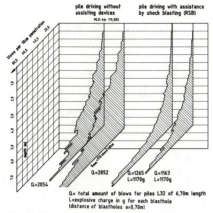

Fig. 6: Records of test drivings, blows per 100 mm

Some typical driving records together with the used amount of explosives are shown in the following figure.

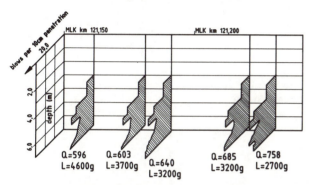

Fig. 7: Records of test drivings, blows per 100 mm

The function of the RSB-method has been described by Dadson, 1983, and the extent of the shattered zone has been examined by Mayer and Eberstadt, 1983. By variation of the distance between the bore holes and the amount of explosives per bore hole a short-term adaption to changing strengths of the ground is possible.

During execution of work at site 2 the effect of the RSB-method has been investigated by use of test pits and by large scale ultrasonic measurements with the pulse transmission method (Krautkrämer, Krautkrämer, 1980).

This method has prooved to be good suited to measure the geometry and the decrease of strength of the loosened zone (Prange, 1984). The results are given in detail by Mayer and Eberstadt, 1983. A limited slot of fragmented material on both sides of the axis of blasting was clearly identified by visual examination (fig. 8).

With the aid of ultrasonic measurements of sound velocity, wave-and material damping before and after blasting the loosened zone has been investigated in large scale. The measurements, which have an accuracy of 0,1 m, confirm the findings won at the test pit and indicate the width of the shattered slot with 0,6 to 0,8 m. A typical example for this measurements is given in fig. 9.

Fig 8: View of slot produced by blasting according to the RSB-method, site 2.

SITE 3

At this site at the eastern part of the Mittelland Canal at km 197,15 zo 198,4 the ground consists of lime marl stone and difficult driving works were expected. Therefore the use of the RSB-method has been dictated for driving the 9,0 to 11,5 m long sheet piles. The lime marl stone proved to be slablike joined rock with an overlying weathering zone of 4 m thickness.

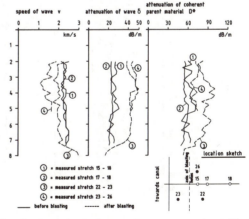

Fig. 9: Record of ultrasonic measurements, site 2.

The bedding planes are striking N-S and have a slight inclination towards E. The first family of joints strikes Se-NW and is inclined with an angle of 90⁰ towards NE, the second group main joints strike N-S and dip with an angle of 90⁰ towards E. In most cases the joints are opened and filled with soft clay.

Because it was demanded - and therefore the RSB-method should be used - to loosen only a narrow zone on both sides of the axis of the sheet pile wall, in order to make the ground drivable, it was necessary to proof the effect of the blasting. This was done again by visual investiga-

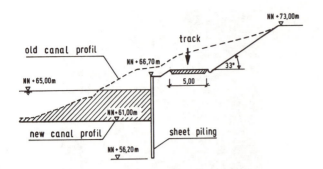

Fig. 10: Cross section of the canal at site 3.

tion of test pits and by ultrasonic measurements with the pulse transmission method.

On the southern bank of the canal the test pit showed that there was a slot like zone of fractured rock with particles in the size of crushed coarse gravel and small stones. In proceeding with excavation the material from this slot slided into the test pit, as can be seen on fig. 11. The width of the slot was between 0,4 and 0,5 m, it was smaller than at site 2. At the ground surface due to blasting parallel cracks appeared. From the ultrasonic measurements it could be stated, that according to the tender conditions the effect of creating a narrow zone of fractured material by blasting was fulfilled.

Fig. 11: View of shattered slot, produced by blasting according to the RSB-method, site 3.

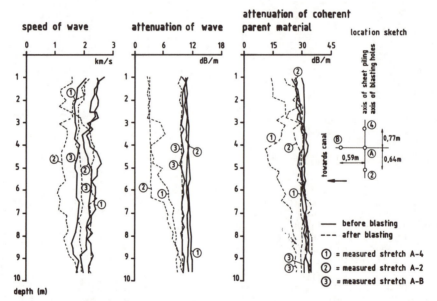

Fig. 12: Records of ultrasonic measurements, site 3

So at the two measuring sections A-4 and A-2, both directed parallel to the axis of blasting, distinct differences in velocity of sound v [km/s] and wave damping δ [db/m] after blasting are given. In contrary, the material damping D, defined as $D = v \cdot \delta$ [dB/m] has changed less. For measuring section A-B transverse to the axis of blasting and only 0,59 m in length, the blasting showed no effect. This results and others, because of lack of space not presented, confirm the finding from the visual investigation of the test pit, which showed a narrow zone of loosened or fractured material, that was drivable for sheet piles.

REFERENCES:

J. Dadson (1983) Blast control takes press. off Piling New Cicil Engineer

I. + H. Krautkrämer Werkstoffprüfung mit Ultraschall, Springer 1980

Chr. Eberstadt, B.K. Mayer (1983) Abgrenzung der Sprengzone mit Ultraschall. Symp. Messtechnik im Erd- und Grundbau, München, Deutsch. Gesellsch. für Erd- und Grundbau

B. Prange (1984) Generalbericht, Themengruppe 2, Symp. München

Point resistance of piles in sand

Résistance de pointe des pieux dans le sable

N. MIURA, Professor of Construction Engineering, Saga University, Saga, Japan

SYNOPSIS   The point resistance of piles in sand is mainly considered from the   viewpoint of the particle-crushing energy around the pile tip.   It is shown that the work dissipated in the particle-crushing of sand is as much as 80 - 90% of the total work done by the external force and that the point resistance of piles in sand greatly depends on the particle-crushing property of the sand.

INTRODUCTION

Past studies on the bearing capacity of piles in sand (De Beer, 1963, BCP Committee,1969, Takano et al., 1974) suggest that the point resistance of piles closely relates to the particle-crushing of sand around the pile tip. This study makes it clear how the particle-crushing affects the point resistance of piles by the detailed investigations on model pile tests.

EXPERIMENTS

Main properties of the sand used in this study are as follows: Maximum diameter ≈ 2.00 mm, fifty percent diameter ≈ 0.84 mm, specific gravity=2.66, maximum void ratio= 1.07 and minimum void ratio= 0.627, respectively.   Figure 1 is the schematic diagram of the sand container used for the model pile test.   This apparatus is an assembly of two pieces of cylindrical walls, a bottom plate and a ceiling plate and a steel pile of 5 cm in diameter and 32 cm in length.   The wall friction was decreased by coating a small amount of grease on the inner wall of the cylinder and by attaching double layers of polyvinyl sheets with soapy water between them to the wall.

Air-dried sand of water content of 0.3 to 0.5 percent was compacted in 28 cm thick in a dense state (void ratio is 0.60 and wet density is 1.66 g/cm^3) and the model pile was placed on the sand surface using a supporting frame.   After that, a sand layer of 13 cm thick was filled additionally, and thereby a buried model pile of 13 cm depth was prepared.   A ceiling plate was set and two rubber bags were inserted through the holes as shown in Fig. 1, for applying the vertical pressure σ_v to the sand surface.

For the pile loading test, the sand container was set on a compression machine, and pile stress was applied in controlled steps, with each step being approximately one-twentieth of the contemplated maximum stress. At each step, the stress was sustained until the rate of settlement became 0.01 mm/min, and then the incremental stress for the next step was applied. After the pile loading test, water was supplied

to the container so that the sand sample can stand itself by the capillary force for the convenience of extruding the sample from the container. A CBR mold attached a cutter head was then pushed into the sand sample as illustrated in Fig. 2.   For sectional sampling, the CBR mold was placed on a sample-extruder and thin-wall rings of diameters 10 cm, 6 cm and 4 cm were inserted in order, as seen in Fig. 3. The sampling sections are shown later in Fig. 5.

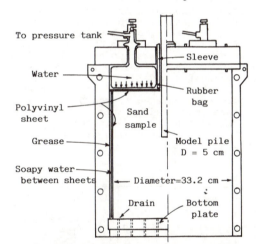

Fig. 1 Sand Container for Pile Test.

Fig. 2 Sampling of Sand Around the Pile Tip

Fig. 3 Sectional Sampling Using Thin-Wall Rings

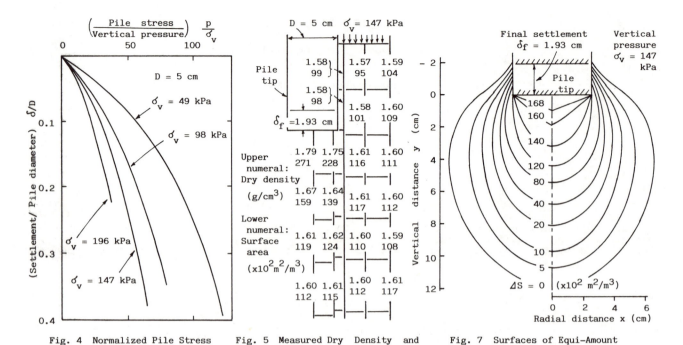

Fig. 4 Normalized Pile Stress
– Settlement Curves

Fig. 5 Measured Dry Density and
Surface Area in Each Section

Fig. 7 Surfaces of Equi-Amount
of Particle-Crushing

PARTICLE-CRUSHING REGION

Figure 4 shows the normalized pile stress and settlement relationships of four cases of different vertical pressures, explaining that all the curves continue to slope as the case of actual pile load tests and that the characteristics of these curves are of local shear failure. In the previous study, where the experiments were carried out using the model pile of 3.5cm, the author pointed out that the pile stress - settlement curve could be simulated reasonably by a mathematical model proposed by Shioi et al. (Miura, 1983). Situation is the same for the present data, but here the discussion is not made on this problem.

Now, for investigating the effect of particle-crushing on the point resistance of piles in sand, it is necessary to know the particle-crushing distribution around the pile tip in detail. Previous study proved that the amount of particle-crushing could be evaluated reasonably by the surface area S, which is calculated by $S = S_w \times \rho_d$, where S_w and ρ_d indicate specific surface area (m^2/g) and dry density. The value of S_w can be obtained through the sieving test and the Blaine test, and the details of them appear elsewhere (Miura et al. 1977).

Assuming that S value determined by the above-mentioned method represents the value at the center of each sampling section depicted in Fig. 5, the changes of surface area in vertical direction below the pile tip (y direction) and the radial direction (x direction) can be depicted as shown by Fig. 6, which is for the case of vertical pressure of 147 kPa and the final settlement δ_f of 1.93 cm. The broken lines in the figure represent the curves obtained by extraporation or interporation.

Based on the y - S curve and x - S curve, we may depict the contour lines of equi-amount of particle-crushing around the pile tip as illustrated in Fig. 7, where ΔS means an increase of surface area from the original value of $S_o = 110 \times 10^2$ m^2/m^3. It can be seen that the cone, the strongly crushed region, grows just below the pile, and that the surfaces of equi-amount of particle-crushing extend spherically around the cone. It is also known that the diameter of the bulb-shaped particle-crushing zone is two to three times of the diameter of the model pile.

Figure 8 comparably indicates the development of particle-crushing zone for various vertical pressures and settlements. The outermost line of ΔS being zero indicates the particle-crushing regions which essentially the same with the plastic region. As for the shape of the plastic

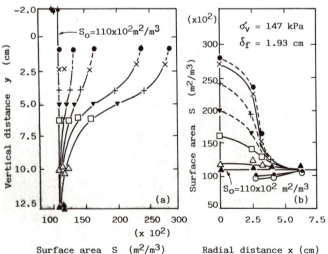

Fig. 6 Distribution of the Amount of Particle-Crushing
(Surface Area S) Around the Pile Tip

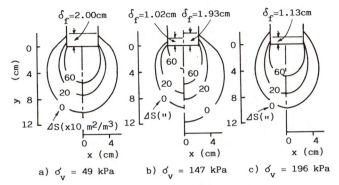

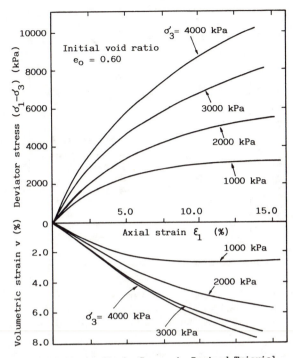

Fig. 8 Comparison of the Particle–Crushing
Regions for Various Test Conditions

zone that develops around the pile tip, several ideas
have been proposed, and among them we can find a
bulb-shaped one (Vesić, 1967). Aboshi(1975) also
found experimentally the plastic zone around the
tip of deep pile to be bulb-shaped. These investigations stated above support the present shape
of the plastic region, i.e., the particle-crushing region.

CONSIDERATION ON ENERGY BALANCE

The point resistance of piles in sand is discussed
in the following from the viewpoint of energy
balance by evaluating the energies dissipated in
the particle-crushing around the pile shaft and sand.
the friction between the pile shaft and sand.
First, the energy dissipated in particle-crushing
can be estimated on the basis of S - w relationship, where w is plastic work done per unit
volume (kN·m/m^3) (Miura et al., 1977). The
S - w curve for the present sample was determined
through drained triaxial compression tests carried out on the sand specimen of 5 cm diameter
and 12.5 cm height with a void ratio of 0.61 to
0.65, being the nearest possible to the void
ratio of the pile test sample. The conditions
of the triaxial compression tests are:strain rate
= 0.2%/min and confining pressure of 500 kPa to
4000 kPa.

Stress-strain curves obtained are represented in
Fig. 9, showing that no peak appears even at an
axial strain of 15 percent when the confining
pressure is higher than 2000 kPa. Fig. 10 shows
the failure envelope; the convexity of the failure envelope may be caused by the particle-
crushing. The internal friction angle at confining pressures under the particle-crushing region, i.e. $\sigma_3 \leqq 300$ kPa is determined as 39.0°.
The sample experienced various axial strains were
taken out from the triaxial chamber for measuring
the specific surface area S_w. The dry density
ρ_d corresponding to the S_w value was determined
on the basis of the volume change during the
shear, and the product of these values gives the
surface area per unit volume, S. The plastic
work done per unit volume w is given from the
stress-strain curves, q - ε, and p - v, i.e.,

$$w = \int (\sigma_1 d\varepsilon_1 + 2\sigma_3 d\varepsilon_3)$$
$$= \int (q d\varepsilon + p dv) \qquad (1)$$

where, $q = \sigma_1 - \sigma_3$, $p = (\sigma_1 + 2\sigma_3)/3$, $d\varepsilon = d\varepsilon_1 - (dv/3)$

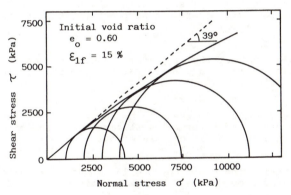

Fig. 9 Stress-Strain Curves in Drained Triaxial
Compression Tests at σ_3 = Constant

Fig. 10 Failure Envelope of the Tested Sand

and $dv = d\varepsilon_1 + 2d\varepsilon_3$. The above-mentioned equation neglects the elastic component since it oc-
cupies only a few percent of the total work. The
author found in the previous study that there was
a unique relationship between the surface area S
and the plastic work done w independent of the
stress level and the magnitude of the confining
pressure (Miura et al., 1977). This is also true
for the present sample as seen in Fig. 11.

Now, the plastic work done per unit volume w_i
corresponding to each value of ΔS in Fig. 7, can
be read on the curve in Fig. 11. For example,
$\Delta S_1 = 168 \times 10^2$ m^2/m^3 (S=168+110=278 ") in Fig.7
corresponds to $w_1 = 12.3$ N·m/m^3 in Fig. 11.
While, the volume of each section of Fig. 7 is
measured graphically and denoted by v_1. Hence,
the summation of the products of w_i and v_i might
be the total work dissipated in particle-crushing,

$$W_c = \sum w_i \times v_i \qquad (2)$$

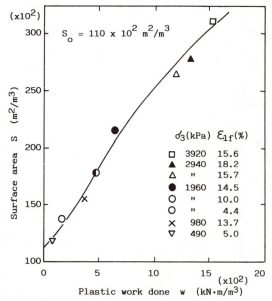

Fig. 11 Relationship between Surface Area S and
Plastic Work Done w per Unit Volume

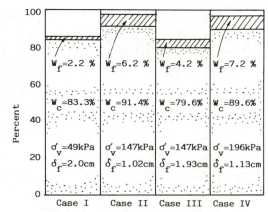

Fig. 12 Percentage of the Dissipated Energy for
Particle-Crushing W_c and Shaft Friction W_f

The value of W_c for the experiment shown in Fig.7 is $W_c = 190.2$ N·m. Next, the frictional work dissipated at the contact face of the pile shaft and sand, W_f, may be evaluated in the following ways. The horizontal stress acting on the pile shaft σ_h', is expressed using Jaky's equation for the coefficient of lateral pressure at rest, $K_O = 1 - \sin \phi_d$, as

$$\sigma_h' = \sigma_v' \times K_O \qquad (3)$$

Assuming that the frictional angle between the pile and sand is $\phi_f = 2\phi_d/3$, then the coefficient of friction is

$$\mu = \tan (2\phi_d/3) \qquad (4)$$

The diameter of the pile being D, the buried length L and the final settlement δ_f, the frictional work W_f is calculated by

$$W_f = \sigma_h' \, \mu \, \pi \, D \, L \, \delta_f \qquad (5)$$

Substituting D = 5 cm, L = 13 cm and $\phi_d = 39°$ for the case of $\sigma_v' = 147$ kPa, we obtain $W_f = 9.9$ N·m.

The total work done by the external force W_e was evaluated by the enclosed area of the pile stress-settlement curve and for the case of $\sigma_v' = 147$ kPa and $\delta_f = 1.93$ cm, W_e was 239.0 N·m. Therefore, the work done by the external force at the pile tip,

$$W = W_e - W_f = 229.1 \text{ N·m} \qquad (6)$$

To this value, the rate of the work dissipated in particle-crushing W_c (= 190.2 N·m) becomes a high percentage of 83%. Figure 12 summarizes the experimental results of four cases, indicating that the particle-crushing energy covers in fact as much as 80 to 90% of the total energy. The results stated above clearly indicate that the point resistance of piles in sand greatly depends on the particle-crushing property of sand below the pile tip to a depth of several times of the pile diameter.

CONCLUSIONS

The point resistance of piles in sand was mainly investigated from the viewpoint of particle-crushing by carrying out model pile tests, and the following conclusions were derived.

(1) A bulb-shaped particle-crushing region of a dimension of two to three times of the diameter of piles develops around the pile tip.

(2) The work dissipated in the particle-crushing of sand is as much as 80 to 90 percent of the total work done by the external force.

(3) The point resistance of piles in sand greatly depends on the particle-crushing property of sand below the pile tip to a depth of several times of the pile diameter.

ACKNOWLEDGEMENTS

The author wishes to thank Mr. Yohichi Asakami, a graduate student of Yamaguchi University, who conducted the experiments of this study. The author also acknowledges the support of the grant received from the Ministry of Education, Science and Culture.

REFERENCES

Aboshi,H. (1975). On the deformation and failure of sand underneath deep foundations. Tech.Conf. of The Inst.of Engs., Australia, 185-189.
BCP Committee (1971). Field tests on piles in sand. Soils & Foundations, (2), 2, 29-49.
De Beer,E.E. (1963). The scale effect in the transposition of the results of deep sounding tests on the ultimate bearing capacity of piles and caisson foundations, Geotechnique, (13),1.
Miura, N. (1983). Point resistance of piles in sand. Tech. Reps. of the Yamaguchi Univ.,(3),129-139.
Miura, N. and Yamanouchi, T.(1977). Effect of particle-crushing on the shear characteristcs of a sand. Trans. of JSCE, (9), 198-202.
Shioi, Y. et al..(1978). A method for evaluating the bearing capacity of piles by non-linear analysis, 23rd Symp. on SM&FE, 9-16.
Takano, A. et al..(1974). Load settlement characteristics of piles buried in sand. 9th Annual Meeting on SM&FE, 533-535.
Vesic, A.S.(1967). Ultimate loads and settlement of deep foundation in sand. Bearing Capacity and Settlement of Foundation. Duke Univ., North Carolina, 53-68.

Pile groups under static and dynamic loading

Les groupes des pieux sous des charges statiques et dynamiques

M. NOVAK, Professor, University of Western Ontario, London, Canada
B. EL SHARNOUBY, Assistant Professor, University of Alexandria, Egypt

SYNOPSIS   Behaviour of pile groups under static loading, low frequency loading and dynamic loading is discussed with special attention being paid to pile-soil-pile interaction. A direct solution of the group flexibility, stiffness and settlement is described, examples are given and the accuracy of the interaction factor approach is evaluated. The effect of pile separation on pile group stiffness is considered. Approximate formulae for the estimate of group damping are proposed for low frequency excitation and high frequency effects are outlined.

INTRODUCTION

The behaviour of pile groups is affected by interaction between individual piles unless the piles are very far apart. This interaction increases group settlement, redistributes the loads on individual piles and modifies group flexibility and thus also its stiffness and, under dynamic loads, its damping. Much research effort has been devoted to the study of these effects in recent years. Only a few typical approaches can be mentioned here. Poulos based most of his work on Mindlin's (1936) solution for the displacement field in an elastic half-space and collected his results in a monograph (Poulos and Davis, 1980); Wolf and von Arx (1978) employed the finite element method; approximate analytical methods were formulated eg. by Sheta and Novak (1982); the boundary element method was used by Banerjee (1978) and Wolf and Darbre (1983) while a hybrid method was established by Waas and Hartmann (1981). Most of the results presented in this paper were obtained using a direct group analysis based on the Mindlin solution.

The behaviour of pile groups depends on the properties of the piles and their arrangement, the properties of the soil and, also, on the type of loading. Three basic types of loading are discussed separately: static loading, low frequency loading and dynamic loading.

THE METHOD OF ANALYSIS

The most popular method of evaluating the group effects is the interaction factor approach. This approach is easy to use and is readily applicable because the interaction factors are available in the form of charts and formulae (Poulos and Davis, 1980; Randolph and Poulos, 1982; Kaynia and Kausel, 1980).

To assess the accuracy of the interaction factor approach and to alleviate some of its limitations, the authors formulated a direct solution of the whole group. As in Poulos's approach, the soil reactions to pile displacement are established by means of the Mindlin (1936) solution for the displacement field in the elastic halfspace and the piles are modelled by finite elements. However, to make the direct solution of large groups computationally feasible, the soil flexibility is calculated using equivalent point loads and symmetry of pile groups is exploited. The method is described in full detail elsewhere (El Sharnouby and Novak, 1984b). Because of the nature of the Mindlin solution, the method is fully justified only for homogeneous soil; but as approximate it can be used for any soil profile by defining the soil modulus by the average of the values pertinent to any two locations in question. Some results obtained by means of this method are described below. The focus is on pile stiffness rather than settlement because stiffness is more often used when evaluating response of pile supported structures to loads.

STATIC LOADING

Vertical Response

In practice, the stiffness (and settlement) of pile groups is most often evaluated using interaction factors derived for two piles and superimposed for all piles in the group (Poulos and Davis, 1980). This approach is approximate because the interaction factors to be superimposed are calculated for any two piles neglecting the stiffening effect of the other piles. The scope of this inaccuracy is apparent from Fig. 1 which shows the variation of the group efficiency ratio with the stiffness of the underlying stratum characterized by the ratio E_b/E_s. The group efficiency ratio = K_G/Nk where K_G = stiffness of the group, N = number of piles and k = stiffness of a single pile considered in isolation; E_b = Young's modulus of the bearing stratum and E_s = Young's modulus of the soil around the piles. The group efficiency is calculated for two spacing ratios S/d, where S = pile spacing and d =

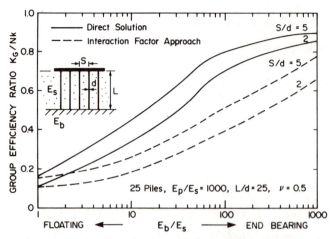

Fig. 1 Vertical Stiffness of Square Group of 25 Piles vs Stiffness of Under-lying Stratum

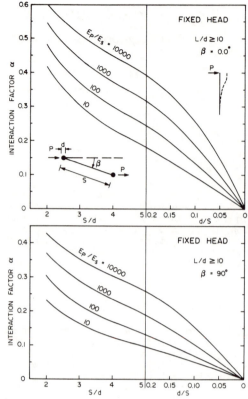

Fig. 2 Horizontal Interaction Factors for Fixed Head Piles

pile diameter, using both the direct solution and the interaction factor approach. For floating piles ($E_b/E_s = 1$), both approaches give the same result but as E_b/E_s increases, the two approaches diverge with the direct analysis consistently giving higher group efficiency, i.e. higher stiffness. The magnitude of this difference depends on the parameters of the group. Nevertheless, Fig. 1 indicates that the interaction factor approach may exaggerate the group effects for large groups of endbearing piles but works very well for floating piles.

Horizontal Response

Interaction factors. - For the horizontal response, the interaction factor approach was found to work quite well for small and moderately large groups. The interaction factors obtained using the authors' technique are plotted for angles $\beta = 0°$ and $90°$ in Fig. 2. For free head piles, these factors are similar but markedly smaller than those of Poulos and Davis (1980). The second feature of the interaction factors presented is that they are given for the ratio E_p/E_s, where E_p = Young's modulus of the pile, rather than for the more commonly used stiffness ratio $K_r = E_p I_p / E_s L^4$ in which L = pile length and I_p = second moment of cross-sectional area. The interaction factors presented in Fig. 2 are valid for all piles whose length $L \gtrsim 10d$. This presentation is made possible by the observation that for $L \gtrsim 10d$, the horizontal interaction factors are largely independent of pile length; thus, for typical piles, the inclusion of pile length into the dimensionless stiffness parameter K_r is not necessary. Finally, the horizontal interaction factors were found to be practically independent of the soil profile. With the simplifications resulting from the small effects of pile length and soil profile, the data plotted in Fig. 2 are of rather general validity.

For fixed head and pinned head piles, the horizontal interaction factors can be calculated

using the approximate empirical expression

$$\alpha_h = A\left(\frac{E_p}{E_s}\right)^B \left(\frac{d}{S}\right)^C \tag{1}$$

where A, B and C are constants. Suitable values of constants A, B and C are given in Table 1.

TABLE 1

Constants A, B and C for Calculation of Interaction Factors

Head	β	A	B	C
Fixed	0°	0.480	0.075	0.600
	90°	0.270	0.110	0.700
Pinned	0°	0.410	0.095	0.725
	90°	0.203	0.134	0.838

For intermediate angles β, the interaction factors may be calculated from the extreme values using the relation suggested by Randolph and Poulos (1982), i.e.

$$\alpha_h(\beta) = \alpha_h(0°)\cos^2\beta + \alpha_h(90°)\sin^2\beta \tag{2}$$

The greatest limitations to the accuracy of pile group analysis stem from the assumptions of linear elasticity. One effect for which corrections should be made is pile separation from the soil. This is likely to occur in the topmost layer of soil where the confining pressure is small, especially under cyclic loading. A simple approximate way of accounting for this effect is to represent the separation zone by a free pile length, e, as if the pile were sticking out of the ground. Such a free length considerably reduces the stiffness of the pile (Fig. 3) and also the interaction factor as can be seen from Figs. 4 and 5. Fig. 4 shows the values of α_h vs dimensionless separation e/d for a range of E_p/E_s and two typical soil profiles, namely the homogeneous soil profile and the linear (Gibson) soil profile. In Fig. 5, the same interaction factor is presented as the dimensionless interaction reduction factor

$$F_E = \alpha_h\left(\frac{e}{d}\right) / \alpha_h\left(\frac{e}{d} = 0\right)$$

i.e., interaction factor for separation e/d divided by interaction factor for fully embedded pile. The values shown in Figs. 4 and 5 were calculated for S/d = 5, L/d = 25 and β = 0°; however, with an error of up to about ± 10%, Fig. 5 can be used for other parameters as well.

Horizontal response of pile groups. - The behaviour of a pile group under horizontal loading can be predicted using either a direct analysis of the whole group or interaction factors. Extensive parametric studies (El Sharnouby and Novak, 1984b) indicated that for small and medium size groups the superposition of the interaction factors yields sufficient accuracy. This superposition can be implemented in an approximate way or rigorously.

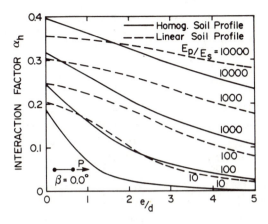

Fig. 4 Effect of Pile Separation on Interaction Factor

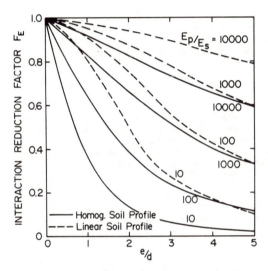

Fig. 5 Interaction Reduction Factor vs Separation e/d

The approximate superposition of the interaction factors for a group yields the group stiffness as

$$K_G = \frac{\sum_r k}{\sum_r \alpha_h} \qquad (3)$$

in which k is stiffness of individual piles considered in isolation and α_h are the interaction factors between a reference pile and the rth pile with r = 1,2,...,N where N is the number of piles. For the reference pile α_h = 1. With equal piles characterized by stiffness k, $\sum k$ = Nk. Equation 3 is easy to use but the results are not quite accurate and depend on the choice of the reference pile which, therefore, should not be in the centre or at the periphery of the group.

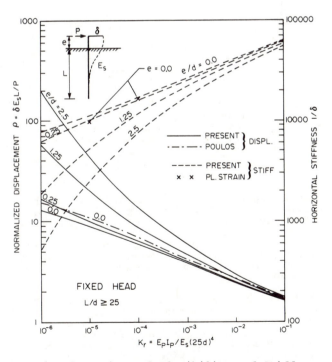

Fig. 3 Horizontal Flexibility and Stiffness of Fixed Head Single Piles With Free Length

The more rigorous formula for group stiffness for piles with a rigid cap can be written as (Novak, 1979)

$$K_G = k \sum_i \sum_r \beta_{ir} \qquad (4)$$

in which β_{ir} are the elements of the inverted matrix $[\alpha_{ir}]^{-1}$ of all interaction factors. The matrix $[\alpha_{ir}]$ lists the interaction factors α_{ir} between any two piles and all diagonal terms $\alpha_{ii} = 1$. Both i and r run from 1 to N. Thus, the matrix $[\alpha_{ir}]$ is N by N. The assembly of the matrix $[\alpha_{ir}]$ can be facilitated using Eq. 1 but its inversion for a large group becomes tedious. For smaller groups, the difference between the results of Eq. 3 and Eq. 4 is usually not great as can be seen from Fig. 6. This figure shows the group efficiency ratio of a square group of 9 and 25 piles evaluated for different pile free lengths e/d using three approaches: the direct analysis, the interaction factors with Eq. 3 and the interaction factors with Eq. 4. The direct analysis yields consistently greater stiffness than the interaction factor approach and Eq. 4 gives better results than Eq. 3. The differences increase with the number of piles and may become quite significant for large groups (El Sharnouby and Novak, 1984).

Fig. 6 also indicates that group efficiency ratio increases with the pile free length (separation). Despite that group stiffness decreases with increasing free length, as can be seen from Fig. 7; this decrease is not quite so abrupt as it is for single piles.

Nevertheless, for both single piles and pile groups, the reduction of stiffness due to pile separation can be very substantial and may be

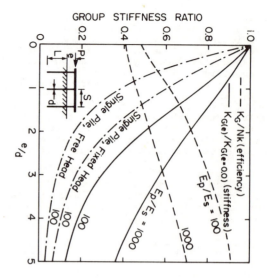

Fig. 7 Effect of Pile Free Length on Group Efficiency and Stiffness

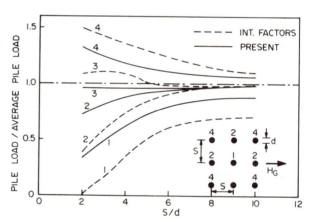

Fig. 8 Distribution of Horizontal Loads in Group of 9 Piles Calculated Using Interaction Factors and Using Direct Group Analysis

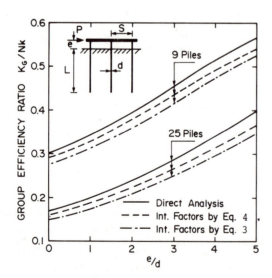

Fig. 6 Stiffness of Square Group vs Pile Free Length (Homogeneous Soil, $E_p/E_s = 1000$, $L/d = 25$, $S/d = 2.5$, $\nu = 0.5$)

further aggravated by diminishing soil shear modulus towards ground surface. These two effects have to be included in the analysis if a realistic prediction of pile behaviour is to be made. This suggestion was confirmed by experiments (Novak and El Sharnouby, 1984) but further research into the representative free pile length is needed.

Distribution of pile forces. - Pile-soil-pile interaction produces one more effect, i.e. redistribution of the loads acting on individual piles of the group. It has been recognized that the peripheral piles are more heavily loaded than the other piles with the differences increasing with decreasing pile spacing. However, the interaction factor approach may exaggerate the nonuniformity of pile load distribution as can be seen from Fig. 8 in which the pile loads evaluated using interaction factors are compared with those obtained by means of the direct group analysis.

LOW FREQUENCY LOADING

Many large structures such as skyscrapers, nuclear power plants or offshore towers are exposed to dynamic loads which produce responses whose dominant frequency is lower than the fundamental natural frequency of the soil stratum. In such a case, no progressive wave is generated in the soil medium and geometric damping is absent. Consequently, the low frequency dynamic stiffness of the group can be assumed to be approximately equal to the static stiffness and damping can be evaluated only from material (hysteretic) damping of the soil and piles. For homogeneous strata, the limiting fundamental natural frequencies are

$$\omega_v = \frac{\pi V_s}{2h} \sqrt{\frac{2(1-\nu)}{1-2\nu}} \ , \ \omega_h = \frac{\pi V_s}{2h} \qquad (5)$$

for the vertical and horizontal directions respectively; V_s = soil shear wave velocity, h = stratum depth and ν = Poisson's ratio. For non-homogeneous media similar formulae are also available.

Material damping can be described in terms of complex shear modulus of soil G^* and complex Young's modulus of piles E_p^*, i.e. as

$$G^* = (1+i2\beta_s) G \qquad (6a)$$

$$E_p^* = (1+i2\beta_p) E_p \qquad (6b)$$

in which β_s = soil material damping ratio, β_p = pile material damping ratio and G = real soil shear modulus. The complex moduli can be introduced into the equations of equilibrium of the soil-pile system. The solution yields complex dynamic stiffness (impedance function) of the group $K_G = K_1 + iK_2$ in which K_1 = the real stiffness and K_2 = the imaginary part of stiffness which accounts for energy dissipation due to material hysteresis in both the soil and piles. For low frequencies, inertia effects are insignificant and real stiffness K_1 is equal to the static stiffness of the group discussed above. The damping can also be expressed in terms of the equivalent viscous damping constant $c = K_2/\omega$ where ω = circular frequency.

The question arises of whether the group damping has to be evaluated using the direct solution of the whole group. Detailed parametric examination indicates that, for low frequencies, the group damping can be estimated just on the basis of soil material damping ratio β_s and static stiffness K_1 as

$$K_2 = 2\beta_s K_1 \varepsilon \qquad (7)$$

in which ε = coefficient given for the vertical

response of floating piles and horizontal response of all types of piles in Table 2.

TABLE 2

Coefficient ε For Evaluation of Pile Group Damping at Low Frequencies

Direction Soil Profile	Vertical Any	Horizontal Homogeneous	Parabolic
ε	1	0.85	0.75

For the vertical response of endbearing piles, the damping K_2 may be less than that obtained by Eq. 7 with $\varepsilon = 1$ and close to pile material damping ratio, depending on the parameters of the system.

HIGH FREQUENCY RESPONSE

A number of solutions are available to analyze high frequency response of pile groups. They indicate that the interaction effects are quite complicated and much more frequency dependent than properties of single piles. This is indicated by Fig. 9 in which the variation of group stiffness and damping is shown for horizontal response of a group of four piles. The plots shown were calculated using the theory and numerical data due to Sheta and Novak (1982) considering pile interaction and for comparison, neglecting it. Both group stiffness and damping show sharp peaks which are absent if pile interaction is not considered. These peaks are reduced but not eliminated if a weak zone around the piles is considered to account for non-linear contact phenomena (Novak and Sheta, 1980). The peaks in the stiffness and damping can result in two peaks in the response to horizontal excitation even if rocking is not considered (Fig. 10). Sharp peaks also show in group efficiency ratio variation with pile spacing. All features of pile interaction should be verified by experiments.

CONCLUSIONS

A direct efficient analysis suitable for static and low frequency loading of pile groups is reported and used to examine the validity range of the applicability of the interaction factor approach. The interaction factor approach was found to be sufficiently accurate for vertical response of floating piles and horizontal response of small and medium groups; it is much less accurate for the evaluation of vertical response of endbearing piles and distribution of loads on individual piles.

Simple formulae for the evaluation of low frequency damping are proposed and the more complex nature of high frequency response of pile groups is exemplified.

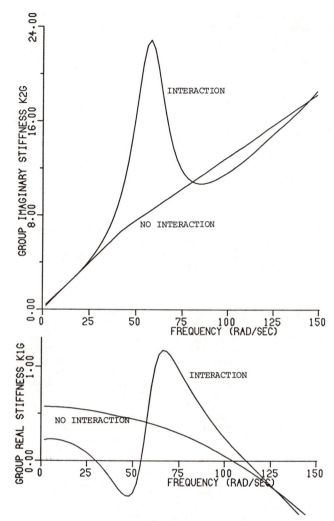

Fig. 9 Effect of Pile Interaction on
Horizontal Stiffness and Damping
of Group of Four Piles

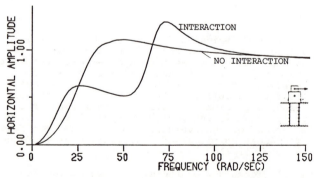

Fig. 10 Effect of Pile Interaction on
Horizontal Response of Footing
Supported by Four Piles

ACKNOWLEDGEMENTS

The research reported was supported by a grant
from the Natural Sciences and Engineering Research Council. The assistance of M. Sheta is
acknowledged.

REFERENCES

Banerjee, P.K. (1978). Analysis of axially and
laterally loaded pile groups, Ch. 9, Developments in Soil Mechanics, ed. C.R. Scott,
Appl. Sci. Pub., London, pp. 317-346.

El-Sharnouby, B. (1984). Static and dynamic behaviour of pile groups, Ph.D. Thesis, Fac.
of Engrg. Sc., Univ. of West. Ont., London.

El-Sharnouby, B. and Novak, M. (1984a). Dynamic
experiments with a group of piles, J. of
Geotech. Engrg. ASCE, pp. 719-737.

El-Sharnouby, B. and Novak, M. (1984b). Analysis of pile groups exposed to static and low
frequency loading, Res. Rept. GEOT-7-84, Fac.
of Engrg. Sc., Univ. of Western Ont., London.

Kaynia, A.M. and Kausel, E. (1980). Dynamic behavior of pile groups, 2nd Int. Conf. Num.
Methods in Offshore Piling, Austin, Texas.

Mindlin, R.D. (1936). Force at a point in the
interior of a semi-infinite solid, Physics,
7, pp. 195-202.

Novak, M. and El-Sharnouby, B. (1984). Evaluation of dynamic experiments on a pile group,
J. Geotech. Engrg. ASCE, pp. 738-756.

Novak, M. and Sheta, M. (1980). Approximate
approach to contact effects of piles, Dyn.
Response of Pile Fdns: Analytical Aspects,
ASCE, Florida, pp. 53-79.

Poulos, H.G. and Davis, E.H. (1980). Pile Foundation Analysis and Design, John Wiley and
Sons, pp. 397.

Randolph, M.F. and Poulos, H.G. (1982). Estimating the flexibility of offshore pile groups,
Proc. 2nd Int. Conf. on Num. Methods in Offshore Piling, Austin, Texas, pp. 313-328.

Sheta, M. and Novak, M. (1982). Vertical vibration of pile groups, J. Geotech. Engrg. ASCE,
pp. 570-590.

Waas, G. and Hartmann, H.G. (1981). Pile founda-
tions subjected to dynamic horizontal loads,
Eur. Simul. Mtg. "Modelling and Simulation of
Large Scale Structural Systems", Capri, Italy.

Wolf, J.P. and von Arx, G.A. (1978). Impedance
functions of a group of vertical piles, ASCE,
Earthq. Engrg. and Soil Dyn., Pasadena, Cal.
II, pp. 1024-1041.

Wolf, J.P. and Darbre, G.R. (1983). Dynamic
stiffness matrix of embedded and pile foundations by indirect boundary element method,
7th SMIRT, Chicago, K(b), pp. 245-258.

Pile driving of soil-displacing piles through soft soils

Enfoncer des pilots, des pilots qui se pressent à travers du sol mou

JACK P. OOSTVEEN, Delft University of Technology, Netherlands
JEAN A. G. KUPPERS, Delft University of Technology, Netherlands

SYNOPSIS   The first soil-displacing pile of a group to be driven, will display different settlement as a result of influence caused by driving the other piles of the group than for example the last to be installed. This causes one pile to react more rigidly than another and co-operating in the whole construction of the foundation one pile is bound to take a greater load than another. This leads to consequences in the distribution of forces and deformation of the construction. The effect observed during the penetration of a clay layer is the upheaveal of the groundlevel which causes upward frictional forces on piles. Therefore lifting of piles from their base or cracking of the piles may occur. The latter may occur with the cast-in-place type of piles which are just installed and have little strength.

INTRODUCTION

The phenomenon coming up for discussion here, is the following:
the through soil-displacement interposed pile is bound to load the existing piles during the installation period, which will influence their behaviour.
This influence concerns not only the recently installed piles but also the already situated piles of adjacent constructions
Now here is discussed the upheave of the landlevel as a result of pile driving through clay-layers, which causes uplift and tension forces on the existing piles.

1. CASE HISTORIES

Although several data are available the following locations are selected:
- Rotterdam, The Netherlands
- The Hague, The Netherlands
- Bagdad, Iraq.

1.1 Rotterdam, The Netherlands

For the benefit of negative adherance research in the Rotterdam area several piles were being equipped with strain gages, in the last 20 years.
These testpiles were provided with strain gages to achieve measurements of the axial forces that are active in the pile shaft especially in units of time.
These piles of the vibro-type were so constructed that before placing the reinforcement, an assembled pilesegment was placed into the shaft in a layer of grout. The assembled pilesegments were fitted out with strain gages at the required levels, in relation to the pile feet.
Fig. 1 shows two of the measurements, which were obtained during piledriving at 1.75m c.t.c. ($r/r_0 = 6,7$) both about 13 hours after the installation of the cast-in-place testpiles. These testpiles were vibro-casing piles respectively wrapped round by bentonite (fig. 1a) and with a bitumen coating (fig. 1b).
At the start of driving the adjacent piles the inital forces presented in the shaft of the testpiles (gage 1) were about -34 kN and -43 kN respectively, in the pilefoot (gage 2) these forces were respectively -74 kN and -64 kN. Broadly outlined it may be concluded that below the landlevel a layer consisting of sand and silt originating from dredging works down to 7.00m is encountered. While penetrating this layer hardly any change of the forces in the shaft as well as in the pile foot was registered.

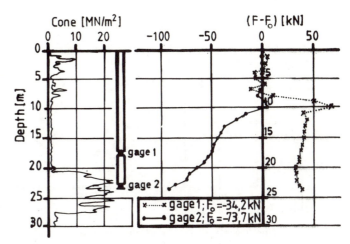

a. test pile, wrapped around by bentonite

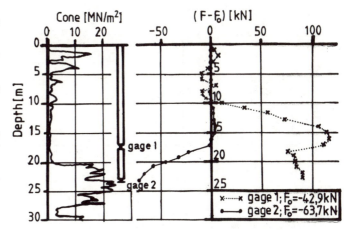

b. testpile, with bitumen coating
fig.1   Rotterdam; The behaviour of the testpiles during piledriving at 1.75 m c.t.c.

Underneath this layer a 12m thick soft clay and peat layer
is found, followed by sand. Penetrating this layer, in the
shaft a very fast increasing tension force superposed the
initital force introducing a total tension force, while
the force in the pile foot hardly shows any change.
Also during driving through this soft clay and peat layer
the tension force in the pile shaft suddenly breaks down to
about zero, while from that moment in the pilefoot an increasing compression force is introduced.
During penetration into the deep sand layer the force in
the pile shaft hardly remains about zero, while the compression force in the pilefoot is still increasing.
Measurements at another vibro-casing pile show similar
results.

1.2 The Hague, The Netherlands

In the Hague the following measurements have been worked
out during pile driving for an actual foundation.
- The vertical movement of the landlevel during the
  driving activities of 14 piles (fig.2).
- The vertical movement of the top of a test pile, which
  was installed 15 days before, during driving of 5
  surrounding piles (fig.3).
- The piezometric variations at 2 gages in the clay layer
  at 9.00 m below landlevel, that occur as a result of
  driving 27 piles (fig.4).

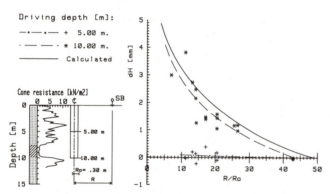

Fig. 2; The Hague, the upheave of the landlevel

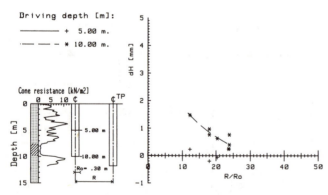

Fig. 3; The Hague, the uplift of piles

All piles involved in the measuring belong to one of the
pileconcentrations of the foundation.
The piles ϕ 0.60 m have got a driving depth of about 12.00m
below landlevel. The situation of the pileconcentration,
the piezometric gages (P.G.1 and P.G.2), the test pile (TP)
and the settlement beacon (SB) are given in fig.5.

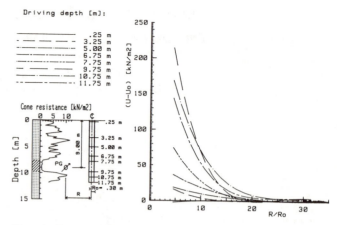

Fig. 4; The Hague, the pore excess in relation to the
driving distance and depth.

The landlevel measurements all show the same tendency.
During the penetration the first 5.00 m upheave kept within
the marginal (dH < 0.25 mm). Further penetration between
5.00 m and 10.00 m shows an upheave varying according the
distance to the driven pile: from about 4 mm at a distance
of about 2.50 m ($r/r_o \approx 8$) to 1 à 2 mm at 6.00 m ($r/r_o \approx 20$)
and 0 mm at 13.00 m ($r/r_o \approx 45$).
The subsidence of the landlevel during penetration into the
the pleistocene sand below a depth of 10.00 m varied from
1 mm at 2.50 m ($r/r_o \approx 8$) to 0 mm at 10.00m ($r/r_o \approx 33$) or
more.
The measurements at the pile top show similar results, movements were even smaller.
Pore pressure measurements in the clay layer show hardly
any change during penetration over the first 5.00 m either
Between 5.00 m and 10.00 m penetration the pore pressure
changes rapidly, depending on the distance to the pile.
During penetration of the pleistocene sand, the pore
pressure went down considerably in the vicinity of the
pile, with a slight ascent in the beginning at some distance away from the pile.
At distances over 7.50 m ($r/r_o = 25$) hardly any change in
pore pressure is seen.
Fig.4 shows the strong decrease in pore pressure within
the radius of 3.00 m ($r/r_o = 10$) as a result of the penetration into the pleistocene sand, and the way in which
this concurs with a wave of pore pressure increase as one
moves away from the pile.

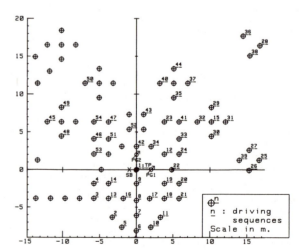

Fig 5; The Hague, the layout of the pile concentration

1.3 Bagdad, Iraq

During piledriving works for an actual construction at the Bagdad Airport, problems had risen with the foundation. The already situated piles were uplifted with the upheave of the landlevel.
Several measurements were made to diagnose the problems.

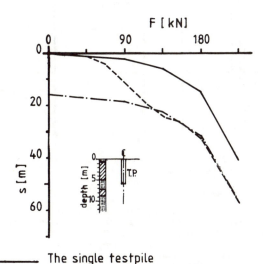

The single testpile
After driving 2 piles at 1.50 m c.o.c.
The fitted curve of the single testpile

Fig. 6; Bagdad, the testloads on a testpile before and after driving two adjacent piles (1.50 m c.o.c. both).

Fig. 6 shows the results of two testloadings on the same pile. The first one on a single pile, the second after driving two more piles at a distance of 1.50 m ($r/r_o=6.25$). During driving these two piles the test pile rose respectively 17 mm and 28 mm.
During the second testloading the test pile acted less rigidly to begin with. At $F=135$ kN the first testloading shows a settlement of only 5 mm while the second one gives a settlement of 25 mm. Although there was deterioration of the settlement behaviour, the bearing capacity had hardly changed.
This is shown by fitting the two load-settlement curves together which gives a similar respons after attaining $F = 135$ kN. Other measurements are shown in fig.7.
During driving of several piles the upheave was measured at various distances, as well as uplift of the top and the foot of a test pile. This test pile was fitted out with an installed shaft, in which a free-standing rod was placed, in order to measure the deformation of the pile foot.
This measurement consists of two parts. In the first part piles are driven in a normal manner, the second part consists of driving two adjacent piles, which are driven in pre-drilled holes to try out the pre-drilling effect in order to avoid the uplift.

2. The Phenomenon

From these case histories and other cases not described here, it is found that the landlevel will heave up by pile driving through clay and peat layers. This upheaveal is caused by displacing a volume of soil which is equal to the volume of the pile.
The rate of upheave will be dependent on the following aspects:
- The volume of soil displaced by one pile.
- The number of piles and their driving sequence.

- The initial compressibility of the soil which is determined by water and air contents in relation to permeability.
- The deformation resistance of the upperlaers penetrated.
In the upheaved area upward friction on the piles already installed will occur.
This causes uplift of these piles from their foundationbase, if there is an insufficient retaining force on the pile foot. In the other way if the retaining-force has a sufficient magnitude tension forces in the pile shaft will occur. The cast-in-place piles which exist of very fresh concrete with hardly any strength can be cracked, if these piles have an insufficient reinforcement.
In 1974 the latter phenomenon had led to the failure of the foundation of a new unit of a power station nearby Amsterdam, the Netherlands.
In this case the cast-in-place piles were driven through a 18-23 m thick soft clay and peat layer into the sand layer in which the piles were based.

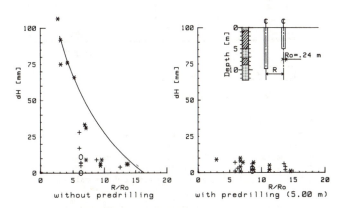

without predrilling   with predrilling (5.00 m)

*   Upheave of the landlevel
+   Uplift of the piletop
O   Uplift of the pilefoot

――――― Calculated upheave

Fig. 7; Bagdad, upheave and uplift at 5.00 m drivingdepth

3. Analytical model

In order to determine the rate of upheaveal caused by driving a single pile a simple analytical model can be defined. This model exists of a three-layer system (fig.8).
- A lower layer (layer 0), presumed to be infinitely rigid. This layer represents for example e deep sand layer in which the piles are based.
- A middle layer (layer 1), presumed to be displaced during the process. This layer with a low permeability consists of three elements: water, air and soil particles, so that the compressibility can be computed by

$$C_o = \frac{c_p}{1-n} + \frac{1}{n\{\frac{s}{c_w} + \frac{s-1}{p}\}}$$

in which
- c_o compressibility of the soilmixture
- c_p compressibility of the particle material
- c_w compressibility of pure water
- n porosity
- s saturation degree
- p pore pressure

As a simplification this layer is assumed to react like a homogeneous elastic medium. Otherwise the displacement caused by penetration of the pile is simulated by a cylindrical expansion over the whole depth of this layer: $u(r_o) = r_o$.

- A top layer (layer 2), presumed to be a layer already
  penetrated. So in this layer there is only vertical
  deformation as a result of the upheave of layer 1. The
  resistance against this deformation is caused by shear
  stresses in the vertical plane only.

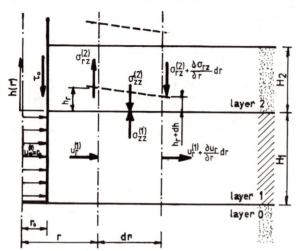

Fig. 8; The analytical model.

4. Recommendations

A computer model for working out the analytical model is
available. In fig.2 and 7 the output of the computer-
program is compared to the field observations.
From the upheave due to a single pile the magnitude of the
upheave caused by a group of piles can be calculated:

$$h = f \times \sum_{i=1}^{n} h_i(r_i)$$

in which: $h_i(r_i)$ = the upheave at a distance r_i caused
                by pile i
        n = the number of piles
        f = the reduction factor.

The reduction factor depends on the permeability of
layer 1, the installation velocity and the driving sequence as well as the time between pile driving.
If it becomes evident that the upheave will be considerably
and uplift of piles will occur, the following actions should
be taken:
- re-driving of the uplifted piles.
- pre-drilling of the piles like the Bagdad case.
- a minimum penetration depth inti layer 0 by which a
  sufficient retaining force is guaranteed.
  Inthis case sufficient reinforcement of the cast-in-place
  piles are necessary.

By neglecting the friction forces in layer 1 the foundation-
depth in layer 0 can be calculated by (fig.9):

$$H_o = \frac{\tau^{(2)}}{\tau^{(o)}} H_2$$

The minimum tension force for dimensioning the pile
shaft will be determined by:

$$N = 2\pi \, r.H_2.\tau^{(2)}$$

The minimum reinforcement will be:

$$A_a = \frac{2\pi \, r.H_2.\tau^{(2)}}{\bar{\sigma}_a}$$

while the minimum elongation, which may occur will be:

$$\varepsilon_{pile} = \frac{2\pi \, rH_2\tau^{(2)}}{E_a A_a} < \varepsilon_f$$

in which ε_f is the rupture elongation of fresh concrete.

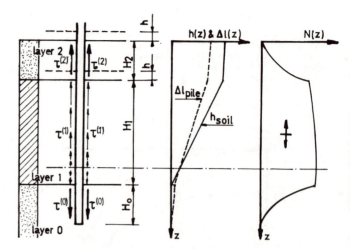

fig.9 The deformation and force distribution in a pile
       due to the upheave.

5. Acknowledgement

This research, which was sponsored by the Applied Research
of the Public Works department of the Dutch Government, was
performed in co-operation with the State Building department, the Rotterdam Public Works department and the International Foundation Group, Ltd at Gouda.

6. References

Cole, K.W. (1972). Uplift of piles due to driving displace-
    ment. Civil Engineering and Public Works Review,
    March, pp.263-269.
Cooke, R.W., Price, G. and Tarr, K. (1979). Jacked piles
    in London clay: a study of load transfer and settlement
    under working conditions. Geotechnique 29 no.2,
    pp.113-147.
Hagerty, D.J. and Peck, R.B. (1971). Heave and lateral
    movements due to pile driving. ASCE. J. of S.M.,
    Nov., pp.1513-1532.
Klohn, E.J. (1963). Pile heave and redriving. ASCE-
    transactions, Vol.128, pp.557-577.
Hammond, A.J., Mitchell, J.M. and Lord, J.A. (1979).
    Design and construction of driven cast-in-situ piles in
    stiff fissured clays. Proc. ICE conf. on recent develop-
    ments in the design and construction of piles.
Kremer, R.H.J. (1976). Uitbreiding Centrale Hemweg, van de
    streken van het Oer.IJ. Publikaties Grondmechanica,
    Dienst der Publieke Werken van Amsterdam, bureau
    Grondmechanica, Nov. (in Dutch).
Verruijt, A. (1970). Theory of groundwaterflow.
    MacMillan and Co, London.

Designing of the pile tip level at bridge foundation in loose and soft deposits

Desseinant du niveau de pointe d'un pieu à un fondation du pont dans des dépôts lâches et tendres

LÁSZLÓ RÓZSA, B.Sc., M.Sc., Ph.D., Head of the Underground Designing Department UVATERV, Associate Professor, Budapest, Hungary

SYNOPSIS   Bearing capacity of the piles at the bridge foundations in loose and soft deposits under rivers on great plains is, in general, less than that given in publications. Short piles give great settlements in the clay layers. Relatively long piles are convenient to apply to prevent the movement of the foundations. The settlement of the piles is less and the bearing capacity is greater if the lower part of the pile embedded in the sandy layers.

1. INTRODUCTION

Rivers on great plains change their beds frequently and below the river relatively young deposits are to be found to a considerable depth. Mostly this is the case at such plains where the surface, settled in geological ages, are filled up by river and sea deposits.
Under such soil conditions pile-foundations are made mostly, as usually in the recent period. In connection with the piled foundations the following three interrelated problems are encountered:

1/ Design of the piling depth, that of the required pile length

2/ Estimation of the piles' diameter and the bearing capacity

3/ Calculation of the expected settlement of the pile foundation.

Deposits under the river bed are loose, easy to compress the layers. Foundations near the surface involve, generally, considerable settlement, deformation and displacement of the foundation. In case of several bridges structural defects were encountered because of the piers' movements, due to the settlement, tilting and movement of foundation, elimination of which required considerable maintenance work.

2. LOOSE SEDIMENT UNDER THE RIVER BED

Five bridges were constructed in the last decades to span the River Tisza/Hungary. In connection significant exploration work was carried out. The exploration have revealed clayey layers of varying softness and medium stiffness and sandy layers of different composition, laying under each other from the surface to the depth of the exploration. Majority of the granular layers is fine sand. The void ratio of the clay is relatively high, it varies between

$$e = 0,8-1,17 \qquad /1/$$

Their plasticity index is

$$I_p = 46-52 \ \% \qquad /2/$$

Smaller than the above value has been encountered only at some thinner layers. The angle of internal friction of the clay is:

$$\emptyset \ 5-13^\circ$$

Angle of internal friction of the granular layers is 20-25°. Coefficient of uniformity

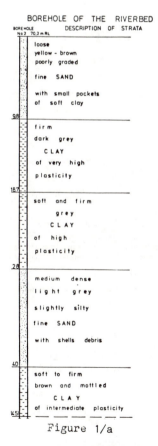

BOREHOLE OF THE RIVERBED

BOREHOLE No 2 70,2 m RL	DESCRIPTION OF STRATA
	loose
	yellow - brown
	poorly graded
	fine SAND
	with small pockets
	of soft clay
9,8	firm
	dark grey
	CLAY
	of very high
	plasticity
18,7	soft and firm
	grey
	CLAY
	of high
	plasticity
28	medium dense
	light grey
	slightly silty
	fine SAND
	with shells debris
40	soft to firm
	brown and mottled
	CLAY
45	of intermediate plasticity

Figure 1/a

Characteristic borehole
Boring on the site of the highway-bridge
spanning the River Tisza at Szeged

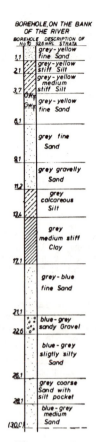

Figure 1/b

Characteristic borehole

Boring on the site of the motorway at Tiszapalkonya

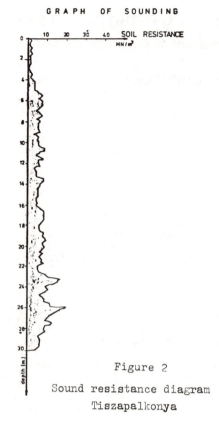

Figure 2

Sound resistance diagram Tiszapalkonya

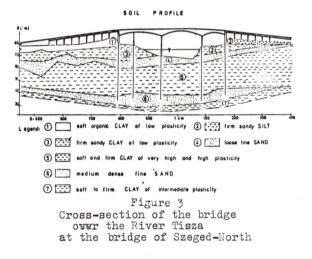

Figure 3

Cross-section of the bridge over the River Tisza at the bridge of Szeged-North

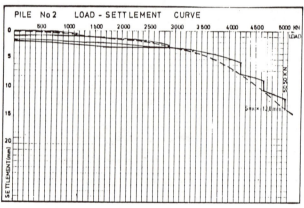

Figure 4/a

Load-settlement curve bored pile with dia. of o,8o m /Bridge at Csongrád/

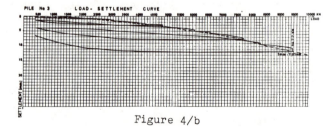

Figure 4/b

Load-settlement curve pile with dia of 1,2 m /Bridge at Csongrád/

is U = 2-6. The water content of the cohesive layers is near the plastic limit, only some layers have higher water content

The natural water content of the granular layers is about 25 to 30 %
Characteristic boring profiles is shown in Figure 1/a and 1/b.

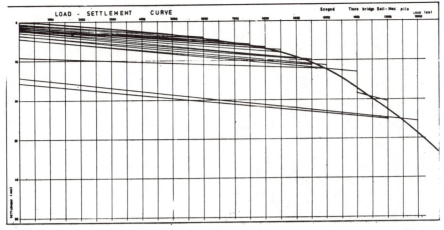

Figure 4/c

**Load-settlement curve Soil-Mec type bored pile
with dia of 1,2 m at the bridge of Szeged-North**

At other exploration the loose granular layers are prevalent. Sounding of the granular layers showed relatively low soil resistance although it was not possible to eliminate the skin friction entirely at these probes /Fig.2/

Scouring-outs are also to be considered because of the considerable flow regime of the river, as a consequence of which the level of the bed bottom can not be considered as an exact line. The scouring-outs and the deposits change their places quite frequently /Fig.3./

3. PILE-SKIN FRICTION IN LOOSE, GRANULAR DEPOSIT

Pile foundations made in relatively young loose deposits are to be generally considered as friction piles, i.e. the skin friction has basic role in the bearing capacity. The performed different tests, test piling, sounding and loading, equally have shown that the load acting on the piles, serving as bridge foundations, is basically carried by the skin friction.

4. TEST PILING

The loading tests in the course of design were carried out mostly on the bank. To eliminate the skin friction of the layers above the bed bottom we enclosed the upper part of the piles with pipes thus limiting the acting of the skin friction only from the depth of the bed bottom. It was a simulation of the work of the river piles. Of the performed loading tests /Fig. 4a/ a shorter and a longer piles have been chosen for this paper /Fig. 4b/. Loading tests were made at the actual sites of piling during construction.

These tests also justified the above-explained facts. When performing loading-tests on Soil-Mec piles with dia. of 1,2 we obtained bearing capacity of 13,000 k/N and settlement of 28 mm. For load-settlement curve see Fig. 4/c.

The ultimate load capacity of the shorter Ø O,80 m pile – 26 m – was 5050 kN, while that of the longer Ø 1,20 m pile, –33 m,–was as much as 9477 kN. The acting skin friction was the same at both piles, because at the longer pile on the upper part the friction was eliminated by casing tube.
The loading tests at other bridges have shown that the compression under the shorter piles was several times more than under the longer ones.
The experiences of constructed bridges have shown that the foundations on long bored piles suffered no remarkable settlement and there was no tilting or movement.

5. EVALUATION OF THE PILE LOADING

The loading tests carried out for different bridge foundations have not, of course, scientific aims, they have been intended to serve practical goal, checking of the designed bearing capacity of the pile. The general lesson that can be drawn from the numerous loading tests performed in loose sediments is that the load acting on the piles is mostly carried by the skin friction. If we attribute the results obtained for bearing capacity by loading tests solely to the skin friction and if we calculate the friction coefficient from the acting load based on the well-known formula of the skin friction

$$P = \frac{q}{2} K.f \qquad /3/$$

where q – is the geostatical pressure kPa
K – is the skin surface sq.m., and
f – is the friction coefficient
and take the f = tg Ø value into account we obtain for the value of Ø angle is in good coordination with the average friction angle of the penetrable layers.

6. SELECTION OF THE FOUNDATION LEVEL

When selecting the foundation level the problems connected with movement are to be necessarily taken into account. The experiences
gained with formerly built bridges have shown
that at bridges with shallow foundations considerable settlement, tilting and movement
have been encountered. Such phenomena were observed at several bridges spanning the River
Tisza and Danube. Especially big movements were
observed at the road-bridge built over the River Tisza at Szeged toward the end of the last
century and founded in the soft clay layers
relatively near the bed bottom by caisson method. The test has revealed that the movements
were caused by the soft clay layer interchang-
ed by uniform sized quick-sand to be found
under the river bed. The colloid content of
the clay is very high.
Thick and unfavourable from the foundation-
aspect layers lying under the riverbed require
long bored piles with big diameter /o,8 m and
over/ for bridge foundation. Such long piles
prevent settlement and movement of pile
foundations.

Prediction of the behaviour of friction piles in non-cohesive soils

Prédiction sur le comportement des pieux flottants dans des sols pulvérulents

E. SELLGREN, Ph.D., AB Jacobson & Widmark, Lidingö, Sweden

SYNOPSIS

The choice of foundation method is an important matter both economically and technically. For the design of the foundation, testing of the soil is needed to obtain information about its geotechnical properties. When designing piled foundations in non-cohesive soils, it is necessary to know the deformation properties of the soil. The pressuremeter is a suitable piece of equipment to determine stress/strain relationship. Theories and calculation methods have been developed to use the results in foundation design.

In this study, 24 full scale tests on driven precast piles are presented where the calculation of the bearing capacity and the settlement have been based on pressuremeter test results.

Three different calculation methods have been studied. The results show a large scatter in the accuracy of the prediction, both between the methods and within each method. Therefore new design diagrams have been proposed, which are based on this experience.

A new way of determining the whole load/settlement relationship for a loaded pile is presented. This method is based on the hyperbolic equation, and the pressuremeter modulus and limit pressure are used in the analysis. The agreement with measured data is very good.

BEARING CAPACITY

Point resistance

When determining the bearing capacity of friction piles by means of the results from pressuremeter tests, the point resistance and the shaft resistance are added, as in most other calculation methods. The method was proposed by Ménard (1963). The ultimate unit point resistance p_{pf} is determined as

$$p_{pf} = q_o + k p_1^* \qquad (1)$$

where

k = bearing capacity factor

q_o = overburden pressure at the foundation level

p_1^* = $p_1 - p_o$ = net limit pressure

p_o = the lateral earth pressure at rest.

The bearing capacity factor, k, is dependent on a number of different variables, primarily; type of soil, depth of embedment, shape of pile and installation method.

According to Centre d'Etudes Ménard (1975), the soil is divided into four categories. In Fig. 1, the bearing capacity factor, vs the ratio of the depth of embedment and pile diameter, is presented.

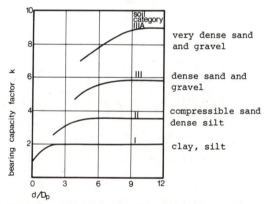

Fig. 1   Bearing capacity factor, k, vs the ratio of the depth of embedment and the pile diameter according to Centre d'Etudes Ménard (1975)

Bustamante & Gianeselli (1981) proposed a slightly altered classification of soil categories as well as bearing capacity factors. This proposal implies a decrease of the previously mentioned k-factors of about 25 percent, see Fig. 2.

Baguelin et al (1978) presented the k-factors in a more differential way with one graph for each type of soil. This proposal gives higher values than the two other. In Fig. 3, the k-factors for silt and sand/gravel are presented.

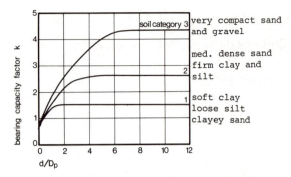

Fig. 2   Bearing capacity factor, k, vs the ratio
of the depth of embedment and the pile
diameter according to Bustamante &
Gianeselli (1981)

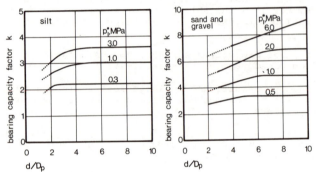

Fig. 3   Bearing capacity factor, k, vs the ratio
of the depth of embedment and the pile
diameter according to Baguelin et al
(1978)

Shaft Resistance

The shaft resistance of friction piles in non-
cohesive soil is also determined as a function
of the limit pressure of the soil measured by
pressuremeter tests. It is also dependent on
the type of soil, pile material, pile dimensions and installation method. In Fig. 4, three
different proposals of maximum unit shaft resistance are given.

Creep Load

The creep load (or the critical load), defined
as the load at the minimum radius of curvature
of the creep curve, can be calculated, in
essence, in the same way as the bearing capacity. By replacing the net limit pressure by the
net creep pressure in Eq. (1), and in the design
curves for point resistance and shaft resistance, it is possible to calculate the creep
load with great accuracy.

LOAD/SETTLEMENT RELATIONSHIP

Calculation Methods

The settlement analysis of friction piles in
non-cohesive soils is a rather complex problem.

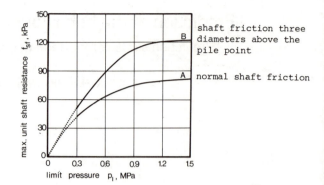

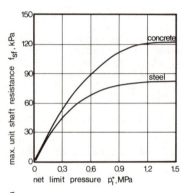

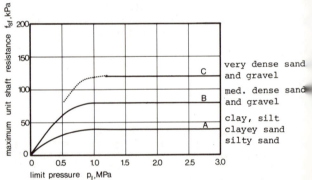

Fig. 4   The maximum unit shaft resistance for
driven piles, vs the limit pressure and
the net limit pressure according to

a) Centre d'Etudes Ménard (1975)
b) Baguelin et al (1978)
c) Bustamante & Gianeselli (1981)

The driving of the piles causes changes in the
deformation characteristics of the soil. Large
residual stresses in the pile due to the driving are sometimes obtained, and this can have
a great influence on the load/settlement characteristics. Many of the solutions for determining the settlement of single piles and pile
groups are roughly approximate. Many of them
determine only one point on the load-displacement curve or give only a linear relationship
for the initial part of the curve or are only
valid for rather small loads compared with the
ultimate load, see for example Gambin (1963)
and Cassan (1966).

For friction piles driven in cohesive soils, there are, however, calculation methods which determine the load/settlement relationship with great accuracy, even in the vicinity of the ultimate load. For example, Torstensson proposed an idealized relationship between load and displacement. By slightly changing this relationship it has been found that this method predicts very well the behaviour of friction piles in non-cohesive soils if the shaft resistance is larger than the point resistance, see Sellgren (1981). The idealized relationship is normalized with respect to the maximum unit shaft resistance, f_{sf}, and the displacement, s_f, when the ultimate load is reached, see Fig. 5.

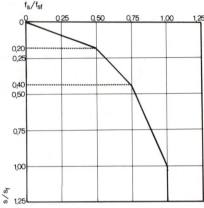

Fig. 5   Idealized relationship for friction piles in non-cohesive soil between the relative shaft resistance and the relative displacement of the pile according to Torstensson (1973) and revised by Sellgren (1981).

The displacement modulus, K_s (at half the bearing capacity), is determined by the relationship, E_p/G_{pr}, and, l_p/D_p, where E_p = Young's modulus of the pile material, G_{pr} = shear modulus of the soil determined by pressuremeter tests, l_p = pile length and D_p = pile diameter, see Fig. 6.

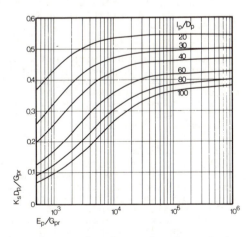

Fig. 6   Diagram for determination of the initial displacement modulus, K_s, according to Bengtsson & Hansbo (1979)

Proposed Method

The author has in a thesis (Sellgren 1981) stated a calculation method which predicts with great accuracy the load/settlement relationship up to the ultimate load. The load/settlement relationship for a friction pile in non-cohesive soil is here expressed by means of the equation of a hyperbola. The settlement, s, is thus determined as

$$s = a \frac{P}{1-P/P_f} \qquad (2)$$

where

a = initial slope of the load/settlement relationship

P = load on the pile head

P_f = predicted bearing capacity

The initial slope for a pile with circular cross-section can be expressed as

$$a = \frac{4}{\pi D_p} \frac{1+\tanh\theta l_p (\beta/\theta E_p D_p)}{\beta+\tanh\theta l_p (\theta E_p D_p)} \qquad (3)$$

where

β = $13.5 E_{pr}$ for $\nu_s = 0.3$

θ = $\sqrt{4B/E_p D_p}$

B = $1.25 E_{pr}$ for $\nu_s = 0.3$

ν_s = Poisson's ratio for the soil

For piles with square cross-section there is no term $4/\pi$ in the expression, and the side length is used instead of the diameter. The simplest way to determine the initial slope, a, is to use the nomographic in Fig. 7. By the nomograph, "a" is determined for a concrete pile with E_p = 30 GPa and a square cross-section.

For driven piles the cyclic pressuremeter modulus is used instead of the standard modulus.

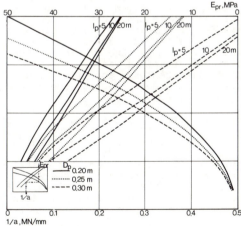

Fig. 7   Nomograph for determination of the initial slope of the load/settlement relationship for driven friction piles in non-cohesive soils. The nomograph is made for piles with square cross-section, with E_p=30 GPa and ν_s=0.3.

The cyclic modulus is determined by carrying out a number of loading and unloading cycles in the pseudo-elastic phase, i.e. the straight part of the pressuremeter curve. If the pressuremeter test only is carried out as a standard test, an approximate value of the cyclic modulus can be obtained as 2 to 4 times the standard modulus. The lower limit is valid for a fine soil and the upper for coarser material.

The asymptote to the hyperbola representing in this case the failure load, P_f, calculated from the pressuremeter test results.

CASE RECORDS

In order to study the behaviour of friction piles in non-cohesive soils, a number of full scale tests have been carried out. In all cases, the bearing capacities and the settlement characteristics of the piles, have been predicted on the basis of the pressuremeter test results. They have, thereafter, been compared with results from load tests or a stress wave analysis using the computer program CAPWAP. In the following, the test sites and the results are described.

A. Luleå, Sweden

A bridge over a railway and a road was to be founded on friction piles. The soil consisted of deep layers of sand and silt. Pressuremeter tests were performed both before the driving of the piles and after the driving of the whole groups was completed. The upper 4 m consisted of loose organic silt with the mean limit pressure, p_1 = 0.59 MPa, and the mean pressuremeter modulus, E_{pr} = 4.9 MPa. Below the silt was dense sand with the corresponding values, 1.94 MPa and 12.0 MPa, respectively. After the driving of the pile group, the limit pressure decreased to 0.38 MPa in the loose silt and increased to much more than 2.2 MPa in the sand. The modulus increased in the silt to 5.5 MPa and in the sand to 54 MPa.

The square concrete piles with the side length 270 mm were driven 10.7 m into the soil by means of a 4 tonnes drop hammer directly to the intended pile point level. The load tests included two different piles in the outer abutments, one pile in the middle of each group. One of the piles was tested twice, the first time when only the pile in question was driven and the second time after the whole group was driven.

The results of the load test only gave a bearing capacity of 0.78 MN on the single pile (A1). The other piles (A2 and A3) had a bearing capacity of 1.48 MN and 1.35 MN, respectively. For determining the bearing capacity, the rules proposed by the Swedish Pile Commission (1979) have been used, which implies that the bearing capacity is determined at a displacement, s_o, of the pile head, which is

$$s_o = Pl_p/E_p A_p + 20 + D_p/20, \text{ mm}$$

B. Göteborg, Sweden

The soil consisted originally of about 12 m of soft organic clay above a very deep layer of loose to dense sand. The mean limit pressure in the sand was 1.3 MPa and the mean modulus was 7.3 MPa. The undrained shear strength of the clay was only about 10 kPa.

Two piles, which constituted a part of a pile deck for a small bridge, were tested. The test piles were made of concrete with a square cross-section and a side length of 235 mm. They were driven by means of a 3 t falling hammer, 18.6 m (B1) and 18.1 m (B2) into the soil.

The bearing capacities observed for the two piles were 1.19 MN and 1.11 MN, respectively. There were no measurements of the point resistance and the shaft resistance during the tests, but the CAPWAP-analysis of a redriven pile gives 0.30 MN and 0.70 MN respectively.

C. Pitsundet, Sweden

The soil consisted of layered medium dense silt and sand. The geotechnical investigations indicated a slight increase in the strength at depth with a lower strength around the pile points. Test piles were driven at two different sites, with two piles in the first and six piles in the second. The mean limit pressure at the first site was 0.92 MPa and at the second, 0.81 MPa. The corresponding pressuremeter moduli were 8.1 MPa and 9.0 MPa, respectively. The piles were concrete driven piles with a width of 270 mm and lengths varying between 11.7 m and 13.0 m.

No load tests on the piles were carried out, but they were tested by stress wave analysis. At the first site, the bearing capacity varied between 1.55 MN and 1.75 MN with a shaft resistance of 1.44 MN to 1.66 MN. At the second site, the bearing capacity was 1.10-1.50 MN with a variation in shaft resistance between 0.90 MN and 1.40 MN.

D. Hjälmaresund, Sweden

At the site for the bridge, the soil consisted mainly of non-cohesive soil of sand and gravel to great depth. Down to 15-20 m it was sand, which is loose to medium dense for 10 to 15 m depth and under that, rather dense. In one of the bridge abutments, the mean limit pressure was 0.65 MPa and in the other 0.62 MPa in the non-cohesive soil. The corresponding mean pressuremeter modulus was 13.1 and 6.5 MPa, respectively.

Five piles in two abutments were tested by stress wave analysis. They were of concrete and had a side length of 275 mm and length 18-19 m. They were driven at an inclination (4:1) into the soil. The analysed bearing capacity varied between 0.70 MN and 1.55 MN and the shaft resistance between 0.63 MN and 0.95 MN.

E. Amsterdam RAI, Holland

In connection with ESOPT II (European Symposium on Penetration Testing), one test pile was driven into laminated sand, clay and peat. The soil was soft down to 12 m depth where there was a rapid increase in strength. The limit pressure varied between 0.1 and 0.3 MPa in the soft soil, whereas it was up to 2.0 MPa in the dense sand. The mean limit pressure along the pile was 0.41 MPa and the mean pressuremeter modulus, 2.7 MPa.

One test pile was driven 14.1 m into the soil.
The dimensions of the pile were 250x250 mm.

The bearing capacity of the test pile was
determined as 1.10 MN, but there were no
separate measurements of point and shaft
resistance. Nor was a CAPWAP analysis carried out.

F. Fittja, Sweden

In Fittja there were two different test
sites. At test site 1, the soil consisted of
1 m dry crust, 10 m soft clay and below that a
deep layer of non-cohesive soil, which was very
loose sand/silt down to 25 m and rather dense
sand/gravel at greater depth. The length of the
piles at this site varied between 20 and 28 m.
The mean limit pressure was 0.54-0.80 MPa and
the mean pressuremeter modulus 4.6-8.2 MPa.

At the other test site it was silt and sand
from the soil surface to great depth. Down to
15 m depth the soil was loose, while the remainder was medium dense. The length of the
test piles varied between 16 and 27 m. The mean
limit pressure was 0.38-0.60 MPa and the mean
pressuremeter modulus, 6.1-7.3 MPa.

In total five piles were tested, both by load
tests and by stress wave analysis using CAPWAP.
The bearing capacities for the two test piles
(F1 and F2) at test site 1 varied between
0.31 MN and 0.54 MN. The corresponding values
for the three piles (F3, F4 and F5) at test
site 2 were 0.75-1.21 MN.

ANALYSIS

Bearing Capacity

There is a considerable scatter in the results,
both between the three calculation methods and
within each method. It is not easy to see a
clear trend, but the proposals of Baguelin et
al (1978) and Centre d'Etudes Ménard (1975)
give similar results with quite good agreement
with the measured bearing capacities if the
piles are installed in medium dense to dense
soil. For loose soil, they overestimate it by
up to 2-3 times, whereas the prediction by
Bustamante & Gianeselli gives good agreement
for these soils, but is, on the other hand,
very conservative for dense soils.

By splitting up the bearing capacity into its
two components, it is clear that the same trend
for the shaft resistance as for the total
bearing capacity, but it is more obscure for
the point resistance, because in the CAPWAP
analysis this can be underestimated if insufficient energy is transferred to the point
during the pile driving. However, for almost
all of the piles analysed, the point resistance
is only a fraction of the total bearing capacity even in the case where load tests have been
performed. It appears that if there is a very
low share of measured point resistance, the
bearing capacity is overestimated by the calculation methods, but if most of the load is
carried at the point, the prediction is quite
accurate.

As Baguelin et al overestimate the shaft resistance for loose layered soils, but otherwise
predicted it very well, the author has proposed
a change in the design diagram shown in Fig. 8.

TABLE I

Selected data from piles studied and the
calculated results of the measured bearing
capacity.

Site pile No	l_p m	$\bar{p}_1$ MPa	$\bar{E}_{pr}$ MPa	Bearing capacity, MN			
				CM*	BA*	BU*	Meas.
A1	10.7	1.33	8.7	1.34	1.57	0.89	0.78
A2	10.7	>2.0	32.2	1.38	1.57	1.24	1.48
A3	10.7	>2.0	32.2	1.33	1.49	1.14	1.35
B1	18.6	1.30	7.3	1.08	1.20	0.84	1.19
B2	18.1	1.30	7.3	1.04	1.15	0.79	1.11
C1	13.0	0.92	8.1	1.13	1.49	0.81	1.75
C2	13.0	0.92	8.1	1.13	1.49	0.81	1.55
C3	12.8	0.81	9.0	1.16	1.28	0.58	1.10
C4	11.7	0.81	9.0	1.02	1.26	0.57	1.10
C5	12.8	0.81	9.0	1.16	1.28	0.57	1.20
C6	11.7	0.81	9.0	1.02	1.26	0.57	1.40
C7	11.7	0.81	9.0	1.02	1.26	0.57	1.50
C8	11.7	0.81	9.0	1.02	1.26	0.57	1.50
D1	19.0	0.65	13.1	2.68	2.60	1.78	1.08
D2	19.0	0.65	13.1	2.08	2.60	1.78	0.70
D3	18.0	0.62	6.5	2.65	2.55	1.75	1.55
D4	19.0	0.62	6.5	1.17	1.61	0.71	1.20
D5	19.0	0.62	6.5	1.17	1.61	0.71	1.25
E1	14.1	0.41	2.7	1.24	1.28	0.66	1.10
F1	28.1	0.80	8.2	2.97	3.78	1.75	0.54
F2	20.0	0.54	4.6	1.60	1.90	0.72	0.31
F3	26.7	0.60	7.0	2.38	2.65	1.32	1.21
F4	21.7	0.51	7.3	1.29	1.83	0.83	0.82
F5	15.7	0.38	6.1	1.10	1.41	0.69	0.75

*CM = Centre d'Etudes Ménard (1975)
 BA = Baguelin et al (1976)
 BU = Bustamante & Gianeselli (1981)

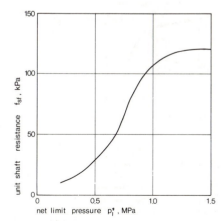

Fig. 8 Proposed design diagram for determination of unit shaft resistance of driv-
en friction piles in non-cohesive soil.

By using this diagram, the shaft resistance can be predicted with great accuracy. The mean value of the predictions for the studied piles differs by only 3% from the measured, with only a small variance.

Also, the design diagram for the bearing capacity factor is changed so that they better predict the point resistance, even when there is a considerable share of shaft resistance in the total cpacity, see Fig. 9.

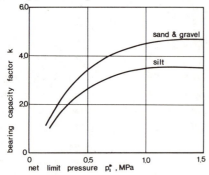

Fig. 9   Proposed design diagram for determination of the bearing capacity factor for driven friction piles in non-cohesive soil.

This proposal will not give such great accuracy for the measured values from the CAPWAP analyses as for those obtained for the shaft resistance, because the CAPWAP analyses often underestimate the point resistance results compared to those obtained in a load test, as too little energy is transferred to the point if the shaft resistance is too high.

Load/Displacement Relationship

The load/displacement relationship calculated by means of the hyperbolic equation, Eq. 2 and by using Eq. 3, shows for almost all piles a very good concordance with the corresponding measured relationship. In Fig. 10, an example is shown of the comparison between the measured and calculated relationship. The example shown is one of the piles (F5) at Fittja. The bearing capacity has been calculated by means of the design diagram in Fig. 8 and 9.

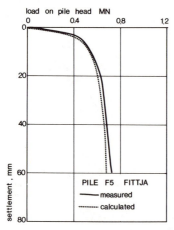

Fig. 10   Comparison between the measured and calculated bearing capacity for pile F5.

CONCLUSIONS

The following concluding remarks can be drawn from the study performed:

- the pressuremeter is an excellent instrument for determining the deformation properties of the soil in situ

- the common calculation methods for the design of friction piles in non-cohesive soils are not sufficiently accurate in all cases

- the shaft resistance of driven friction piles in non-cohesive soils is predicted with great accuracy by the new proposed design diagram, Fig. 8

- the point resistance is best predicted by Eq. 1 and the new proposal for bearing capacity factors, Fig. 9

- the load/settlement relationship can be determined with great accuracy by means of the hyperbolic equation, Eq. 2, and by using Eq. 3 to calculate the initial slope of the curve

- pile design, based on pressuremeter test results, may allow for a considerable reduction in pile lengths and, consequently, in foundation costs.

REFERENCES

Baguelin, F., Jézéquel, J.F. and Shields, D.H., 1978.   The Pressuremeter and Foundation Engineering. Trans. Tech. Publications, Clausthal.

Bustamante, M.G. and Gianeselli, L., 1981.   Réajustement des paramètres de calcul des pieux. Proc. of the 10th International Conference on Soil Mechanics and Foundation Engineering, Vol. 2, pp. 643-646, Stockholm.

Cassan, M., 1966.   Le tassement des pieux. Synthèse des recherches récentes et essais comparatifs. Sols-Soils, Vol. V, No. 18-19, pp. 43-52, Paris.

Centre d'Etudes Ménard, 1975.   Règles d'utilisation des techniques pressiométriques et d'exploitation des résultats obtenus pour le calcul des fondations. Publication D/60/75, Longjemeau.

Gambin, M.P., 1963.   Calcul de tassement d'une fondation profonde en fonction des résultats pressiométriques. Sols-Soils, Vol. 2, No. 7, pp. 11-23, Paris.

Ménard, L., 1963a.   Calcul de la force portante des fondations sur la base des résultats des essais pressiométriques. Sols-Soils, Vol. II, No. 5, pp. 9-24, Paris.

Sellgren, E., 1981.   Friction Piles in Non-Cohesive Soils. Evaluation from Pressuremeter Tests. Thesis. Department of Geotechnical Engineering, Chalmers University of Technology, Gothenburg.

Torstensson, B-A., 1973.   Friction piles in soft clay. A field study in model scale (in Swedish). Thesis. Department of Geotechnical Engineering, Chalmers University of Technology, Gothenburg.

Notes concerning analysis of drilled piers

Remarques sur le calcule des pieux de grand diamètre

J. ŠIMEK, Professor of Civil Engineering, Czech Technical University, Civil Engineering Department, Prague, Czechoslovakia

Z. BAŽANT, Professor Emeritus of Civil Engineering, Czech Technical University, Civil Engineering Department, Prague, Czechoslovakia

O. SEDLECKÝ, Research Assistant, Czech Technical University, Civil Engineering Department, Prague, Czechoslovakia

SYNOPSIS   Part I, for which is responsible Z.Bažant, treats the evaluation of coefficient of structural strength of soil.Analysis of elastic settlement of drilled piers by linear elastic theory needs to introduce the appropriate value of the active depth in dependence of structural strength of soil. This strength can be found if coefficient of structural strength is known. Verification of this coefficient is possible by measurements of settlement of pier base. - Part II, for which are responsible J.Šimek and O.Sedlecký, shows a method for evaluation of skin friction from load test results and draws conclusions for analysis of bearing capacity of drilled piers.

PART I.COEFFICIENT OF STRUCTURAL STRENGTH

Structural strength is equal to the stress induced by applied load, which is not causing a measurable settlement. This is the zero settlement condition which arises when the soil grains compress only elastically, negligibly in compasiron to the settlement caused by the relative movement of grains. Measurement of structural strength in laboratory is difficult because the stress due to the own weight of apparatus may be greater than the structural strength. On the contrary the contact stress acting at drilled pier base may be equal or smaller than structural strength. This allows to determine the structural strength by drilled piers load tests.

When the elastic settlement analysis of drilled piers by linear theory of Poulos /Poulos 1980, Bažant 1979/ was introduced by the writter into the Czechoslovak Standard ČSN 731004 the question emerged of the appropriate value of Young´s modulus of soil to be used in the analysis. It was ascertained /Bažant 1984/ that this modulus is equal to triaxial modulus of deformation, if the assumption is made, that the soil on which the drilled pier is bearing undergoes compression in a thin layer below the pier base only. The thickness of this layer, the active depth, can be evaluated from the condition that the compression of soil arises when the increment of stress in subsoil is greater than the structural strength of soil. Structural strength is defined as the geostatic stress multiplied by coefficient of structural strength. Coefficient is given in literature /Bažant 1984/. However, for complicated geological conditions and great applied loads it is preferable to determine the coefficient of structural strength on site. His value can be obtained from the pier load tests delivering a zero settlement at pier base for small load, usually the first load increment. When the coefficient is known, the length of drilled pier producing a minimum settlement can be obtained.

EVALUATION OF COEFFICIENT OF STRUCTURAL STRENGTH

In the active depth concept the hypothesis is made that the structural strength equals the normal geostatic effective stress σ_v' multiplied by the coefficient of structural strength n. The compression of soil develops in the layer above the plane in which the vertical normal stress σ_z' produced by pier head is greater than structural strength. The condition of zero compression is

$$\sigma_z' \leqslant n\,\sigma_v' \qquad\qquad /1/$$

Solution of Eq.1 requires the knowledge of the coefficient n which can be found, if the stress is known at which the zero settlement arises.

In the literature /Bažant 1984/ the recommended values of the coefficient n vary between 0.1 and 0.4 according to the kind of soil. These values have been derived from the telltale measurements of displacements in the subsoil below loaded areas of shallow footings. The question may be raised, if these values apply to the subsoil below the drilled pier bases. The more precise values of n are also needed, if complicated geological conditions and/or great loads are involved.

Drilled piers load tests offer the method of finding the coefficient n,a method based on the fact, that the zero settlement of pier base occurs at the beginning of loading. If sufficiently small first load increment is realized, a zero settlement occurs as it was revealed by pier load tests /Reese and al. 1976, Wright and Reese 1979/ at which the instrumentation allowed to measure the settlement of pier base.

To find the coefficient n we insert into Eq. 1 the vertical normal stress

$$\sigma'_z = c_z \, Q_o \, / \, D^2 \qquad /2/$$

where D = length of pier, Q_o = head load at zero base settlement. Q_o should be the maximum
load at which the base settlement is zero. If
the load rises over Q_o /point b in Fig.3/, the
structural failure occurs which is manifested
by abrupt settlement, albeit a small one. Coefficient c_z tabulated by Sankaran /1981/ for
Poisson´s ratio γ = 0.5 depends on depth z,
slenderness ratio D/d, where d = diameter of
pier, and K = E_p/E_s, the stiffness ratio of
Young´s moduli of concrete shaft E_p and of soil
around pier E_s /Fig.1/.

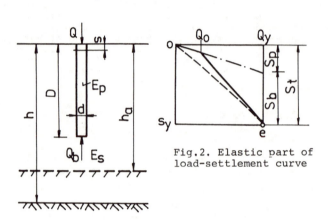

Fig.2. Elastic part of
load-settlement curve

Fig.1. Parameters of drilled pier problem

Coefficient of structural strength is according to Eq. /1/ and /2/ expressed by

$$n = c_z \, Q_o \, / \, (\sigma'_v \, D^2) \qquad /3/$$

The vertical normal effective geostatic stress
in a homogeneous soil

$$\sigma'_v = \gamma_d \, z - \gamma_w \, h_w \qquad /4/$$

in which γ_d = unit weight of dry soil, z =
depth of the point for which the stress is
calculated, γ_w = unit weight of water, h_w =
depth of the point under the groundwater table.
The measurements of the settlement of pier base s_b requires the instrumentation which is
not applied at usual load tests, where only the
head settlement s_t is measured. However, in this
case it is also possible to find the load Q_o
at which s_b is zero from the equation

$$s_b = s_t - s_p \qquad /5/$$

where s_p is the compression of concrete pier
shaft /Fig.2/. If $s_t = s_p$, the settlement of base s_b = 0. In homogeneous soil it can be assumed
that the load Q acting on the head of pier
shaft decreases linearly from the head to the
tip. When the base load Q_b = 0, the compression

of concrete pier shaft is given by

$$S_p = 0.5 \, Q \, D \, / \, (A_p \, E_p) \qquad /6/$$

where A_p, E_p are the area, resp. Young´s modulus
of concrete. However, the linear decrease of
load is not always assured. The compression of
the shaft is greater, when the load is transmitted to the surrounding soil by skin friction in more compressible layer at base. On the
contrary, the compression of the shaft is sma-
ler, when the load is transmitted to the soil
in cavings situated near the pier head. Therefore in these circumstances one can not skip
the measurement of the settlement of base.

If the coefficient n is known, it is possible
for given load Q and D to find the relative
active depth h_a/D from the graphs published
by Bažant /1984/. Knowing h_a/D, one can find out
the depth correction factor R_{ha}, and in turn,
the Poulos settlement influence factor
$I_{sa} = I_1 \, R_k \, R_{ha}$. The graphs of factors I_1, R_k
and $R_h = R_{ha}$ were published by Poulos to enab-
le the practical estimate of settlement /Pou-
los 1980, Bažant 1979/. The elastic settlement
is given by equation

$$s = I_{sa} \, Q \, / \, (E_o \, d) \qquad /7/$$

When the factor I_{sa} is introduced, the modulus
of the layer under the pier base should be
used in conjunction.

DRILLED PIERS WITH MINIMUM SETTLEMENT

If the coefficient of structural strength n is
verified by the load test, the length of pier
D_o can be computed assuring for given load Q
the zero settlement at base. Expressing the
geostatic stress by

$$n \, \sigma'_v = n \, \gamma_n \, D_o \qquad /8/$$

and inserting σ'_z from Eq. 2 the length of pier
follows from Eq. 1

$$D_o = (c_z \, Q \, / \, n \, \gamma_n)^{1/3} \qquad /9/$$

Drilled piers having the length D_o produce the
contact stress at pier base which is equal to
structural strength. If this condition is satisfied, the soil below the base undergoes no
compression, the drilled pier is behaving as a
column bearing on rock and his settlement derives only from the compression of concrete.
Drilled piers of the length D_o are useful on
compressible soils of great depth in the case
the rock is out of reach when foundations sensitive to settlement should be built.

RESULTS OF COMPUTATIONS

Sand

The drilled pier Q1 in Houston, Texas /Wright
and Reese 1979/ is bearing on saturated dense
silty sand to fine snad SP, exhibiting N = 32.

The length of pier $D = 16.71$ m, the diameter $d = 0.914$ m, $D/d = 18$ and groundwater level at 11.22 m above base. Coefficient n can be inferred from the head load at zero base settlement $Q_o = 401$ kN /Fig.3/. Vertical normal stress σ'_z in the middle of pier base according to Eq.2 is $\sigma'_z = 25 \times 401/16.71^2 = 36$ kPa which equals the structural strength. Coefficient $c_z = 25$ holding for D/d 18, $K = 500$ and $\gamma = 0.5$ was interpolated between the values tabulated for $D/d = 10$ and 25 /Sankaran 1981/. Vertical normal geostatic stress at base according to Eq.4 is $\sigma'_v = 20 \times 16.71 - 10 \times 11.22 = 222$ kPa. Introducing these values into Eq. 3 we get the coefficient of structural strength of saturated sand $n = 36/222 = 0.16$. The load $Q_o = 401$ kN fulfills the condition that it is on the verge of equilibrium before the failure of structural strength starts /Fig.3, point b/.

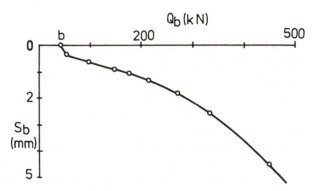

Fig.3. Settlement at base of pier Q1

Gravelly sand

The drilled pier T1 of Honshu-Shikoku Bridge, Japan /Takahashi 1981/ is bearing on saturated very dense gravelly sand having $N = 40$ to 50. The pier has the extreme length of $D = 70$ m and diameter $d = 3$ m, D/d 23. Groundwater level is 63.5 m above base. The greatest load attained at the test is 40 000 kN. Even if the pier is not bearing on the rock, his settlement is minimum as if it was so. From the graph of permanent settlements the guess can be made that the zero base settlement is achieved for head load $Q_o = 30\ 000$ kN. For interpolated $c_z = 33$ the vertical normal stress is $\sigma'_z = 33 \times 30\ 000/70^2 = 202$ kPa. The ensuing load $Q_b = 1\ 436$ kN is apparently below the sensitivity of measurement. Vertical effective geostatic stress $\sigma'_v = 21 \times 70 - 10 \times 63.5 = 835$ kPa Coefficient $n = 202/835 = 0.24$. The length which assures zero settlement at base follows from Eq. 9 as $D_o = (33 \times 30\ 000/0.24 \times 21)^{1/3} = 58.13$ m. The actual length of 70 m is greater than needed.

Clay

The drilled pier S1 in Houston, Texas /Wright and Reese 1979/ is bearing on fissured clay CH. The length $D = 7.05$ m, $d = 0.76$ m, $D/d = 9$ and groundwater level 2.47 m above base. Head load at zero base settlement $Q_o = 107$ kN. Vertical normal stress for $c_z = 10$ is $\sigma'_z = 10 \times 107/7.05^2 = 22$ kPa. Vertical normal effective geostatic stress $\sigma'_v = 20 \times 7.05 - 10 \times 2.47 = 116$ kPa. Coefficient $n = 22/116 = 0.19$.

CONCLUSIONS

Under the assumption that the limit Q_o was securely ascertained computations of the coefficient of structural strength have given the following results:
/a/ saturated dense silty sand $n = 0.16$
/b/ saturated very dense gravelly sand $n = 0.24$
/c/ fissured clay $n = 0.19$
For these kinds of soils the value advocated in literature /Bažant 1984/ is $n = 0.2$. The agreement is satisfactory and it holds for drilled piers of lengths between 7.05 m and 70 m and of diameters between 0.76 m and 3 m.

REFERENCES

Bažant,Z. /1979/. Methods of Foundation Engineering, 616 pp. Elsevier, Amsterdam and New York.

Bažant,Z. /1984/. Estimating Soil Moduli from Drilled Piers Load Tests, ASCE Journal Geotech. Engg. /110/.

Poulos,H.G. and Davis,E.H. /1980/. Pile Foundation Analysis and Design, 397 pp. Wiley, New York.

Reese,L.C. and al. /1976/. Behavior of Drilled Piers under Axial Loading. ASCE Journal Geotech.Engg.Div., /102/ GT5, 493-510.

Sankaran, K.S. and al. /1981/. Stresses of Soil around Vertical Compressible Piles, ASCE Journal Geotech.Engg.Div. /107/, GT1, 107-112.

Takahashi,K. and al. /1981/. Investigation of Bearing Capacity of Foundation Ground of Honshu-Shikoku Bridge, Case History Volume, 9th ICSMFE, 132-156, Tokyo.

Wright,S.L. and Reese,L.C. /1979/. Design of Large-Diameter Bored Piles. Ground Engineering London, /12/, Nov.17-23 and 50-51.

PART II. BEARING CAPACITY

The influence of shaft resistance on the bearing capacity has been known since the beginning of pile foundation.Its significance has
considerably increased owing to the introduction of technologies of cast-in-place piles.
According to the results of in situ loading
tests the shaft (skin) resistance equals 60-
80% of the overall bearing capacity. The exception is represented by the point-bearing piles
supported at the bottom by rocks. The results
of more then 300field loading tests consider:
the activation of shaft resistance, the coefficient of earth pressure on the pile, the
active zone around the pile, the distribution
of the vertical and horizontal stresses, the
values of the limit stage coefficients etc.
The activation of shaft resistance occurs even
under a minor settlement of the pile,even if
this one is less than 1mm. Such a small displacement of pile is possible even under small
loading of the pile top or even in the case
of slightly compressible subsoil under the bottom. According to our expiriences may be considered rock, weak rock with the modulus of deformation more then 500 MPa. A further phenomenon bas been observed in the case of piles
concreted directly in the boring - the shear
area is formed arround the pile shaft. The soil
in the immediate surroundings of pile surface
hardens due to the concreting and the shear
area is at a distance of 20-50 mm from the actual pile surface (Fig.4).During the application of pressure grouting, during separate
concreting (prepac system) the shear area is
situated essentially at a greater distance. In
the case of permeable soils and weak rocks
their strengthening is achieved by the use of
cement grouting or by grouting suspension. In
the case of less permeable soils or impermeable soil the strengthening during concreting
and grouting is due to the hydratation of the
concrete or of the cement suspension. The other
case is the protection of pile shaft by PE or
PVC foils. Essentially it may be said that the
technology has a considerable influence on the
bearing capacity of boring piles. During the
observation of individual soil strata, deformations increase in the direction toward the
pile surface and become apparent.

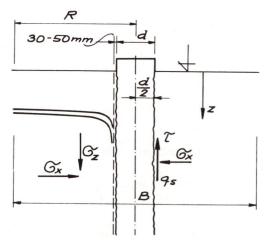

Figure 4. The active zone around
the pile

The distance from the pile centre is denoted
as R and designated as the active zone around
the pile.It is the area to which the effects
of the vertical loading of the pile are trans-
fered in the soil and also the deformations.
For non-cohesive soils it is approximatelly
R = 4d, for cohesive soils R = 3d, where d is
the diameter of pile. It is evident that a greater deformation of soil and therefore also vertical stress was measured in the vicinity of
the surface.According to the measurement the
deformation and the vertical sterss σ_z were zero
at the distance delimited by the boundary of
active zone. The other measurement was for the
estimation of the horizontal stress σ_x to receive the value K, the coefficient of earth
pressure on the pile (Fig.5a,5b). The value is
generaly used as a constant even if actually
is not. The pile surface is rather uneven,this
value can reach the coefficient of passive
earth pressure. Some authors consider coefficient at rest K = 1 - sinφ. From the tests carried out in the laboratory and in the field
different values of K were obtain, but never
less than K = 1 and never K = 1 - sinφ. These
results, testing of vertical and horizontal
contact stresses on the shaft and at the bot-
tomof piles were the bases for the equations
for determination of the bearing capacity of
large diameter boring piles. These types of
piles are the main technology of deep foundation in Czecholovakia, where about 200 000
meters of piles are realised every year.

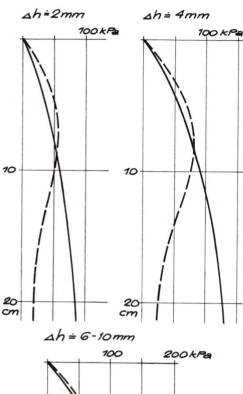

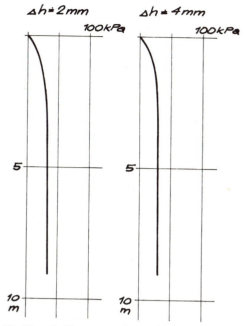

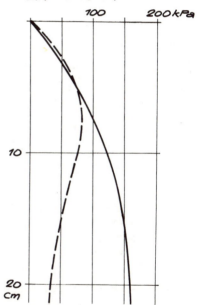

Fig.5a The influence of vertical displacement
Δh for vertical and horizontal stresses
(in laboratory).

Fig.5b The influence of vertical displacement
Δh for horizontal stresses on pile.

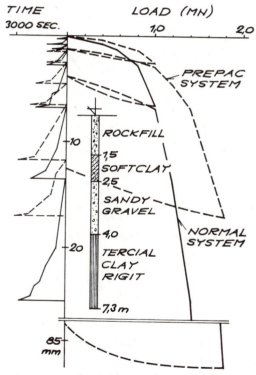

Fig.6 Loading diagram

The equation (10) takes into account many main
influences, technology, protection by PE or
PVC foils, theory of limit stages, activation of
shaft resistance, system of concreting etc.
Fig.6,7 shown the loading diagram for normal
system of conreting and for prepac system and
loading diagram for single pile and pile group.

PERMISSIBLE BEARING CAPACITY
Permissible bearing capacity according to the
Regulation for foundations of multi-storied
slab concrete structure (Šimek 1975) is

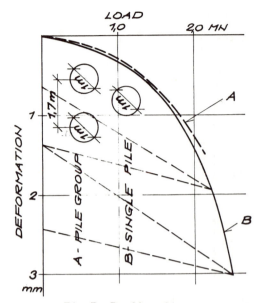

Fig.7 **Loading** diagram

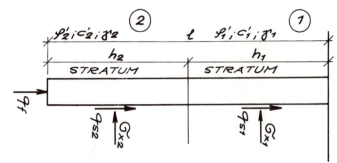

$$q_{s1} = m_3 \gamma_1 \frac{h_1}{2} tg(\alpha_1 m_1 \varphi_1') + m_2 c_1'$$

$$q_{s2} = m_3 (\gamma_1 h_1 + \gamma_2 \frac{h_2}{2}) tg(\alpha_2 m_1 \varphi_1') + m_2 c_2'$$

$$q_f = \frac{1}{2} m_3 \gamma_2 \alpha N_{\gamma R} + m_3 (\gamma_1 h_1 + \gamma_2 h_2) N_{qR} + m_2 c_2' N_{cR}$$

Fig.9 Equation (10) for determination permissible bearing capacity

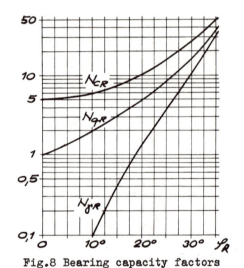

Fig.8 Bearing capacity factors

$$Q_p = 1,3 A q_f + u \sum_{i}^{n} h_i q_{si} \qquad (10)$$

q_f...resistance at the bottom of pile

A ... area of the cross-section of pile

u ... perimeter of pile

h_i... thickness of the i-stratum of subsoil

q_{si}.. unit shaft resistance of the i-stratum of subsoil

$$q_f = 0,5 \gamma_{1R} N_{\gamma R} + \gamma_{2R} l N_{qR} + c_R' N_{cR} \qquad (11)$$

or

$$q_f = 0,1 q_d \qquad (12)$$

Coefficient of limit stages are :
$m_1 = m_3 = 0,9$ and $m_2 = 0,5$

It means $\varphi_R = m_1 \varphi$, $c_R' = m_2 c'$, $\gamma_R = m_3 \gamma$ where φ', c', γ are the soil properties from the engineering geology investigation.

In the equation (10) and (11) are
l ... total length of pile
$q_{si} = \sigma_{xi} \tan(\alpha \varphi_{iR}) + c_{iR}'$
$\sigma_{xi} = \sigma_{zR} K$

σ_{zR} ... reduced geostatic effective stress in the centre of i-stratum of subsoil

α ... technology coefficient

$\alpha = 0,8$ for using the bentonite suspension,

$\alpha = 0,8$ for using PE or PVC foils (thickness max 0,25 mm),

$\alpha = 0,9$ for using steel tubes,

$\alpha = 0,9 - 1$ for separate concreting (grouting, prepac system),

$\alpha = 0,6$ for using PE or PVC foils (thickness over 0,25 mm),

In the equation (10) the coefficient of earth pressure on pile is supposed to be K = 1. For the settlement over 25 mm it may be K = 1,2.

Loading tests on closed and open ended pure piles

Essais de chargement de pieux tubulaires à pointe ouverte et fermée

I. SOVINC, Professor, IMFM, Edvard Kardelj University, Ljubljana, Yugoslavia
J. LIKAR, Assistant, IMFM, Edvard Kardelj University, Ljubljana, Yugoslavia
G. VOGRINČIČ, Lecturer, IMFM, Edvard Kardelj University, Ljubljana, Yugoslavia
F. ŽIGMAN, Researcher, IMFM, Edvard Kardelj University, Ljubljana, Yugoslavia

SYNOPSIS   The results of extensive dynamic and static tests on steel pipe piles are described. The piles tested were open ended, close ended, equipped with an enlargement of the pile section (vanes) and with a plate with a circular opening inside the tube. The favorable effect of the soil plug was ascertained and the parameters influencing the bearing capacity calculation by the wave equation method are discussed.

INTRODUCTION

The main aim of the investigations, described in this paper, was to estimate the driving resistancy and the bearing capacity of steel pipe piles, driven through 30 m thick layer of very soft marine clay into the bearing gravely and sandy soils. The pipe piles investigated were open ended, partially or fully close ended, equipped with an enlargement of the pile section (vanes) or ordinary pipes without lagging.

The tests were performed at a site of grain silo situated on a pier at one of the Adriatic ports. The very close spaced driven displacement piles could damage the existing storage foundations or even threaten the stability of the quay wall constructions, and the underwater slopes. Therefore the most of the tests on driving and bearing capacity were performed on open ended pipe piles to prevent the lateral displacements

and the heave of more than $5\,000$ m^3 of the soil at the site area of $2\,200$ m^2.

SOIL CONDITIONS AT THE SITE OF THE TEST PILES

The soil profile at the site of the test piles is shown in Figs.1 and 2. In this report only some test results will be reproduced for the typical soil layers.

<u>Layer a- silty sand</u>: average angle of internal friction and cohesion intercept in terms of effective stress
$\varphi'= 26^0\ 40'$ Translatory and rotatory
$c'= 7.5$ kPa   direct shear tests

<u>Layer b- marine clay</u>: average cohesion in terms of total stress
$c_u = 21$ kPa   ... In situ vane tests

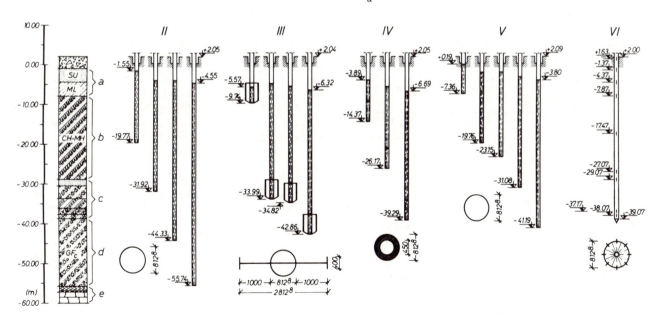

Fig.1 Geometry of the test piles and heights of the soil plug inside the piles II, III, IV and V during driving

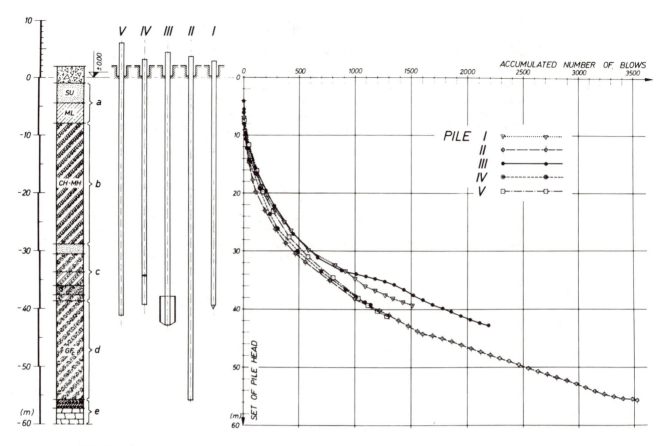

Fig.2 Scheme of the test piles and plots of accumulated number of blows versus depth

$\varphi' = 19^{\circ}$
$c' = 20$ kPa   ... Triaxial shear tests

Layers c and d- silty and clayey gravel and sand intercepted in section c by thin layers of clay:

TABLE I

Layer	El. (m)	SPT N	Grain size distribution			
			> 20	20/6	6/2	< 2
			(mm)			
c	- 28	33	9	22	20	49
	- 33		9	11	7	73
d	- 43	34	18	11	13	58
	- 53	45	20	17	11	52

Layer e- Eocene flysh

DESCRIPTION OF THE TEST PILES

The schemes of the six test piles are shown in the Figs.1 and 2. Piles are steel tubes with the outside diameter of 812.8 mm and the wall thickness of 12 mm. Piles I to V were driven with a single acting Diesel hammer with the theoretical maximum energy of 146 kN m/blow. The pile VI, located about 45 m apart from the group of piles I to V, was driven with a single acting Diesel hammer with theoretical maximum energy of 115 kN m/blow.

Pile I and Pile VI are closed at the bottom with a metal cone. The pile I was driven to the el. of -39.34 m (0.74 m underneath the upper face of the bearing gravely layer d) and the pile VI to the el. of -39.07 m (1.90 m underneath the upper face of the bearing gravely layer d).

Pile II and Pile V are open ended tubes. The pile II was driven to the el. of -55.74 m (17.14 m underneath the upper face of the bearing gravely layer d) and reached the base of the firm eocene flysh. The pile V was driven to the el. of -41.19 m (2.59 m underneath the surface of the gravely layer d).

Pile III is an open ended tube with vanes, located 5 m above the base level. The pile was driven to the el. of -42.86 m (4.26 m underneath of the upper face of the bearing layer d).

Pile IV is an open ended tube with a plate with a circular opening, located 5 m above the base level and has the inside diameter of 450 mm. The pile was driven to the el. of -39.29 m (0.69 m underneath the surface of the gravely layer d).

MEASUREMENTS DURING DRIVING AND TEST LOADING

The following measurements were carried out during driving and test loading on piles I to V:
a) the settlement of the pile head during driving

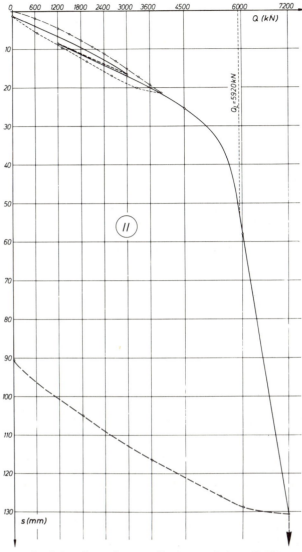

Fig. 3 Load settlement diagram of the pile II

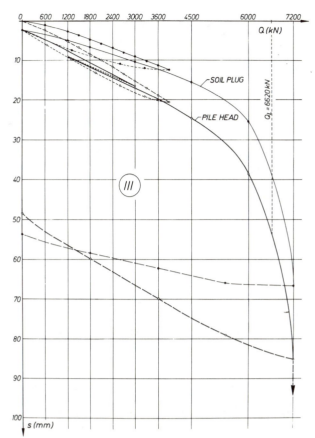

Fig. 4 Load settlement diagram of the pile III

b) the settlement of the pile head during loading by axial compressive and cycling load on piles II, III and IV

c) the upwards movement of the pile head during pulling of the piles I, II, III, IV and V

d) the movement of the upper part of the pile during horizontal loading of piles I and II

e) the upper face of the soil plug inside of the open ended piles III and IV

f) the heave of the surrounding soil during driving of the pile I.

Pile VI was instrumented with strain gauges for measurements of driving stresses in the pile shaft as well as the transfer of the axial load in the pile during test loading.

Due to the scarcity of space available not all of the test results will be given and discussed in this paper. They will be published elsewhere.

Results of measurements during driving

The settlements of the pile head during driving versus the accumulated number of blows for piles I to V are given in Fig. 2. In order to measure the driving stresses in the pile VI at 9 levels A to I strain gauges were fitted on the pile shaft (see Figs. 1 and 7). The maximum tensile stresses in the pile shaft were registered during driving through less resisting soil when the compressive wave reflected in the upwards direction (as tensile). The maximum tensile stresses of 76 MPa were observed at the level G, located 7 m from the head of the pile. The maximum impact (compressive stress 194 MPa) was measured at the level H, 4 m from the pile head. By using the wave equation and Smith's damping parameters the maximum stresses at the last set of blows would be 135.5 MPa in tension at the level 6.70 m underneath the pile head and 162.5 MPa in compression 4 m under the pile head.

Results of the measurements of the height of the soil plug inside the pile during driving

The upper face of the soil plug formed inside the open ended piles II to V during driving was measured by using a metal disk connected to a measuring device located near the pile head. The results of measurements (the base level of the pile and the height of the soil plug inside the pile) are shown in Fig. 1.

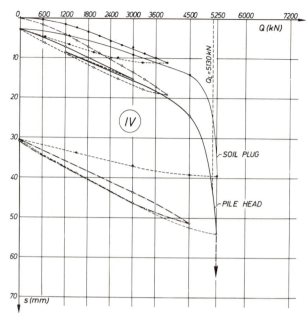

Fig. 5 Load settlement diagram of the pile IV

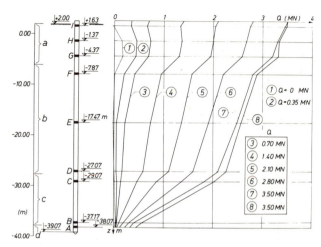

Fig. 7 Measured load distribution curve of the pile VI
(No 8 ... after 27 hours)

Heave of the surrounding soil

The measurements were made by very precise surveying in a square area 10 m x 10 m around the close ended pile I. It was stated that the most of the displaced volume of the soil was in the lateral direction.

Measurements during test loading of the piles

The test piles were subjected to a stress controlled loading test 35 to 44 days after driving. In the first phase the load was increased to 3 900 kN in 5 loading steps. The vertical movements were observed at each step 2 hours or until the increment of settlements of the pile head in 20 minutes became equal or less than 0.1 mm. After reloading, in the second phase, the load was increased again in steps until the failure load was reached. In this way all the piles except the pile VI were loaded. The full instrumented pile VI was tested according to a different procedure.

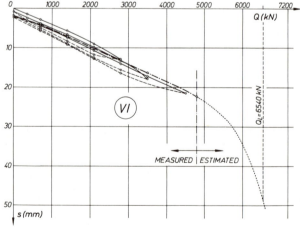

Fig. 6 Load settlement diagram of the pile VI

The load on test piles was realized by using 4 hydraulic jacks (4 x 1 800 kN). The reaction of the jacks was taken by a steel beam supported by two tension piles. The piles I and III, II and IV, and III and V were used as tension piles for the piles II, III, and IV, respectively. A platform weighted with concrete blocks was used for the pile VI.

The load settlement diagrams of the test piles II, III, IV and VI are shown in Figs. 3 to 6. For the determination of the limit load Q_L the criterium of the German DIN 4026 was chosen.

The results of the measurements of the upper face of the soil plug inside the open ended piles III and IV during test loading are shown in Figs. 4 and 5. It is evident that inside the piles a plug was formed and therefore the bearing capacity of the piles increased (especially for the pile IV) considerably.

By using the results of measurements during driving and the test loading of the pile VI, the static bearing capacity was evaluated by means of the wave equation and Smith's damping parameters. For skin friction and toe damping factors 0.16 s/m and 0.49 s/m were introduced, respectively. Limit load of 5 450 kN is probably very close to the load test results. To get a satisfactory agreement for measured and calculated limit load for pile IV the Smith's damping factors need to be changed to 0.03 s/m for the skin friction and to 0.10 s/m for the toe damping.

CONCLUSIONS

- The bearing capacity of open ended pipe piles, provided with an enlargement of the outside cross section (vanes) or with a plate with a circular opening inside the tube, can be increased considerably.

- In predicting the static bearing capacity by means of the wave equation the Smith's damping parameters should be reduced for the piles with the soil plug inside in comparison to the close ended empty pipe piles.

Application of in situ tests for evaluation of pile bearing capacity

Application des essais in situ pour l'estimation de la capacité portante des pieux

A. TEJCHMAN, Professor, Technical University of Gdańsk, Faculty of Hydrotechnics, Poland
K. GWIZDALA, Senior Assistant, Technical University of Gdańsk, Faculty of Hydrotechnics, Poland
J. KLOS, Senior Assistant, Technical University of Gdańsk, Faculty of Hydrotechnics, Poland

SYNOPSIS   On the basis of the load tests of many Vibro-Fundex piles performed in different soil conditions, the verification and analysis of the use of static sounding results of soil for evaluation of the pile bearing capacity has been carried out.
        Besides determining the allowable piles bearing capacity, the comparison of interpretation of the loading tests results by means of different methods has been performed. The analysis of the comparison is given and own proposal of the interpretation of loading test results is presented, taking into account real behaviour of piles /conventional and large diameter/ in subsoil.

INTRODUCTION

Static sounding /CPT/ is one of more popular methods of in situ testing of soil. Geotechnical parameters obtained /the unit resistance of soil under the penetrometer cone q_c and the unit resistance of soil at the friction sleeve wall f_s / make it possible to relatively well evaluate the bearing capacity of piles at the design stage. However, comparative calculations show that different bearing capacities of piles are obtained for different calculation methods adopted. It is known that proper verification of calculation results can be provided by test loading of piles, which is regarded as one of most reliable methods of in situ pile testing. However, correct determination of the bearing capacity of piles based on such tests depends also on the method adopted for interpreting the pile load versus settlement curve.

To verify bearing capacity calculations carried out for Vibro-Fundex piles by several penetrometer methods, test loading of 18 piles has been conducted on the site of sounding. The permissible bearing capacity of the piles was evaluated using several different methods of interpretation and comparison of the results was made. The analysis served the authors as a basis for developing a new method of determining the bearing capacity of piles based on loading test. The methods takes fairly well into account the actual behaviour of piles, typical as well as large-diameter ones and eliminates use of any conventional safety factors.

DESCRIPTION OF TESTS CARRIED OUT

All the testing was done on the sites of building of bridge supports in Gdańsk. The construction works involved making about 1200 Vibro-Fundex piles situated under 15 supports. The piles were cast in steel casings of 457 mm diameter driven with Delmag hammers. The pile tip was ended by steel cone of 600 mm diameter leaving in the soil. After filling with concrete the pipes were pulled out by means of a vibrator mounted on a pile driver. The pile

length varied on the average between 12 and 16 m. Within each support area the soil was sounded and at least one test loading of a pile was carried out after driving of piles group.

Sounding was done with Gouda penetrometer provided with a Begemann tip. The unit cone resistance q_c and unit shaft friction f_s were measured. On the whole 21 soundings down to the depth of up to 22 m were carried out.

For test loading of piles a hydraulic lift was used. The testing was carried out according to a special research program as presented in the next section.

Soil conditions on the site of brigde construction were diverse. The subsoil consisted mainly of fine and medium sand, loose /I_D = 0,30/ or of medium compaction degree /I_D = 0,50/ as well as clayey sand, sandy clay and silty clay characterized by liquidity index varying on the average from /I_L = 0,0 to I_L = 0,4./

RESULTS AND ANALYSIS OF THE TEST LOADING OF PILES

The methods of determining the permissible bearing capacity of a pile can be divided into the following groups:

a/ determining the ultimate capacity and decreasing the value by a conventional safety factor. When the ultimate bearing capacity of a pile was not attained during the testing then graphic methods or approximation of the loading function might provide its value,

b/ test loading according to a special procedure in order to directly obtain the permissible load /also including here instrumented piles/

c/ graphic examination of the load vs settlement curve aimed at determining the so called characteristic points of the curve from which the permissible load can be established /without use of safety factors/.

In the building site in question total of 18 test loadings was carried out. Among them for 11 piles test loading and interpretation of the results according to different methods were done. Group a was represented by the methods of Van der Veen (1978), Rollberg (1976), and the method described in the Polish standard PN-69/B-02482 (1969), group b was represented by the Szechy (1978) and LPCP /Laboratoire Central des Ponts et Chaussées/ (1970) methods, group c – by the method developed by the authors and introduced into the new Polish standard PN-84/B-02482 (1984).

The last method was developed as it had been found that the other methods did not provide a unique answer as to the permissible pile load, especially when the ultimate load had not been reached.

The method proposed consists in an analysis of a graphically constructed diagram of the reciprocal of the first derivative of pile settlement vs load relation. To this end a segment of unit length /OM/ as chosen for both axes of the co-ordinate system should be laid off above the load axis along the production of the settlement axis s. Then straight lines parallel to tangents to the load /settlement curve at its selected points should passed through the point obtained in such a way. These parallel lines define on the load axis Q values of dQ_1/ds_1 corresponding to the analyzed points of the load /settlement relation. These segments, when laid off above the Q axis on straight lines perpendicular to that axis and passing through the respective tangency points, define the points of dQ_1/ds_1 curve. The procedure is illustrated in figure 1. The common feature distinguishing the phase of considerable plastic strain of soil is rectilinearity of the corresponding part of dQ_1/ds_1 curve.

The permissible pile load has been defined as the load corresponding to the beginning of this strain phase.

One or two rectilinear segments of the curve can be distinguished depending on the kind of pile operation in the soil. The curve in fig.1 corresponds to behaviour of a typical pile of diameter up to 60 cm, the curve in fig.2 shows the behaviour characteristic for large diameter piles. The beginning of the first segment /curve of "a" type as per fig.1/ or the second one /curve of "b" type as per fig.2/ defines the bearing capacity Q_{bt} of the pile, the point of the segment intersection with the load axis defines the value of the ultimate load Q_u of the pile.

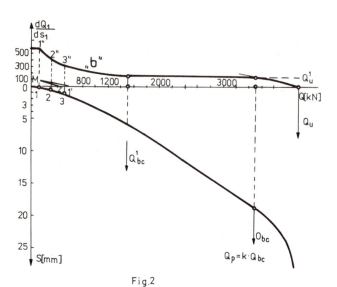

Fig.2

Determination of the permissible pile load Q_p involves only introduction of a coefficient k for variation of soil parameters. Its value varies between 0,9 and 0,7 /$Q_p = k\, Q_{bc}$/ In the case under consideration k equal to 0,7 was assumed because of high heterogenity of the subgrade and variation of parameters defining the strenght of the soil. For the new Polish standard PN-84, tree values of the coefficient k have been chosen depending only on type of curve, namely: k = 1 for a diagram of "a" type, k = 0,8 for a diagram of "b" type and k = 0,9 when Q_{bc} is assumed as Q_{max} /see Fig.3/.

The method proposed may be used also when the ultimate load has not been reached during test loading. In such case the curve is analyzed in the following way:
a/ if $Q_{bc}/Q_u \geqslant 0,4$, the curve is of "a" type and $Q_{bc} = Q_{bc}^1$
b/ if $Q_{bc}/Q_u < 0,4$, the pile settlement curve is of "b" type and $Q_{bc} = Q_{max}$ is assumed at k = 0,9
Interpretation of such case is shown in fig.3

A detailed description of the method proposed and the procedure of analyzing the graphically determined diagram of dQ/ds depending on the form of the load /settlement curve obtained as a result of pile test loading can be found in (1982) and in the new Polish Standard concerning pile foundations (1984), worked out by Authors.

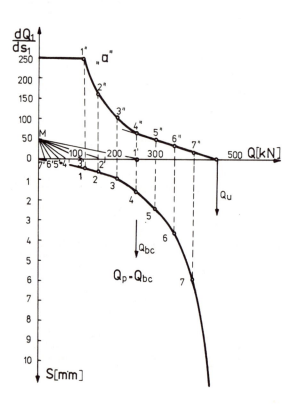

Fig.1

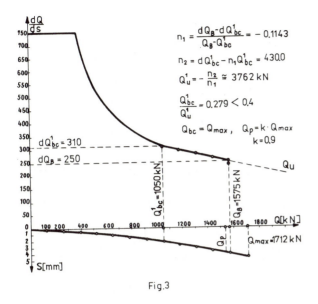

$$n_1 = \frac{dQ_B - dQ^1_{bc}}{Q_B - Q^1_{bc}} = -0.1143$$

$$n_2 = dQ^1_{bc} - n_1 Q^1_{bc} = 430.0$$

$$Q_u = -\frac{n_2}{n_1} \cong 3762 \text{ kN}$$

$$\frac{Q^1_{bc}}{Q^1_u} = 0.279 < 0.4$$

$$Q_{bc} = Q_{max}, \quad Q_p = k \cdot Q_{max}$$
$$k = 0.9$$

Fig.3

Table I shows results of interpretation of test loading of selected piles carried out according to several known methods in use and the method proposed.

TABLE I

Comparison of results of pile test loading by different methods /permissible loads Q_p in MN/

Pile No	per PN-69	Van der Veen method	Rollberg method	Szechy method	LCPC method	proposed method k=0.7
VI	0.90	0.90	0.95	0.87	—	1.15
VII	1.20	—	1.28	1.35	—	1.35
VIII	1.09	1.00	1.32	1.05	—	1.20
IX	0.98	0.83	1.23	0.98	—	1.12
X	0.75	1.00	1.00	—	0.92	1.22
XII	0.80	0.80	0.96	—	—	0.84
XIII	0.60	0.80	0.87	—	—	0.70
XIV	0.70	0.70	0.82	—	0.85	1.10
XV	1.00	—	1.01	—	1.20	1.19
XVI	1.15	—	1.06	—	1.09	1.20
XVIII	0.75	0.60	0.84	—	0.79	0.77

It follows from Table I that the value obtained of the permissible pile load depends on the method applied. On the average, the differences amount to 25-30%. This is a result of somewhat subjective interpretation of the load settlement curve, whose form depends essentially on the manner of pile work in the soil, and of assumption of conventional /in a sluse arbitrary/ factor of safety. The method proposed by the authors defines the permissible pile load with respect to the form of the load /settlement curve, taking thus into account in the analysis the actually occurring pile - soil interaction, and eliminating simultaneously the need of use of conventional safety factors. The results obtained by this method proved to be very close to results of calulations carried out based on the new Standard PN-84. In the authors opinion the method utilizes the bearing capacity of piles better than other methods.

COMPARISON AND ANALYSIS OF SOIL SOUNDING RESULTS

Soil was sounded on the site of building of each bridge support. The values of q_c and f_s obtained from the sounding were used to calculate the bearing capacacity of piles according to three chosen methods. Philipponat (1979), Bustamante - Gianeselli (1981) and a USSR Standard (1974) in which the pile bearing capacity is determined as the sum of soil resistance under the base and along the shaft.

For the Philipponat and Bustamante - Gianeselli methods general factors of safety equal to F = 2 were adopted, while for the method as presented in the USSR Standard F = 1,4 was used. Table II shows the results of calculations together with a comparison of pile bearing capacity values obtained from test loading.

Determination of the permissible bearing capacity of piles from field test was based on the old Polish Standard PN-69/B with the value of the safety factor F equal in the majority of cases to 2.

The comparison shows that in each case the calculated values of the bearing capacity of Vibro-Fundex piles were too high. It is thus evident that the bearing capacities of piles

TABLE II

Comparison of the results of sounding with those of pile test loading /permissible loads Q_p in MN/

Pile No	Philipponat method	Bustamante method	Method of USSR Standard	Loading tests
I	2.16	1.17	2.28	1.00
II	1.43	0.97	1.99	0.90
III	1.31	0.98	1.79	1.10
IV	1.88	1.32	2.05	0.85
V	2.21	1.43	1.83	1.15
VI	2.15	1.73	3.15	0.90
VII	2.47	1.78	2.81	1.20
VIII	1.20	1.28	1.30	1.09
IX	1.43	1.61	2.93	0.98
XI	1.95	1.69	2.81	0.85
XII	1.64	1.51	2.61	0.80
XIII	1.06	1.32	2.79	0.60
XIV	1.37	1.35	2.62	0.70
XV	1.17	1.29	2.56	1.00
XVIII	0.72	0.83	1.37	0.75

determined on the basis of sounding had been overestimated. Confirmation of this opinion may be found in the paper (1983) which is concerned also with piles of other types and various soil conditions. It is therefore important that the factors of safety be appropriately selected for the caluclation methods, or correction factors be used when calculating the resistances of pile base and shaft. In the case under consideration the choice was as follows: for the Philipponat method a generalized factor of safety F = 3,0, for the Bustamante method partial coefficients F_s = 3,5 for the shaft and F_b = 2,0 for the base and for the method of the USSR standard F = 3,5. Fig.4 presents a comparison of the calculated permissible bearing capacity N_{cal} obtained based on the above mentioned methods but after using the proposed correction with the values N_{test} determined from the loading tests of piles.

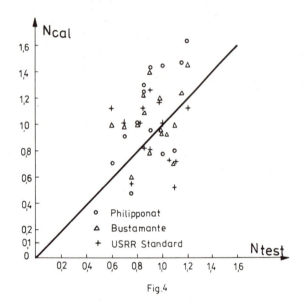

Fig.4

It follows from the investigations reported in this paper that methods known and widely used for engineering purposes both for interpretation of pile test loading and sounding reslts need further verification aimed at better taking into account the actual behaviour of piles in subsoil when calculating their bearing capacity.

It appears that for large and important structures or nonhomogeneous subsoil the bearing capacities of piles calculated in the design stage based on static formulae or sounding data ought to be verified by test loading.

REFERENCES

Bustamante, M., Gianeselli, L. (1981) . Prevision de la capacite portante des pieux isolés sous charge verticale, Bull. Liaison Lab. des Ponts et Chaussées, V-VI, 83-108, Paris.
Cassan, M. (1978) .Les essais in situ en mechanique des sols. Vol. I, II, Eyrolles, Paris.
Klos, J. (1982) . Interpretation of results of pile test loading based on graphic differentiation of the settlement versus load curve /in Polish/. Arch. Hydrotechniki, no.4, 491-505.
Lab. Central des Ponts et Chaussées (1970) . Essai statique de fondations profonder.
Philipponat, G. (1979) . Methode practique de calcul d un pieu isolé à l'aide du pénétromètre statique. Revue Francaise de Géotechnique, no.10, 55-64.
Polish Standard PN-69/B-02482 (1969) .Foundations. Bearing capacity of piles and pile foundation /in Polish/. Wyd. Normalizacyjne, Warszawa.
Polish Standard PN-84/B-02482 (1984) . Foundations. Bearing capacity of piles and pile foundation (in Polish) . Wyd. Normalizacyjne, Warszawa.
Rollberg, D. (1977) . Determination of the bearing capacity and pile driving resistance of piles using soundings. Publ. of the Inst. for FE, SM, RM and WWC, RWTH (University) Aachen, vol.3, 43-227.
Trofimenkov, Y.G. (1974) . Penetration testing in USSR. Proc. ESOPT, I, 147-154, Stockholm.
Tejchman, A., Klos,J., Gwizdala, K. (1983) . Calculation methods of bearing capacity of conventional and large diameter piles according to the limit state and displacements and on the basis of sounding results (in Polish) , Technical University of Gdańsk.

An instrumented bored pile with soil improvement for increased shaft resistance

Un pieu foré instrumenté avec amélioration du sol pour la résistance augmentée du fût

W. H. TING, Consultant Engineer, Kuala Lumpur, Malaysia
C. T. TOH, Consultant Engineer, Kuala Lumpur, Malaysia

SYNOPSIS   In a limestone area in Malaysia, the limestone occurs in the form of thin slabs with soil in between. Loose alluvium overlie the limestone slabs. Large diameter bored piles were constrained to be founded on the thin slabs. The limestone slabs in combination with the poor overburden soil were considered inadequate to support the piles. The soil in the overburden shaft zone was then improved by jet grouting technique which is briefly described. The pile was then instrumented and load tested to determine the load transfer pattern as well as its general behaviour. In another part of the site one large diameter bored pile with no improvement of shaft resistance was load tested, and the results were analyzed and compared with the behaviour of the pile with shaft zone soil improvement. A cluster of jet grout columns was also constructed in the overburden material and load tested. A finite element model study was also made to obtain a better understanding of the mechanisms involved.

1. INTRODUCTION

Some parts of Kuala Lumpur, the Capital city of Malaysia, is underlain by limestone formation with karst topography. It was proposed to construct a 26 storey building on such a site. The building has three basements and is supported by bored piles.

2. SUBSURFACE CONDITION

On the building site, the soil profile consists of loose clayey silty sands of quaternary age overlying weathered Upper Paleozoic Sedimentary rock deposits which in turn lies on the Lower Paleozoic limestone formation.

At this location, the limestone appears to have been weathered into rock lenses and slabs of varying thickness with soil deposits between the layers instead of the pinnacled limestone structure, typical of Kuala Lumpur limestone elsewhere.

A typical cross-section is shown in Figure 1.

3. GEOTECHNICAL CONDITION

In some areas, the large diameter bored piles are founded on limestone layers which are more than 3m thick, provided that the subsurface condition below the layer is adequate for supporting each pile group. Where there are frequent occurrences of rock layers, the piles were constructed by drilling through the rock slabs using the reverse circulation method.

In some areas (eg. Borehole 54, see Figures 1 and 2), the upper limestone strata was found to be less than 3m thick, and thicker layers can only be found at great depths. The strength of the strata at various levels is shown in Figure 2.

It was then decided to found a pile of 1.2m diameter (near Borehole 54) on a limestone layer of about 1.2m thick and to increase the load carrying capacity of the pile by improving the soil surrounding the shaft. The pile was keyed 0.5m into the limestone.

4. SOIL IMPROVEMENT

The technique of soil improvement adopted was the formation of jet-grouted columns around the pile. The vertical section is as in Figure 2 and a cross-section is as in Figure 3(a).

A jet-grouted column is formed by lowering a 19mm diameter tube into the ground until the desired depth is reached. Two water jets at the bottom of the tube under a pressure of 20 bars loosen the soil as the tube is lowered. Then, under a pressure of up to 250 bars, jets of grout are pumped into the ground as the tube is raised. The jet delivers the grout as well as mixes the grout with the soil within a certain radius to form a grouted column. Under average soil conditions, a column of about 0.4m diameter is formed by this technique. The grout consists of a mixture of 1 part cement to 3.4 parts of water by volume. Up to 15% of sodium silicate by weight of water was added to improve gel time.

5. LOAD TESTS ON JET GROUT COLUMNS

A load test was carried out on a 3 piled cluster as shown in Figure 3b to determine the efficiency of the jet grouted columns.

The jet grouted columns were formed in loose alluvium to a length of 3.7m. The load-settlement results of the test are shown in Figure 4. The piles failed at a pile/soil cylindrical interface of about 1.4m diameter when pile stress was less than about 2.3MPa.

The back-computed modular ratio between pile and soil (E pile/E soil) was approximately 10.0 indicative of a compressible pile.

6. PILE TESTS AND INSTRUMENTATION

The 1.2m diameter bored pile (near Borehole 54) with the soil surrounding the shaft improved by jet grouting was tested to twice its working load. Loading of the pile was by use of kentledge.

In order to observe the manner of load transfer down

the shaft, four sets of strain gauges were installed at various depths along the pile (Figure 2).

The bored pile was installed and tested from R.L. 90ft (R.L. 27.43m or 9.2m above the final pile cut off level) as basement excavation at that juncture was not complete. The top of the jet grout columns was at R.L. 59.8ft (18.23m) the final pile cut off level. The configuration for load testing is as shown in Figure 2.

During testing, load was maintained at various levels to observe creep behaviour. Additionally, some cyclic loading was carried out.

A second pile load test was carried out on a 1.4m diameter bored pile which however did not have its shaft zone improved by jet grouting. The pile was embedded 18.6m into material with S.P.T. greater than 50. This second pile was however not instrumented with strain gauges.

7. RESULTS AND DISCUSSION

7.1 Load-Settlement Behaviour

Figure 5 illustrates the load-settlement behaviour of the instrumented bored pile with shaft zone improvement and of the bored pile without shaft zone improvement.

It can be seen that the pile with shaft-zone improvement is distinctly more stiff at the head than the conventional pile.

7.2 Maintained Load Behaviour

The first cycle load was taken to 800t and maintained for 42 hours. As shown in Figure 5 and 6, the second cycle was taken up to 1,600t. The loads were maintained at 1,400t for 62 hours and at 1,600t for 25 hours to observe creep behaviour.

The maintained load tests show that creep occurs with transfer of load down the shaft and the equivalent change in load in the pile can amount to about 180t. The creep decreases with stress level and duration.

The changes in the strain profile due to creep at 1,400t and at 1,600t are shown in Figures 7 and 8.

7.3 Load Transfer Phenomena

Figures 2, 7 and 8 show that large load transfer occur in the unimproved portion of the pile (R.L. 90ft to 60ft) and in the upper few feet of the improved length of the pile (to R.L. 36ft).

This is somewhat surprising as it was assumed that the transfer would be within the length of the pile where the soil around the shaft was improved by jet grouting ie. below R.L. 60ft. The average shaft support between gauges 2 (R.L. 67ft) and 3 (R.L. 36ft) is about 523kpa, and between gauges 3 and 4 (R.L. -34ft) about 166kpa.

The former value is somewhat high and a possible explanation is that during grouting of the lower section i.e. below R.L. 60', the soil heave due to grouting may have induced an upward "preload shaft friction".

Figure 9 illustrates how "preloading" due to heave could have affected the load transfer results, in producing an exaggerated load transfer curve at the upper portions of the pile.

7.4 Finite Element Analysis

An elasto-plastic finite element analysis using 8 node Isoparametric Quadrilaterals was carried out for the bored pile with shaft improvement and resting on a 1.2m thick layer of limestone. The assumed properties are shown in Table 1.

Table 1

Material	E	ν	C	ϕ	ψ
Bored Pile	19GPa	0.3	–	45°	45°
Jet Grout Columns	320MPa	0.3	640KPa	0.0	0.0
Soil From R.L. 90ft to R.L. 60ft	32MPa	0.3	0.0	30.0	30.0
Soil Surrounding Jet Grout Columns	32MPa	0.48	134KPa	0.0	0.0
Limestone Beneath Bored Pile	30GPa	0.3	300MPa	0.0	0.0
Soil Beneath Limestone	64MPa	0.48	200KPa	0.0	0.0

The load settlement results from the Finite Element analysis in Figure 6 shows a less stiff response compared to the measured results.

Figure 10 compares the computed strains from Finite Element analysis with the measured strains from the second cycle. The Finite Element analysis showed less load transfer with depth compared to the measured results.

In an attempt to estimate the degree of "preload" on the pile, the computed strains were subtracted from the measured strains and plotted in Figure 11.

The estimated "preload shaft friction" ranged from 75KPa to 190KPa depending on the applied load level. The shape of the curve resembled that suggested in Figure 9.

7.5 Tensile Strains From Cyclic Loading

The cyclic loading test has two interesting features. The first is the presence of residual strains in the pile shaft after the pile has been loaded and unloaded. The other is that at the end of the second unloading, tensile strains begin to appear at gauge point 3.

Figure 12 illustrates the measured strains for the second and fourth loading and unloading cycles with tensile strains in the lower portion of the pile in the latter cycle.

8. CONCLUSION

.. The soil surrounding the shaft of a large diameter bored piled pile has been improved by the formation of jet grouted columns.

.. The instrumented pile load tests indicate the benefit of improved soil surrounding the shaft.

.. "Preloading" of the upper portion of the shaft due to heave caused by grouting may have taken place possibly resulting in:

• Large load transfer along the upper portion of the shaft.

• Residual strains after unloading some of which are tensile strains.

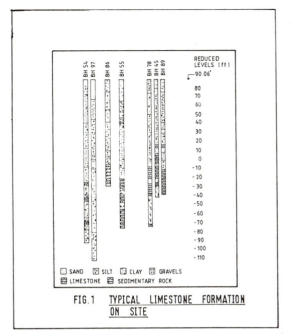

FIG.1 TYPICAL LIMESTONE FORMATION ON SITE

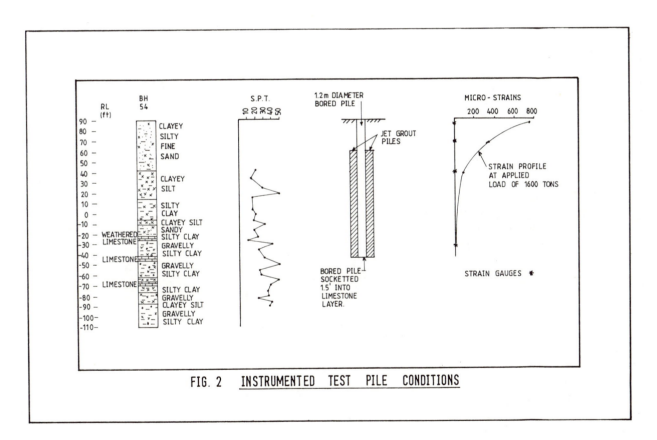

FIG. 2 INSTRUMENTED TEST PILE CONDITIONS

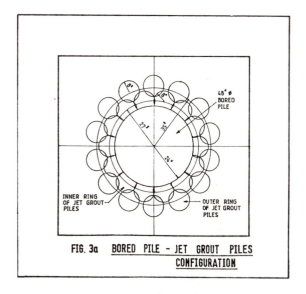

FIG. 3a   BORED PILE - JET GROUT PILES
CONFIGURATION

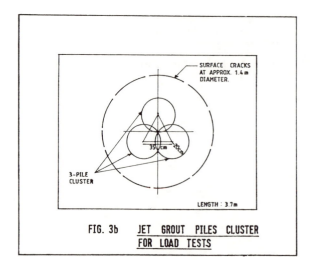

FIG. 3b   JET GROUT PILES CLUSTER
FOR LOAD TESTS

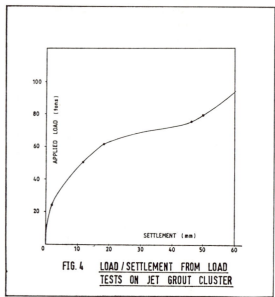

FIG. 4   LOAD / SETTLEMENT FROM LOAD
TESTS ON JET GROUT CLUSTER

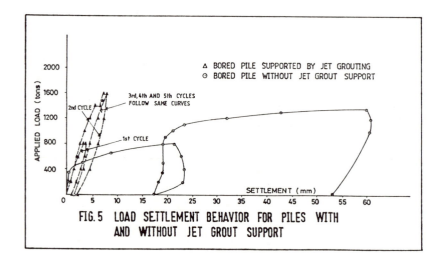

FIG. 5   LOAD SETTLEMENT BEHAVIOR FOR PILES WITH
AND WITHOUT JET GROUT SUPPORT

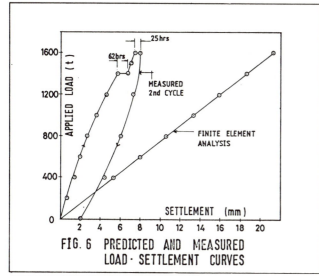

FIG. 6 PREDICTED AND MEASURED
LOAD · SETTLEMENT CURVES

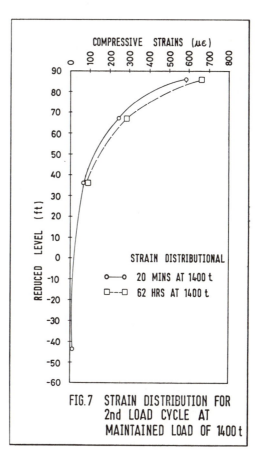

FIG.7 STRAIN DISTRIBUTION FOR
2nd LOAD CYCLE AT
MAINTAINED LOAD OF 1400 t

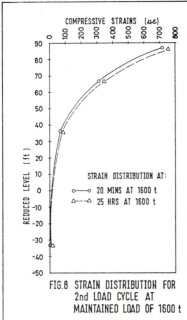

FIG.8 STRAIN DISTRIBUTION FOR
2nd LOAD CYCLE AT
MAINTAINED LOAD OF 1600 t

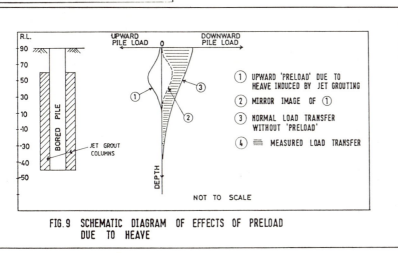

FIG.9 SCHEMATIC DIAGRAM OF EFFECTS OF PRELOAD
DUE TO HEAVE

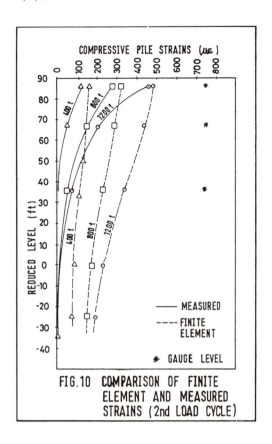

FIG.10 COMPARISON OF FINITE
ELEMENT AND MEASURED
STRAINS (2nd LOAD CYCLE)

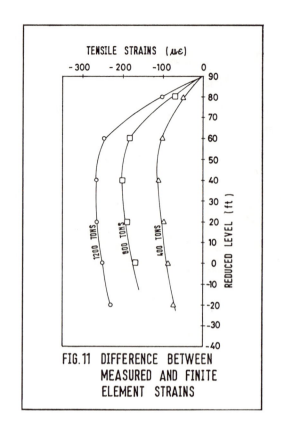

FIG.11 DIFFERENCE BETWEEN
MEASURED AND FINITE
ELEMENT STRAINS

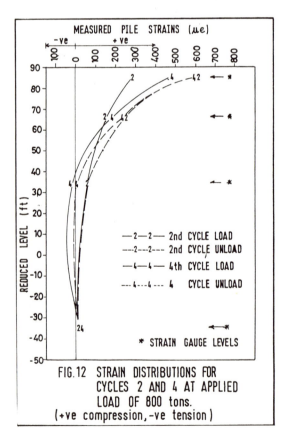

FIG.12 STRAIN DISTRIBUTIONS FOR
CYCLES 2 AND 4 AT APPLIED
LOAD OF 800 tons.
(+ve compression, -ve tension)

Analysis of the relationship between the bearing capacity and diameter of piles in sands

Variation de la force portante des pieux en fonction du diamètre en milieux sableux

YU. G. TROFIMENKOV, Director, Cand. Sc., Fundamentproject Institute, Moscow, USSR
R. E. KHANIN, Engineer, Fundamentproject Institute, Moscow, USSR
G. M. LESHIN, Engineer, Fundamentproject Institute, Moscow, USSR

SYNOPSIS   Load testing of instrumented piles 73-325 mm in diameter driven in sands have been carried out. The portion of the load carried by the point and by the shaft was measured during pile loading. The relationship between the bearing capacity and diameter of piles was determined. This permits the bearing capacity of production piles to be accurately estimated by the tests of small diameter sectional steel piles driven to the predetermined depth.

The reliable data on the bearing capacity of piles can be derived by the results of static load tests. But these tests are very laborious. During site investigations it is much easier to drive and load test small diameter sectional steel piles of the same length as presupposed production piles.

To evaluate the expediency of the use of these piles, the test results of steel instrumented piles of 73 to 325 mm in diameter were compared. The toe of these piles was equipped with a cone and an electric strain gauge to measure point loads. The strain gauges were also placed along the pile shaft to measure the distribution of skin friction.

The tests of piles of equal length and of 4 different diameters provided data for evaluation of the change of the bearing capacity of piles with the diameter.

Correlations made earlier (Trofimenkov, et al., 1983) showed that in clayey soils the bearing capacity of piles of equal length is directly proportional to diameter of the piles. In sand soils such a relationship is not observed.

Comparison of the bearing capacity of production piles in clays and in sands determined by the load tests (Q_t) and by compution from the results of the load tests of small piles (Q_c) assuming that bearing capacity is directly proportional to the pile diameter is given in Fig. I. The results of both determinations are close in clays and differ in sands. This departure from linear proportionality in sands is the result of a significant role of base load of a pile on its bearing capacity. Therefore the distribution of the load along the pile shaft and pile base was analyzed.

The tests were carried out in alluvial medium sand of medium density with the following characteristics at the level of pile point:

unit weight – 18.5 kN/m^3, angle of internal friction –35°, modulus of deformation – 30 MPa, cone penetration resistance, q_c, 7 MPa

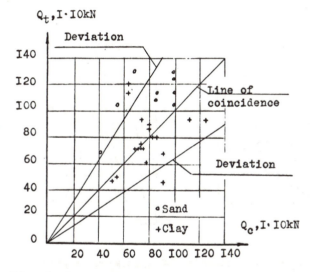

Fig. I Comparison of the bearing capacity determined by tests of production piles and pile of small diameter.

The length of tested piles – 6 m. In Fig 2 the load-settlement diagrams of the test piles of four different diameters are presented. In these diagrams each curve is a mean of the two tests. The distribution of force along the pile shaft is shown in Fig. 3. In this figure it is seen that the part of the total load taken by pile base changes in the process of loading and constitutes more than 40 percent. All the date on results of the tests are given in Table I. As not all load - settlement curves show a definite peak load, the ultimate load was defined as the load causing total pile settlement equal to 10 percent of the radius.

As it is seen from the Table I : the ultimate load, Q_u is increased by 8.3 when the diameter of a pile is increased by 4.4; the ratio of the point load Q_p to the cross section area

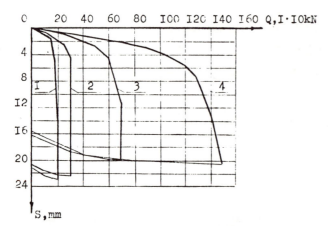

Fig. 2 Load - settlement diagrams of the test piles
       I. Dia. 73mm 2. Dia. II4 mm
       3. Dia. 2I9mm 4. Dia. 325 mm

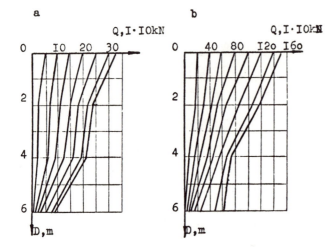

Fig. 3   Distribution of load along a pile shaft
       a - pile II4 mm in diameter
       b - pile 325 mm in diameter

is approximately constant and does not depend on the pile diameter.
For the determination of the relationship between the bearing capacity and dimensions (length and diameter) of a pile, equation (I) may be written following the technique of dimensional analysis:

$$\frac{Q}{q_c rs} = f(L/r) \qquad (I)$$

where Q - load on a pile, kN;
q_c - cone resistance, MPa;
r   - radius of a pile, cm;
s   - pile settlement, cm;
L   - pile length,   cm;

TABLE I

Results of Pile Testing

Description	Unit	Pile diameter, mm			
		73	II4	2I9	325
Pile radius (r)	cm	3.65	5.7	I0.95	I6.25
Ratio of pile Length (L) to pile radius (r)	-	I64	I0.5	55	37
Ultimate load (Q)	kN	I70	300	690	I420
Point Load (Q_p)	kN	30	80	290	600
Ratio Q_p/Q_u	-	0.I75	0.267	0.420	0.423
Unit base resistance (q_o)	MPa	7.07	7.7I	7.60	7.08
Unit skin resistance (f)	MPa	0.I00	0.I46	0.095	0.I32
Value for function 0.I f(L/r) by Eq. 2		I8.2	I3.2	8.2	7.7

As was indicated above ultimate load corresponds to settlement equal to 0.I r. In this case

$$\frac{Q_u}{q_c r^2} = 0.I f\left(\frac{L}{r}\right) \qquad (2)$$

Value for function 0.I f (L/r) calculated by equation (2) is given in Table I and the graph of this function is shown in Fig. 4. As it is seen in the graph all the experimental points are practical on a straight line. The equation of this line is:

$$0.I f(L/r) = 0.09I5 (L/r) + 3.I6 \qquad (3)$$

As a result the following formula is obtained

$$Q_u = q_c r^2 \left(0.09I5\frac{L}{r} + 3.I6\right) \qquad (4)$$

After some transformations the formula (4) may be expressed as

$$Q_u = A_s\frac{q_c}{70} + A_b\ q_c \qquad (5)$$

where A_s; A_b - the bearing areas of a pile skin base, respectively.
This expression shows that the unit resistance under a pile point for all diameters is equal to cone resistance divided by 70.

From the formula (5) the relationship between the ultimate loads of piles with different slenderness ratio (L/r) may be found

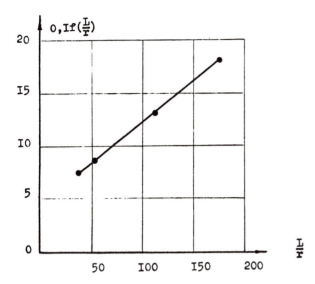

Fig. 4 Value of function 0.I f (L/r)

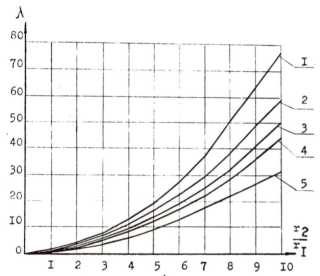

Fig. 5 Variation of λ with r_2/r_I and L/r_I

1. $L/r_I = 20$ 2. $L/r_I = 50$ 3. $L/r_I = 75$
4. $L/r_I = 100$ 5. $L/r_I = 200$

$$\lambda = \frac{r_2}{r_I} \times \frac{I + 35 \frac{r_2}{L}}{I + 35 \frac{r_I}{L}} \qquad (6)$$

The variation of λ with r_2/r_1 and L/r_I is shown in Fig. 5

From the formula (6) and the graph in Fig. 5, it is seen that the bearing capacity of a pile in sand is increasing not proportional to the diameter but much more rapidly as it

was indicated above on the basis of the tests. The fraction of the load taken by the base is (from Eq. 5)

$$\frac{Q_b}{Q_u} = \frac{I}{I + \frac{L/r}{35}} \qquad (7)$$

In Table II the comparison of the ratio Q_b/Q_u determined experimentally and by Eq. 7 is given.

Table II

Fraction of the load taken by pile base

Q_b/Q_u r_{cm}	3.65	5.70	I0.95	I6.25
experimentally	0.I76	0.27	0.42	0.42
by Eq. 7	0.I75	0.25	0.39	0.48

The obtained relationship between the bearing capacity and the slenderness ratio of piles enabled to widely use sectional steel piles of II4 mm in diameter for the determination of the bearing capacity of production piles.

Reference

Trofimenkov, Yu. G., Matjeshevich, I.A., Leshin, G.M., Khanin, R.E., (I983). Reliability of different methods for determination of bearing capacity of driven piles. Foundations and soil mechanics N I, pp. I5-I7, Moscow (in Russian).

The bearing capacity of screwed piles in cohesive layers

La capacité portante des pieux vissés dans les sols cohérents

W. F. VAN IMPE, Professor, Laboratory of Soil Mechanics, Ghent State University, Ghent, Belgium

SYNOPSIS

Two pile loading tests up to failure were performed on continuous screwed concrete piles of the Atlas-type, in a uniform tertiary clay layer. The type of pile mentioned and its related screwing method is described by Imbo (1984). From the results of the test loading an analysis is made concerning the total point and shaft bearing capacity in respect also with the cone penetration results. Some considerations are made about the influence of the time interval between performing and test loading of the piles.

INTRODUCTION

The Atlas-type pile is a concrete auger pile, cast in place while screwing out a thickwalled steel tube equiped at its bottom with an hollow exchangeable auger. This augered end with helical shape also bears a helical flange. At the bottom the casing is closed off by a non-retrievable cast-iron drilling tip (Fig.1a). Screwing in the steel tubes this tip grips, while screwing out it loses its grip and is left behind allowing to cast the concrete, (Fig. 1b).
Two of such screw piles were made, as test piles, near Kortrijk-Belgium in a quite uniform thick tertiary eocene clay layer (Ieper-clay). At the location of the two test piles (Fig. 2) a number of static cone penetration tests (CPT) were performed. Their results are shown in Fig. 3. Some of these test results were obtained before bringing in, others after performing the piles. No appreciable differences in CPT-results could be measured with respect to this time factor.
The two identical test piles were installed on April 6, 1984. The loading up to failure for

test pile P1 was made on May 8 ; for test pile P2 on July 7, 1984. At the mentioned loading dates (30 days, respectively 90 days after performing the piles, small differences in test results also were expected from the point of view of reconsolidation of the clay surrounding the pile shaft.
Each loading and unloading step of the loading program was kept constant for one hour. The shaft diameter (Fig. 1), due to the special way of casting the concrete while screwing out the steel tube equals at least its diameter of D_s = 360 mm. The full shaft and base diameter, due to the flanges at the screw in this case was D_b = 460 mm.

THE TEST LOADING RESULTS

The loading program on each pile can be deduced from Fig. 4 and Fig. 5.
For the test pile P1, failure occurred as a continuous and rather quick penetration at the loading level of about Q = 1560 kN (Fig. 5a).Following outer load had to be decreased immediately as to maintain and later on to decrease the penetrating rate of the pile into the soil.
The failure at test pile P2 was introduced at Q =

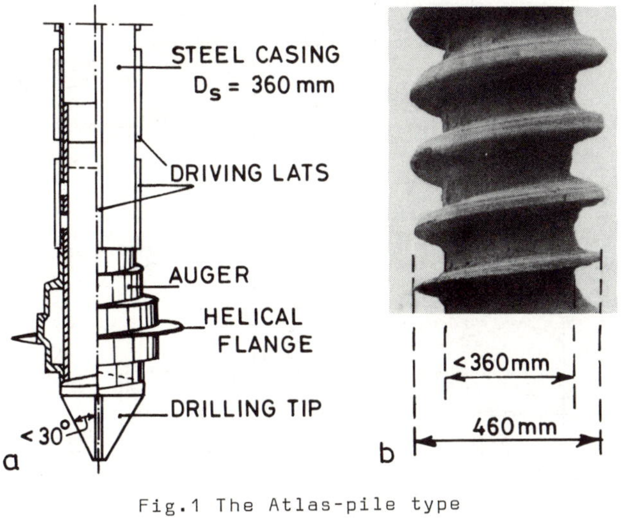

STEEL CASING
D_S = 360 mm

DRIVING LATS

AUGER

HELICAL
FLANGE

DRILLING TIP

< 30°

a

< 360 mm

460 mm

b

Fig.1 The Atlas-pile type

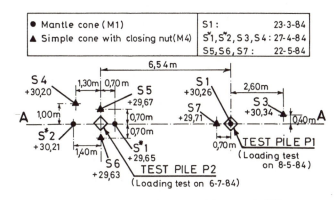

● Mantle cone (M1)	S1:	23-3-84
▲ Simple cone with closing nut(M4)	S*1,S*2,S3,S4:	27-4-84
	S5,S6,S7:	22-5-84

Fig.2 Location of test piles and CPT

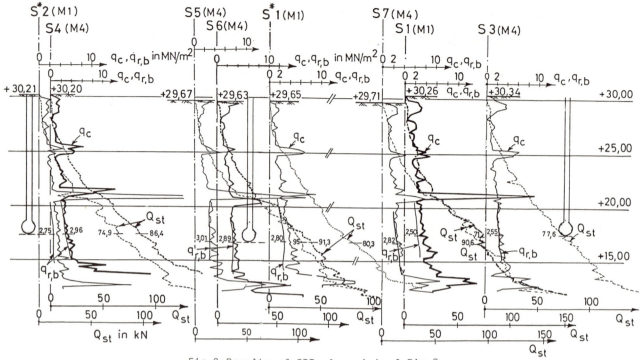

Fig.3 Results of CPT along A-A of Fig.2

1700 kN although continuous penetration at a rate of about 30 mm/hour only was obtained at a constant total load of 1765 kN, which so was considered as the rupture load.

Out of this loading-settlement results, the failure criteria of Van der Veen (1953) and Christiaens (1970) as described by De Beer (1967) are used.

For the first mentioned criterion an appropriate straight line on Fig. 6 is indicating the failure load Q_r. From Fig. 6 for the test pile P1 the Van der Veen's value becomes $Q_r^{(L)}$ = 1580 kN ; for the test pile P2 it rises up to be $Q_r^{(L)}$ = 1755 kN.

The application of the Christiaen's criterion, describing the failure load at the intersection point Y of two best fitting straight lines in a semi-logaritmic load settlement diagram, (Fig. 7), brings the $Q_r^{(L)}$-values up to $Q_r^{(L)}$ = 1550 kN for pile P1 and $Q_r^{(L)}$ = 1680 kN for P2. In Table I such failure loads are gathered.

ANALYSIS OF THE PILE BEARING CAPACITY

a)Using De Beer's method (1971) for driven piles, taking into account the scale effect of pile base diameter versus cone diameter, out of each mentioned CPT-result the ultimate unit point bearing capacity $q_{r,b}$ is deduced from the cone resistance values q_c.

The CPT-results obtained from mantle cone tests although beforehand were adapted, because with this extended cone type some resistance measured at levels above its point in fact also is included in the cone resistance measurement. In

TABLE I

Assumed total failure load $Q_r^{(L)}$ from test results

Test pile	Observed	Van der Veen criterion	Christiaens criterion
P1	1560 kN	1580 kN	1550 kN
P2	1765 kN	1755 kN	1680 kN

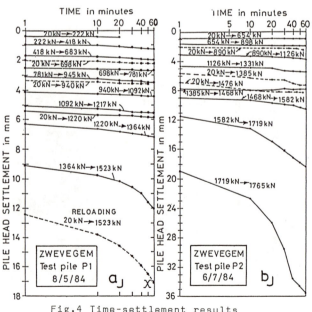

Fig.4 Time-settlement results

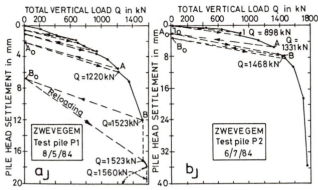

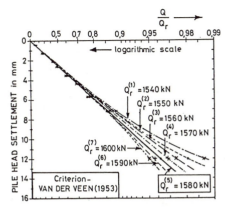

Fig.5 Vertical load versus pile head settlement

Fig.6 Failure load from Van der Veen-criterion

comparison with the simple cone with closing nut therefore a decrease has to be taken into account. For clays and values of the cone resistance q_c (Fig. 3) of 2 MN/m² $< q_c <$ 4 MN/m² such decrease Δq_c here is described proportionally as :

0,4 MN/m² $< \Delta q_c <$ 0,8 MN/m².

On Fig. 3, each of the corresponding $q_{r,b}$-curves is drawn, allowing to obtain the $q_{r,b,o}$-value at the pile tip level, corresponding to each of the CPT-results. At the same level, $Q_{s,t,o}$ is the cumulated lateral resistance measured on the cone penetration tubes (d_s = 0,036 m).

In Table II, for all CPT-results (adapted for the extended mantle cone results), the values of $q_{r,b,o}$; $Q_{s,t,o}$; $Q_{r,b}^{(c)}$; $F_{p,c}^{(c)}$ and $Q_r^{(c)}$ are given, in which

$$Q_{r,b}^{(c)} = q_{r,b,o} \cdot \frac{\pi D_b^2}{4} \; ; \; \text{ultimate point bearing} \quad (1)$$

$$F_{p,s}^{(c)} = Q_{s,t,o} \cdot \frac{D_s}{d_s} \; ; \; \text{ultimate shaft bearing} \quad (2)$$

and

$$Q_r^{(c)} = Q_{r,b}^{(c)} + F_{p,c}^{(c)} \quad (3)$$

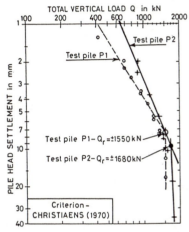

Fig.7 Failure load from Christiaens-criterion

$$P_n = \frac{1}{\eta_1} \cdot \left(\frac{Q_{r,b,max}^*}{\eta_2} + \frac{F_{p,s,max}^*}{\eta_3} \right) \quad (4)$$

or, with η_1 = 1,4 :

P_n for test pile P1 becomes : P1 = 730,9 kN

P_n for test pile P2 becomes : P2 = 944,8 kN

b) The devision into point and shaft bearing capacity can be made using Van Weele's method (Van Weele, 1957).
In Table IV the data, out of the test loading results, needed in this respect, are gathered.
The ultimate shaft bearing capacity $F_{p,s}^{(L)}$ then is calculated (Van Impe, 1984) as :

$$F_{p,s}^{(L)} = \frac{Q_A \cdot \frac{\Delta V}{\Delta Q} - V_A}{\frac{\Delta V}{\Delta Q} - (1 - n) \cdot \frac{\ell}{E\Omega}} \quad (5)$$

where

$$n = \frac{\int_o^\ell Q_{s,t,x} \cdot dx}{\ell \cdot Q_{s,t,o}} \quad (6)$$

ℓ = 13 m

E = 28,5 kN/mm²

Ω = 0,1159 m²

Out of the CPT-results ; CPT-S1 for test pile P1

TABLE II

Results of calculated bearing capacities out of CPT

CPT	$q_{r,b,o}$ ($\frac{MN}{m^2}$)	$Q_{s,t,o}$ (kN)	$Q_{r,b}^{(c)}$ (kN)	$F_{p,s}^{(c)}$ (kN)	$Q_r^{(c)}$ (kN)
(adapted)S1	2,50	71	415,5	907,2	1322,7
S3	2,55	77,6	424,0	991,6	1415,6
S7	2,82	90,6	469,3	1157,7	1627
(adapted)S*1	2,80	80,3	465,3	1026,1	1491,4
(adapted)S*2	2,75	74,9	457,0	957,1	1414,1
S4	2,96	86,4	491,9	1104,0	1595,9
S5	3,01	95,0	500,2	1213,9	1714,1
S6	2,89	91,3	480,3	1166,6	1646,9

Out of the data in Table II, some maximum and minimum values are derived in Table III in order to get an estimation of the allowable bearing capacity.
From the Table III-data, (on next page), allowable bearing capacities P_n were calculated as :

TABLE III

Derived values from table II

CPT nr	Test pile nr	Values from CPT at or around the test pile				Values from CPT-overall spreading					
		$Q^{(*)}_{r,b,max}$ (kN)	$Q^{(*)}_{r,b,min}$ (kN)	$F^{(*)}_{p,s,max}$ (kN)	$F^{(*)}_{p,s,min}$ (kN)	$Q^{(o)}_{r,b,max}$ (kN)	$Q^{(o)}_{r,b,min}$ (kN)	$F^{(o)}_{p,s,max}$ (kN)	$F^{(o)}_{p,s,min}$ (kN)	$n_2 = \dfrac{Q^{(o)}_{r,b,max}}{Q^{(o)}_{r,b,min}}$	$n_3 = \dfrac{F^{(o)}_{p,s,max}}{F^{(o)}_{p,s,min}}$
S1, S3, S7	P1	415,5		907,2		500,2 for P1 and for P2	415,5 for P1 and for P2	1213,9 for P1 and for P2	907,2 for P1 and for P2	1,20 for P1 and for P2	1,34 for P1 and for P2
$S^{*}1$, $S^{*}2$, S4,S5, S6	P2	500,2	457,0	1213,9	957,1						

TABLE IV

Data from Fig.3a,b-pile loading tests

Pile nr	Total measured settlement of pile head (mm)	Measured plastic settlement of the pile head (mm)	Elastic uprising $V_x = s_x - s_{x_o}$ (mm)	Pile load (kN)	$Q = Q_B - Q_A$ (kN)	$V = V_B - V_A$ (mm)
P1	$s_A = 5,555$ $s_B = 12,058$	$s_{A_o} = 2,140$ $s_{B_o} = 6,785$	$V_A = 3,415$ $V_B = 5,273$	$Q_A = 1217$ $Q_B = 1523$	306	1,858
P2	$s_A = 5,493$ $s_B = 7,793$	$s_{A_o} = 2,113$ $s_{B_o} = 3,163$	$V_A = 3,380$ $V_B = 4,630$	$Q_A = 1331$ $Q_B = 1468$	137	1,250

and CPT-S6, for test pile P2, one gets :

$$n_{(P1)} = 0,306 \quad \text{and} \quad n_{(P2)} = 0,333$$

From equation (5) and Table IV, it can be derived :

for pile P1 : $F^{(L)}_{p,s} = 1190$ kN

for pile P2 : $F^{(L)}_{p,s} = 1350$ kN

The ultimate point bearing capacities $Q^{(L)}_{r,b}$ out of the loading test results, then become :

test pile P1 : $Q^{(L)}_{r,b} = Q^{(L)}_{r} - F^{(L)}_{p,s} = 1560 - 1190 = 370$ kN

test pile P2 : $Q^{(L)}_{r,b} = 1765 - 1350 = 415$ kN.

Following this calculating method the increase of the rupture load by about 11% is almost entirely due to the ultimate shaft bearing uprising. Comparing of these results with all from surrounding CPT-results calculated values (in Table II), leads to table V-results.
Although at start a much higher failure load to be measured in the testing of P2 (versus P1) was expected, (being in accordance with the assumption of some reconsolidation of the clay layer) out of the ratio $Q^{(L)}_{r}/Q^{(c)}_{r}$ in Table V it was discovered this is not the case. In this case no influence of any reconsolidation on the bearing capacity was deduced. This probably can be attri-

buted on the one hand to the fact that the time interval of 60 days between the two loading tests in this case was rather small ; on the other hand it is thought the effect of the plastic remoulding and disturbing of the soil while screwing in the flanges at the tip, was neutralized by the noticed dragging out of some clay around the driving lats, screwing out the steel tubes.
From equation (5) and Van Weele's method the bearing capacity share of the pile shaft $\left(\dfrac{F^{(L)}_{p,s}}{Q^{(L)}_{r}}\right)$ in this case of pile loading tests seems to exceed the predicted ratio $\left(\dfrac{F^{(c)}_{p,s}}{Q^{(c)}_{r}}\right)$ by about 10%.

TABLE V

CPT nr	Pile nr	out of CPT-results around pile			out of pile loading tests			
		$Q^{(c)}_{r}$ (kN)	$F^{(c)}_{p,s}$ (kN)	$\dfrac{F^{(c)}_{p,s}}{Q^{(c)}_{r}}$ (%)	$Q^{(L)}_{r}$ (kN)	$F^{(L)}_{p,s}$ (kN)	$\dfrac{F^{(L)}_{p,s}}{Q^{(L)}_{r}}$ (%)	$\dfrac{Q^{(L)}_{r}}{Q^{(c)}_{r}}$
S1 S3 S7	P1	1322,7 1415,6 1627	907,2 991,6 1157,7	68,6 70,0 71,1	1560	1190	76,3	1,18 1,10 0,96
$S^{*}1$ $S^{*}2$ S4 S5 S6	P2	1491,4 1414,1 1595,9 1714,1 1646,9	1026,1 957,1 1104,0 1213,9 1166,6	68,8 67,7 69,2 70,8 70,8	1765	1350	76,5	1,18 1,25 1,11 1,03 1,07

CONCLUSION

For the Atlas pile of Fig. 1b, the total bearing capacity, as a first approximation, can be predicted from CPT-results using a calculation method developed for driven piles, after correcting measured CPT-cone resistances when using extended mantle cone. Loading test results in this case are showing failure loads exceeding about 10% the mentioned predicted values.

The calculated predictions for $F_{p,s}^{(c)}$ starting from the total lateral friction $Q_{s,t,o}$ in CPT-results, are underestimating the real shaft bearing capacity $F_{p,s}^{(L)}$ of this type of screw pile.

Out of the test results of measured rupture load and using equation (5), it looks (Table V) as the share of the shaft bearing in total failure load with this Atlas-pile is about 10 % higher than predicted from CPT-results.

No influence was detected of some reconsolidation effect on the bearing capacity in a time interval of 60 days between the two loading tests.

REFERENCES

De Beer, E. (1967).   Proefondervindelijke bij-
     drage tot de studie van het grensdraagver-
     mogen van zand onder funderingen op staal.
     Bepaling van de vormfactor s_b.   Tijdschrift
     Openbare Werken van België, nr. 6, december
     1967 ; nr. 1, februari 1968 ; nr. 4, augus-
     tus 1968 ; nr. 5, october 1968 ; nr. 6,
     december 1968.

De Beer, E. (1971).   Méthodes de déduction de la
     capacité portante d'un pieu à partir des
     résultats des essais de pénétration.
     Annales des Travaux Publics de Belgique,
     n° 4, août 1971 ; n° 5, octobre 1971 ; n°
     6, décembre 1971.

Imbo, R. (1984).   The Atlas screwpile : an
     improved foundation technique for the vibra-
     tion free performing of piles with larger
     bearing capacity.   6th Budapest Conference
     on Soil Mechanics and Foundation Enginee-
     ring, October.

Van der Veen, C. (1953).   The bearing capacity of
     a pile.   Proc. 3rd. International Confe-
     rence on Soil Mechanics and Foundation En-
     gineering, Zürich, Vol. II, p. 84-90.

Van Impe, W. (1984).   Pile loading test results
     on an Atlas auger pile.   6th Budapest Con-
     ference on Soil Mechanics and Foundation
     Engineering, October.

Van Weele, F. (1957). A method of separating the
     bearing capacity of a test pile into skin
     friction and point resistance.   Proc. 4th
     International Conference on Soil Mechanics
     and Foundation Engineering, London, Vol.II,
     p. 76-80.

The influence of vibrations on Ateneum

L'influence des vibrations à Aténeum

R. G. M. WIKSTRÖM, M.Sc., IPT Foundation Consultants Ltd., Helsinki, Finland
J. T. HEIKKILÄ, M.Sc., National Board of Public Building, Helsinki, Finland
P. K. PAAVOLA, M.Sc., IPT Foundation Consultants Ltd., Helsinki, Finland
M. K. PELKKIKANGAS, M. Pelkkikangas Consulting Engineers, Helsinki, Finland

SYNOPSIS   Driving of piles close to a building once placed upon wood piles, later underpinned by megapiles, without damaging the already affected frame is a task where calculations must be supported by tests.   The proposed slim circular ductile iron piles and the tests described in this paper proved that the vibrations and settlements can be kept within allowable limits.   Through a large monitoring some interesting phenomena concerning the acting of the megapiles and the distribution of the vibrations could be observed.

Renovation of Ateneum

The building of Ateneum is located in the heart of Helsinki. The wood piling was done in the years 1885-1887. The base of the building was 3000 m² the volume 48.000 m³. It consists of cellar, 3 floors and ceiling. In 1900 it was enlarged for the first time. The whole building was underpinned by megapiles in 1968. From the beginning the Ateneum has been the seat of art, museum, Finnish Academy of Art aso. Through this renovation the cellar and ceilings will be utilized as well as the space below the yards. The old cellars are made deeper to the same level as the new ones, 0.4...0.7 m below the waterlevel. Due to difficult conditions and type of foundations the project is geotechnically requiring and interesting. The renovation will be performed during three years under the supervision of the National Board of Public Building. Planning and realization is done by private consultants and contractors.

Ground conditions and foundations

The building is situated on the area of the former Kluuvi Bay, filled in 19th century. The ground level is now at +2.0. The bedrock is at a depth of 20 meters, and it is overlied by a relatively dense glacial till, consisting of silt, sand and gravel. The clay layer above is separated from a silty loam by a thin uniform beach sand. The fill has a thickness of up to 5 meters and it is built up mainly of silt, sand, stones and boulders. The fill has partially plunged into the loam. The upper groundwater level above the clay is around +0, but the real or lower one is around -1.0. In the neighbourhood are several buildings on wood piles.
Originally Ateneum was on wood piles driven to refusal in the dense layer of till. Upon the piles was built a mattress of timber and

Fig.1   Ateneum

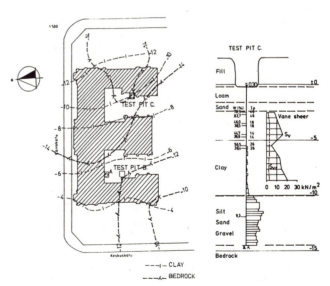

Fig.2   Soil conditions

the stone walls. In 1968 the building was underpinned with megapiles as the wood foundations were damaging and differential settlements with accompanying cracks occured. The piles were driven with hydraulic jacks through the clay and stopped when they reached the silt, sand and gravel. See picture 3.

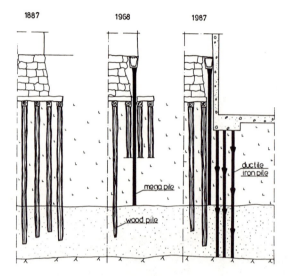

Fig.3   Evaluation of piles

THE BASIC ASPECTS FOR THE PLANNING

The effects of dynamic loadings from foundation engineering works

Referring to the ground conditions, the type of the existing foundations and the state of the frame it was obvious that the building is very sensitive to dynamic loadings. The influence of the traffic was earlier measured and reached values of ≤ 1.0 mm/s in vertical direction. Different piling methods were studied regarding costs v. vibrations. Especially the piling to be made in the existing cellars with limited height had a great influence in the choice. The underpinning made in 1968 was naturally a vibrationless method but nowadays it is very costly and not very suitable for newbuilding. Experiences from representative piling jobs were collected. Some years ago precast, in-situ and bored piles were used closed to a building underpinned by megapiles. Although only settlements (10...20 mm) were measured it brought a clear picture of how sensible a construction of this type is. Recently some more detailed studies and comparisons of the effects of driven piles of different sizes had been carried out. I.e. a 300 x 300 mm² concrete pile caused in clay formations twice as much vibrations as a Ø 170 mm ductile iron pile, although they were driven with the same drop weight. In another project the use of slim profiles combined with light pneumatic

hammers gave very small vibrations. Much less facts about the vibrations caused by the breakdown of structures were to be found. Is this a forgotten topic? . The only field where vibrations are plentifully measured is that of blasting of rock. But the range of the frequencies are roughly about ten times greater than those of piling so the experiences are not directly valid. All together too little sources could be found to make a theoretical realistic study of the problems at Ateneum. The owner agreed upon a test piling and with future projects in mind asked for a serious study of as well the test as the final execution.

TEST PILING

General

The goal for the test piling was to check the degree of vibrations when using slim steel piles driven by a light hammer and the influence of the vibrations on the building, megapiles and ground. The correlation of size of the pile, distance, number of blows and penetration of the ground was to be studied. Also the bearing capacity of the piles and driving instructions for the final piling should be fixed. There were three test pits chosen so that the adjacent structural shape was each time of a different type as corner, long wall and braced wall. The fill was removed so the piling started directly into the natural soft layers of loam and clay.

Piles and equipment

The test piling consisted of six Gustavsberg ductile iron piles. Two piles had a diameter of 118 mm and a wall thickness of 8.4 mm and the rest respectively 170 mm and 11 mm. The piles were delivered in pieces of 5 m and coupled with rigid conical sleeves. See picture 4. The smaller weighed 26 kg/m and the larger 48 kg/m. The piles were equipped with flat shoes. As hammer was used an Atlas Copco pneumatic hammer PH 180. The total weight was 880 kg and the piston 112 kg. Nominal speed was 330 strokes/min with an airpressure of 600 kPa. The guidance of the hammer was very primitive, which allowed horizontal deflections and uncentered strokes. The piles were placed 1...2 meters from the building and the distance to the megapiles varied from 1.35 meters to 2.1 meters.

INSTRUMENTATION

Vibrations

The velocity and acceleration were measured with 13 vertical geophones and 6 horizontal ones. 2 geophones were fixed to the ductile iron pile to be driven, 2 to the cut-off megapile and 2 to the adjacent megapile. The rest of the geophones were spread out in the building and the fill. For comparison some geophones were moved from first floor to second floor when driving the second pile of the test pits. The results were registered on UV-plotters.

Settlements

Eventual vertical movements were checked in 22 points through accurate levelling points and all significant existing cracks were registered and monitored by small "bridges" of gypsum. One megapile per test pit was exposed and cut off and furnished with a dial indicator. A hydraulic jack was installed to keep the cut megapile under a constant load of 400 kN during the piling or as in some cases without load. See picture 4.

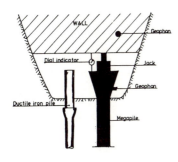

Fig.4   Test pit

Pile Driving Analysis

All piles were measured during the whole driving process with a PDA-instrument. The results were registered on a tape for further detailed studies. See picture 5.

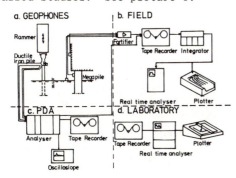

Fig.5   Instrumentation

MEASUREMENTS

Vibrations

The velocities and frequencies were registered in correlation to the applied force on the pile cap and the depth of the pile toe. In those points where the velocity vectors were measured in three directions they were transformed to a resultant.

Building

The highest value for the resultant was 1.6 mm/s measured in a column on the first floor when driving a 170 mm pile at a distance of 1.05 m. The pile point was at a depth of 6.5 meters just reaching the sand layers. The corresponding force of the hammer was 550 kN. The horizontal velocity was as high as 1.2 mm/s due to the weak guidance of the piling equipment. All the other calculated resultants in the building stayed clearly below 1 mm/s. See diagram 6.

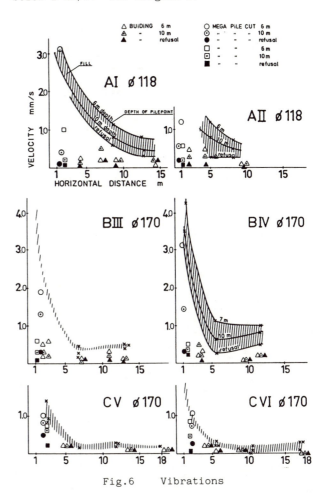

Fig.6   Vibrations

Megapiles

The highest values in the cut and jacked megapile were vertically 3.4 mm/s when the Ø 170 mm pile reached the sandlayer with an applied force of 590 kN. There was no significant change in the vibrations of the megapile when it was unloaded. The vertical vibrations of the uncut pile were always less than 1.0 mm/s. The horizontal velocity reached a peak of 5.8 mm/s. Due to the weak guidance the horizontal values did not show any correlations to earthlayers and resistance. When the stroke was well-centered the horizontal values were much less than the vertical ones. The vibrations in

the megapiles decreased with an increasing
depth when the pile point had passed the
megapiles and reached their minimum when the
pile driving came to refusal.   See
diagram 7.

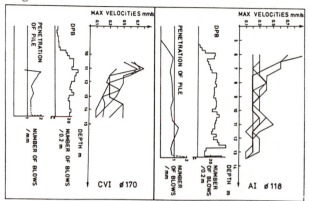

Fig.7   Vibrations, blows and DPB

Fill

Again the bad guidance caused peak values of
11.3...11.5 mm/s vertically measured
1.0...1.5 m from the piles. At a distance of
6 meters the corresponding value was only
0.5...0.8 mm/s. In general the values
measured close to the piles when the hammer
struck correctly were about 2...3 mm/s.

Settlements

The dial indicators attached to the megapiles
showed values of 0...0.02 mm in those piles
where the load was kept constant at 400 kN.
In the two piles where the load was released
during a part of the driving the settlements
were 0.15 mm and 0.24 mm. No cracks were
noticed in the gypsum bridges and the final
accurate levelling control of the building is
yet to be done.

PDA

With the CASE-calculation and a J-factor of
0.1...0.2 the ultimate bearing capacity of
the ∅ 118 pile is 390...400 kN and the ∅ 170
pile 800...840 kN. The corresponding
penetration was 0...1 mm/min respectively
0...2 mm/min. As the soft clay layer with a
reduced cu-strength will allow with respect
of buckling a load of 280 kN respectively 500
kN, it is obvious that the pile must be
tested with a larger hammer or a drop weight
when it has come to refusal.

CONCLUSIONS

Vibrations

With a strict guidance of the hammer the
values of velocity will stay below 1 mm/s in
the building. As this is less than the
continuous stress caused by the traffic it

can be allowed. The slight difference in the
diameters had no significant influence as
long as the hammer is the same.

The larger piles should thus be driven with
an undersized hammer when passing the
sandlayers into which the megapiles are
supported. For the final ultimate bearing
capacity a more effective hammer should be
used.   The frequencies where the maximum
velocities occured were 5...20 Hz. The self
frequency of the structural parts are in this
range which results in a slight increase of
the horizontal vibrations in the upper floors
but staying still below 1 mm/s.

Some phenomena observed from the test
results:
- The vibrations decreased considerably when
  the piles came to refusal.
- The vertical vibrations in the building and
  the fill decreased normally in relation to
  distance when driving ∅ 118 mm piles, but
  when driving the 0 17∅ mm the values
  increased at a distance greater than the
  depth to the sandlayer (due to
  superimposition of R-, P- and S-waves).
- The point of the megapile was the most
  sensible conductor of vibrations.
- The megapiles when rigid fixed were damped
  by the mass of the building.
- No noticable change of vibration in the
  megapile when it was unloaded.
- The factor of transfer from ground to
  building was 0.25...0.30 at a distance
  of 2 meters from the pile.

Settlements

As the test piling caused none or minor
settlements in the adjacent megapiles it is
obvious that the final piling due to its
great number of piles can be predicted to
reach values of 1...4 mm. But as the new
piles are evenly spread there will be no
abrupt differential settlements.

Piling equipment

A well guided piling device with a centered
stroke and if necessary a reduced air
pressure when passing the critical layers
will keep the vibrations and settlements at a
minimum.   The number of blows for the
smaller pile was about 9.400 and for the
larger about 14.700. Some of the larger
piles should be tested with a heavier hammer
or testloaded in order to get a maximum load.

Piles

The slim profiles and round shape proved to
be suitable for penetrating the layers and
reach the hard strata with a light equipment.
The pile has a favourable circular shape
against buckling. As the smaller pile is
manufactured in pieces down to 1 meters it is
very suitable for indoor works. Due to the
hollow section they can always be inspected
for integrety and deflection thus keeping the
safety factor at a reasonable level.

A study on behaviour of long H-piles in soft ground

Une étude sur le comportement des pieux-H longs dans la terre tendre

S. M. WOO, Moh and Associates (S) Pte Ltd., Singapore
Z. C. MOH, Moh and Associates (S) Pte Ltd., Singapore

SYNOPSIS   Many highrise buildings are supported by long H-piles. In cases where these piles penetrate into a deep bearing layer underneath a thick layer of soft clay, the verticality of these long piles and the behaviour of pile under compression loading are the important points for considerations in design.

This paper describes a study of 11 instrumented H-piles driven at a site to investigate the vertical alignment after driving, the induced lateral movement of pile from driving the adjacent piles, the deformation of pile, especially at the splicing joints under loading test.

Measurements of inclinometer tubes installed on the H-piles indicate that the vertical profiles of the H-piles often exceed the specified tolerances. Significant lateral movement of pile in the soft clay layer may be induced by driving adjacent piles. The movement is related to the distance of the adjacent pile driven. The vertical alignment of a pile and its loading capacity can be affected by the strength of splicing joints. A weak joint may cause joint failure or buckling of pile under loading. Splicing joints stronger than normal should be designed for long piles. Piles with strong splicing joints can pass pile loading tests to two times the design working load, even with large lateral deflection after driving.

Whilst bending of pile appears to be unavoidable, the importance of quality control and field supervision for piling work cannot be overemphasized.

INTRODUCTION

Many long steel H-piles have been driven into soft grounds to support highrise buildings around the world. It is not commonly possible to check the actual verticality of long H-piles after driving into the ground, although many designers do realize that the driven long H-piles are usually not absolutely vertical.

This paper reports the field behaviors of 11 H-piles driven into a thick marine clay deposit. The piles were instrumented with inclinometer casings to study their vertical alignment and the effects of driving of adjacent piles. Six of these piles were load tested to verify the load carrying capacity and the possibility of buckling. The effects of weak splicing joints on the pile alignment and the pile capacity were investigated on one of the instrumented piles.

PREVIOUS STUDIES

The use of inclinometer to monitor the alignment of piles have been reported in several literatures, e.g. JOHNSON (1962), HANNA (1968), and FELLENIUS (1972). JOHNSON (1962) measured the alignment of a bent tapered composite pile and found a sharp break between the top section and bottom section of the pile. The approximate out-of-alignment at the pile tip was 3.15 m. HANNA (1968) monitored the curvature and direction of three H-piles after being driven. Very large deflections which occurred about the weak axis of the piles were measured. Small bending radii were measured to be about 60 m. FELLENIUS (1972) reported measurements of driven slender precast concrete piles by means of an inclinometer. Bending or out-of-vertical alignment of piles is not only limited to driven piles; FLEMING and LANE (1971) experienced lateral deviation up to 0.9 m at a depth of 30 m for bored piles placed in London Clay.

The causes of pile bending or out-of-alignment have been attributed to: (a) pile-driving technique (MOHR, 1963); (b) assymetrical soil displacement occurred near pile tip (HANNA, 1968); (c) presence of obstruction (BJERRUM, 1957); (d) effect of splicing (FELLENIUS, 1972). A few practical measures have been suggested to prevent pile bending, such as preaugering (HANNA, 1968), using straight pile segment and strong joints, providing rock-shoe (FELLENIUS, 1972) and improving driving technique (MOHR, 1963; FELLENIUS, 1972).

Analytical methods were proposed by PARSONS and WILSON (1954), JOHNSON (1962) and BROMS (1963) to determine the allowable bearing capacity of bent piles taking into account the stress of pile material and soil resistance. Many researchers actually carried out full load test of the bent piles to verify their capacities (MOHR, 1963; FELLENIUS, 1972).

SUBSOIL CONDITIONS AT THE TEST SITE

The subsoil formation at the test site is a typical soft marine deposit overlying old formation. Within the depth of 20 to 30 m, the soil is a layer of young marine deposit material and black organic clays. The special feature of the subsoil formation at the test site is the existence of a 3 m thick stratum of medium stiff reddish brown silty clay at the depth of about 19 m below the ground surface. This medium stiff layer lies in the middle of the soft marine clay deposit and divides the whole stratum into two substrata.

Underlying the lower marine clay layer is a layer of loose clayey sand, which gradually becomes a very dense clayey sandy silt with increasing depth. This dense layer is a good supporting stratum for foundation piles.

The general properties of the various subsoil strata are summarized in Table 1.

Table 1:
Summary of Soil Properties at Test Site

Soil Description	Depth (m)	N blows	W_n %	γ_t kN/m^3	q_u kN/m^2
Top Fill	0-2	-	-	18.0	-
Organic Clay	2-5	0	63.2	15.1	-
Marine Clay	5-18	0	62.3	15.2	32.4
Medium Stiff Silty Clay	18-20	6-8	30.6	18.6	93.0
Marine Clay	20-26	0	53.4	16.0	50.8
Loose Clayey Sand	26-36	5-25	18.3	20.5	-
Very Dense Clayey Sandy Silt	below 36	>100	13.2	21.5	-

METHOD OF STUDY

A total of eleven H-piles were instrumented for the study. Ten of the H-piles had the same size (350 x 350 x 131 kg/m) and the eleventh pile was 400 x 400 x 197 kg/m. All the piles were driven into the underlying dense sandy silt layer. The length of piles varies from 36 m to 52.8 m, depending upon the location and depth of the bearing layer. Diesel hammers of K-45 and KB-45 were used to drive the piles to set.

For each pile, steel pipes of 114.3 mm O.D. were attached to both sides of the web of the H-pile by welding and brackets. The distance from the base of the steel pipe to the pile tip was about 5 m.

After driving and cutting the head of the pile a plastic inclinometer casing was inserted into one of the pipes and the annulus between the pipe and the casing was filled with cement grout. Initial readings were taken after the grout was set.

Deflections of the test piles at different times were measured by a SINCO Digitilt inclinometer. Measurements of the inclinometer casings were made at the following stages: (a) after driving (b) during and after driving of adjacent piles and (c) before and during static load test.

INTERPRETATION OF TEST RESULTS

Vertical Alignment of Piles After Driving

All the test piles were designed to be vertical with a verticality tolerance of 1 to 100. Figure 1 shows the measured alignments of the ten H-piles of the same size. It can be seen that all the piles deviated from the vertical alignment.

Except for Piles No. 1 and No. 10, the maximum lateral deflection of the piles occurred at the bottom of the casing. No sharp break of the alignment is observed throughout the profile which indicates a gentle sweep type of pile deformation. The amount of the maximum deflection of the pile appears to be not related to the pile length.

The maximum deviation and their corresponding slopes and radii of the overall curvatures are summarized in Table 2.

Five out of the ten piles show relatively small maximum deviation of less than 40 cm. Three piles give maximum deviation over a meter.

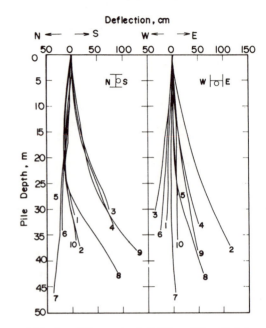

Fig. 1: Alignment of H-Piles After Driving

Table 2:
Measured Deviations of Piles After Being Driven

Pile No.	Pile Length (m)	Maximum Deviation (m)	Slope	Radius of Overall Curvature, (m)
1	36.0	0.18	1:172	601
2	41.6	1.18	1:32	579
3	36.0	0.80	1:36	618
4	42.0	0.97	1:33	518
5	51.3	0.22	1:123	1408
6	52.8	0.32	1:105	1194
7	52.3	0.37	1:125	4898
8	48.1	1.06	1:40	138
9	45.3	1.36	1:28	144
10	43.8	0.11	1:334	802

As seen in Figure 1 more piles show larger deflection about the weak axis which is identical to the findings of HANNA (1968). Actually, most of the piles deviated diagonally, i.e. about two axes. Although most of the piles were installed in the same direction, no dominant direction of the pile deviation can be observed.

It is interesting to note that soon after the largest maximum deviation was detected in Pile No. 9, the piling contractor was advised to devote better check on the verticality of the pile before driving Pile No. 10. The measured verticality of this pile became almost perfect. This clearly indicates the importance of installation process for the individual piles. Bending of piles can be avoided or greatly reduced with improved driving technique.

The "slope" of the pile as given in Table 2 is taken as the ratio of the maximum deviation of a pile to the corresponding pile depth at which the maximum deviation occurred. Common specifications like the British Code CP 2004 and ICE (1978) specify that the maximum permitted deviation of a vertical pile is 1 in 75. Using this specification as a guideline, only five piles in this test series could be accepted. However, as discussed in a later section of this paper, even Pile No. 9 which had the largest slope of 1:28 after driving could support the static load test with no excessive settlement.

BJERRUM (1957) reported that the Norwegian authorities would reject steel piles with a bending radius smaller than 366 m. In this study, most of the piles had a radius of curvature greater than 366 m. However, for two of the piles, i.e. No. 8 and 9, although they had radius of curvature smaller than 366 m, they nevertheless passed the static load tests. From the inclinometer monitoring results, it is not possible to detect directly any twisting of the test piles. However, from the projected plan views of the initial profiles after driving as shown in Fig. 2, significant changing in direction of the piles No. 1, 8 and 10 can be observed. The three piles No. 1, 8 and 10 might have twisted during driving, though they are acceptable as judged by offset.

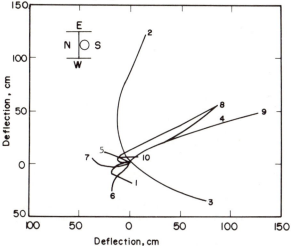

Fig. 2: Projected Plan View of Piles

Pile Movement Due to Driving of Adjacent Piles

Inclinometer readings were taken to monitor the pile alignments immediately before, during and after driving of adjacent piles. In this series of monitoring, all the piles were assumed to be fixed at the bottom of the inclinometer tube. The measured lateral movements of one typical instrumented pile during driving of adjacent piles are shown in Fig. 3. The sequence of driving of the adjacent piles are also shown in the same figure. The significant results obtained from these measurements are: (1) pile deflection is affected by driving of adjacent piles within a distance of about 4-5 m. (2) the maximum lateral movement induced is in the order of 5-6 cm. (3) all the piles show larger lateral movements about the weak axis. (4) most of the piles tend to move in the north or northeast direction disregarding the driving sequence of the adjacent piles. (5) the maximum lateral deflection of a pile occurred either at the pile top or in the middle of each marine clay layer. When driving adjacent piles within a distance of 5 m, the lateral movement is more pronounced in the soft marine clay layer. The medium stiff clay layer, although only 3 m thick tends to give good restraint to the piles. When driving piles at a larger dis-

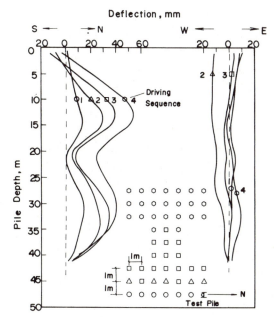

Fig. 3: Effect of Driving of Adjacent Pile on Pile Alignment

tance away, the instrumented piles tend to move more at the pile head. The exact cause of this movement is not certain.

Lateral Deflection During Static Load Test

Five of the instrumented piles (No. 1, 2, 5, 8 and 9) were subjected to static load test and the pile profiles were measured before and during load application. For all five piles tested, no significant changes in curvature which might suggest buckling or joint failure had occurred. Plotted in Fig. 4 are the pile settlements under various stages of loading against the reverse of a pile slope. The results indicate that settlements of piles under static loads are unrelated to the pile verticality. The settlements measured were all within the elastic shortening range of the piles. The results of the load tests are satisfactory which meet the specification requirements for settlement under sustained load and residual settlement on unloading.

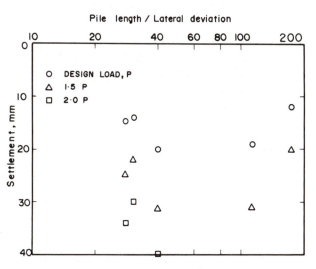

Fig. 4: Settlement vs Pile Length/Lateral Deviation Ratio Under Static Load

Behavior of a Pile with Weak Joints

The strength of the splicing joint is a controlling factor for the alignment of the pile under driving. Splicing joints commonly used by local contractors only have two splicing plates fillet welded onto the outer faces of the flanges of the H-pile and the sections are then butt welded throughout.

The design was adopted for Pile No. 11 with no special check on the splicing joints. After driving the pile was found bent throughout its entire length with a total offset of 76 cm at the tip. The bending of the pile was found to be more severe at splicing joints between sections. Figure 5 shows the measured deflection components of the pile after driving with the joints circled.

This pile was designed to be load tested up to 720 tons. However, when it was loaded to about 500 tons large settlement occurred and the pile could not sustain the next increment to 600 ton load. Large residual settlement of 22 mm was obtained after unloading. Figure 6 plots deflections of the pile under 180 ton and 600 ton loads. The pile deflected in one direction at the top 30 m under 180 ton load. When it was loaded to 600 tons, maximum deflection occurred at 6 m and 13.6 m below the ground surface and the pile bent into an S-shape. It indicates that yielding of the joints might have occurred under large load.

CONCLUSIONS

Based on the results and discussions presented, the following conclusions can be drawn in regard to the behavior of steel H-piles driven through soft ground: (1) the measured profiles of instrumented piles indicate that large deviation from vertical alignment may be induced by pile driving. Load tests to twice the design working load on piles having deviations larger than normally allowed in pile specifications have however, confirmed that the piles perform satisfactorily. (2) the lateral displacement of piles during driving of adjacent piles were measured and significant movements were observed along the section in the very soft clay layer. The lateral deflection is dependent upon the distance of the adjacent pile driven. For piles tested in the present study, driving of pile at distance more than 4 to 5 m provided insignificant effect. (3) the vertical alignment of a pile and its loading capacity can be affected by the strength of the splicing joints. A weak joint may cause joint failure or buckling of pile under loading. Splicing joints stronger than normal should be designed for long piles. (4) larger pile spacing should be allowed for pile groups to avoid piles coming across each other at the tips. Whilst bending of pile appears to be unavoidable, the amount of deviation from true alignment can be reduced by careful and improved driving technique. Importance of quality control and field supervision for pile work cannot be overemphasized.

REFERENCES

Bjerrum, L. (1957). Norwegian Experiences with Steel Piles to Rock. Geotechnique, Vol. 7, pp. 73-96.
British Standards Institution, (1972). Code of practice for Foundations, CP 2004, p. 105.
Broms, B.B. (1963). Allowable Bearing Capacity of Initially Bent Piles, J.SMFD, ASCE, Vol. 89, SM 5, pp. 73-89.
Fellenius, B.H. (1972). Bending of Piles Determined by Inclinometer Measurements. Canadian Geotechnical Journal, Vol. 9, No. 25, pp. 25-32.
Fleming, W.G.K. and Lane, P.F. (1971). Tolerance Requirements and Construction Problems in Piling, Behavior of Piles. Institution of Civil Engineers, London, pp. 175-178.
Hanna, T.H. (1968). The Bending of Long H-Section Piles. Canadian Geotechnical Journal, Vol. V, No. 3, pp. 150-172.
Institution of Civil Engineers (1978). Piling, Model Procedures and Specifications, ICE, London, p. 56.
Johnson, S.M. (1962). Determining the Capacity of Bent Piles, J.SMFD, ASCE, Vol. 88, No. SM 6, pp. 65-79.
Mohr, H.A. (1963). Discussion on Johnson S.M. Paper, J.SMFD, ASCE, Vol. 89, SM 4, pp. 213-216.
Parsons, J.D. and Wilson, S.D. (1954). Safe Loads on Dog-Leg Piles, Transactions, ASCE, Vol. 121, pp. 695-716.

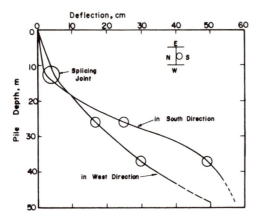

Fig. 5: Alignment of a Pile with Weak Joints After Driving

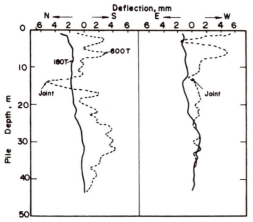

Fig. 6: Lateral Deflection of Pile with Weak Joints Under Test Load

Field evaluation of diesel hammer performance

Evaluation de champ de fonctionnement d'un marteau diesel

M. J. WU, Associate, Shannon & Wilson, Inc., Seattle, WA, USA
T. M. GURTOWSKI, Principal Engineer, Shannon & Wilson, Inc., Seattle, WA, USA
G. YAMANE, Vice President, Shannon & Wilson, Inc., Seattle, WA, USA

SYNOPSIS   Six single-acting open-end diesel hammers were used to drive 61-cm octagonal prestressed concrete piles into alluvial deposits during the design and construction of the West Seattle Freeway Bridge. These six hammers had almost identical characteristics specified by the manufacturers. Dynamic test results revealed that the efficiency of these hammers ranged from 57 to as low as 17 percent. The large variations in the hammer efficiency impacted the pile driving resistances. For piles driven into similar soils, the differences in driving resistances were as much as 300 to 500 percent. Dynamic testing should be performed to evaluate hammer efficiency, especially when unusual changes are observed in driving resistances and/or hammer performance. Diesel hammer performance cannot be evaluated by observations only.

INTRODUCTION

The use of diesel hammers has increased rapidly in the U.S.A. because of their lighter weight in comparison with steam and air hammers, their ability to deliver variable energies and their efficiency in driving long piles. However, the energy output of a diesel hammer could vary widely and is difficult to detect unless dynamic tests are performed using a pile driving analyzer similar to that developed by Goble, et al. (1975)

During design and construction of the new 1.8-km long, six-lane West Seattle Freeway Bridge located in Seattle, Washington, U.S.A. (Yamane and Wu, 1982), a total of six single-acting open-end diesel hammers were used to drive 61-cm concrete piles into alluvial deposits. Based on the manufacturer's specifications, these hammers had almost identical ram weight, ram stroke, rated energy, and explosive force. Dynamic tests using pile analyzers were performed on all six hammers by Goble & Associates (1980, 1981, and 1982). The test results revealed that the hammer efficiency (e) defined as the ratio of the maximum energy measured at the pile top (E_{max}) to the ram weight times stroke (E_h), ranged from about 57 to as low as 17 percent. Because of the efficiency variations, driving resistances varied as much as 300 to 500 percent for piles driven into similar soils. The low hammer efficiency resulted in driving resistances in excess of the specified maximum allowable of 144 blows per 30 cm for controlling driving stresses. The pile driving time for 30 m pile penetration increased from about one hour to 3 to 5 hours. This paper describes the results of the dynamic tests and hammer efficiency.

SOIL CONDITIONS, PILE AND HAMMERS

The site of the new West Seattle Freeway Bridge is underlain by about 3-5 m of hydraulic fill. The alluvial deposits underlying the fill are as much as 85 m thick and consist of loose to dense sand with scattered layers of slightly plastic silt. Very dense glacial deposits underlie the alluvial deposits.

A 61-cm octagonal prestressed concrete pile was selected to support the approach and interchange structures (Yamane and Wu, 1982). The design capacity was 1,780 kN.

The piles were driven approximately 30 m into the alluvial deposits. Four representative boring logs are presented in Figure 1, which includes standard penetration resistance (N-values) and pile driving blow counts. The subsurface conditions encountered at these four boring locations are very similar except Figure 1b boring has a distinct dense sand layer and Figure 1c boring has relatively high N-values overall. The Figure 1d boring has the lowest overall N-values.

A total of six individual single-acting open-end diesel hammers were used. These included two Kobe K45, three Kobe KC45, and one Delmag D46-13. Based on the manufacturer's specifications listed in Table I, these diesel hammers have almost identical ram weight, range of rated ram stroke, rated energy, and explosive force.

A Kobe K45 hammer (K45-I) was used in the initial test pile program. Based on the test results, pile driving criteria were developed for a K45 hammer. One criterion

TABLE I

Hammer Data - Manufacturers Specifications

Hammer	Ram Weight kg	Max. Rated Stroke meter	Rated Energy (E_h) KN-m	Explosive Force KN
Kobe K45	4,500	2.9	53.7 to 127.5	1,872
Kobe KC45	4,500	3.0	78.2 to 132.3	1,668
Delmag D46-13	4,580	3.2	65.6 to 142.4	1,690

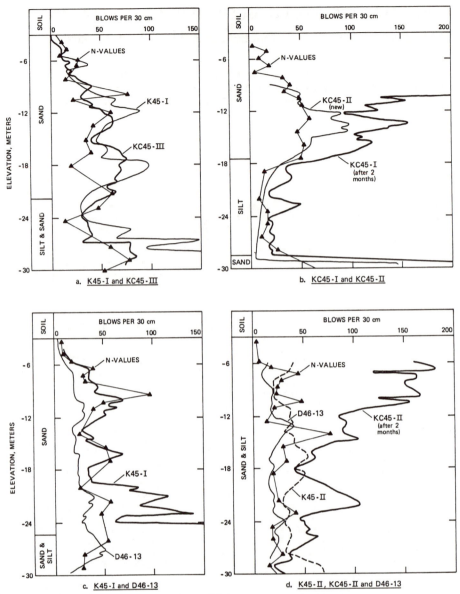

a. K45-I and KC45-III

b. KC45-I and KC45-II

c. K45-I and D46-13

d. K45-II, KC45-II and D46-13

NOTES: 1. ALL PILES WERE 61 cm OCTAGONAL PRESTRESSED CONCRETE HOLLOW PILES DRIVEN WITH FIR-PLYWOOD CUSHIONS.
2. ALL PILES WERE DRIVEN INTO ALLUVIAL FINE TO MEDIUM SAND WITH SILT LAYERS.

Fig. 1 N-Values and Pile Driving Resistances Versus Elevations

was to keep the driving resistance less than 144 blows per 30 cm to control the driving stresses. Another K45 hammer (K45-II) was used to drive production piles until the hammer emitted excessive smoke and violated the U.S. EPA (Environmental Protection Agency) air pollution standards. A Kobe KC-45 hammer (KC45-I) was then used. According to the manufacturer, the specifications for the two hammers were almost identical except the KC45 used high pressure fuel injection for more complete combustion to reduce air pollution.

The KC45-I was used to drive about 120 piles in a 2-month period. Near the end of the 2-month period, the efficiency of the hammer decreased so much that it took more than three hours to drive a pile 30 m which normally took

one hour. A new KC45 hammer (KC45-II) was then brought to the site, which was very efficient in the beginning. However, its efficiency also decreased rapidly within about a 2-month period. Near the end of the 2-month period, it took 3 to 5 hours to drive a pile 30 m. Finally, a Delmag D46-13 hammer was used to complete the project over a two year period. This hammer drove a pile 30 m in about 0.7 hours. The performance of the D46-13 hammer was efficient and consistent.

A KC45 hammer (KC45-III) was also used at another portion of the project. The performance of this hammer was relatively efficient and consistent during the entire 2.5-year period. It took about one hour to drive a pile 30 m.

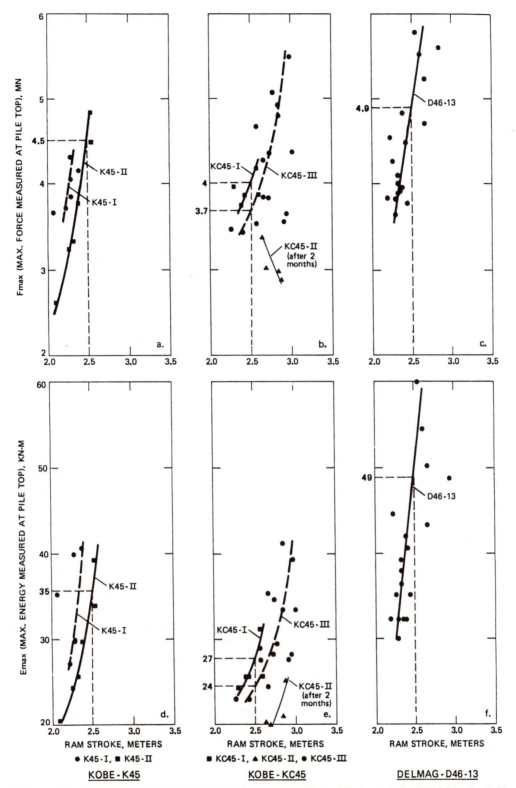

Fig. 2 Hammer Performance Evaluation

NOTES: 1. ALL DATA SHOWN WERE OBTAINED FROM FIELD DYNAMIC TESTS PERFORMED BY GOBLE & ASSOCIATES.
2. ALL DATA SHOWN WERE FOR DRIVING 61 cm PRESTRESSED CONCRETE PILES WITH FIR-PLYWOOD CUSHIONS.

N-VALUES AND DRIVING RESISTANCES

Representative N-values and pile driving resistances versus elevations for the six diesel hammers are presented in Figure 1. During pile driving, no limit was placed on the ram stroke for the K45-I, K45-II, KC45-I, KC45-II, and KC45-III hammers. However, for the D46-13 hammer, the maximum ram stroke was often limited to about 2.5 m to prevent excessive driving stresses. A 27-cm thick fir-plywood cushion was placed on top of all piles. A review of Figure 1 indicates the following:

1. Of the six hammers used, the D46-13 required the least amount of hammer blows. The driving resistance ranged 20 to 30 blows (Figures 1c and 1d).

2. The driving resistances of K45-I and K45-II generally followed the N-values. In general, the driving resistance was about 30 to 200 percent greater than with a D46-13 hammer (Figures 1a, 1c, and 1d).

3. The driving resistances for the K45-I and KC45-III were about the same (Figure 1a).

4. Figure 1b shows driving resistances of two piles located 1.8 m apart, driven with a KC45-I and a KC45-II. When these two piles were driven, the KC45-I was at the end of the 2-month driving period and the KC45-II was new. As shown, the total driving blow-counts for the KC45-I was approximately three times greater than those for the new KC45-II.

5. The KC45-II efficiency decreased rapidly with time. Representative driving resistances obtained with the KC45-II at the end of the 2-month driving period are presented in Figure 1d. The total driving blow-counts for the KC45-II were about three to five times greater than those for the K45-II and the D46-13, respectively.

HAMMER PERFORMANCE EVALUATION BY DYNAMIC PILE TESTS

Dynamic tests using Goble's pile analyzers were performed on each diesel hammer. The analyzer measures acceleration and strain at the top of the pile which are converted to energy and force and used to calculate pile capacity. The test results are summarized in Figure 2 which include the maximum energy (E_{max}) and the maximum force (F_{max}) measured at the pile top versus ram stroke. The KC45-I was tested at the beginning of its use while the KC45-II was tested at the end of the 2-month driving period. A review of Figure 2 reveals the following:

1. For a constant ram stroke of 2.5 m, the E_{max} are less than 20, 24, and 49 kN-M for the KC45-II, KC45-III, and D46-13 hammers, respectively.

2. The measured hammer efficiency (e) ranged as follows:

Hammer	Range of Efficiency (e)
	percent
Kobe K45-I	28 to 39
Kobe K45-II	22 to 35
Kobe KC45-I	18 to 28
Kobe KC45-II	17 to 20
Kobe KC45-III	22 to 33
Delmag D46-13	30 to 57

The above range of e-values clearly explain the reason for the differences in pile driving resistances shown in Figure 1. The rated energies of the K45, KC45, and D46-13 hammers are listed in Table I.

3. Assuming that the KC45 hammers functioned properly as specified by the manufacturer, such as the KC45-III, it

still required higher ram strokes of about 0.4 to 0.7 m to achieve the same E_{max} when compared with the K45 and D46-13 hammers. Apparently, the high pressure fuel injection of KC-hammers reduces hammer efficiency.

CONCLUSIONS

1. Dynamic tests were performed on six individual diesel hammers with almost identical ram weight, ram stroke, rated energy, and explosive force. The test results revealed that the efficiency of these hammers ranged from a high of 57 to as low as 17 percent. The variations in e-values were large for comparable hammers made by different manufacturers. Variations were also noted for hammers of the same model but different serial numbers.

2. The KC45 diesel hammers with high pressure fuel injection for controlling air pollution required about 0.4 to 0.7 m longer strokes to deliver the same energy to the pile top when compared with the K45 and D46-13 hammers.

3. Although diesel hammers may be delivering identical E_h-values, the differences in driving resistances could be as much as 300 to 500 percent because of variations in the hammer efficiency.

4. Dynamic testing should be used to measure hammer efficiency especially when unusual changes are observed in driving resistances and/or hammer performance. Diesel hammer performance cannot be evaluated by observations only. Pile driving criteria are meaningful and useful only if the hammer is maintained and performs properly as specified by the manufacturer.

ACKNOWLEDGEMENTS

The authors gratefully acknowledge the U.S. Corps of Engineers, project administrator, for providing pile driving data and Goble & Associates for performing dynamic tests reported herein. Permission of the Seattle Engineering Department to publish this paper is also appreciated.

REFERENCES

Goble & Associates (1980, 1981, and 1982). Reports on Pile Dynamic tests for West Seattle Freeway Bridge.

Goble, G. G., Likins, G. E., Jr., and Rausche, F. (1975). Bearing Capacity of Piles From Dynamic Measurements. Final Report, Dept. of Civil Engineering, Case Western Reserve University, March.

Yamane, G. and Wu, M. J. (1982). Pile Foundation: West Seattle Freeway Bridge Replacement. Transportation Resarch Record 884, pp. 29-37.

Calculation of bearing capacity of laterally loaded pile groups

Calcul des fondations sur pieux à la force horizontale

V. V. ZNAMENSKY, Kuybyshev Moscow Civil Engineering Institute, Moscow, USSR
A. V. KONNOV, Kuybyshev Moscow Civil Engineering Institute, Moscow, USSR

SYNOPSIS.   The behaviour of a single pile is radically different from the behaviour of a pile in group. The new method of calculation involves the group effect coefficient as a product of the two coefficients - a coefficient of interaction of piles K_i , which take in account the interaction of piles and coefficient of restraint K_r , taking in account a rigid restraint of a pile in a cap.

INTRODUCTION

A complicated geological structure at construction sites, especially in constructing projects on developed territories, makes it difficult to determine design characteristics of upper soil layers, which affects the accuracy of calculations of laterally loaded pile foundations. To avoidboth major errors and overstimated safety margins, the most reliable method of determination of a pile resistence to lateral load is used: a pile test under a static test load. This technique provides for an integrated account of all features of soil properties varying with depth and, which is not least important, changes in soil properties owing to consolidation during pile driving.

Groups of piles are used in the majority of applications in the mass construction, which are united into a system by a stiff reinforced concrete cap. The behaviour of a single unrestrained pile is radically different from the behaviour of a pile in a group. This resides in different resistance to the action of lateral load with one and the same pile head deflection at the ground level.

Now the abovementioned difference in bearing capacities of laterally loaded piles is assessed by a group effect coefficient $K_{g.e.}$. According to the experimental results, the group effect coefficient is always greater than unity, it varies over a wide range and depends on a number of factors including also soil conditions and parameters of a group of piles so that it is very difficult to determine this coefficient in each specific application. As a result, the load bearing capacity of laterally loaded piles in the majority of applications is not used to the full extent, and engineering and economic characteristics of pile groups are undervalued. The new method of calculation involves the determination of the group effect coefficient as a product of two coefficients - a coefficient of interaction of piles K_i taking into account the interaction of piles when they are used together in a foundation, and a coefficient of restraint K_r taking into account a rigid restraint of a pile in a reinforced concrete cap:

$$K_{g.e.} = K_i \cdot K_r . \qquad (1)$$

This approach to the determination of the group effect coefficient makes it possible to take into account the influence of various factors on its value in a more correct manner thus substantially improving the accuracy of calculations.

A method has been worked out on the basis of comprehensive experimental studies of operation of model and field laterally loaded pile foundations conducted at the Chair of Soil Mechanics, Bases and Foundations of the Kuybyshev Moscow Civil Engineering Institute. The use of up-to--date strain gauge techniques made it possible to conduct individual investigations into the influence of pile restraint by a cap and their interaction on the load bearing capacity of laterally loaded pile groups.

The experimental studies showed that the interaction of piles in laterally loaded groups increased with an increase in the number of piles and decreased with an increase in the distance between the piles, being practically independent of the embedment length. On the basis of these results, an assumption was made that it is possible to determine the coefficient of interaction only depending on two factors: the number of piles in a group and their spacing.

It is very difficult if possible to obtain a rigorous mathematical solution for the determination of the coefficient of interaction of piles which would be based on real soil properties, variation of its physical characteristics with depth and also such an important factor as non-uniform consolidation of soil during pile driving, rather than on an idealized elastic medium. For these reasons it seemed most expedient to determine the coefficient of interaction using experimentally obtained relationships. These include:

- regularity of variation of the coefficient of interaction depending on the number of piles in a foundation;
- regularity of variation of the coefficient of interaction depending on the pile spacing.

Using these regularities, diagrams of the relationship of the ratio $1/K_i$ verssus the pile spacing for groups with different number of piles were plotted which are given in Fig.1. Mathematical computer handling of these diagrams by the least square technique made it possible to obtain the following formula for the determination of the coefficients of interaction within the range of pile spacing from 3 to 10 d:

$$K_i = \frac{a^{0.016n+0.39}}{0.14n + 2.08} \qquad (2)$$

wherein n is the number of piles in a group;
a is the pile spacing.

For laterally loaded foundations having from 3 to 20 piles, with a pile spacing between 3 and

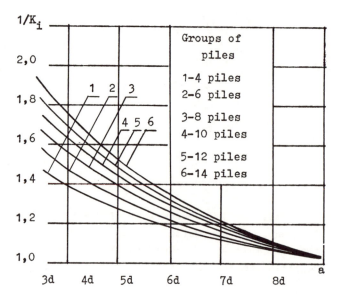

Fig.1. Diagrams of the Relationship $1/K_i = f(a)$

6d, the values of the coefficients of interaction determined by fromula (2) are given in Table I.

Table I.

Coefficients of Interaction of Piles in Laterally Loaded Groups

n	a	3d	4d	5d	6d
3		0.649	0.737	0.813	0.881
4		0.626	0.713	0.800	0.858
6		0.585	0.673	0.751	0.821
9		0.539	0.628	0.708	0.781
12		0.504	0.596	0.678	0.755
16		0.470	0.566	0.654	0.736
20		0.446	0.546	0.640	0.729

According to the results of the experimental studies, the coefficient of restraint taking into account rigid restraint of a pile head in the cap does not depend on the number of piles in a laterally loaded group. This makes it possible to consider two individual piles which differ only in the conditions of restraint of their heads to determine this coefficient. Assuming that under the action of a lateral load the pile behaves as an elastic rod having its lower part fixed in soil at a certain depth, the upper part being bent, we can find the values of horizontal forces that are necessary to cause a unit deflection of the pile head:

for unrestrained pile

$$P_h^{ur} = \frac{3EI \cdot 1}{1_{o.ur}^3} \qquad (3)$$

for restrained pile

$$P_h^r = \frac{12EI \cdot 1}{1_{o.r}^3} \qquad (4)$$

wherein EI is the bending stiffness of pile, kN/m^2 ;

$1_{o.ur}$ is the embedment length of an unrestrained pile, m;

$1_{o.r}$ is ditto, for a cap-restrained pile. As the coefficient of restraint is the ratio of the lateral resistance of a cap-restrained pile to the lateral resistance of unrestrained pile wiht one and the same deflection at the ground level, obtain:

$$K_r = \frac{P_r^h}{P_{ur}^h} = 4 \frac{1_{o.ur}^3}{1_{o.r}} \qquad (5)$$

The values of $1_{o.ur}$ and $1_{o.r}$ were determined according to K.S. Zavriev, depending on the dimensionless penetration of pile into soil $\bar{l}$:

$$\bar{l} = _d\bar{l} \qquad (6)$$

wherein l is the depth of pile penetration, m;

$_d$ is the coefficient of deformation, m^{-1} determined by the formula:

$$_d = \frac{5\sqrt{\bar{k} (1.5d + 0.5)}}{EI} \qquad (7)$$

wherein $\bar{k}$ is the coefficient of proportionality, kN/m^4;

is the pile diameter, m;

EI has the same meaning as in (4).

The values of the coefficients of restraint calculated by formula (5) for various values of dimensionless pile penetration depth are given in Table II.

Table II

Coefficients of Restraint

I	K_r	I	K_r	I	K_r
2.6	2.92	3.0	2.48	3.4	2.32
2.7	2.80	3.1	2.42	3.6	2.27
2.8	2.67	3.2	2.38	3.8	2.23
2.9	2.57	3.3	2.35	4.0	2.22

With the known values of the coefficients of interaction and restraint, the load bearing capacity of a laterally loaded group of piles is determined by the formula:

$$P_{l.g.} = nK_r K_i P_{l.s.} \qquad (8)$$

wherein $P_{l.g.}$ is the design lateral load permissible for a group of piles, kN;

$P_{l.s.}$ is the design lateral load permissible for an individual unrestrained pile, kN.

The design permissible lateral load for an individual unrestrained pile is determined by the static test of the pile.

Table III

Test and Calculation Data on Resistance of Laterally Loaded Pile Groups

Number of piles in a group	Load bearing capacity of laterally loaded pile group, kN		
	Test results	Theory	Difference,%
2 piles	114	96	15
4 piles	210	178	15
5 piles	290	214	26
6 piles	310	250	16
9 piles	405	346	14

It can be seen from the above that the new calculation method makes it possible to determine the load bearing capacity of a laterally loa-

ded group of piles with a low cap based on static test results obtained for an individual
unrestrained pile. The method has been worked
out for long flexible piles (I 2,5), taking
into account both the parameters of a pile
group and characteristics of a soil base.
Table III gives test and calculation results
for the load bearing capacity of piles of
30x30 cm cross-section, 6.0 m long tested in
the test field under lateral static load.

It can be seen from Table III that the disagreement between the theory and test data averages 15%. The exception is the group of five piles, wherein the difference was 26%.

Comparison of the test results and theory makes
it possible to recommend the new method for
the practical calculations.

Session 4B
Piles and other deep foundations
B. Pier foundations

Séance 4B
Pieux et autres fondations profondes
B. Fondations sur caissons

Variation in time of capacity of pile foundations in clays

Changement dans le temps de la capacité des fondations pieux dans les argiles

A. A. BARTOLOMEY, Professor, D.Sc., Eng., Perm Polytechnical Institute, USSR
B. S. YUSHKOV, Cand.Sc., Eng., Perm Polytechnical Institute, USSR

SYNOPSIS   The paper presents the results of comprehensive experimental and theoretical investigations of the increase in bearing capacity in time of various pile foundations in clays. Data on variation of single pile capacity in time as dependent upon pile location within a foundation are cited. The variation of capacity of a pile foundation as a whole depending on the number of piles is also discussed. To determine pile foundation capacity formulae, a regression equation and a nomogram are suggested.

The increase in time of bearing capacity of single piles in clays have been investigated in detail recently(Bartolomey,1966;Novozhilov, 1966,1970) whereas relevant data on the similar process in pile foundations are in fact not available. In order to elucidate the regularities of variation in time of pile foundation capacity comprehensive empirical and theoretical investigations have been carried out at the Perm Polytechnical Institute. Based on the experimental testing of small-scale pile foundations the regularities of pile foundation capacity variation in time have been determined and relationships which hold for group behaviour of foundation piles in service obtained. To study the regularities of interaction between a pile foundation and surrounding saturated clay small- and large-scale instrumented pile foundations comprising 4 to 25 piles as well as full scale instrumented pile foundations were tested. Piles were 5 to 15m long, 25 x 25, 30 x 30 and 35 x 35cm in section and with the spacing of 3d. A foundation consisted of up to 9 piles. The experiments were conducted in clays of different consistencies (J_L = 0.25 - 0.8)

Numerous experiments have demonstrated that bearing capacity along the lateral surface of driven piles in saturated clays reaches its ultimate value after the seepage consolidation and tixotropic strengthening process is over. The tests show a 80% increase in capacity of four-pile groups tested 40-45 days after driving as compared to the data obtained 6 days after. The bearing capacity of nine-pile groups (5,7 and 9m long piles) registered 45 days after driving increased by 70% as compared to the data obtained 6 days after driving (Fig. 1,2) (Bartolomey & Yushkov,1980)

The analysis of load distribution between pile tip and lateral surface showed that for all piles (except central) in a 9-pile group the load carried by lateral surface is 35-50% larger than that of the pile tip whereas the tip of central pile carries twice as much load as the lateral surface. Comparison of bearing capacities measured 6 and 45 days after driving demonstrated that corner pile resistance

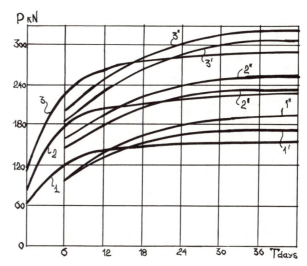

Fig.1. Pile capacity increase in time(consistency=0.7):1-single 5m long pile;1'-5m long pile in a group of 4 piles;1''-5m long pile in a group of 9 piles;2-single 7m long pile;2'-7m long pile in a group of 4 piles; 2''-7 m long pile in a group of 9 piles; 3- single 9m long pile; 3'-9m long pile in a group of 4 piles; 3''-9m long pile in a group of 9 piles.

increases by 15% 45 days after driving as compared to 6 days after and friction forces along lateral surface grow 4 times for the same period. Pile tip resistance of middle piles in an outside row grows by 36% for 45 days while friction forces along lateral surface increase by 220%. Central pile tip resistance increases by 70 % and the corresponding friction forces values indicate a 3-times increase for the same period.

The increase in capacity of corner and middle piles in the outside row is mainly due to the growth of unit friction along the lateral surface. The increase in pile tip frontal resistance of the central pile is due to consolidation of the underlying soil.

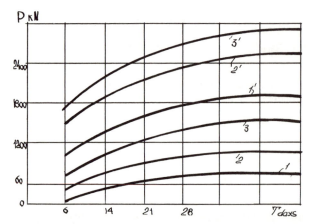

P кN

Fig.2. Pile foundation capacity variation in time for 4-and 9-pile groups.1,2,3-4-pile foundations,5,7,9m long piles,respectively;1',2'3'- 9-pile foundations,5,7,9m long piles respect.

A number of experiments indicate that an accurate evaluation of the actual bearing capacity of pile foundations might be based on ultimately allowable settlements of buildings and structures (Bartolomey, 1982).

The analysis of load distribution among piles in a 9-pile foundation 6 and 45 days after driving has shown that bearing capacity values in corner piles are the highest ones whereas central piles carry the lowest load among other piles in both cases.

The change of physical-mechanical soil characteristics as an immediate result of driving as well as the variation of soil characteristics in time are the factors which affect the variation in time of pile foundation bearing capacity. Pile driving brings about the consolidation of soil adjoining a pile so that physical and mechanical properties of soil change. The degree to which the initial soil properties change might be a criterion to distinguish several zones of different consolidation. Soil unit mass increases by 20-27% in consolidated zones adjoining piles as well as in inter-pile spacings.

Based on the analitical solution of the problem of soil displacement during pile driving formulae have been obtained for determining consolidation zone dimensions. A width of consolidation zone for a 4-pile foundation is determined using the formula:

$$L = \frac{(\varepsilon - \varepsilon_{min}) \cdot (\sqrt{\frac{1+\varepsilon}{\varepsilon - \varepsilon_{min}}}) d}{(1+\varepsilon)(1+\varepsilon_{min}) J} \quad (1)$$

For a 9-pile foundation (3 x 3):

$$L = \frac{(\varepsilon - \varepsilon_{min})(1,5 \cdot \sqrt{\frac{1+\varepsilon}{\varepsilon - \varepsilon_{min}}} - 3,5) d}{(1+\varepsilon)(1+\varepsilon_{min}) J} \quad (2)$$

For a 16-pile foundation (4 x 4)

$$L = \frac{(\varepsilon - \varepsilon_{min})(2 \cdot \sqrt{\frac{1+\varepsilon}{\varepsilon - \varepsilon_{min}}} - 5) d}{(1+\varepsilon) \cdot (1+\varepsilon_{min}) J} \quad (3)$$

The value J in the denominator is determined using the formula

$$J = \frac{1}{2\sqrt{1+\varepsilon} \cdot \sqrt{\varepsilon - \varepsilon_{min}}} \cdot \ln \frac{\sqrt{\varepsilon - \varepsilon_{min}} + \sqrt{1+\varepsilon}}{\sqrt{1+\varepsilon} - \sqrt{\varepsilon - \varepsilon_{min}}} - \frac{1}{1+\varepsilon} (4)$$

where ε is the coefficient of porosity for undisturbed soil; ε_{min} is the coefficient of porosity for soil after driving; L is the inter-pile spacing.

The bearing capacity of pile foundation is minimal immediately after driving because the emergence of additional pore pressure results in the effective stress decrease as well as decrease in soil resistance along the lateral surface of piles. Eventually, additional pore pressure drops while effective stresses, soil resistance along the lateral surface and bearing capacity increase. The variation of pile foundation bearing capacity depends on effective stresses and, therefore, to determine it a degree of effective stress increase(consolidation) should be used. The tests indicate that a relationship exists between a growth of pile foundation bearing capacity in time and variation of additional pore pressure along the pile-soil interface and at different distances from a foundation depending on the radius of soil consolidation zone which appears as a result of driving. On the basis of the solution of a seepage consolidation theory problem and taking into account pile foundation parameters, regularities of load transfer to adjoining soil and some other factors we obtained the formulae for determining pile foundation bearing capacity in time

$$\Phi_t = \Phi_0 \cdot \left[1 + f \left(\frac{P_w(\tau t)}{P_{w_0}(\tau)} \right) \right] \quad (5)$$

where Φ_t is the bearing capacity of pile foundation at any time interval; Φ_0 is the bearing capacity of pile foundation as registered after driving; P_w is the additional pore pressure; P_{w_0} is the initial value of additional pore pressure.
When $P_w = P_{w_0}$ effective stresses are equal to zero and the pile foundation capacity is minimum. When $P_w(\tau t) = 0$ effective stresses reach the maximum value and the bearing capacity becomes maximum. The bearing capacity grows as the ratio $\frac{P_w(\tau t)}{P_{w_0}(\tau)}$ decreases.

The analysis of experimental data indicates that the bearing capacity is influenced by the variation of $f\left(\frac{P_w(\tau t)}{P_{w_0}(\tau)}\right)$ just as by the degree consolidation. Thus, the resulting formula for determining pile foundation bearing capacity is reduced to

$$\Phi_t = \Phi_0 \times \left[1 + U_3 \right] \quad (6)$$

Based on the solution of a seepage consolidation problem and taking into account pile foundation parameters and regularities of load transfer to adjoining soil, formulae have been obtained to determine a degree of consolidation (U_3).

The degree of consolidation values for practical purposes are prespecified in a table for different values of F and K,

$$K = \frac{R}{\tau_0} \qquad F = \frac{c_v' t}{\tau_0^2}$$

where $R = L + z_0$ is the distance from the centre of foundation to the consolidation zone border; z_0 is the radius of pile foundation as determined using the formula $z_0 = \frac{1}{\pi} \cdot 2(a+b)$

where a and b are the plane dimensions of foundation (m).

$$F = \frac{C_v' \, t}{z_0} \qquad (7)$$

where   is the time "at rest" for piles (in days);   is the consolidation index.

$$C_v' = \frac{K_\varphi \, \delta_0 \, E \, (1 + 2\xi)}{3 \, \gamma_B \cdot \left(\beta + \frac{E \, n}{E_w}\right)} \qquad (8)$$

where K_φ is the seepage coefficient; δ_0 is the coefficient of initial pore pressure; ξ is the coefficient of soil lateral pressure; γ_B is the unit mass of gas-containing liquid; n is the porosity of soil; E_w is the modulus of volumetric compression of gas-containing liquid; β is the dimensionless coefficient equal to

$$1 - \frac{2\mu^2}{1-\mu}$$

The specified values of consolidation degree depending on "K" and "F" are reproduced in Table I. For a single pile $K = 8$, for a 4-pile foundation $K = 4$ and for a 9-pile foundation $K = 2$.

Given the initial bearing capacity value obtained from static penetration or pile driving data and having analytically specified the consolidation degree we can obtain the pile foundation bearing capacity with regard for time factor.

A regression equation was obtained based on the available experimental data which have been processed using mathematical statistics procedures:

$$\begin{aligned} \Phi = \; & 886.57 + 219x_1 + 834x_2 + 259x_3 - \\ & - 106.57x_1^2 + 198.75x_1x_2 + 248.43x_2^2 + \\ & + 208.75x_2 \cdot x_3 \end{aligned} \qquad (9)$$

TABLE I

Consolidation Degree Values as Dependent on F and K

No.	U_3	F			K
		2	4	6	8
1	0.05	0.034	0.280	0.720	1.327
2	0.25	0.126	0.964	2.450	4.563
3	0.50	0.256	1.914	4.430	9.000
4	0.75	0.473	3.482	8.795	16.333
5	0.95	0.975	7.114	17.905	33.400

The coefficients of regression in the Eq.(9) were specified using the least squares method and proceeding from the condition that the bearing capacity depends on three factors: time, number of foundation piles, pile length. These factors, intervals of their variation and the fixed levels are presented in Table II where x_1 is the number of days since driving (t); x_2 is the number of piles in a foundation (n), x_3 is the pile length (ℓ).

In accordance with the conditions of the expe-

TABLE II

Levels and Intervals of Variation

Levels	Factors		
	x_1 (days)	x_2 (the number of piles)	x_3 (pile length)
Zero level (0)	25,5	5	7
Lower level (−1)	6	1	5
Upper level (+1)	45	9	9
Interval of variation	19,5	4	2

riment tabular (x_i) and given (X_i) values of the factors are related by the ratio

$$x_i = \frac{X_i - X_{0i}}{J_i} \qquad (10)$$

where X_{0i} is the given value of a factor at the zero level ($t = 25,5$ days; $n = 5$ piles; $\ell = 7$m); J_i is the given value of variation interval ($t = 19,5$; $n = 4$; $\ell = 2$). Solving the regression equation we can specify variations of pile foundation bearing capacity as dependent on the number of foundation piles and their length for any time period.

To determine pile foundation bearing capacity in engineering practice a nomogram based on empirical and theoretical solutions was composed (Fig. 3). The nomogram consists of two binary scales $x_1 x_2$ and $x_2 x_3$, and the scale Φ on which bearing capacity values are plotted. Scale $x_1 x_2$: the ordinate is the number of foundation piles, the abscissa is the time "at rest" for piles. Scale $x_2 x_3$: the ordinate is the number of foundation piles, the abscissa is the pile length. Bearing capacity values should be determined following the procedure: 1. A point is specified in the $x_1 x_2$ scale which corresponds to a given number of piles and time "at rest". 2. This point is plotted onto the $x_1 x_2$ axis. 3. A point is specified in the $x_2 x_3$ scale which corresponds to the same number of piles and to the given pile length. 4. This point is plotted onto the $x_2 x_3$ axis. 5. Connecting the point plotted on the $x_1 x_2$ axis with the one plotted on the $x_2 x_3$ axis we obtain the point where the line crosses the Φ axis. The point thus specified corresponds to the bearing capacity value to be determined.

Example: The bearing capacity of a 5-pile foundation has to be determined 6 days after driving (pile length is 8m). First, the unknown $x_1; x_2; x_3$ are specified.

$$x_{1;2;3} = \frac{X_i - X_{0i}}{J_i} \qquad (11)$$

where X_i are the given values of the given factors; X_i^0 are the given values of the factors at zero level taken from Table II; $X_1^0 = 25,5$ (time); $X_2^0 = 5$ (number of piles); $X_3^0 = 7$ (ℓ - pile length); J_i are the given values of variation intervals taken from Table II; $J_1 = 19,5$ (t - time); $J_2 = 4$ (number of piles); $J_3 = 2$ (ℓ - pile length).

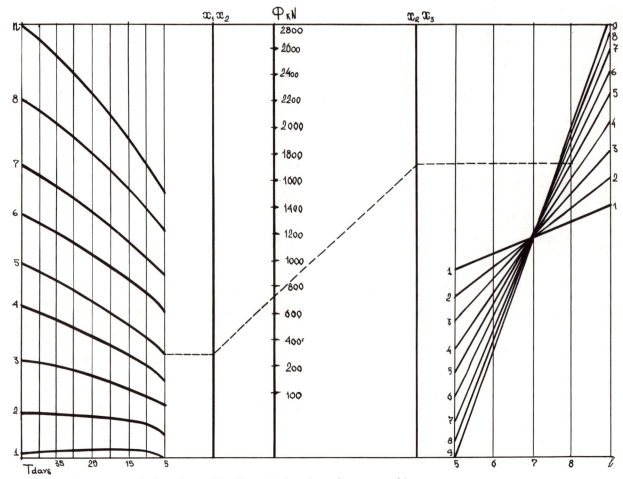

Fig. 3. Nomogram to determine pile foundation bearing capacity.

For 6 days $\quad x_1 = \dfrac{6 - 25.5}{19.5} = -1$

For 5 piles $\quad x_2 = \dfrac{5 - 5}{4} = 0$

For 8m-long piles $\quad x_3 = \dfrac{8 - 7}{2} = 0.5$

The values of $x_1 = 1; x_2 = 0; x_3 = 0.5$ are then substituted into the regression equation and solving the equation we obtain $\varphi = 690.5$ kN. The given values $x_1 = 1; x_2 = 0; x_3 = 0.5$ are substituted into the regression equation to determine the bearing capacity of the same foundation 45 days after driving. The equation solves to give $\varphi = 1128.5$ kN.

Thus the bearing capacity of pile foundation for 45 days "at rest" increases by 438 kN as compared to the 6 days period. The empirical and theoretical investigations have demonstrated that bearing capacity of pile foundations in clays increases by 65-70% in 40-45 days. Thus the design efficiency is raised when bearing capacity increase in time is taken into consideration.

REFERENCES

Bartolomey A.A., Golofeevsky G.F.(1966). Pile driving experience in the city of Perm and problems of efficient design. In:Seminar on Pile Foundation Design.-Moscow:Orgselstroy, pp.1-6. (In Russian).

Bartolomey A.A.(1872).Variation of deformation modulus, unit weight and cohesion forces of clays in the active zone.In:Problems of Construction Efficiency,No.108.-Perm:PPI Press, pp.18-32. (In Russian).

Bartolomey A.A.,Yushkov B.S.(1980).Variation in time of bearing capacity of pile founda- tions in soft clays.In:Footings and Founda- tions.-Perm:PPI Press, 1980,pp.22-28. (In Russian).

Novozhilov G.F.(1970). Investigation of bearing capacity increase in time of piles in soft clays in Leningrad. In: Construction in Soft Soils. - Riga, pp. 235-240.

Dynamic pre-loading of large diameter bored piles

Préchargement dynamique des pieux forés de grand diamètre

B. BERGGREN, Swedish Geotechnical Institute, Linköping, Sweden
P. E. BENGTSSON, Swedish Geotechnical Institute, Linköping, Sweden
B. LUNDAHL, Stabilator AB, Foundation Division, Danderyd, Sweden
E. MAGNUSSON, Skanska AB, Danderyd, Sweden

SYNOPSIS   Foundation on large diameter bored piles in loose and medium dense non-cohesive soils is not economic in Sweden. If the non-cohesive soil beneath the pile is made more dense and if the stiffness of the soil could be measured the situation for bored piles would be better. A method to pre-load non-cohesive soil beneath bored piles dynamically has been described by Eresund (1972). Several field and laboratory tests have shown positive results, Berggren (1981). In 1983, the Swedish contractor Stabilator AB decided on development of equipment for production of bored piles. Development work was supported by the National Swedish Board for Technical Development (STU).

This paper describes the theoretical background for dynamic pre-loading and the results from a field test. The test shows that the analysis of the dynamic pre-loading gives a good estimate of the static behaviour of the pile tip. The test also shows that the pile can take considerably more load, 5-10 times, after dynamic pre-loading than if it was cast in an untreated soil.

1. RELATIONSHIP BETWEEN DYNAMIC AND STATIC LOADING

The relationship between the dynamic and the static force giving the same displacement of a weightless foundation on soil may according to Lysmer & Richert (1966), be expressed by:

$$\frac{P_{dyn}}{P_{stat}} = k_1 + c_1 \frac{D}{2v_s} \cdot \frac{\dot{s}}{s} \tag{1}$$

where

P_{dyn} = dynamic force

P_{stat} = static force

k_1 = coefficient dependent on the elastic behaviour of the soil

c_1 = coefficient dependent on the viscous behaviour of the soil

D = diameter of the foundation

v_s = shear wave velocity

s = displacement

$\dot{s}$ = displacement rate

The assumptions for equation (1) are a weightless foundation and that the dynamic loading is a continous sinusodial one. Now introduce the additional assumptions that the force induced in the soil by the blow from a free-falling weight follows a sinusodial course and that the time to reach maximum load is t_0. The mean value of the displacement rate is then

$$\dot{s} = s/t_0 \tag{2}$$

which, introduced into equation (1), gives

$$\frac{P_{dyn}}{P_{stat}} = k_1 + c_1 \frac{D}{2v_s t_0} \tag{3}$$

The coefficients k_1 and c_1 are dependent on the frequency factor a_0 which may be expressed by (Lysmer & Richart, 1966)

$$a_0 = w \frac{D}{2} \sqrt{\frac{\rho}{G}} \tag{4}$$

where

w = angular frequency of the loading
ρ = density of the soil
G = shear modulus of the soil

It is stated that

$$v_s = \sqrt{\frac{G}{\rho}} \tag{5}$$

$$w = 2\pi \frac{1}{T} = 2\pi \frac{1}{4t_0} \tag{6}$$

where

T = period

The expression (4) of the frequency factor a_0 can thus be rearranged

$$a_0 = \frac{\pi D}{4v_s t_0} \tag{7}$$

An analysis of the equation (3) shows that only one graph is needed to obtain the relationship between the dynamic force and the static force at the same displacement for different foundation diameters D. Figure 1 is valid for the diameter $D_0 = 1.0$ m. If another diameter D_1 is needed the graph in Figure 1 can be used by changing the parameter v_s to v_s/α where

$$\alpha = \frac{D_1}{D_0} \tag{8}$$

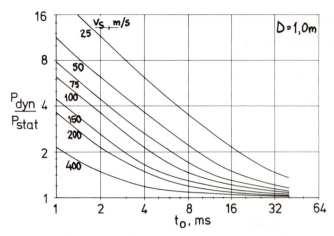

FIG. 1. The relationship between the dynamic and static force P_{dyn}/P_{stat} at the same displacement, the shear wave velocity v_s and the time t_0 from zero-force to maximum force.

2. MEASUREMENTS DURING DYNAMIC PRE-LOADING

The dynamic loading can be transferred to the soil by a heavy ram that is allowed to fall freely on a foundation standing on the soil. The contact pressure between the foundation and the soil can be evaluated by measuring the stress in the foundation and the acceleration of the foundation according to the idea described by Eresund (1972). The steel stress and acceleration are measured at a certain level, x, of the foundation.

$$\sigma_x A - F = m_x \ddot{x} \qquad (9)$$

where

A = cross section of the foundation
m_x = the weight of the foundation below the level x

The contact pressure between the foundation and the soil will be

$$p = \sigma_x - \frac{m_x \ddot{x}}{A} \qquad (10)$$

The displacement of the foundation during the blow is evaluated by double integration of the acceleration curve, i.e.

$$x = \int\int \ddot{x} dt \qquad (11)$$

3. EARLIER EXPERIENCE FROM DYNAMIC PRE-LOADING

Laboratory dynamic pre-loading tests on dry sand were made by Eresund (1972). The positive effect of the pre-loading was very evident. One of the factors that describes the effect of the pre-loading is the plastic ratio s_{pl}/s_{max}, the ratio between the residual and the maximum displacement caused by a blow. The plastic ratio s_{pl}/s_{max} is a measure of the plasticity created by the dynamic loading. A decreasing ratio indicates

a hardening of the soil and the smaller the ratio the more elastic the soil. The agreement between calculated and measured force is best at a low plastic ratio. Eresund's conclusion was that the hardening effect of the dynamic pre-loading was low after the plastic ratio had reached 0.1. He also stated that the pre-loading should not be stopped until the platic ratio was 0.1.

Later experiments, Berggren (1981), in the field and in the laboratory on saturated fine sand show that the plastic ratio can not reach a value as low as 0.1 even at relatively low loads. Realistic final values are instead 0.15 to 0.25. The measured increase in stiffness of the soil before and after dynamic pre-loading reached 5 to 10 in Eresund's and Berggren's tests.

Eresund (1972) found that the loading rate must be limited so that the pressure in the soil beneath the foundation increases at the same rate as the pressure on the contact base. Later laboratory tests show that if the loading rate is too high shear deformations spread deeper in the soil than the accumulating displacement of the foundation. A low dynamic loading rate has an effect positive on the displacement of a foundation during a later static loading. At high dynamic loading rates, deterioration can also occur compared to the original situation.

One other important factor is development of pore pressure, especially in fine, non-cohesive soil, where the rate of pore pressure dissipation is low. What happens during a pore pressure increase is not entirely evident. However, it is essential that the load cycles are slow enough to ensure pore pressure dissipation.

The conclusion that can be drawn is that dynamic pre-loading ought to be performed in steps of increasing load levels and so that the plastic ratio s_{pl}/s_{max} decreases during each step.

4. EQUIPMENT FOR DYNAMIC PRE-LOADING

The equipment developed by Stabilator AB consists of five parts:

1. Weight 3.8 t, length 4 m
2. Guide line for weight
3. Steel foot foundation 1.4 t, diameter 850 mm
4. Measuring unit, diameter 300 mm
5. Measuring equipment, station for data acquisition and analyzing equipment.

In order to register acceleration and steel stress a measuring unit is placed directly above the steel foot foundation. Accelerometers and resistance strain gauges are mounted inside this measuring unit. The signals from the strain gauges and the accelerometers are distributed by a cable to the station, where the signals are recorded on a digital oscilloscope. If required the signals can be stored on diskettes. A microcomputer with plotter is used for analyses and plotting.

5. PERFORMANCE OF DYNAMIC PRE-LOADING

Macadam is placed at the bottom of the bored hole to a thickness equal to half the diameter of the hole. The risk of suction is thereby decreased in the event of up-lifting of the equipment. The suction otherwise loosens the bottom and must be avoided.

The dynamic pre-loading should be started with a low fall height, 20 cm. Continuous registration of residual axial displacement of the foundation shows whether the soil is hardening or not, i.e. whether the residual displacement and the plastic ratio decrease with the number of blows. When the residual displacement and the plastic ratio are lower than certain criteria a larger fall height (the double) is ordered and the procedure is repeated.

6. EVALUATION OF DYNAMIC PRE-LOADING

In order to calculate the relationship between the dynamic and the static force according to Chapter 1 above, the shear modulus of the soil must be determined. This is achieved interactively, starting with an empirical value G_0.

The shear modulus G for a stiff foundation on the surface of an elastic half-space may be expressed by:

$$G = \frac{p}{s} \cdot \frac{D}{4} \cdot \frac{1-\nu}{2}$$

where

P = contact pressure (static)
D = diameter of the foundation
ν = Poisson's ratio

Since the displacement is the same in the dynamic and static cases the shear modulus should be the same. If the calculated value of G differs from G_0 the calculation is repeated with another value of G_0.

The dynamic pre-loading is finished when the required values of load and displacement are reached. The required safety margin to bearing--capacity failure of the soil is achieved if

● the soil is hardening
● the residual axial displacement follows a linear path with increasing fall height
● the displacement at maximum contact pressure is less than 2% of the diameter of the foundation.

7. FIELD TEST

7.1 Soil conditions

The soil layers at the test site consists of

    0.5 m fill
    3 m clay
    silty, sandy moraine.

7.2 Dynamic pre-loading

When the boring reached a "firm" moraine layer at 6 m depth the dynamic pre-loading equipment was installed in the hole and an extensive test

was performed. The measured residual displacement and a "shear modulus" G_{dyn} are shown in Figure 2 ($\nu = 0.3$)

$$\text{where} \quad G_{dyn} = \frac{P_{dyn}^{max}}{s(\text{at } P_{dyn}^{max})} \frac{\pi D}{4} \frac{1-\nu}{2}$$

Figure 2 shows that the residual axial displacement decreases within every drop series (series with constant fall height) as long as the fall height does not exceed 2.0 m. At the fall heights 2.0 m and 4.0 m no hardening effect can be noticed. Similarly, the "shear modulus" is constant, in contrast to an increasing course at lower fall heights. The observation indicates that the soil is still elastic but that the bearing capacity has not been reached, even at a fall height of 4 m.

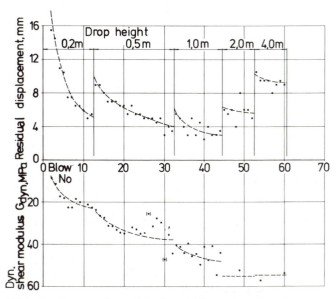

FIG. 2   Measured residual settlement and calculated dynamic "shear modulus".

7.3 Analysis of dynamic pre-loading

The calculation of the load displacement relationship of the pile tip (according to Chapter 6) shows that at 20 mm displacement a static pressure of 2.85 MPa is required on a foundation with a diameter of 0.85 m (dynamic pressure 4.4 MPa). The analysis also shows that the shear modulus of the soil is 40 MPa. The static pressure, 2.85 MPa, corresponds to the load 2.36 MN at 20 mm displacement of a pile tip with a diameter of 1.0 m.

The skin friction capacity of a pile is normally reached after a relatively small displacement, 5-10 mm. The calculated skin friction capacity for the test pile is 0.53 MN.

The total calculated load supported by the test pile is 2.89 MN at 20 mm displacement.

7.4 Static load test

After dynamic pre-loading of the pile bottom the pile itself was cast.

The static pile load test arrangement is shown in Figure 3.

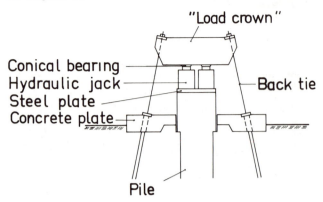

FIG. 3   Test arrangement for the static load test.

Axial displacement of the pile cap and two other points along the pile length were measured.

The load test was performed as loading in steps of the same duration. The load steps were basically 250 kN, with a duration of 16 minutes. Unloading and reloading for a short duration (4 minutes) was performed on some occasions.

During the static load test the displacement of the concrete plate (see Figure 3), followed that of the pile. At a pile-top load of 8.5 MN the displacement of the concrete plate was 50 mm. The ultimate strength of the connection between the pile and the plate was calculated to be 1300 kN.

The skin friction capacity of the pile part in clay was calculated to be 300 kN and that of the pile part in non-cohesive soil to be 300 kN.

Figure 4 shows a calculated load-displacement curve for the pile/plate connection and for the skin friction of the pile in clay and in non-cohesive soil.

The general load-displacement relationship for pile skin friction in clay given by Torstensson (1973) has been used for all given loads in Figure 4.

The total bearing capacity of the pile is 8.5 MN of which that of the pile point is 5.6 MN.

The non-linear load-displacement relationship given by Torstensson (1973) has also been used to describe the function of the pile point.

Addition of the parts in Figure 4 gives a load-displacement curve according to Figure 5, which shows the measured load-displacement curve. The load-displacement curve calculated according to Swedish quidelines for large diameter bored piles (not dynamically preloaded) is also shown in the figure.

Figure 5 shows clearly that dynamic pre-loading can be used to considerably increase the soil stiffness and that analysis of the pre-loading will give a good estimate of the static behaviour of the pile point.

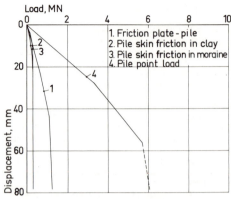

FIG. 4   Calculated load-displacement relationships.

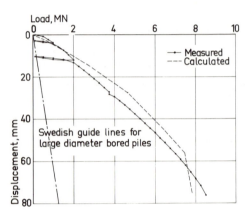

FIG 5.   Calculated and measured load-displacement curves of the pile load.

8.   REFERENCES

Berggren, B. (1981). Large diameter bored piles in non-cohesive soils - settlements and bearing capacity. Dep. of Soil Mechanics and Foundation Engineering, University of Chalmers, Göteborg. Thesis (Swedish).

Eresund, S. (1972). Settlement of circular, stiff foundations on non-cohesive soils. Effect of dynamic pre-loading. Dep. of Soil Mechanics and Foundation Engineering, University of Chalmers, Göteborg. Thesis (Swedish).

Lysmer, J. & Richert, R.E. Jr. (1966). Dynamic Response of Footings to Vertical Loading. Journal of the Soil Mechanics and Foundations Division, ASCE, Vol. 92, SM1, Jan, 1966, pp. 65-91.

Torstensson, B-A. (1973). Friction piles in soft highplastic clay. A field study in model scale. Dep. of Soil Mechanics and Foundation Engineering, University of Chalmers, Göteborg. Thesis (Swedish).

Bearing capacity of piers and piles with large diameters

Capacité portante des fondations sur puits et pieux de gros diamètre

H. BRANDL, Professor, Dr.techn., Dipl.-Ing., Technical University Vienna, Austria

SYNOPSIS   The paper gives a correlation between diameters from 1,0 to 8 m and skin friction of piers and piles in medium dense soils (silty-sandy gravels). For comparison bored piles with diameters down to 0,2 m and pressure piles as well as grouted piles are dealt too. Though the diagrams have been derived from measurements in coarse and mixed grained soils, they can be transferred to fine grained soils to a certain extent. But they are not valid, if the toe of the piers or piles is embedded in layers, being essentially stiffer or harder than those along the shaft.

INTRODUCTION

Deep foundations being heavily loaded in vertical as well as horizontal direction are special cases of design method. Foundations of bridges, cableways and high masts in steeply inclined or sliding slopes frequently require relatively large depths and cross-sectional areas.

VERTICAL BEARING CAPACITY

Usually the vertical bearing capacity of pier foundations and piles consists of two components: skin friction and point resistance. Only if a very weak soil is underlain by extremely stiff layers (moraines, rocks), skin friction becomes negligibly small. Skin friction depends not only on the soil characteristics, foundation depth and way of construction but also on the diameter of the pile or pier foundation and some other parameters.

The aim of the paper is not to present another theory for calculating point resistance (load taken by base). Generally may be stated that some design methods which have proved for shallow foundations, provide good results for large diameter-piers too, if those are not too deep. For evaluating the vertical bearing capacity DIN 4017 or $q_{krit.}$ by O.K.FRÖHLICH (1954) may be used then. In cases of relatively weak subsoil or if the resudual shear strength is very small, the latter method should be preferred:

$$q_{krit.} = \frac{\pi \cdot (\gamma \cdot L + c \cdot ctg\, \varphi)}{ctg\, \varphi - (\frac{\pi}{2} - \hat{\varphi})} \qquad (1)$$

γ .... unit weight above the base

φ ,c .. shear parameters under the base

L .... depth of foundation

$q_{krit.}$ is the idealized base pressure, when the deformations under the horizontal foundation joint are just beginning to become plastic (from the outer to the inner zone). The allowable pressure may be increased to about

$$\sigma_{allow.} \cong 1,2 \cdot q_{krit.} + \gamma \cdot L$$

As measurements showed, this formula should be limited to about L = 15 to 20 m (25 m), depending on the soil characteristics and the cross-sectional area of the foundation. For larger depths the value $q_{krit.}$ doesn't grow so much or even remains constant.

Comparative calculations show that the theoretical bearing capacity of piles and piers may vary between some hundred percents, if the specific limits of application or assumptions of the several design methods are not taken into account correspondingly.

For evaluating skin friction, most theoretical design methods are more or less insufficient. The way of constructing piers or piles on the sites plays an important role too. Therefore in engineering practice the results of in situ measurements and experience are of greatest importance.

Deriving from about hundred deep foundations in mainly mountainous regions (Fig.1) a correlation could be found between large diameter piles and piers and their skin friction. The subsoil consisted of medium dense silty-sandy gravels with variing contents of clay ($\leqq$ 10 %) or stones, blocks resp. ($\leqq$ 30 % per mass). Usually these slope deposits were mixed-grained, with an uniformity degree of about $U = d_{60}/d_{10} = $ 50 to 200. The construction was as follows (Fig. 2):

diameter D $\leqq$ 1,5 m: bore holes with casing strings

1,5 $\leqq$ D $\leqq$ 3 m: open shafts; skin surface usually protected by shotcrete (partially)

diameter D $\gtreqless$ 3 m: skin surface always protected by shotcrete
lining (10 - 25 cm)

The graph is valid only for single piles or
piles of a mutual axial distance of at least
2,5 D and for piers with a distance of the skin
surfaces of at least 3 m.

The cross-sectional areas of the large piers
(D = 3 to 8 m) were circular or elliptical. The
latter was preferred mainly in steeply inclined
or sliding slopes, in order to gain a great
modulus of resistance.

The lenghts (depths) of the foundations which
were considered for a statistical evaluation
varied between (10)14 to 21(25) m. Generally
can be stated that the percentage of point
resistance of the whole load decreases with increasing length and increases with the diameter
of the pile or pier foundation. A schematical
correlation is shown in Fig. 3.

Though the ratio L : D influences the ratio
skin friction : point resistance too, it has
not been drawn in Fig. 2. But Fig. 4 shows that
the percentage of load taken by base clearly
increases for compact foundations and increasing
total load. This effect is especially significant when the maximum value of skin friction
is exceeded and the total load Q is gradually
approaching the ultimate bearing capacity.

Other factors of influence are the ratio of
stiffness pier : soil and the Poisson's ratio
γ of the soil.

In case of an axially loaded pile or pier
embedded in an elastic-isotropic halfspace the
load transfer to the elastic medium can be
computed according to formula (2),(2a):

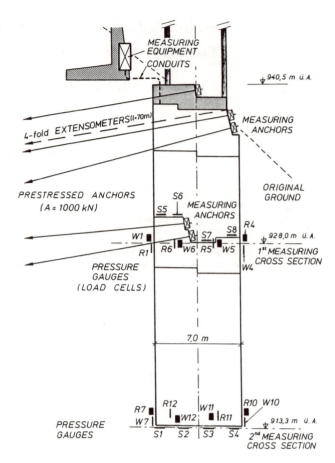

Fig. 1: Measurement systems in a foundation
pier of reinforced concrete for a
bridge column in a steeply inclined,
sliding slope

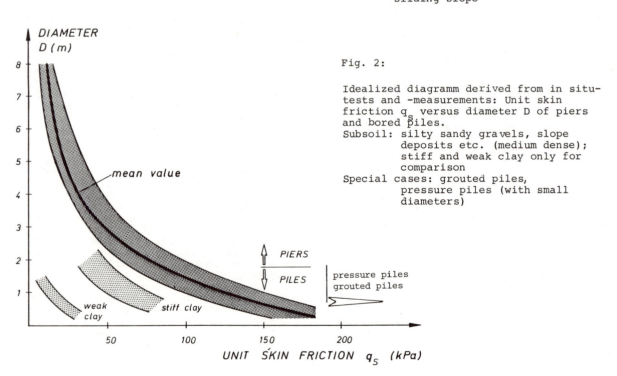

Fig. 2:

Idealized diagramm derived from in situ-
tests and -measurements: Unit skin
friction q_s versus diameter D of piers
and bored piles.
Subsoil: silty sandy gravels, slope
deposits etc. (medium dense);
stiff and weak clay only for
comparison
Special cases: grouted piles,
pressure piles (with small
diameters)

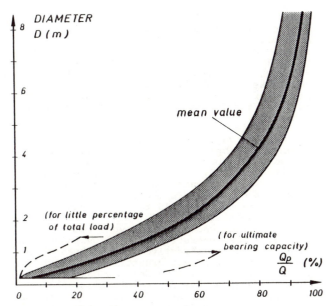

Fig. 3: Percentage of point resistance versus diameter of piers and bored piles: simplified for a length (foundation depth) of L = (10)15 m to 20(25); usual permanent service loads of structures

Q_p ..... point resistance force
Q ..... total load
(Q_{max} = ultimate bearing capacity of the pier or pile

Derived from measurements; according to Fig. 2

$$\frac{Q_p}{Q} = \frac{k_o}{(1 - \frac{E}{E_p}) + \frac{E}{E_p} \cdot \frac{8L^2}{3D^2} \cdot k_o} \qquad (2)$$

$$k_o = \frac{\ln \frac{2L}{D} - 0,25}{\ln \frac{2L}{D} - 1,5 + \frac{2L}{D}} \qquad (2a)$$

E .... modulus of elasticity of soil
E_p ... modulus of elasticity of pile

This formula is valid for Poisson's ratio ν = 0,5 (Borowicka, 1976). Table 1 shows that the theoretical values are smaller than the measured ones, mainly for compact foundations (little ratio L/D - Fig. 4). This could be expected because the usual service loads exceed the elastic state of load transfer to the soil. But nevertheless the theory proviedes usuable limit values for comparative evaluations - at least for long piles.

Therefore the diagram in Fig. 2 should give only a simplified range of the correlation between the diameter D and skin friction q_s. When taking into account the several parameters in all de-

Table 1

Percentage of load, taken by point resistance force within the elastik state: Q_p/Q
Theoretical results for the elastic-isotropic halfspace (from formula (2))

$\frac{L}{D}$	$E_{soil} : E_{pile}$		
	1:100	1:1000	1:10000
5	17,0	18,8	19,0
10	9,6	12,4	12,8
15	6,8	9,3	9,8
20	4,4	7,5	8,1
25	3,2	6,2	6,9

tails, the figure would have to be extended to about 25 graphs. For instance, elliptical cross sectional areas have been converted theoretically into circular ones (with a medium diameter), though even that factor is of certain influence: in case of all the other parameters being constant, skin friction of elliptical piers is a bit greater.

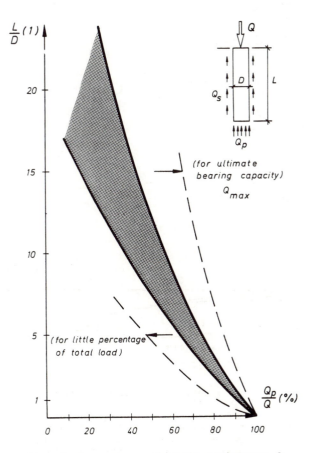

Fig. 4: Percentage of point resistance Q_p versus ratio L/D of piers and bored piles; according Fig. 3

The amount of load itself plays an important role too: Increasing vertical loads Q on the top of the foundation also raises skin friction. In many cases this value can be registered very exactly, when during the construction procedure sudden settlements occur or settlements become larger and larger - till point resistance is activated fully. In such cases the maximum value of skin friction has been exceeded and the subsoil under the piers or piles suddenly is pressed relatively high. Therefore Fig. 2 predominantly refers to permanent service loads with an ultimate capacity of the unit skin friction. The corresponding settlements do not exceed $s \lessgtr 2 - 3$ cm (in non cohesive soils or stiff clay).

For comparison, some results for stiff and weak clays have been drawn in Fig. 2 too (range of scattering). Furthermore some hints on the effect of injecting piles are given.

Frequent loading and unloading reduces skin friction, what must be considered when designing.

Though skin friction is not constant along the surface of piers or piles, this approximate assumption has been made for Fig. 2. Measurements showed that there exists a maximum value (mainly in the upper third or half of the foundation depth), and that the friction clearly decreases in large depths. As the investigated soils were somewhat similar, this approach can be justified for practical purposes and simplifications.

The bearing capacity of piles or piers can be essentially improved by grouting along the shaft or/and in the base. Fig. 5 shows one of the results for sandy gravels with little contents of silt (medium dense). By using grouting pressures of 1 - 3 MPa the unit skin friction could be raised about 40 to 60 %, point resistance up to 250 %.
Bustamante/Gouvenot (1983) give a survey of several sites, wherefrom can be concluded that this treatment is effective in all types of soil, with relatively modest quantities of grout (1 - 2 m³): The gains in bearing capacity measured were 25 - 30 % for point resistance and 60 - 600 % for unit skin friction - the soils variing from clay to gravel. The grout components were cement + water (+ bentonite).

Skin friction is further increased if using pressure piles with a very small diameter (e.g. root piles). The scattering range of results gained by in situ-tests is drawn in Fig. 2 for comparison.

HORIZONTAL BEARING CAPACITY

For evaluating the shear forces and bending moments in pier foundations or large diameter piles loaded by horizontal forces and moments, the earth-pressure theory and the theory of subgrade reaction have proved. But both methods must be compared and used critically as they are based on theoretical simplifications. In engineering practice these approximations usually are allowable, but when designing and calculating complicated structures, the following hints should be considered:

- limit analyses with variing parameters

- comparison of the results gained by both methods

Usually the earth pressure theory can be interpreted more clearly from soil mechanical point of view - even if the earth-pressure distribution is rearranged. The disadvantage is that such limit theories usually do not provide undemiable results for deformation values. On the other hand the most important parameter of the second theory, i.e. the modulus of subgrade reaction, is not a constant at all, but depends on several factors itself. The run of the modulus with depth frequently influences the results more than its absolute value. Even if assuming a modulus of subgrade reaction which seems thouroughly plausible, comparitive calculation may show that the passive earth pressure stress is exceeded near the ground surface (Fig. 6). This discrepancy needs not to be overestimated: measurements and experience showed that a rearrangement of earth pressure distribution will take place in such cases.

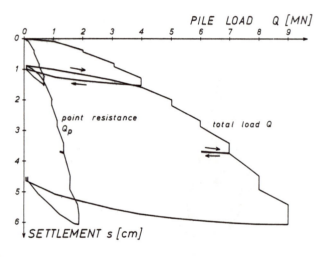

a) not grouted

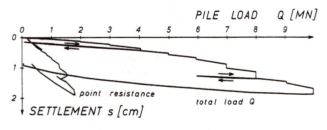

b) grouted (1 - 3 MPa pressure)

Fig. 5: Field tests on bored piles (diameter D = 90 cm, total length L = 11 m): effect of grouting the base and the lowest 7 m of the shaft; medium dense to dense sandy gravels
Q .... vertical pile load

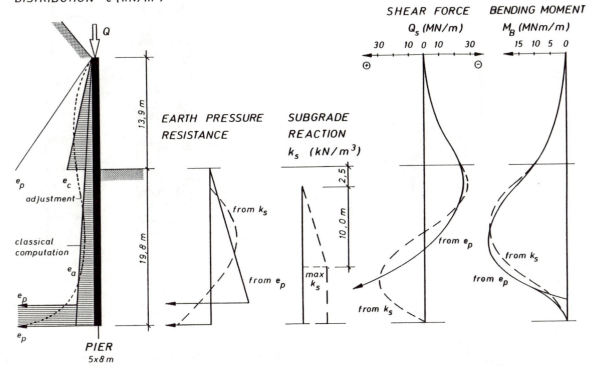

Fig. 6: Predominantly horizontally loaded piers (cross sectional area: 5 x 8 m; axial distance 10 m): Comparative calculations according to earth pressure theory (e_p) and theory of subgrade reaction (k_s).
e_c ... earth pressure in creeping, sliding zone;

$$e_o < e_c < e_p$$

Similar to the vertical bearing capacity also the horizontal one can essentially be improved by grouting along the shaft of piles or piers.

A special theoretical treatment and practical experience require piers with prestressed anchors along their shaft (Fig. 7,8), as they may be necessary in steeply inclined, sliding slopes (Brandl, 1980, 1982). These foundations are heavily loaded by the structure as well as by the slope. Furthermore various load cases have to be computed for bridges etc. Measurements showed that the prestressed anchors influence the vertical load transfer from the piers to the subsoil too (i.e. the ratio Q_p:Q), though their statical purpose is to take over only horizontal forces.

CONCLUSION

The bearing capacity of piers and large diameter bored piles depends on the following parameters:

- Increasing diameters D raise the point resistance force Q_p, i.e. the ration Q_p:Q.

- The ratio Q_p:Q decreases with an increasing ratio L:D.

- The ratio Q_p:Q increases with an increasing total load Q, mainly after the limit value for skin friction force is exceeded.

- The reatio Q_p:Q increases with a higher stiffness (modulus) of the pier or pile.

- The influence of the Poisson's ratio γ on the ratio Q_p:Q is negligibly small.

- The shape of the cross section of piers (circular, elliptical) is only of little influence on the vertical load transfer.

- Frequent loading and unloading reduces skin friction to a limit value.

For the usual service loads, the ratio Q_p:Q, the point resistance force resp. is greater than theoretically computed on the basis of the elastic isotropic halfspace. In engineering practice, design methods based on approximations and simplifications are unavoidable - but they should be developed in connection with in-situ measurements. A generalization is not always valid then, but modifications are easily possible

according to the methods of construction, local experience etc.
For evaluating the horizontal bearing capacity, comparative design methods are recommended too.

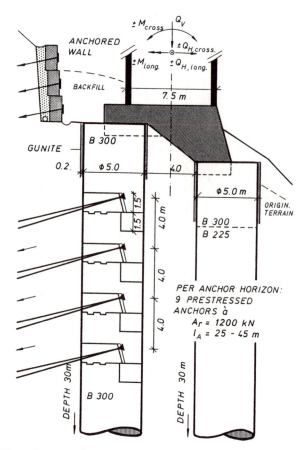

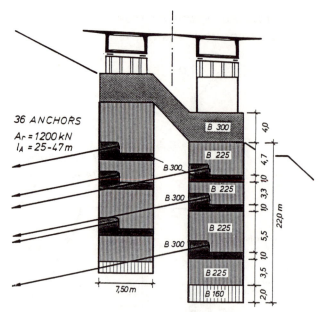

Fig. 8: Foundation of a pair of bridge columns in a sliding steep slope. Prestressed anchors, constructed in the shafts of the piers; elliptical cross section of the piers: 7,5 x 5 m

Brandl, H., Brandecker, H. (1982): Autobahnbau unter extremen geotechnischen Bedingungen. Mitteilungen für Grundbau, Bodenmechanik und Felsbau, Nr. 1, Technische Universität Wien.

Bustamante, M., Gouvenot, D. (1983): Grouting: a method improving the bearing capacity of deep foundation. Proc.VIII ECSMFE, Helsinki.

Fröhlich, O.K. (1954): Über den Beginn des fortschreitenden Bruches bei örtlicher Belastung eines gleichartigen Baugrundes. Vorträge der Baugrundtagung, Stuttgart.

Fig. 7: Foundation of a high bridge column in a sliding, steep slope. Two piers acting as a frame with a great section modulus. External loads Q,M (from the structure) on the top of the foundation:

$\pm Q_{H,long.}$, $M_{long.}$ .... horizontal forces and moments in the longitudinal axis of the bridge

$\pm Q_{H,cross.}$, $M_{cross.}$ ... horizontal forces and moments in the transverse axis

A_r .... fixed anchor forces (permanent service loads)

l_A .... total length of the anchors

B225, B300 .... quality of the reinforced concrete

REFERENCES

Borowicka, H. (1976): Über die zulässige Belastung von Großbohrpfählen. VI.ECSMFE, Vienna.

Brandl, H. (1980): Fundierung und Sicherung von Brücken in Rutschhängen. Proc.11th Congress, Int.Association for Bridge and Structural Engineering, Vienna.

Expander bodies – A new concept for underpinning of structures

'Expander bodies' – Un concept nouveau pour étayant des structures

BENGT B. BROMS, Professor, Nanyang Technological Institute, Singapore

SYNOPSIS

A new type of pile, the expander body pile, is described in the paper which can be used for underpinning of structures. A folded thin steel sheet is used which is wrapped around the lower part of the pile. The folded steel sheet, the expander body, can be inflated in the ground after the pile has been driven or placed in a predrilled hole. The bearing capacity of the pile is thereby increased. The ultimate bearing capacity of the pile can be estimated from the maximum grout pressure required for the inflation of the expander body or from the results from penetration tests.

INTRODUCTION

The new pile is driven or jacked down into the soil or placed in a predrilled hole as shown in Fig. 1a depending on the soil conditions and on the required bearing capacity of the pile. Cement grout is then injected into the folded steel sheet, the expander body, at the bottom of the pile through a small diameter grout pipe inside the pile shaft. The pipe is sealed by a packer just above the expander body. A foot or bulb is formed when the expander body is inflated as shown in Fig. 1b. The steel sheet controls the grout so it does not penetrate into the surrouding soil. The volume of the grout and the pressure required for the inflation are measured. From the measured volume-pressure relationship the ultimate bearing capacity of the pile can be estimated as described below.

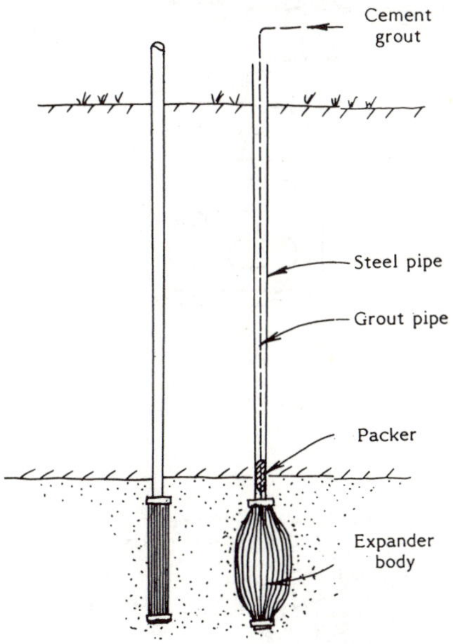

With the new pile relatively thin (> 2 m) sand or gravel layers can be utilized close to the ground surface even when the sand or gravel is loose. The length of the piles and thus the costs can then be reduced. Relatively light equipment can be used for the installation of the piles especially if small diameter expander bodies are used. The piles can be installed, for example, from the basement of an existing building with restricted headroom. If the piles are placed in predrilled holes or jacked down using the existing building as reaction then the vibrations accused be the installation of the piles will be small.

Different sizes of the expander bodies are available (0.3 m, 0.5 m and 0.8 m) as shown in Table 1. Small diameter (0.3 m) expander bodies may be chosen for the underpinning of relatively light one to two storey buildings. The large expander bodies can be used as anchors in soft to medium stiff clays where the tensile resistance otherwise may not be sufficient.

a. Folded   b. Expanded

Figure 1 : The Expander Body Pile

TABLE I: DIMENSIONS OF EXPANDER BODIES

	300	500	800
Diameter, mm	300	500	800
Length, mm			
Before expansion	1,000	1,700	2,500
After expansion	900	1,550	2,300
Cross sectional area, m^2	0.07	0.20	0.50
Surface area, m^2	0.47	1.57	3.64
Weight, kN (with grout)	0.95	4.6	14.0

UNDERPINNING OF BUILDINGS USING EXPANDER BODIES

The new pile has been utilised in Sweden, primarily for underpinning of buildings as illustrated in Fig. 2.

The piles are placed in holes drilled through the outside rubble walls. Percussion drilling is usually required. After expansion of the base and filling of the pile shafts with cement grout, the shafts are grouted to the rubble walls so that the weight of the building can be transferred safely to the piles. The steel pile shafts function as reinforcement in the walls. The piles will in this case carry the total weight of the including the weight of the walls.

In Fig. 3 is shown a building which has been lifted using expander piles. The building has been strengthened by concrete beams that extend into the outside walls. The piles are driven or jacked down through holes left in the concrete slab or in the beams. It is possible to locate the expander body in a relatively thin sand or gravel layer relatively close to the ground surface in order to reduce the length of the piles. After expansion of the expander bodies and filling of the pile shafts with concrete the building can be raised using hydraulic jacks. Each jack should be controlled individually so that the building can be lifted uniformly. With this system, it is not necessary to carry the weight of the relatively heavy rubble walls and the number of the piles can be reduced. After the elevation of the building has been checked and corrected if necessary, the piles are grouted to the beams or the slab.

INFLATION OF THE EXPANDER BODIES

Cement grout normally is used for the inflation of the expander bodies. The water/cement ratio is usually 0.4 to 0.5. The required grout pressure depends on the soil conditions. It is mainly governed by the angle of internal friction ϕ_d or ϕ' and by the modulus of elasticity E_s of the surrounding soil. In dense sand or gravel grout pressures of up to 3 MPa may be required.

Both ϕ_d and E_s are difficult to evaluate from laboratory tests because of the disturbance caused by the sampling and the changes that takes place during the installation of the piles. It is therefore preferable to evaluate the limit pressure and the volume-pressure relationship during the inflation from pressuremeter tests. It is expected that the limit pressure and the volume-pressure relationship will be similar since the inflation of the expander body is similar to that of the main cell at a pressuremeter test.

Both the limit pressure and the maximum grout pressure are expected to be affected by the chosen installation method. The limit pressure will probably be somewhat higher for driven piles than for piles which have been placed in predrilled holes because of the compaction of the soil that takes place during the driving.

ULTIMATE BEARING CAPACITY

The ultimate bearing capacity of the new pile (Q_{ult}) depends on both the base and skin friction resistances of the expander body, Q_{point} and Q_{skin}, respectively.

$$Q_{ult} = Q_{point} + Q_{skin} \qquad (2)$$

A deformation of 3 to 5% of the diameter is normally required to reach the maximum base resistance, while only a few millimetres are required to mobilize the skin friction resistance.

The base resistance of the new pile is expected to be large in silt, sand and gravel compared with the skin friction resistance because of the relatively short

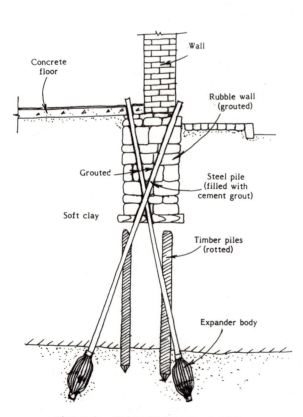

Figure 2 : Underpinning of a building

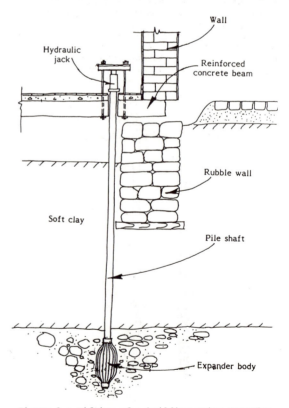

Figure 3 : Lifting of a building using expander bodies

length and small surface area of the expander body. The bearing capacity can be estimated from the maximum grout pressure required for the inflation or from penetration and pressuremeter tests as described below.

BEARING CAPACITY IN COHESIONLESS SOILS

Calculation from the maximum grout pressure p_{grout}. Test data indicate that the ultimate bearing capacity can be estimated from the maximum grout pressure and that the calculation methods which are based on the pressuremeter test can be used.

The net base resistance q_{point}^* of a pile can according to Baquelin et al (1978) be estimated from the limit pressure p_1 determined from a pressuremeter test

$$q_{point}^* = k(p_1 - p_o) \qquad (3)$$

where p_o is the initial total horizontal stress in the ground and k is a coefficient that depends on the depth of embeddment L, the diameter of the pile D, the soil type as well as on the limit pressure. The coefficient k increases with increasing limit pressure and with increasing pile length. It is suggested that the values on k derived by Baquelin et al (1978) for bored piles can be used to estimate the bearing capacity of the new pile.

The net base resistance which is equal to the difference between the maximum bearing capacity of the soil and the total overburden pressure corresponds to the bearing capacity of the soil or rock neglecting the weight of the pile since the weight of the pile is approximately equal to the weight of the displaced soil. The difference is usually small and can be neglected.

The difference $(p_1 - p_o)$ the net limit pressure (p_1^*) is equal to

$$p_1^* = p_{grout} + z \int grout - p_o \qquad (4)$$

where p_{grout} is the grout pressure measured at the ground surface z is the depth below the ground surface and and $\int grout$ is the unit weight of the grout. However, the height of the grout column above the expander body corresponds approximately to the initial total horizontal pressure p_o $(z \int grout \approx p_o)$. Therefore Eq. (3) can be written as

$$q_{point}^* = k\,p_{grout} \qquad (5)$$

Test results indicate that Eq (5) will give reasonable values on the base resistance when the expander bodies are used as compression members. However, when they are used as anchors the resistance will be reduced due to the reduction of the overburden pressure when the expander bodies are loaded in tension. It is suggested that a reduction coefficient equal to 0.7 can be used.

For cohesionless soils (silt, sand and gravel) the skin friction resistance (f_s) of a steel pile normally varies between 0.5% and 2% of the base resistance. Since the skin friction resistance is small compared with the base resistance only an estimate is required. The ultimate bearing capacity of the expander bodies with 0.3 m, 0.5 m and 0.8 m diameter has been

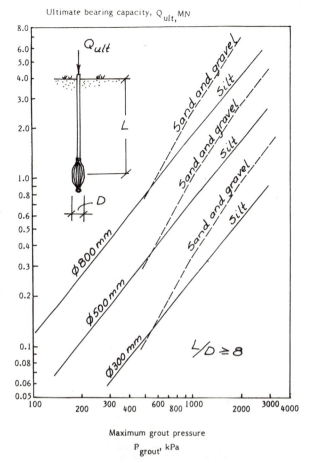

Figure 4 : Prediction of bearing capacity from the maximum grout pressure, p_{grout}

calculated for silt, sand and gravel in Fig. 4 as described above. It has been assumed that the skin friction resistance (f_s) is 1% of the base resistance (q_{point}^*) for sand and gravel and 2% for silt. It can be seen that the bearing capacity increases rapidly with increasing grout pressure.

The depth of the expander bodies below the ground surface should be at least 8D (D is the diameter of the expander bodies). This is normally the case. If the depth is less than 8D and the relative density of the soil is high then the bearing capacity should be reduced.

Calculation from penetration tests. The bearing capacity of the new pile in silt, sand and gravel can also be estimated from the results from penetration tests. A comparison between different penetration testing methods is shown in Table II (Broms, 1981; Broms and Bergdahl, 1982). However the results are affected by such factors as soil type (silt, sand or gravel), the depth below the ground surface and the location of the ground water table. For sand the relationship $q_c = 0.4$ N (MPa) is frequently used. The skin friction resistance affects the results from weight soundings since this test is not carried out in a predrilled hole. The relative density may therefore be overestimated when the depth exceeds 10 m to 15 m.

Pile load tests in sand and gravel (e.g. van der Veen and Boersma, 1957; Meyerhof, 1956; Vesic 1967) indicate

TABLE II

COMPARISONS BETWEEN CONE PENETRATION TEST (CPT), STANDARD PENETRATION TEST (SPT) AND WEIGHT SOUNDING TEST (WST).

Relative Density, R_D	CPT. Cone resistance q_s, MPa	SPT. Penetration resistance, N_{30} blows/0.3 m	WST. Penetration resistance, N_w ht/0.2 m
Very loose	< 2.5	< 4	< 10
Loose	2.5 - 5	4 - 10	10 - 30
Medium	5 - 10	10 - 30	30 - 60
Dense	10 - 20	30 - 50	60 - 100
Very dense	> 20	> 50	> 100

that the net base resistance (q_{point}^*) of a pile can be estimated from the cone penetration resistance (CPT)

$$q_{point}^* = q_c \qquad (4)$$

where q_c is the average cone resistance within a zone that extends one pile diameter (D) below and 3.75 D above the pile point (van der Veen and Boersma 1957).

Test data show that the unit ultimate bearing capacity will decrease with increasing diameter. It is suggested, that the bearing capacity should be reduced when the diameter of the expander bodies exceeds 0.3 m and that reduction coefficients of 0.8 and 0.5 can be used at a diameter of 500 mm and 800 mm, respectively. The pull-out resistance will be lower than the bearing capacity due to the reduction of the overburden pressure when the expander bodies are loaded in tension. It is therefore suggested that the resistance should be reduced by 30% when the expander bodies are used as anchors in cohesionless soils.

The skin friction resistance will vary with the soil type as mentioned above. It has been assumed that the skin friction resistance is 1% of the base resistance since only an estimate is required. The total skin friction resistance (Q_{skin}) is then 12% of the total point resistance (Q_{point}). With these assumptions the total ultimate bearing capacity will be 0.08 q_c, 0.2 q_c and 0.3 q_c (MN) for expander bodies with 0.3 m, 0.5 m and 0.8 m diameter, respectively. These values should be reduced by 30% when the expander bodies are used as ground anchors.

BEARING CAPACITY IN COHESIVE SOILS

The ultimate bearing capacity in clay depends mainly on the undrained shear strength as evaluated by e.g. field vane tests. When the expander bodies are located at least four to six diameters below the ground surface the net base resistance neglecting the weight of the pile can for overconsolidated clays be estimated from the relationship

$$q_{point}^* = 9 c_u \qquad (5)$$

The base resistance at c_u = 30 kPa is thus estimated to 270 kPa or 19 kN, 54 kN and 135 kN for expander bodies with 300 mm, 500 mm and 800 mm diameter respectively.

The bearing capacity is often low immediately after installation due to the remoulding of the soil during the inflation of the expander bodies. The capacity will increase gradually with time up to one to three months after the installation due to reconsolidation of the soil.

The skin friction resistance along the sides of the expander body can be estimated from the relationship

$$f_s = \alpha \, c_u \qquad (6)$$

where α is a reduction factor that depends on the undrained shear strength of the clay. For medium to stiff clays when the undrained shear strength c_u > 50 kPa, the reduction factor is about 0.5. For soft clays with $c_u \leq$ 50 kPa a reduction coefficient of 0.8 is commonly used (Broms, 1966, Broms and Hansbo, 1977).

The ultimate bearing capacity in kN at will then be 1.0 c_u, 3.1 c_u and 7.4 c_u for expander bodies with 0.3 m, 0.5 m and 0.8 m diameter respectively at c_u < 50 Pa where c_u is the undrained shear strength in kPa. The correspondence capacities at c_u > 50 kPa are 0.86 c_u, 2.6 c_u and 6.3 c_u, respectively.

SUMMARY

A new type of pile, the expander body pile, is described which can be used for the underpinning of structures which have been damaged, for example, by excessive settlements.

The bearing capacity and pull-out resistance of the expander bodies can be evaluated from the maximum grout pressure p_{grout} required for the expansion. The methods that have been developed for bored piles which are based on the results from the Menard pressuremeter can be used. The ultimate bearing capacity can also be estimated from the penetration resistance as determined by different penetration tests (CPT, SPT and WST).

The expander bodies have been tested in silt and sand at two locations in Sweden. The test data indicate that the proposed design methods will in general give results which are on the safe side and thus conservative.

REFERENCES

Baquelin, F., Jézéquel, J.F. and Shields, D.H., 1978. The Pressuremeter and Foundation Engineering. Trans Tech Publications, Clausthal, Germany, 617 pp.

Broms, B. B. 1966. Methods of Calculations the Ultimate Bearing Capacity of Piles - A Summary, Sols-Soils, Vol. 5, No. 18-19, Paris, 1966.

Broms, B. B. and Bergdahl, 1982. The Weigh Sounding Test (WST), State-of-the-Art Report, ESOPT II, Amsterdam, 12 pp.

Meyerhof, G.G., 1956. Penetration Tests and Bearing Capacity of Cohesionless Soils. Journ. Soil Mech. a. Found. Div., ASCE, Vol. 82, SM1, pp. 1-19.

van der Veen, C. and Boersma, L., 1957. The Bearing Capacity Predetermined by Cone Penetration Test. Proc. 4th Int. Conf. Soil Mech. a. Found. Engng., Vol. 2, pp 72-75.

Vesic, A.S., 1964. Investigations of Bearing Capacity of Piles in Sand, Proc. North America Conf. on Deep Foundations, Mexico City, Vol. 1, pp 197-224.

Bearing capacity and driving stresses of open-ended steel pipe piles of Oritkari Quay

La capacité portante et les tensions d'enforcement dans les pieux de tuyau de fer avec bouts ouverts dans le Quai d'Outkari

J. HARTIKAINEN, Professor, University of Oulu, Finland
P. HASSINEN, Research Engineer, Technical Research Centre of Finland
H. KOMULAINEN, Research Assistant, University of Oulu, Finland
E. SLUNGA, Assistant Professor, Helsinki University of Technology, Finland

SYNOPSIS

The quay wall of the Oritkari harbour was constructed of 20 m long, 762 mm in diameter, open-ended steel pipe piles, which were driven through clayey silt into a dense sandy silt layer by a 80 kN hydraulic hammer using a drop height of 0.5...0.8 m. Pile Driving Analyzer (PDA) measurements were done in two stages for 5+5 piles. The ultimate bearing capacities determined by CAPWAP analyses at the end of continous pile driving were 2.7...3.2 MN, which are approx. 35% greater than the geostatically calculated bearing capacities without a soil plug. The dynamic point resistances of the piles were found to be very low, and no solid soil plug developed during driving, although an obvious about 0.5 m long compacted zone inside the pile tip was observed by soundings. Driving stresses of three piles were measured using strain gauges, the results being at the most 60% higher than the stresses calculated by the CAPWAP program.

SITE AND CONSTRUCTION OF THE QUAY

The Oritkari harbour is located on the mouth of the Oulu river south of the city of Oulu. The first stage in the construction of the harbour was completed in 1970.

The stage in the construction work concerned here consisted of a quay designed to accomodate both stern and side-loading vessels with an along-shore length of 170 m and a stern loading breadth of 40 m at right angles to the quay line. The quay is adequate for one or two vessels depending on their size, and could be extended along the shore later if required to take one more vessel. The water depth at the quay is 11.5 m and the height of the quay side above mean water level is 2.4 m.

The dense soil deposit at the site lies at a considerable depth, and is overlain by looser material with a poor bearing capacity which can easily be removed by dredging. Since the water depth at the site was no more than 1.5...2 m, construction of the quay on dry land behind a diversion dam was an obvious solution.

A cross-section showing the construction of the quay is given in Fig. 1. The wall consists of a row of steel pipe piles 762 mm in diameter joined by L and T-angles welded to their sides and fixed rigidly to an edging structure of reinforced concrete, which is also supported by a row of concrete piles. The steel piles extend some 3...4 m into the dense silty sand layer, i.e. to a level of -19.0... -20.5 m.

The head of every second steel pile is anchored by means of a 25 m tie rod to a reinforced concrete anchorage wall which functions by means of passive earth pressure against a

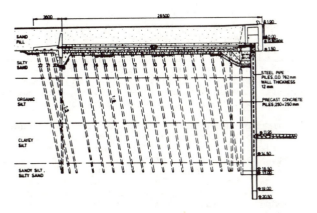

Fig. 1. Cross-section of the quay structure and a soil profile.

granular soil fill. The area lying between the anchorage wall and the wall of steel piles has a foundation of wooden piles 16 m in length driven in at an inclination of 6:1 and fitted with pile caps.

The quay structure contains a total of 307 steel pipe piles, 136 concrete piles and 3680 wooden piles. The granular soil fill has a thickness of 3.4 m. Some 266.000 m³ of soil had to be dredged from the dock basin.

SOIL CONDITIONS

The sea bed was composed of 4...5 m of loose silty sand, beneath which was a 4...6 m layer of highly compressible organic sulphide silt having a water content of 40...60%. Below these fluvial sediments was 3...6 m layer of hard clayey silt of glacial origin. (Fig. 1) The substrate beneath this consisted largely of dense silty sand.

The weight sounding penetrated to a depth of 16...17 m, thus reaching the dense silty sand layer. The resistance increased markedly at around -14...-18 m. The dynamic probing resistance increased relatively little in the clayey silt layer, but became considerably greater in the silty sand lying below this.

The strength parameters for the soil layers, as used for planning purposes, are shown in Table 1.

Table 1. Dimensioning parameters of soil layer

Soil layer	Effective unit weight γ' (kN/m^3)	Effective friction angle ϕ (^{O})
1. silty sand	8,5	30
2. organic silt	8,0	27
3. clayely silt	9,5	32
4. silty sand	11,0	35

PURPOSE OF THE MEASUREMENTS

The purpose of the stress wave measurements was to obtain information on the behaviour of an open-end steel pipe pile upon driving and ensure that the driving stress would remain within reasonable limits. It was also hoped to compare the ultimate bearing capacities measured at the moment of driving with values calculated from the geostatic stresses. A further topic of interest involved the necessary specifications for the pile driving equipment, and in particular the driving efficiency.

The measurements were performed at two stages in the work, the first being at the beginning of pile driving, with the aim of avoiding damage to the piles while at the same time obviating any unnecessary reductions in the driving force used. The plan was to perform the stress measurements using two complementary methods, a Pile Driving Analyzer (PDA) at the top of the pile and strain gauges placed at various levels along the lower half of the pile.

MEASUREMENT METHODS

The Case method (Goble et al., 1975) involves measurement of the acceleration and the strain of the pile head as functions of time, from which the PDA calculates the particle velocity and plots a force curve. The equipment then uses these velocity and force data to calculate the so called Case bearing capacity, a figure which is recorded separately for each blow of the pile driver in accordance with the adjustments put in by the user. If one wishes to examine the force and velocity curves immediately, an oscilloscope can be linked directly to the PDA. In any case the data are recorded on magnetic tape for later inspection, graphical presentation and further analysis where necessary.

A general outline of the PDA equipment as a whole is presented in Fig. 2, which shows the acceleration and strain transducers attached to the pile, the cables with their junction boxes, the analyzer, based on an MC 68 000 microprocessor, an oscilloscope and a multi-channel tape recorder.

INSTRUMENTATION ON THE PILES

Strain gauges were installed at four levels on pile no. 29 and at five levels on nos. 204 and 211, where the numbers are assigned in accordance with the order of driving. The gauges were glued symmetrically on the outer surfaces of opposite sides of the pile, on the positions shown in Fig. 2. The uppermost gauges were located at a level which more or less coincided with the upper boundary of the clayey silt layer towards the end of the pile-driving process, which is also close to the point of maximal bending moment exerted on the pile. This enabled the bending strain to be measured after the dock basin had been dredged. The performing of measurements at different levels also provided an opportunity for assessing the residual stresses remaining in the pile after it had been driven into position.

All the gauges and cables were protected with steel L-angles welded onto the side of the cylinder, and a steel wedge larger in size than the L-angles was welded onto the tip of the pile with a gap of 1 mm between it and the L-angle. This gap avoids the forces exerted on the wedge to be transmitted to the gauges. Although the protective angles themselves transmit some of the force, the error arising in this way is small, as the effect of this force is spread over a broad area of the cylinder at the point where the gauge is located.

The 8...10 cables reaching the top of the pile (20 on pile no. 204) were plugged into connect-

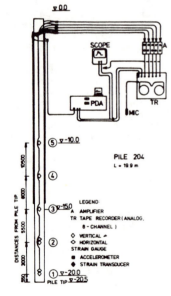

Fig. 2. Scheme of instrumentation.

ing cables, these then leading to the amplifier unit. The five amplifiers available effectively restricted the number of signals to be recorded to five, although a sixth gauge could also be monitored by alternation. The connection scheme is to be seen in Fig. 2. Two of the eight channels on the tape recorder were used to record the PDA force and velocity signals, five for the force curves and one for voice recording.

PILE-DRIVING EQUIPMENT

The driving of steel pipe piles 762 mm in diameter required an unusually large hammer and pile helmet, while the length of the piles, 20 m, and the order in which they were to be driven necessitated a rig of considerable height, which in turn meant ensuring that the base machine was sufficiently heavy to guarantee stability (Fig. 3a).

Fig. 3a) Driving of the pipe pile wall and
3b) the 80 kN hydraulic drop hammer, Junttan.

The hydraulically operated hammer constructed on an excavator chassis by Savonvarvi Oy employed at Oritkari proved highly suitable for this purpose (Fig. 3b), the two parallel lifting hydraulic cylinders being capable of maintaining a frequency of 60...70 blows per minute with a 80 kN hammer at a drop height of 0.5 m. The maximum drop height attainable was 0.8 m. The height of the rig was 38 m and the total weight of the equipment something over 1000 kN.

The pile helmet consisted of 100 mm thick steel plate, a centering cone, an elastic part made of azobe wood and a steel frame

surrounding this. The elastic part was 370 mm high and square in cross-section (450x450 mm). The grain of the azobe wood ran in a vertical direction.

INITIAL STRESS WAVE

The driving of steel piles does not always require the use of a pile helmet, since steel is a sufficiently tough material to withstand short peak stresses, even ones in excess of the static yield point. Without the helmet, the stress wave is of short duration and rapidly rising in form, which is undesirable as far as the penetration velocity of the pile is concerned. The form of the stress wave can be adapted by a pile helmet with suitable properties or by an elastic hammer construction.

When a blow is applied to an elastic pile using a rigid hammer without a pile helmet the resulting initial stress wave obeys the equation, (Bredenberg, 1982)

$$F_i(t) = Z \cdot v \cdot e^{-\frac{Z}{m}t} \tag{1}$$

where, F_i = impact force
   Z = $\frac{AE}{c}$ pile impedance,
   A = cross-sectional area of pile
   E = elastic modulus of pile
   v = particle velocity of the head of the pile, = hammer velocity in this case,
   m = mass of the hammer,
   t = time.

In practice the wave front is not vertical but shows a brief rising phase. Similarly the wave never reaches its theoretical peak.

The piles studied here were driven using a pile helmet with a static spring constant of 8592 MN/m, corresponding to 54% of the rigidity of an equal length of pile (370 mm), i.e. the pile helmet was fairly rigid. The mass of the hammer was 8000 kg and its legth 3.0 m.

The initial stress wave (Fig. 4) was measured early in the pile driving process, when the tip was still only at a depth of 3.5 m. The first reflected wave was the tension wave from the tip, so that the initial stress wave

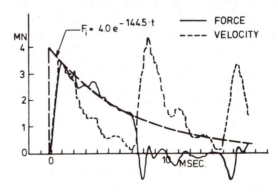

Fig. 4. Force and velocity of the head of pile 204 as functions of time at the beginning of driving.

alone could be examined during a time of $\frac{2L}{c}$. The wave diminished exponentially in the manner given by equation.

$$F_i(t) = Z \cdot v \cdot e^{-144.5t} \qquad (2)$$

Its rise time is 0.6 ms and the strain velocity brought about by the wave front $\dot{\varepsilon} = 0.88 \frac{1}{s}$.

The acceleration of the pile head is obtained from the equation

$$\ddot{x} = \dot{\varepsilon} \cdot c \qquad (3)$$

in which c = wave velocity = 5139 m/s. This gives an acceleration of 4500 m/s², or 460 g.

Since the pile helmet was highly rigid, it caused rather little alteration in the form of this wave, protracting the time slightly, but scarcely reducing its maximum amplitude. The maximum measured stresses varied in the range 105...163 N/mm² with drop heights of 0.5...0.75 m (Table 2).

Table 2. Calculated and measured maximum driving stresses (MPa)

Pile no.	drop height (m)	max.imp.stress calc.	max. measured stresses meas.at pile head	at diff.levels	
25	0,5	121	83	121	
27	"	"	118	140	
29	"	"	80	105	
29	0,8	156	114	138	95 ②
204	0,5	121	137	137	146 ③
"	0,75	151	163	163	160 ③
211	0,7	145	140	140	148 ③ ④

About 60...75% of the kinetic energy of the hammer was transmitted to the pile, this proportion being unaffected by the above variations in drop height. Figures of around 90% have been obtained for the efficiency of a rigid hammer without pile helmet in laboratory experiments (Bredenberg 1982).

REFLECTION OF STRESS WAVES

No strong reflected compression waves are created provided that the dynamic skin resistance of the pile is relatively evenly distributed and the point resistance is small, in which case the sum of the gradually weakening initial wave and the reflected waves does not exceed the strains imposed by the initial wave. If one pictures the skin friction of the pile as being concentrated in a set of points, the amplitude F_i of the incoming wave decreases at each point by (Fischer, 1984):

$$F_{i,j+1} = F_{i,j} - \frac{R_j}{2}, \qquad (4)$$

in which $F_{i,j}$ = amplitude of wave which has passed point j,
R_j = skin resistance at point j.

The compression wave $F_R = \frac{R_j}{2}$ is reflected upwards at point j, whereas if $R > 2 F_i$, the whole wave will be reflected in the form of a compression wave, summing with the incoming

waves. If the skin frictions caused by the upward and downward-moving stress waves are equal, a residual compressive force $\frac{R}{2}$ remains between two consecutive friction points in the pile. The following stress wave will then tend to be reflected as a compression wave under the influence of this residual force. The soil model is assumed here to be a rigid-plastic one.

A number of computer programs have been devised for analysing reflected waves recorded at the head of a pile. The CAPWAP program (Goble et al., 1975), which employs one-dimensional wave equation, enables one to calculate the distribution of the dynamic skin friction along the length of the pile and the stresses at any given point on the pile. The program uses parameters supplied by the user together with the resistance distribution to plot a curve for the force developing at the head of the pile, which is fitted as closely as possible to the measured power curve.

CAPWAP analyses were performed on the last blows applied to 6 piles. The skin resistance distributions for piles nos. 25, 29 and 33 are presented in Fig. 5a and for piles nos. 204 and 211, situated about 150 m away, in Fig. 5b. The friction in piles 25 and 29 is seen to be concentrated in an area about 4...7 m from the tip, the strongest skin friction of pile 33 being noted 1...5 m from the tip. The point resistances of all the piles are very small, and a half of the total skin resistance is shown to be concentrated in an area 3...6 m from the tip.

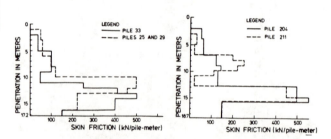

Fig. 5. Skin friction during driving calculated by CAPWAP a) piles 25, 29 and 33 b) piles 204 and 211.

Force and velocity curves for pile no. 25 are presented in Fig. 6a, in which the force wave includes a strong reflected compression wave with its peak 5.2 ms after that of the initial wave. The location of the skin friction concentration is given by the equation

$$x = \frac{c \cdot t_{max}}{2} , \qquad (5)$$

in which x = distance of skin friction concentration from measurement point,
t_{max} = time differential between peaks in the initial and reflected waves.

The calculated skin friction in pile 25 is greatest 13.4 m below the measurement point, i.e. 3.8 m from the tip of the pile, a result which is at variance with the situation in Fig. 5a, which shows the skin friction to be concentrated approx. 2 m upper.

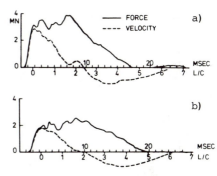

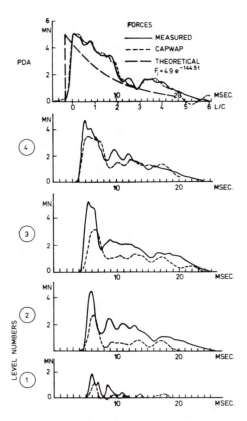

Fig. 6. Force-time and velocity-time curves of the head of a) pile 25 at final penetration b) pile 29 1,0 m above final penetration.

The driving stresses recorded by the gauges on pile 29 reached their maximum after a pause of 1½ days. This stress was only 10% greater than the impact stress. This is illustrated in Fig. 6b, which depicts the first blow after the interval. In this case the CAPWAP analysis places the concentration of friction somewhat higher.

The force curve recorded on the top of pile no. 204 shows a local minimum value some time after the peak in the initial wave (Fig. 7a). The wave reflected from the tip must thus be a tension wave with a simultaneous increase in velocity. The amplitudes of the compression waves reflected from the skin surface of the pile are relatively small during the $0 \ldots \frac{2L}{c}$. The exponentially decreasing initial stress wave is represented by a dotted line.

Stress waves recorded at the top of pile no. 204 and at the levels 1...4 are depicted in sections b...e of Fig. 7, on which the corresponding force curves obtained from the CAPWAP analysis are indicated with dotted lines. The measured and theoretical curves correspond relatively well at level 4, but at levels 2 and 3 the measured wave amplitudes are 60% greater than the calculated ones. The overall lengths of the waves more or less correspond. The tension wave from the tip is slightly earlier noticed at levels 2, 3 and 4 than is given by CAPWAP, while the incoming compression and tension waves at level 1 are practically simultaneous, the time discrepancy, approx. 0.2 ms, being shorter than the rise time of the compression wave, so that the amplitude remains small. The strength of the tension wave is roughly 70...80% of that of the compression wave.

The differences between the calculated and measured stresses may be caused by residual stresses, which were highest near the tip of pile 204. The max. residual stress was approx. 100 N/mm² in tension, measured 5 hours after pile driving had been finished. The highest compressive residual stress was 140 N/mm² in pile 29.

BEARING CAPACITY

The bearing capacity of a pile as determined by the Case method may be regarded as being most reliable in noncohesive soils. Thus the

Fig. 7. Measured and calculated force-time curves at different levels of pile 204 at the last blow.

ultimate bearing capacities calculated by the method in silty soils are those which deviate most markedly from the actual values, due to the great variation and poor predictability of the damping constant J_c in such soils. The damping constant can be evaluated more precisely using the CAPWAP program.

The ultimate bearing capacity was determined by means of CAPWAP analysis for 6 piles, the results varying in the range 2.7...3.2 MN, corresponding to Case damping constants of 0.40...0.55. By this stage the tip of the pile was in the silty sand layer, for which a damping constant of 0.15 is recommended. The value for the clayey silt is much higher, 0.55 on average. The quake parameter was 0.17 ...0.23 cm for pile no. 204 and otherwise consistently 0.20 cm.

It is difficult to calculate the point resistance of an open-ended pipe pile. The figure is obviously low provided that a soil plug does not form at the tip, but the probability of this phenomenon depends on the soil type, the coarse of the inner surface of the cylinder and the diameter of the cylinder at least. In a dense sand layer a plug can develop even during the driving of the pile. Also, plugging due to static loading and plugging due to dynamic loading are two quite different things.

Since the piles studied here are relatively short, the point resistance has a considerable effect on bearing capacity, the geostatically calculated ultimate bearing capacities varying according to the method used (Table 3), ("Vei-ledning ved pelefundamentering", 1973; Meyerhof, 1976; Poulos, Davis, 1980) and the degree of plugging within the range 1.8... 3.4 MN. The external and internal skin resistances are assumed in the calculations to be equal. The observed permanent sets at last blows varied between 4...8 mm.

Table 3. Bearing capacity (MN) of pipe piles according to three calculation methods, Case and CAPWAP. (Lower limit without and upper with plug.)

CALC. METHOD	Pile No.			
	25	29	204	211
Meyerhof (1976)	2.0...3.1	2.0...3.1	2.3...3.3	2.3...3.3
Poulos (1980)	3.3	3.3	3.4	3.4
Veiledning.. (1973)	2.1...2.8	2.1...2.8	2.2...2.6	1.8...2.3
Case, J_C = 0.45	3.4	4.3	3.0	2.7
CAPWAP	3.0	3.0	3.0	2.8

The dynamically determined ultimate bearing capacities lie in the upper half of the range of variation of the statically calculated values, a pattern which would seem to gain support from the mild plugging effect observed in the dynamic probing tests (Fig. 8), although the CAPWAP analysis does show any evidence of plugging near the tip of the pile.

CONCLUSIONS

The bearing capacities of the piles, as determined by CAPWAP analysis, were in the range 2.7...3.2 MN, corresponding to damping constants of J_C = 0.40...0.55 in the Case method. All the piles had a point resistance of less than 0.2 MN.

The above values were about 35 % greater than the ultimate bearing capacities, calculated geostatically and including only the skin resistance. It can be expected that the bearing capacity would still increase considerably after the dissipation of excess pore water pressure. The skin friction, as calculated using the CAPWAP program, was with one exception concentrated in the clayey silt horizon 3...7 m from the tip of the pile, whereas the dynamic probing resistance was greatest close to the tip. This suggests, that the dynamic and static skin resistances are located at different depths.

The soundings showed considerable compaction of the soil inside the pipe pile about 0.5 m from the tip. This could be interpreted partly as representing a soil plug, but at least it did not increase the point resistance. The data on the progress of the first blows after a pause tended slightly to point to the possible formation of a static soil plug upon the dissipation of the excess pore water pressure.

The initial stress wave followed the theoretical wave form relatively closely, the calculated stresses proving quite valid. The stresses existing in the bottom half of the pile were found to be much greater than those calculated by the CAPWAP program, however, exceeding them by as much as 50...60%. When only PDA measurements are used to monitor stresses

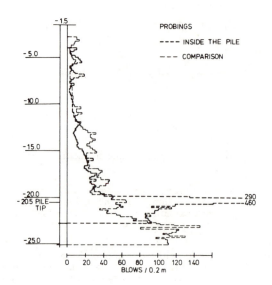

Fig. 8. Dynamic probing through pile 206 in comparison with a probing 5 m away.

in the pile a 60% increase is too large when operating close to the yield point of steel. The highest stresses observed in this research were nevertheless very much smaller than the maximum permitted values.

Construction of the steel pipe pile wall was highly successful, and the pile driving operation was carried through efficiently without increasing the risk of damaging the piles.

ACKNOWLEDGEMENTS

This research was sponsored by Rautaruukki Ltd (The finnish state owned steel company) and it was supported by the client, City of Oulu and by the contractors, YIT Ltd and OMP Ltd. Structural design of the quay was made by Voimarakenne Ltd and geotechnical design by PSV Ltd.

REFERENCES

Goble, G.G., Garland Likins Jr., Rausche, F. (1975). Bearing capacity of piles from dynamic measurements. Final report, Dept. of Civil Engineering, Case Western Reserve University, Ohio.

Fischer, H.C. (1984). Stress wave theory for pile driving applications, lecture. Second Int. Conf. on the Application of Stresswave Theory on Piles, Stockholm, pp. 43-46.

Bredenberg, H. (1982). Dynamic test loading of point bearing piles. Doctor thesis, Royal Institute of Technology, Dept. of Soil and Rock Mech., Stockholm, pp. 56-80,250-262.

"Veiledning ved pelefundamentering". Rules for Pile Foundation (1973). The Norwegian Pile Committee. Oslo, pp. 25-33.

Meyerhof, G.G. (1976). Bearing capacity and settlement of pile foundations. ASCE J. Geotech. Div. vol 102, GT3, pp. 199-217.

Poulos, H.G., Davis, E.H. (1980). Pile foundation analysis and design. J. Wiley & Sons, New York, pp. 18-30.

Horizontal loading tests on actual closed wall foundations

Chargement horizontal d'une fondation réelle avec parois moulées

TAKAYA KAINO, Deputy Director, Structure Design Office, Japanese National Railways, Japan

SYNOPSIS   The Japanese National Railways engineers developed and actually constructed the rigid foundation in which diaphragm wall are placed to form a box-shaped inclosure as an alternative to the caisson foundation. Two horizontal loading tests on the actual foundations were carried out. Pulling with pre-stressing strands between a pneumatic caisson and a new-type foundation of approximately the same size the displacement of the former was four times that of the latter. It was confirmed that the displacement of the new-type foundation could be presumed approximately using a calculating model in which the resistance of skin friction around the foundation side walls was accounted for in addition to the normal reaction of the soil.

INTRODUCTION

The caisson foundation has a much smaller plane-to-bridge size ratio than all other traditional foundations. However the caisson has a major disadvantage. It is apt to move considerably during earthquake tremors.

As an alternative to the caisson, several Japanese National Railways engineers have developed the closed wall foundation (hereinafter referred to as the CWF). With the CWF, diaphragm walls are placed to form a □-shaped or ⊟-shaped inclosure. The CWF is designed under the premise that the horizontal reinforcing bars must be sprit in the vertical joints between its sections. However, the construction is arranged so as to enable transmission of both bending moment and shearing force, causing the vertical joint to act as a sort of lap joint (Fig. 1). Before adopting the vertical joint for the actual work, preliminary experiments were done pertaining to its bending and shearing strength.

TEST I (IIZAKA-KAIDO VIADUCT)

Horizontal loading test

Three pier foundations of the Iizaka-kaido viaduct are CWF and the others are pneumatic caissons. The horizontal load test was carried out by pulling with prestressing strands between P7 (pneumatic caisson foundation) and P8 (CWF) (Fig. 2). The caisson foundation of P7 is cylinder-shaped with an exterior diameter of 10.5 m (the exterior diameter of the friction cutter part is 10.7 m), an interior diameter of 7.7 m, and a length of 25 m. The CWF of P8 is a square with an exterior size of 10 m, an interior size of 7 m and a length of 25.3 m.

The initial geological conditions were similar to those of boring No. 4 in Fig. 3 and mainly comparatively dense gravel. Fig. 3 represents

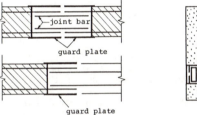

Fig. 1   Examples of the Vertical Joint

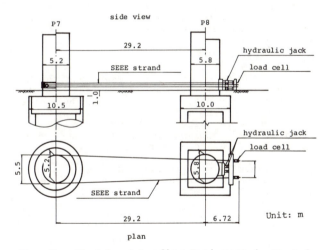

Fig. 2   Sketch of Loading Equipment in Test 1

the results of the standard penetration tests in the ground surrounding the foundations after construction work. Borings No. 2 and No. 3 were only 0.3 m from the surface of the side wall of the caisson. Their N-values lowered to about one fifth of those before the work. Boring No. 5 also was only 0.3 m from the

surface of the diaphragm wall. Its N-values
lowered very little compared to the pre-work N-
values. The test was carried out under these
geological conditions without grouting around
the caisson.

The loading height of 1.5 m above the top of the
foundations was selected to facilitate the loading work. A maximum horizontal load of 11.8 MN
was selected. The repetition of loading was 4
cycles. The loads were fixed for more than an
hour against each maiden load-step.

Test results

Fig. 4 represents horizontal displacement of the
top of each foundation and each rotary angle at
the maximum load of each cycle. Although P8 was
similar in size to P7, the horizontal displacement of the top of the foundation of P8 was
3.7 mm at the most and its residual displacement
was only 0.3 mm with a load of 11.8 MN. In
contrast, the horizontal displacement of the top
of the foundation of P7 was 18 mm, and its
residual displacement was approximate 10 mm with
a load of 11.8 MN. The rotary angle of P7 was
also approximately four times that of P8. For,
the pneumatic caisson has minimal skin friction.
Since it has a smooth side wall and slackens the
surrounding ground. Contrarily, the CWF has
considerable skin friction since it slackens the
surrounding ground little and the concrete which
is placed into the trench is close to the surrounding ground.

Fig. 5 represents the changes in earth pressure
against load in P8. Earth-pressure meters were
pressed against the side surface of the trench
to indicate earth pressure at rest. We supposed
its coefficient of 0.5. It is natural that the
front earth pressure increased considerably
while the rear earth pressure decreased, with a
60~90% rate of change in front earth pressure.
There was little change of pore water pressure
at these points. The change of vertical earth
pressure at the bottom of the CWF, the stress of
skin friction, and the stress of reinforcement,
etc. were small.

Analysis

The calculation of the displacement and the
rotary angle of the CWF as well as soil reaction,
with both horizontal and vertical loads applied,
was done according to the model shown in Fig. 6.
The values were calculated by balancing the
vertical load, horizontal load and rotary moment
assuming the CWF to be a rigid body.

Coefficients of soil reaction k_1, k_3, k_7 are
involving normal stress against the surface of
the wall. They are calculated as follows:

$$k_1 = k_3 = 0.4 E_O B_h^{-(3/4)} \quad \text{------------ (1)}$$

$$k_7 = 0.4 E_O B_v^{-(3/4)} \quad \text{------------ (2)}$$

where E_O is modulus of deformation (E_O(MPa)=2.5N
N: N-value for sand), and B_h and B_v are pseudo-
widths of the side and the bottom of the foundation for calculation (cm). Since k_3 is a
coefficient of the reaction from the inner soil,
if it moves together with the CWF, $k_3 = 0$. Then,
$k_3 = 0$ away from the bottom. For residual
slime, k_7 is lowered to 50% of its calculated

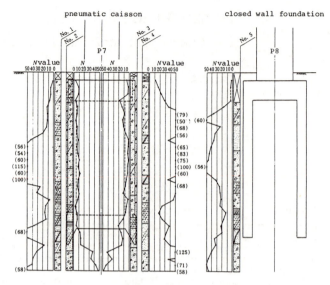

Fig. 3 Soil Profile near P7, P8 after the
Execution of Work

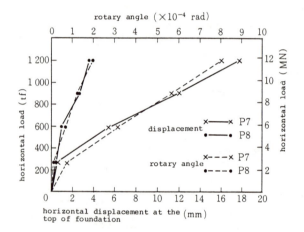

Fig. 4 Displacement and Rotary Angle
against Load

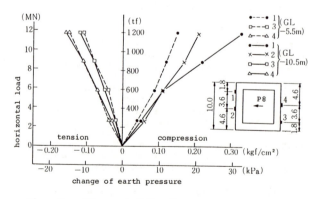

Fig. 5 Change of Earth Pressure against
Load

value using Eq. (2).

The other coefficients of soil reaction concern tangential stress against the surface of the wall due to skin friction and the shearing deformation of the ground. They were calculated from k_1 and k_7 using the finite element method on horizontal and vertical planes, as no accurate data was available. That is, $k_5 = k_6 = 0.6 k_1$, $k_2 = k_4 = 0.4 k_1$ and $k_8 = 0.5 k_7$. However, $k_6 = k_4 = 0$ away from the bottom of the CWF like k_3.

According to the degree of displacement of the diaphragm wall, the soil reaction increased or decreased between the passive and active earth pressure (Fig. 7). Shearing soil reactions were also similar. The average skin friction strength, (based on the results of many vertical loading tests on cast-in-place piles) was taken to be altmate strength of the shearing soil reaction, τ_u, with $\tau_u = 5N \leqq 200$ (KPa) for sandy soil, and $\tau_u = C$ or $10N \leqq 150$ (KPa) for clayey soil.

For the caisson foundation, k_1, k_5, k_7 and k_8 are the only valid coefficients of the soil reaction. As there is no slime at the bottom k_7 can be calculated by Eq. (2). Since there is little skin friction, $k_2 = 0$ and $k_5 = 0.1 k_1$.

Table I shows the results of both the CWF and the caisson calculating methods for the CWF of P8 based on the above-mentioned premises. These values result when a horizontal load of 11.8 MN, a vertical load of 8.2 MN and a bending moment of 17.6 MN·m, are exerted on the center of the CWF top face.

With a load of 11.8 MN, both the horizontal displacement and the rotary angle of the top of the CWF of P8 comprised 75% of the calculated value using the CWF method. It was rather coincidental. Concerning the resultant force of the horizontal normal soil reaction acting on both sides, the measured values were 30 KPa at GL-5.5 m and 40 KPa at GL-10.5 m, while the calculated values were 70 KPa at GL-5.5 m and 80 KPa at GL-10.5 m.

TEST II (OJI VIADUCT)

Horizontal load test

The six pier foundations of the Oji viaduct are CWF. The horizontal load test was carried out by pulling with prestressing strands between P2 and P3 as in Test I. The soil profile and structural features of P3 are shown in Fig. 8. The distance from P3 to P2 is 74 m long. The loading points were 3.6 m above the top of the CWF. The loading method and items of measurement were similar to those of Test I. However, in this case the deformation of the CWF was measured with insert-type inclinometer.

Results and analysis

The horizontal displacement and inclination of the body of the CWF with a load of 11.8 MN are shown in Fig. 9. In Fig. 9, the calculated values using the CWF method are represented by a solid line. While the CWF of the Oji viaduct is considerablly smaller than that of Iizaka-

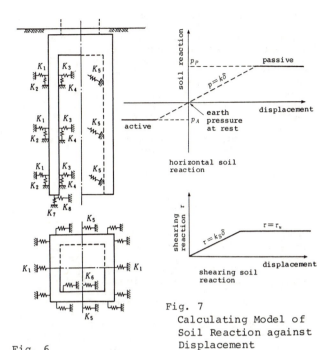

Fig. 6
Calculating Model of
Closed Wall Foundation

Fig. 7
Calculating Model of
Soil Reaction against
Displacement

TABLE I

Comparison of Calculating Method between
Closed Wall Foundation and Caisson

Calculating Method	Horizontal displacement at the top of foundation		Rotary angle	
Closed Wall F.	0.50 cm		2.65×10^{-4} rad.	
Caisson	1.28 cm		7.73×10^{-4} rad.	
	Max. horizontal normal reaction			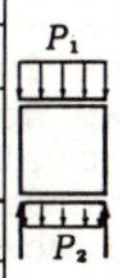
	Situation from the top	p_1	p_2	P_1
Closed Wall F.	3.0 m	72 KPa	7 KPa	
Caisson	4.0 m	185 KPa	-13 KPa	P_2
	Normal reaction at the bottom			
	Max. changing value		Initial	
Closed Waff F.	+69 KPa	-18 KPa	659 KPa	
Caisson	+130 KPa	-35 KPa	238 KPa	

kaido viaduct, the horizontal displacement at the top of the former was similar that of the latter. Therefore, in order for the calculated values to coincide with the measured values we had to double the value of the coefficient of soil reaction which had been determined from the results of a standard penetration test.

The values represented by a broken line in Fig. 9 were calculated on condition that only k_1, k_5

(the only horizontal component), k_8 and k_7 were accounted for in Fig. 6 and that the CWF was an elastic body. With the calculation a computer program of an elastic beam of finite length on the elastic floor was used. However, all co-efficients of the soil reaction were multiplied by 1.23 in order to compensate for the dis-regarded k_2 and k_5 (vertical component). Naturally, concerning the inclination, it was appreciably better to regard the body of the CWF as an elastic body than a rigid one. Vertically, the difference in bending moments calculated between the two methods was 5%.

Now,

$$\beta = \sqrt[4]{\frac{kD}{4EI}} \quad \text{-------------- (3)}$$

where k is the horizontal coefficient of soil reaction, D is the pseudo-width of the foun-dation and EI is the bending rigidity of the foundation body. ℓ is the length of the foundation. Using the coefficients of soil reaction that were counted backwards in order to coincide with measured displacement, $\beta\ell$ for this CWF is 1.9 (In Test I, $\beta\ell$ for the CWF was 0.8). Using the coefficient of soil reaction that was derived from the soil investigation, $\beta\ell$ for this CWF is 1.6. The displacement and the incli-nation at the top of this CWF calculated according to the model in Fig. 6 were safer than the measured values. The calculating method in which the CWF is regarded as an elastic body of finite length is considerably complicated. Therefore, in case that $\beta\ell$ is less than 2, it is considered possible to design regarding the CWF as a rigid body according to the model in Fig. 6.

In Test II, changes of earth pressure measured by earth-pressure meters which were set on the front side and the rear side of the CWF were only 10∼30% of the calculated values. However, the skin friction measured by two gauges which were set on the right side and the left side of the CWF reached 70% of the calculated values.

CONCLUSION

The following facts were confirmed by means of two horizontal loading test. In dense sand and gravel, the displacement of the closed wall foundation (CWF) was considerably less than that of the pneumatic caisson under the same condi-tion. This fact also could be presumed by calculations. For, in the case of the pneumatic caisson the effective resistance of skin friction is marginal.

The displacement and the rotary angle of the CWF to which the horizontal load was applied can be approximately presumed by the calculating model in which the resistance of skin friction is accounted for in addition to the normal reaction of the soil, assuming that the CWF is a rigid body. From the result of measurement of the inclination when $\beta\ell$ is approximately 2, the body of the CWF moves as an elastic body rather than a rigid one. However, the difference in the displacement due to the two calculating methods is not large.

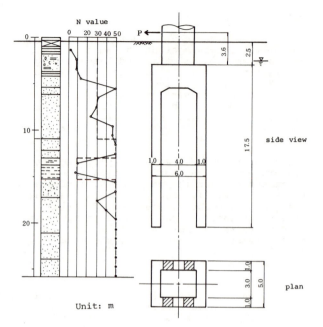

Fig. 8   Closed Wall Foundation of P3 in the Oji Viaduct

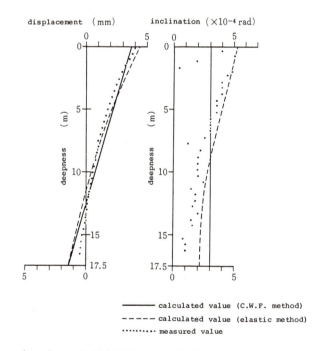

Fig. 9   Distribution of Horizontal Displacement and Inclination of CWF of P3 Loaded Horizontally 11.8 MN

REFERENCE

Japanese National Railways   (1974). Foundation design standard.

Large scale instrumented well foundation studies in cohesive soil media

Etudes sur une grande échelle instrumentée aux fondations de puits aux milieux de sol cohérent

R. K. KATTI, Professor of Civil Engineering, Indian Institute of Technology, Bombay, India
P. S. BANSOD, Former Jr. Research Officer, Department of Civil Engineering, IIT Bombay, India
D. R. KATTI, Jr. Project Engineer, Department of Civil Engineering, IIT Bombay, India
D. N. NARESH, Former Jr. Project Engineer, Department of Civil Engineering, IIT Bombay, India

SYNOPSIS   A large number of caisson foundations generally known as well foundations in India are used for supporting heavy axial loads, horizontal thrust and moments for bridges and other heavy structures.   The problem is statically indeterminate in nature with respect to moments taken by the base and sides,etc.   Large scale model studies on an instrumented well of dimensions 120 cm diameter and 525 cm height for different embedment ratios with cohesive soil around base and sides were conducted in a large scale multipurpose soil testing bed having facilities to apply 1000 kN vertical and horizontal loads.   This paper describes the results obtained and the various integration procedures adopted to solve the problem.   Guidelines for selection of parameters for design of well foundations based on non-dimensional parametric considerations are also indicated.

INTRODUCTION

Well foundations which are also known as Caisson foundations are normally used for supporting piers of long span bridges and tall structures wherein the hard strata is not encountered at shallow depths and the loads supported consist of heavy axial loads combined with moments and horizontal thrust. Normally these foundations are circular in nature and having diameters varying from a few meters to as high as 30 m. The depth to diameter ratio may vary from 0.5 to 2.0 and above. In majority of the cases, they are around 1.0. Although the depth to diameter ratio may be closer to shallow foundations, because of high magnitude of depth, the sides are expected to contribute in resisting a certain amount of moment. The problem is indeterminate and three dimensional in nature.

To evaluate the moments taken by base and sides, several theories were postulated by various research workers. The first attempt was to use Terzaghi's bulk head theory which is meant to deal with two dimensional problems. Realising the three dimensional aspect of the problem, Pender indicated the probable nature of stress distribution on the sides, based on the concept of centre of rotation[4]. Subsequently different research workers conducted studies on small scale well models using cohesionless soil and applying the load above the mud level and by measuring the deflections, indicated the nature of passive resistance developed[5]. Katti et al. for the first time conducted studies on instrumented well models by mounting pressure cells at the base and sides of the well and indicated the moments shared by base and sides[1,2].

Realising the importance of the problem for bridge construction in India, a series of studies have been undertaken by the author using large scale instrumented well models having 120 cm diameter and 525 cm height. In this paper, the studies conducted on the well model with cohesive soil at the base and sides have been presented, analysed and discussed.

EXPERIMENTAL INVESTIGATION

The soil selected for study was a cohesive soil which when mixed with 33 % moisture and compacted to a density of 1600 kg/m^3 would give a cohesion of 80 kPa. The plasticity index and the liquid limit of the soil were 32 and 75 % respectively.

The multipurpose soil testing bed designated as MSTB in which the studies were conducted has dimensions 610 cm x 305 cm x 488 cm deep with facilities to apply 1000 kN vertical and horizontal loads as shown in Figs.1(a,b)

Keeping in mind the dimensions of the MSTB and the boundary effects, a rigid well of diameter 120 cm x 525 cm in height having self weight of 145 kN was selected. Pressure cells 7.5 cm in diameter were placed at the base and along the sides. 13 cells are located at the base and a maximum of 95 on the sides as shown in Figs.1. (a,c). There are facilities such as LVDTS, settlement gauges, strain indicators, etc. to scan and record automatically the tilt, deformations and stresses.

The depth to diameter ratios designated as d/b ratios studied were 0.0, 0.5, 1.0, 1.5, 2.0 and 2.5.

Procedure for Conducting the Test

Below the base of the well, the soil was compacted to a height of 180 cm to obtain a density of 1600 kg/m^3 and cohesion of 80 kPa. After placing the well at a specified location, the soil was placed and compacted along the sides to obtain the required embedment for a given test. Care was taken to prevent damage to pressure cells during compaction.

The ultimate bearing capacity of the soil was 456 kPa. For experimental purposes, the allowable bearing capacity adopted was around 150 kPa, giving a factor of safety around 3. Thus the total vertical load applied was limited to 225 kN including the dead weight. The vertical load was applied in increments of 10 kN. After applying vertical loads, the horizontal loads were applied in suitable increments until the tilt was significant.

At the end of each increment, sufficient time was allowed for readings to stabilize. The readings with respect to rotation, vertical displacement and stresses at various pressure cell locations were recorded. At the end of the test, samples were taken to evaluate shear strength, compression, density, etc.

RESULTS

Zero Embedment Case

An embeded well is statically indeterminate to evaluate moments taken by the base and sides, it is necessary to develop contact pressure distribution diagram for the base and sides. For this purpose, rigid body concept and equilibrium condition for zero embedment case has been utilized to obtain correlation between edge stresses and other pressure cells both for axial load conditions and for combined axial load and moment condition by developing appropriate integration technique.

The results show that under axial load condition, the stresses at a given radius from the centre are nearly the same. The minimum stress is at the centre and increases as shown in Fig. 1.d. This is in confirmity with the work done on cohesive soils. Assuming variation in stress between two adjacent pressure cells in radial direction as linear shown in Figs.1(c,d) and by integrating the contact pressure diagram and equating to the axial load, the following equation is developed to evaluate the unknown edge stress P_3 in terms of the known P_0, P_1, P_2 and the applied load.

$$P_3 = 3.8583 \times 10^{-4} V - 0.2045 P_0 - 1.2272 P_1 - 1.9318 P_2$$

where P_0, P_1, P_2 are pressure at O, 22.5 and 45 cm from the centre and V is the vertical load acting on the base.

Under an applied horizontal thrust, it is observed that the stresses due to moment increase on the rear side and decrease on the loading side as shown in Fig.1.e. Taking moment across the axis, the incremental increase and decrease at the edges is obtained. It is assumed that the stresses parallel to the axis are constant See Figs.1 (e,f).

$$P_3 = 5.6484 \times 10^{-5}(M - M_E) - 3.0384 \bar{P}_1 - 3.5355 \bar{P}_2$$

The correlations between P_3, P_1 and P_2 and $\bar{P}_3$, $\bar{P}_1$ and $\bar{P}_2$ are shown in Figs. 2a and 2b.

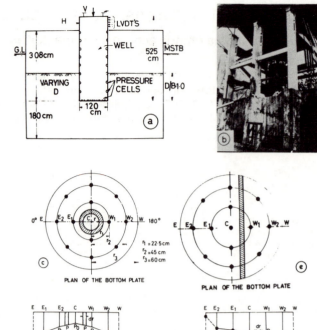

Fig.1(a) Sketch showing section of Well and MSTB (b) Photograph of Well and MSTB (c) Base plate showing pressure cell locations and integration procedure for base contact pressure (d) Section through base plate showing pressures at cell locations and integration procedure (e,f) Integration procedure for moments.

Embedment Cases

Load Transfer to Base and Sides under Axial Load

In these cases due to side friction, the load transmitted to the base due to the application of the incremental load is different. The actual load transmitted to the base is evaluated by completing the base contact pressure diagram after obtaining the edge stress from the correlation graph. See Fig.2a. This helps in knowing the percentage of load transmitted to the base. For various d/b ratios, the load transmitted to base and sides are shown in Fig.2c. From this, it may be noted that for same load, as d/b ratio goes on increasing, the load transmitted to base decreases and for a given d/b ratio, as the load increases, the percentage of load transmitted to base goes on increasing.

Moment Shared by Base and Sides

When horizontal load is applied, due to moment, the stresses acting at the base and sides alter See Figs.2 (d,e). To complete the contact pressure diagram at base under various horizontal loads, by knowing various values of recorded pressure increments $\bar{P}_1$, $\bar{P}_2$, etc. the edge pressures are obtained from the correlation graph as shown in Fig.2b. On the basis of the contact pressure diagram, the moment across the axis passing through the centre of the base is calculated. This gives the moment taken by the sides. The applied moment is obtained across the same axis, and the moment taken by base is subtracted from above. These are evaluated in terms of percent of applied moments. The values are plotted in Fig.2e. It is seen that as a/b ratio increases, the moments taken by base decreases and the moment taken by sides increases.

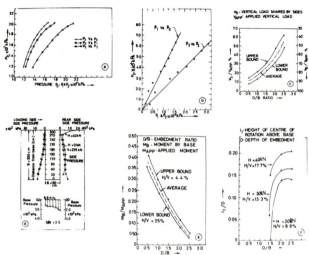

Fig.2(a) Correlation for axial loads
(b) Correlation for moment
(c) Load transmitted to base and sides
(d) Alteration of stresses at side and base due to horizontal load.
(e) Moments shared by base and sides.
(f) Height of centre of rotation for various d/b ratios.

The contact pressure diagrams are important for the design of steining of the wells. The pressure cells record predominantly the normal stresses acting on its surface. The unknown contact pressures on the sides are, one at the top tier and one at the bottom tier. Thus for completing the contact pressure distribution diagram which is three dimensional in nature, an attempt is made to evaluate the surface stresses by equating the moments due to side contact pressures to the moment shared by the sides. With respect to the unknown contact pressure at the bottom edge of the side, it is considered reasonable to extrapolate linearly the existing curve. To evaluate the centre of rotation, surface edge stress and the position of the resultant force, the following approach has been developed.

The centre of rotation is found by utilising LVDT readings at various levels above the mudline. The centre of rotation changes with applied horizontal load for a given embedment and also changes with change in embedments. These values are plotted for various values of embedment ratios as shown in Fig.2f. For horizontal loads upto 5 % of the vertical load, the centre of rotation remains almost near the base in all embedment cases. Also for a given horizontal load, as the d/b ratio increases, the centre of rotation remains almost at the base upto

d/b = 1.5 and later on starts shifting upwards for higher d/b ratios.

To develop contact pressure diagram, the following approach is adopted.
1) The three dimensional stress distribution is integrated to give a two dimensional force distribution as shown in Fig.3a.
2) Determine the resultant force and the point of action. The two dimensional force system is integrated to give a resultant force and point of action above and below the centre of rotation.

By resolving the stresses recorded by pressure cells parallel and perpendicular to the axis of rotation, it is observed that due to symmetry, the stresses parallel to axis of rotation get cancelled and stresses perpendicular to the axis cause moments to resist the force. Taking a unit width and assuming a linear variation between adjacent pressure cells in a given tier, the following integration is carried out to obtain the resultant force designated as unit depth resultant force (UDRF). See Fig.3b. Being axisymmetric, the force acts parallel to the direction of applied horizontal force.

$$F_H = \int_0^{\pi/4} P_s \, R \, \sin \phi \, d\phi + \int_{\pi/4}^{\pi/2} P_s' \, R \, \sin \phi \, d\phi$$

on integrating and inserting the value of radius R, we have

$$F_H = 34.414 \, P_{s0} + 160.82 \, P_{s1} - 75.234 \, P_{s2}$$

To evaluate the unknown surface force, the force diagram is divided into strips as shown in Fig.3c and moments are taken through axis passing through the base and equated to the known side moment. After integration, for the portion above the centre of rotation the equation takes the form :

$$M_s = \left[\sum_{i=0}^{n} Q_{i-1} \; a_n \left(l_1 + \sum_{i=0}^{i=n-1} a_i + \frac{a_n}{2} \right) \right] + \left[\sum_{i=0}^{n} (Q_i - Q_{i-1}) \; \frac{a_n}{2} \left(l_1 + \sum_{i=0}^{n-1} a_i + 2/3 \, a_n \right) \right]$$

Similar equation is obtained for portion below the centre of rotation. Knowing the unknown surface force and taking the same ratio of distances between the adjacent pressure cells in the lower tier, the calculated pressure cell readings are worked out backwards. The maximum stress should not exceed 3 C_u.

After computing the stress diagram, the resultant of forces above and below the centre of rotation are obtained by normal methods. See Fig.3d. It may be noted that the point of action of the resultant force is closer to 2/3rd of depth between centre of rotation and the surface and centre of rotation and the bottom. Thus an attempt is made to replace the earlier distribution with and equivalent reverse triangular distribution as shown in Fig.3d. This distribution is compatible with the stress deformation characteristics of the cohesive material system.

The coefficient of vertical subgrade reaction

k_v for various d/b ratios and various vertical loads are evaluated by taking the average stress at the base and dividing it by the corresponding settlement.

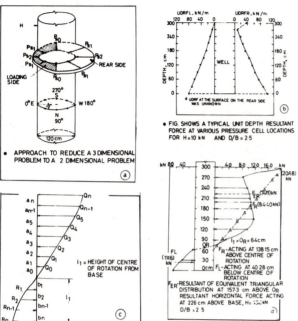

- APPROACH TO REDUCE A 3 DIMENSIONAL PROBLEM TO A 2 DIMENSIONAL PROBLEM (a)

- FIG. SHOWS A TYPICAL UNIT DEPTH RESULTANT FORCE AT VARIOUS PRESSURE CELL LOCATIONS FOR H=10 kN AND D/B=2.5 (b)

l_1 = HEIGHT OF CENTRE OF ROTATION FROM BASE (c)

F_{ER} RESULTANT OF EQUIVALENT TRIANGULAR DISTRIBUTION AT 157.3 cm ABOVE O_R RESULTANT HORIZONTAL FORCE ACTING AT 226 cm ABOVE BASE, H=130 kN D/B=2.5 (d)

Fig.3(a) Approach to convert 3-D stress system into 2-D.
(b) UDRF Vs. depth.
(c) Approach to determine resultant force.
(d) Resultant force and equivalent triangular distribution.

The modulus of horizontal subgrade reaction k_h would be of use to determine the horizontal displacements and the tilt. To find k_h, the relation $k_h = P_h/y$ is used wherein by using the rigid body consideration, the average stress p_h is evaluated by dividing the UDRF by the diameter and unit depth, wherein y is the deflection at that depth. It is found that k_h/k_v values vary between 11 to 16 for various d/b ratios and for design purposes k_h/k_v may be taken as 10. This high value of k_h indicates that it is not a function of soil alone but a combined function of the soil and the structure.

From the above analysis, it may be noted that the moments taken by base and sides, centre of rotation, etc. are changed to non-dimensional parameters such as percent and embedment ratios to facilitate its adaption to proto-type wells in cohesive soil system. The following guidelines may be adopted to select parameters for design purposes.

After ascertaining the depth of embedment based on the subsurface and bearing capacity criteria in cohesive soils, evaluate d/b ratio. On the basis of d/b ratio using relations based on non-dimensional parameters, obtain moments shared by base and sides, centre of rotation, equivalent triangular distribution, etc. from Figs. (2c, e, f and 3d). Based on the resultant force, evaluate maximum surface stress values and also the stresses at the bottom. Check whether these values are less than 3 cu. Evaluate the tilt using the following equation.

Displacement at mudline, $\delta = \left(\dfrac{Q_{R\ max.}}{unit\ width}\right) / k_h$

and angle of tilt, $\theta = \delta/y$
where $Q_{R\ max.}$ is maximum force per unit width at the surface. Evaluate k_v directly or by using E_s obtained from stress strain curve. It is reasonable to assume $k_h = 10\ k_v$. Settlement of well under axial and live loads can be evaluated using normal settlement analysis. Detailed guidelines have been given in Ref.3.

SUMMARY AND CONCLUSION

On the basis of above studies, it is realised that in case of majority of the well foundations, wherein the d/b ratio is between 1.0 and 1.5, almost 66% of the moment is taken by the sides. This would help in reducing the diameter of the well. The non-dimensional parameters are helpful in evaluating the moments shared by base and sides, centre of rotation, equivalent forces and developing contact pressure diagrams which are used for design of steining. The integration procedures adopted are found to be helpful in evaluating various unknowns. The k_h values appear to be a combined function of the soil and structure. These studies are found to be helpful in developing guidelines for wells surrounded by cohesive soil at base and sides.

ACKNOWLEDGEMENT

Thanks are due to Ministry of Transport, Government of India who have sponsored this project.

Thanks are due to Prof. A.K. De, Director, I.I.T. Bombay for the keen interest taken in the work. Authors appreciate the help rendered by Sarvashri H.D. Golani, B. Suresh, K.K. Moza and C.P. Chavan.

Thanks are also due to Miss Asha Shetty and Miss Ajita Parab for typing this paper.

REFERENCES

1. Katti; R.K., Deokule and Vyas J.N. (1972) : 'Soil structure interaction of well foundations model studies. Jour. Ind. Geotech. Soc.

2. Katti; R.K., Dewaikar, D.M. and Vasandani, A.S. (1977) : 'Studies on circular well foundation in clay media'. Fifth South East Asian Conf. on Soil Engg. Bangkok, Thailand.

3. Katti; R.K., Bansod, P.S., Naresh, D.N. and Golani, H.D. (1983) : 'Studies on estimating resistance of cohesive soil at base and sides of a model well foundation of bridges subjected to moments, horizontal loads and varying direct loads'. Report submitted to Ministry of Shipping and Transport, Govt. of India, pp. 1-294.

4. Pender. (1947) : 'Lateral support afforded to piers founded in sand'. Jour. Inst. of Engineers, Australia.

5. Sankaran and Muthukrishniah (1969) : 'Wells subjected to horizontal forces-model study'. Jour. I.R.C. paper No. 273.

Drained uplift capacity of drilled shafts

Capacité sous-pression drainée du puits forés

FRED H. KULHAWY, Professor of Civil Engineering, Cornell University, Ithaca, NY, USA

SYNOPSIS   A general analysis/design model is presented for the drained uplift capacity of drilled shaft foundations. This model has evolved from extensive research to define the failure mechanisms and establish the controlling parameters. Detailed guidelines are given to evaluate these parameters, and the results of field load tests are used to illustrate the model reliability.

INTRODUCTION

Drilled shafts (also known as drilled piers, bored piles, etc.) have become the foundation of choice in many design situations, stimulating research to develop improved design methods. This paper presents a general analysis/ design model for the drained uplift capacity of drilled shafts, which is based upon extensive research by our group during the past ten years and has included analytical studies, laboratory testing, large-scale model testing, and evaluation of full-scale field load tests. For brevity, the term shaft is used herein.

BASIC CONSIDERATIONS

In principle, the uplift capacity of shafts is given as in Fig. 1a by the vertical equilibrium equation below:

$$Q_u = W + Q_{tu} + Q_{su} = W + Q_{tu} + \int_{surface} \tau(z)dz \quad (1)$$

in which Q_u = uplift capacity, W = foundation weight, Q_{tu} = tip resistance, Q_{su} = side resistance, and τ = shearing resistance along a general shear surface. The use of this equation is limited only by our ability to predict the shear surface and the shearing resistance along it, and the tip resistance.

Studies to define the shear surface have been summarized recently by Kulhawy, et al. (1983), who showed that shafts fail principally along the soil-shaft interface leading to an overall cylindrical shear, as implied by Fig. 1a. The corresponding load transfer which normally occurs is shown in Fig. 1b (Stewart and Kulhawy, 1981b). Typically, the displacement to mobilize the full side resistance is about 5 to 10 mm.

The mechanism by which this type of failure occurs has been examined by Stewart and Kulhawy (1980, 1981a), as shown in Fig. 2. During initial uplift loading, Riedel shears develop in the soil along planes on which Mohr-Coulomb

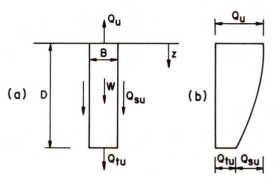

Fig.1 Shaft in Uplift

failure conditions are satisfied (Fig. 2a). Large displacements along the Riedel shears are not kinematically possible, so the soil is forced to develop displacement shears with further foundation movement (Fig. 2b), which finally result in a continuous displacement shear (Fig. 2c). This continuous shear is very close to the soil-shaft interface, and effectively defines a cylindrical shear surface.

However, in some cases the Riedel shears constitute a kinematically permissible failure mode before a continuous displacement shear develops. For this condition, a composite failure surface occurs, represented by a cone of soil near the ground surface with a cylindrical shear below. Fig. 3 illustrates this composite surface and gives suggested guidelines for determining the depth of the failure cone. In this figure, developed for both drained and undrained loading, the mean values over the depth, D, are used for the effective

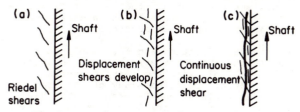

Fig.2 Development of Shear Surface

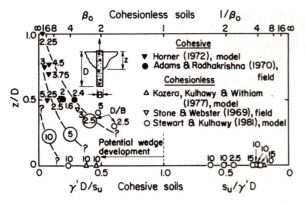

Fig.3 Composite Failure for Shafts in Uplift
(Stewart and Kulhawy, 1981a)

unit weight, γ', the undrained strength, s_u, and β_0, defined as $K_0 \tan\delta'$ in which K_0 = in-situ horizontal soil stress coefficient and δ' = soil-shaft interface friction angle. Examination of this figure shows that cone development only occurs for small shaft D/B ratios when the shafts are installed in high strength soils with high in-situ stresses (large β_0).

SIDE RESISTANCE

For the dominant failure mode, the integral in Eq. 1 can be expressed as the shearing resistance on the surface of a vertical cylinder, or:

$$Q_{su} = \int_0^D P(z) \sigma_h'(z) \tan \delta'(z) \, dz \qquad (2a)$$

$$= \int_0^D P(z) \sigma_v'(z) K(z) \tan \delta'(z) \, dz \qquad (2b)$$

in which P = foundation perimeter, σ_h' = horizontal effective stress which acts as a normal stress on the soil-shaft interface, δ' = effective stress angle of friction for the soil-shaft interface, σ_v' = vertical effective stress, and K = operative coefficient of horizontal soil stress (σ_h'/σ_v'). These terms are often grouped to define $\beta = K \tan\delta'$ and the unit side resistance, $f = \beta \sigma_v'$. This grouping obscures behavioral factors and is not used herein.

The perimeter and vertical effective stress terms can be evaluated simply. The perimeter is computed from the foundation geometry and will be a constant for a straight shaft. The vertical effective stresses are computed from the soil unit weight and the water table location. For design purposes, the highest seasonal location normally is appropriate.

The interface friction angle commonly is related to the effective stress friction angle of the soil, ϕ', with the results expressed as a δ'/ϕ' ratio. Detailed study of soil-concrete interfaces (Kulhawy and Peterson, 1979) has shown that when the interface is rough, $\delta'/\phi' > 1$. Normal cast-in-place concrete with a slump

greater than about 100 mm will yield a rough interface in granular soils. A ratio greater than 1 is of little design significance because it means that the failure surface will move out from the interface into the adjacent soil, giving a design ratio of 1.

The most difficult term to evaluate is K, because it is a function of the original in-situ K_0, and the stress changes caused in response to construction, loading, and time. Considering these factors, there may be either an increase or decrease from the original K_0. Values of K reported in the literature for a wide range of foundation types indicate low values approaching 0.1 and high values approaching 5. These bounds correspond roughly to the range from minimum active to maximum passive stress states.

The first step is to evaluate K_0. Most natural soil deposits are overconsolidated to some degree, at least near the surface. Therefore, assuming an at-rest $K_0 \approx 1-\sin\phi'$ will almost always be overly conservative for design. What is necessary is to establish the K_0 profile with depth which reflects the in-situ conditions more correctly. Measurements made by a pressuremeter or other evolving field devices can provide direct in-situ estimates (e.g., Baguelin, et al., 1978). A second approach is to construct the K_0 profile based on the stress history of the soil (Mayne and Kulhawy, 1982). And thirdly, the K_0 profile can be estimated from empirical correlations with field and laboratory test indices (Stas and Kulhawy, 1984).

Once the in-situ K_0 profile has been estimated, the operative K can be determined. Studies by Kulhawy, et al. (1983) have shown that the K/K_0 ratio for shafts varies between 2/3 and 1 when normal concretes are used. The lower range corresponds to slurry construction which leaves a thick cake on the shaft wall or causes softening in cohesive soils, while the upper range corresponds to dry construction and minimal sidewall disturbance. Casing construction below the water table is an intermediate case. Obviously, caving shaft walls or running sands will allow the ground stresses to relax much more and reach a minimum active state in the limit. These problem conditions require special study.

A further factor to consider is the use of expansive cement for the shaft concrete, which has the potential to increase K/K_0 above 1. A preliminary study by Sheikh, et al. (1983) on shafts in stiff clay indicates as much as a 50% increase in capacity with expansive cements. Although comparable detailed data are not available for shafts in granular soils, there is every reason to suggest that K/K_0 will be greater than 1 when expansive cements are used. This issue will have to be clarified in the future.

Incorporating all of these side resistance factors yields the following general equation:

$$Q_{su} = \frac{K}{K_0} \int_0^D P(z) \sigma_v'(z) K_0(z) \tan\left[\phi'(z) \cdot \frac{\delta'}{\phi'}\right] dz \quad (3)$$

with $\delta'/\phi' = 1$ and $K/K_0 = 2/3$ to 1.

MODIFICATIONS FOR CONE BREAKOUT AND BELLS

When it is determined from Fig. 3 that a cone breakout may develop, leading to a composite shear surface, the side resistance will be reduced because the uplifted cone of soil is no longer exerting a shearing resistance to the shaft wall. Based on examination of the available data, Stas and Kulhawy (1984) suggested that a reduced β be used, defined as $\beta_r = (2 + \beta_o)/3$. The reduced side resistance then is:

$$Q_{su}(\text{reduced}) = Q_{su}(\text{from Eq. 3}) \, \beta_r/\beta_o \quad (4)$$

with β_o as defined previously. However, if D/B is larger than about 5, or if the determined z/D is less than about 0.25, the reduction should be disregarded because it is minor.

When a belled shaft is loaded in uplift, the shear surface changes from a cylindrical shape to a more complex one. No rigorous theory is available to evaluate this problem at the present time. However, observations made by the writer after reviewing the results of many load tests lead to the following tentative conclusions: (1) for deeper shafts with depth to shaft diameter ratios (D/B) greater than about 10, there is little apparent influence of the bell on side resistance, (2) for shorter shafts with D/B ratios less than about 5, a design assumption of an operative mean diameter appears to give computed side resistances in general agreement with the load tests, and (3) intermediate lengths can be treated by a linear interpolation between D/B of 5 to 10. This operative mean diameter is defined as B_{shaft} plus $(B_{bell} - B_{shaft})/3$ and is used herein.

TIP RESISTANCE AND WEIGHT

The tip resistance of shafts in uplift commonly is assumed to be zero, but this assumption may be overly conservative in some cases. Stewart and Kulhawy (1980, 1981b) discussed this problem and showed that tip resistance can be developed from both tension and suction. Suction is an undrained phenomenon and is not present during drained loading. However, tip tension can develop when the shaft concrete bonds with the soil at the tip. During uplift, the tensile strength of the soil would be mobilized over the area of the tip. However, common construction practices usually result in a thin "altered" zone of very low tensile strength at the tip. Also, the tensile strength of soil is low, commonly on the order of several percent of the compressive strength. These two points lead to the prudent conclusion of assuming zero tip tension. Conversely, where very careful cleanout is accomplished and the soil at the tip has significant tensile strength (e.g., basal till), tip tensions can develop which will add to the uplift capacity. The same is true for rock at the tip, in which case the tip tension will be controlled by the lower tensile strength of either the rock or the concrete.

The final term to evaluate in Eq. 1 is the shaft weight. This is computed simply from the shaft geometry, being certain to include the

water table location to compute the effective shaft weight. For belled shafts, the operative mean diameter would be used.

FIELD LOAD TEST COMPARISONS

To evaluate the analysis/design approach outlined above, a comparison was made between the predicted uplift capacity, Q_{up}, and the measured uplift capacity, Q_{um}, as determined from 17 load tests available in the literature which were conducted on shafts installed in entirely granular soil deposits. The basic parameters are listed in Table I, with further details given by Stas and Kulhawy (1984). In all cases, δ'/ϕ' was taken as 1, and K/K_o was 1 except for the two 40 foot deep shafts with $K/K_o = 5/6$ because of casing construction under water. Customary U.S. units were used because these data were reported in that format.

Fig. 4 shows the results of the comparison. The agreement is very good with the solid line which represents a 1 to 1 or perfect prediction. A linear regression of these data resulted in the following:

$$Q_{up}(\text{tons}) = 1.7 + 0.91 \, Q_{um}(\text{tons}) \quad (5)$$

with a correlation coefficient of 0.961. The data were analyzed further by normalizing Q_{up} by Q_{um}, resulting in:

$$Q_{up}/Q_{um} = 1.04 - 0.0016 \, Q_{um}(\text{tons}) \quad (6)$$

This normalized fit gave a mean of 0.98 and a coefficient of variation of 28.8%. Overall, these results show a very good comparison with a small (and conservative) tendency for underestimation.

When it is considered further that as-built diameters are usually larger than the as-designed diameters, by as little as a few percent to as much as 15% in sands (Stewart and Kulhawy, 1981a), the correlations would be even better. Unfortunately, the load test data were not detailed enough to include the as-built diameters.

A final observation to be made relates to the mean value of K, back-calculated from the load tests and shown in the last column of Table I. The mean value of K is large and substantially higher than the 0.4 to 0.6 expected for normally consolidated (NC) soil. Only deep shafts approximate the NC case, while the data show very clearly that high horizontal stresses exist at shallow depths. These high stresses must be determined for economical design.

SUMMARY AND CONCLUSIONS

A general analysis/design model has been presented to compute the drained uplift capacity of straight-sided drilled shaft foundations,

TABLE I. Load Test Parameters

Shaft Depth (ft)	Shaft/Bell Diameter (ft)	Ground Water Depth (ft)	Total Unit Weight (pcf)	Effective Friction Angle (deg)	W (tons)	Q_{su} (tons)	Q_{up} (tons)	Q_{um} (tons)	Mean K from Q_{um}
8.0	3.00	b[a]	110[c]	31[d]	4.2	21.5[g]	25.7	24.0	1.96
10.0	3.00	b[a]	110[c]	32[d]	5.3	33.2	38.5	49.0	2.62
8.0	2.00	b[a]	120[c]	40[d]	1.9	34.2	36.1	45.0	4.25
10.0	3.00	7.5[a]	110[c]	31[d]	4.8	34.9	39.7	40.4	2.33
9.0	2.00/3.00	b[a]	120[c]	36[d]	2.9	41.0	43.9	27.7	1.92
11.0	2.00/3.00	b[a]	120[c]	36[d]	3.5	53.1	56.6	58.0	2.82
4.0	2.00/3.00	b[a]	120[c]	36[d]	1.3	5.6[g]	6.9	14.3	5.09
7.0	2.50	2.5	111	31[e]	1.9	3.3	5.2	8.4	1.31
10.0	3.00	0.0	122	31[e]	3.1	26.3	29.4	43.1	4.71
4.5	1.10	1.0	120[c]	36[d]	0.2	3.0	3.2	2.5	2.26
8.0	1.20	3.0	120[c]	36[d]	0.5	9.6	10.1	7.0	1.56
12.0	1.20	1.0	120[c]	36[d]	0.6	13.5	14.1	14.3	2.08
21.0	3.50	2.0	120[c]	32[d]	9.4	80.2	89.6	93.7	1.62
21.0	3.50	2.0	120[c]	32[d]	9.4	80.2	89.6	100.0	1.74
6.5	2.00/3.50	b	110	30[d]	2.4	15.8	18.2	22.5	3.79
40.0	1.75	4.0	115	33[f]	4.5	45.5	50.0	38.4	0.45
40.0	1.25	4.0	115	33[f]	2.3	32.5	34.8	33.8	0.59

a - inferred from boring logs   b - water level below shaft tip   c - assumed
d - estimated from field SPT   e - from direct shear test   f - test type unknown
g - reduced for cone breakout

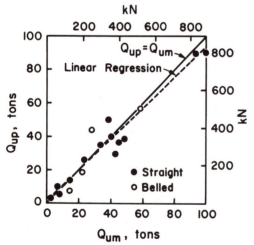

Fig.4 Capacity Comparison in Drained Uplift

and detailed guidelines have been given to evaluate the model parameters. Recommendations are also given to analyze cone breakout conditions if they are present, and to extend the model to belled shafts. Comparisons with available full-scale field test data are very good and support the model well.

ACKNOWLEDGEMENTS

This research has been supported largely by the Niagara Mohawk Power Corporation and the Electric Power Research Institute, with R. M. White and P. G. Landers as the respective project managers. Many colleagues and former students participated in this research and their contributions are appreciated. L. Crouse has done her usual superb job in preparing this manuscript.

REFERENCES

Baguelin, F., Jézéquel, J.F. and Shields, D.H. (1978). Pressuremeter and Foundation Engineering. 617p., TransTech, Clausthal.

Kulhawy, F.H. and Peterson, M.S. (1979). Behavior of Sand-Concrete Interfaces. Proc. 6th Pan-Am.Conf.SMFE, 2, 225-236, Lima.

Kulhawy, F.H., Trautmann, C.H., Beech, J.F., O'Rourke, T.D., McGuire, W., Wood, W.A. and Capano, C. (1983). Transmission Line Structure Foundations for Uplift-Compression Loading. Rpt.EL-2870, 412p., Elec. Power Res. Inst., Palo Alto.

Mayne, P.W. and Kulhawy, F.H. (1982). K_O-OCR Relationships in Soil. ASCE J.Geotech.Eng. Div., 108, GT6, 851-872.

Sheikh, S.A., O'Neill, M.W. and Mehrazarin, M.A. (1983). Expansive Cement in Drilled Shafts. Rpt.UHCE 83-14, 183p., Univ. Houston.

Stas, C.V. and Kulhawy, F.H. (1984). Critical Evaluation of Foundation Design Methods for Axial Loading. Rpt. in press, Elec. Power Res. Inst., Palo Alto.

Stewart, J.P. and Kulhawy, F.H. (1980). Behavior of Drilled Shafts in Axial Uplift. Geotech.Rpt. 80-2, 261p., Cornell Univ., Ithaca.

Stewart, J.P. and Kulhawy, F.H. (1981a). Investigation of Uplift Capacity of Drilled Shafts in Cohesionless Soil. Geotech.Rpt. 81-2, 422p., Cornell Univ., Ithaca.

Stewart, J.P. and Kulhawy, F.H. (1981b). Interpretation of Uplift Load Distribution Data. Proc. 10th ICSMFE, 2, 277-280, Stockholm.

Load-deformation characteristics of drilled piers

Les relations effort-déformation pour les barettes

I. MANOLIU, Professor, Civil Engineering Inst. Bucharest, Romania
D. V. DIMITRIU, Assistant Professor, Civil Engineering Inst. Bucharest, Romania
N. RADULESCU, Assistant, Civil Engineering Inst. Bucharest, Romania
GH. DOBRESCU, Senior Research Eng., Building Research Inst. Bucharest, Romania

SYNOPSIS   Foundations on drilled piers are very efficient for carrying large loads to a deep bearing stratum. Pertinent data on the behaviour of such elements are quite rare due to the difficulties encountered with the large scale test programs. Field tests on 8 axially loaded drilled piers and 9 laterally loaded piers have been performed on 5 different sites in Romania. Behaviour under axial load was sarongly affected by the nature of the soil at the base of the pier. Under lateral load, piers behaved satisfactorly, regardless the direction of the load and the soil nature. Based on the interpretation of the results, analytical procedures wewe deve - loped for defining the load - settlement and load - deflection relationship.

INTRODUCTION

Long drilled piers, constructed by using trench walls equipments and techniques, are increas - ingly used as high bearing capacity foundation units. The number of piers in a foundation is, usually, small, which explains the importance attached to proper construction technique, in - suring the fulfillment of the design bearing capacity. Minimizing the number of piers and, by this way, the cost of the foundation, requi - res a clear understanding of the behaviour of piers under various load conditions. The best approach is still represented by the field tests on instrumented or uninstrumented piers. Due to the high values reached normally by the loads, field tests on drilled piers become very cumbersome. Therefore, available results of the not very numerous undertaken tests, must be carefully checked in order to define the para - meters which govern both the bearing capacity and the load-deformation relation. In this way data can gradually accumulate, in order to allow the improvement of computation methods.

FIELD TESTING PROGRAM

The present paper is based on the results of field test performed in Romania at the sites of 5 industrial buildings. A total number of 8 axial and 9 lateral load tests have been performed.

Typical drilled piers test load set-up

Romanian specifications for the design and construction of drilled piers (P.106-79) con - sider the field test as mandatory in order to determine the axial bearing capacity, R_u and the horizontal bearing capacity, H_{cr}. In or - der to avoid handling of large counter-weight and to perform on the same job both vertical and horizontal loads, the set-up shown in the fig.1 is currently used.

Sometimes, after completing the tests, the re - action frame is incorporated in the foundation provided the foundation is large enough.

Criteria for defining the critical loads

Tests performed under the above mentioned spe - cifications are of the stress-control type.The loading is applied in increments of 1/10 ..1/15 of the presumed critical load, and is maintained until stabilization of deformations is reached. The axial critical load is defined by one of the following criteria :

a) the load which correspond to a settlement s_o of the pier head equal to 1/10 of the width, b, of the pier ;

b) the load preceding the one for which sta - bilization of the deformation is not reached within 24 hrs ;

c) the largest load which could habe been applied to the pier, without fulfilling criteria "a" or "b".

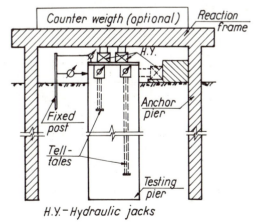

Fig.1   Typical test load set - up

The horizontal critical load is defined as :

a) the load which corresponds to a deflection y_0 of the pier head at the ground level equal to 25 mm ;

b) the load preceding the one for which stabilization of the deformation is not reached within 24 hrs.

RESULTS OF THE FIELD TESTS

Fig.2 summarizes data referring to stratigraphic columns, dimensions of the piers and types of loading. As one can remark, except pier Vd, all laterally loaded piers have been previously submitted to axial load. Piers Va, Vb, Vc have been tested only in compression. Piers I, IIa, IIb and III have been instrumented with tell-tales. Settlement marks were placed under the base of the pier IIa and IIb. Testing piers have been also provided with steel pipes incorporated in the concrete in order to check by means of sonic sounding the quality and the continuity of the concrete.

Results of the compression load tests are given in table I and those of horizontal load tests in table II. In the case of piers I, IIa and III, the above formulated criteria "a" or "b" could not apply. For design purpose, the maximum load reached during the test has been assigned as critical load, according to criterion "c". In the case of pier IV the critical load corresponded to a settlement $s_0 = 78.4$ mm $\approx$ $0.1 \cdot b = 80$ mm. In all other cases, critical load was established based on criterion "b". Among piers subjected to lateral load, at piers IIa, IIb and III the critical load has been conventionally defined as corresponding to a deflection $y_0 = 25$ mm. In fact, none of the laterally loaded pier exhibited ground failure during the load test.

By placing tell-tales instruments at various depths into the pier, one can obtain the diagram of settlement along the pier, s(z), the Young modulus of the concrete E, the relation between the frictional τ (z) and s(z), the force transmitted to the base, Q_b. Data obtained by processing tell-tales readings at the 4 instrumented piers are summarized in tables III and IV.

TABLE I
Axial load test results

Q_0 (MN)	Settlement s_0 (mm) for pier no.							
	I	IIa	IIb	III	IV	Va	Vb	Vc
0.5	0.27	—	0.14	—	—	0.15	0.15	0.25
1.0	0.59	—	0.32	—	0.68	1.17	1.17	1.16
1.5	1.19	—	—	0.76	—	1.71	1.35	1.49
2.0	1.85	0.44	0.68	—	1.55	2.43	1.61	3.08
3.0	3.58	0.71	1.14	—	4.00	4.03	2.61	11.65
3.5	4.61	—	1.31	—	—	4.90	4.54	16.00
4.0	5.56	1.18	—	2.12	21.72	5.79	7.08	23.45
4.2	—	—	106.41	—	—	—	—	—
4.5	6.56	—	—	2.71	—	6.75	10.55	—
5.0	7.78	1.77	—	3.33	50.20	—	17.37	—
5.5	—	—	—	3.37	—	10.40	25.30	—
6.0	—	1.92	—	—	78.40	14.05	—	—
6.5	13.53	—	—	—	—	17.85	—	—
7.0	—	2.61	—	7.18	140.00	—	—	—
8.0	18.37	4.34	—	9.87	191.70	—	—	—
9.0	—	5.38	—	11.92	248.00	—	—	—
10.0	34.92	6.95	—	16.02	274.00	—	—	—
11.0	42.04	8.50	—	20.46	334.50	—	—	—
12.0	55.20	10.29	—	—	377.80	—	—	—
13.0	—	12.90	—	—	—	—	—	—

BAHEVIOUR OF AXIALLY LOADED PIERS

Interpretation of the field test results

Experimental values of the critical load $R_{u,m}$, defined by using previously given criteria and included in tab.III have been compared to the

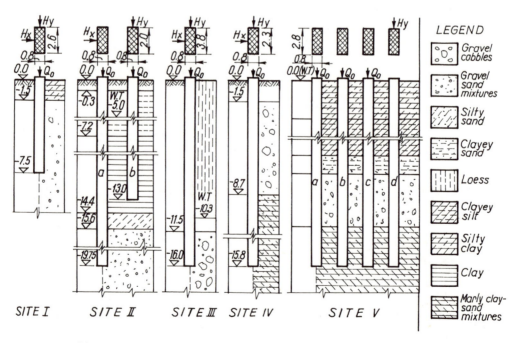

Fig.2   Layout of soil profiles and test conditions

TABLE II
Lateral load test results

H (MN)	\multicolumn{9}{c}{Deflection y_0 (mm) for pier no. and direction}
	I-x	I-y	IIa-x	IIb-y	III-x	III-y	IV-x	IV-y	V d-y
0.1	0.18	—	1.17	—	2.54	—	2.00	0.54	—
0.15	—	0.165	—	—	—	—	4.25	—	—
0.2	0.45	—	3.09	0.90	7.42	2.12	—	—	0.30
0.25	—	—	—	—	—	—	7.00	1.30	—
0.3	0.77	0.26	5.81	—	11.00	—	—	—	0.50
0.32	—	—	—	—	—	—	10.00	2.13	—
0.4	1.18	—	9.08	1.81	16.90	7.90	13.00	2.80	0.65
0.5	1.68	—	15.90	—	23.40	—	21.79	—	0.80
0.6	2.27	0.91	27.90	4.49	—	12.50	—	—	1.00
0.7	2.94	—	37.50	—	—	—	—	—	1.25
0.8	3.54	—	52.27	8.93	—	20.50	—	9.88	1.40
0.9	—	2.16	—	—	—	—	—	—	1.70
1.0	—	—	—	17.73	—	—	—	—	2.70
1.2	—	3.92	—	32.09	—	38.30	—	27.77	—
1.4	—	—	—	51.32	—	—	—	—	—
1.5	—	6.38	—	—	—	—	—	—	—
1.6	—	—	—	83.47	—	—	—	—	—

ones computed by using formula recommended by Romanian specifications P.107-79. According to the specifications, the critical load (the ultimate bearing capacity) is expressed :

$$R_{u,c} = R_f + R_b \qquad (1)$$

where R_f represents the friction component and R_b the base resistance component.
R_f is obtained by using values of the unit friction, f, given in tabelar form in function of the soil type and depth. R_b is computed in terms of the pier dimensions and of the strengths characteristics of the soil at the pier base (angle of internal friction $\emptyset$ or undrained cohesion c_u).
The comparison lead to some conclusions, as follows :

Piers with base in non-cohesive soil

The ratio $R_{u,m}/R_{u,c}$ is exceeding unity (except pier III where $R_{u,m}/R_{u,c} = 0.63$). Since in all these cases, including pier III, the true ultimate bearing capacity could not be reached during the test, the maximum experimental load being defined as $R_{u,m}$, one can conclude that design recommendations of the Romanian specifications are on the safe side.
The "efficiency index" of the pier foundation was defined as a ratio between the critical load R_u ("external" bearing capacity) and the allowable load of the concrete section, R_p ("in-

ternal" bearing capacity).
All piers were made of reinforced concrete with a 28 day strength of at least 200 daN/cm², therefore a value of $R_p = 5000$ kN/m² x A, where A is the section area, in m², was assigned.
All piers with base in non-cohesive soils had an efficiency index above 1, proving a full use of both soil and concrete resistance.
Settlements recorded under maximum loads varied between 12.9 mm and 55 mm.

Piers with base in cohesive soils

In all cases critical load was defined by the criteria "a" or "b" previously mentioned. The ratio $R_{u,m}/R_{u,c}$ was sistematically less than unity, so the design recommendations were not on the safe side in these cases. The efficiency index was below 0.5.
Given the results of the sonic soundings and of the lateral load tests, the unsatisfactory behaviour of the piers could not be atributted to a lack of continuity of their bodies, or to the poor quality of the concrete. Several circumstances could explain the clear differences observed between the two types of piers. In first place, the ultimate pressure at the pier's base does not increase with depth in the case of cohesive soils in the same manner as it does increase in the case of non-cohesive soils. Secondly, when construction requirements are not strictly observed, a cushion of slurry is trapped between the base of the pier and the soil; in the case of coarse and medium non-cohesive soils, the fluid from the cushion can be "squeezed" into the voids of the surrounding soil under the weight of the column of fresh concrete ; in the case of cohesive soils, with a much smaller permeability, the cushion cannot be "squeezed".
As a matter of fact, only differences in the construction process can explain the differences in the behaviour of piers Va, Vb and Vc, constructed and tested close to each other.
In the case of instrumented piers I, IIa, IIb and III it was possible to compare the measured ultimate load in friction, $R_{f,m}$, with the computed one, $R_{f,c}$, and they proved to be in good agreement (except the short pier I).
In the case of uninstrumented piers V, knowing the strength characteristics of the soil it was possible to simulate analytically the load transfer. Computations were repeated until a coincidence was reached between computed and measured settlements (Dimitriu, 1982). Using these data, the friction resistance, R_f, was expressed, showing also a very good agreement with values ob-

TABLE III

Interpretation of axial load test results in terms of bearing capacity

Pier no.	L (m)	A (m²)	\multicolumn{3}{c}{Computed by prescriptions}	\multicolumn{3}{c}{Measured}	$R_{f,m}/R_{f,c}$	$R_{u,m}/R_{u,e}$	$R_{u,m}/R_p$
			$R_{f,c}(kN)$	$R_{b,c}(kN)$	$R_{u,c}(kN)$	$R_{u,m}(kN)$	$R_{f,m}(kN)$	$s_0(mm)$			
I	7.5	2.08	2.040	4.915	6.955	12.000	4.000	55.0	1.96	1.73	1.15
IIa	19.75	1.6	5.160	9.785	12.945	13.146	6.670	12.9	1.29	1.015	1.64
IIb	13.5	1.6	3.276	1.200	4.470	3.682	3.700	1.31	1.13	0.82	0.46
III	14.0	3.04	5.920	17.900	23.820	15.000	6.500	40.20	1.09	0.63	1.20
IV	15.8	1.84	4.340	1.840	6.180	6.000	—	78.4	—	0.97	0.65
Va	20.0	2.24	4.926	2.240	7.166	5.500	4.449	10.4	0.93	0.76	0.49
Vb	20.0	2.24	4.926	2.240	7.166	4.500	4.218	10.5	0.856	0.67	0.40
Vc	20.0	2.24	4.926	2.240	7.166	3.500	5.082	16.0	1.031	0.48	0.312

tained by specifications P.106-79.

Analytical study on the load-settlement relation

In a previous paper (Manoliu, Dimitriu, 1979) it has been suggested to use for purely frictional piers an interaction parameter $\beta = \sqrt{\alpha U/EA}$ in which α is the slope of the relation $\tau - s$, τ being the side friction. It was shown that the load-settlement relation ($Q_o - s_o$) can be well approximated if it is known the way in which the parameter β varies with the ratio Q_o/R_f.

As a result of studies carried out afterwards by the authors, it is proposed to consider β as a constant of the behaviour in the linear range of the frictional contact, defining à priori the following relation between Q_f and s_o, Q_f being the part of the external load Q_o transmitted to the lateral surface of the pier :

$$\frac{dQ_f}{ds_o} = k_{of} \cdot \left(1 - \frac{Q_f}{R_f}\right)^q \quad (2)$$

where q is a shape coefficient which is deduced from boundary conditions put to the eq (2). Thus when $Q_f = R_f$, $s_o = s_\ell$ (fig.3), where s_ℓ is the settlement at which the friction resistance is fully mobilized. By solving eq (2) for $q \neq 1$ and the mentioned boundary conditions, it follows :

$$Q_f = R_f \left[1 - \left(1 - \frac{s_o}{s_\ell}\right)^{\frac{k_{of} \cdot s_\ell}{R_f}}\right] \quad (3)$$

The relation (3) is valid for $s_o \in [0, s_\ell]$; for $s_o > s_\ell$, $Q_f = R_f$.
It is assumed that the base resistance Q_b varies linearly with the base settlement, s_b :

$$Q_b = k_b \cdot s_b \quad (4)$$

or, in function of the settlement s_o :

$$Q_b = k_b' \cdot s_o \quad (4')$$

The coefficient k_b' is no more constant, its value depending on the magnitude of the mobilized force Q_f. By neglecting the shortening of the body of the pier under the load Q_f, one can write :

$$k_b' = (k_b \cdot k_p)/(k_b + k_p) \quad (5)$$

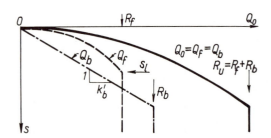

Fig.3   Definition of the load - displacement parameters

where $k_p = EA/L$, L being the length of the pier. The relation (4),(4') is valid for the range $Q_b \leq R_b$; afterwards Q_b remains constant for $Q_b = R_b$.
The parameter k_{of} of the relation (2) is deduced from the transfer equation in the hypothesis of a linear behaviour :

$$k_{of} = Q_f/s_o = \beta EA \frac{1 - \exp(-2 \cdot \beta \cdot L)}{1 + \exp(-2 \cdot \beta \cdot L)} \quad (6)$$

The parameters which govern the load settlement behaviour are, besides the ones of the pier itself (E,A,U,L) : R_f, R_b, s_ℓ, k_p and α . Because α signifies in this approach the slope of the tangent in origin of the $\tau - s$ curve, the following relation is proposed :

$$\alpha = \frac{\tau_{max}}{\eta \cdot s_\ell} = \frac{R_f}{UL} \cdot \frac{1}{\eta \cdot s_\ell} \quad (7)$$

where η is a coefficient bellow unity expressing how many times the initial slope α is larger than the slope of the secant corresponding to the point of full mobilization of the shear resistance, τ_{max}, for the settlement $s = s_\ell$ (fig.4).

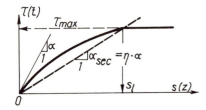

Fig.4   Definition of the soil-shaft interaction parameters

With the given elements, the diagrams $Q_o - s_o$ have been reconstructed for all instrumented piers, using parameters from experimental results, except coefficient η which has been estimated. Pertinent data are summarized in tab.IV.

TABLE IV

Interpretation of axial load test results in terms of load-settlement relation

Pier no.	E(*) (MN/cm²)	$R_{f,m}$ (MN)	$s_{2,m}$ (mm)	$k_{p,m}$ (MN/cm)	k_b (MN/cm)	η	$10^3 \times \beta$ (m⁻¹)	k_{of} (MN/cm)
I	2.8	4.00	20.0	1.80	1.76	0.25	42.6	7.66
IIa	2.8	6.67	2.26	6.60	5.11	0.50	81.6	33.74
IIb	2.8	3.70	2.0	0.	0	0.50	82.8	29.15
III	1.9	6.50	6.0	2.30	2.18	0.50	51.7	18.50

(*) derived from tell-tales records

In fig.5 computed load-settlement curves are plotted against measured points. In fig.6 computed loads, $Q_{o,c}$ and measured loads $Q_{o,m}$ leading to the same settlement s_o have been plotted for the 4 tests. The most part of the results are located within a range of $\pm 10\%$. This tests have shown, as many others reported elsewhere, that the frictional resistance R_f is fully developed at very small settlements, in

the range of 2 ... 10 mm in cohesive soils and 10 ... 30 mm in non-cohesive soils.
The following empirical procedure is recommended to estimate the load-settlement relation, in lieu of field tests, when soil characteristics are at hand :

a) Critical loads $R_{u,c}$, $R_{f,c}$ and $R_{b,c}$ are computed ;
b) Limit settlement s_ℓ is estimated as follows :
   - $s_\ell = 5$ mm when the soil surrounding the pier is predominantly cohesive (more than 80 % of the embedment) ;
   - $s_\ell = 20$ mm when the soil surrounding the pier is predominantly non-cohesive ;
   - s_ℓ is averaged, considering the thickness of the each layer, between 5 mm and 20 mm, in non-homogeneous soil ;
c) Coefficient η is estimated as follows :
   - $\eta = 0.5$ for $s_\ell = 5$ mm ;
   - $\eta = 0.25$ for $s_\ell = 20$ mm ;
   - η is obtained by linear interpolation between 0.5 and 0.25 when $5 < s_\ell < 20$;
d) k_b is computed by using the elastic solution :

$$k_b = \frac{\dot{E}_s \cdot \ell}{I_w \cdot F (1 - \nu^2)} \qquad (8)$$

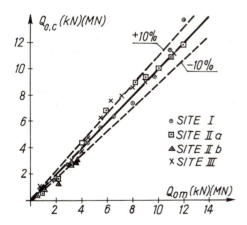

Fig.5   Computed and measured load vs settlement diagrams

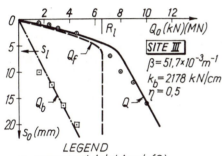

Fig.6   Computed vs measured load for all tests

where ℓ is the great side of the pier section, E_s is the deformation modulus of the soil at the base of the pier, I_w is a shape coefficient function of the ratio ℓ/b (in the case of rigid foundations I_w varies between 1.2 and 1.7 for $\ell/b = 2$ and respectively $\ell/b = 5$), F is a depth correction factor (for practical purpose F = 0.5) and ν is Poisson ratio of the soil. Once these parameters are established, the load-settlement diagram can be computed by using eq (4) and (5).

BEHAVIOUR UNDER LATERAL LOADS

Two aspects have been considered, when interpreting the results of field tests : the load-deflection diagram and the lateral critical load H_{cr}.
It was assumed that the load-deflection relation (H-y) is governed by a hyperbolic law of Kondner - Zelasko type, expressed as :

$$H = K_o \frac{y}{1 + y/y_r} \qquad (9.1)$$

or

$$y = H/K_o \frac{1}{1 - H/P_u} \qquad (9.2)$$

where P_u is the ultimate lateral load, for which resistances of both soil and pier are fully mobilized, K_o is the slope in the origin of the H-y relation and $y_r = P_u/K_o$ (fig.7). One can remark that the behaviour of the pier, in terms of displacements, is governed solely by two parameters of the soil-pier system, namely P_u and K_o.

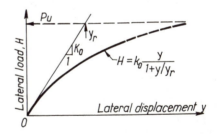

Fig.7   Definition of the lateral load-deflection curve parameters

In this paper, an empirical approach is used in order to determine these parameters. The approach allows to develop the entire H-y diagram and to define the critical load H_{cr} from a field test in which that load has not been reached.
In theory, by choosing arbitrarily two experimental pairs of values (H_1,y_1), (H_2,y_2) the parameters P_u and K_o have the expressions :

$$P_u = \frac{H_1 \cdot H_2 \cdot (y_2 - y_1)}{H_1 \cdot y_2 - H_2 \cdot y_1} \qquad (10.1)$$

$$K_o = \frac{H_1 \cdot P_u}{y_1 \cdot (P_u - H_1)} = \frac{H_2 \cdot P_u}{y_2 \cdot (P_u - H_1)} \qquad (10.2)$$

In order to reduce the effect of experimental errors, all combinations of pairs of experimental points are processed averaging then the values P_u and K_o. In practice, experimental values are well matched by computed ones by selecting only 5 points, namely the first two loads, to define the modulus K_o, the last two loads to define P_u and one arbitrary point in the middle zone of the diagram.
Using this approach, computations were performed for the laterally loaded piers. Results are summarized in tab. V. Diagrams in fig.8 show computed and measured values.

TABLE V

Interpretation of lateral load test

Pier no.	P_u (MN)	K_0 (kN/mm)	H_{cr} (MN)	$10^{-7} \times EI$ (MN·cm²)	n_h (daN/cm³)	m (MN/m⁴)	m' (MN/m⁴)
I-x	1.21	5.60	1.11	3.106	3.84	14.70	10.60
I-y	2.02	9.85	1.86	32.80	1.89	23.60	11.10
IIa-x	0.91	81.0	0.63	2.39	0.552	2.76	1.84
IIb-y	1.76	180.0	1.27	14.93	0.527	5.58	3.76
III-x	0.94	42.8	0.50	3.08	0.32	0.89	0.69
III-y	1.77	99.0	1.03	69.50	0.134	1.65	0.61

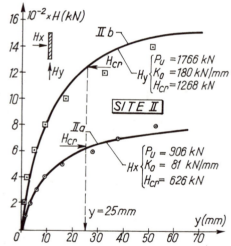

Fig.8 Computed and measured lateral load vs deflection diagrams

Since in no field test a load leading to unstabilized deflection was reached, H_{cr} was computed for a deflection $y_{cr} = 25$ mm.
Considering the pier embedded in a Winkler-type soil, with a modulus of soil reaction varying linearly with depth $E_s = n_h \cdot z$, n_h was computed by using the relation:

$$n_h = \frac{EI}{\left[(y_{cr}/H_{cr}) \cdot (EI/A_y)\right]^{5/3}} \qquad (11)$$

where EI is the stiffness of the pier and A_y is a coefficient which depends on the ratio $L/T = L(n_h/EI)^{0.2}$. For practical purpose $A_y = 5$ for short piers and $A_y = 2.5$ for medium and long piers (Reese, Allen, 1977).
In the Romanian specifications is given for n_h the expression :

$$n_h = m \cdot d_c \qquad (12)$$

where $m(FL^{-4})$ depends on the soil type and d_c is the design value of the pier width, usually taken as the side of the pier perpendicular to the direction of the load, plus 1.0 m. Coefficient m has been computed with the relation (12). Large differences were obtained for the same pier, depending on the direction of the load, along the shortest side, b, or along the largest side, ℓ. If in this last situation, a design width $d' = (\ell + b)/2$ was used instead of $d_c = (b+1.0)$, values obtained for m' were practically the same, regardless the direction of the load, in the case of piers I and III and closer to each other in the case of pier II.

CONCLUSIONS

Long drilled piers proved to be efficient as elements of high axial bearing capacity when penetrating with their base in a non-cohesive dense soil.
Analytical procedures, based on the processing of field tests data, have been proposed in order to describe load-displacement and load-deflection relationships. These empirical procedures can be useful for the interpretation of the results of large scale test, which remains the basic tool for the design of pier foundations.

REFERENCES

Dimitriu, D., V. (1982) "Some comments on the nature and reliability of the parameters used in numerical modelling". Proc.Int.Sym. on Numerical Models in Geomechanics, Zürich.

Manoliu, I., Dimitriu, D.V. (1979) "A parameter to define the soil-pier interaction for axially loaded piers", The 7th ECSMFE, vol.3, Brighton.

Reese, L.C., Allen, J.D. (1977) "Drilled shaft design and construction guidelines manual", U.S. Dept.of Transportation, Washington, D.C.

x x x "P.106-79. Technical prescriptions for the design and construction of drilled piers", INCERC, Bucharest (in Romanian)

Field testing on large driven piles

Essais de charge sur grands pieux battus

R. MEY, Ing. Caminos, TECAR, S.A., Spain
C. S. OTEO, Dr. Ing. Caminos, Lab. de Carreteras y Geotecnia, CEDEX, Spain
J. SANCHEZ DEL RIO, Ing. de Caminos, Dragados y Construcciones, S.A., Spain
A. SORIANO, Dr. Ing. Caminos, Univ. Politécnica de Madrid, Spain

SYNOPSIS

A new pier for supply coal to the Los Barrios Power Plant has recently constructed. The pier is founded on cylindrical prestressed piles, driven into fine silty sand. In order to complete the available geotechnical information, a series large-scale load tests were carried out. In this paper, horizontal and vertical (compression and pull-out) load tests on 36" and 54" Ø piles are described. The deformation of the soil-pile system and the load distribution along the pile shaft are analyzed from the measurements carried out during the tests.

INTRODUCTION

In order to supply coal to the fossil-fuel Power Plant at Los Barrios in Cadiz, Spain, the company Gibraltar--Intercar, S.A. has recently constructed a new pier for docking and unloading of 150,000 DTW vessels. The work, carried out by the Temporary Association Tecar (Dragados y Construcciones, S.A. and Entrecanales y Tavora, S.A.), basically consists of a pier with and L-shaped plan, entailing one module 380 m long by 28 m wide (the Unloading Pier), parallel to the coast, and another module, joining up the first to land (the Connecting Pier), which is 208 m long by 40 m wide. Figure 1 shows the plan of this facility.

The Connecting Pier is built of a site-poured concrete slab supported by beams of the same material for which a total of 68 prestressed (54" Ø, 5" thick) cylindrical Raymond piles make up the foundation.

The Unloading Pier, or Main Pier, has a similar structure and is also supported by prestressed cylindrical piles, which are 66" Ø and 6" thick, forming 60 three-pile moduli, as shown in Figure 1.

The work is located on the inside of the Bay of Algeciras on a sea floor where the draught of the water varies considerably. As indicated in Figure 1, the sea floor is at elevation -8.0 at the start of the Connecting Pier, and at -32 elevation at the eastern corner of the Unloading Pier.

GEOTECHNICAL CONDITIONS

The subsoil has a relatively uniform stratigraphical profile, and it is made up of the following layers of soil:

- Mud and silt, 1.5 m thick.

- Fine grey somewhat silty sand of thicknesses varying between 15 and 22 m.

- Grey sandy silt containing organic materials and shells, from soft to medium consistency; its thickness varies from 1 to 7 m.

- Silty sand with silt pockets (5-10 m thick).

- Gravel and sand overlaying the boltom sandstone rock.

After analyzing several different solutions for building the two piers, it was decided that driven prestressed piles would be used in order to avoid the major problems that the water draught (approximately 30 m at the Main Pier) and the low to medium strength of the ocean floor presented in other foundation alternatives.

Whith that idea in mind, the work was designed to be supported on prestressed Raymond piles, with diameters of 54" and 66", of great structural strength, with a length of 18 m driven into the ground. In this manner, the pile tips would generally remain in the upper layer of somewhat silty fine grey sand. Nevertheless, in the Pier Project design it was also taken into account that it was probable that some of the piles could remain above the intermediate silt layers, bearing in mind the effect of this silt layer both on the bearing capacity of the piles and on their deformability. The latter was especially important because of the effects that differential settlements could have on the pier structure.

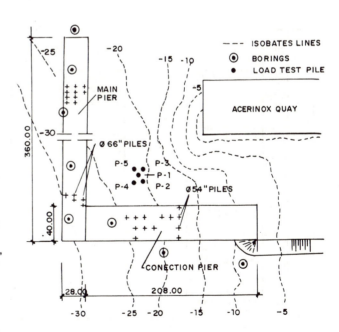

Fig. 1.- Plan of the Gibraltar-Intercar pier

LOAD TESTS

Given the importance of the work and its exceptional natu- re (piles 1.68 m Ø and 55 m long driven into the sea floor) it was decided to complete the available geotechnical information (test boring, penetration and laboratory tests, etc). Therefore, a series large-scale load tests were carried out "in situ" to study the following aspects, mainly:

- Strength and lateral deformability of the soil-pile system, or location of the fictitious fixed point, established according to the Oteo method (Oteo, 1981) since the piers had no external dolphins.

- Real distribution of the vertical load applied to the pile between shaft and tip. (It was wanted to test the real strength at the shaft in view of the possible pre- sence of silt at the tip of some of the piles).

- Pile settlement (for its vital significance in the design stress of the pier structure).

In order to study these points, and for practical reasons, it was decided to concentrate a series of vertical load tests (compression and traction) and horizontal load tests practically on one point. Additionally, in orden to obtain complementary information on the joint behaviour of the piles and soil at other points, several pile driving tests were decided on. More than 30 piles were equipped with accelerometers and strain-gauges in order to monitor the driving by means of P.D.A. equipment. Part of the re- sults of these dynamic controls have been described in a previous report (Sanchez del Rio y Bernal, 1984).

The stratigraphical profile of the site of the load tests has been reproduced in Figure 2, together with some statistics that give an idea of the nature (fines content) and state of the soil: water content, plasticity and S.P.T. tests. These last values are those obtained by test boring, although their validity is questionable, given the problems that usually arise in this type of test.

The load tests were carried out using five piles, driving four 54" Ø piles into the vertices of a square 6.35 m on each side, and the fifth pile - 36" Ø - in its centre. The situation is shown in Figure 1.

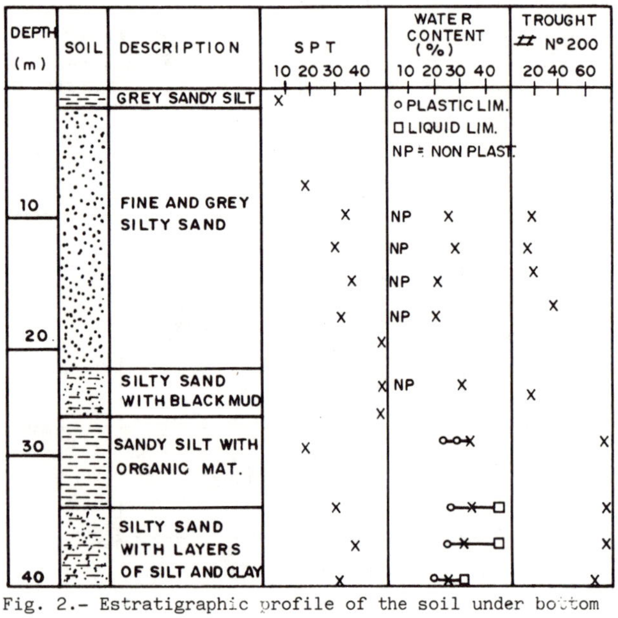

DEPTH (m)	SOIL	DESCRIPTION	SPT 10 20 30 40	WATER CONTENT (%) 10 20 30 40	TROUGHT π N°200 20 40 60
		GREY SANDY SILT	X	o PLASTIC LIM. □ LIQUID LIM. NP = NON PLAST	
10		FINE AND GREY SILTY SAND	X		
			X	NP X	X
			X	NP X	X
			X	NP X	X
			X	NP X	X
20			X		
		SILTY SAND WITH BLACK MUD	X NP	X	X
			X		
30		SANDY SILT WITH ORGANIC MAT.	X	o o X	X
			X	o X □	X
		SILTY SAND WITH LAYERS	X	o X □	X
40		OF SILT AND CLAY	X	o X □	X

Fig. 2.- Estratigraphic profile of the soil under bottom sea at the load test

The test plan was as follows:

1. A horizontal load test between two 54" Ø piles (P-2 and P-3).

2. A compression test (up to 3,5 MN) subsequently to be followed by a traction test (up to 2,2 MN) on the cen- tre 36" Ø, P-1, using the other piles for reaction.

3. Pile P-1 to be re-driven, monitored by the P.D.A., the same as the initial driving - a length of 1.10 m.

4. Repetition of the compression and traction tests, up to 5 MN and 3 MN respectively.

Pile P-1 was instrumented with 14 vibrating wire extenso- meters, placed along two vertical lines on opposite sides, in order to determine the load distribution throughout the pile during the compression and traction tests.

ASSEMBLY AND LOAD TESTING

To carry out the horizontal load test a steel frame was set up attached to pile P-2 by a steel sheet fixed to the pile by the prestressed wires of the pile and corres- ponding wedges. A hydraulic jack was attached to the frame, the mobile element of which was attached to the other pile, P-3, by means of a steel girder (figure 3).

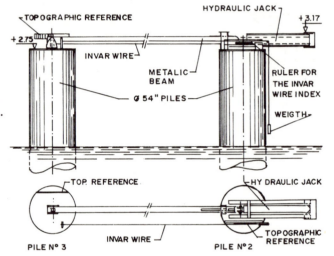

Fig. 3.- Lay-out of the horizontal load test

The maximum horizontal load applied in this test was 50 KN, to stay under the piles bending strength, sin ce they had no restrains at the head. First, a cycle of up to 40 KN was applied separating the piles; then the same cycle, to bring the piles close together. After- wards, a 40 KN cycle was applied separating the piles, and then, as rapidly as possible, 5 complete cycles, bring- ing the piles together and separating them, with the same maximum load value. Lastly, the load was increased to 50 KN to apply a new cycle of separating and bringing the piles together.

The horizontal movements at the head of each pile were measured from the land. To do this, two stations were installed on fixed bases and two references were fixed to the piles. Moreover, the sum of both movements was measured, thanks to the installation of a small fixed scale on pile P-2 and a movable index -counterweighted- joined to P-3 by an invar thread.

For vertical load tests, it was necessary to assemble a

steel platform to join up the four reaction piles. This platform (Figure 4) consisted of two large steel girders, each one supported by and anchored to the prestressed wires of two of the piles (by conical wedges). Two other girders were joined to the original two, in the middle, leaving pile P-1 in the centre of the empty space formed by the four girders.

After the platform was installed, at the head of pile P-1 a 5 MN hydraulic jack was installed, the upper part of which was provided with an articulated hinge. The latter was joined to the two central reaction girders by 32 cables. In this manner, when the piston of the jack was pressed, the load was transmitted to the platform (and from the platform to the piles), thanks to these cables.

To apply traction to pile P-1, two hydraulic jacks were installed, resting on the platform and thanks to a steel brace previously glued to the pile with Epoxy resin (Figura 4).

During the vertical load tests, the following magnitudes were measured:

a) The absolute vertical settlement of pile P-1 and two

of the reaction piles by topographic methods, with a N-3 precision level. This level was installed from a relatively fixed point closeby (land, already constructed work, etc). This was a problem because of the action of wind, waves, etc.

b) The relative vertical settlement of the pile with respect to the reaction platform, with a minimum precision of 0.25 mm.

c) The vibrating wire extensometers installed in pile P-1 to ascertain the load distribution throughout its shaft.

Given the rigidity of the platform and the greater diameter of the reaction piles, the deformation to be expected from these elements proved to be very small. For this reason the movement of pile P-1 measured with respect to the platform was almost the same as the absolute value, with a maximum error of approximately 5%.

In the vertical load tests, the load was also applied in at least three cycles, with practically zero under no load conditions. This was done to check the measuring methods, the effect of future cyclical stress and the residual deformation of the soil.

RESULTS OBTAINED

Due to the brevity of this report, only the most outstanding results of the load tests are outlined.

For example, Figure 5 shows the 40 KN load cycles in pile P-2 during the horizontal load test. This figure shows how there is a quasi linear relationship between load and shift in each cycle, with a certain rigidization process occurring between the first cycle and subsequent cycles of the same load.

On increasing the horizontal load to 50 KN, the behaviour continued to be almost linear, with a residual deformation of only approximately 12% (similar to that in Figure 5). The aplication of sucessive cycles did not add significant residual effects.

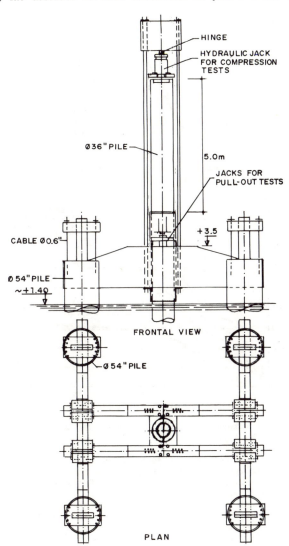

Fig. 4.- Lay-out of the load test facilities

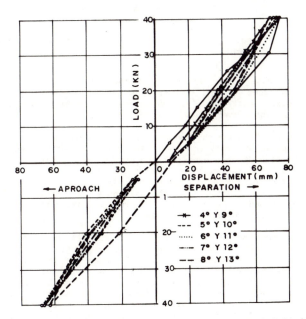

Fig. 5.- Diagram load-displacement in the horizontal load test

In all cases, it was observed that bringing the piles closer created somewhat grater movements (10%) than separating them, due to the interference between piles, which gave an idea as to the group effect.

The measurements carried out during the compression and traction tests, which were more detailed, supplied greater knowledge on the behaviour of the piles. In fact, in addition to knowing the settlement of the pile head, the distribution of the load throughout the pile shaft could be deduced as also the mobilization of the frictional resistance in terms of the pile settlement.

In Figure 6.a, there is a graph of the load applied versus settlement at the head of the pile for compression test number 1, and Figure 6.b shows the same graph corresponding to test number 2 (after having re-driven pile P-1).

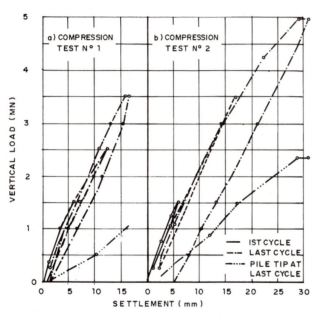

Fig. 6.- Relationship between load and settlement in the compression tests.

The quasi linear behaviour of the pile can be seen in both cases, though somewhat less in the re-driven pile: residual settlements of 14% as compared to 9% in compression test number 1.

Figure 7 shows the variation, throughout the pile, of compression loads in three load cycles in test number 2. These loads have been inferred on the basis of the measurements of the vibrating wire extensometers, with an elasticity modulus of 45.000 MN/m^2 for the concrete. This value was deduced from the extensometers located above the ground. In test number 1, before redriving the piles, it was approximately 10% higher.

Figures 8 and 9 have been deduced from all these measurements. The first shows the mobilized friction along the shaft, as a function of the settlement of the section being considered, and Figure 9 shows the variation of the maximum mobilized friction with the depth (greater than that assumed in the design). As can be deduced from these figures, the friction was completely mobilized in the upper half of the pile, whereas it appears that approximately 20% was not mobilized in the lower half. As illustrated in Figure 9, the unit friction measured was

practically linear with the depth.

A maximum of 45% of the external load applied reached the pile tip (last cycle of Test 2). The measurements carried out confirmed that resistance was not completely mobilized at the pile tip. Nevertheless, more load was not applied during the test for fear of the theoretic danger of buckling presented by P-1.

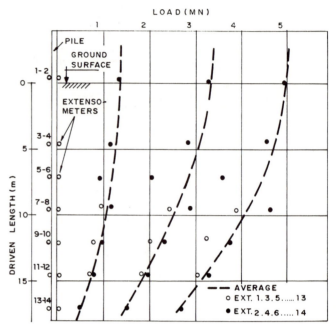

Fig. 7.- Compression load test Nº 2: load distribution with the depth.

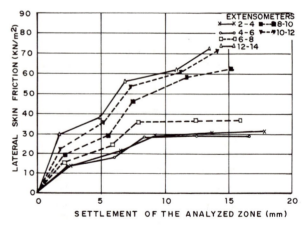

Fig. 8.- Lateral skin friction mobilized along the compression test Nº 2.

It should be pointed out that during the pull-out tests, the total resistance of the pile was mobilized in Test 2 (Figure 10), with an external load of 2,5 MN. The lateral skin friction measured on this occasion was somewhat less than that measured in traction test 1, due to the series of compression-traction cycles. Its distribution along the pile shaft (figure 11) was more uniform than in the compression test, showing an average value of approximately 33 KN/m^2, similar to the design assumption made for lateral skin friction under compression.

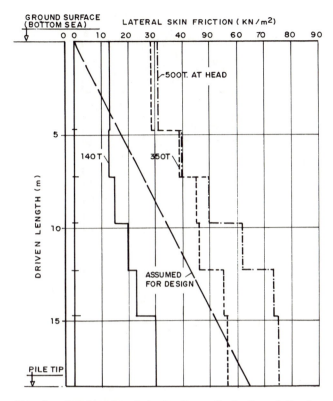

Fig. 9.- Relationship between the soil depth and the lateral skin friction for several loads at head (compression test № 2).

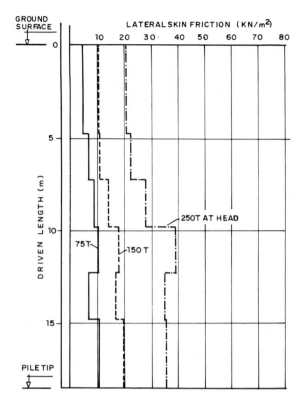

Fig. 11.- Relationship between the soil depth and the lateral skin friction in the pull-out test № 2.

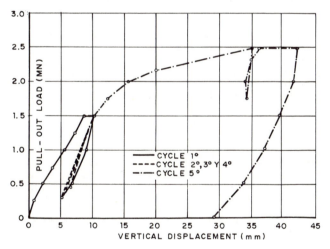

Fig. 10.- Pull-out test № 2: relationship between load and displacement.

ANALYSIS OF THE RESULTS

In order to interpret the results of the horizontal load tests the method proposed by Oteo (see reference) has been followed, the same approach was taken at the previous design stage. According to this method, piles can be simulated by equivalent prismatic beams fixed at some equivalent depth L' measured from the mud line. Since the behaviour of the piles on this load test has been quite li-

near , the desplacement at the top, δ , allows for the evaluation of L' (with a free standing length l):

$$L' = \sqrt[3]{\frac{3 \, \delta \, E_p \, I_p}{H}} - l$$

where H is the total load applied to the pile head, E, the pile material modulus and I_p is the moment of iner-tia af the pile cross section respect to a diameter.

Taking the values of $E_p = 45.000$ MN/m^2, as was obtained from the vertical load test and some laboratory test, the value of L' resulted on the order of 4.1 to 5,6 m for the different load steps and different piles tested. The com-pressibility of the soil can be derived from this length since, according to Oteo (1981).

$$L' = 1, 2 \, f \times \sqrt[4]{\frac{E_p \, I_p}{E_{sl}/3}}$$

where, E_{sl} is the modulus of the soil at the pile point and f is a coefficient related to E_{so}/E_{sl}, being E_{so} the soil modulus at the mud line (a linear increase with depth is assumed).

From laboratory tests it was expected that the ratio E_{so}/E_{sl} could change from 0,3 to 1 and the factor f could then be estimated on the order of 1,4 to 1,0. These last values allow an estimate for the range of modulus values.

The compressibility of the soil may as well be derived by interpreting vertical load test according to Poulos method (Poulos y Davis, 1980). For this method, the set-tlement of the pile head, w_c, is

$$w_c = \Delta L + \frac{P}{D E_s} I_o R_k R_h R_v$$

where, ΔL is the shortening of the free length of the pile, P is the total applied load, D is the external diameter of the pile, E_s is the average soil modulus and I_o, R_k, R_h and R_v are influence coefficients tabulated by Poulos that take into account the pile compressibility, its slenderness, the Poisson effect, etc.

For the total load of 3,5 MN (within the range of the linear behaviour) a modulus value $E_s = 33,7$ MN/m^2 would be obtained, this value being larger than that assumed at the design stage.

Figure 12 presents the variation of E_s versus depth that was assumed for design purposes (deduced from the interpretation of triaxial tests according to a hyperbolic model) and the range of values of E_s that are obtained from horizontal and vertical load tests. It can be seen that the average value of E_s obtained from field tests is 2 to 3 times larger than that assumed in design.

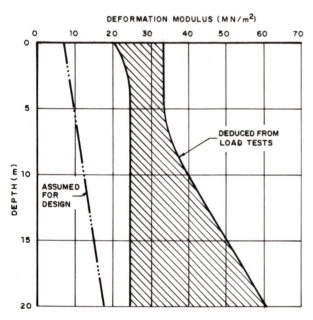

Fig. 12.- Comparison between assumed and deduced deformation moduli.

On the other hand, the unit skin friction was estimated as $f_s = \beta . \sigma'_v$. The API code suggests values of β in the range of 0.26 to 0.50 for the type of soils at this site. To evaluate ultimate vertical loads at the design stage a value of $\beta = 0,36$ was taken.

These values have been represented in Fig. 13 together with those derived from the interpretation of compression test n. 2 (the skin friction al the lowest part has been extrapolated). This figure shows that for the middle part of the shaft the tests values are somwhat larger than those assumed for design but within the range of the API recommendations while close to the pile point that recommendation is exceeded.

From the pull-out test 3 the value of this coefficients results somwhat lower (figure 13) probably due to the alternating character of the applied loads.

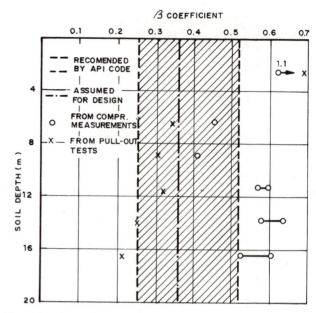

Fig. 13.- Comparison between measured and theoretical values of β coefficient.

CONCLUSIONS

On the basis of the information reported within this paper the following conclusions could be advanced.

- The compressibility of the soil as obtained from the interpretation of load tests (horizontal and vertical) is lower , by a factor of 2 to 3, than that obtained from interpretation of laboratory tests.

- The unit skin friction along the shaft estimated from compression tests is somewhat larger thant that recommend by the API Code for this type of soils, particularly close to the pile point. For the pull-out test with cyclic loading such a difference has not been observed.

- The mobilization of the skin resistence has been almost fully developed in the compression tests when the point resistance is still increasing. A larger load (displacement) is needed to reach the failure condition at the point than that needed to get that situation along the shaft.

ACKNOWLEDGEMENTS

The authors wish express their deep gratitude to Gibraltar-Intercar S.A. for the cooperation and permission to publish this information. Also the colaboration of the organizations and people involved in the load test Tecar, Dragados y Construcciones S.A., Entrecanales y Tavora and Laboratorio de Carreteras y Geotecnia is appreciated.

REFERENCES

Oteo, C. and Valerio, J. (1981). "A Simplified Analysis of Piles with Lateral Loads". Proc. X Int. Conf. on Soil Mech. and F.E. Stockholm, Vol. 1.

Poulos, H.G. and Davis, H. (1980). "Pile foundations analysis and design". John Willey Ed. N.Y.

Sanchez del Rio, J. and Bernal, A. (1984). "Stress-wave measurements on large Raymond-type piles". 2nd. Int. Conf. on the Application of Stress-wave Theory on piles. Stockholm, pp. 221-28.

Foundations for the rehabilitation of an ancient building

Fondations pour la réhabilitation d'un ancien bâtiment

F. MUZAS, Dr. Ingeniero C.C.P., Rodio, Madrid, Spain
F. MORENO-BARBERA, Dr. Arquitecto, Madrid, Spain
A. URIEL, Dr. Ingeniero C.C.P., Agromán, Madrid, Spain

SYSNOPSIS The problems are described in connection with a rehabilitation project of a 15th Century building in Burgos (Spain) involving the excavation of three basement levels below groundwater level and having to conserve several parts of the ancient building. An analysis is made of the different problems encountered. The solution finally adopted, at present being carried out, includes a perimeter retaining wall constructed just below two façade walls, by means of the soil freezing technique and the temporary underpinning of the interior walls by means of a reinforcing structure consisting of micropiles.

1 - INTRODUCTION

The "Casa del Cordón" Building is a fortified palace built in the city of Burgos (Spain) during the last years of the fifteenth Century. Its architectural construction corresponds to the transition between the Gothic and Renaissance styles.

Nowadays the building belongs to the "Caja de Ahorros Municipal of Burgos" which decided to rehabilitate it to instal the company's head offices. The projet includes the excavation of a cellar 11.5 m high, with three levels, to lodge a Conference Hall, safe box facilities for clients and underground parking.

The Fine Arts Authorities have given permission for the rehabilitation works of the Building but have imposed the condition that several parts of the palace must be conserved, such as two façades,the central cloister and a lateral arcade.

Fig. 1 shows the plant of the Building and the parts that must be conserved during the works. The total surface area is about 4,000 m2,70% corresponding to the palace and 30% to old houses, the grounds of which are incorporated into the palace building.

Fig. 2 shows a view of the Building corresponding to the façade onto Calvo Sotelo Square.

The walls of the palace are constructed of cut limestone blocks laying on a spread foundation 1.5 m wide, made of stone and lime mortar.The foundation depth is about 2.0 m from ground level.

2 - GROUND CONDITIONS

The geological soil profile of the ground is as follows:

i)   backfill, about 2.0 m deep;

ii)   gravel and sand down to 4.0 to 6.5 m depth;

iii)   silty-sandy clay lying 2.0 to 3.0 m thick in some zones;

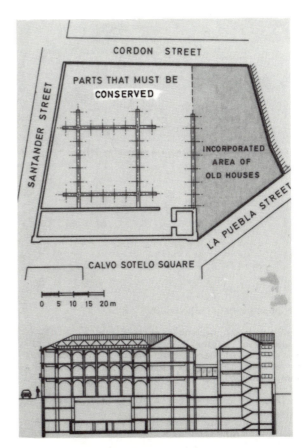

Fig. 1 - Plant of the "Casa del Cordón" and cross-section of the new Building.

iv) marl with gypsum lying from about 6.0 to 10.0 m depth downwards.

Fig. 2 - View of the "Casa del Cordón" Building

Fig. 3 shows the mean soil profile. The water table lies at about 2.5 m depth with a small gradient towards the Arlanzon River that flows parallel to the façade onto Calvo Sotelo Square and about 150 m away.

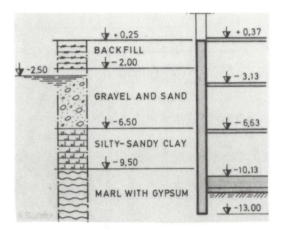

Fig. 3 - Mean geological soil profile and building underground levels.

3 - DESIGN PROBLEMS ENCOUNTERED

Due to the ground conditions, mainly the presence of ground water and the permeability of the gravel and sand layer, and also due to the above mentioned project characteristics, several problems arose.

These problems may be resumed as follows:

i) need of a water-proof screen surrounding the area to be excavated.

ii) need of a supporting structure to bear the ground and water thrusts.

iii) need to brace some parts of the ancient building, during the cellar excavation works, until the permanent supports were constructed.

iv) need to restrict as much as possible the movements of those structural parts of the palace that must be conserved in order to avoid damage during the works.

4 - SOLUTIONS ADOPTED

In order to solve the problems that have just been resumed, Rodio Company collaborated with the Project Manager Dr. of Architecture F. Moreno-Barberá.

The possibilities of several foundation techniques were analized to answer the requirements and to solve the problems. Subsequently, the solution adopted was as follows:

i) Temporary underpinning of all the structural elements that must be conserved inside the Building.

ii) Perimetric reinforced concrete wall, embedded in the marls, in order to create a resistant and water-proof enclosure, permitting the ground to be excavated inside this.

Initially, for this last purpose, a diaphragm wall, constructed by the slurry trench tecnique, was designed, sited along the perimeter line except along the façades to be conserved where the diaphragm wall was sited just inside. The solution could be carried out along all the perimeter line except in three separate zones located in the façades, where the machynery was not able to work. In those three zones the soil freezing technique was envisaged as a way to complete the perimeter wall. Finally, the need for space inside the cellar made it necessary to locate the perimeter wall just below the existing façades. So for all this zone of the building the soil freezing technique was adopted in order to construct a continous pier foundation, also serving as perimetric retaining wall.

5 - TEMPORARY UNDERPINNING CHARACTERISTICS

The purpose of the underpinning was to transfer the loads of the structural elements that must be conserved from the existing foundations to the ground below the cellar excavation bottom.

For this, the system designed was as follows:

i) The existing foundations had to be strengthened by two reinforced concrete beams (0.5 x 1.3 m) which had to be pressed over the spread foundations by means of stressed steel bolts, as indicated in Fig. 4 (2 steel bars 40 mm Ø every 2.0 m, stressed to 500 kN).

ii) The foundations had to be underpinned

with "Ropress" micropiles that have a steel pipe reinforcement, fitted with non-return grout valves in the lower part of the pipe, in order that the bonding to the ground could be created by grouting cement mixture at high pressure.

The micropiles were also to be fitted with an inner steel rod in order to preload the micropiles before they were bonded to the foundation beams. After that the rods were to be relieved and the pipe filled with cement mixture. Two types of micropiles, 250 and 450 kN allowable load, were designed, which had to be preloaded to 200 and 350 kN respectively.

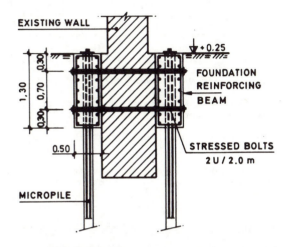

Fig. 4 - Foundation reinforcement and temporary underpinning.

6 - CONTINUOUS PIER FOUNDATION WITH SOIL FREEZING TECHNIQUE

As we mentioned above, to construct the perimeter retaining wall below the façades of the Building, it was decided to make adjacent piers by using the soil freezing technique.

First of all, it was considered advisable to strengthen the spread foundation of the walls by placing two reinforced concrete beams (0.40 x 1.50 m) in a similar way as described above for the temporary underpinning.

After that, the construction process was to be the following (see Figs. 5 and 6):

i)   In a first phase, 16 thick hollow cylinders of frozen soil were to be constructed, with the following characteristics:
   - inner Ø: 4.0 m to 4.5 m
   - thickness: approx. 1.0 m
   - distance between axes: 6.5 m. to 7.0 m approx.

ii)   Exacation was to be carried out inside the cylinders in alternate order and rectangular piers were to be concreted, 2.0 or 3.0 m long.

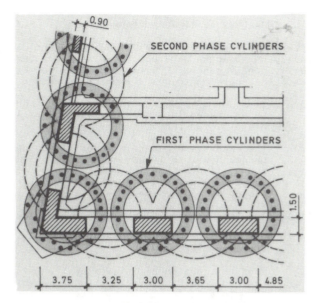

Fig. 5 - Plant of frozen soil cylinders and pier foundation panels.

iii) The cylinders were to be filled with properly compacted soil.

iv)   In a second phase, 15 intermediate cylinders of frozen soil were to be constructed (5.0 m inner Ø).

v)   Excavation was to be carried out inside the second phase cylinders and rectangular piers 4.0 or 4.5 m long were to be concreted, joined to those of the first phase.

vi)   The second phase cylinders were to be filled with properly compacted soil.

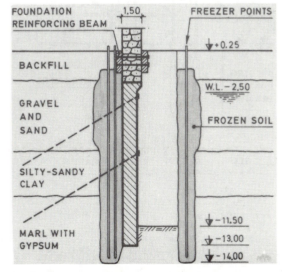

Fig. 6 - Section of a frozen soil cylinder and a pier foundation panel. Anchors are placed during general excavation.

7 – GENERAL EXCAVATION PROCEDURE

After the perimeter wall and the inside underpinning works were completed, as described above, the general excavation was to be executed according to the following procedure:

i) First of all the ancient structures had to be braced in order to obtain overall rigidity for them.

ii) The excavation had to progress in three phases down to levels -2.8 m, -6.5 m and -11.5 m placing two rows of temporary anchors grouted into the ground at -2.8 m and -6.5 m levels.

iii) As the excavation progresses the micropiles are to be conveniently braced each 2.0 m in order to create temporary supports (Fig. 7)

iv) When the bottom of the excavation is reached (-11.5 m level) the permanent structure is to be constructed and the micropiles then removed.

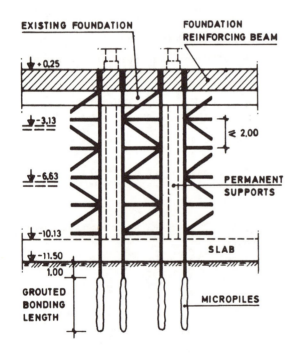

Fig. 7 – Temporary supporting structure made with micropiles during general excavation.

8 – CONSTRUCTION

The works for the rehabilitation of the "Casa del Cordon" Building began in June 1.983. They were contracted to Agroman Company associated with Rodio Company to perform the soil freezing works.

To date (june 1.984) the works of underpinning

and the perimeter retaining wall have been completed and the general excavation has just started. During the perimeter retaining wall construction the water table level rised about 50 cm.

For the construction of the pier foundation panels below the façades, using the frozen soil technique, two freezing plants were used, of 160,000 Kcal/h refrigerating power each.

Along the perimeter of each cylinder of frozen soil, about 24 freezer points were installed, approx. every 0.80 m, to freeze soil in about 1.0 m thickness. As cooling fluid, a terpene mix was used instead of brine.

Each cylinder of frozen soil took about 15 days to create. The soil temperatures and the frozen soil evolution was monitored by thermo-electric couples installed in the ground and automatically controlled by microcomputer.

Excavation inside the cylinders could be started when the temperature at the theoretical excavation boundary reached -5ºC.

The works for inner excavation, reinforcement, framework and concreting took about 25 to 30 days per cylinder. Fig. 8 shows the construction of a pier foundation panel inside a frozen cylinder.

During the works no relevant movements of the façades were observed nor any damage to same.

Fig. 8 – Construction of a pier foundation panel inside a frozen soil cylinder.

9 – CONCLUSION

The case history reported here indicates that the frozen soil technique may be used for building underpinning works, at least in similar cases where the configuration of the fabrics and foundations, (conveniently reinforced when necessary) prevents heaving risk.

Horizontal load tests on files of large diameter bored piles

Essais de chargement horizontal sur files des pieux moulés

H. G. SCHMIDT, Bilfinger + Berger Bauaktiengesellschaft, Mannheim, FRG

SYNOPSIS   Piers for bridges are often founded on large diameter bored piles arranged in a single file. German codes of practice differ as to the group efficiency under lateral load. Some large-scale horizontal load tests were run, each on two or three piles simultaneously, situated one behind the other. The loading device as well as the test programme are described, and the load bearing behaviour of the test piles is discussed. Additional investigations are suggested.

INTRODUCTION

In the Federal Republic of Germany, piers for road or railway bridges are often founded on a single file of large diameter bored piles, see fig. 1. If pile groups are subjected to lateral loads, German Standard DIN 4014 Teil 2 yields that the modulus of horizontal subsoil reaction k_s must be reduced as a function of the interspace, and that to the same degree for each pile of the group, whereas the code of practice EBK recommends reductions that differ from pile to pile, depending on its position within the group, see fig. 2. There are no special rules for single files of piles.

The group action of laterally loaded piles has been investigated mostly by model tests and/or analyses, hence involving always some doubts as to their relevance for the prototype. Large-scale tests are scarce, yielding very often only the behaviour of the pile group related to that of a single pile, and results of load distribution and pile-soil interaction are missing. For this reason, some tests were run on files of two or three free-headed, large diameter bored piles located one behind the other.

HORIZONTAL LOAD TESTS

To facilitate the test procedure, a new loading device was designed (Schmidt 1981), see fig. 3. It may be

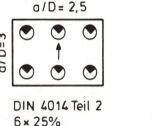

Fig. 2 German codes of practice concerning group action under horizontal load

adapted to pile diameters ranging from D = 0.9 m to 1.5 m, and to any distance of the test piles. Total loads up to 1.0 MN may be applied. The tensile rods are stressed by two double-acting hydraulic jacks, which are supported by working piles or by two sections of a pile casing embedded in the soil. The load is transferred to steel beams and induced in the test piles by two more hydraulic jacks, acting as load cells, and which may be used to correct the pile distance during the test, if necessary.

This paper concentrates on a test series run on 7 piles with lengths L = 8.5 metres and diameters D = 1.2 metres, embedded in uniform, medium dense sand above the ground water level. Two piles were constructed with a casing, 3 piles using a bentonite slurry, and for two piles the boreholes were excavated using a casing, but were filled with bentonite slurry for 7 hours before concreting. Three groups were tested: C 2/2, B 3/2.2, and CB 2/3. The letter denotes the construction procedure, the first number the number of piles, and the second number the pile spacing, related to the pile diameter. The following test procedure was adopted for each group:

(1) Maintained load test of the pile group, 5 increments for both loading and unloading;
(2) cyclic loading of the pile group, 10 cycles;
(3) reloading and unloading of the pile group by steps as described above;
(4) reloading and unloading of the individual piles one after the other by steps as described above.

Fig. 1 Typical bridge piers founded on a single file of large diameter bored piles

Fig. 3 Loading device for two-pile files

The measuring device was described by Nowack and Gartung (1983).

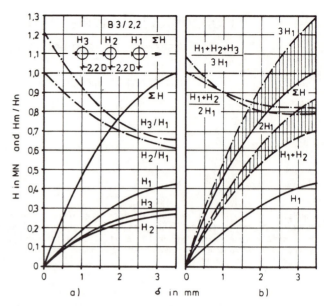

Fig. 5 Results of horizontal load test on three-pile file

TEST RESULTS

The test results proved the suppositions derived from the behaviour of single piles (Schmidt 1981).

Effect of interspace

The test results for the groups C 2/2 and CB 2/3 are plotted in fig. 4, showing that the load bearing behaviours of the piles with a distance a = 3 D are almost identical, whereas in the group C 2/2 with a distance a = 2 D the bearing capacity of the rear pile differs from that of the front pile more and more with increasing load and displacement, respectively. Results of incremental reloading corroborate that three of the four piles show the same behaviour as part of the group and as single piles, except the rear pile of group C 2/2. From these results may be concluded that the front piles of the files behave as single piles, and that the bearing capacity of pile files is not reduced by group action, if the pile distance equals or exceeds 3 pile diameters.

Load distribution

File no. B 3/2.2 consisted of 3 piles, see fig. 5 a). The load-deflection-curves of piles no. 2 and no. 3 coincide, but differ from that of the front pile. This pattern of the load distribution indicates that the behaviour of the center pile is influenced by the movement of the front pile, but not in addition by the

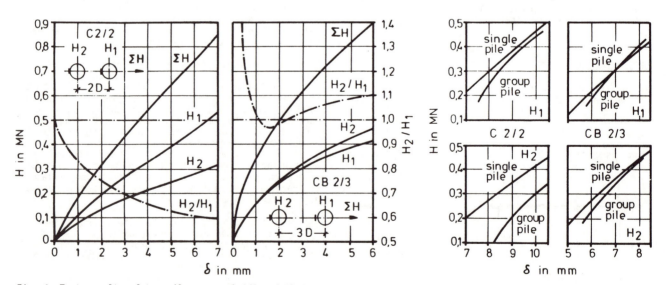

Fig. 4 Test results of two-pile groups C 2/2 and CB 2/3

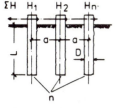

c = cohesive soil
n = non-cohesive soil

no	n	D	L	a/D	Soil type
-	-	m	m	-	-
1	2	1,0	5,0	2,0	n
2	2	1,2	8,5	2,0	n
3	2	1,35	8,5	2,2	n
4	2	1,2	8,5	3,0	n
5	3	1,35	8,5	2,2	n
6	2	1,2	12,5	4,0	c, n
7	2	1,2	28,0	2,4	c, n
8	2	1,2	16,0	1,33	c
9	2	1,5	25,0	1,67	c

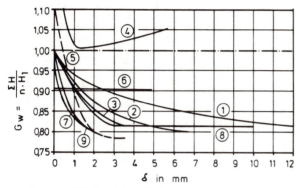

Fig. 6 Group efficiencies of laterally loaded pile files

displacement of the rear pile. This fact is in good agreement with suppositions made before (Schmidt 1981), and corroborates the above statement, that the front pile behaves as a single pile. Hence, piles no. 1 and no. 2 may be considered as a 2-pile file, and group efficiency may be evaluated by relating the bea-

ring capacity of any pile file to that of the front pile, see fig. 5 b).

Group efficiency

In this way, the group efficiencies of all the pile files tested were evaluated and plotted in fig. 6. Files no. 4 and no. 6 with piles spaced at three or more pile diameters showed no group effect. Differential behaviour of the piles in file no. 6 resulting in Gw = 0.9 is due to non-homogeneous soil conditions, as it is often measured in tests on identical single piles. The curve for file no. 5 starts at Gw = 1.1, as the rear pile initially showed a better bearing behaviour than the front pile. Some differences in the geometries of the pile shafts were to be expected due to the production procedure (see above), affecting the behaviour under small loads. All the results yield that the group efficiency decreases with increasing displacements (and loads), down to values of Gw 0.75-0.8 for the two-pile files. As test conditions differ, definite rules concerning the effect of the interspace or of the load on the group efficiency may not yet be derived from these results.

Bearing behaviour

In a number of tests, the bending moments of the pile shafts were measured, and the moduli of horizontal subsoil reaction were evaluated from the test results. The bending moments measured on the pile file C 2/2 are plotted in fig. 7, showing that the depth of the maximum bending moment does not vary very much with increasing loads. In spite of the fact, that the horizontal loads carried by piles no. 1 and no. 2 differ more and more with increasing load, the bending moments of both piles are approximately equal. Cyclic loading affects the bending moments of the rear pile to a greater degree than those of the front pile. In the lower section of the pile shafts, the residual moments after unloading are noteworthy. Measurement results corroborated the rule of thumb, saying that cracking of the concrete starts, if the tensile stresses exceed some 3 MN/m², and by this effect, the stiffness of the pile shafts was reduced to fifty percent of the initial value.

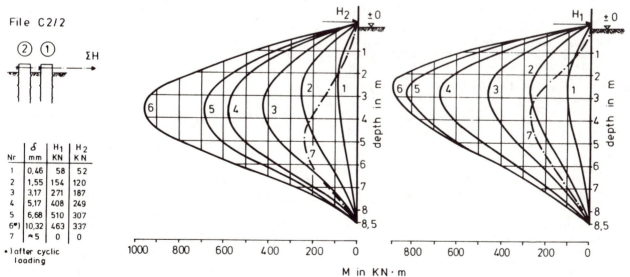

File C2/2

Nr	δ mm	H₁ KN	H₂ KN
1	0,46	58	52
2	1,55	154	120
3	3,17	271	187
4	5,17	408	249
5	6,68	510	307
6*)	10,32	463	337
7	≈5	0	0

*) after cyclic loading

Fig. 7 Bending moments measured on file C 2/2

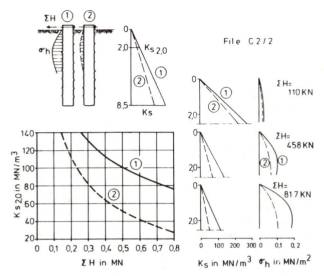

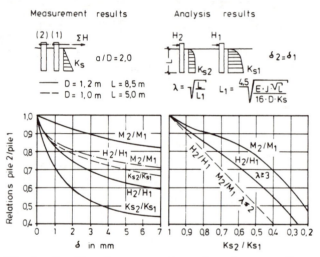

Fig. 8 Moduli of horizontal subsoil reaction and contact pressures evaluated for file C 2/2

Moduli of horizontal subgrade reaction were evaluated from the measurement results, see fig. 8. The common statement that the reaction modulus increases proportionally to the depth below the soil surface was proved. Various patterns were tried, yielding that good agreement was achieved in any case, if the values coincided approximately from the soil surface down to a depth of some two metres, whereas the values at the pile base showed ratios up to 6:1. As different patterns for the increase of the reaction modulus with depth are in common use in Germany, it is felt that the modulus of horizontal subsoil reaction should be defined at a depth of approximately two meters, see fig. 8. The investigations yielded that the maximum value of the contact pressures, too, was located approximately at that depth, for all the piles tested. Once more, the results illustrate the effects of group action on the modulus of horizontal subsoil reaction, and hence on the contact pressures.

Apparently, the displacement of the front pile reduces the soil resistance for the rear pile in the upper region, and this pile tranfers a greater part of its load to lower sections, resulting in higher bending moments. Therefore, the ratio of loads carried is improved compared with that of the soil resistances, and bending moments are approximately equal, see fig. 9. Short piles behave in a different way. Comparing the bearing behaviour of the front pile with that of the rear pile in the two-pile group no. 1 in fig. 6 yielded that for approximately rigid piles the relations of the loads carried, of the bending moments, and of the soil moduli are almost equal.

"Induced displacements"

In a two-pile file, group efficiency is governed by the bearing behaviour of the rear pile, which is affected by the displacements of the front pile. It was felt, therefore, that on the other hand displacements induced in the front pile by loading the rear pile alone could be a means to judge group efficiency. Test results proved that such "induced settlements" indicate reliably, whether group action is to be expected or not. But there was no definite relation between group efficiency and the induced displacements, see fig. 10,

maybe due to the fact, that group efficiency was evaluated from the initial loading of the whole file, whereas the induced displacements were measured in the final reloading of the individual piles.

Effect of cyclic loading

File CB 2/3 was subjected to four cyclic loadings, see fig. 11. In each case, the number of cycles amounted to n = 10, and the loads applied ranged from some 150 kN per pile to some 450 kN per pile. Keeping the initial distance of the piles constant resulted in the fact, that the displacements and the total loads of the pile group differed to a small degree for each cycle. Hence, those loads were evaluated, that would have induced constant displacements. The results show that unloading and reloading did not affect the displacements up to a definite amount of the horizontal load, and that the ten cycles applied were not sufficient to reach stable, quasi-elastic conditions under higher loads. Results of files C 2/2 and B 3/2.2 yielded that the load distribution may be influenced by cyclic loading, but results do not allow for definite conclusions.

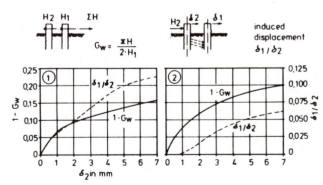

Fig. 9 Results of measurements and analyses on the effect of pile stiffness on the load bearing behaviour of pile files

Fig. 10 Relation between group efficiency and ratio of induced displacement

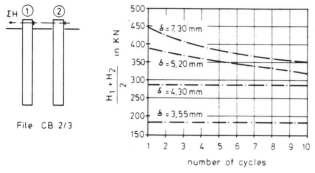

Fig. 11 Results of cyclic load tests run on file CB 2/3

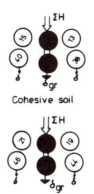

Cohesive soil

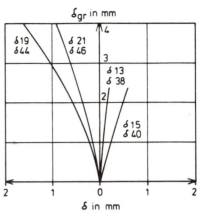

Fig. 13 Displacements of unloaded piles beside a laterally loaded pile file

Effect of bentonite slurry

It is often suspected that the bearing behaviour under horizontal loads is deteriorated, if bentonite slurry is used for the pile construction. The test series reported in this paper yielded the opposite result. Using bentonite slurry instead of a casing resulted in an enlarged pile diameter and hence improved the bearing behaviour, and even for piles showing the same diameter (file C compared with file CB, see above), those constructed with a slurry showed improved bearing behaviour under small loads. It is to be supposed that the sand above the ground water table was cemented to a short distance around the pile, and that the bentonite cake might have reacted with the pile concrete.

PILE-SOIL INTERACTION

Pile-soil interaction in a pile file is not yet fully understood. Two simplified models are plotted in fig. 12. As the soil in between the two piles is compressed, whereas the pile distance remains unchanged, a joint will develop around the backside of the front pile in the upper region. Hence, stresses transferred to the soil from the rear pile must be "diverted", resulting in a more intense compression of the soil, thus reducing the modulus of reaction. Shearing resistance along a soil slice between the piles may be supposed to govern the pile-soil interaction. In non-cohesive soils it depends on the lateral pressure, which might vary from earth pressure at rest to passive pressure. Substantially, these models are corroborated by the results of two tests, see fig. 13, showing the displacements of piles situated beside two test files

(see no. 9 in fig. 6). Additional investigations are necessary on this subject, and it is felt that the FE method would be a powerful tool. It may be concluded as well, that pile-soil interaction in groups consisting of a definite number of pile files is more complicated, resulting in a smaller group efficiency than measured on pile files.

CONCLUSIONS

The behaviour of the pile files tested may be characterised as follows: Group action vanished at pile distances equal to or greater than three pile diameters; in pile files with smaller distances, the front pile behaved as a single pile, and group efficiency was governed by the bearing capacity losses of the rear piles, which were equal for each pile in a file; for long piles, bending moments were approximately the same for all the piles of the file, in spite of different load ratios of the front pile and of the rear piles, respectively; bentonite slurry did not deteriorate the horizontal bearing behaviour, and displacements induced in an unloaded, neighbouring pile indicated that group action must be taken into account. Additional investigations on the group action of pile groups that consist of a number of pile files are necessary.

REFERENCES

Nowack, F. and Gartung, E. (1983). Messungen bei Probebelastungen vertikal und horizontal belasteter Großbohrpfähle. Geotechnik (1), 1-10, Deutsche Gesellschaft für Erd- und Grundbau e. V. Essen.

Schmidt, H. G. (1981). Group action of laterally loaded bored piles. Proc. 10th ICSMFE, (2), 833-837, Stockholm.

Schmidt, H. G. (1977). Horizontale Belastbarkeit lotrechter Großbohrpfähle. Proc. Pfahlsymposium München 1977, 127-134, Deutsche Gesellschaft für Erd- und Grundbau e. V. Essen.

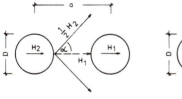
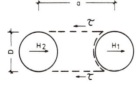

Fig. 12 Simple models for pile-soil interaction in pile files

Pier foundations of the Saudi Arabia – Bahrain causeway

Les fondations sur puits de la route sur digue entre Arabie Saoudite et Bahrain

J. Y. TONNISEN, Chief Design Engineer, Ballast Nedam Group NV, Amstelveen, Netherlands
E. J. DEN HAAN, Project Engineer, Delft Soil Mechanics Laboratory, Delft, Netherlands
H. J. LUGER, Project Engineer, Delft Soil Mechanics Laboratory, Delft, Netherlands
M. J. D. DOBIE, Manager, Delft Geotechnics (UK) Ltd, Singapore Branch, Singapore

SYNOPSIS   Of the total 25 km of the Saudi Arabia - Bahrain Causeway, 11.5 km consists of bridges supported on piers embedded directly into the bedrock. This paper describes the geology, site investigation for these piers and correlations between various soil parameters. Comparisons are presented between predicted vertical and horizontal pier deflections and the results from loading tests.

INTRODUCTION

The Saudi Arabia - Bahrain Causeway, presently nearing completion, provides a 25 km link across the Gulf of Salwa between the island of Bahrain and the mainland of Saudi Arabia. The Causeway consists of five bridges with a total length of 12.5 km and seven sandfill embankments. The island of Umm Nasan is included in the alignment as shown on figure 1.

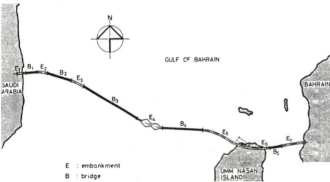

Figure 1 Location of Saudi Arabia - Bahrain Causeway

Four of the five bridges are founded on 3.5 m diameter hollow prestressed concrete cylinders, which form both the foundation pile and pier shaft in a single element. These piles are grouted into predrilled holes in the weak Tertiary bedrock as indicated on figure 2. The bridge closest to Bahrain is founded on caissons to avoid penetrating one of Bahrain's fresh water aquifers.

In this paper various geotechnical aspects of the pier foundations are described, with emphasis on the methods used to predict pile performance and comparison with actual behaviour.

GEOLOGY

Over the whole length of the Causeway superficial Quaternary layers overlie Tertiary bedrock. The bedrock consists almost entirely of Miocene and Pliocene argillaceous carbonate rocks. A cyclothemic sequence of deposition is evident with repeated cycles of claystones, siltstones and sandstones, and frequent brecciated contact zones. The layers are almost horizontally bedded with maximum dips of about 3°. Weathering of the bedrock is associated with exposure of the present day upper surface during the late Pleistocene. Leaching, dolomisation and dessication occurred, combined with subsequent submer-

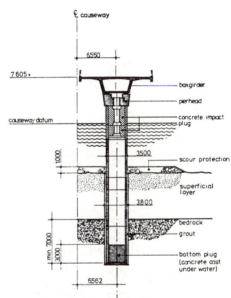

Figure 2 Typical Pier Foundation

gence, and have resulted in colour changes and reduction in strength of the usually weak claystones and siltstones to soil consistencies in the upper few metres.

The Quaternary layers form a veneer of superficial deposits, from 0 to 12 m thick, on top of the bedrock. They consist mainly of carbonate and quartz sands, and are cemented in places to form limestones and sandstones. A layer of caprock is present on the seabed in most places.

SITE INVESTIGATION

Two jack-up platforms were used to drill boreholes at every pier location. The boreholes were advanced by light cable percussive methods in the superficial layers and wireline triple tube rotary core drilling in the bedrock. With a pier every 50 m along the bridges this resulted in more than 10 km of borings. Unconfined compression tests were carried out on specimens of borehole core on the drilling platforms. On average one test was carried out every 2 m. SPT's were executed both in the sand using a split spoon and in the bedrock using a solid cone. The frequency of these tests was every 1.5 m or 3.0 m depending on ground conditions.

In the laboratory uniaxial unconfined, quick undrained triaxial and consolidated undrained triaxial compression tests were carried out. In addition classification tests such as water content, density, particle size distribution and Atterberg limits were executed.

At approximately 25% of pier locations Ménard pressuremeter tests were carried out in a separate borehole. In the superficial sands, an AX probe with a protective slotted casing was driven into the soil or placed in a predrilled hole. For the bedrock a BX probe was used with a laminated steel sheath. Altogether 810 pressuremeter tests were carried out.

SOIL PARAMETER CORRELATIONS

To assist in establishing complete profiles of stiffness and strength at each pier location, an extensive correlation study of various measured soil properties was undertaken. Figure 3 summarises the particle size distribution for the Tertiary bedrock. Silt is clearly predominant.

symbols : ▲ PI : 0 to 9
          x PI : 10 to 24
          ● PI : 25 and greater
numeral at symbol indicates % gravel

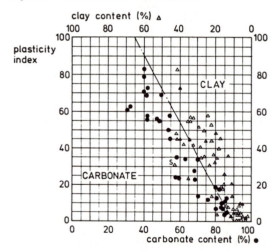

Figure 3   Particle size distribution

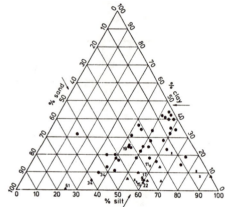

Figure 4   Clay-carbonate phase diagram

The relationship of carbonate content and clay content to plasticity index (PI) is summarised on figure 4. This represents a simple phase diagram which indicates that silt sizes and larger consist mainly of carbonate. The predominant carbonate mineral is dolomite. From the point of view of plasticity, most test results fall on or

just below the A - line reflecting the high silt content. In logging the boreholes, distinction was made between claystone (PI>25), siltstone (PI<25) and sandstone (non-plastic).

Correlations between mechanical properties (such as E_p, Q_c and N) were also established. As an example figure 5 shows the relationship between E_p and Q_c taking into account ranges of PI. This correlation was based on tests in adjacent boreholes carried out at similar depths. A detailed study of these correlations is given by Tonnisen and Dobie (1985).

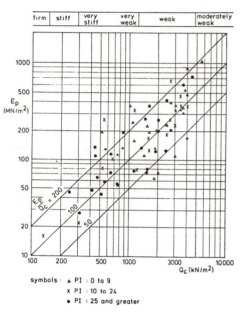

symbols : ▲ PI : 0 to 9
          x PI : 10 to 24
          ● PI : 25 and greater

Figure 5   Modulus (E_p) versus strength (Q_c)

BEARING CAPACITY OF PIERS

Existing bearing capacity theories for foundations subjected to inclined and eccentric loads are not valid for the pier, due to the fact that the rotation centre lies well above the base. It was therefore decided to use the stress-characteristics method. This method works well in a cohesive soil in undrained conditions (ϕ=0) and it is considered that the bedrock can be treated in this manner.

The stress-characteristics method yields a lower bound value of the bearing capacity. That is, if for a given external load a stress field can be found which can support the load, then the failure load is higher than or equal to this load. The stress field is governed by two conditions, one consisting of the equilibrium equations, the other being the Mohr-Coulomb failure criterion. Combination of the two sets of equations yields a pair of hyperbolic differential equations, which can be solved by integration along lines in characteristic directions. The design loads (earthquake loading is most important in this respect due to the relatively large horizontal force and moment) are applied to the pier at the level of the bedrock surface. These loads are then multiplied by a factor. The highest value of this factor for which a stress field can be constructed that results in equilibrium of the pier will never be greater than the actual safety factor for the assumed conditions. A computer program PILE was developed to find the maximum value of the multiplication factor.

Figure 6 shows a result of the method. It was established that ample bearing capacity is present for an L/D ratio of 2 if C_u>400 kPa. The site investigation showed that this soil strength is usually present in this bed-rock.

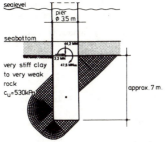

Figure 6   Result of stress-characteristics method

LATERAL DEFLECTIONS

The specification for the piers required that the maximum lateral deflection at the top of the pier should be 40 mm. To check the lateral deflections, a simple pocket calculator program RIGID was developed. RIGID is based on a paper by Vallabhan and Alikhanlou (1982) and models the pier as a rigid body with 3 degrees of freedom: horizontal and vertical displacement, and rotation. The pier-soil interaction is modelled by a number of linearly elastic springs as shown in figure 7.

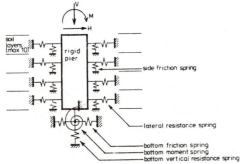

Figure 7   Spring constant model

The different springs in RIGID model lateral soil resistance, shaft friction, bottom vertical and moment resistance and bottom friction. The lateral spring constants k_h are derived from the Menard pressuremeter modulus E_p:

$$k_h = 3E_p/\{0.4 (4.417 D)^\alpha + 0.5\alpha D\} \quad [MN^{-3}] \quad (1)$$

where α is an empirical factor.

The shaft friction spring constant, denoted by k_s, describes the development of shaft friction for increasing relative shaft-soil displacement. From an early vertical load test, a value $k_s= 66$ MN/m³ was derived for the bedrock, and as correlations of k_s with stiffness or strength parameters were not found in existing literature, k_s was assumed constant. The bottom spring constants are based on elastic solutions for vertical, moment and shear loading of an embedded plate. Once again, E_p is the input parameter. However, the empirical factor α, also included in equation (1), relates Youngs modulus of the soil to the pressuremeter modulus: $E= E_p/\alpha$.

An early horizontal load test was conducted at a site devoid of Quaternary sand, and an excellent fit between the measured lateral deflections and those calculated by RIGID was obtained for $\alpha= 0.5$. This value was then assumed in the bedrock at all sites. From comparison of RIGID and another early load test where 4 m of medium-dense sandcover was present, it appeared that in the sand $E_p \cong 7$ MPa at the sea bottom increasing with about 0.6 MPa for each metre of depth. In the sand $\alpha= 1/3$ was assumed.

Predicted and measured horizontal pier top displacements

are given in table I for the load tests completed up to July 1984.

TABLE I
Predicted and measured horizontal pier deflection

Test pier	Horizontal load kN	Socket length m	Horizontal pier top deflection (mm)	
			predicted	measured
3-96-1	1000	11.0	5.4	10.7
3-96-3	1000	6.5	9.1	10.0
3-64	900	7.7	15.9	15.9
3-10	1000	9.3	12.3	13.4

At test pier 3-96-1, the large socket length resulted in much too small a predicted displacement due to the assumption of the pier being rigid over its full socketed length. Thus it is necessary to limit the use of RIGID to piles with small L/D ratio. Figure 8 shows deflection measurements of pier 3-64S and the prediction made using RIGID.

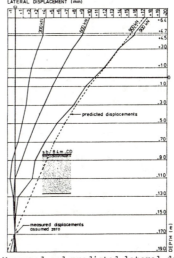

Figure 8   Measured and predicted lateral deflections load test 3-64S

The measurements were made using an optical inclinometer system in which a light source is lowered down a duct cast into the pile. The position of the light source is measured by theodolite and is accurate to within 1 mm over a 20 m pile length.

PIER SETTLEMENTS

Three 20 MN vertical load tests were conducted to check pier settlements. Vibrating wire strain gauges were cast in the piers at 3 different levels (4 gauges at each level) to determine the distribution of the load over the shaft. A prediction of the first load test using a elastic solutions for rock-socketed piles (Donald, Sloan and Chiu in Pells, 1980) was found to be pessimistic, even though the Youngs modulus was obtained from pressuremeter tests using $E = E_p/\alpha$ with $\alpha= 0.5$.

Better predictions for the remaining load tests were obtained by a load transfer method. The pier is divided into several elements over its socketed length and springs model pile stiffness, shaft adhesion and bottom resistance. Figure 9 gives the method for 3 elements, which can easily be extended to a larger number.

Assuming a value for F_1, the equations are solved one by one, at last finding F. This process is continued for other values of F_1 until the resulting value of F equals the applied load. The deformations of the various springs are then summed (C_1 to C_4) to find the pier settlement at the rock surface.

For a system of 3 elements, the system equations are

$$F_1(C_1 + \tfrac{1}{4}C_2 + c_2) + F_2(\tfrac{1}{4}C_2 - c_2) = 0$$

$$F_1(C_1 + \tfrac{1}{4}C_2) + F_2(\tfrac{1}{4}C_2 + \tfrac{1}{4}C_3 + c_3) + F_3(\tfrac{1}{4}C_3 - c_3) = 0$$

$$F_1(C_1 + \tfrac{1}{4}C_2) + F_2(\tfrac{1}{4}C_2 + \tfrac{1}{4}C_3) + F_3(\tfrac{1}{4}C_3 + \tfrac{1}{4}C_4 + c_4) + F(\tfrac{1}{4}C_4 - c_4) = 0$$

where

$$c_1 = 1/k_v A$$

$$c_{2-4} = 1/E_{pier} A$$

$$c_{2-4} = 1/k_s \pi D l$$

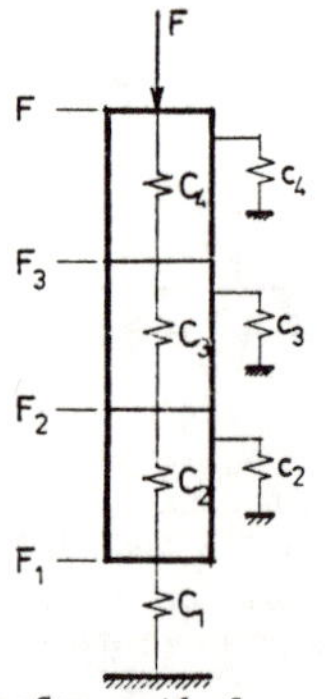

Figure 9 Load transfer method

Values of k_v and k_s were obtained from the first load test, using the load transfer method in reverse order. Extremely linear stress-strain relations were found for both shaft friction in the bedrock, and the bottom resistance: k_s= 66 MN/m³, k_v= 440 MN/m³. In the sand deposit, k_s= 7.8 MN/m³ at the design load of 16 MN. The side friction spring constants for the 2 predictions were established rather arbitrarily, taking the results of the first load test into account. The bottom spring constants were assumed equal. Table II summarises the predictions and measurements, showing the load transfer method to be a useful tool for settlement calculations of rock socketed piles.

TABLE II

Predicted and measured vertical pier deflections

Pier no.	Max. settlement of pile top (mm)			$F_{base} : F_{applied}$		
	measured	elastic solution	Load transfer method	measured	elastic solution	Load transfer method
4-10S	4.2	7.5	*	40%	34%	*
3-13S	4.4	8.0	3.6	20%	30%	23%
3-96-3	4.8	7.5	4.6	56%	32%	41%

*The load transfer method was used in reverse order to establish the friction spring constants for the remaining tests.

After the tests, a tentative correlation was established from the shaft friction measurements:

$$k_s/E_p = 0.62 - 0.16 \log_{10} E_p \qquad [m^{-1}] \qquad (3)$$

where E_p is in MPa.

CONCLUSIONS

(1) From the results of the many insitu and laboratory tests carried out, correlations were established between various physical and mechanical soil and rock properties to assist in establishing profiles of strength and modulus at each pier location.

(2) The assumption of linear deformation behaviour within the working stress range for the Tertiary bedrock was justified by full scale loading tests.

(3) Simple spring models were found to be suitable for predicting both lateral and vertical pier deforma-

tions. However for larger pier embedment, the assumption of a rigid element for the pier resulted in underestimation of lateral deflection.

(4) The factor α relating measured pressuremeter modulus to real soil modulus was found to be approximately 0.5.

ACKNOWLEDGEMENTS

Apart from the authors, K.W. Talsma and A.H. Rol, both of Delft Soil Mechanics Laboratory, contributed significantly to the work described in this paper.

SYMBOLS

PI   plasticity index

Q_c unconfined compressive strength (MPa)

C_u undrained shear strength (MPa)

N   S.P.T blowcount

E_p pressuremeter modulus (MPa)

E   Youngs modulus (MPa)

α empirical factor $E = E_p/\alpha$

k_h, k_s, k_v lateral, shaft friction and bottom bedding values (MNm^{-3})

C, c spring compliance (MN^{-1}m)

D   pier diameter (m)

L   socket length (m)

REFERENCES

Pells, P.J.N. (1980) (editor) Structural foundations on rock. Proc. Int. Conf on Structural foundations on rock, Sydney, 7-9 May 1980. A.A. Balkema, Rotterdam.

Vallabhan, C.V.G. and Alikhanlou, F. (1982) Short rigid piers in clays. Journal of the Geotechnical Engineering Division, ASCE, vol 108, no GT10. pp 1255-1272.

Tonnisen, J.Y. and Dobie, M.J.D. (1985) Geotechnical aspects of 3.5 m diameter drilled piles for the Saudi Arabia - Bahrain Causeway. Proceedings 8th South East Asian Geotechnical Conference, Kuala Lumpur.

Session 4C
Piles and other deep foundations
C. Foundations for offshore structures

Séance 4C
Pieux et autres fondations profondes
C. Fondations pour les structures 'offshore'

Remarks on instrumented driving for offshore platform piles

Notes sur le battage instrumenté des pieux pour plateformes offshore

L. F. ALBERT, Studio Geotecnico Italiano, Milan, Italy
G. F. ROCCHI, Studio Geotecnico Italiano, Milan, Italy
D. VARISCO, Tecon, Milan, Italy
P. VERONELLI, Interconsult, Milan, Italy

SYNOPSIS   The writers have been in charge of the design and assistance during installation of three large off-shore platforms at Campos basin, Brazil. The Owner has requested the execution of instrumented driving. Possible effects of static weight and residual stresses are discussed. Interpretation of experimental results is continued in terms of average gradient of soil adhesion with depth.

1. GENERAL

The writers have been in charge of the design and assistance during installation of three large off-shore platforms already completed at Campos Basin, Brazil. Main characteristics of the platforms are given in Table I.

Considering the very high required pile resistances (P_{lim}) in all cases the Owner (PETROBRAS) accepted the suggestion advanced by the Designers and carried out some instrumented driving, in order to check some basic assumptions and obtain parameters for future projects. Instrumented drivings have been monitored by three different Contractors, although in all cases experimental data have been interpreted by means of CAPWAP, to asses the total pile capacity at the time of driving and its distribution along the shaft and at the base; obtained results have kindly been forwarded to the writers.

Soil conditions are generally characterized by a covering layer of calcareous sand about 10 to 30 m thick, followed by very thick deposits of very likely normally consolidated silty clay or clayey silt with granular interlayers; Fig.1 shows schematically the distribution of static point resistance (q_c) with depth and some of the plasticity characteristics of cohesive layers.

Pile points at final penetrations at Garoupa and Enchova platforms were located within sandy layers. As already reported in the literature [Dahlberg and De Matos (1983), Dahlberg (1983), De Matos and De Mello (1982)] once the piles passed through the covering layer sometimes slightly cemented, very large initial penetrations under the effect of pile self-weight have been observed (see table I, P_{in}).

In the following paragraphs some of the experiences gained from these and similar cases history will be discussed.

2. INFLUENCE OF STATIC WEIGHT OF PILE AND HAMMER IN THE DEFINITION OF PILE LIMIT CAPACITY

The influence of the static weight has been neglected in all quoted cases, and endeed it seems to be so for all cases reported in the literature. If this is not important in on-shore conditions, for the off-shore environment such approach leads to an underestimation of soil limit bearing capacity.

Let us consider (as actually occurred for the three platforms under discussion) that the pile has reached a large initial penetration under own weight, because of the presence of normally consolidated, cohesive (soft) materials near sea bottom. Before actual driving is started, very long (and heavy) "followers" are placed on top of pile head, together with the hammer. Also if an underwater hammer is used (as it was at Cherne platform), the static (submerged) weight of the part of the pile above sea bottom and of the hammer may very well be of 3 to 5 MN. During the life of the platform they will obviously be removed and the

TABLE I   Platforms and piles characteristics

PLAT-FORM	WATER DEPTH (m)	PAY LOAD (MN)	JACKET WEIGHT (MN)	PILES WITH INTER. SHOE					P_{in} (m)
				N (-)	D (in)	P_{lim} (MN)	P (m)		
GAROUPA	120	162	72.2	36	48	20.3	85		≅50
ENCHOVA	116	216	144.4	32	66	34.8	75-89		59
CHERNE	142	216	163.6	24	72	45.4	80-110		45÷67

N = number of piles;   D = pile diameter
P = design penetration; P_{in} = initial penetration

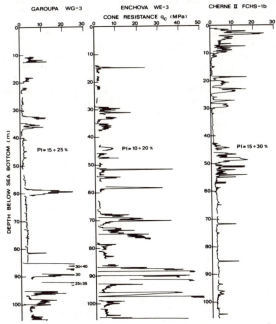

Fig.1   Soil Profiles at Campos Basin, Brazil

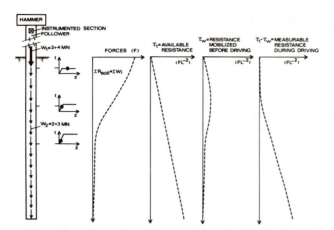

Fig.2 Influence of Static Weight on Pile Resistance to be Measured during Driving

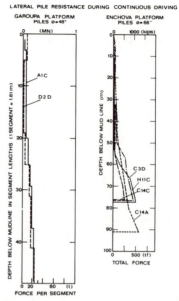

Fig.3 Results from CAPWAP Analyses as Given in Original Reports by Contractors

weight of the part of the pile above sea bottom will be considered as "external" load.
If one looks at the static equilibrium of the part of the pile already into the soil (simply calculated for example by means of the t-z approach), in the case of linear increase of pile-soil adhesion with depth (typical of a normally consolidated soil) the distribution of forces and mobilized soil resistances shown by Fig.2 is obtained.
At the limit, if the weight of the part of the pile above sea bottom and of hammer is large and very near to the limit resistance of the supporting soil (as it may occur for short penetrations below sea bottom or when very soft soils are encountered) one blow of even a light hammer may produce large additional penetrations; obviously in these conditions the soil resistance measured in an instrumented section would be negligible.
Any subsequent analysis of experimental data performed by CAPWAP would lead to accordingly negligible computed shaft (and base) resistances. However, the conclusion that the soil under examination has no resistance is wrong, being obviously the reality that the entire available resistance has already been spent to ensure the static equilibrium of the pile.
Experimental evidencies gathered at Campos basin are strongly in support of this conclusion;Fig.3 shows in the original form produced by Contractors in charge of the interpretation of instrumented driving some of the distributions of shaft resistances with depth at the sites of Garoupa and Enchova (initial driving). In both cases it can be noticed that negligible soil resistances are computed along the shaft down to $40 \div 50$ m depth. This is not consistent with any type of soil, not even if calcareous. Remembering that in both cases the static weight of pile, followers and hammer was in the range of $3.5 \div 5.5$ MN, a comparison between Fig. 2 and 3 shows a good match between theory and measured data.
The simplest way of taking into account this phoenomenon is to add (in first approximation) to the limit shaft resistance calculated by CAPWAP the total static weight (submerged) of pile and hammer ($\overline{W}$).
Then the following conclusions (Studio Geotecnico Italiano, 1982) can be advanced:
a) failure of considering the self-weight of pile and hammer leads to a significant underestimation of the total limit bearing capacity of the foundation soil. This is particularly true for offshore conditions, where static weights are lar-

ge,and may be particularly misleading for all soft soil sites, specifically during initial pile driving when the available soil resistance is strongly reduced by remoulding.
b) actual total pile capacity may simply be obtained by adding to CAPWAP results the value of $\overline{W}$; in order to obtain the "available" limit pile capacity, to the value calculated as above one shall subsequently subtract the self-weight of the part of the pile penetrated into the soil ($\overline{W}_2$).
c) soil "sensitivity" or "set-up" ratio values, (generally defined as ratio of the resistance measured in redriving to the one obtained during initial installation) may largely be overestimated if the appropriate value of the term $-\overline{W}-$ is not included above and below the division line. That may be one of the reasons why sensitivities not matching with soil properties are sometimes reported in the literature.

3. RESIDUAL STRESSES

Because of the large axial compressions induced by the blow applied by the hammer, large residual stresses may remain "locked-in" after pile driving, as demonstrated for example by Holloway et al. (1975, 1978). This may be particularly important for interpretation of experimental measurements of forces and accelerations when high point resistances are encountered (as in some instances at Garoupa and very often at Enchova).
Fig.4 shows schematically the mechanism involved (in presence of negligible external static weight); once the stress wave applied by the hammer has caused the maximum tip penetration, the pile starts to rebound. The relative displacements at pile soil interface change in direction: in the upper part of the pile, where the deformations in compression have been larger, the final "negative" (upwards) pile displacements relative to the soil will be larger and the soil will stay finally in "tension", similarly to what occurs in a "negative skin friction" kind of situation. Near the pile tip the rebound of each pile section will be smaller, because limited by the downwards thrust applied by the soil in the upper part of the pile;

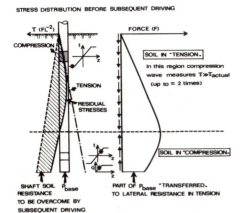

STRESS DISTRIBUTION BEFORE SUBSEQUENT DRIVING

Fig.4 Effect of Residual Stresses for Piles Driven in Dense Sand

therefore the soil will still remain partly in compression, as well as the soil below the pile tip. A large residual compression may be locked in at pile base, mobilizing a corrisponding force in "tension" along the upper part of the shaft. During a subsequent blow, the stress wave will have first to cancel the "tension" in the soil by displacing down to a point of zero mobilized lateral resistance all the sections in the upper part of the pile; however the downward movement of the pile relatively to the soil will continue to the point of full mobilization of the available "compressive" soil resistance also.

Conversely, near the pile tip where the soil is already in compression, the residual resistance still to be mobilized by the incoming stress wave is smaller than τ_{lim} and than the limit base resistance.

Consequences of not taking into consideration such mechanism when interpreting experimental measurements are:

a) the total (measured) calculated soil resistance in principle stays the same, as the pile has to be in equilibrium (no external forces are present);

b) however, its distribution along the pile changes and unrealistically high lateral soil adhesions (up to $1.5 \div 2$ times actual values) may result in the upper zone of the pile shaft, where part of the base resistance has been "transferred" by the mechanism of residual stresses;

c) unrealistically low τ values are measured in the bottom part of the pile shaft, as well as largely underestimated limit base resistances are evaluated. This is not depending on soil properties but on relative pile-soil rigidity, compressibility of materials present along the shaft and at pile base, type of stress-wave applied by the hammer, etc;;

d) if data gathered from direct interpretation of measurements are not filtered through such type of considerations, wrong and/or unsafe design parameters may be issued.

4. REINTERPRETATION OF DATA OBTAINED WITH CONVENTIONAL CAPWAP ANALYSES

Results of interpretation of instrumented driving finally submitted by the three different Contractors at Garoupa, Enchova and Cherne Platforms have been partly reevaluated taking into consideration the observations briefly discussed above; as actual records of driving were not available to

TABLE II - Garoupa - D=48" - Menck 5000

PILE No.	PEN. (m)	CAPWAP RESULTS P_{lat} (MN)	P_{base} (MN)	$P_{lat\ lim}$ = $\overline{W}+P_{lat}$ (MN)	P_{lim} (MN)	TIME FROM PREVIOUS DRIVING (Hours)	$k=\frac{\tau}{z}$ kN/m²/m
A1/C	77.2	21.6	1	25.3	25.8	1480(2)	2.22
	77.3	18	1.3	21.8	22.4	1480(57)	1.9
	88.6	6.2	0.9	9.9	10.2	1480(750)	0.66
A2/C	88.2	24.8	1.9	28.6	29.8	1325(2)	1.92
	88.2	23.2	0.8	26.9	27.1	1325(10)	1.81
	88.4	17.2	1.2	20.9	31.5	1325(152)	1.4
D1/C	82.2	17.5	0.7	21.3	21.3	1475(2)	1.64
	87.7	11.7	0.9	15.5	15.7	1475(803)	1.05
D2/D (*)	88.1	6	0.6	8.8	8.8	CONT.DR.	0.6

(*) Hammer: Vulcan 560; $\overline{W} \cong 2.85$ MN
$\overline{W}$: Submerged weight of hammer and pile $\cong 3.7$ MN

TABLE III - Enchova - D=66" - Menck 5000 & Vulcan 560

PILE No.	PEN. (m)	CAPWAP RESULTS P_{lat} (MN)	P_{base} (MN)	$P_{lat\ lim}$ = $\overline{W}+P_{lat}$ (MN)	P_{lim} (MN)	TIME FROM PREVIOUS DRIVING (Hours)	$k=\frac{\tau}{z}$ kN/m²/m
C3D	77.5	4.7	4.2	8.9	11.8	CONT.DR.	0.56
	77.8	17.3	9.4	22.4	30.5	1536(7)	1.4
		10.3	10.2	15.3	24.3	1536(20)	0.96
H11C	70	0.1	3.6	4.2	6.7	CONT.DR.	0.33
	76.7	3.6	5.3	7.7	11.8	CONT.DR.	0.49
	76.7	4.4	4.9	8.5	12.2	CONT.DR.	0.55
	76.7	12.4	7.8	16.5	23.1	1080(21)	1.06
		12.4	7.8	16.5	23.1	1080(39)	1.06
C14A	76.5	2.4	4	6.7	9.5	CONT.DR.	0.44
	90.5	2.6	7.8	6.9	13.4	CONT.DR.	0.32
	90.5	5.6	7.8	9.9	16.3	CONT.DR.	0.46
	90.8	20.9	12.5	26.1	37.2	624 (10)	1.20
		14.7	12.0	19.9	30.5	624 (50)	0.92
		6.2	13.4	11.4	23.4	624 (129)	0.53
C14C	76	2.9	4.2	7	10.0	CONT.DR.	0.46
	76.2	3.4	3.8	7.5	10.0	CONT.DR.	0.49
	76.2	4.1	1.6	8.2	8.5	CONT.DR.	0.54
H3C	91	4.7	5.8	9	14.8	CONT.DR.	0.41
H14D	91.7	0.4	5	4.7	9.7	CONT.DR.	0.21

$\overline{W}$: Submerged weight of hammer and pile $\cong 4.1 \div 5.2$ MN

TABLE IV - Cherne II - D=72" - Menck MHU 1700

PILE No.	PEN. (m)	CAPWAP RESULTS P_{lat} (MN)	P_{base} (MN)	$P_{lat\ lim}$ = $\overline{W}+P_{lat}$ (MN)	P_{lim} (MN)	TIME FROM PREVIOUS DRIVING (Hours)	$k=\frac{\tau}{z}$ kN/m²/m
5	83.2	8.8	1.7	13.8	14.2	4H 22'	0.69
	87.0	7.8	1.2	12.8	12.7		0.59
	98.0	7.5	1	12.5	12.0		0.45
	111.0	8.5	0.1	13.6	11.9		0.38
6	82.2	10.7	0.9	15.7	15.4	4H 45'	0.81
	90.0	4.7	1.1	9.7	9.4		0.42
	110.5	5.4	1.3	10.4	10.0		0.29
17	58.5	2.1	1.4	7.1	7.6	2H 27'	0.72
	88	4.1	1	9.1	8.8		0.41
	98	2.6	1.6	7.6	7.7		0.28
	110	7.1	0.9	12.1	15.7		0.35
18	51.5	12.5	2	17.5	18.7	184H	2.29
	60.0	3.4	0.8	8.4	8.2		0.80
	70.0	2.9	1.1	7.9	7.9		0.56
	80	3.7	0.8	8.7	8.3		0.47
	96	4.3	1.1	9.3	8.9		0.35
	102	5.2	1.4	10.2	10.1		0.34
	109.5	8.4	1.4	13.4	13.1		0.39
18	109.5	15.7	6.4	20.7	25.4	14H	0.60
	110.0	12.5	1.5	17.5	17.3		0.50
	110.8	12	0.4	17	15.7		0.48

$\overline{W}$: Submerged weight of hammer and pile $\cong 5.0$ MN

the writers, the basic correction introduced is the one depending on self-weight (see para.2). Tables II to IV contain the following data:
- pile number (or code) and penetration below sea bottom (Pen.) at which the interpretation of instrumented driving has been performed;
- results of "CAPWAP" interpretation, given by the Contractor in charge of instrumentation in term of soil resistances at the time of driving; P_{lat} and P_{base} are shaft and base limit resistances;
- correction of lateral resistances, adding the submerged weight $(\overline{W})$ of pile, followers (where used) and hammer $(P_{lat\ lim})$, according to para.2;
- evaluation of P_{lim}, representing the available limit pile resistance at mud line, obtained adding, $P_{lat}+P_{base}$ (CAPWAP) and $\overline{W}$ but subtracting the submerged weight of the part of the pile penetrated into the soil $(\overline{W}_2)$; this is the value to which the Designers make usually reference for the evaluation of available factors of safety;
- conditions of driving: continuous driving, or redriving after a certain period allowed for "set up"; values in brackets represent the number of the blow considered, in the redriving sequence.

Furthermore, because of the normally consolidated state of most of the soil layers, a simplified assumption of lateral limit pile - soil adhesion linerally increasing with depth has been considered, neglecting (for sake of simplicity) the differencies between cohesive strata and granular interbeddings (into which it is very likely that some of the softer material has been dragged). Then the following relationships hold:

$$\tau = k \cdot z = \text{limit pile-soil adhesion} \qquad (1)$$

$k = const = $ gradient of adhesion with depth below mud line (z)

$$P_{lat\ lim} = 0.5 \cdot \pi \cdot D \cdot L^2 \cdot k \qquad (2)$$

$$k = \frac{2 \cdot P_{lat\ lim}}{\pi \cdot D \cdot L^2} \qquad (3)$$

The last column of Tables 2 to 4 shows the values of $-k-$ back calculated using the lateral resistances evaluated in the fifth column; they have been plotted as function of depth in figure 5. "Set up" ratios may be evaluated for all piles for which data in initial driving and redriving conditions are available.
Comparing values of P_{lat} (CAPWAP) and $P_{lat\ lim}$, one can immediately realize the importance of $\overline{W}$ when actual limit pile capacity or "set up" ratio are to be evaluated.
From Fig. 5 it is interesting to note that:
- piles of different geometry, installed at different locations indicate the same trend of behaviour during driving and subsequent reconsolidation;
- it has been postulated that the solution in terms of pile capacity to the problem of the interpretation by CAPWAP of an instrumented blow is unique; however it is not uncommon that differencies of up to 30-40% in P_{lim} may occur with two subsequent examinations of the same experimental registration (see for example Table III). In spite of this fact, values of $-k-$ for "initial driving" conditions are remarkably similar for the three platforms; they fall in a range of 0.3 to 0.6 kN/m²/m.
- all k values for "initial driving" conditions seem to be very low and smaller than usually expected on the basis of soil sensitivity;
- because of the large displacements occurring during penetration and the large number of blows applied at pile top, such k values could be considered as representative of the lower limit of

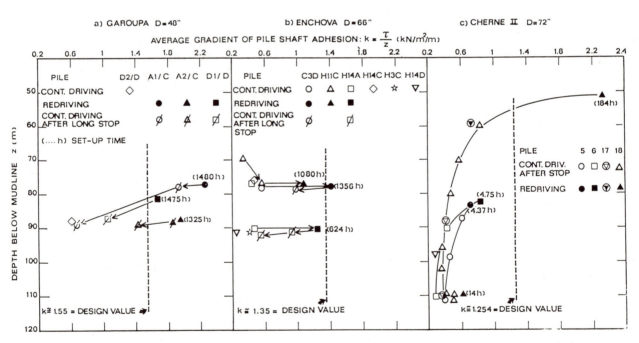

Fig. 5 Average Gradient of Soil-Pile Adhesion (Data from CAPWAP + Static Weight)

cyclic pile resistance both in compression and in tension (introducing the correction for Poisson's ratio effect);
- it is well evident the strong increase in soil resistance produced by any "set-up" time, even if of very limited extent, as it was for Cherne platform; also in this latter case where few hours only have been allowed for reconsolidation the trend is quite clearly established and with the help of data obtained at Garoupa and Enchova (see the invaluable advantage of the availability of experimental measurements in similar soil conditions! ...) one can clearly assess that, hopefully, with time, the design k value will be reached.
"Experimental" k values range from 1.2÷1.46 for Enchova to 1.64÷1.92 at Garoupa platform where relatively large "set-up" times were observed. In spite of the consideration of the effect of static weight, resulting "set-up" ratios seem to be rather high.
- application of a large number of blows, even after full reconsolidation causes a dramatic drop of resistance, to nearly the same level of "initial driving" (see: Fig. 5a, pile A1/C; Fig.5b, piles C3D and C14A and Fig.5c, all piles). This should not be surprising if one consider the fact all the piles under discussion are "low displacement" piles (open end, with a limited thickness of the internal shoe); pore pressure generated during initial installation is limited as well as the subsequent increase in effective stresses.

Some of the same data have been arranged in Fig.6; k has been plotted as function of the Log of the Number of blows: where the instrumented measurements have been taken after any significant "set up" time, the number of blows has been calculated from starting of redriving operations; for "continuous driving" conditions, the number of blows has been calculated from the last significant stop of operations.
In spite of some dispersion, a clear trend is established, where the lower limit is the same value obtained for continuous driving: a progressive degradation of soil resistance is observed towards a common lower limit, more or less indipendent from initial conditions (continuous driving or after large "set up" time). The same behaviour has been reported elsewhere (see for example: Heerema, 1978 and 1979) and can quite clearly be followed on a single pile also from Fig.5c, pile 18.
Some basic aspects, of soil mechanics should now

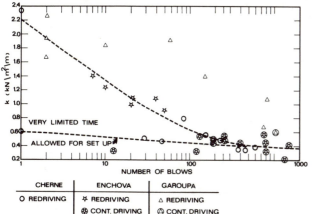

Fig. 6 Degradation of Average Soil Resistance with Driving

be mentioned, namely:
a) the shear strength of sandy material is independent from strain or stress velocity (Lambe and Whitman, 1968; Heerema, 1979).
b) the peak shear strength of clayey soil is strongly dependent on strain velocity, particularly with increasing plasticity index or liquid limit. However, at large strains and under cyclic loading the particles interlocking along a predetermined failure surface is progressively lost. The resistance of the material is then only conditioned by the residual shear strength (i.e.: residual angle of shearing resistance) and becomes practically independent from strain velocity (Atkinson and Bransby, 1978; Lupini et al. 1981; Mizikos and Fournier 1984).
Then there are also no physical reasons why so high damping factors, as traditionally used in wave equation analyses should be applied for continuous driving in soft cohesive materials.
c) the reconsolidation after installation around a low displacement pile causes mainly a rearrengement of particles along the failure surface (and consequently the recovery of ϕ from residual to peak value) but little increment of horizontal effective stress [Carter et al. (1980)].
d) clay soil specimens subjected to cyclic loading exhibit a progressive increment of the critical displacement; the increment is more pronounced when the deviatoric cyclic stress is equal to the available shear strength. Because of that, "traditional" values of quake are to be used when analysing the first few blows but definitively much larger values should be applied for all blows where large relative pile-soil displacements have already been attained.

For a possible improvment of soil models for cohesive soils in wave equation analyses or in interpretation of experimental measurements one should then take into account the following:
- in initial redriving (first few blows) large values of damping and limited values of "quake" should be adpoted. The soil is still working at or near "peak" shear strength and limited deformations have been imposed;
- for continuous driving, damping factors should be strongly reduced (see point b) above) and a relatively large quake is to be applied.

It can be noted that with the above working hypotheses, minimum values of - k - would very likely increase (because of the increase of the corresponding pile shaft limit capacity) in the range of 0.9-1.2 kN/m². Two main consequencies are then to be considered:
- if it is also true that the resistance of internal plug during redriving may account for a significant percentage of measured pile capacity (Dahlberg, 1983), set up ratios would drop even more, to less than 2.
- the lower limit of residual resistance so evaluated would very nearly approach friction values measured during the site investigation with down the hole, static cone penetration tests.

ACKNOWLEDGEMENTS

The kindness of PETROBRAS in allowing a free use of experimental measurements is gratefully aknowledged as well as the permission of MICOPERI, Milan (the Contractor for construction and installation of the three platforms) to publish much of the quoted information.

REFERENCES

Atkinson J.H. and Bransby (1978). The Mechanics of Soil - An Introduction to Critical State Soil Mechanics. McGraw-Hill, University Series of Civil Engineering.

Carter J.P., Randolph M.F., Wroth C.P. (1980). Some Aspects of the Performance of Open - and Closed Ended Piles. Numerical Methods in Offshore Piling, I.C.E. London.

Dahlberg R. (1983). Dynamic Pile Testing. An Important Aid in Verification of Offshore Piles. Dynamic Measurement of Piles and Piers, ASCE, Preprint 83-033, Philadelphia, Pennsylvania, May 16-19.

Dahlberg R. and De Matos S.F.D. (1983). Dynamic Testing and Analysis of Garoupa PGP-1 Piles. Proc. of the Conference on Geotechnical Practice in Offshore Engineering, Univ. of Texas, Austin, April 27-29.

De Matos S.F.D. and De Mello J.R.C. (1982). Piling of Garoupa Platform. Proc. of Offshore Technology Conference, Houston, Texas, May 3-6.

Heerema E.P. (1978).Prediction of Pile Driveability: Heather as an Illustration of the Friction Fatigue Theory. Proc. of European Offshore Petroleum Conference and Exhibition, London, October.

Heerema E.P. (1979). Relationship between Wall Friction Displacements Velocity and Horizontal Stress in Clay and in Sand for Pile Driveability Analyses. Ground Engineering, January.

Holloway D.M., Clough G.W. and Vesic A.S. (1975). The Mechanics of Piles-Soil Interaction in Cohesionless Soils. Soil Mechanics, Series n° 39, School of Engineering Duke University, December.

Holloway, D.M., Clough G.W. and Vesic A.S. (1978). The Effect of Residual Driving Stresses on Pile Performance under Axial Loads. Proc. of Offshore Technology Conference, Houston, Texas, May 8-11.

Lambe T.W. and Whitman (1968). Soil Mechanics. Hohn Wiley & Sons.

Lupini J.F., Skinner A.E. and Vaughan P.R. (1981). The Drained Residual Strength of Cohesive Soils. Géotecnique 31, n° 2.

Mizikos J.P. and Fournier J. (1984). Dynamic and Static Frictions of Open - Ended Piles in Cohesive Soils. II Int. Conf. on the Application of Stress-Wave Theory on Piles, Stockholm, May.

Studio Geotecnico Italiano (1982). Discussion on the Results of Driving Obtained during Pile Installation, Enchova Platform, Brazil. Internal Report.

Chargements latéraux sur un groupe des pieux

Static and cyclic lateral loads on a pile group

F. BAGUELIN, Laboratoire Central des Ponts et Chaussées, Bouguenais, France
J. F. JEZEQUEL, Laboratoire Régional des Ponts et Chaussées, Saint-Brieuc, France
Y. MEIMON, Institut Français du Pétrole, Rueil-Malmaison, France

RESUME   Un groupe de six pieux instrumentés, battus dans un bicouche argile-sable saturé, a été soumis à un programme de chargement latéral statique et cyclique longue durée. L'instrumentation permet de déterminerl'effet de groupe et les courbes de réaction à différents niveaux. On présente certains résultats concernant l'effet de groupe et l'effet du temps suivant le type de chargement.

INTRODUCTION

L'étude expérimentale présentée a été menée conjointement par l'ARGEMA (Association de Recherche en Géotechnique Marine) et le Laboratoire Central des Ponts et Chaussées.

1. EXPERIMENTATION

Le groupe est constitué de deux files de trois pieux de section carrée (B = 0,3 m) reliés entre eux par un chevêtre rigide dans lequel ils sont articulés. Dans chaque file, les pieux sont espacés de deux largeurs centre à centre et les deux files sont espacées de trois largeurs (figure 1). Le groupe est fiché de 6,50 m dans un sol constitué d'une couche de 4,0 m d'argile peu plastique surmontant une couche de 4 m de sable fin et graviers. Afin de simplifier l'interprétation on a, préalablement au battage, décapé la partie superficielle de sol surconsolidé puis maintenu le niveau de l'eau dans cette fouille au niveau du terrain naturel.

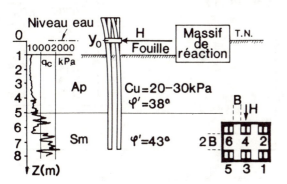

Fig. 1   Coupes du dispositif d'essai et caractéristiques de sols.

Les essais de chargement latéral, statiques et cycliques, sont automatisés et les informations recueillies concernent la distribution des efforts dans le groupe, les déplacements et les pentes des têtes des pieux, ainsi que les moments et les pentes le long du fût des pieux. Au total, 250 voies de mesure sont auscultées à raison de 20 mesures par seconde. L'originalité du programme de chargement (tableau I) est qu'il comporte des essais de longue durée : charges statiques maintenues 40 jours et sol-licitations cycliques jusqu'à 10 000 cycles de période 14 secondes simulant l'effet de la houle sur les plateformes off-shore.

Tableau I. Chronologie du chargement.

Essai	Nom	Durée	N (cycles)	H (kN)
Statique	SH-1	40 j	–	120
Cyclique	CH1-1	4 h	1000	40-80
"	CH2-1	40 h	10000	40-120
"	CH2-1	4 h	1000	40-80
Statique	SH-2	34 j	–	160
Cyclique	CH1-3	40 h	10000	40-80
"	CH2-2	40 h	10000	40-120

2. RESULTATS

Du fait de la rigidité du chevêtre reliant les pieux en tête, le déplacement y_0 est pratiquement le même pour les six pieux. La figure 2 donne l'évolution de y_0 en fonction de l'effort total H appliqué au groupe. On y constate notamment l'effet de l'écrouissage lors des chargements successifs. La stabilisation complète n'a jamais été obtenue ni sous l'effet des charges statiques, ni sous l'effet des charges cycliques. Cependant, au bout de quelques milliers de cycles la vitesse de déplacement $\dot{y}_0$ devient très faible (figure 3).

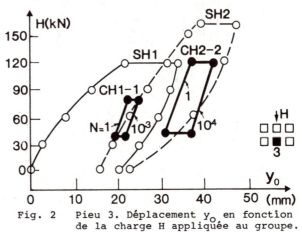

Fig. 2   Pieu 3. Déplacement y_0 en fonction de la charge H appliquée au groupe.

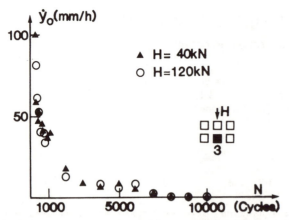

Fig. 3 Pieu 3. Essai cyclique CH2-1. Vitesse de déplacement en fonction du nombre de cycles.

La mesure des moments dans la partie de pieu hors du sol permet de calculer l'effort tranchant T_0 dans chacun des pieux du groupe et donc de connaître la répartition de l'effort total H dans le groupe (fig. 4). On constate que l'effort tranchant T_0 est pratiquement le même pour les pieux d'une même file. En revanche la file avant reprend une part de l'effort H d'autant plus importante que le niveau de chargement est plus élevé. En fin de chargement il y a stabilisation - voire chute - de l'effort repris par la file arrière. A la figure 5 est représentée la distribution des moments le long du pieu 1 pour un chargement cyclique. Pour un effort tranchant T_0 à peu près constant, on constate - entre le 1° et le 1000° cycle - une augmentation de la valeur du moment maximum et un abaissement de son point d'application mettant ainsi en évidence un ramollissement important du terrain sous l'effet des cycles. Sur la figure 5 on vérifie que le moment au point d'application de la charge est très faible et que l'on a bien une articulation à la liaison pieu-chevêtre. En raison du nombre important de mesures de moments (un niveau de 2 jauges de déformations tous les 0,25 m pour les pieux 1, 2, 3 et 4) et de la qualité de ces mesures, il est possible de déterminer les cour-

bes de réaction globale (pB, y) tous les 0,25 m de profondeur par double dérivation des courbes M(z) et donc de déterminer l'effet du temps, des cycles et de l'interaction entre pieux à différents niveaux dans le sol. Un exemple de courbe de réaction est donné à la figure 6.

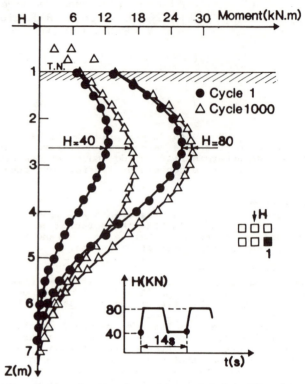

Fig. 5 Pieu 1. Essai cyclique CH1-2. Effet des cycles sur la distribution des moments.

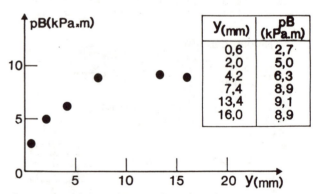

y (mm)	pB (kPa.m)
0,6	2,7
2,0	5,0
4,2	6,3
7,4	8,9
13,4	9,1
16,0	8,9

Fig. 6 Essai statique SH1. Pieu 3. Courbe de réaction à Z = 2,5 mètres.

CONCLUSIONS

Ces essais ont permis d'analyser le comportement d'un groupe de pieux de faible espacement sous charge statique et cyclique de longue durée. En 1984 on a étudié le comportement d'un pieu isolé voisin du groupe soumis exactement au même programme de chargement. En outre on a effectué des essais au pressiomètre autoforeur, notamment cycliques, afin de mettre au point une méthode de calcul adaptée à ce type de fondation.

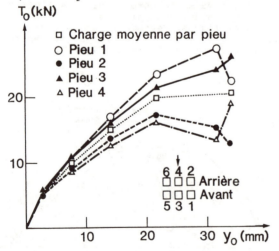

Fig. 4 Essai statique SH1. Répartition en tête des pieux de l'effort total H appliqué au groupe.

Soil/structure interaction study for a piled concrete platform

Interaction sol-structure pour une plateforme en béton sur pieux

C. J. F. CLAUSEN, Consulting Engineer, Copenhagen, Denmark
O. KJEKSTAD, Civil Engineer, Norwegian Geotechnical Institute, Norway
O. E. HANSTEEN, Civil Engineer, Norwegian Geotechnical Institute, Norway

SYNOPSIS   The development of the large Troll gas field in the Norwegian sector of the North Sea will, as a result of deep water and very soft soils, require fixed platform solutions different from those used previously in the northern North Sea. The paper describes one of the candidate fixed platforms being considered, the CONDEEP T300. Details are presented related to static and dynamic analysis of soil/structure interaction.

INTRODUCTION

The Troll offshore oil and gas field was discovered by Norske Shell A/S in September 1979. This field, located some 100 km north-west of the city of Bergen in Norway, will be producing by 1995, provided a market can be found for the huge gas quantities. With its estimated $1.6 \cdot 10^{12}$ cubic metres of gas, Troll could for example meet the present UK gas consumption for a period of 30 years.

The possible development of the Troll field represents a major technical challenge as a result of

- Shallow reservoir, located only 1600 m below the surface.
- Water depth of 330 m, close to twice as deep as any North Sea field developed so far.
- Presence of soft, normally consolidated clay from seabed to 24 m depth.

Norske Shell A/S has since the discovery studied a number of fixed and floating platform concepts (Offshore Engineer, 1983; Norwegian Oil Review, 1984) to check their ability to meet the demanding requirements. The present paper describes some of the design studies carried out for one of these concepts, the CONDEEP T300 platform proposed by Norwegian Contractors.

Two alternative T300 platforms have been studied for the Troll field, with and without piles. Only the piled version is addressed below.

SOIL CONDITIONS

Extensive soil investigations have been carried out at the Troll field (Cuckson, 1983; Moeyes and Hackley, 1983). They include undisturbed sampling with X-ray checking of quality, samples maintained under high ambient pressure, and in situ vane and cone penetrometer tests. A typical soil profile is summarized in Fig. 1 (Eide and Andersen, 1984).

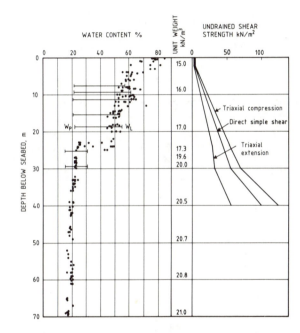

Fig. 1:   Summary of Troll Soil Conditions (Eide and Andersen, 1984)

THE CONDEEP T300 CONCEPT

The base of the T300 platform will be built in a dry-dock, then towed to a protected deepwater site for slipforming of the concrete superstructure and mating with the deck structure. On tow-out the draught will be 225 m and the pay load some 45 000 tons (Schjetlein, 1983). Figure 2 shows a sketch of this structure after installation at the field.

The piled version of T300 will have circular steel skirts penetrated 12 m into the soft upper clays to give sufficient stability until the foundation piles have been installed. The concept studied has 75 piles of outer diameter 3.0 m, wall thickness 75 mm and penetration to 80 m below mudline. The piles are placed in 3 groups, 25 piles underneath each foundation pod.

The structural and dynamic analysis and design of T300 is done by Norwegian Contractors with Norwegian Offshore Consultants (NOC) as consultants. The Norwegian Geotechnical Institute (NGI) is the geotechnical consultant. Figure 3 shows in principle the two structural models of the T300 that were analysed as a part of the design studies, a space frame model and a detailed finite element model.

It is the responsibility of the geotechnical consultant to present the boundary conditions for these two models to the designers, such as displacements and stresses at any point of the structure/foundation interface for given loading acting upon the superstructure.

PRINCIPLES FOR INTERACTION ANALYSIS

An intimate interaction between the T300 platform and the foundation will govern both the distribution and the magnitude of the stresses in the platform. The problems associated with reliable analyses of all aspects of this interaction are formidable. There appeared to be no procedure available that was able to handle adequately all of these aspects simultaneously, and it was decided to carry out two separate interaction analyses:

- A static analysis, which aims at giving a detailed picture of the stress distribution in the foundation pods, the piles, the girders between the pods, the lower parts of the legs and the area around the riegel (Fig. 2).

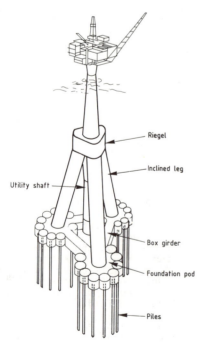

Fig. 2: CONDEEP T300 Platform.

- A dynamic analysis, which aims at giving an overall picture of the dynamic behaviour of the structure, including dynamic amplification factors by which the statically computed stresses are multiplied.

ANALYSIS FOR STATIC INTERACTION

Basic principles

The forces acting upon the structure must be transferred into the supporting soils, partly through the piles, and partly through the platform base areas in direct contact with the soil. The distribution of the support reactions, and hence the stresses in the structure, will depend upon the relative stiffnesses of the different parts of the foundation system and the structure.

It was decided to carry out a foundation analysis that included the following points:

- A fully coupled solution that allows for the stiffness of both superstructure and foundation system.
- Three-dimensional geometry.
- Interaction effects between the various parts of the foundation system (for example pile group effects).
- Non-linear load/displacement behaviour of individual foundation elements (for example local soil yielding along the edge of the platform base).

For a complex system of this type it is not possible to give a single set of conservative soil properties that will govern the required dimensions of all parts of the structure. As an example, one may expect that a "soft" soil will give the highest displacements and thus the highest bending stresses in the piles, whereas a "strong" soil will allow high base edge loads and thus give high bending stresses in the pod.

The analyses of the combined structure/foundation system were therefore carried out for two soil profiles, for simplicity referred to as "soft" and "strong". These two profiles were obtained from one set of characteristic soil stiffnesses and strengths, determined taking the cyclic nature of the wave loading into account.

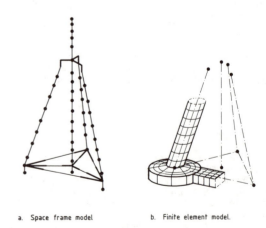

a. Space frame model   b. Finite element model.

Fig. 3: Structural Models of T300

The "soft" soil profile was obtained by dividing the strengths by the partial coefficient of 1.30 required by the Norwegian code (Norwegian Petroleum Directorate, 1977). This code does not give any guide on how to develop the "strong" soil profile. It was therefore decided to simply mulitply the strengths by 1.30 for the "strong" soils.

In addition to uncertainties in soil behaviour, the foundation analysis must also include the variations in platform support conditions that occur with time. The following three support conditions have been considered:

1. The platform has just been placed and the piles not yet installed. Loading is a low submerged platform weight combined with summer storm conditions.

2. The piles have been installed and the platform ballasted to its final weight. This weight is partly carried by the piles and partly by the base. The design 100 year wave then occurs.

3. After some time the submerged weight may be carried by the piles only. The design 100 year wave then occurs.

Linear elastic methods

The structural designers selected 16 interface joints where the space frame model was to be connected to the foundation system, Figure 4. Each of the three pods were assumed to be rigid in the foundation analysis, i.e., the displacements of any point on a pod can be expressed in terms of the six displacements at the pod centre.

The foundation piles were modelled as individual 6 by 6 stiffness matrices representing the relation between pile head forces and displacements. The foundation base and skirts were modelled as a number of plate elements with 3 degrees of

freedom at their centre. For this elastic foundation system there exists a linear relationship between displacements $\mathbf{v}$ and forces $\mathbf{S}$:

$$\mathbf{v} = \mathbf{FS} \qquad (1)$$

where $\mathbf{F}$ is a flexibility matrix. The size of this system of equations will be 3 times the number of plate elements plus 6 times the number of piles. Procedures used to find the different elements in the $\mathbf{F}$ matrix are explained below.

The elastic relationship between interface joint displacements $\mathbf{p}$ and sum of foundation element forces w.r.t. the joints $\mathbf{R}_f$, is given by:

$$\mathbf{R}_f = \mathbf{K}_f \cdot \mathbf{p} \qquad (2)$$

where $\mathbf{K}_f$ is the stiffness matrix of the foundation system referred to the interface joints. For the superstructure the same type of relationship exists:

$$\mathbf{R}_S = \mathbf{K}_S \, \mathbf{p} \qquad (3)$$

where $\mathbf{R}_S$ are superstructure forces referred to the interface joints and $\mathbf{K}_S$ the superstructure condensed stiffness matrix.

Equilibrium of the interface joints require that:

$$\mathbf{R} - \mathbf{R}_f - \mathbf{R}_S = 0 \qquad (4)$$
$$\mathbf{R} = (\mathbf{\bar{K}}_f + \mathbf{\bar{K}}_S) \cdot \mathbf{p} \qquad (5)$$

where $\mathbf{R}$ is the given load vector acting upon the interface joints when displacements are prevented. Equation (5) is the governing equation for the combined elastic system of superstructure and foundation. With 16 interface joints this system contains $16 \cdot 6 = 96$ equations only, compared to say 1500 for Equation (1).

The stiffness matrix $\mathbf{K}_f$ is determined from Equation (1) by a condensation process where 96 unit displacements are assumed for the interface joints, the corresponding vectors $\mathbf{v}$ computed, and Equation (1) solved for $\mathbf{S}$. This results in the matrix $\mathbf{K}_f$ and two other matrices that relate interface joint displacements to pile head and base element forces.

The above are straight forward matrix operations that only require matrix $\mathbf{F}$ to be known. It consists of the following submatrices:

$\mathbf{F}_{BB}$ = Base element displacements due to base element unit forces.

$\mathbf{F}_{PP}$ = Pile head displacements due to pile head unit forces.

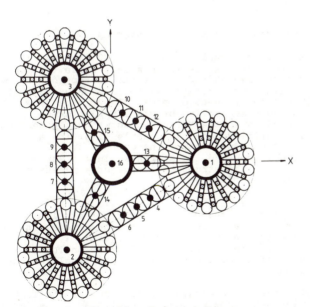

Fig. 4: Coupling Joints between Superstructure and Foundation

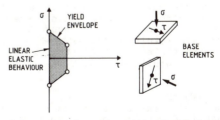

Fig. 5: Base Elements with Yield Envelope

F_{BP} = Base element displacements due to pile head unit forces.

The submatrix F_{BB} is formed by the computer program SPRINT (Clausen, 1983), based upon a numerical integration of Mindlin's point load solutions (Mindlin, 1936). These solutions have been adjusted to approximately account for the effect of increasing soil stiffness with depth.

The submatrices F_{PP} and F_{BP} are computed with the computer program SPLICE (Clausen et al., 1982). The pile is modelled as beam elements embedded in an elastic half space with a soil modulus that increases linearly with depth.

Pile/soil/pile interaction values were actually computed for distances between two piles of 5, 10 and 20 metres. For other distances an interpolation formula for the interaction value I was used:

$$I = A \cdot e^{-B} \cdot x \qquad (6)$$

where A and B are constants determined from the SPLICE results, and x is the distance between the two piles. Similar procedures were used for pile/soil/base interaction values.

Non-linear corrections

The above matrix F assumes a linear elastic behaviour of the foundation system. After an elastic solution has been found, one could in theory compute a new F matrix with adjusted stiffnesses and repeat the condensation process. However, this would be highly impractical and very costly in terms of computer time, as one elastic solution requires of the order 5 hours CPU time on a Prime 750 computer.

The CONDEEP T300 studies were therefore carried out with a basic elastic solution subjected to correction forces to account for non-linear effects. For each base element a yield envelope as indicated on Figure 5 was defined. The maximum value of normal stress was determined from bearing capacity considerations (Lauritzsen and Schjetne, 1976). For each pile an axial and a lateral load/displacement diagram as indicated on Figure 6 was defined. An approximate non-linear solution could then be found by the following steps:

1. Solve the linear elastic system.
2. For each base element and each pile compute the unbalanced forces caused by the element being unable to exceed the yield or load/displacement curve.
3. Form the sum of these unbalanced forces at the interface joints and add to the given vector R.
4. Solve the system once more and repeat until convergence has been obtained.

This procedure may tend to overestimate the interaction effects between the different foundation elements, but it will ensure that all elements have resulting forces that are compatible with the strength of the supporting soils, and in equilibrium with the external forces.

Example results

The above numerical model was analysed with 53 different load combinations, 2 soil types and 3 support conditions. This resulted in 189

complete solutions for a detailed structural study. A few (10-15) of these cases were found to be of particular interest, and therefore analysed further by the large finite element model of the structure.

Table 1 gives a summary of some computed results for a "soft" soil case. Values given are displacements and forces for the most heavily loaded pod when the structure is subjected to self weight, and 100 year wave loading in the +X-direction (Fig. 4) multiplied by a load factor of 1.30.

TABLE 1

Pod 1 Computed Results	Linear analysis	Non-linear analysis
Displacements		
δ_x, mm	36	51
δ_z, mm	45	74
θ_{yy}, mrad	0.22	0.38
Vertical Forces		
Piles, MN	780	994
Base Elements, MN	510	284
Horizontal Forces		
Piles, MN	93	100
Base Elements, MN	96	119

The somewhat surprising increase in horizontal shear taken at the pod, is due to local overstressing underneath other parts of the base, with lower bearing capacity than the large leading pod.

The axial pile forces were found to vary between 23 to 48 MN for the linear case, and 37 to 42 MN for the non-linear case.

ANALYSIS FOR DYNAMIC INTERACTION

The dynamic analysis of the T300 platform is based upon a space frame model, where the foundation pile/skirt/soil system is represented by 3 axial and 3 rotational springs under each of the three foundation pods. Experience from performance monitoring of gravity platforms installed in the North Sea shows that even such a simplified model is capable of giving a satisfactory prediction of the overall dynamic behaviour, provided the stiffness in the various parts of the structure is adequately determined (Hansteen, 1979).

Soil model

The regulations of the Norwegian Petroleum Directorate allow use of a linear model in the dynamic analysis of the structure. If non-linear effects have a significant influence on the safety of the structure, they shall be considered.

The dynamic analysis carried out for the T300 platform was a stochastic analysis of the design storm, assuming stationary conditions during the 6-hour storm duration. In such an analysis, the

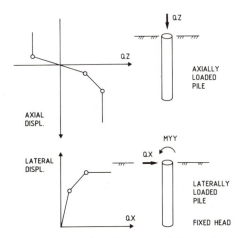

Fig. 6: Axial and Lateral Non-Linear Behaviour of Piles

power density spectrum $S_r(\omega)$ of the response quantity r (r is, say, a stress component) and its standard deviation σ_r is computed. The expected maximum value r_{max} is found as

$$r_{max} = f \cdot \sigma_r \qquad (7)$$

where f is computed from the power density spectrum, and is normally in the range 3.5-4.0.

In determining the stiffnesses of the foundation springs, it is the cyclic stiffness (secant modulus in hysteresis loop) that is of interest. This modulus is strongly dependent upon the cyclic stress amplitude. When a large number of stress cycles occurs, it is also necessary to consider the decrease in modulus with increase in number of stress cycles, due to pore pressure build-up. A method to predict the development of strain amplitudes in clays subjected to a large number of stress cycles of variable amplitude (Andersen, 1976; Andersen, 1983) was used to compute the appropriate secant shear modulus for the soil elements. In principle, the procedure implies that each soil element is subjected to stress cycles corresponding to the stresses during the design storm. In the present case, the design storm consisted of altogether 1800 load cycles, ranging from 900 cycles with 20% of the maximum amplitude to 1 cycle with 100% of the maximum amplitude. The maximum amplitude varies from element to element. The equivalent linear secant modulus was then determined as the ratio between the standard deviation of the stress and the standard deviation of the corresponding strain during the storm. This definition of the equivalent modulus ensures that the total energy of the computed displacements are reasonable, even if the frequency distribution (shape of the power spectrum) may be somewhat inaccurate due to non-linearities.

Computer implementation

The soil model outlined above has been built into NGI's non-linear finite element program FEAST84, which was used to compute the foundation spring stiffnesses. This program can only handle a two-dimensional plane strain model. The computational model used had the same base area and the same moment of inertia as the complete T300 foundation, and also contained the axial effect of piles with the same moment of inertia about the platform centreline as the T300 piles.

Horizontal loads and moments corresponding to the standard deviation of the loads during the design storm were applied in steps, and one iteration was carried out for each step. An equivalent horizontal spring stiffness for the whole platform was then found as the ratio between applied horizontal load and the resulting horizontal displacement, and a similar rotational spring as the ratio between moment and rotation.

The total rotational stiffness of the T300 foundation results partly from the vertical axial springs under the pods, and partly from the rotational springs under each pod. From static elastic halfspace solutions, it was estimated that the first of the above contributions accounted for 70% of the total rotational stiffness. From this assumption, the stiffness of all the axial springs and the rotational springs about horizontal axes could be computed. The stiffnesses of the rotational springs about the vertical axes have a negligible influence on the computed dynamic response.

Results

The computed dynamic axial spring stiffnesses under each pod were 6500 MN/m horizontally, and 43000 MN/m vertically. For comparison, the non-linear results from the static analysis given above correspond to an apparent horizontal spring stiffness of 4295 MN/m. The static equivalent vertical stiffness, which also includes the immediate settlement due to the submerged weight of the platform, is 17300 MN/m.

The difference in equivalent stiffnesses between the two procedures is significant. Note that the "static" values represent a much higher load level than the "dynamic" values. Also, the static analysis was primarily aimed at obtaining the distribution of soil reactions under the platform, while the dynamic analysis aimed at obtaining representative displacements of the platform during the design storm.

In the subsequent dynamic analysis, the first natural period of the platform was found to be 4.0 sec. If the softer static spring stiffnesses had been used, a significantly higher natural period would have been predicted, giving rise to higher dynamic amplification of the wave forces.

CONCLUSIONS

The paper has summarized the procedures used to analyse the interaction between superstructure and foundation for the piled version of the CONDEEP T300 proposed for installation at the Troll field.

It is the opinion of the authors that for complex foundations of this type, it is necessary to undertake separate interaction analyses, each focusing on interaction effects of particular significance for the subsequent analyses to be carried out. It is also necessary to analyse a wide range of possible soil behaviour and support conditions, as it is highly unlikely that one critical combination will govern the design of all superstructure members.

ACKNOWLEDGEMENTS

The authors wish to thank Norske Shell A/S and Norwegian Contractors for the permission to present some results from the CONDEEP T300 studies that are still in progress. The valuable discussions with our colleagues at the Norwegian Geotechnical Institute are gratefully acknowledged.

REFERENCES

Andersen, K.H. (1976). Behaviour of clay subjected to undrained cyclic loading. International Conference on the Behaviour of Off-shore Structures, 1. BOSS'76. Trondheim 1976. Proceedings, Vol. 1, pp. 392-403. Also publ. in: Norwegian Geotechnical Institute, Publication, 114.

Andersen, K.H. (1983). Strength and deformation properties of clay subjected to cyclic loading. Norwegian Geotechnical Institute, Oslo, report 52412-8. 54 p.

Clausen, C.J.F. (1983) "SPRINT" a computer program for analysis of a rigid three-dimensional structure supported by an elastic half space. Report 8207-1, Copenhagen 22nd February, 1983.

Clausen, C.J.F., P.M. Aas and E. Hasle (1982) SPLICE, a computer program for analysing structure-pile-soil interaction problems. International Symposium on Offshore Engineering, 3. Rio de Janeiro 1981. Proceedings, London, Pentech Press, pp. 129-145.

Cuckson; J. (1984) Specification and performance of new equipment for a site investigation at a deep water soft soil site. Foundations for Offshore Installations; Seminar. London, January 1984, Society for Underwater Technology.

Eide, O. and K.H. Andersen (1984) Foundation engineering for gravity structures in the northern North Sea. Paper presented at Conf. on Case Histories in Geotechnical Engineering. St. Louis, Mo 1984. Norwegian Geotechnical Institute, Oslo. Report, 51500-2. 52p.

Hansteen, O.E. (1980) Dynamic performance. Shell Brent 'B' Instrumentation Project; Seminar. London 1979. Proceedings, pp. 89-107. Org. by the Society for Underwater Technology, London. Also publ. in: Norwegian Geotechnical Institute. Publication, 137.

Lauritzsen, R. and K. Schjetne (1976) Stability calculations for offshore gravity structures. Offshore Technology Conference, 8. Houston 1976. Proceedings, Vol. 1, pp. 75-82. Also publ. in: Norwegian Geotechnical Institute. Publication, 113.

Mindlin, R.D. (1936) Force at a point in the interior of a semi-infinite solid. Journal of Applied Physics, Vol. 7, No. 5, pp. 195-202.

Moeyes, B. and M. Hackley (1983) Soil investigations in the Troll area. Offshore Northern Seas; Advanced Projects Conference. Stavanger 1983. Proceedings, T6, 37p.

Norwegian Petroleum Directorate (1977) Regulations for the structural design of fixed structures on the Norwegian Continental Shelf. Stavanger.

Schjetlein, I.O. (1983) CONDEEP T300 concrete gravity platform for deep waters. Offshore Northern Seas; Advanced Projects Conference. Stavanger 1983. Proceedings, T10, 33 p.

The Troll field (1984) Norwegian Oil Review, Vol. 10, No. 3, pp. 17-44.

Troll, The story so far (1983) Offshore Engineer, December, pp. 22-29

Behavior of a large scale pile in silty clay

Comportement d'un pieu à grande échelle dans l'argile silteuse

EARL H. DOYLE, Staff Research Engineer, Shell Development Company, Houston, Texas, USA
JOHN H. PELLETIER, Senior Civil Engineer, Shell Oil Company, Houston, Texas, USA

SYNOPSIS   A large scale pile test was performed to obtain information for the design of an offshore platform in 700 feet (213 m) of water. The pile was tested under a variety of loading conditions. This report discusses the results of the load test program as they relate to pile foundation response under various load rates and cyclic load conditions.

INTRODUCTION

A large scale pile load test was conducted in Long Beach, California, to better determine the axial behavior of the piles designed for a 700 foot (213 m) water depth platform located 15 miles (24 km) offshore of the test site. The Long Beach location was chosen because it is onshore and has soil properties similar to the offshore site at a deep enough penetration to show significant differences between various axial pile capacity predictive methods. This test has been referred to as the Beta Pile Test.

The 30-inch (762 mm), 1.5-inch (38 mm) wall thickness test pile was lowered through a cleaned out 42-inch (1067 mm) sleeve pile which had been driven to 190 feet (58 m) and later cleaned out. The test pile was then driven with a Delmag D-62-12 diesel hammer from a penetration of 190 feet (58 m) to 263 feet (80 m) below ground level. The soil at the test penetration is a very stiff to hard silty clay with frequent sand seams below 256 feet (78 m). Details of the pile test setup, soil conditions, static pile capacity and pile capacity predictive results are discussed by Pelletier and Doyle (1982). The purpose of this report is to present further results of the load tests.

TEST PLAN AND OBJECTIVES

Three load test series were conducted. Test Series One was conducted as soon as the pile was driven to grade in order to examine the ability of pile driving analysis procedures to compute short and long term pile capacity and to acquire an additional pile capacity value to compare with effective stress analyses. After this initial test, the pile was driven to a final penetration of 264 feet (80.5 m) to remove any possible testing effects. The second and most complex load test series started 60 days after driving, when piezometers indicated that 95% of the excess pore pressures had dissipated. This series was conducted to determine: (1) long term static capacity, (2) load rate effects, (3) the influence of previous load history on capacity, (4) pile capacity under both one-way and two-way cyclic loading, and (5) tension versus compression capacity. The last test series was started 87 days after driving to determine if pile capacity regained with time following cyclic degradation.

TEST PROGRAM RESULTS

Loading was applied to the pile at the +8 foot (2.4m) elevation. Pile top loads and displacements were measured at that elevation. Pile top load was measured by three independent full strain gage bridges. Each bridge consisted of four pairs of strain gages spaced 90 degrees around the pile at the same elevation in order to cancel bending strains. Displacement at the pile top was measured by a calibrated linear slidewire which was attached to an overhead reference beam. A Microhead Level and an engineer's level were also used whenever possible to verify the displacement readings.

The pile was loaded by hydraulic jacks which were arranged so that either tension or compression loads could be incrementally or continuously applied to the pile top.

A summary of the designated test numbers and test procedure is given in Table I. The measured maximum pile top load and pile top load rate is also given for each test. In addition, pile top load versus pile top displacement is plotted in Figure 1 for each test. This seven part figure shows the load-deflection data for each day of testing. A zero displacement corresponds to the pile location at the start of each load test series.

Test Series One
The first load series started 71 minutes after driving and lasted two hours. The first test (1-1) was run to obtain the short term static capacity under both incremental and continuous loading conditions. The load rate was increased in the second test (1-2) to investigate load rate effects.

Test Series Two
The second test series was started 60 days after driving and lasted three days. Seven tests were conducted. Three load tests were performed on the first day. The first test (2-1) was similar to Test 1-1 and its purpose was to obtain the long term static capacity. Test 2-2 was run at a fast rate to investigate load rate effects while the third test (2-3A) was conducted to determine whether there was any change in capacity since Test 2-1.

Three tests (2-3B, 2-4, 2-5) were conducted on the second day. Test 2-3B was a duplication of Test 2-3A and was conducted to provide a reference capacity for the subsequent test (2-4). Test 2-4 was a cyclic

TABLE I
Test Program Load Series

Test Number	Procedure	Maximum Load, kN	Load Rate mm/min
1-1	–Load in 100 kip increments	3123	–
	–Bleed off some hydraulic pressure		
	–Load continuously to failure then unload to zero	3634	0.8
1-2	–Load continuously to failure then unload to zero	3870	1.8
2-1	–Load in 100 kip increments	10707	–
	–Load continuously to failure	11040	1.5
	–Increase load rate	11877	17.8
	–Shut in hydraulic pressure and allow pile to creep then unload to zero	10809	–
2-2	–Load continuously to failure then unload to zero	11935	17.8
2-3A	–Load continuously to failure then unload to zero	11806	7.6
2-3B	–Load continuously to failure then unload to zero	14417	1.3
2-4	–One-way cyclic tension test. Ten cycles each at percentage levels of: 25-30, 25-40, 25-50, 25-60, 25-67, 25-83, and 5 cycles at 25-100 (where 100% is the Test 2-3B capacity)	–	12.7
	–Continue last load cycle to large deflection then unload to zero	14337	12.7
2-5	–Load continuously to tension failure, then conduct 16 cycles of fully reversed (two-way) loading (see Table II)	13816	4.1
2-6	–Load continuously in compression to failure then unload to zero	-10249	15.2
	–Load continuously to failure until pile is pushed into virgin soil below tip	-11285	15.2
	–Conduct 6 cycles of fully reversed loading cycle 1	10409 / -8932	
	cycle 6	9052 / -8060	
3-1	–Load continuously to failure	11596	1.3
	–Increase load rate	11730	12.7
	–Shut in hydraulic pressure and allow pile to creep then unload to zero	11846	–
3-2	–Load continuously to failure	13096	12.7
	–Conduct 9 cycles of fully reversed loading then 6 cycles of progressively less loading cycle 1	+13096 / -10578	
	cycle 9	+10542 / -9595	
	–Load continuously to compression failure	-8661	12.7
3-3	–Load continuously to failure	10542	7.6

(Unless otherwise stated, all load values in this report include the pile weight and, for Test Series One, the hammer weight. Positive values denote a tension test.)

tension test where the pile was cycled at several tension bias load levels. A tension test to failure at the end of Test 2-4 was run to determine if cyclic tension loading caused any degradation in pile capacity. The final test of the day was a fully reversed (tension and compression) cyclic test. Shown

in Figure 1 is the pile top-displacement relationship for cycles 1, 5, 10 and 16.

The last day consisted of a compression test and a fully reversed cyclic test. During the compression part of the fully reversed cyclic test, the displacement slidewire bottomed out at -7.8 cm. Thus, that portion of the curve in Figure 1 is not correctly shown.

Test Series Three
Test Series Three was conducted 30 days after test series two. This last series lasted three days and consisted of three tests (3-1, 3-2, 3-3).

Test 3-1 was a static test conducted for the purpose of determining whether capacity had recovered since completing Test Series Two.

Test 3-2 was a fully reversed cyclic test. After nine fully reversed load cycles to failure, the level of loading was progressively reduced over the next six cycles in order to develop a backbone curve. A compression test immediately followed to determine if degradation continued during the reduced cyclic tests.

The last test (3-3) of the program was a static test to failure.

DISCUSSION

The testing program was developed to provide information about static and cyclic capacity, load history and rate effects. These are discussed below.

Static pile capacity
The static capacity was determined in Test 2-1 (Figure 1). A variety of load application methods was used during Test 2-1. The pile was initially loaded in tension in 100 kip (445 kN) increments. At a pile top load of 2407 kips (10707 kN), the pile began to pull out of the ground. A slow continuous load was then applied at a rate of 0.06 inches/minute (1.5 mm/minute). The pile reached a maximum load of 2482 kips (11040 kN). This load, minus the pile weight of 144 kips (640 kN), has been taken by Pelletier and Doyle (1982) as the static pile capacity. The loading rate was then increased to 0.7 inches/minute (17.8 mm/minute) and the load reached 2670 kips (11877 kN). The hydraulic jacks were then shut off and the pile was allowed to creep. The pile load dropped to 2430 kips (11809 kN) before creep movement ceased. For this test, the difference between incremental capacity, slow continuous capacity and post-failure creep capacity was less than 3%.

Short-term versus long-term capacity
The first load test (Figure 1) started 71 minutes after driving. The maximum load measured during the continuous portion of the test was 760 kips (3381 kN). Subtracting the pile weight of 144 kips (641 kN) and weight of hammer of 33 kips (147 kN) gave a net pile load of 583 kips (2593 kN). A piezometer located at a penetration of 239 feet (73 m) and 17.8 feet (5.4 m) from the pile wall showed an excess pore pressure at the time of testing of 30 psi (207 kPa) above hydrostatic of 93 psi (641 kPa). The test capacity for the first test (2-1) after 60 days showed a net pile top load of 2338 kips (10400 kN). Thus, the ratio between the long-term and short-term capacity (set up factor) is four. It is likely that the "immediate" capacity would have been less than 583 kips (2593 kN) if the pile was tested sooner than 71 minutes after driving since some pore pressure dissipation was observed before the test started.

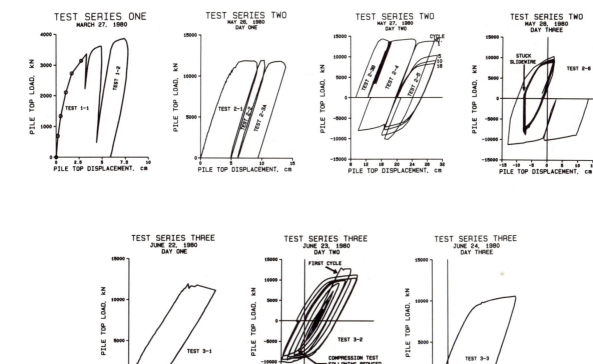

Fig. 1 – Pile top load versus pile top displacement diagrams.

Rate effects

The pile was tested under a variety of continuously applied loading rates which varied from 0.03 to 0.7 inches/minute (0.76 to 17.8 mm/minute). In terms of load rates, these correspond to 100% to 1500% of ultimate capacity per hour in Test Series Two, for example. The loading rates are indicated in Table I. Pile capacity increased approximately 8% per tenfold increase in strain rate in Test Series Two, while the capacity increased by 8% when the strain rate was doubled in Test Series One. The large increase in Test Series One may have been affected by the dissipation of pile driving induced pore pressures along the pile wall during testing.

Load history effects

One of the objectives of Test Series Two was to determine set up capacity and to investigate effects of load history on measured pile capacity. As shown in Table I, the fast rate portion of Test 2-1 and Test 2-3A had essentially the same capacity. These tests were conducted on day one. Thus, the accumulation of large displacements from Test 2-1 through Test 2-3a did not affect capacity. The next morning (day two), the first test (2-3B) showed a 32% increase in capacity as compared to the first test on day one (Test 2-1). Tests 2-1 and 2-3B were run at similar load rates. Even after one-way cycling (Test 2-4), the capacity was unchanged from that morning's first test. The overnight increase in capacity may be due to dissipation of shear induced pore pressures which were generated during the previous day's testing. For example, during Test Series Two, near field excess pore pressures showed a gradual rise of 25 psi (172 kPa) during the first day's testing.

These had dissipated by the next morning.

Test Series Three was conducted in a similar manner as Test Series Two except that the pile loading rates were 0.5 inches/minute (12.7 mm/minute) for each load test. The load test results were similar to Test Series Two except the effect was smaller. Pore pressures rose 10 psi (69 kPa) during the first day of testing, while the overnight capacity increased 9%.

Cyclic pile capacity

Tests were conducted under both one-way and two-way loading conditions. For the one-way tests (Test 2-4), cyclic load was applied ten times each between levels of 25-30%, 25-40%, 25-60%, 25-67%, and 25-83% of the ultimate capacity. No permanent pile deformations occurred until the pile was cycled five times between 25-100% of ultimate capacity. The measured pile top capacity prior to the one-way cycling was 3241 kips (14417 kN) as indicated in Table I, Test 2-3B. Following cycling at ultimate capacity, the measured pile top load of 3232 kips (14377 kN) was essentially unchanged. Because of the limited number of cycles, however, no criteria were developed to predict the response of deep penetration piles under a large number of cycles.

Displacement controlled two-way cyclic tests to failure were conducted. Tests 2-4, 2-5 and 3-2 consisted of 16, 7 and 9 fully-reversed cycles, respectively. The cycling at ultimate capacity resulted in a significant reduction in pile capacity. Degradation began as soon as two-way loading occurred. Degraded values ranged between 61% to 85% of the precyclic values. The measured pile top loads for Test 2-5 are shown in Table II. By the last three cycles, the degraded capacity was 61% of the original capacity and the rate of degradation had decreased. The reduction in ultimate tension capacity approximates a straight line on a semi-logarithmic plot for cycles 2-14. This behavior is similar to the degradation model proposed by Idriss, et al (1976) for clay. The degradation was, however, temporary and had healed by the end of the 30 days separating Test Series Two and Three, as indicated by the first load test results from each test series (Table I). Thus, for these soils, capacity degradation is substantial but temporary.

TABLE II
Pile Top Loads For Test 2-5

Cycle Number	Peak Tension (kN)	Peak Compression (kN)	Half Of Absolute Difference (kN)
1	13816	-10338	1739
2	11921	-10449	743
3	11338	-10133	605
4	10818	-9693	565
5	10382	-9274	556
6	10035	-8928	556
7	9755	-8821	467
8	9635	-8394	623
9	9323	-8105	609
10	9128	-7887	623
11	8928	-7762	583
12	8776	-7562	609
13	8630	-7326	654
14	8460	-7388	538
15	8478	-7322	578
16	8429	-7162	636

After cycle nine of Test 3-2, two-way cycling was continued except that maximum tension and compression loads were progressively reduced. One of the purposes for running this test was to determine if degradation continued under reduced two-way cycling. The loads were reduced to .93, .88, .75, .52 and .27 of the last full cycle failure load. The pile was then loaded to failure in compression. If no degradation had occurred under the reduced cycling levels, the load-deflection curve obtained from the last compression test should have gone through the tips of the previously run reduced cycling curves. As shown in Figure 1 the reload went through the tips of the .27 and .52 load level curves but was progressively less at the higher load levels. At the .93 load level, the load was about 8% less on the reload cycle. About one-third of that was caused by the continued degradation of the last reload. The rest of the degradation was, therefore, caused by the reduced load levels. It appears that load levels less than about 50% of the maximum did not cause further reduction in the load-displacement curve. Above that level, the three reduced level cycles contributed to the degradation at about the same level as the fully reversed failure load cycles.

Tension versus compression capacity

The two-way cyclic tests provide a means to examine the question of tension versus compression capacity of large scale piles. Since the pile tip had been pulled up by previous tension loadings, pile tip effects were minimal. If tension and compression capacities are the same, then the midpoint of a symmetric load-displacement

hysteresis loop would be biased by the weight of the pile and the plug (if the pile was plugged during the test). During driving, the plug was monitored and the pile did not plug. The measured weight of the pile was 144 kips (640 kN) and the submerged weight of the plug was about 30 kips (133 kN). The results of Test 2-5 are shown in Table II where half of the absolute difference between the peak tension and compression values after the first few cycles is about equal to the pile weight. During cyclic loading, the plug apparently played no measureable part in the pile capacity. Thus, the two-way cyclic data indicate that the tension and compression capacities are equal. Similar results were obtained for Tests 2-6 and 3-2.

SUMMARY

The results of Beta Pile Test contribute to the understanding of the behavior of axially loaded piles under a variety of loading conditions. Pile set up factors are at least four for these soils. Pile capacity increased about 8% for every tenfold increase in load rate. During Test Series Two and Three, overnight pile capacity increases of 9-32% were measured and may be explained by measured dissipation of shear induced pore pressures. For a limited number of cycles, one-way loading did not degrade pile capacity. Two-way loading at ultimate load capacity caused a significant but temporary reduction in pile capacity. After fully reversed cycling, degradation continued to occur at two-way load levels above about 50% of the ultimate load. Finally, the capacity of the pile was the same in both tension and compression.

ACKNOWLEDGEMENTS

This study, conducted by Shell Development Company, Fugro-Gulf, Inc. and Raymond International, was funded by Shell Oil Company and its partners in the Beta Oil Field. Special thanks are due Messrs. T. K. Hamilton, D. W. Bogard, R. L. Boggess and H. Matlock for their design and installation efforts during the pile test.

REFERENCES

Pelletier, J. H. and Doyle, E. H. (1982). Tension capacity in silty clays - Beta pile test. Proc. 2nd Int. Conf. Numerical Methods in Offshore Piling, 163-182, Austin, Texas.

Idriss, I. M., Dobry, R., Doyle E. H. and Singh, R. D. (1976). Behavior of soft clays under earthquake loading conditions. Preprints, Offshore Technology Conf, Paper 2671, 605-616, Houston, Texas.

Ultimate axial bearing capacity of piles driven into coral rock and carbonate soils

Capacité portante critique relative à la pression axiale des pieux battus dans des couches de sol et de rocher contenant du carbonate

J. HAGENAAR, Deputy Head Geotechnical Department, PRC Engineering Inc., Hague Office, Netherlands
A. VAN SETERS, Geotechnical Engineer, PRC Engineering Inc., Hague Office, Netherlands

SYNOPSIS   Recorded load tests have shown that the ultimate bearing capacity of piles driven into coral formations and carbonate deposits is less than would have been expected from in-situ Standard Penetration Test (SPT) data. This paper presents the results of 25 axial load tests on steel pipe and prestressed concrete piles driven into such formations for offshore projects along the Red Sea coast of Saudi Arabia. A comparison is made between the soil resistances predicted by dynamic analysis and the actual measured capacities from the load tests.

INTRODUCTION

A static analysis is done usually prior to load testing, in order to provide a preliminary indication of the pile penetration depths that are to be expected for the design ultimate pile capacities. The engineering properties of weak coral-derived rock and carbonate sediments can be established from standard penetration resistances (SPT N-values) measured during sub-surface investigations. Limiting values of unit frictional resistances and end bearing to be adopted, should be in accordance with those recommended by McClelland (1974), Agarwal et al (1977), and Hagenaar (1982).

The ultimate capacities calculated for the various pile types can then be used in a wave-equation analysis in order to establish suitable hammer sizes and penetration rates.

The soil resistances predicted by the dynamic analysis for 25 test piles are compared statistically in this paper with the measured ultimate bearing capacities from the load tests.

A linear relationship is established between the computed and measured capacities, in order to obtain a more accurate simplified prediction of the static bearing capacity of piles driven in coral and carbonate sediments.

SUB-SURFACE CONDITIONS

All test piles are installed in coral formations and the mainly cohesionless carbonate sediments encountered offshore along the Red Sea coast of Saudi Arabia, near Jeddah and Yanbu. A generalized cross section showing typical geological surface features is shown in Figure 1. A detailed description of sub-surface conditions encountered at the location of the test piles can be found in the publications by Hagenaar et al (1981, 1982, 1983).

COMPUTED PILE BEARING CAPACITIES

The first series of load tests revealed that the side friction of the driven steel piles was very low, and did not increase significantly with depth (Hagenaar, 1982). A

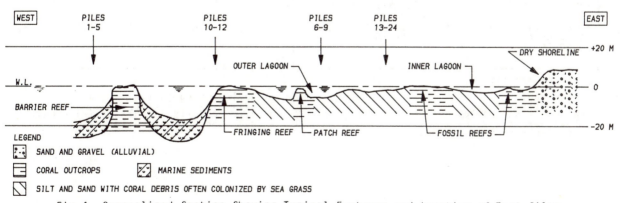

Fig.1 Generalized Section Showing Typical Features and Location of Test Piles

TABLE 1

Description of Test Piles and Dynamic Analysis

Pile No	Pile Data Description	L (m)	D (m)	Hammer Data Type	E_R (kN-m)	Driving Record N (bl/25cm)	e_i (%)	Dynamic Analysis JP (sec/m)	JS (sec/m)	Q_c (kN)	Load Test Q_m (kN)
1	1422 mm o.d. steel (open)	66.5	37.7	Diesel Kobe KB 80	216	27	90	0.45	0.3	6,200	6,541
2	" (open)	73.2	44.4	"	216	80	90	0.45	0.3	11,000	7,846
3	" (plugged)	22.3	10.8	"	216	19	90	0.45	0.3	3,800	2,239
4	" (plugged)	42.0	30.4	"	216	42	90	0.45	0.3	7,800	5,786
5	" (plugged)	48.3	36.8	"	216	170	90	0.45	0.3	14,000	>6,070
6	614 mm o.d. steel (closed)	29.0	28.0	Diesel Kobe K-45	132	8	65	0.49	0.16	932	1,765
7	" (closed)	15.0	11.5	"	132	21	76	0.49	0.16	1,961	2,314
8	" (closed)	27.0	26.5	"	132	18	76	0.49	0.16	1,765	2,550
9	" (closed)	24.0	20.5	"	132	19	76	0.49	0.16	1,814	2,942
10	914.4 mm o.d. steel (open)	31.1	30.5	Diesel Delmag D-46	143	21	60	0.49	0.16	2,599	3,315
11	" (closed)	46.0	45.0	"	143	57	76	0.49	0.16	5,345	6,600
12	" (closed)	31.5	30.7	"	143	37	72	0.49	0.16	4,756	5,982
13	" (open)	56.2	33.7	Delmag D-62	143	20	83	0.49	0.16	4,609	4,904
14	864 mm o.d. steel (open)	56.6	34.9	"	143	23	83	0.49	0.16	5,149	3,530
15	" (open)	37.6	15.5	"	143	6	83	0.49	0.16	1,716	1,916
16	" (open)	46.0	26.1	"	143	38	83	0.49	0.16	5,688	4,904
17	762 mm o.d. steel (open)	31	20.2	"	143	11	83	0.49	0.16	2,403	2,354
18	864 mm o.d. steel (open)	48	23.8	"	143	16	83	0.49	0.16	2,942	4,021
19	" (open)	47	24.0	"	143	10	72	1.48	0.49	1,863	2,256
20	" (open)	48.4	11.3	Steam Vulcan 360	245	22	70	1.48	0.49	4,904	5,639
21	762 mm o.d. steel (closed)	37.1	10.3	Diesel Mitsubishi MH 72 B	212	31	82.5	1.31	0.49	4,413	4,904
22	" (closed)	30.4	11.5	"	212	29	90	1.48	0.49	3,236	3,089
23	914 mm o.d. steel (closed)	46.8	19.2	Steam Menck 1500	184	35	88	1.48	0.49	4,413	>4,904
24	762 mm o.d. steel (closed)	27.5	10.5	Diesel Mitsubishi MH 72 B	212	15	82.5	1.31	0.49	2,354	3,531
25	60 cm octagonal prestressed concrete	34	18.1	Diesel Kobe KB 45	132	18	76	0.49	0.16	3,000	2,354

Description of Symbols:

L = Pile Length
D = Penetration
E_R = Maximum rated energy
N = Blows per last 25 cm
e_i = Efficiency of hammer impact

JP = Soil damping factor at tip
JS = Soil damping factor along shaft
Q_c = Pile capacity calculated (wave-equation)
Q_m = Measured ultimate pile capacity

limiting value of 20 kN/m2 for the unit shaft friction was adopted for the static analysis.

Limiting values for unit point resistances were correlated with SPT N-values measured in boreholes near or at the location of the test piles. Figure 2 shows the relationship established (Hagenaar, 1982), for both open- and closed- ended piles.

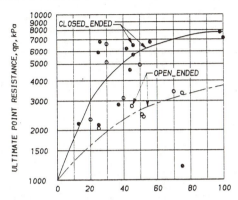

Fig.2 Limiting Point Resistance vs. SPT N - values.

The slow maintained load method referred to as standard loading procedure in the ASTM Designation D-1143 was used for the testing. Figure 3 shows the load/settlement curves of 4 test piles.

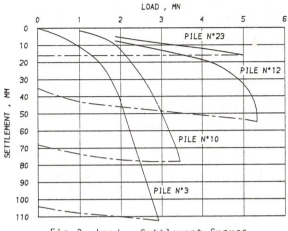

Fig.3 Load - Settlement Curves

DYNAMIC ANALYSIS

The wave equation analysis by computer (WEAP, PANWEQ, etc.) was used for hammer selection and to establish driving criteria for installation of the piles upon completion of the load tests.

The pile capacities Qc calculated by dynamic analysis, for the final number of blows per last 25 cm measured during installation of the test piles, did not correspond with the ultimate bearing capacities Qm established from the load test results (Table 1).

The data presented in this paper were not available during installation of the piles for the various offshore projects involved. Consequently, the bearing capacity versus penetration rates curves, established by the wave equation analysis, were reconstructed by applying a site specific ratio Qm/Qc. Final sets were then established for installation of the piles.

A second method consisted of varying soil damping factors. It seemed that damping factors of 1.48 sec/m at the tip and 0.49 sec/m along the shaft were more appropriate than the Smith's values of 0.49 and 0.16 sec/m respectively. However, as can be seen from Table 1, differences still existed (test piles 19 - 34).

PILE INSTALLATION AND LOAD TESTS

Table 1 shows the pile and hammer data, the number of blows per last 25 cm at which driving was stopped, and the efficiency of the hammer during the final blows.

The ultimate compression capacities were derived using various interpretation methods. Allowable pile loads were established by using a factor of safety of 2, or by employing maximum settlement criteria (for example test pile 3 in Figure 3).

RELATIONSHIP BETWEEN COMPUTED AND MEASURED CAPACITIES

Interpretation of Data

Figure 4 shows the measured pile capacities versus the predicted pile capacities from the wave equation analysis (Table 1).

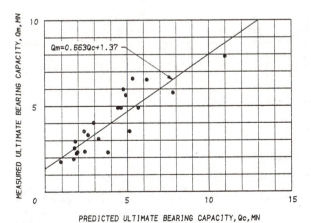

Fig.4 Relationship between Measured and Computed Pile Capacities

The following statistical interpretation method, suggested by Rausche et al (1972), and Olsen and Flaate (1967), has been used to predict the ultimate pile bearing capacity in the field.

Applying linear regression analysis, the most probable values of A and B can be estimated in order to establish the best fit linear relationship between Q_m and Q_c according to:

$$Q_m = A Q_c + B \qquad (1)$$

The linear relationship derived is shown in Figure 4. The correlation factor 0.87 indicates a good correlation.

Adjustment of Dynamic Analysis

To check the degree of conformance with the pile load test results, the pile capacities established by the wave equation were recalculated using the statistically adjusted form of equation (1), that is :

$$Q_c^a = 0.663 \, Q_c + 1.37 \qquad (2)$$

The measured versus recalculated pile capacities are shown in Figure 5.

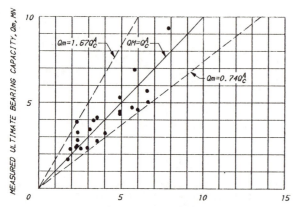

Fig.5 Comparison of Measured and Recalculated Pile Capacities (from
statistical adjusted form).

The regression line is now $Q_m = Q_c^a$, with a correlation coefficient of 0.89. The mean value of $Q_m/Q_c^a = 1.03$ and the standard deviation 0.2. The coefficient of variation is 20%, that is about 67% of the piles have calculated capacities within 20% of the measured values.

CONCLUSIONS

The comparisons show that the pile dynamic analysis by wave equation gives a good correlation with the static measurements on the test piles. The statistically adjusted form gives an acceptable prediction of the ultimate bearing capacity of piles driven into coral and carbonate sediments.

It is essential that the hammer energy applied to the pile is measured during installation, as this may differ significantly from the values used in the dynamic analysis.

A selection of a safety factor, for establishing allowable pile design loads, should not only consider inaccuracies in the calculations, but also ensure that settlements under design loads remain relatively small. The safety factor of 2 used in the evaluation of axial pile load test results should, therefore, be multiplied with the factor 1.67 (Figure 5) needed to account for the inaccuracies. Consequently, a factor of safety of 3.34 is recommended for predicting allowable pile loads from the recalculated ultimate pile capacities by wave equation.

REFERENCES

Agarwal, S.L., Malhotra, A.K. & Banerjee, R. (1977). Engineering Properties of Calcareous Soils affecting the Design of Deep Penetration Piles for Offshore Structures. 9th annual O.T.C., Houston, Texas, OTC 2792, 503-512.

McClelland, B. (1974). Design of Deep Penetration Piles for Ocean Structures, Journal of the Geotechnical Engineering Division, Proc. of the ASCE, Vol. 100, No. GT7, July, 705-747.

Hagenaar, J. and van den Berg, J. (1981). Installation of Piles for Marine Structures in the Red Sea, X ICSMFE, Stockholm, 8/29, 727-730.

Hagenaar, J. (1982). The use and interpretation of SPT results for the determination of axial bearing capacities of piles driven into carbonate soils and coral. Proc. of ESOPT II, Amsterdam, 51-55.

Hagenaar, J., Sijtsma, H., and Wolsleger, A. (1983). Selection and use of piles for marine structures in coral formations and carbonate sediments. Conference on piling and ground treatment for foundations, the Institutions of Civil Engineers, London, 47-56.

Olsen, R.E., and Flaate, K.S. (1967). Pile-Driving Formulas for Friction Piles in Sand. Journal fo the Soil Mechanics and Foundations Division, Proc. of the ASCE, Vol. 93, no. SM6, November, 279 - 296.

Rausche,F., Moses, F., and Goble, G.G. (1972). Soil Resistance Predictions from Pile Dynamics. Journal of the Soil Mechanics and Foundations Division, Proc. of the ASCE, Vol. 98, No. SM9, Sept., 917 - 937.

Full scale load tests for offshore piles

Essais de charge à grande échelle pour des pieux offshore

IQBAL H. KHAN, Associate Professor of Civil Engineering, University of Garyounis, Benghazi, Libya

SYNOPSIS   Results of compression and tension load tests on offshore piles are presented. The piles were driven about 12.0 metres below the sea bed level into the soft limestone formation. The load settlement behaviour was found to be almost linear elastic. The ultimate load capacity predicted from static formulas is found to correlate well with the load test. Dynamic formulas are found to underestimate the pile capacity in the present case.

INTRODUCTION

A load test on one or more prototype piles is usually an integral part of all important works founded on piles. Such tests are carried out to determine the load carrying capacity of piles or to obtain values of in-situ soil parameters to be used for back analysis of data or for design. Reliable and useful data can be obtained from such tests only if the test pile is carefully instrumented, properly installed and the test carried out under expert supervision. Offshore testing work introduces many other problems as well eg. wind and wave attacks. Such tests are therefore highly expensive and very few have been reported in literature.

Construction of docks and harbours and more recently offshore oil, gas and sea bed mineral wealth exploration, has resulted in a large increase in offshore construction activity. This paper describes the results of compression and tension tests carried out on driven steel piles during the construction of a jetty. The results are compared with the theoretical estimates and some conclusions of practical significance are drawn.

SOIL AND PILE DATA

The jetty 1.6 kilometers long has been constructed to accommodate oil tankers of upto 50,000 tons DWT. The jetty is supported on 243 driven steel piles, their diameter varying from 0.86 m to 2.2 m; and length varying from 22 m to 25 m. These piles were driven by a Delmag (D-55) hammer; 9.0 to 12.0 metres below the sea floor level and grouted into the soft limestone layer, which is the main formation encountered. The limestone is fissured, weak and of organic origin, overlain by a shallow layer of calcareous sand (Unit weight 2.0 g/ec). The Stress-Strain relationship of limestone is found to be of the brittle type with a peak value of the resistance at a relatively small strain. It has a cohesion (c_v) of 1.3 kg/cm^2 and angle of internal friction ($\emptyset$) of 35°. The average unit weight is 2.1 g/c.c.

For structural design the maximum wave height is taken to be 8.0 metres with a period of 10 seconds. A maximum wind velocity of 150 kilometre/hour and a maximum current velocity of 2.0 knots was assumed. The temperature range was taken to be 15° to 50^oC.

Fig. 1 gives the general view of the jetty. Fig. 2 give the borehole log of the test site, sea water depth and the pile position. Typical driving record of the test pile is shown in Fig. 3. Table I gives the relevant pile and hammer data.

Test Set Up

Load on test piles was applied by four hydraulic jacks acting against a steel beam welded to anchor piles. Loading sequence is shown in Figs.4 and 5. Movement of pile head as well as of anchor piles and the beam were recorded by micrometer gauges.

RESULTS

Though several piles were tested only typical results are being presented. All tests were carried out to 2-3 times the design load. Fig.4 and Fig. 5 give, respectively, typical pile behavior in compression and tension load tests. In the compression test, total settlement at maximum test load is 17.6 mm and most of it is recovered on release of load, the net settlement being only 2.9 mm. The rate of settlement at the last increment of loading is 0.029 mm/ton. The tension pile is found to heave 24 mm at full test load. On release of load the net heave is only 9.5 mm.

ANALYSIS

Various criteria are employed to determine the ultimate load capacity of pile from a load test data. Chellis (1961) has given as many as seventeen different rules, based on such criteria as

Fig.1 General View Of Jetty under Construction.

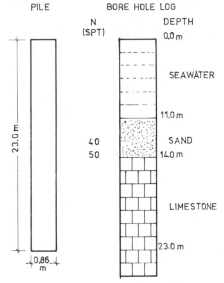

Fig.2 Bore hole Log of Site and a Test Pile.

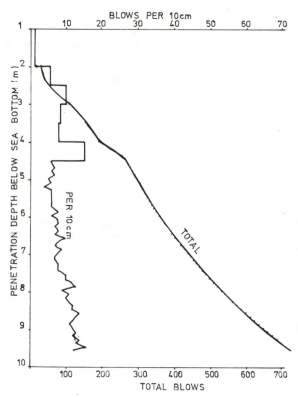

Fig.3 Typical Driving Record of Test Piles.

For a single compressible pile, end bearing on a rigid layer, Poulos and Davis (1974) have shown that the pile top displacement is a function of L/d and E_p/E_R (symbols are defined in Table I). Following their procedure, the pile top displacement in the present case is computed to be about 8.0 m.m. The actual measured elastic displacement is about twice this value. Obviously, this difference is due to the fact that the limestone formation is not rigid but soft and compressible.

settlement, net settlement, elastic settlement, rate of settlement etc. etc. Judged by any of these criteria, it is obvious that the load capacity of piles tested is at least 700 tons in compression and may actually be much more. Much of the settlement is linear elastic. Similarly for the pullout test, the Uplift capacity is at least equal to the test load and major portion of heave (14.5 mm) is elastic. Since the piles have not been loaded to failure a detailed analysis is difficult. Whittaker and Cooke (1966) have shown that the full mobilisation of skin and base resistance does not proceed simultaneously. Pull out tests have been carried out by many workers eg. Ireland (1957), Vesic (1970); Das and Seeley (1975). Their conclusion is that the skin friction is approximately the same in tension as in compression. In practice, however it is taken to be smaller in tension (Tomlinson 1971).

TABLE I

Pile and Hammer Data

Parameter	Symbol	Value
Length of Pile	l	23.0 m
Embedded length	L	9.0 m
Diameter - outer	d	0.86 m
- Inside		0.83 m
Pile Weight	W_p	9.1 tons
Hammer Weight	W	5.4 tons
Fall of Hammer	H	3.0 m
Final Set	S	0.0083 m/blow
Modulus of Elasticity		
i) Pile	E_p	21×10^6 tons/m^2
ii) Limestone	E_R	20×10^4 tons/m^2

Note: 1 ton equal 9.8 KN

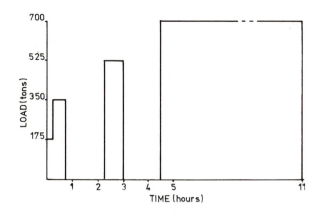

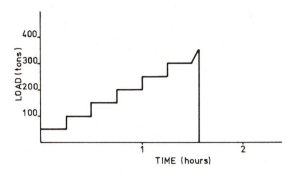

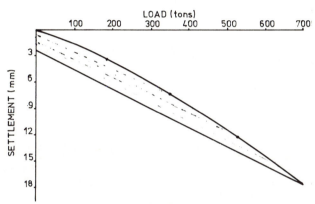

Fig.4 Loading Sequence and Load-Settlement
Behaviour of Pile (Compression Test)

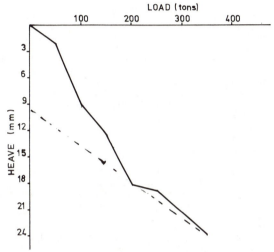

Fig.5 Loading Sequence and Heave of Pile
(Tension Test)

Estimates of the load capacity of piles are usually based on the so called static and dynamic
formulas. Dynamic formulas do not take into account the soil properties but the static formulas are heavily dependent on the correct evaluation of various soil parameters. The precise
expressions for the various formulas, their
derivation and their limitations are given in
all standard texts, eq. Chellis (1961); Bowles
(1982). Table II gives the load capacity of the
test pile according to some of the more common
formulas. All parameters required in these calculations are given in Table I. The 3.0 m thick
loose sand layer (Fig.2) is taken into consideration as a surcharge but neglected for skin friction. The factor of safey from static formulas
is about 5 in compression and about 3 in tension. This correlates well with the actual test
data. All the dynamic formulas however appear to
underestimate the pile capacity in the present
case. The Michigan Study (1965) however concluded that the dynamic formulas predicted higher
estimates in some cases and lower in some other
cases.

CONCLUSIONS

Results of a full scale load test on offshore
piles are presented. For these large diameter,

TABLE II

Ultimate Pile Capacity From Formulas

FORMULA	Reference	Capacity (tons)	
	Number	Shaft	Base
Static			
Tomlinson	9	1557	450
Vesic	10	1387	450
Meyerhof	6	1823	450
Dynamic			
HILEY	1,2	501 tons	
JANBU	2,5	526 tons	
Engg. News	1,2	480 tons	
Navy-Mekay	1,2	1296 tons	

Coeff. of Earth Pressure K=1.5 and α=0.7(assumed)

driven steel piles, bearing on soft limestone
the load settlement behaviour is found to be
almost linear elastic. It is suggested that at
least some tests should be carried out to failure to give a better insight of pile behaviour
upto the yield point.

The ultimate capacity predicted from static formulas correlates well with the observed pile
behaviour but correct evaluation of soil and
rock parameters is necessary. Dynamic formulas
appear to underestimate the pile capacity in
the present case.

ACKNOWLEDGEMENT

The author wishes to express his thanks to Engineers El Fariha and S. Zakaria who painstakingly
collected most of the data presented in this
paper.

REFERENCES

1. Bowles, J. E.; (1982) Foundation Analysis and
    Design; 816pp; McGraw Hill.
2. Chellis R. D.; (1961), Pile Foundation, 704pp
    McGraw Hill.
3. Das, B. M. and Seeley, G. R. (1975) Uplift
    Capacity of Burried Piles in Sand, ASCE,
    JGED (10); 101, October, pp 1091 - 1094,
4. Ireland, H. O. (1957), Pulling Tests on
    Piles in Sand, Proc. 4th, ICSMFE (2) pp 43-45
    London.
5. Janbu N. (1976) Static Bearing Capacity of
    Friction Piles. Proc. 6th. European Confer-
    ence on SMFE (1), pp 479-488.
6. Meyerhof G. G.(1976) Bearing Capacity and
    Settlement of Pile Foundations ASCE JGED
    (3) 102 March pp 195-228.
7. Michigan State Highway Commission (1965). A
    Performance Investigation of Pile Driving
    Hammers and Piles. Lansing, Michigan 338pp
8. Poulos, H G. and Davis E. H. (1974). Elas-
    tic Solutions for Soil and Rock Mechanics
    411pp. Wiley.
9   Tomlinson, M J.(1975). Foundation Design and
    Construction 785pp Pitman
10. Vesic, A, S. (1970) Testson Instrumented
    Piles, Ogeechee River Site, ASCE JSMFD (2)
    96, March, pp561-584,
11 Whittaker T. and Cooke, R. W.(1966) An In-
    vestigation of shaft and Base Resistance of
    Large Bored Piles in London Clay Proc
    Conf. on Large Bored Piles ICE London pp
    7 - 49,

Pieux battus sollicités en tension

Tension load tests on driven piles

J-F. NAUROY, Institut Français du Pétrole, Rueil-Malmaison, France
F. BRUCY, Institut Français du Pétrole, Rueil-Malmaison, France
P. LE TIRANT, Institut Français du Pétrole, Rueil-Malmaison, France

RESUME   Le développement prévu des plates-formes à lignes tendues pour l'exploitation des gisements d'hydrocarbures par grandes profondeurs d'eau pose le problème nouveau de la tenue des pieux d'ancrage sollicités en tension. Dans ce contexte, trois pieux très instrumentés ont été battus dans différents sols : limons, sables lâches et formation carbonatée. Après mise en place, les pieux ont été soumis à divers types de sollicitations, en particulier des chargements statiques et cycliques en tension. Les résultats obtenus ont permis de préciser notamment :
- l'évolution des contraintes effectives dans le sol durant le battage et la reconsolidation du sol après battage,
- la mobilisation du frottement latéral en chargement statique,
- l'influence des sollicitations cycliques et de la vitesse de chargement sur le frottement latéral et le déplacement du pieu.

INTRODUCTION

Le développement prévu de plates-formes à lignes tendues (tension leg platforms) pour l'exploitation des gisements d'hydrocarbures en mer par des profondeurs d'eau de 200 à 300 mètres à plus d'un millier de mètres, pose le problème nouveau de la tenue des pieux d'ancrage sollicités en tension statique et cyclique. En règle générale, le comportement d'une fondation est jugé satisfaisant lorsque les déplacements réversibles et irréversibles, résultant de l'application des cas extrêmes de chargement, demeurent en-deçà de certaines limites tolérables vis-à-vis des critères de rupture du sol de fondation et des impératifs fonctionnels de l'ouvrage. Dans le cas d'une plateforme à lignes tendues, les déplacements réversibles des pieux d'ancrage resteront toujours négligeables vis-à-vis de l'allongement propre des lignes; en revanche, il est essentiel de savoir estimer les risques de déplacements irréversibles des pieux et leur évolution dans le temps car, contrairement au cas des pieux travaillant en compression, tout mouvement irréversible du pieu vers le haut se traduit par une baisse de capacité.

Dans ce contexte, un important programme d'expérimentation a été entrepris, dès 1978, dans le cadre de l'Association de Recherche en GEotechnique MArine (ARGEMA), sur le comportement des pieux soumis à des charges statiques et cycliques en tension. Puisque les pieux de fondation ou d'ancrage en mer sont, le plus souvent, mis en place par battage, trois pieux d'une trentaine de centimètres de diamètre, très instrumentés, ont été battus dans trois types de sols représentatifs de sédiments fréquemment rencontrés en mer: limons normalement consolidés, limons et sables lâches, formation carbonatée plus ou moins cimentée. Une étude géotechnique très complète a été effectuée sur les trois sites d'expérimentation par carottages et mesures in situ. Parallèlement des études de laboratoire ont été conduites sur le comporte-

ment statique et cyclique des sols concernés et sur la tenue de petits pieux dans ces matériaux. Dans cette communication, on a choisi de traiter trois aspects importants :
- le battage et la reconsolidation du sol autour du pieu,
- la mobilisation du frottement latéral en chargement statique en tension,
- le comportement des pieux sous sollicitations cycliques.

1 - EXPERIMENTATION EFFECTUEE

1.1. Sols

L'étude expérimentale du comportement des pieux en tension a été conduite à terre dans des dépôts de sédiments représentatifs des sols rencontrés couramment en mer :
- limons très plastiques (IP $\geqslant$ 50), normalement consolidés : site de Cran,
- limons peu plastiques et sables lâches : site de Plancoët,
-formation carbonatée d'âge tertiaire, constituée de sables coquilliers et coralliens (faluns) très compressibles et fragiles, de granulométrie étalée, avec des couches légèrement cimentées de quelques centimètres d'épaisseur : site de Plouasne.

Une campagne très complète de reconnaissance des sols a été préalablement menée sur chacun des sites : carottages, profils pénétrométriques, pressiométriques (pressiomètres Ménard et autoforeur) et scissométriques, diagraphies nucléaires. Une étude géotechnique assez exhaustive a été effectuée en laboratoire sur les carottes prélevées : identification, essais oedométriques, essais triaxiaux standards et cycliques ....
La coupe lithologique de chacun des sites est reportée sur la figure 1.

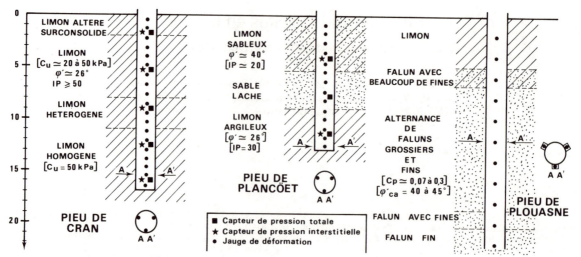

Fig. 1 - Coupe lithologique des sols et descriptif des pieux battus, instrumentés.

1.2. Pieux

Les pieux expérimentaux sont des tubes en acier d'environ 30cm de diamètre, mis en place par battage. A Cran et à Plancoët les pieux sont fermés à leur extrémité inférieure et battus respectivement jusqu'à 17 et 13 mètres de profondeur. A Plouasne, le pieu est ouvert (à la manière des pieux offshore en général) et battu jusqu'à 22,5m de profondeur. L'instrumentation des pieux comprend des jauges de déformation et des capteurs de pression interstitielle et de contrainte totale (Fig. 1)

De plus, à Cran, des piézomètres disposés à différentes distances du pieu permettent de suivre l'évolution de la pression interstitielle durant la reconsolidation du sol après le battage.

1.3. Sollicitations appliquées

Après mise en place par battage, différents types de sollicitations ont été appliquées à ces pieux:
- essais dynamiques par chute libre d'une masse de 400 kg sur la tête du pieu,
- essais statiques en tension par paliers,
- essais cycliques en tension (de 1000 à 10 000 cycles) entre deux bornes de chargement et essais "tempête". Quelques essais statiques et cycliques en compression ont été également effectués sur le pieu de Cran.

2 - BATTAGE DES PIEUX ET RECONSOLIDATION DU SOL

2.1. Diagrammes de battage et caractéristiques du sol.

Les diagrammes de battage et les profils pressiométriques et pénétrométriques sur les trois sites de Cran, Plancoët et Plouasne sont réunis sur la figure 2. Indépendamment de la puissance des marteaux utilisés, on constate que les diagrammes de battage demeurent pratiquement uniformes (nombre de coups quasiment constant par unité de longueur) :
- dans le limon de Cran, sur les 17 mètres de pénétration,
- dans la formation carbonatée de Plouasne entre 5 et 19 mètres de profondeur.

Bien que la surface latérale des pieux dans le sol croisse linéairement avec la pénétration, les forces réactives demeurent pratiquement constantes : on en conclut que le frottement latéral sol-pieu au battage est quasiment nul et que la résistance au battage provient uniquement des efforts en pointe et, éventuellement, du frottement de la couche supérieure de limon à Plouasne.

Mais si les diagrammes de battage sont comparables, les phénomènes mis en jeu sont fondamentalement différents suivant la nature du sol :

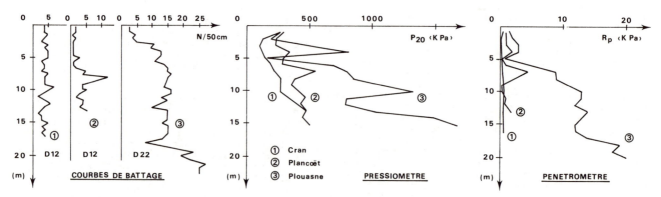

Fig. 2 - Courbes de battage et profils pénétrométriques et pressiométriques sur les trois sites d'essais.

- dans le limon de Cran, la pression interstitielle s'accroît durant le battage, de sorte que
les contraintes effectives et le frottement à
l'interface sol-pieu tendent vers zéro. La même
explication prévaut probablement pour le site de
Plancoët dans les couches de limon encadrant la
couche de sable,

- dans la formation carbonatée très perméable de
Plouasne, l'annulation du frottement latéral observée ne peut être imputée à l'accroissement de
pression interstitielle mais se trouve reliée à
la grande compressibilité du matériau. Des essais
de laboratoire réalisés avec le même matériau
ont en effet montré que la contrainte normale
σ'_r au fût du pieu battu est inférieure à la contrainte σ'_{r_0} dans le sol au repos, de sorte que
le frottement latéral est considérablement réduit (Nauroy et al. 1983). Ce mécanisme s'est
avéré irréversible.

2.2. Reconsolidation des sols fins après battage.

Dans les sols fins, on observe une reconsolidation du sol après battage. Ce phénomène a été
particulièrement étudié dans le cas du limon
très plastique de Cran (Fig. 3).

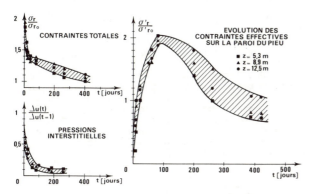

Fig. 3 - Reconsolidation du sol après battage.

D'après les mesures effectuées, on observe que :
- les surpressions interstitielles induites au
cours du battage se dissipent relativement vite,
- les contraintes totales sur le fût du pieu,
qui avaient considérablement augmenté du fait du
refoulement du sol par la pénétration du pieu
fermé (en pointe), diminuent aussi, mais plus
lentement.

Cette décroissance des contraintes totales ne
peut provenir que d'une diminution du volume du
sol remanié et comprimé qui entoure le pieu,
c'est-à-dire d'une reconsolidation : consolidation liée d'abord à la dissipation des surpressions interstitielles, puis à un réarrangement des
particules fines. Tant que la contrainte totale
sur le fût du pieu est supérieure à la contrainte totale horizontale du sol, on obtient une
consolidation du matériau, qui entraîne à son
tour une diminution des contraintes (relaxation)
de façon que le système évolue vers l'équilibre.

Il résulte des mesures effectuées que la contrainte radiale effective σ'_r s'exerçant sur le
pieu (Fig. 3), probablement voisine de zéro
après battage, croît d'abord jusqu'à un maximum
correspondant à la dissipation des surpressions
interstitielles, puis tend progressivement vers

une limite qui paraît être la contrainte horizontale du sol au repos. L'importance du maximum
est liée au refoulement résultant de l'extrémité
fermée du pieu.

Puisque le frottement latéral est directement
proportionnel à la contrainte effective radiale
σ'_r normale au pieu, il convient d'être très
prudent dans les conclusions à tirer d'un essai
statique en tension ou bien de mesures dynamiques
effectuées sur un pieu battu dans un sol fin.

3 - MOBILISATION DU FROTTEMENT LATERAL DES PIEUX EN CHARGEMENT STATIQUE.

La charge est appliquée par paliers d'incréments
égaux, de durée une heure. La détermination de
la répartition des charges dans le pieu s'effec-
tue à partir des déformations du pieu à différents niveaux.

3.1. Pieu battu dans le limon plastique de Cran.

L'essai de tension a été réalisé 260 jours après
le battage ; les surpressions interstitielles
sont alors dissipées, mais les contraintes conti-
nuent d'évoluer (Cf. 2.2.). A chaque niveau, le
frottement latéral est mobilisé progressivement
jusqu'à une valeur limite liée à la résistance
au cisaillement du sol. Le frottement limite est
atteint pour une même valeur du déplacement local (environ 1,5 mm, soit 5/1000 du diamètre du
tube) quel que soit le niveau considéré (Fig.4)

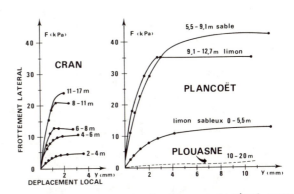

Fig. 4 - Mobilisation du frottement latéral sous
chargement statique en tension

Par ailleurs, les contraintes sur le pieu évoluent
très peu au cours du chargement.

3.2. Pieu battu dans les limons et sables de Plancoët.

Les courbes de mobilisation du frottement latéral
représentées sur la figure 4 sont calculées pour
un essai en tension réalisé 120 jours après le
battage, par conséquent après dissipation des
surpressions interstitielles. La mobilisation du
frottement latéral est complète pour un déplacement local du pieu d'environ 7 mm dans le sable,
5 mm dans le limon sableux et 2,5 mm dans le limon argileux (soit respectivement 25/1000,
18/1000 et 9/1000 du diamètre du tube). Ce déplacement local critique semble être caractéristique du sol. Par ailleurs, on constate que la contrainte latérale du pieu augmente généralement
au cours de l'essai en tension et ceci d'autant
plus que le matériau est sableux.

3.3. Pieu dans la formation carbonatée de Plouasne

Le frottement latéral du pieu battu à Plouasne est négligeable dans les faluns (≤1 kPa). Comme indiqué plus haut (Cf. 2.1) la mise en place a quasiment annulé les contraintes radiales.

En revanche, il faut signaler à cette occasion qu'un pieu foré et cimenté réalisé sur le même site a mobilisé un frottement latéral de plus de 100 kPa. Ces résultats seront détaillés par ailleurs.

4 - COMPORTEMENT DES PIEUX SOUS SOLLICITATIONS CYCLIQUES.

On se propose ici d'illustrer un aspect du comportement des pieux sous sollicitations cycliques. On peut reporter sur les diagrammes de mobilisation du frottement latéral déjà présentés plus haut (Fig. 4) les points correspondants à la charge cyclique. Il apparaît sur l'exemple présenté

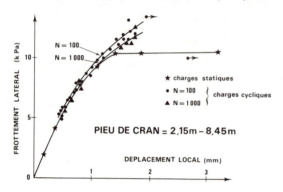

Fig. 5 - Frottement latéral sous charges statiques et cycliques.

figure 5 que le comportement de la fondation est globalement semblable sous les deux types de sollicitations statiques et cycliques. Cependant une analyse plus fine montre que pour un même déplacement local le frottement latéral diminue en fonction du nombre de cycles, traduisant un phénomène de dégradation cyclique. En revanche, l'effet favorable de la vitesse de chargement sur la rigidité de la fondation est mis en évidence par la position relative des points issus des essais de charge statique (vitesse lente) et cyclique (vitesse rapide). La figure 6 montre également l'effet de la vitesse de

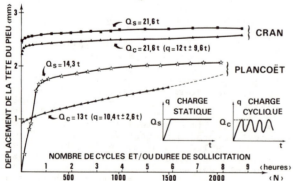

Fig. 6 - Déplacements en tête du pieu sous charge statique et cyclique.

chargement sur le comportement en tête du pieu. Dans le cas de Plancoët, la dégradation cyclique apparaît nettement si on compare les vitesses de déplacement en tête sous charge statique et cyclique (Fig. 6). En fait, comme on l'a montré par ailleurs (Puech, 1982), cette dégradation devient prépondérante par rapport à l'influence de la vitesse de chargement.

Ces quelques éléments confirment différentes observations publiées dans la littérature sur les effets contraires de la dégradation cyclique et de la vitesse de chargement cyclique.

CONCLUSIONS

Trois pieux très instrumentés ont été battus dans différents sols puis soumis à des sollicitations axiales statiques et cycliques. Les données recueillies sont très nombreuses ; on a fait ressortir les aspects suivants :
1. Suivant la nature du sol, l'annulation du frottement latéral au cours du battage ne recouvre pas nécessairement les mêmes phénomènes : augmentation de la pression interstitielle dans les argiles et limons, chute des contraintes effectives par compressibilité dans les sables carbonatés.
2. La contrainte effective normale au pieu évolue considérablement (dans les limons) au cours de la reconsolidation du sol après battage. Ce résultat incite à la plus grande prudence dans l'interprétation des résultats d'essais de chargements subséquents.
3. Le frottement latéral se mobilise progressivement avec la sollicitation axiale et atteint un palier pour un déplacement local du pieu dont la valeur est caractéristique du sol considéré.
4. Les essais de chargement cyclique mettent en évidence l'influence contraire de la vitesse de chargement et de la succession des cycles sur la rigidité de la fondation.

REMERCIEMENTS

Les auteurs remercient les membres de l'Association de Recherche en GEotechnique MArine de l'autorisation de publier les résultats de cette étude.

Les essais ont été effectués par le Laboratoire Régional des Ponts et Chaussées de St. Brieuc.

REFERENCES

Nauroy, J-F. and Le Tirant, P. (1983). Model Tests of Piles in Calcareous Sands. ASCE Speciality Conference : Geotechnical Practice in Offshore Engineering, pp. 356-369, Austin.

Puech, A., Brucy, F. and Ma, E. (1982). Tension Pile Design using Self-Boring Pressuremeter Test Results. Symposium on the Pressuremeter and its Marine Applications, Editions Technip, pp. 361-371, Paris.

Puech, A., (1982). Basic Data for the Design of Tension Piles in Silty Soils. Boss'82, 3rd International Conference on Behavior of Offshore Structures, pp. 141-157, MIT, Boston.

Side friction of piles in calcareous sands

Friction latérale des pieux dans les sables calcaires

I. NOORANY, Professor of Civil Engineering, San Diego State University, San Diego, California, USA

SYNOPSIS   Steel piles driven in calcareous sands develop considerably less side resistance than those driven in silica sands. This paper describes an investigation of the strength behavior and soil-steel friction of two noncemented calcareous sands, with particular emphasis on the effects of grain crushing on these properties. Results indicate that calcareous sands have very high friction angles, and average soil-steel friction angles. Grain crushing does not appear to reduce these properties. It is concluded that low side friction of steel piles driven in calcareous sands is caused by low effective soil-pile interface stresses rather than small soil-pile friction angles.

INTRODUCTION

Calcareous sands are composed primarily of calcium carbonate ($CaCO_3$) and are abundant in coastal zones and continental shelves of the warm equatorial regions of the ocean. They are composed of shells and skeletal remains of benthos (bottom dwelling) organisms such as corals, molluscs, and calcareous algae. Coral sands are products of erosion and slumping around coral reefs and atolls. Coral reefs are formations of calcium carbonate laid down by living plants (coraline algae) and animals (corals). They develop in shallow waters between 30 degrees south and 30 degrees north latitude (McClelland, 1974). Because calcareous sands are biogenic in origin, and are derived from mechanical erosion and breakdown of coral reefs and shells by wave action (a mechanism similar to the process of erosion of clastic rocks), they are referred to as bioclastic sediments (Seibod and Berger, 1982; Noorany, 1983).

During the past decade, it has been recognized that the geotechnical properties of calcareous sands are different from those of silica sands (McClelland, 1974 and 1980; Datta, et al., 1979; several papers in Demars and Chaney, 1981; Nauroy and Le Tirant, 1983; and Dutt and Cheng, 1984). In particular, experience with pile foundations driven in uncemented and partially cemented calcareous sands indicates that friction resistance on the sides of these piles is considerable lower than that in silica sands. (Angemeer, et al., 1973 and 1975; McClelland, 1974 and 1980; Agarwal, et al., 1977; Sullivan and Squire, 1980; Cottrill, 1982; Puyuelo, et al. 1983, Dutt and Cheng, 1984 among others). When this phenomenon was first noted, it was attributed to the relative softness of calcium carbonate compared to quartz. However, it was later realized that some calcareous sands develop higher interparticle friction than most terrestrial soils (McClelland, 1980; Beringen, et al., 1981; Noorany, 1982; Dutt and Cheng, 1984), indicating that factors other than soil friction might be responsible for the abnormally low side resistance of piles driven in calcareous sands.

SCOPE OF STUDY

The objective of this study was to investigate the internal friction and soil-steel friction of two noncemented calcareous sands, and to evaluate the influence of particle crushing on these properties. The sands were taken from two beaches: one on the island of Guam and the other in southern Florida. Isotropically consolidated-drained (ICD) triaxial compression tests were run on each soil to measure the stress-strain behavior and the effective friction angle, ϕ', in loose and dense states. The effective confining pressure varied from 100 kPa to 400 kPa. The loose condition was obtained by pouring (raining) the soil in the specimen mold. The dense condition was obtained by placing the soil in five layers and tamping. The controlling factor for each set of specimens was void ratio. The tests on crushed soil were run on the material which was partially crushed to obtain a finer grained soil with the same coefficient of uniformity as the natural soil shown in Figure 1. A few tests were also run on thoroughly crushed (ground) soil samples.

Soil-steel friction was measured in direct shear mode by sliding a 9cm x 9cm steel plate on the surface of compacted soil. The effect of particle crushing on soil-steel friction angle, δ, was also measured.

For comparison, a silica sand having a grain-size distribution similar to the two calcareous sands, was also tested. The test results were analyzed to evaluate the influence of soil crushing on shear behavior, and on soil-steel friction angle of calcareous sands.

SOIL DESCRIPTION AND PROPERTIES

The calcareous sand from Guam was a uniformly graded material with a carbonate content of more than 90%. The grain-size distribution curves for this soil, in natural, crushed and ground states, are shown in Fig. 1. The soil had both rounded and elongated particles with rough texture, and

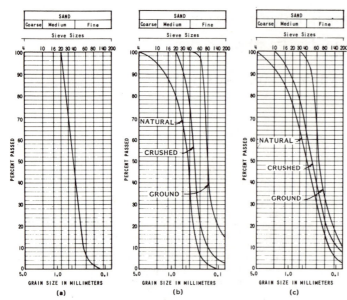

(a)   (b)   (c)

Fig. 2.   Electron Photomicrograph of Calcareous Sand from Guam

Fig. 1   Grain Size Distribution Curves for (a) Silica Sand, (b) Calcareous Sand from Guam and (c) Calcareous Sand from Florida

it also included some hollow particles as shown in Fig. 2. The specific gravity of solids was 2.80. The grain-size distribution curves for the calcareous sand from Florida are shown in Fig. 1. The specific gravity of solids was 2.84. The soil contained some flat pieces of broken shells as well as bulky particles with rough texture. The percentage of calcium carbonate was about 92.

The silica sand tested was a uniformly graded sand with a grain size distribution shown in Fig. 1. The soil consisted of bulky particles with smooth surfaces. The specific gravity of solids was 2.61.

RESULTS OF STRENGTH TESTS

The stress-strain and volume change characteristics of each sand under loose and dense conditions were measured in ICD triaxial compression tests. Tests were run both on dry and fully saturated samples. Back pressures of 400 to 500 kPa were used to obtain B values over 97%. To study the effect of particle crushing on the strength properties, tests were run at equal soil densities on natural, crushed and ground soil conditions.

Typical stress-strain and strain-volume change data measured on the calcareous sand from Guam are shown in Fig. 3, and a typical p-q plot is shown in Fig. 4. Similar results were obtained from a large number of triaxial tests on both calcareous sands; complete data can be seen in Noorany, 1982. A summary of the soil friction data is given in Table I.

The salient points of the triaxial test results are summarized below:

a. When compacted in identical manner, the calcareous sands tested had considerably higher void ratios than the silica sand (Table I). However, because a significant part of the voids were intraparticle voids they did not affect soil shearing resistance, especially at low stress levels. As stresses built up, some grain crushing occurred, but the amount of crushing in triaxial samples loaded to failure was very minor. This was determined from a comparison of grain size distribution curves before and after testing.

b. Despite a higher void ratio and crushability, calcareous sands possess very high internal friction angles. The friction angles of the two calcareous sands tested (44° to 49°) are significantly higher than those for most silica sands. The high values for loose condition are particularly surprising, although the limited data available support this finding (Datta et al., 1979 and 1980; Beringen et al., 1980; and Dutt and Cheng, 1984).

c. The high friction angles of the calcareous sands tested were not due to dilatational behavior during shear. In loose states both soils exhibited volume decrease, yet they had friction angles in the range of 44 to 46 degrees. Surface roughness at grain contact points, and the reinforcing effects of elongated flat particles in the soil matrix, might be responsible for high frictional resistance of calcareous sands.

d. The friction angle of the calcareous sands tested decreased with increase in confining pressure (Fig. 4). The decrease in ϕ' was noticeable at confining pressures higher than 300 kPa; at a confining pressure of 400 kPa, the amount of reduction in ϕ' value for both sands was from 2 to 4 degrees.

e. At equal void ratios, the friction angles of crushed calcareous sands were essentially the same as those of natural soil.

TABLE I

Results of Triaxial and Soil-Steel Friction Tests

Soil Type	Specific Gravity, G_s	Soil Condition	Void Ratio, e	Friction Angle, ϕ, Degrees	Soil-Steel Friction Angle δ, Degrees
Silica Sand	2.61	loose	0.90	35	21
		dense	0.73	40	20
Calcareous sand from Guam	2.80	loose	1.36	46	18
		dense	1.18	49	18
		loose,crushed	1.32	46	21
		loose,ground	1.32	46	--
		dense,crushed	1.12	48	22
Calcareous sand from Florida	2.84	loose	1.44	44	20
		medium	1.30	45	20
		dense	1.19	47	23
		medium,crushed	1.30	45	23
		medium,ground	1.30	45	--
		dense,crushed	1.06	49	23

Even when a thoroughly crushed (ground) soil was tested at the same void ratio as the natural soil, it had the same friction angle (Fig. 4).

RESULTS OF SOIL-STEEL FRICTION TESTS

The results of soil-steel friction tests are summarized in Table I. These results indicate that unlike ϕ' values, δ values for calcareous sands appear to be comparable to those of silica sands. The test results also indicate that the soil-steel friction angle, δ, did not change significantly with soil density. Also, as was the case for ϕ', the δ values for the natural and crushed soils were about the same. This finding was similar to the test results reported by Beringen et al. (1981), but Dutt and Cheng (1984) have reported higher δ values for another calcareous soil.

CONCLUSIONS

The side resistance developed on the surface of a pile driven in a soil can be expressed as:

$$f = \sigma'_n \tan \delta = K \sigma'_v \tan \delta \qquad (1)$$

where f is side friction; σ'_n is effective normal stress; σ'_v is effective vertical stress; K is coefficient of lateral pressure; and δ is soil-pile friction angle.

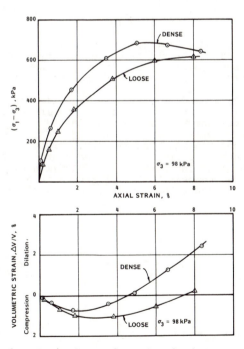

Fig. 3. Typical Results of Triaxial Compression Tests on Calcareous Sand from Guam

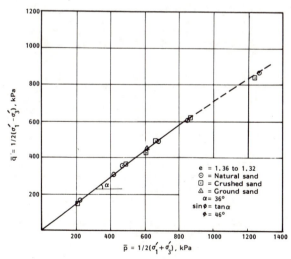

Fig. 4. p-q Diagram and Failure Line for Loose Calcareous Sand from Guam

The results of this study have eliminated the possibility that the frictional characteristics of calcareous sands are responsible for the low shaft resistance of piles. Therefore, by eliminating this factor, and on the basis of effective stress principles applied at the pile-soil interface, it appears that the only remaining cause of the observed low capacities of driven straight steel pipe piles in calcareous sands is that the effective normal stress, σ'_n acting perpendicular to the pile surface is much lower than expected. The possibility that the soil-pile interface stress is abnormally low was suggested by McClelland (1980), Nauroy and LeTirant (1983), and Dutt and Cheng, (1984).

The soil-pile interaction mechanism in calcareous sands is different from silica sand. When a pile is driven in a silica sand, the soil packs tightly around the pile and builds large soil-pile interface stresses. In calcareous sands, however, the soil is naturally very loose and pile driving vibrations are not very effective in densifying this type of soil which is composed of many flat particles and some bulky hollow particles. A driven pile causes the soil grains to crush rather than displace laterally. Consequently, the soil-pile interface stresses will be small.

Soil cementation can further influence the soil-pile interface stress. In a partially cemented soil, pile vibration during driving may create a small gap between the soil and the pile, decreasing the soil-pile interface stresses to very small values. The combination of these factors appears to be responsible for the low side resistance of piles in calcareous sands.

REFERENCES

Agarwal, S.L., Malhotra, A.K. and Banerjee, R., (1977). Engineering Properties of Calcareous Soils Affecting the Design of Deep Penetration Piles for Offshore Structures, Proc., 9th Offshore Tech. Conf., Vol. 1, 503-512, Houston.

Angemeer, J., Carlson, E.D. and Klick, J.H., (1973). Techniques and Results of Offshore Pile Load Testing in Calcareous Soils, Proc. 5th Offshore Tech. Conf., Vol. 2, 677-692, Houston.

Angemeer, J., Carlson, E.D., Stroud, S., and Kurzeme, M., (1975). Pile load Tests in Calcareous Soils Conducted in 400 ft of Water from a Semi-Submersible Exploration rig, Proc., 7th Offshore Tech. Conf., Vol. 2, 657-670, Houston.

Beringen, F.L., Kolk, H.J., and Windle, D., (1981). Cone Penetration and Lab. Testing in Marine Calcareous Sediments, Symp. Proc., Geotech. Prop., Behavior and Performance of Calcareous Soils, ASTM, STP 777, 179-209.

Cottrill, A., (1982). Concrete Plugs to the Rescue as Rankin's Piles Plunge Deeper, Offshore Engineer, Dec. 1982, p. 17.

Datta, M., Gulhati, S.K., and Rao, G.V., (1979). Crushing of Calcareous Sands During Shear, Proc., 11th Offshore Tech. Conf., Vol. 3, 1459-1467, Houston.

Datta, M., Gulhati, S.K., and Rao, G.V., (1980). An Appraisal of the Existing Practice of Determining the Axial Load Capacity of Deep Penetration Piles in Calcareous Sands, Proc., 12th Offshore Tech. Conf., Vol. 4, 119-130, Houston.

Demars, K.R. and Chaney, R.C., (Eds.), (1981). Geotech. Properties, Behavior and Performance of Calcareous Soils, ASTM, STP 777, 414 pp.

Dutt, R.N. and Cheng, A.P. (1984). Frictional Response of Piles in Calcareous Deposits. Proc., 16th Offshore Tech. Conf., Vol. 3, 527-534, Houston.

McClelland, B., (1974). Design of Deep Penetration Piles for Ocean Structures; Journal of the Geotech. Engineering Division, ASCE, Vol. 100, No. GT7, 705-747.

McClelland Engrs., Inc., (1980). Geotech. Considerations for Nearshore Foundation Design in Calcareous Material, Civil Engr. Lab., Naval Const. Battalion Center, Port Hueneme, PO No. N62583/80 M R028.

Nauroy, J.F. and LeTirant, P., (1983). Model Tests of Piles in Calcareous Sands, Proc., Conf., on Geotech. Practice in Offshore Engineering, ASCE, 356-369.

Noorany, I., (1982). Friction of Calcareous Sands, San Diego State Univ., Dept. of Civil Engineering, 1-68.

Noorany, I., (1983). Classification of Marine Sediments, San Diego State Univ., Dept. of Civil Engineering, 1-26.

Puyuelo, J.G., Sastre, J. and Soriano, A., (1983). Driven Piles in a Granular Calcareous Deposit, Proc., Conf., on Geotech. Practice in Offshore Engr., ASCE, 440-456.

Seibold, E. and Berger, W.H., (1982). The Sea Floor: An Introduction to Marine Geology, Springer-Verlag, Berlin, 288.

Sullivan, R.A. and Squire, J.M., (1980). Geotechnical Properties of West and North African Continental Shelf Sediments, Proc., 7th Regional Conf., of Africa on Soil Mech. and Found. Eng., Accra, Vol. 1, 43-53.

Dynamic and static tests on large diameter piles in hard calcareous clays

Essais dynamiques et statiques sur des pieux à grand diamètre dans des argiles dures calcaires

TED K. PARK, Senior Engineer, Dames & Moore, San Francisco, CA, USA
D. MICHAEL HOLLOWAY, Principal Engineer, InSituTech, Oakland, CA, USA
ROBERT D. DARRAGH, Partner, Dames & Moore, San Francisco, CA, USA
WAY Y. CHOW, Principal Engineer, International Engineering Co., San Francisco, CA, USA

SYNOPSIS   This paper presents case histories of 1.8 and 1.0 meter diameter pipe piles driven in very stiff to hard calcareous clays at the nearshore of the Port of Puerto Bolivar, Colombia. A field test program was performed to resolve uncertainties in estimating soil set-up, ultimate static capacity and pile driveability in calcareous clays. Pile driving behavior during initial and restrike driving was monitored with a pile driving analyzer for four 1.8 meter diameter piles driven by a Hydroblok HBM 1500 and two 1.0 meter diameter piles driven by a Delmag D80-12. A static load test also was performed on one 1.8 meter diameter pile in order to verify pile penetration criteria and to calibrate the dynamic test results. Based on the results of the test program the installation criteria, in terms of blowcount and minimum pile penetration, were refined and eased significantly once the large and rapid soil set-up contributions to long-term pile capacity were demonstrated.

INTRODUCTION

From June through December 1983, a major pile test program was conducted at a new port being built in Guijira Province, Colombia. High capacity piles were designed to support the Commodities Pier and adjacent Coal Berth facilities, founded in very stiff to hard calcareous cohesive soils underlying Puerto Bolivar.

The Commodities Pier, 282 meters long and 30 meters wide, was built in three sections, comprised of jack-up type steel hull barges. A total of 56 steel pipe piles (1.8-m-OD X 32mm wall thickness), open-ended, were installed to resist an ultimate compression load of 1520 tonnes. The piles were driven, or jacked and driven to final grade using a Hydroblok HBM 1500 with a maximum rated energy of 57 tonne-m (net impact energy of 40 tonne-m). A plan view of the Commodities Pier is given in Figure 1.

In addition to the large-diameter piles, the bridgeway connecting the Commodities Pier to shore employed smaller pipe piles (1.0-m-OD x 19mm wall thickness) driven vertically with a Delmag D80-12 having a maximum rated energy of 27 tonne-m. The Coal Berth facilities, located north of the Commodities Pier, also will be supported on 1.0-m-OD piles, some of which must develop ultimate compression loads as large as 860 tonnes, with batters as severe as 1H:2.5V.

It is well recognized that the predictions of long-term pile capacity and pile driveability for large diameter high capacity piling in calcareous clays involves considerable uncertainty. The relative contribution of cementation, the degree of remolding caused by pile installation, and the rate and amount of set-up (capacity gain) to be expected in such soils are not easily determined. Conventional design procedures were developed primarily for smaller piles and weaker clays. The effects of impact pile driving on the long-term bearing capacity in these calcareous soils could not be predicted with confidence, and the presence of carbonate-cemented concretions above the minimum design penetrations raised pile driveability concerns. Given

these significant uncertainties, a detailed field test program was a design requirement. Pertinent aspects of the program are highlighted in this paper.

SUBSURFACE CONDITIONS

Based on geophysical survey data, 13 exploratory borings and laboratory analyses of selected samples, the subsurface soils were characterized in terms of differing geologic age and engineering properties into three distinctive strata, as described below. The seafloor varied from 0 to 15m below sea level, with a tidal range of 15cm.

o Upper sand layer (SM) - Holocene deposits of loose to medium dense silty sands, 7 to 22 m thick, with occasional silts, shells and gravels.

o Middle clay layer (CL/CH) - Pleistocene deposits of stiff to very stiff calcareous silty clays (OCR = 4), 6 to 20m thick, with fair amount of the lag deposits at the base. The undrained shear strength was in the range of 0.65 to 1.9 kg/cm^2 with an average value of 1.0 kg/cm^2.

o Lower clay layer (CH) - Miocene marine deposits of hard calcareous clay (OCR = 5) with occasional layers of carbonate-cemented concretions. The average undrained shear strength was 2.0 kg/cm^2 per meter.

The pile design unit skin friction values were computed using shear strength reduction factors of 0.5 to 0.7 for the clay layers, estimated from the empirical criteria (1,5) that relate the adhesion between pile and soil to the undisturbed shear strength of clays. The minimum penetration depths were estimated based on the outside skin friction and the fully mobilized end bearing which is about 50 percent of the outside friction. The maximum penetration depths were estimated based on outside friction and end bearing on the steel cross section area only. The conservatism applied to the maximum design penetration was intended to account for variation

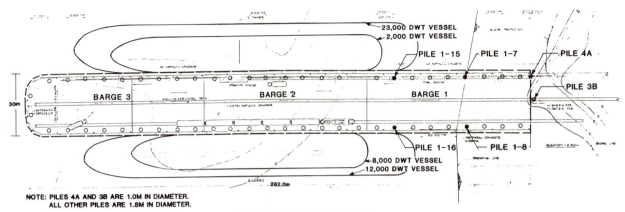

NOTE: PILES 4A AND 3B ARE 1.0M IN DIAMETER.
ALL OTHER PILES ARE 1.8M IN DIAMETER.

FIG. 1 COMMODITIES PIER PLAN

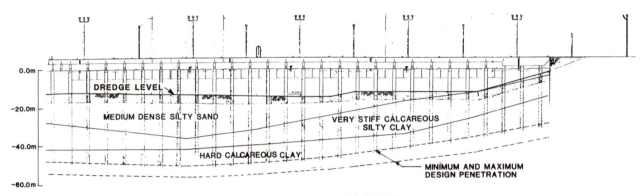

FIG. 2 SIMPLIFIED SOIL PROFILE

in soil strengths and the uncertainty in characterizing the behavior of the overconsolidated calcareous clays. This also considers the possibility of removing the soil plug if necessary to drive through the cemented zones.

TEST PROGRAM

The primary objectives of the field test program included:

o Establishment of suitable installation criteria for the Commodities Pier and Coal Berth piles;

o Verification that satisfactory long-term axial pile capacities could be achieved, and

o Evaluation of performance of the HBM 1500 and D80-12 pile drivers.

Dynamic monitoring of installation and restrike driving, using force and acceleration measurements at the pile butt, was performed to accomplish the above objectives. Pile driving episodes were monitored with a Pile Driving Analyzer for four 1.8m-OD piles and two 1.0-m-OD piles. A static load test was performed on one of the 1.8-m-OD piles in order to verify satisfactory pile penetration criteria and to calibrate the dynamic test results.

A total of eleven driving episodes were monitored using dynamic measurements. Both initial and restrike driving data were obtained for 1.8m-OD piles No. 1-7, 1-8 and 1-15 (the prefix 1-designating piles supporting

jack-up barge No. 1), as well as for 1.0m-OD bridgeway piles No. 4A and 3B. Only initial driving data were collected for pile No. 1-16, as it was subsequently loaded statically. Test pile locations and soil profile are shown on Figures 1 and 2.

Hammer Performance

The Hydroblok HBM 1500 performed consistently in driving the 1.8-m-OD piles, delivering maximum forces and transferred energies at the pile butt on the order of 1600 tonnes and 25 tonne-m, respectively. The transferred energies were 25 percent less than those predicted (32 tonne-m) in pre-field wave equation analyses, although the maximum butt force was well modeled.

During the first test stage, the Delmag D80-12 delivered only half the energy values predicted by wave equation analyses (11.0 tonne-m), and the 1.0m-OD Pile No. 4A could not be driven to the penetration required for the test. After thorough checkup of the hammer, and substitution of a new capblock material as recommended by the manufacturer, the field-measured performance during the second test stage was markedly improved. The maximum delivered energy to the piles was on the order of 8.5 tonne-m.

Field Estimated Pile Capacities

The piles drove rather easily to the required penetrations, indicating that only moderate soil resistance had to be overcome during pile installation, and that

no obstructions were encountered. The blowcounts with
the HBM hammer were 17 to 23 blows for the last 30 cm
penetration at the end of initial driving.

At the beginning of restrike, however, even only four
hours after installation, the blowcounts increased
from 20 to 48 or more for the first 30 cm penetration.
Clearly, substantial set-up had occurred in these
overconsolidated clays.

Case Method (2) predictions of pile capacity, and those
based on wave equation predictions for the monitored
driving episodes, are shown in Figure 3.

It is interesting to note that as restrike penetration
progressed, the blowcounts remained much higher than
those found at the end of initial driving, signifying
that setup effects were not completely reversed in
redriving.

Detailed Analyses

Further analyses of the dynamic measurement data were
performed in the office using the computer program
CAPWAP (4). The iterative wave equation solution procedure permits determination of soil resistance distribution and rheologic parameters that provide the best
prediction of field-measured force at the pile butt,
using the measured acceleration record as input to the
model. Ultimate pile capacities obtained from CAPWAP
results are also plotted in Figure 3. The higher
capacity predicted by the conventional wave equation
model relative to the CAPWAP predictions, is largely
attributable to a more optimistic estimate of hammer
performance than was observed in the field. The over-
prediction of Case Method capacities with respect to
CAPWAP results suggests that the Case damping parameter
(0.5) assumed in the field was too low. The CAPWAP
results should provide better estimates of pile capacity at the time of driving/restrike, since the soil
response is approximated most rigorously. However,
the CAPWAP method has difficulties in modeling soils
behavior for large diameter piles, especially under
the hard driving conditions.

Soil Resistance Distributions

Predictions of unit soil resistance versus depth
based on CAPWAP results, are presented in Figures 4
and 5 for piles No. 1-8 and 1-15, respectively. Data
from the end of initial (EOI) and beginning of restrike
(BOR) driving are included in these figures, along with
the laboratory-determined undrained shear strength
data of the samples obtained from the nearby borings.

The CAPWAP restrike results clearly illustrate soil
set-up effects. Most of the soil resistance increase
is detected in the middle clay stratum, where the hammer blow was able to fully mobilize the available soil
resistance. Since for pile 1-15 the beginning of restrike blowcount was extremely high (42 blows per first
2.5cm 47 hours after installation) it must be recognized
that neither the full shaft resistance in the lower
clay nor full toe capacity for this pile could be
detected by the blow. Therefore, the actual ultimate
capacity of this pile was appreciably higher than could
be determined from the dynamic tests alone.

Figure 6 shows the average value of skin friction (estimated from CAPWAP) divided by undrained shear strength
vs. rest period in the middle clay stratum. The average
skin friction values determined from initial driving
were in the range of 16 to 25 percent of the undrained
shear strength; at the beginning of restrike, the average skin friction increased to 47 to 68 percent of the
undrained shear strength depending on the rest period.

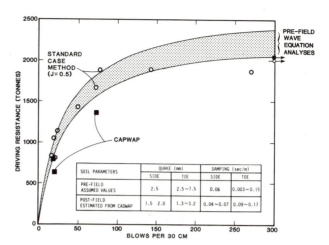

**FIG. 3 PREDICTED RESISTANCE VS BLOWCOUNT-
1.8mØ PILES/HBM1500**

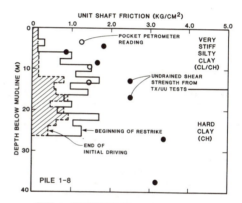

**FIG. 4 ESTIMATED UNIT SHAFT FRICTION
FROM CAPWAP**

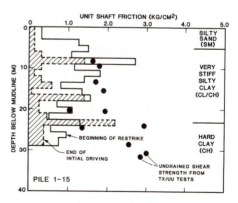

**FIG. 5 ESTIMATED UNIT SHAFT FRICTION
FROM CAPWAP**

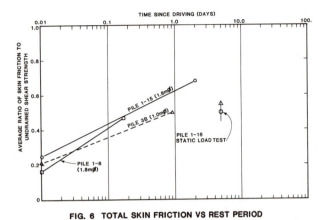

FIG. 6 TOTAL SKIN FRICTION VS REST PERIOD

If it is assumed that the inside friction is half of the outside friction (3), the skin friction developed at the beginning of restrike 47 hours after initial driving for pile 1-15, can be estimated as 45 and 23 percent of the undrained shear strength for the outside and inside shafts, respectively. The ultimate average outside friction values with time eventually is expected to exceed half of the undrained shear strength, which was assumed in design.

Static Load Test Results

The fundamental questions regarding pile capacity predictions based on dynamic analysis methods concern the correspondence between resistance mechanisms developed under dynamic and static loading conditions. Furthermore, the influence of inner soil plug behavior on the capacity predictions is not easily determined. (The soil plug rose to 2m ± of the mudline in all cases observed.) Obviously, a static load test provides the most certain evaluation of static pile performance under axial compression loads and the correlation between dynamic predictions based on restrike behavior and static behavior. Five days after installation to the minimum penetration, Pile No. 1-16 was statically loaded to 1520 tonnes (twice its design load) without reaching failure. Load levels were determined from strain gauges near the butt, which corrected for minor jack and loading eccentricities. The load-settlement data from the static test on Pile No. 1-16 are shown in Figure 7, along with CAPWAP analysis predictions based on restrike results from nearby Pile No. 1-15.

Damage to pile strain measurement systems below the mudline prevented the evaluation of static load transfer characteristics directly. Without achieving failure under static loading, it was not possible to fully calibrate the dynamic test results.

CONCLUSIONS

The consistent, satisfactory performance of the Hydroblok HBM 1500 provided a reliable means to achieve the penetration required at the Commodities pier. Installation criteria, in terms of both blowcount and minimum pile penetration, were significantly eased once the large soil set-up contributions to long-term pile capacity were demonstrated.

The static load test verified that sufficient axial capacity was available. Unfortunately, it precluded an accurate assessment of the ultimate soil capacity for correlation with total and unit resistance values obtained in the dynamic analyses.

Finally, the relatively poor performance of the Delmag D80-12 hammer at the outset was a cause for major concern. The dynamic measurements provided immediate means to document the difficulties, and thereafter to verify their effective remedy. The installation criteria at the Coal Berth were revised significantly based on the test program results on the bridgeway piles.

References

1. API RP2A, "Recommended Practice for Planning, Designing, and Construction Fixed Offshore Platform," American Petroleum Institute, Dallas, Texas, 1981 Edition.

2. Goble, G.G., Likins, G. and Rausche, F., "Bearing Capacity of Piles From Dynamic Measurements," Final Report, Case Western Reserve University, Cleveland, Ohio, March 1975.

3. Heerema, E.P., "Pile Drivings and Static Load Tests on Piles in Stiff Clay," Paper No. 3490, Proceedings, Eleventh Annual Offshore Technology Conference, Houston, Texas, April 1979.

4. Rausche, F., Goble, G.G., and Mosses, F., "A New Testing Procedure for Axial Pile Strength," Third Annual Offshore Technology Conference, Houston, Texas, 1971.

5. Tomlison, M.J., "Foundation Design and Construction," John Wiley & Sons, 1976.

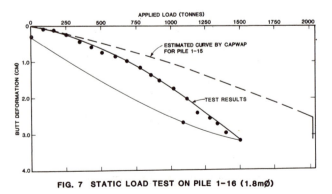

FIG. 7 STATIC LOAD TEST ON PILE 1-16 (1.8mØ)

Bearing capacity of foundations on calcareous sand

Force portante des fondations sur les sables carbonates

H. G. POULOS, Professor of Civil Engineering, University of Sydney, Australia
E. W. CHUA, Engineer, Urban Development Authority, Malaysia

SYNOPSIS   The paper describes a series of model footing tests on calcareous and silica sands under carefully-controlled laboratory conditions. The influence on bearing capacity of overburden pressure, relative density and cyclic loading is considered. The highly compressible nature of the calcareous sand results in substantially lower bearing capacities than for the silica sand. Measured bearing capacities are compared with theoretical values and it is demonstrated that the most satisfactory theory is one based on a cavity expansion approach.

INTRODUCTION

Calcareous sands are prevalent in many offshore oil- and gas- producing areas of the world. Such soils are frequently of biological origin and are characterised by their susceptibility to crushing on shearing, and to post-depositional cementation. Because of the compressible nature of these soils, they have been observed to provide poor support for foundations, particularly driven piles (Angemeer et al, 1975).

In an attempt to better understand the behaviour of foundations on calcareous sands, a series of laboratory model footing tests was undertaken on a Bass Strait calcareous sand. The influence on bearing capacity of overburden pressure, relative density and cyclic loading was studied. Comparative tests were also carried out on a silica sand. This paper describes these tests, compares measured and theoretical bearing capacities, and presents values of soil modulus backfigured from the experimental load-settlement curves.

ENGINEERING PROPERTIES OF SOILS TESTED

The calcareous sand was from Bass Strait, Australia, and consisted largely of uncemented grey biogenic particles. The soil was well-graded with maximum and minimum particle sizes of about 3 mm and 0.06 mm respectively. The silica sand was from Sydney, Australia and was composed of relatively angular quartz particles which were uniformly graded. The general physical characteristics of the soils are summarised in Table 1. Further details are provided by Chua (1983).

Drained triaxial compression tests on isotropically consolidated samples were carried out to determine strength, volume change and deformation characteristics of the sand. While isotropic consolidation does not seriously influence strength characteristics (as compared with anisotropic consolidation), it was recognised that the measured deformation parameters could be influenced significantly.

For both sands, the Mohr–Coulomb failure envelope was curved, so that the drained friction angle ϕ decreased with increased confining pressure σ'_c. The following approximate relationship was found:

$$\phi = a - b \log_{10} \sigma'_c \qquad (1)$$

where σ'_c = effective confining pressure, in kPa

For the calcareous sand at a relative density of about 50%, a = 54.2 and b = 4.3. For the silica sand at a relative density of about 85%, a = 49.4 and b = 3.7.

The volumetric strain at failure Δ_v varied with σ'_c according to the following approximate relationship:

$$\Delta_v = c + d(\sigma')^{0.5} \% \qquad (2)$$

For the calcareous sand, c = -1.13, d = 0.07; for the silica sand, c = -11.5, d = 0.26. The calcareous sand thus changed from a dilatant material to one exhibiting volume reduction at relatively low confining stress.

TABLE 1

GENERAL PHYSICAL CHARACTERISTICS OF SILICA
AND CALCAREOUS SANDS

PROPERTY	SILICA SAND	CALCAREOUS SAND
Coefficient of Uniformity	1.67	4.75
Mean Diameter (mm)	0.32	0.30
Specific Gravity	2.65	2.73
Maximum Density (t/m^3)	1.63	1.77
Minimum Density (t/m^3)	1.46	1.28

MODEL FOOTING TESTS

The tests were carried out in apparatus similar to that described by Poulos et al (1976). The soil was contained in a vessel 305 mm internal diameter and 229 mm deep, with drainage provided at both ends. Overburden pressure was provided by pressurised water acting on a rubber membrane above the soil surface. The footings were 25 mm diameter with the base roughened and were generally located on the surface, although a few tests were carried out on footings located up to 5 diameters below the surface. Loading was applied via a testing machine which was controlled through a micro-computer which also controlled a data acquisition system.

Beds of sand were prepared by raining sand dry through a double-mesh sieve into the body of the vessel, maintaining a constant height of fall. The majority of tests on calcareous sand were carried out using a 0.4 m height of fall, which produced a relative density of about 50%. The relative density of the silica sand was substantially larger, ranging between 78% and 100%. Following placement of the sand, saturation was effected by allowing an upward flow of water through the base. After assembly of the apparatus, the desired overburden pressure was applied and consolidation permitted. Primary consolidation took only a few minutes, but a consolidation period of 8 hours was allowed in all tests.

In the static loading tests, the footing was loaded statically to failure at a rate slow enough to ensure drained conditions (0.1 mm/min). In the cyclic loading tests, the footing was subjected to a specified number of cycles of one-way repeated loading at a predetermined stress level, after which the footing was loaded statically to failure.

In interpreting the model test results, it was necessary to adopt a consistent definition of the bearing capacity since failure was not clearly defined; therefore, it was taken to be the average applied stress at which a settlement of 10% of the footing diameter was reached.

MODEL TEST RESULTS

Typical load-settlement curves for each type of sand are shown in Fig. 1 for an effective overburden pressure of 103 kPa. Clearly, the stiffness and bearing capacity of the footing on the calcareous sand is much smaller than for the silica sand.

Fig. 2 plots the footing bearing capacity q_u against the effective overburden pressure σ'_{vo}. For both sands, q_u increases as σ'_{vo} increases, but the relationship is highly non-linear. For the calcareous sand in particular, there is a very slow rate of increase of q_u for σ'_{vo} in excess of 200 kPa.

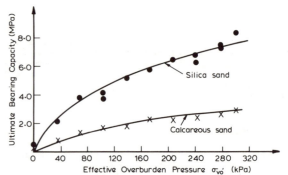

FIGURE 2   BEARING CAPACITY AT VARIOUS EFFECTIVE OVERBURDEN PRESSURES

Some of the difference between the bearing capacities on the two sands may be attributed to the higher relative density of the silica sand. The influence of initial relative density was studied by performing a series of tests at an overburden pressure of 103 kPa, and the results are shown in Fig. 3. q_u clearly depends on the initial relative density, but nevertheless, the value for calcareous sand is still substantially less than for silica sand of comparable relative density. Fig. 3 also shows the results of tests on the buried footings, and indicates no significant difference between these and the results for surface footings.

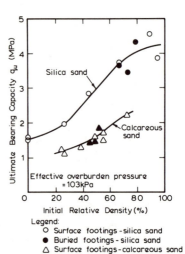

Legend:
O Surface footings - silica sand
● Buried footings - silica sand
△ Surface footings - calcareous sand
▲ Buried footings - calcareous sand

FIGURE 3   INFLUENCE OF INITIAL RELATIVE DENSITY AND FOOTING EMBEDDMENT ON ULTIMATE BEARING CAPACITY

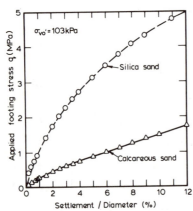

FIGURE 1   TYPICAL LOAD-SETTLEMENT CURVES

Effect of Cyclic Loading

From the tests carried out in which cyclic loading was performed prior to static loading to failure, the following observations were made:

(i) the permanent settlement increased with cyclic load level and number of cycles, and could be reasonably closely represented by an empirical expression of the same form found by Diyaljee and Raymond (1982).

(ii) the cyclic stiffness of the footing increased with increasing numbers of cycles, the major increase occurring in the first few cycles.

(iii) the ultimate load capacity after cycling tended to decrease due to cyclic loading. The reduction was small for cyclic load levels less than about 30% of ultimate, but at higher cyclic load levels, significant reductions in ultimate load capacity occurred due to the rapid accumulation of permanent settlements which could exceed 10% of the diameter (hence causing "failure") in a few cycles. Fig.4 summarises the results for the calcareous sand tests; similar results were found for the silica sand tests.

c) Vesic's spherical cavity expansion theory (Vesic, 1972) with a curved Mohr-Coulomb envelope.

In all cases for the cohesionless soils considered here, the theoretical expression for q_u could be simplified, with adequate accuracy, to the following:

$$q_u = N_q \sigma'_{vo} \qquad (3)$$

where N_q = dimensionless bearing capacity factor, and σ'_{vo} = initial effective overburden pressure.

In Terzaghi's theory, for a given footing shape, N_q is a function only of the friction angle ϕ', and in the calculations, the value of ϕ' used was adjusted according to the initial effective confining stress, as indicated by the laboratory test results (Eq. 1). This confining stress was calculated as the mean initial effective stress, taking the coefficient or earth pressure at rest, K_o, to be 0.33).

In Vesic's cavity expansion theory, the value of N_q depends both on the friction angle ϕ' and the plastic volume strain characteristics of the soil, and it was therefore necessary to carry out an iterative analysis to determine N_q. The equivalent confining stress σ'_c was taken to be the approximate mean principal stress below the footing at failure.

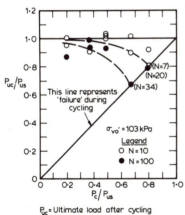

P_{uc} = Ultimate load after cycling
P_{us} = Ultimate static load capacity
P_c = Maximum load during one-way cycling

FIGURE 4   EFFECT OF CYCLIC LOADING ON ULTIMATE LOAD CAPACITY FOOTINGS ON CALCAREOUS SAND

COMPARISONS BETWEEN THEORETICAL AND MEASURED BEARING CAPACITY

Three methods were used to compute the ultimate bearing capacity q_u of the footings:

a) Terzaghi's theory for general shear failure (Terzaghi, 1943)

b) Terzaghi's theory for local shear failure, which uses the same bearing capacity factors as for general shear, but reduced strength parameters

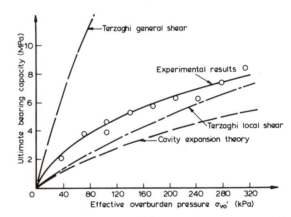

FIGURE 5   COMPARISON OF EXPERIMENTAL AND COMPUTED BEARING CAPACITY OF MODEL FOOTINGS ON SILICA SAND

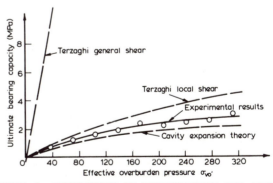

FIGURE 6   COMPARISON OF EXPERIMENTAL AND COMPUTED BEARING CAPACITY OF MODEL FOOTINGS ON CALCAREOUS SAND

Figs.5 and 6 compare experimental and predicted bearing capacity of the footings on calcareous sand the silica sand respectively.

For both soils, the Terzaghi general shear and local shear equations give poor predictions. In particular, the general shear equation significantly overpredicts bearing capacity in most cases.

It must be borne in mind that the experimental results are derived from the arbitrary assumption that "failure" occurs at a displacement of 10% of the diameter; nevertheless, Figs.5 and 6 demonstrate that the cavity expansion theory more closely models the stress conditions beneath the footing than do conventional bearing capacity theories. A similar conclusions was reached by Ismael and Vesic (1981).

BACKFIGURED VALUES OF SOIL MODULUS

From the elastic solution for a rigid circular footing on a finite layer (Poulos and Davis, 1974), values of drained Young's modulus E'_s were derived for a stress level of one-third of the bearing capacity. Fig.7 plots E'_s against effective overburden pressure σ'_{vo} for both soil types and reveals that, in both cases, E'_s increases almost linearly with σ'_{vo}. Detailed comparisons between measured and predicted settlements for these tests are discussed by Poulos et al (1984).

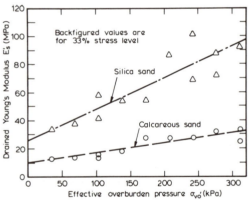

FIGURE 7 BACKFIGURED SOIL YOUNG'S MODULUS FOR MODEL FOOTING TESTS

CONCLUSIONS

The unusual nature of calcareous sands has a major effect on foundation behaviour. Despite the high angle of internal friction of these sands, the bearing capacity of model footings is significantly less than on silica sands. The main reason for this difference is the compressive plastic volume strain of the calcareous sand at relatively low confining pressures, which contrasts with dilatant plastic volume strains in the silica sand. Conventional theories seriously overestimates bearing capacity on calcareous sands, but reasonable predictions are provided by a cavity expansion theories which takes into account the variation of friction angle and plastic volume strain with mean normal stress.

Cyclic loading tends to reduce the bearing capacity due to the development of permanent settlement; however, the reduction is unlikely to exceed 10% if the maximum load during cycling is less than about one-third of the ultimate static load capacity.

Values of soil modulus backfigured from the footing tests are significantly less for calcareous sand than for silica sand.

ACKNOWLEDGEMENTS

The work described in this paper forms part of a project on the Engineering Behaviour of Bass Strait Carbonate Sands, which is being carried out at the University of Sydney with the support of a Marine Sciences and Technology Grant from the Australian Government. The second author was the recipient of a University of Sydney Postgraduate Reserach Scholarship. The authors are indebted to K. Chan, K. Larymore, M. Uesugi, T. Hull and R. Fraser for assistance with the experimental work.

REFERENCES

Angemeer, J., Carlson, E., Stroud, S. and Kurzeme, M. (1975). Pile Load Tests in Calcareous Soils Conducted in 400 Feet of Water from a Semi-Submersible Exploration Rig. Proc. 7th Annual OTC Conf., Houston, paper OTC 2311.

Chua, E.A. (1983). Bearing Capacity of Shallow Foundations in Calcareous Sand. M.Eng.Sc. Thesis, Univ. of Sydney.

Diyaljee, V.A. and Raymond, G.P. (1982). Repetitive Load Deformation of Cohesionless Soils. Jnl. Geot. Eng. Divn, ASCE, Vol.108, No.GT10, pp.1215-1229.

Ismael, N.F. and Vesic, A.S. (1981). Compressibility and Bearing Capacity. Jnl. Geot. Eng. Divn, ASCE, Vol.107, No. GT12, pp.1677-1691.

Poulos, H.G. and Davis, E.H. (1974). Elastic Solutions for Soil and Rock Mechanics. John Wiley and Sons, New York.

Poulos, H.G., De Ambrosis, L.P. and Davis, E.H. (1976). Method of Calculating Long Term Creep Settlement. Jnl. Geot. Divn, ASCE, Vol.102, No.GT7, pp.787-804.

Poulos, H.G., Chua, E.W. and Hull, T.S. (1984). Settlement of Model Footings on Calcareous Sand. Res. Rep. No.490, Univ. of Sydney.

Terzaghi, K. (1943). Theoretical Soil Mechanics. John Wiley and Sons, New York.

Vesic, A.S. (1972). Expansion of Cavities in Infinite Soil Mass. Jnl. Soil Mechs. Fndns. Divn, ASCE, Vol.98, SM3, pp.265-290.

Analysis of batter piles

Analyse des pieux inclinés

SHAMSHER PRAKASH, Director, Central Building Research Institute, Roorkee, UP, India
GOPAL RANJAN, University of Roorkee, Roorkee, India
G. R. S. TYAGI, California Department of Transportation, Los Angeles, California, USA

SYNOPSIS
A method of analysis of batter piles in sands based upon realistic non-linear p-y relationship has been developed.
Its application has been demonstrated both for small scale pile and full scale field pile tests.

INTRODUCTION

Reese and Matlock (1956) had developed non-dimensional solutions for deflections, moments and soil reactions along fully embedded vertical piles based upon the concept of beam on elastic foundation. Several tests on model and full scale batter piles have been interpreted by resolving the load perpendicular to the pile and applying the above solutions as for vertical piles, which is not correct.

The behavior of a batter pile is non-linear and the concept of p-y relationship has been applied for analysis of a single batter pile in non-cohesive soils under horizontal load. The p-y relationship used is of the form

$$p = kxy^n \qquad (1)$$

in which k is a function of batter angle β and relative density D_r, 'x' is depth coordinate along the pile (Fig.1), 'y' is deflection and exponent 'n' is a function of relative density only (Tyagi 1983).

THEORETICAL ANALYSIS

.The analysis is based on the assumptions that 1) the pile is free standing and wholly embedded (Fig. 1); 2) the lateral load is horizontal and acts at the ground surface; and 3) axial deformation of soil along the axis of pile may be neglected.

For pile shown in Fig. 1, the equation of bending of pile is:

$$\frac{d^4 y}{dx^4} + \frac{Qg}{EI} \sin\beta \frac{d^2 y}{dx^2} + \frac{1}{EI} kxy^n = 0 \qquad (2)$$

in which EI is flexual stiffness of pile, Qg is the horizontal load, and β is batter angle. The differential Eq. 2 can be solved by finite difference method as a two point boundary value problem (T.P.B.V.P.).

For numerical solution of differential Eq. 2 one requires the actual variation of soil-reaction in terms of p-y relation which were developed from tests on instrumented small size piles (Tyagi 1983).

TEST PROGRAM

Hollow aluminium piles 2.2 cm O.D. and 0.15 cm I.D. and 110 cm long were tested with batter angles of $\pm$ 15°, $\pm$ 30° and $\pm$ 45°. Each pile was instrumented with 28 foil gauges and calibrated to monitor bending moments. The soil used was dry medium sand at relative densities of 40, 57.5, and 66 percent. Sand was deposited by rainfall method in a 1.5 m square tank, in which the piles had already been placed. Strains under lateral load and hence bending moments along each pile were monitored (Tyagi 1983).

DEVELOPMENT OF p-y CURVES

The basic data was obtained in terms of bending moments along the length of the piles. This was differentiated and integrated twice to obtain soil reactions (p) and deflection (y) values. Typical bending moment (m), deflection (y), and soil reaction (p) plots for a test with $\beta = -15°$ and $D_r = 40$ are shown in Figures 2,3, and 4 respectively.

p-y curves for the above conditions and for depth along the pile (x) of 12.5 cm, 17.5 cm, 22.5 cm, and 27.5 cm are shown in Fig. 5. Similar p-y curves were obtained for all other tests (Tyagi 1983). An examination of these p-y curves shows that the p-y relationship for batter piles is non-linear.

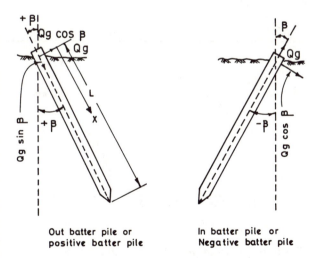

Out batter pile or
positive batter pile

In batter pile or
Negative batter pile

Fig.1. Notation

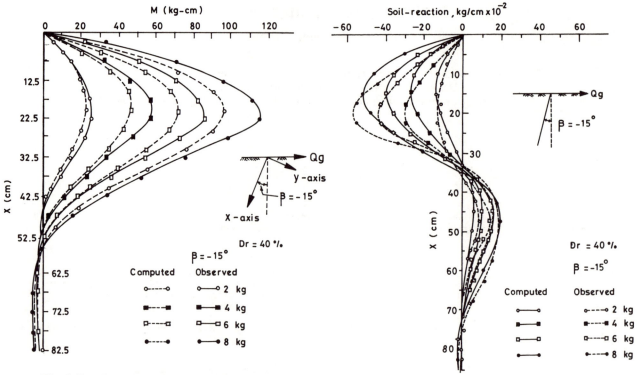

Fig. 2. Bending moments along the pile

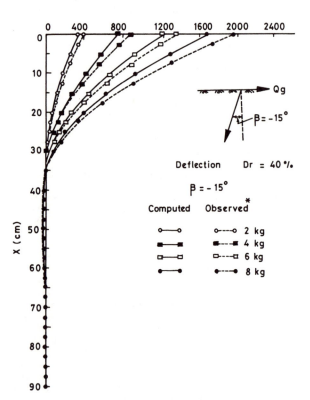

Fig. 3. Deflections along the pile
*reduced from bending moments

Fig. 4. Soil reaction along the length of the pile

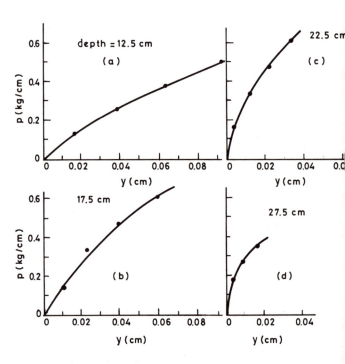

Fig. 5. p-y curves for different depths for pile,
$\beta = -15°$, Dr = 40 %

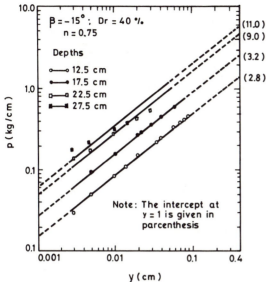

Fig.6. p-y plot on log-log scale for different depths

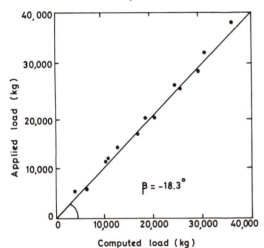

Fig. 7. Computed and applied loads in field pile

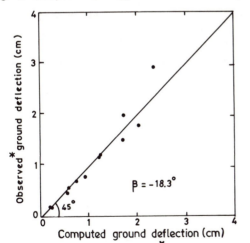

Fig. 8. Computed and observed* ground deflection
* reduced

DETERMINATION OF k AND n

If we take logs on both sides of eqn. 1, we get

$$\log p = n \log y + \log (k\, x) \qquad (3)$$

By plotting p-y on double log paper for different depth, Fig. 6 is obtained. The slope of this line is 'n' and equals 0.75. The curves when extrapolated to y = 1, give the intercepts on p-axis as 'kx' for a particular depth. These are shown in Fig. 6. It will be seen from this figure that the straight lines on log-log graph have been drawn with a uniform slope and these represent the observed points well. This exercise was repeated with each test series and the values of 'n' for relative densities of 40, 57.5 and 66 percent were 0.75, 0.63 and 0.6 respectively. It was further found that the exponent 'n' does depend upon batter angle. Thus 'n' is a function of relative density (Dr) only and was expressed as

$$n = (0.99 - 0.6\, Dr) \qquad (4)$$

Further the intercept (kx) at y =1 for depths of 12.5 cm, 17.5 cm, 22.5 cm and 27.5 cm is listed in Fig. 6. The ordinates for all tests at 40, 57.5 and 66 percent relative densities and batter angle of -15° are listed in Table 1.

TABLE 1
kx Values for β = -15° and Relative Densities (Dr) of 45, 57.5 and 66 percent

Dr	kx (intercept)	(x) cm	k	Adopted value of k
1	2	3	4	5
40	2.8	12.5	0.224	
	3.2	17.5	0.297	
	9.0	22.5	0.400	0.35
	11.0	27.5	0.400	
57.5	1.9	12.5	0.152	
	3.4	17.5	0.194	
	4.2	22.5	0.187	0.187
	5.1	27.5	0.185	
66	0.96	12.5	0.077	
	1.30	17.5	0.074	
	1.85	22.5	0.082	0.083
	2.4	27.5	0.087	

The variation of 'k' is not very large at different depths. Therefore one average value for one relative density in column 5 has been adopted in subsequent analysis. Similar data for other batter angles was obtained by Tyagi (1983). Thus k is a function of both battler angle β and relative density 'Dr'. To determine a relationship between k, β and Dr, k was first expressed as a function of β as k = mβ + c. (5.)

Both 'm' and 'c' were found to be dependent on 'Dr' and a general expression for 'k' is

$$K = (0.00815\, Dr - 0.00634)\beta + (0.475 - 0.59\, Dr) \qquad (6)$$

The general form of 'p' is given by eqn. 1, in which 'k' is expressed by eqn. 6 and 'n' by eqn. 4. Now, eqn. 2 can be solved by finite difference method to obtain (a) pile deflections, (b) moments and (c) soil reactions along its length (Tyagi 1983).

As a check on the fitted soil reaction curve, the component of load normal to the pile axis was determined for each test. The ratio of the (a) applied load to the (b) computed load for all relative densities and batter angles varied from 0.983 to 1.008. This shows that the soil modulus function and the parameters which define it have been realistically determined.

Computed values of bending moments, deflections normal to the axis (y) along the length of the pile, and soil reactions for batter angle -15° and tested in sand with relative density 40% are plotted in Figures 2,3, and 4 respectively, along with the observed values. The computed and measured (reduced) deflections are fairly close. For soil reactions, the location of maximum value is slightly shifted, otherwise the maximum computed values are reasonably close to the observed values. The fit of bending moments is excellent.

The above establishes the fact that soil-pile behavior in batter piles is non-linear and a realistic method for determination of design parameters in actual piles has been developed. There is, however, a need to check the validity and applicability of this method to the field conditions. Although several field tests on batter piles are available, the parameters needed for this analysis cannot be evaluated from many such data. However the available field data reported by Alizadeh and Davisson (1970) has been analysed as per the above method, which will now be presented.

ANALYSIS OF FIELD DATA

Alizedah and Davisson (1970) report lateral load tests on 2 batter piles -18.3^o and $+18.3^o$ inclined with the vertical for Lock and Dam 4 of the Arkansas River navigation project. The steel piles (14BP73) were 43.1 ft long and had been instrumented with electric resistance strain gauges.

The soil at the site was medium to fine sand and silty sand, had medium densities and was classified as SM-SP on the Unified Soil Classification System. The submerged unit weight of sand was 62.8 lbs per cubic feet. The angle of internal friction of sand sub-grade was 32° (range 31° to 35°).

The data in deflection is as follows:

Batter angle β	Load for 1/4" pile head deflection	Load for 1/2" pile head deflection
-18.3^o	25k (11340 kg)	42k (19051 kg)
$+18.3^o$	27k (12247 kg)	44k (19958 kg)

Moment versus depth curves have been plotted by Alizedah and Davisson (1970). These have been used to 1) define the p-y relationship at depths of 37.5 cm, 75 cm, 112.5 cm and 150 cm and 2) determine k and n as in eqn. 1 in the same way as for the laboratory data. The expression for 'k' as a function of batter angle β is

$$k = (-9 \times 10^{-3} \beta + 1.46) \qquad (7)$$

It must be noted that the tests had been performed only at one relative density, Dr. Therefore 'k' in equation 7 cannot be expressed as a function of Dr for field conditions. The value of 'n' is 0.5 for both β's of $+18.3^o$ and -18.3^o. Thus eqn. 1 defines soil reaction for eqn. 2 and the soil pile response is solved for deflection, bending moments and soil reactions along the pile length.

Computed and applied load is plotted in Fig. 7 whereas computed and measured ground deflection is plotted in Fig. 8. The two sets of data show a good fit between the computed and applied or measured quantities.

COMPARISON OF FIELD & LABORATORY VALUES OF CONSTANTS

Exponent 'n' is defined for the laboratory data by eqn.4.

If we assume 50% relative density for the field, the value of 'n' for field condition is 0.69. By independent analysis of field data, the n-value was determined to be 0.5, which is not very much different from practical considerations. The value of 'k' is defined by eqn.6 from laboratory test data. Again, for Dr=0.5 and $\beta = -18.3^o$, the value from field data is 1.624. This is a large variation from small size piles to large size piles. There is thus a need to define the range of 'k' values for field piles and for different relative densities. More data is being analyzed by the senior author to fill this gap and to revise eqn. 7 for different relative densities also.

LIMITATIONS

The investigation may be criticized because of the following limitations:

1) Sand is defined by Dr only and not by its "structure".

2) In Figure 6, the extrapolation is of 1 order due to limited test data.

3) The field values of 'k' and 'n' need be further determined.

4) Although it is not apparent from this analysis, but vertical pile for $\beta = 0$ cannot be solved by this method.

5) It is too brief a presentation because of space limitations.

CONCLUSIONS

Despite the above limitations, the following conclusions can be drawn from this investigation:

1) The soil pile behaviour of batter piles is non-linear. Soil reaction 'p' is expressed as $p=kxy^n$.

2) The proposed solution of beam on elastic foundation for batter piles with non-linear soil reaction may be used to determine pile response.

REFERENCES

Alizedah, M. and Davisson, M.T. (1970), "Lateral Load Tests on Piles - Arkansas River Project," Soil Mech. and Found. Div. ASCE, Vol. 96, No.SM5, pp. 1583-1604.

Reese, L.C. and Matlock, H. (1956), "Non-Dimensional Solutions for Laterally Loaded Piles with Soil Modulus Proportional to Depth", Proc. Eighth Texas Conf. on Soil Mech. and Found. Engrg., Austin, TX.

Tyagi, G.R.S. (1983), "Behavior of Batter Piles", Ph.D. thesis, University of Roorkee, Roorkee, India.

Prediction of time dependent displacement of anchors

Prédiction de déplacement de temps dépendant des plaques d'ancrage

GOPAL RANJAN, Professor of Civil Engineering, University of Roorkee, Roorkee, India
SWAMI SARAN, Professor of Civil Engineering, University of Roorkee, Roorkee, India
A. S. NENE, Lecturer in Civil Engineering, VR College of Engineering, Nagpur, India

SYNOPSIS   A new approach to predict the time dependent behaviour of plate anchors using constitutive laws for cohesive soils has been developed. The proposed stress-strain-time relationship is based on a nonlinear Kelvin model having a strain-softening spring and a time hardening dash pot. The constitutive relationship consists of four interdependent rheological parameters which have been obtained by laboratory triaxial tests under constant deviator stress conditions. The stress-strain-time relationship is incorporated in the analysis for load-time-displacement of anchors. Time displacement data obtained from model tests has been compared with the predicted time-displacement data.

INTRODUCTION

In case of anchors embedded in cohesive soils the long term deformation under load are important. Adams and Hayes(1967) were the first to study this aspect. On the basis of model tests in clay deposit they observed that long term uplift capacity was much less than short term capacity. Later, in 1968 Matsuo also confirmed these observation through field tests. Radhakrishna and Adams(1973) conducted short duration and long duration tests on augered footings and observed that the long term uplift capacity can be predicted using strength parameters under drained conditions. Johnson and Ladanyi(1974) carried out field tests on screw piles embedded in permafrost soil to study the creep behaviour. Based on mathematical model of expanding cylindrical cavity in non-linear viscoelastic plastic medium solutions for creep settlement of deep circular anchor plates were proposed. These studies reveal that no systematic attempt seem to have been made in the past to study the time-dependent deformations of anchors.

Utilizing non-linear constitutive relationship an analytical procedure has been developed to predict pressure displacement characteristics of horizontal shallow plate anchors subjected to axial vertical pullout loads (Nene 1983). Based on constitutive relationship established through suitable rheological model an analysis to evaluate the time-dependent displacement of an anchor subjected to a sustained load has been developed. The theoretical results have been compared with carefully conducted model tests.

TIME DEPENDENT DISPLACEMENT OF ANCHORS

When an anchor is subjected to sustained pullout load vertical normal stresses in the soil change. The change in the vertical stress varies from point to point in the soil mass above the anchor level. Further, if the soil is saturated, distribution of pore pressures,

the drainage boundaries make the problem complex.

A simple approach to study the time dependent behaviour of soils could be through suitable rheological model consisting of some of the basic rheological elements namely Hookean elastic body, Newtonian viscous liquid, Saint-Venant plastic body and Pascals liquid. Several rheological models have been utilized by investigators to study various problems. Murayama and Shibata(1961) proposed a model which consisted of a Hookean spring, connected to a Kelvin unit. A St. Venant unit was introduced in the Kelvin unit to represent threshold stress. Based on this model a stress-strain-time relationship was proposed. Christensen et. al.(1964) and Wu et.al.(1966) proposed a model similar to Kelvin-Maxwell model. They applied rate process theory. Barden(1965,1969) utilized Kelvin models with dash pots having non-linear viscosities to investigate the time-dependent deformation of normally loaded clays. Komamura and Huang proposed a model comprising of Bingham and Voigt units in series for visco-elastic-elastic material. Prakash et al. (1975), Aziz and Laba (1976), Wu et al.(1978), Prakash et al.(1979), Ranjan,et al.(1982) also proposed different models for various problems involving time dependent displacements.

The accuracy of prediction of time dependent displacements very much depends upon correct evaluation of rheological constants.

Model proposed by Wu et al.(1975), or that proposed by Prakash et al.(1979) contains only two constants whereas the ones proposed by other investigators contain four or more rheological constants. The rheological constants are influenced by several factors such as density, water content, stress ratio and stress history etc. Some of these factors may be of major influence whereas others may be of minor influence. It is well established that for the soils the stress-strain curve by both drained or undrained tests is non-linear. It was, therefore, felt that the spring of a rheological model should be strain softening. It was also felt that same rheological model should be suitable for predicting both short term and long term strain by using proper parameters. The strain-time curve is also non-linear and strain rate decreases with time. This suggested for use of time hardening dash pot. In view of this a new rheological model is proposed for predicting time-dependent deformations of anchors under sustained pull-out loads.

Proposed Rheological Model

The proposed rheological model is a nonlinear Kelvin model consisting of Hookean element of spring constant $\tilde{E}$ and a dash pot with constant of viscosity η, both connected in parallel (Fig.1). Further, the spring is assumed to be strain softening such that the spring constant $\tilde{E}$ is given by expression

$$\tilde{E} = \frac{1}{\hat{a} + \hat{b}\,\epsilon} \qquad (1)$$

where, $\hat{a}$ and $\hat{b}$ are constants. The coefficient of viscosity η is given by expression

$$\eta = \eta_o \, (t)^{1-N} \qquad (2)$$

where, η_o and $N(N \leqslant 1)$ are also constants. The equation for stress can be written as

$$\sigma = \frac{\epsilon}{\hat{a} + \hat{b}} + \eta_o \, t^{1-N} \, \frac{d\epsilon}{dt} \qquad (3)$$

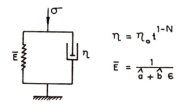

Fig.1 Proposed Rheological Model

The solution of Eqn.3 is obtained as

$$\frac{t^N}{N.\eta_o} = \frac{\hat{b}}{f} - \frac{\hat{a}}{f^2} \, \log_e \left(1 + \frac{f\epsilon}{\hat{a}\,\sigma}\right) \qquad (4a)$$

where, $f = a\sigma - 1$ (4b)

Equation(4) contains four rheological constants which can be conveniently determined from triaxial test.

Estimation of Rheological Constants

The rheological constants are determined by conducting laboratory triaxial tests under constant deviator stress to simulate sustained loading condition. The soil used was a locally available clay classified as clay of high plasticity "CH" as per Unified Classified System. The air dried powdered soil was mixed with required quantity of water and filled in a wooden boxes by kneading compaction. The

water content and bulk density of the soil were 43% and 1.74 g/c.c. respectively. The unconfined compressive strength of the sample was 0.15 kg/cm^2. The samples for triaxial test were collected through thin walled sampling tubes, internal diameter 37.5 mm. The samples were allowed drainage at the ends and through filter paper drains along the length. The soil specimen was consolidated under lateral pressures from 0-2 kg/cm^2. Subsequent to the consolidation of the sample, the cell pressure was maintained constant and the sample was subjected to constant deviator stress by a loading hanger. Axial strain of the sample with time was recorded upto 95% compression. Fresh samples were used for different lateral stresses. The strain-time data was used to computed the rheological constant. It was noted that $t \to \infty$, $\partial \epsilon / \partial t \to 0$ and $\epsilon \to \epsilon_f$ thus equation 3 can be written as

$$\sigma = \frac{\epsilon_f}{\hat{a} + \hat{b}\,\epsilon_f} \quad \text{or} \quad \frac{\epsilon_f}{\sigma} = (\hat{a} + \hat{b}\,\epsilon_f) \qquad (5)$$

Thus the constants $\hat{a}$ and $\hat{b}$ can be computed by plotting ϵ_f/σ vs ϵ_f. For a particular value of σ_3. Figure 2 is the plot obtained for the soil. From Fig.2, the values of constants $\hat{a}$ and $\hat{b}$ are summarized for different cell pressures.

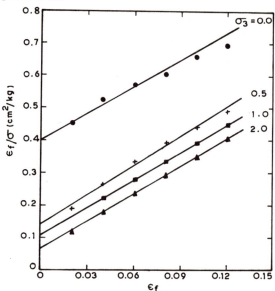

Fig.2 Transformed Stress-Strain Curves

TABLE I

Values of Constants $\hat{a}$ and $\hat{b}$

Cell per (kg/cm^2)	$\hat{a}$ (cm^2/kg)	$\hat{b}$ (cm^2/kg)
0.0	0.400	2.75
0.5	0.140	3.00
1.0	0.110	2.80
2.0	0.065	2.85

Figure 2 and also Table I indicates that for the cell pressures 0-2 kg/cm^2 the value of constant b is more or less constant yielding an average value of 2.847036 cm^2/kg or a value of

0.3512425 kg/cm^2 for 1/$\hat{b}$. However, the constant $\hat{a}$ is influenced by cell pressure. A relation between 1/$\hat{a}$ and σ_3 is plotted (Fig.3) which yields the relation (equation 6)

$$\frac{1}{\hat{a}} = 10.05 \ (\sigma_3)^{0.60206} \qquad (6)$$

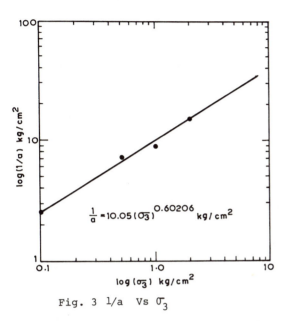

Fig. 3 1/a Vs σ_3

The other constant N and η_0 are obtained (equation 7) by simplifying equation 5 through 4b.

$$F(t) = \frac{t^N}{N\eta_0} = -\frac{\hat{a}}{(1-\hat{b}\sigma)^2} \log_e(1-\frac{\epsilon}{\epsilon_f})-\frac{\hat{b}}{1-\hat{b}\sigma}$$

where F(t) is a function of time t. Thus if F(t) is plotted against t on log-log scale the constants N and η_0 can be evaluated. The constants are determined by method of least square applied to linear regression of log (F_t) vs log (t) plot in which N is the slope of the straight line and the intercept gave the value of log (Nη_0) from which η_0 was computed. The value of N and η_0 are tabulated in Table II. The values of N and η_0 were noted to be mainly influenced by stress ratio, R(R = bσ). Plotting the variation of η_0 and N with R the following equations have been obtained

$$N = 1 - R \qquad (8)$$

$$\eta_0 = (1.2 + 0.25 \ \sigma_3)R^{(-1.8 - \sigma_3)} \qquad (9)$$

Analysis for Time Dependent Displacement

To incorporate the stress-strain-time relationship in the load displacement analysis of eqn.(7) is simplified as

$$\epsilon = \epsilon_f \ (1 - e^\beta) \qquad (10)$$

The equation(10) is transcedental type. The value of ϵ for a given set of values of stress,

TABLE II

Computations of N and η_0

Deviator stress (kg/cm^2)	Stress ratio, R(R=bσ)	N	η_0
Cell pressure 0.0 kg/cm^2			
0.017462	0.0497	0.667883	25.945232
0.056150	0.1599	0.366062	9.954688
0.128110	0.3647	0.560689	5.506643
0.160950	0.4582	0.628892	4.279896
Cell pressure 0.5 kg/cm^2			
0.1117265	0.3181	0.584525	12.790116
0.1232175	0.3508	0.498316	14.969964
0.1648825	0.4694	0.533271	17.546532
0.242267	0.6897	0.486653	3.426814
Cell pressure 1.0 kg/cm^2			
0.1007078	0.2867	0.523874	39.291613
0.1755319	0.4997	0.497668	12.700712
0.2157571	0.6143	0.455420	8.901099
0.252636	0.7193	0.180482	3.802191
Cell pressure 2.0 kg/cm^2			
0.1609812	0.4583	0.469329	29.297581
0.227023	0.6464	0.494516	9.620294
0.258359	0.7356	0.388984	5.225874
0.294809	0.8393	0.293415	2.0101843

where, $\beta = \dfrac{-(1 - \hat{b}\sigma)^2}{\hat{a}} \ (\dfrac{\hat{b}\epsilon}{1-\hat{b}\sigma} + \dfrac{t^N}{N\eta_0}) \qquad (11)$

and $\epsilon_f = \dfrac{\hat{a}\ \sigma}{1 - \hat{b}\sigma} \qquad (12)$

σ time, t and rheological constants, N, η_0 $\hat{a}$ and $\hat{b}$ is computed by iterative process. A subroutine was included in the main programme. Details of the analytical procedure are reported elsewhere (Nene 1983).

COMPARISON

Model tests were conducted on horizontal plates of different shapes and sizes buried at different depths. The properties of soil were as discussed earlier. The pull-out loads of anchors under short duration tests were estimated. The anchors were subjected to half or one-fourth the pull-out loads. The readings of displacement were continuously recorded with time till the displacement became practically negligible. The observed time-displacement curves for some of the tests on various shapes and embedment ratios of anchors are given in Figs. 4 to 7. The predicted curves for the anchors using rheological constants discussed above are also shown. The figure indicates that for smaller magnitudes of pull-out load there is a good agreement between the theoretical and experimental values but at higher loads there is variation. However, the trend of time-dependent curves in most of the cases are identical. More data on rheological constants and comparison with other test data from field/laboratory is being analysed.

CONCLUSIONS

A constitutive relationship, based on a rheological model, is proposed to predict load-time-displacement behaviour of plate anchors subjected to sustained pull-out loads.

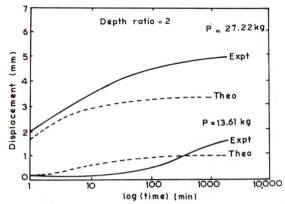

Fig.4 Displacement-Time Curve for Strip Anchor (Depth/Width = 2)

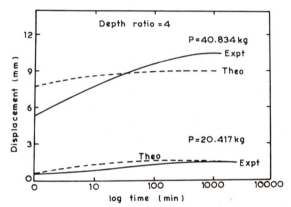

Fig.5 Displacement-Time Curve for Strip Anchor (Depth/Width = 4)

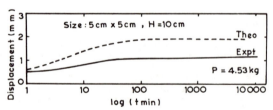

Fig.6 Displacement-Time Curve for Square Anchor

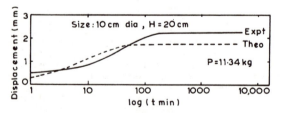

Fig.7 Displacement-Time Curve for Circular Anchor

The rheological constants used in this approach can be evaluated by laboratory tests. However, factors influencing these constants need further investigations.
For sustained loads, upto one-fourth of the breakout loads, this method predicts with reasonable accuracy the load-time-displacement behaviour of plate anchors subjected to axial pull-out loads.

REFERENCES

Adams, J.I. and Hayes,D.(1967. The uplift capacity of shallow foundations. Ontario Hydro Research Quarterly,Vol.19,No.1,1-13.

Aziz, K.A. and Laba,J.I.(1976). Rheological model of laterally stressed frozen soil. Jr.of Geo. Engg Div. ASCE,Vol.102,825-839.

Barden, L.(1965). Consolidation of clays with nonlinear viscosity. Geotechnique, Vol.XV, 345-362.

Christensen, R.W.and Wu,T.H.(1964), Analysis of clay deformation on rate process. Jr. of S.M.& F.E., ASCE, Vol.90,No.SM6,125-157.

Johnson,G.H. and Ladanyi,B.(1974). Fluid tests on deep power installed screw anchors in permafrost. Canadian Geotechnical Journal, Vol. II, 348-358.

Komamura, F. and Huang, R.J. (1974). New rheological model for soil behaviour. Jr. of Geotech Engg Div. ASCE, Vol.100, No. GT7, 807-824.

Matsuo, M.(1968). Study on the uplift resistance of anchor foundations II. Soils and Foundations,Vol.VIII,No.1, 18-48.

Murayama, S. and Shibata, T.(1961). Rheological properties of clay. Proc. 5th ICSMFE I, 269-273, Paris.

Nene, Ashok, S. (1983). Behaviour of shallow plate anchors in soils. Ph.D. thesis, submitted to U.O.R., Roorkee, India.

Prakash, S., Saran, S. and Sharan, U.N. (1975). Prediction of constitutive laws for granular soils. Proc. Istanbul Conf. on SMFE, 120-128, Istanbul.

Prakash,S., Ranjan, G. and Murtaza G.(1979). Time-dependent behaviour of piles under lateral loads. Proc. VI Pan-American Conference on SM & FE, Lima, Peru.

Radhakrishna, H.S. and Adams, J.I.(1973). Long term uplift capacity of augered footing in fissured clay. Canadian Geotechnical Journal, Vol.10, No.4, 647-652.

Ranjan, G.; Prakash, S. and Murtaza, G.(1982). Time-dependent behaviour of batter piles under lateral loads. Commemorative Int. Conf. of Mexican Soil Mech. Society, Mexico City.

Wu, T.H., Resendiz, D. and Neu Kircher,R.J. (1966). Analysis of consolidation by rate process theory. Jr. of SM & FE, ASCE Vol. 92, SM6, 229-248.

Wu, T.H., El Refai and Hsu, J.R. (1978). Creep deformation of clays. Jr. of Geo. Engg. Div. ASCE, No.G71, Vol. 104, 61-76.

Dynamic measurements as a control for offshore piling

Mesures dynamiques pour le contrôle des pieux offshore

J. L. R. ROCHA, Civil Engineer, Instituto de Pesquisas Tecnológicas, Brazil
S. NIYAMA, Civil Engineer, Instituto de Pesquisas Tecnológicas, Brazil
A. B. DA SILVA, Civil Engineer, Instituto de Pesquisas Tecnológicas, Brazil
S. VALVERDE, Civil Engineer, Instituto de Pesquisas Tecnológicas, Brazil
J. R. DE MELLO, Civil Engineer, Petrobrás S.A., Brazil

SYNOPSIS   Extensive dynamic pile driving instrumentation has been used by Petrobras as a control for offshore platform piling. The total number of structures tested to date is 15, with the water depth varying from 16m to 170m and the penetration of the pile varying from 20m to 145m below mudline. The main oil production fields, where the testing was performed, are in the north-east and in the south of the Brazil.

From dynamic measurements of force and acceleration near the pile top, information was obtained, such as the different hammer performances and the bearing capacity estimates.

Some aspects of the calcareous soil, that occur along the Brazilian Continental Shelf are discussed, specially their behaviour during the driving and set-up factor in different fields.

INTRODUCTION

Since 1980, as a part of the offshore platform piling control procedure, dynamic measurements during the driving have been used by Petrobrás. The first one was at the Garoupa platform in the Campos Basin, whose instrumentation was conducted by DnV (Det norske Veritas). After this, a special full-scale driveability testing was carried out by IPT (Instituto de Pesquisas Tecnológicas) and PDI (Pile Dynamics Inc.) in the Curimã field, close to the existing platform PCR-2. Subsequently, other platforms were instrumented as showed in Table I, where the variation of the water depth and the pile penetration below mudline are observed. The schematic location is showed in Fig. 1.

CHARACTERISTICS OF THE SOIL IN DIFFERENT FIELDS

Along the Brazilian Coast, the soil profile presents a certain predominance of the calcareous soils. This paper considers two basic regions: the north-east region and the Campos Basin, located on the south part of the country (Fig. 1).

TABLE I

Offshore Platform Piling Instrumented Since 1980

FIELD	PLATFORM	TESTING BY	WATER DEPTH (m)	MAXIMUM PENETRAT. (m)	NUMBER OF TESTED PILES
GAROUPA	PGP-1	DNV	120	87	4
ENCHOVA	PCE-1	GEO/WCC	116	89	6
NAMORADO	PNA-1	GEO/WCC	146	116	3
	PNA-2	AAN/IPT	170	114	5
CHERNE	PCH-1	AAN/IPT	117	102	2
	PCH-2	FRA/FUG	142	110	4
PAMPO	PPM-1	AAN/IPT	110	87	6
CURIMA	CLOSE/PCR-2	IPT/PDI	52	90	1
	PCR-1	IPT	52	95	15
ATUM	GRID/PAT-2	IPT	55	59	2
	PAT-1	IPT	55	80	8
	PAT-2	IPT	55	80	8
UBARANA	PUB-8	IPT	16	19	2
	PUB-9	IPT	16	19	8
CAIOBA	PCB-4	IPT	27	70	4

NOTE : DNV - DET NORSKE VERITAS   FRA - FRANKI
        GEO - GEOTECNICA   FUG - FUGRO
        WCC - WOODWARD-CLYDE CONS.   IPT - INST. PESQ.TECN.
        AAN - ANTONIO A.NORONHA   PDI - PILE DYNAMICS INC.

Fig. 1 - Schematic Location of the Fields

North-East Region

In this region there are many oil producing fields, with water depth varying from 16m (proximity of Ubarana field) to 55m (other fields). Figure 2-a shows some soil profiles related to the instrumented platforms.

One of the difficulties to the foundation design in this area is related to the evaluation of the soil properties, when the soil presents a high carbonate contents.

In the Curimã field a strong cementation of the calcareous soils was observed, besides considerable coral layers and caverns encountered along the depth. During the driving it was observed continuous degradation of the unit skin friction calculated by CAPWAP analysis carried out at different penetration. This effect was attributed to the crushibility of the cemented calcareous sand (Niyama et al, 1984).

In the Ubarana field, the presence of the strongly cemented calcareous soils at shallow depth (approximately 20m below seafloor) has been considered as the main problem to driven piles. In general, due to the high blow count verified in this stratum, the final pile penetration was less than required by design in view of the significant pull-out load. In those cases, the dynamic measurements led to the strengthening solution.

Campos Basin

The Campos Basin is characterized by oil production structures located in deep waters varying from 110m to roughly 200m. Some of the soil profiles in this area are showed in Figure 2-b, where a complex stratigraphy is observed. Basically, the typical profile is composed by shallow layer of calcareous sand/silt near the sea floor followed by sandy silts and silty clays intermixed with sand layers and shell frangments.

In the South Pole (location of the PCE-1/PPM-1 platform) the pile are supported by the cemented sand layers. In the North Pole, except close to PGP-1/PCH-1 fields, the cohesive soil are prevalent and then, the piles are of floating type, supported practically by skin friction resistance.

Set-Up Effect

One of the main objetives of the instrumentation is the evaluation of the set-up effect of the soils, fundamental parameter to estimate long-term bearing capacity. In some cases, it is possible to conduct ideal redriving program to take set--up factor at various periods after the initial driving. In Fig. 3, three cases of the set-up trends, obtained from redrivings made after up to 87 days, are presented. Note that this figure shows the set-up period versus gain of the mobilized skin friction resistance obtained from CAPWAP analysis. The driving resistance during the redrive conditions after a set-up time of approximately 60 to 70 days indicates a set-up factor of 3 to 4 (Ping et al, 1984) at the Enchova/Namorado field (Campos Basin). Similar value of set-up factor was verified in the Curimã field.

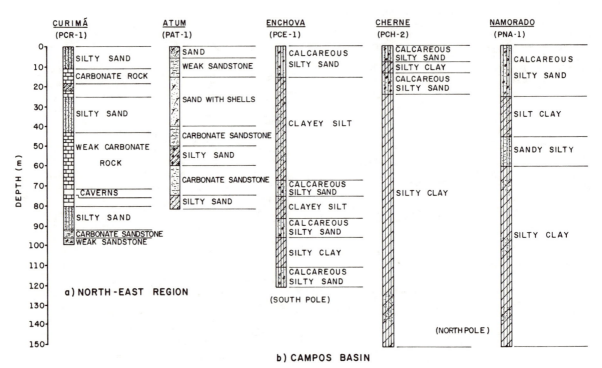

Fig. 2 - Simplified Soil Profiles at Different Fields

Microscopic Analysis

In view of the international tendency to study calcareous soils under some aspects, in laboratory, using scanning electron microscope (SEM), two microphotos of specimens prepared from samples obtained in the boring carried out close to PCR-1 platform, at 63m depth (Sample A) and 93m depth (Sample B), are presented in the Fig. 4 and Fig. 5. The identification of the carbonate mineral by X-ray diffraction analysis revealed calcite in the sample A and dolomite in the Sample B. According to petrographic classification, Sample A was classified as algalic microsparitic limestone and Sample B as algalic very fine cristaline dolomite.

The Fig. 4 shows the preponderant part of specimen (90% to 95%) composed by allochemical components (Rodophitas). The Fig. 5 shows the neomorphic carbonate matrix (80%) involving quartz particles.

This kind of descriptive analysis intend to be the initial phase for a study into the nature and engineering behavior of the Brazilian carbonate soils.

INSTRUMENTATION

As showed in Table I, different contractors carried out dynamic measurements and, basically, in most of the cases both instrumentation and processing methods originally developed at Case Western Reserve University were used. Two accelerometers and strain transducers are attached on opposite sides of the pile, near the top, and the signals are led through a combination box to a analyser. Where IPT conducted the instrumentation, this field unit was a Pile Driving Analyzer, described in more detail in Reference (Goble et al, 1980). This unit determines many driving parameters and some of the most interesting are:

(i)   Maxima of force, velocity and acceleration;
(ii) The maxima of the transferred energy; and
(iii) The bearing capacity according to the Case Method.

Although the Case Method requires the assumption of a damping factor (Rausche, 1978) and its use is limited due to the simplified formulation, the accumulated offshore experience has demonstrated its good usefulness for field decision-making, now and then.

Concerning to special instrumentation, it should be emphasized the monitoring successfully conducted by Franki/Fugro in the PCH-2 platform in the Cherne field, where was used a MHU 1700 underwater hidraulic hammer. Strain transducers and accelerometers were protected by appropriate waterproof casing as well as the special cables and connectors.

HAMMER PERFORMANCES

Table II shows efficiency values for the several hammers used in all platforms listed in Table I. Here the efficiency is the percentage of the rated energy transferred into the pile (ENTHRU). Some hammers, such as Vulcan 040 and Vulcan 340, were air or steam powered, according to the Contractor. In general the Menck hammers performed well with regular efficiency, while the Vulcan hammers presented a not so uniform

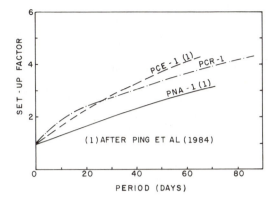

Fig. 3 - Set-Up Trend in Some Fields

Fig. 4 - Microphoto of Specimen from Sample A (x 200).

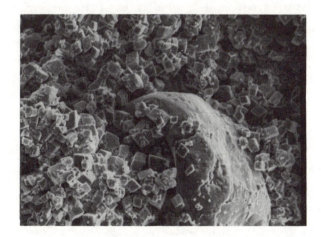

Fig. 5 - Microphoto of Specimen from Sample B (x 300).

performance, i.e., a major range of ENTHRU and the Delmag hammers showed an energy output somewhat less than expected. Some low energy output was observed due to the bad operational conditions, for example, when the compressor was not able to generate proper pressure or even the use of inappropriate cushion capblock. So, those results don't have to be considered as restrictions to the quality of the hammers, but only demonstrate the range of the measured energy.

TABLE II

Transferred Energy of Different Hammers

HAMMER		RANGE OF ENTHRU (kN x m)	RANGE OF EFFICIENCY (%)
VULCAN	0 2 0	17 —— 65	24 —— 78
VULCAN	0 4 0	50 —— 120	30 —— 72
VULCAN	3 4 0	30 —— 101	18 —— 61
VULCAN	5 6 0	120 —— 320	28 —— 66
MENCK	MRBS 3000	190 —— 324	42 —— 72
MENCK	MRBS 4600	290 —— 421	42 —— 61
MENCK	MRBS 5000	250 —— 465	33 —— 62
MENCK	MRBS 7000	220 —— 380	26 —— 45
MENCK	MRBS 8000	468 —— 768	39 —— 46
DELMAG	8 0	59 —— 100	28 —— 49
DELMAG	3 0	5 —— 15	13 —— 17
DELMAG	22/02	17 —— 26	25 —— 39
M H U	1700	160 —— 1005	9 —— 59

ASPECTS OF FIELD DECISIONS

In offshore installation, it is unavoidable to take some decisions in the field, for example, with reference to delimitation of the final pile penetration. Normally, CAPWAP analysis is made in the office, on land, very far from the job site. In this situation, due to the high cost of the installation barge, sometimes it is impossible to wait for post-field analysis. This fact would not be a problem if the pile driving responses are in accordance with the design forecast.

Meanwhile, during the installation of PAT-1 and PAT-2 platforms in the Atum field, some surprises were observed. Near the design penetration depth, for some piles the measured bearing capacity evaluated by Case Method were significantly smaller than required. Then, it was decided to proceed with driving, and monitoring all the piles. Considering Case Method, good sense and previous evaluations on damping factor, as well as set-up factor on similar calcareous sand, the bearing capacity of the piles were estimated. This field estimate was made in terms of the tip and skin friction resistances. Subsequent CAPWAP analysis agreed well with field forecast.

Finally, in view of the monitoring results, the initial installation program was modified and the expensive insert-pile solution was avoided.

These examples show how useful is the pile driving instrumentation whenever it is not possible to determine representative geotechnical properties because of the heterogeneity of such carbonate profiles.

CONCLUSIONS

Dynamic instrumentation of driven piles is an usual procedure to control the offshore platform installation in Brazil. So a significant number of 15 offshore piled structures were monitored to date, since 1980.

The instrumentation cost is considered marginal compared to installation cost (de Medeiros Jr., 1983) and doesn't provoke any delay to the piling operation. Consequently, the cost-benefit analysis has completely justified the use of instrumentation.

The information obtained by dynamic measurements in different fields contributed to gain experience on the better understanding of the hammer-pile-soil interaction, specially concerning to calcareous soils.

REFERENCES

Goble, G.G.; Rausche, F. & Likins Jr. G.E.(1980). The Analysis of Pile Driving - A State of the Art. Proc. Intl. Seminar on the Application of Stress-Wave Theory on Piles, 131-162, June, Stockholm.

de Medeiros Jr., C. & Rodriguez, S.G.H. (1983). Monitoring Driven Piles of PCR-1 Platform. Proc. 4th Intl. Symposium on Offshore Engineering, Rio de Janeiro.

Niyama, S.; de Medeiros Jr., C.; Martins, J. A. A. & Likins Jr. G.E. (1984). Dynamic Pile Instrumentation in a Calcareous Sand Close to PCR-2 Platform, Brazil. Second International Conference on the Application of Stress-Wave Theory on Piles, May, Stockholm.

Ping, W.C.V.; de Mello J.R. & de Matos, S.F.D. (1984). Performance Assessment of Deep Penetration Offshore Piles Driven Into Calcareous Soils. Proc. 16th Offshore Technology Conference, May, 513/526, Houston.

ACKNOWLEDGEMENTS

The authors wish to thank Petrobrás S.A. for their permission to publish the data presented in this paper. The authors also acknowledge the support received by Instituto de Pesquisas Tecnológicas do Estado de São Paulo S.A. - IPT and the all people who participated in the several steps of the works.

The uplift resistance of shallow embedded anchors

La résistance soulevée des ancres enterrées

P. A. VERMEER, Lecturer, Civil Engineering Department, Delft University of Technology, Netherlands
W. SUTJIADI, Student, Civil Engineering Department, Delft University of Technology, Netherlands

SYNOPSIS   Results for the uplift capacity of anchors with depth to breadth ratios of up to eight are presented in this paper. The failure mechanism involves approximately straight rupture lines from the anchor plate to the soil surface. Considering results of finite element computations and scale-model tests, the inclination of a rupture line is found to correspond with the angle of dilatancy. For sand this angle is typically in the range between 0° and 20°, depending on the relative density. A simple formula is derived for the uplift capacity. This formula is shown to give good agreement with empirical data of various researchers.

INTRODUCTION

An embedded anchor consists of a plate which is connected to the anchored structure by means of a cable or tie rod. We consider vertical anchors only, as inclined anchors yield almost the same failure load. The anchors are used for transmission towers, bulkheads and at sea for close station keeping. We will consider a rectangular anchor plate in cohesionless soil, but later the extension to circular plates and cohesive soil is discussed. The classification into shallow and deep anchors is theoretical and relates to the limit load (or failure load). Instead of the depth and the limit load we rather use the embedment ratio and the break-out factor:

embedment ratio = H/B
break-out factor = P/BLHγ

H = depth; B = plate breadth
P = limit load; L = plate length
γ = unit weight of soil

Obviously, the break-out factor increases with embedment ratio and the typical relationship is shown in Fig.1. An anchor in the linear or concave range is considered shallow; otherwise the anchor is deep.

At Delft University the deep anchors are studied experimentally, but the shallow anchors are studied theoretically as plenty of experiments have been reported in the literature. The typical feature of shallow anchors is the formation of approximately straight shear bands from the edges of the anchor plate to the soil surface. However, the literature is not fully unanimous on the straightness of the shear bands and some researchers assume trumpetshaped lines. In the following we will only refer to some recent publications; a complete review of previous work is impossible because of the restricted length of this paper. We will show that the inclination of a shear band coincides to the so-called angle of dilatancy. This soil parameter can either be measured in triaxial testing, or calculated from the friction angle at critical density, ϕ_{cv}.

THE ANGLE OF DILATANCY

Shear dilatancy or shortly dilatancy may be described as the change in volume that is associated with the shear distortion of an element of granular material. Here, an element is assumed to be large enough to contain many particles as micro-elements. Consider for instance a pack of spheres arranged in a state of packing as dense as possible. If any shear distortion is applied, the relative positions of the spheres must change, and the total volume of the pack must increase. This volume change is named dilatancy.

A suitable parameter for characterizing a dilatant material is the dilatancy angle ψ. Originally, this parameter was only used for plane deformation. For such situations with $\varepsilon_2 = 0$ it is defined by the equation (Hansen, 1958).

$$\sin \psi = - \frac{d\varepsilon_1 + d\varepsilon_3}{d\varepsilon_1 - d\varepsilon_3} = \frac{d\varepsilon_v}{-2d\varepsilon_1 + d\varepsilon_v} \qquad (1)$$

where the symbol d is used to denote small increments; $d\varepsilon_v$ is the volumetric strain increment which is considered positive for volume increase. We prefer the definition with the volumetric strain as it also holds for triaxial compression tests with $\varepsilon_2 = \varepsilon_3$ (Vermeer and de Borst, 1984). Typical data for sand is shown in Fig.2. Near and beyond peak strength the dilation rate $d\varepsilon_v/d\varepsilon_1$ attains a constant values, which can be used in eq.(1) to calculate the dilatancy angle. For loose sands this angle tends to zero, but values beyond 15° may be found for dense sands.

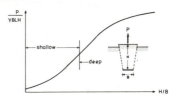

Fig.1

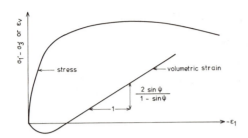

Fig.2 Typical triaxial test data for sand

The meaning of the dilatancy angle is best understood by considering a simple-shear test. Assuming a test with uniform deformation, we have

$$\tan \psi = d\varepsilon_{yy}/d\gamma_{xy} \qquad (2)$$

as illustrated in Fig.3. Hence, ψ is the uplift angle in a simple-shear test or rather in a shear band of arbitrary length.

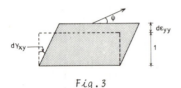

Fig.3

For measuring the dilatancy angle, we recommend a triaxial test rather than a simple-shear test as the latter tends to impose non-uniform stresses in the sample. Instead of a straight-forward evaluation from test results, the dilatancy angle may also be calculated from the friction angle by using one of the following equations:

$$\sin \psi = \frac{\sin\phi' - \sin\phi_{cv}}{1 - \sin\phi'\sin\phi_{cv}} \qquad (3a)$$

$$\cos \psi = \frac{\cos\phi' \cos\phi_{cv}}{1 - \sin\phi'\sin\phi_{cv}} \qquad (3b)$$

where ϕ_{cv} is the friction angle at the critical state (at the critical density). These equations follow from the stress-dilatancy theory by Rowe (1971). The latter gave both theoretical and empirical evidence for the relationship.

$$\frac{d\varepsilon_v}{d\varepsilon_1} = 1 - \frac{R}{K}, \qquad R = \frac{1+\sin\phi'}{1-\sin\phi'}, \qquad K = \frac{1+\sin\phi_{cv}}{1-\sin\phi_{cv}}$$

We find the equations (3) by substituting Rowe's relationship in eq.(1).

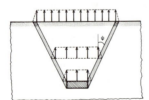

Fig.4 Kinematically admissible failure mechanism

KINEMATICAL SOLUTION FOR PLANE STRAIN

A kinematically admissible failure mechanism for the anchor is shown in Fig.4. A truncated wedge with an apex angle of 2ψ is pulled out together with the anchor plate, which breaks away from the sub soil. Dilating shear bands seperate the truncated wedge from the adjacent soil. Vardoulakis et al.(1981) report a thickness of about 20 times the mean grain diameter. These authors also presented data on the inclination of the shear bands. For a very dense sand with $\phi' = 47^0$ and $\phi_{cv} = 34^0$, the angle with the vertical was measured to be 18^0. This measurement corresponds remarkably well to the dilatancy angle. When using eq.(3a) we obtain $\psi = 17^0$. For a very loose sand the shear bands were found to be vertical. An extremely loose sand is in the so-called critical state with $\phi' = \phi_{cv}$, so that eq.(3a) gives $\psi = 0$. Again this prediction coincides with the observation by Vardoulakis et al.

For $\psi > 0$, the thickness of the shear band increases because of the dilation. However, no material dilates infinitely and the use of a constant dilatancy angle is only a first approximation. In reality the material becomes looser and after intense shearing the critical state with $\phi' = \phi_{cv}'$ is reached. Consider for instance an initially dense sand with a porosity of 36 per cent and $\psi = 17^0$, that dilates to reach the critical state with a porosity of 43 per cent. Then, the shear band thickness increases with 12 per cent. The shear strain that is needed to reach this state is at least 0.4, as can be computed from eq.(2). The value of 0.4 is a lower bound as it is based on the approximation of a constant dilatancy angle, whereas this angle decreases in reality with increase of the porosity. The above exercise leads to the conclusion that the material inside a shear band reaches the critical state when the relative displacement of the shear band boundary is well beyond half the shear band thickness. In other words we need more than 2 mm displacement of the anchor as the thickness of a shear band is about 4 mm. In small-scale model test on rectangular plates we measured less displacement at the limit load, so that the concept of a constant angle of dilatancy is realistic up to and at peak.

For large-scale tests, the concept might be questioned. Near the anchor the displacements may become large, as the truncated wedge does not behave as a rigid block throughout the test. This is best seen from Fig.8 which shows results of finite element computations. Clearly, the shear bands start to develop near the plate and grow up to the surface. In fact, the zone near the plate is sheared very intensively and the dilatancy angle tends to decrease in this region. It would thus seem that the concept of a constant dilatancy angle fails. However, it should be realized that the shear band may displace to "fresh" material. The simplest mechanism would be a shift of the entire shear band into the truncated wedge above the anchor plate. Another mechanism is that only parts of the shear band are shifted inwards, which would result in a curvature of the band. This mechanism seems to prevail as we often observe a slightly trumpet-shaped block above the anchor, rather than exactly straight shear bands.

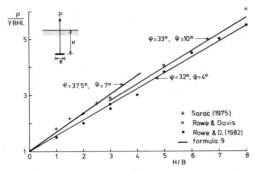

Fig.5 *Comparison of experimental and theoretical limit loads. A data point from Rowe represents the average of 5 tests.*

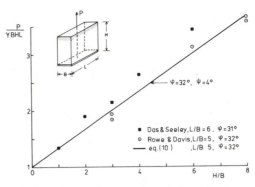

Fig.6 *Comparison of experimental and theoretical limit loads.*

HAND CALCULATION FOR A LONG STRIP ANCHOR

For estimating the limit load, we need information about the stresses in the soil. In fact, we only need the stresses at the shear bands, say the normal stress σ_n' and the shear stress τ_n. Then, the limit load is calculated from the expressions

$$P = P1+P2+P3, \quad P1 = \gamma BLH, \quad P2 = \gamma LH^2 \tan\psi$$

$$P3 = 2L \int_0^1 (\tau_n \cos\psi - \sigma_n' \sin\psi)\,dl \qquad (4)$$

P1 is the weight of the soil column above the anchor; P2 is the weight of the rest of the truncated wedge; P3 is the shearing resistance and l is the length of a shear band. L/B is assumed to be so large that we can neglect the end effects. Short plates will be consider later (eq.10). From the Mohr-Coulomb criterion we know that $\tau_n < \sigma_n' \tan\phi'$, so that

$$P3 < 2L \int_0^1 \cos\psi(\tan\phi'-\tan\psi')\sigma_n'\,dl$$

Hence, a theoretical upper bound is found by substituting $\psi = \phi'$. Then, P3 vanishes and we obtain

$$P/\gamma BLH < 1 + H/B \tan\phi' \qquad (5)$$

This upper bound is very suitable as a first approximation of the limit load, but we are interested in a better estimate because of the unsafe character of an upper bound.

For deriving an accurate approximation of the limit load we may use (Vermeer and Sutjiadi, 1985)

$$\tau_n = \sigma_n' \tan\alpha, \quad \sigma_n' = \sigma_v' \qquad (6)$$

where σ_v' is the vertical stress and

$$\tan\alpha = \sin\phi'\cos\psi/(1-\sin\phi'\sin\psi) \qquad (7a)$$

Note that eq.(7a) gives the range $\sin\phi'<\tan\alpha < \tan\phi'$ depending on the dilatancy angle. The lower bound is obtained for a non-dilatant material ($\psi=0$) and the upper bound correspondence to $\psi=\phi'$. The equation for $\tan\alpha$ becomes extremely simple when we eliminate the dilatancy angle from eq.(7a) by using eq.(3), namely

$$\tan\alpha = \tan\phi' \cos\phi_{cv} \qquad (7b)$$

However, for a further evaluation of the limit load it is easier to use eq.(7a). When substituting the eqs (6) and (7a) in eq.(4), we obtain

$$P3 = \frac{\sin\phi'- \sin\psi}{1 - \sin\phi'\sin\psi} L \int_0^1 2\sigma_v'\,dl$$

In order to proceed the evalution, we need an assumption on the magnitude of the vertical force at the shear bands. The simplest assumption is to take the weight P2 of the two triangles above the shear bands. In fact, this assumption is also made in slip-circle analysis for slope stability. It means that we exclude arching by which the centre soil column (P1) may hang on the shear bands. With this assumption the above equation becomes

$$P3 = \frac{\sin\phi'- \sin\psi}{1 - \sin\phi'\sin\psi} \frac{P2}{\sin\psi} \qquad (8)$$

When adding the contributions P1, P2 and P3 the break-out factor is found to be

$$\frac{P}{\gamma BLH} = 1 + \frac{H}{B}\tan\alpha = 1 + \frac{H}{B}\tan\phi'.\cos\phi_{cv} \qquad (9)$$

VALIDATION BY EMPIRICAL DATA

Results of small-scale tests for rectangular anchors are reported by Rowe and Davis (1982.) Their research work is particularly interesting as it includes data on the dilatancy angle, so that we can use eq.(7a). In fact, they published influence charts for use in a hand calculation which include the effect of the dilatancy angle. When comparing the results of the influence-chart-procedure with the formula proposed here, we obtained differences of less than six per cent. For validating our formula, however, we rather consider the results of model tests as shown in Fig.5. We have some doubts about the high dilatancy angle of 10^0, as a sand with $\phi'= 33^0$ tends to be loose and little dilatant. However, the dilatancy angle is only of minor influence as can be seen from the computational results in Fig.5. The dilatancy angle of 7^0 that goes with the data of Sarac (1975) is estimated: it corresponds to $\phi_{cv} = 32^0$.

Fig.6 shows data for shorter anchor plates. The theoretical line comes from the extended formula

$$\frac{P}{\gamma BLH} = 1 + (\frac{H}{B} + \frac{H}{L}) \tan\phi'\cos \phi_{cv} \qquad (10)$$

This formula reduces to eq.(9) when B/L tends to zero, i.e. for an extremely long anchor plate. The theoretical line in Fig.6 is obtained for $\phi' = 32^0$ and $\psi = 4^0$ as given by Rowe and Davis (1982). Das and Seeley (1975) used a sand with a similar friction angle, so that the theoretical line also applies to their data.

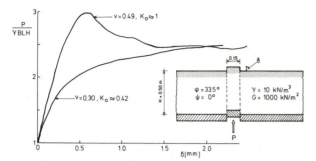

Fig.7 Computed load-uplift curves.

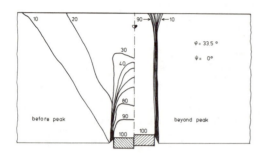

Fig.8 Computed relative velocity contours

VALIDATION BY FINITE ELEMENT COMPUTATIONS

The formules (9) and (10) for the limit load are based on the failure mechanism in Fig.4 and the assumption that the vertical force on the shear band coincides with the soil above. For checking these assumptions, we performed elastoplastic finite element computations. The material model employs an elastic shear modulus and Poisson's ratio and further the constants ϕ', ψ. This so-called perfectly plastic model is among others described in the book by Smith (1982). A special feature of our computer program is the ability to simulate localization of deformation in shear bands (de Borst and Vermeer, 1984).

To facilitate the computations the anchor problem is schematized to a passive trap-door problem. Then the computation proceeds in two stages. First the stresses due to the weight of the soil are computed and subsequently the trap-door is lifted in a number of displacement increments. Fig.7 shows two load-displacement curves for a configuration with $H/B = 3.33$. With the exception of the Poisson's ratio, all parameters were assigned the same value. For the lower curve we used $\nu = 0.3$ giving a K_o-value of 0.43 at the onset of lifting. In contrast to the lower curve, the upper curve shows a marked peak. This is explained by the use of $\nu = 0.49$ which gives a K_o-value close to unity. The high horizontal stresses cause arching between the shear bands and consequently a high peak load. However, this effect disappears at continued deformation, and a unique residual load is found. Although the K_o-value is found to affect the limit load, K_o is not used in the formulas (9) and (10) as we are interested in the unique residual load rather than an unsafe peak load.

The above computations were performed for a non-dilatant material and we obtained vertical shear bands in both situations (Fig.8). In addition,

extremely dilatant material behaviour was considered to observe shear bands at an inclination ψ to the vertical. Obviously, the material model is a rigorous idealisation of real granular material, but it gives an idea of the influence of K_o, the inclination of the shear bands and also on the stresses in the interior of the soil. When summing up the vertical stresses at the shear bands, good agreement was found with the assumption that we made to derive the formulas (9) and (10).

CONCLUDING REMARKS

In the foregoing restriction was made to cohesionless material, but the theory is easily extended to include cohesion. For this purpose, we must use the following relationship between the shear stress and the normal stress at the shear band:

$$\tau_n = (\sigma_n' + c \cdot \cot\phi')\tan\alpha$$

where c is the cohesion and α is defined by eq.(7). Then, it can be derived that

$$\frac{P}{\gamma BLH} = 1 + \left[\left(\frac{H}{B} + \frac{H}{L}\right)\tan\phi' + \frac{2c'}{\gamma B} + \frac{2c'}{\gamma L}\right]\cos\phi_{cv}$$

The dilatancy angle comes in when we use eq.(3b) for ϕ_{cv}. We have shown that the formula is accurate for relatively long plates, say $L>3B$. For shorter anchor plates and also circular plates, the formula is conservative in the sense that the limit load is underestimated. In the special case of a square anchor with $L=B$ we would have a very simple formula which is also useful for circular anchors as we may use an equivalent breadth. However in such cases the limit load is underestimated due to the neglect of higher order terms in H/B. The extension to include circular anchors is given in another paper by the writers (1985). Finally, it is recalled that the formulas are essentially restricted to shallow anchors. They have been validated for depth to breadth ratios of up to eight.

REFERENCES

de Borst, R. and Vermeer, P.A. (1984). Possibilities and limitations of finite elements for limit analysis. Geotechnique 34, No.2, 199-210.
Das, B.M. and Seeley, G.R. (1977). Uplift capacity of shallow inclined anchors. Proc.9th Int.Conf. Soil Mech.Found.Engg.(1). 463-466, Tokyo.
Hansen, Bent (1958). Line ruptures regarded as narrow rupture zones. Proc.Conf. Earth Pressure Probl.(1), 39-48, Brussels.
Rowe, P.W. (1971). Theoretical meaning and observed deformation parameters for soil. Proc. Roscoe Mem.Symp., 143-194. Cambridge.
Rowe, R.K. and Davis, E.H. (1982). The behaviour of anchor plates, Geotechnique 32, No.1, 25-41.
Sarač, Dž.(1975). Bearing capacity of anchors. Report 5, Institute of Geotechnics, Sarajewo.
Smith, I.M. (1982). Programming the finite element Method. Chichester, John Wiley & Sons.
Vardoulakis, I., B. Graf and G. Gudehus (1981). Trap door problem with dry sand. Int. J. Numer. Anal. Methods Geomech., 5, 57-78.
Vermeer, P.A. and R. de Borst (1984). Non-associated plasticity for soils, rock and concrete, Heron 29, No.2.
Vermeer, P.A. and Sutjiadi, W. (1985). The behaviour of vertical anchors in soil. To be presented at 4th Int.Conf. Behaviour Offshore Structures, Delft.

Session 5A
Geotechnical engineered construction
A. Influence of earthwork construction on structures

Séance 5A
Construction employant le génie géotechnique
A. Influence des travaux de terrassement sur les structures

Stability and settlement characteristics of structures in soft Bangkok clay

Caractéristiques de stabilité et tassement des structures dans argile tendre de Bangkok

A. S. BALASUBRAMANIAM, Asian Institute of Technology, Bangkok, Thailand
D. T. BERGADO, Asian Institute of Technology, Bangkok, Thailand
Y. H. LEE, Asian Institute of Technology, Bangkok, Thailand
S. CHANDRA, Asian Institute of Technology, Bangkok, Thailand
Y. YAMADA, Asian Institute of Technology, Bangkok, Thailand

ABSTRACT Field data observed from the full-scale test embankments and excavations at 8 different locations have been analyzed to evaluate the useful engineering parameters and field behavior in soft Bangkok clay. Change of excess pore pressures, ground movements, ground improvement, land subsidence, slope stability analysis and probabilistic analysis are the main topics in this paper. Recent theory considering the concept of local yielding and critical stress in the settlement prediction has been used and reasonably good agreements with the measured value were obtained. Stability analysis with shear strengths at large strain, i.e. critical state, yielded values of safety factor near unity at failure. In addition, abundance of test data in soft Bangkok clay enabled the establishment of probability distributions of strength and compressibility characteristics using Monte Carlo simulation. Consequently, relationships are established between the probability of failure, conventional safety factors, and safety margins. Further, the use of sand drains and lime column techniques for improving the soft Bangkok clay did not have reliable positive results so far. Finally, the effect of land subsidence and the consequent results such as negative skin friction of long piles, differential settlements of structures and the hazardous effects of floods seem the most urgent problem in the Bangkok area at present.

INTRODUCTION

The Chao Phraya Plain in which the sprawling Bangkok Metropolis is located abounds with a thick deposit of marine clay overlying sand. Nearly twenty years of extensive research has been conducted on this deposit at the Asian Institute of Technology (AIT). Thus, a large number of publications is now available on the engineering properties of this deposit including those reported by Moh et al (1969) and Balasubramaniam et al (1977a,b). In the Bangkok area, flooding occurs during rainy season due to land subsidence (maximum of 10 cm/year) caused by excessive groundwater pumping and due to relatively flat gradient of the Chao Phraya River which stagnates its flow during high tides. Except for embankments in flood protection and roadworks, piled foundations are the only form of deep foundations used for tall buildings and bridges. Balasubramaniam et al (1981) described the various aspects of driven piles used in the Bangkok Plain as deep foundations. This paper is on the same series of work on Bangkok subsoils which deal predominantly with the analysis of extensive data collected over the years in relation to the design and performance of low embankments for flood protection purposes as well as in roads and highways to support pavements above flood levels. Much of the pioneer work on Bangkok clay and test embankments were carried out by Drs. Za-Chieh Moh, E.W. Brand and J.D. Nelson at A.I.T.

Two aspects of the design of embankments in soft clays are well studied, namely: the stability and the settlement characteristics. Extensive research has been conducted at AIT on the laboratory and field determination of the geotechnical parameters controlling the stability and settlements of low embankments. These geotechnical parameters were incorporated in sophisticated stress-strain theories such as those developed at the Cambridge University and subsequently modified by other researchers. Furthermore, advanced statistical methods as well as probabilistic analysis were conducted. Thus, both deterministic as well as probabilistic analysis were done with respect to stability and settlement characteristics. In addition, the suitability of using vertical drains in accelerating primary settlements of the embankment was also investigated using full scale load tests. However, only laboratory tests were conducted to study the effects of lime columns on soft clay.

EMBANKMENTS AND EXCAVATION

The test embankments and excavations studies herein are enumerated in Fig. 1. Their locations are also shown in Fig. 1. At the proposed Second Bangkok International Airport (SBIA) at Nong Ngoo Hao (NNH), four full scale test embankments made of sand material and excavation were constructed and studied in 1973. These test sections were designated as:

Test Section I: Embankment of varying height for long term settlement observation
Test Section III: Embankment built rapidly to failure
Test Section IV: Embankment for observation of long term settlement and creep
Test Section V: Excavation

Another full scale test embankment made of clay was constructed at the AIT campus in Rangsit. The test sections also included a drainage channel 80 m long. The construction of the embankment was carried out in two phases. The full scale test section was built in 1969 (Phase I) and was observed for a period of 10 months before being loaded to failure (Phase II). At Pom Prachul Dockyard Site of the Royal Thai Navy, a test embankment was built to assess the performance of sand drains. The test embankment consisted of 3 sections, one with 5 cm diameter sand drains spaced at 1.5 m, the second with spacing of 2.5 m, and the third one without drains. The effectiveness of the sand drains was also studied in an earlier study at the site of Tachang Bridge. In this site, 4 test embankments boxes 6 m square and 4 m high were constructed. Two of them incorporated sand drains while the other two did not have any drains. Two other embankments referred to in this study were in the Bangkok-Siracha Highway and the Thonburi-Paktho Highway. In the Bangkok Siracha Highway Project, 3 test embankments were built; Embankment A was built without berms while Embankment B had berms, Embankment C had bamboo facines at the original ground level without any berms. There were 3 test embankments at the Thonburi-Paktho Highway. Two of the embankments built rapidly to failure are studied in detail in this paper.

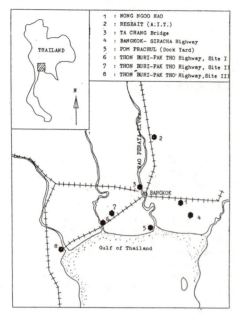

Fig. 1   Location Plan of Test Section in Bangkok Area

GENERAL SOIL PROFILE

A typical soil profile in the Bangkok area is given in Fig. 2. Generally, the upper 1.5 to 2.0 m is a weathered crust which is underlain by 5 to 10 m of soft clay followed by a medium stiff clay layer. The soft clay layer thickness increases towards the sea and decreases towards inland. At the Nong Ngoo Hao site, the top soft clay layer down to a depth of 8 m has a high liquidity index of more than 1.0 and the average natural moisture content is 125% while the liquid and plastic limits are 120% and 50%, respectively. The underlying layer of medium stiff clay from 8-15 m depth has a liquidity index which decreases to about 0.60 at the bottom and the average water content is about 70%, while the liquid and plastic limits are 90% and 30%, respectively. At the AIT campus in Rangsit (see Moh et al, 1972), the soft clay extends to a depth of 8.6 m underlain by about 2 m of medium stiff clay. Hard surface crust and deep vertical cracks extends to 1.5 m below the ground surface. From this depth down to approximately 2.7 m, numerous vertical holes were known to exist. The soil profile at Pom Prachul site, six zones are indicated. The highest water content occurs in zone 1 (1.5-2.5 m depth) and is about 120%. Within the soft clay layer (3 m to 8 m depth), the water content is the lowest at 40-50%. Between 14-17 m depth (zone V), the natural moisture is about 50%. Below 17 m depth, in the medium stiff clay, the water content is very low and is close to the plastic limit. A noticeable feature of the soil profile is the abundant distribution of shell fragments within the soft clay layer. At the Bangkok-Siracha Highway site, the natural water content is close to the liquid limit decreasing from 120% immediately below the drying crust to 110% at a depth of 13 m. The plasticity index is about 80-90% and the soft clay has an overconsolidation ratio of 1.5 to 1.7. At the Thonburi-Paktho Highway, the soft silty clay extends to a depth of 12 m underlain by medium stiff clay down to 15 m. The natural water content varies from 60% to 100% and exceeds the liquid limit. The plasticity index varies from 15 to 25%.

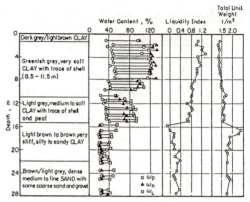

Fig. 2   A Typical Bangkok Sub-soil Profile

PORE PRESSURE OBSERVATIONS DURING EMBANKMENT LOADING

The excess pore pressures developed during embankment loading at seven sites showed gradual build-up at low stress levels increasing at a much higher rate after a certain critical level. D'Appolonia (1971) also observed similar phenomenon and it was explained that the higher rate of increase is due to induced shear stress exceeding the undrained shear strength causing local yielding. This critical stress level was found to be lower than the preconsolidation pressure, p_c, from laboratory one-dimensional consolidation test. Based on the observations from a total of 30 embankment case histories, Leroueil et al (1978b) found that the critical stress, σ'_{vcr}, is slightly less than p_c if OCR is greater than 2.5.

The computed values of the pore pressure parameter, μ, is low when the critical stress is not exceeded. The theoretical values of the parameter, μ, for stress conditions exceeding the critical stress should approach unity, but the measured values in Bangkok clay, especially in Thonburi-Paktho and AIT Campus are on the contrary. This behavior may be attributed to the effect of the weathered crust which allows the dissipation of pore pressures during construction through open cracks, root holes, and others. The parameter, μ, in excess of the critical stress are plotted against OCR in Fig. 3 and shows that the magnitude of μ decreases with the increase in OCR. The estimated value of the parameter, A, is plotted with respect to OCR in Fig. 4. The values of A close to the ground surface are unreasonably low because of neglecting the arching effect between the embankment and the soil. However, Christian (1968) explained that the horizontal stresses

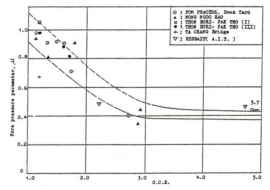

Fig. 3   Relationship between Pore Pressure Parameter, μ, and Overconsolidation Ratio (O.C.R.) for soft BANGKOK Clay.

are strongly influenced by drainage conditions and are over-estimated at relatively shallow depth where significant drainage occurred during construction.

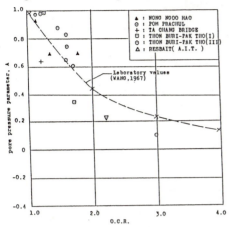

Fig. 4 Pore Pressure Parameter, A, vs O.C.R. Beneath the Centerline of Embankment in Soft Bangkok Clay

Typical effective stress paths using field pore pressures on the centerline beneath the embankments are shown in Fig. 5. The stress paths in the weathered crust are much flatter indicating appreciable consolidation during construction, while stress paths below this zone are relatively steep indicating little dissipation of excess pore pressures during construction. The values of OCR in each depth are also shown. The stress paths do not proceed along the K_O-line, the path followed during routine consolidation test, but are much steeper except for the stress path in the weathered crust wherein appreciable lateral expansion resulted in greater axial strains. The stress path in the weathered zone proceed along the low boundary of the K_O-line because the actual K_O value in the surface layer is greater than the average and that the horizontal stresses are over-estimated by the elastic theory at relatively shallow depths.

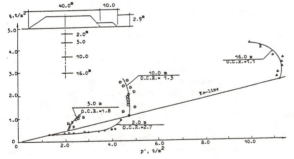

Fig. 5 Effective Stress Path due to Embankment Loading at each Depth (NONG NGOO HAO - IV)

SETTLEMENT CHARACTERISTICS OF TEST EMBANKMENTS

Four test embankments with complete available test data are analyzed for the settlement characteristics. The stiff clay layer below the upper compressible soft clay layer and medium stiff clay layer is assumed to be incompressible. The ratio of the compressible layer thickness to the width of the embankment (Z_O/B) is less than unity except at Tachang Bridge Site embankment. Thus, theoretically, approximate one-dimensional conditions may be assumed in the former case while three-dimensional conditions may be assumed to prevail in the latter case.

The settlements during the construction of embankments can be separated into the following three components (Cox, 1973); (i) the elastic settlement at constant volume due to the imposed shear stresses, (ii) the plastic settlements due to the induced shear stresses exceeding the shear strength, and (iii) consolidation settlement due to dissipation of pore pressure. The consolidation settlement during construction was calculated by the method proposed by the method of Leroueil et al (1978b). All of the four test embankment loads exceeded the critical stress level as indicated from the relationship between pore pressures and embankment loads. The calculated and observed construction settlements are summarized in Table I. The plastic deformation of Pom Prachul Embankment was calculated using the method of D'Appolonia et al (1971). The observed settlements of Nong Ngoo Hao and Tachang Bridge at the end of construction are quite less than the calculated settlements excluding the plastic component. But the other embankments in Thonburi-Paktho and Pom Prachul showed remarkable agreement between the calculated and observed settlements. The method suggested by COX (1973) which includes the elastic deformation, the plastic deformation and consolidation settlement seems to give a practical answer to the magnitude of settlement at the end of construction for soft Bangkok clay, provided correct value of undrained properties can be established.

TABLE I

Calculated and Observed Construction Settlement

Embankment	Test No.	Calculated (cm)				Obser-ved	Reference
		A	B	C	Sum		
TACHANG	3	9.4	-	4.20	13.6	7.1	CIRIDON (1972)
NONG NGOO HAO	IV	12.6	-	16.7	29.3	17.0	YUEN (1975)
THONBURI-PAKTO	I	10.4	41.6	44.6	96.6	103.0	COX (1973)
POM PHACHUL	no drain	11.5	7.7	19.5	38.7	39.2	

A: Elastic Deformation   B: Plastic Deformation   C: Consolidation Settlement

TABLE II

The Total Primary Settlement from Various Methods

Method of Analysis	NONG NGOO HAO	POM PRACHUL	THONBURI PAKTHO (I)	TACHANG
One-dimensional (cm)	214	130	235	30
Three-dimensional (cm)	169	148	225	28
Modified Method	109	73	191	23
ASAOKA's method (cm)	60	80	175	29

The settlement during post-construction period was determined by dividing the entire compressible layer into a series of thin layers. The following methods were used: (i) conventional one-dimensional method; (ii) three-dimensional method (Skempton and Bjerrum, 1957); (iii) the method of Leroueil et al (1978b); and (iv) graphical method (Asaoka, 1978). Since the method of Asaoka (1978) includes the initial construction settlements, the settlements from the method of Skempton and Bjerrum (1957) and that of Leroueil et al (1978b) was added to the observed construction settlement in order to compare with Asaoka's settlements. However, since the conventional Terzaghi settlement fails to recognize the instantaneous deformation, it can be directly compared with that of Asaoka's. The total primary settlements including observed initial settlements are compared in Table II. The settlements as calculated from the modified method proposed by Leroueil et al (1978b) is the one closest to Asaoka's values. Thus, it can be concluded that the method proposed by Leroueil et al (1978b) gives the best estimate of the consolidated settlement in the post-construction period in the soft Bangkok clay.

The coefficient of secondary consolidation, C_α, for specimens of Bangkok clay has been investigated by many researchers. Kulatilake (1978) has investigated the relationship between C_α and the vertical effective stress, and between C_α and voids ratio. C_α are summarized in Table III. Tsai (1982) has obtained the ratio of C_α to C_c to be 0.01. This ratio is quite low compared to the value of 0.05 to $\pm$ 0.02 (Ladd, 1977). The in-situ time-rate of consolidation generally proceed at a more rapid rate than as predicted. Using actual time-settlement records, the C_v values were obtained by Asaoka's method assuming drainage from both ends as tabulated in Table IV. The field values are consistently greater compared to the laboratory values except at Tachang Bridge site where the laboratory values are widely scattered (see Table IV).

TABLE III

Summary of C_α Values (after Kulatilake, 1978)

Sites and Soil Type	C_α (10-4 strain/log cycle)
CHULA-soft clay (non-weathered)	40 – 150
Nong Ngoo Hao-soft (weathered)	10 – 200
Nong Ngoo Hao-soft (non-weathered)	10 – 500
A.I.T.-soft clay (weathered)	0 – 100
A.I.T.-soft clay (non-weathered)	10 – 450

TABLE IV

Summary of Settlement Rate

Embankment	NONG NGOO HAO	POM PRACHUL	THONBURI PAKTHO (1)	TACHANG
Layer Thickness (m)	15.40	17.00	14.50	13.00
Drainage Path (m)	7.70	8.50	7.25	6.50
Range of Cv from Laboratory (cm²/day)	10–950	17–432	9–130	9–2680
Range of Cv from the field (cm²/day) (Asaoka's method)	1980	1859	548	1205

STABILITY ANALYSIS OF TEST EMBANKMENTS

Boonsinsuk (1974) and Ho (1976) calculated the safety of the Nong Ngoo Hao embankment using three different modes of failures; (i) neglecting the strength of the fill, (ii) including the strength of the fill, and (iii) assuming a vertical tension crack in the fill. The factors of safety were obtained by total stress analysis on the critical surface at Nong Ngoo Hao site and comparison among different types of shear strengths. Similarly, results were obtained using effective stress analysis. The factors of safety from the tiraxial $\overline{CAU}$ tests are always higher than those from triaxial $\overline{CIU}$ tests and the predicted pore pressure by Henkel's method always yielded higher safety factor.

Mesri (1975) gave the relationship of $C_u = 0.22\ \sigma_p'$ which correlated well with the average field vane strength and the corrected vane strengths using the correction factor, μ, by Bjerrum (1972). σ_p' is the preconsolidation pressure. The best agreement of Mesri's hypothesis for the strength data from Bangkok clay was obtained in the soft clay layer. Some disagreement, however, occur in the upper zone probably due to the effect of the weathered crust. The comparison between Bjerrum's correction factor, μ, and Mesri's correction on the safety factor is shown in Table V. The average ratio of C_u (vane)/σ_p' of all sites are plotted against the plasticity index, in Fig. 6. The factor of safety corrected by Mesri's relationship for the stability analysis of Nong Ngoo Hao test

embankments was in the range of 0.93 to 1.06. The factor of safety by Bjerrum's correction also approached unity but with greater divergence. Hence, it can be concluded that the available strength at failure under an embankment is independent of the plasticity index and is a unique function of the pre-consolidation pressure in the soft Bangkok clay.

TABLE V

Comparison of Correction Factors

Site	NONG NGOO HAO	BANGKOK-SIRACHA	THONBURI-PAKTHO, II	THONBURI-PAKTHO III	RESBALT (A.I.T.)
BJERRUM's μ	0.70	0.65	0.81	0.74	0.81
MESRI's $\dfrac{0.22\ \sigma_p'}{C_u\ (vane)}$	0.63	0.64	0.88	0.66	0.86

BEHAVIOR OF TEST EXCAVATION

Data from Nong Ngoo Hao Test Excavation and RESBAIT Drainage Channel (Rangsit) in the soft Bangkok clay are analyzed. The Nong Ngoo Hao test excavation which reached a maximum of 4.0 m below the existing ground was fully instrumented. The RESBAIT drainage channel at AIT campus (Moh et al, 1972) which was constructed beside the test bund has been instrumented only with piezometers.

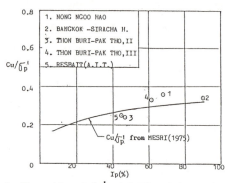

Fig. 6 The ratio, C_u/σ_p' with Plasticity Index in Soft Bangkok clay

Pore pressure due to stress relief has been predicted using conventional methods i.e. one-dimensional, three-dimensional, Henkel's and Skempton's solution. Generally, the one-dimensional theory overestimates to a great extent the excess pore pressures, while the other three methods do not show any significant differences. The piezometric readings in RESBAIT drainage channel generally indicated rapid dissipation of excess pore pressures near the ground surface and at the lower boundary of the soft clay (Moh et al, 1972). This was certainly due to the deep fissuring of the weathered clay and sand seams in bottom layer.

Sivandran (1975) studied the effects of shear modulus, E, on the vertical and lateral movements using empirical relationship. For both the vertical and horizontal movements, the predicted values agrees well with the measured values using the relationship, $E = 250\ S_u$, where S_u is the field vane strength. However, Yuen (1975), using finite element method, found the best agreement with $E = 70\ S_u$ for Nong Ngoo Hao embankment.

The stability analysis of the Nong Ngoo Hao test excavation has been made by ESSA (1974) and Ho (1975). They analyzed the slope using both total and effective stress analysis. The safety factors from average vane shear strength, direct shear strength and $\overline{CIU}$ strength were approximately the same and gave values approaching to unity when Bjerrum's correction factor was applied (Ho, 1975). The safety factor calculated from CK_0U strength was found to be too high and therefore not suitable for the analysis of excavation. The safety factor calculated from unconfined compression strength gave a very low value of 0.59 (Essa, 1974), while Ho (1975), using the unconsolidated undrained strengths from different tests obtained safety factors ranging from 1.03 to 1.84 without considering the effect of tension cracks. The theoretical critical failure surface was found to be different from the observed failure surface. Table VI compares the safety factors computed using the actual failure surface and the theoretical critical failure surface at the end of construction stage. Tension cracks actually occurred at failure of the excavation and Table VI indicates that its occurrence resulted in the reduction of the safety factors in all cases. The tension cracks also altered the position of the critical failure surfaces.

TABLE VI

Actual and Theoretical Safety Factors
(SWEDISH Method, after HO, 1976)

Shear Strength	AA		BB		CC	
	F	F*	F	F*	F	F*
Average vane strength	1.74	1.85	1.59	1.76	1.41	1.54
Unconfined	1.02	1.29	0.99	1.26	0.97	1.24
Shear strength CKoU strength	2.10	2.28	2.07	2.27	1.83	2.06
CIU strength	1.67	1.80	1.62	1.79	1.65	1.53
Undrained - Unconsolidated	1.33	1.46	1.28	1.41	1.23	1.36

AA: Without tension crack   BB: With tension crack
CC: Tension crack with water pressure   F : Theoretical safety factor
F*: Actual safety factor estimated on failure surface

TABLE VII

Theoretical Safety Factors for Final Excavation Depth
(after ESSA, 1974) (Effective Stress Analysis)

Method of Analysis	Shear Strength Parameters	Factors of Safety							
		Predicted Pore Pressures		Pore Pressure Measured at End-of-Const.		Pore Pressure Measured at Failure		Longterm	
		* F	** F_h	F	F_h	F	F_h	F	F_h
Bishop	$\overline{CIU}$	1.82	1.62	1.73	1.54	1.51	1.31	1.27	1.15
	$\overline{CAU}$	2.51	2.26	2.40	2.14	2.06	1.83	1.52	1.37
Janbu	$\overline{CIU}$	1.84	1.57	1.69	1.44	1.45	1.24	1.22	1.10
	$\overline{CAU}$	2.43	2.12	2.28	2.04	2.00	1.80	1.53	1.32

*F = Safety factor without tension cracks.
**F_h= Safety factor corrected for tension cracks with water pressure.

The stability of excavations in soft clays decreases with time because of the dissipation of the negative pore pressure induced due to stress relief. Essa (1974) and Ho (1975) computed the factor of safety for final excavation depth. Table VII contains the safety factors corresponding to the end-of-construction (Day 32), failure (Day 94), and under long term condition. The factor of safety is maximum after the end of construction and minimum under long term condition. The use of $\overline{CAU}$ strength parameters always yielded higher safety factors than that of $\overline{CIU}$ parameters. This factor points out the significant effects of the stress system on stability analysis.

PROBABILISTIC ANALYSIS OF STABILITY AND SETTLEMENT OF STRUCTURES IN SOFT BANGKOK CLAY

Probabilistic techniques were recently introduced by Sivandran (1979), Ananda (1980) and Ganeshanandan (1980) to evaluate the stability and settlements of embankments, excavations and the carrying capacity of pile foundations.

In the stability analysis of full scale test embankments, the probability distribution of the factor of safety and the safety margin were obtained as a direct consequence of the uncertainty of the soil properties, using the Monte Carlo simulation technique. The effect of uncertainty of soil properties on the resulting distribution for safety were also studied. The work was intended to develop a functional relationship to describe the actual probability of failure in terms of the conventional safety factors for soft Bangkok clay. The consolidation settlement of the embankment was also evaluated using the probabilistic technique.

Because the soft Bangkok clay exhibit a slight overconsolidation, the e-log σ_v curve was defined to be made up of two linear portions corresponding to the overconsolidated and normally consolidated ranges. Histograms for NC compression index, C_c, and OC compression index, C_c', were plotted. The C_c was modeled as a normally distributed variable with a coefficient of variation (COV) of 0.18. C_c' was found also to be normally distributed with COV of 0.15. Probability distributions for consolidation settlements were constructed using simulation techniques. In the evaluation of immediate settlements, the probabilistic analysis was applied to an advanced analytical model: finite element technique. Frequency distributions of immediate settlements were constructed. Using soil properties from probability distributions, the immediate settlements were evaluated using bilinear and nonlinear analysis resulting in a COV of 0.112 and 0.067, respectively.

A major application of the probability analysis was accomplished by relating the probability of failure to the conventional safety factor. The stability of the embankment was investigated probabilistically for heights of 2.0, 2.5, 2.8, 3.0, 3.4, 3.7, 4.0 and 5.0 m. Figure 7 shows the distributions for the two moments at embankment heights of 2.0 m and 3.4 m. A relationship between the probability of failure, the factor of safety and the safety margin is established in Fig. 8. The variations of the safety factors with the height of the embankment is shown in Fig. 9. Finally, Fig. 10 shows the relationship derived from the probability of failure and the conventional safety factor. The probability of failure decreases asymtotically with the factor of safety. The probability of failure reached values of less than 0.01 for a safety factor 1.5. Investigations of this region of very low probability of failure was difficult since it involved very high number of simulations. Yet, this is also the region of interest for the soil engineer. Thus, an attempt was made to determine the probability of failure corresponding to a factor of safety of 1.2. The probability of failure was of the order of 10^{-4}. In conclusion, it can be stated that the plot in Fig. 8 can be of practical use to soil en-

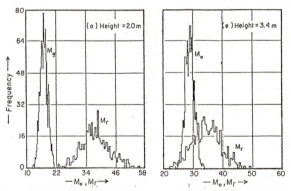

Fig. 7 Frequency Distributions for Overturning and Resisting Moments for Embankment Heights of 2.0 m and 3.4 m

gineers in designing safety factors. With the aid of
this plot, it would be possible to weight alternative
design against actual probability of failure.

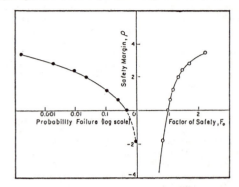

Fig. 8 Safety Margin Vs Probability of Failure and
Factor of Safety

Fig. 9 Height of Embankment Vs Factor of Safety

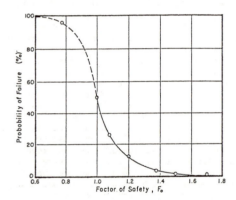

Fig. 10 Probability of Failure Vs Factor of Safety

The stability of the excavation was investigated probabilistically for excavation depths of 1,2,3 and 4 m. Fig. 11
shows the distributions of the two moments for the excavation depths of 3.0 m and 4.0 m. A major application of
the probability analysis is accomplished by establishing
a relationship between the probability of failure and the
factor of safety. Fig. 12 shows the relationship of the
factor of safety and the safety margin plotted against the
probability of failure. The probability of failure is of
the order of 10^{-6} at a factor of safety of 1.91, and it
increases rapidly to the value of 14.4% when the factor of
safety is 1.07. Finally, the relationship between the
safety margin and the factor of safety is shown in Fig. 13.

USE OF SANDWICKS AND SAND DRAINS WITH PRE-LOADING

The performance of sandwicks in accelerating the consolidation of soft Bangkok clay was studied in a full
scale test embankment 90 m long, 33 m wide in
three sections, namely: a section with no drain, a section with drains of 2.5 m spacing, and a section with

drains of 1.5 m spacing. The sand drains consisted of
small diameter (5 cm) sandwicks and were installed by the
displacement method. The finished sandwicks extended to
a depth of 17 m below the ground surface. The embankment
was built in two stages one to a height of 1.45 m and the
other to a final height of 2.35 m. The settlement-time
records obtained from the test embankment showed very
little improvements in the settlement-time performance of
the drained section compared with the no-drain section as
evidenced by time-settlement records in Fig. 14. The
effectiveness of the sand drains was found to be somewhat
significant only in the upper 5 m depth of the subsoil.

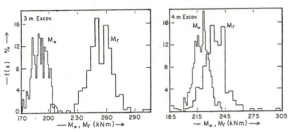

Fig. 11 Histograms of Safety Margin (kNm) at 3.0 m and
4.0 m Depth

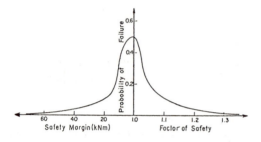

Fig. 12 Plot of Probability of Failure with Safety
Margin and Factor of Safety

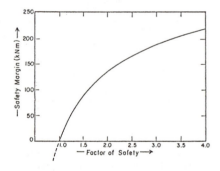

Fig. 13 Plot of Safety Margin and Factor of Safety

LIME COLUMN STABILIZATION OF BANGKOK CLAY

Studies were recently conducted by Anshumali (1980) under
the direction of J.S. Younger to explore the use of lime
column technique in the Bangkok subsoils. The study was
only confined to laboratory tests. The tests were conducted in a Rowe consolidation cell 6" in diameter. Thin
columns of lime were installed in the clay sample and the
influence of the sample size, diameter of lime column and
the curing period of the lime-soil mix on the compressibility and strength characteristics were investigated.
These preliminary tests seem to indicate that the lime
columns have significant effects on both the strength and
compressibility. The samples tested experienced less
settlement and considerable strength gain depending on the

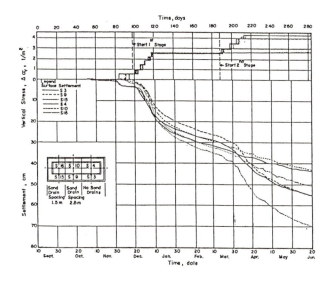

Fig. 14 Typical Settlement Point Readings at Pom Prachul Site

column diameter as well as the curing period. Further studies conducted by Lee (1982) under the direction of J.S. Younger seemed to confirm that a 38% reduction in settlement could be obtained with a 15% lime content after a 12 day curing period. The high salt content and the high organic matter seemed to be the major factors in reducing the effectiveness of lime columns in the soft Bangkok clay. Accordingly, lime column technique may be more effective in the central Bangkok area than towards the seashore.

LAND SUBSIDENCE AND THE EFFECT OF DEEP WELL PUMPING

The land subsidence and the effects of deep well pumping seem to have a very predominant effect on the construction of tall buildings as well as bridges and road embankments in the Bangkok Plain. Especially in the case of runway embankments and roadworks, uneven settlement can take place with long period of time due to subsidence effect. Furthermore, the effects of flood on highways and roads in Bangkok metropolis have now reached an intolerable limit with heavy congestion of traffic and permanent submergence of a large number of roads and houses for a prolonged period of time. A detailed subsidence study conducted by Nutalaya et al (1979-1982) seemed to indicate that subsidence as much as 20 to 80 cms have taken place as compared to the elevations established some 30 to 40 years ago. These studies seemed to indicate that the contribution from the compression of the upper clay layer (20 to 50 m thick) is about 40% of the total surface settlement. The elevation of the Bangkok area is at the alarmingly low level of about 1.0 to 1.5 m above mean sea level. In addition to the hazardous flooding effects which takes place annually for nearly a third of the year, subsidence effects will have a pronounced effect in the surface settlement of roads, and differential settlement of bridges and tall buildings. Substantial effect could also be anticipated from negative skin friction in very deep foundations.

CONCLUSIONS

The excess pore pressures beneath structures in the soft Bangkok clay built-up gradually for low load levels increasing at a much higher rate after a certain critical stress level. A relationship is derived between the critical stress and the preconsolidation stress from oedometer test. The field pore pressure parameters are relatively low when the critical stress is not exceeded. Due to the effects of the weathered crust, these parameters do not show reasonable values even in excess of the critical stress level. The effective stress paths during construction plotted using pore pressures measured in the field do not proceed along the K_O-line but with much steeper slope except in the weathered zone. The construction settlements with three components were in good agreement with the measured field value. The method of Leroueil et al (1978b) gave the best estimate of consolidation settlement in the post-construction period. Due to the effect of the weathered crust and the existence of internal drainage layers, the field C_V values were greater than the laboratory values. All the corrected safety factors at failure including the correction of Bjerrum (1972) and Mesri (1975) were near unity. The excess pore pressures in the test excavation were always overpredicted by the one-dimensional theory. The elastic method and the methods of Henkel and Skempton did not show significant difference but still gave values greater than the measured one. The Monte Carlo simulation technique was used to obtain probability distributions for consolidation settlements, the safety margins and the factor of safety. Relationships were established between the probability of failure, conventional safety factor, and safety margin. A non-linear finite element analysis was also carried out to determine the immediate settlements of the structures using probabilistic approach. A brief presentation is also made on the soil improvement techniques and land subsidence in the Bangkok area. The use of sand drains with pre-loading and lime column techniques did not appear to be appealing to consultants and contractors engaged in major projects. The effects of land subsidence and the hazards of floods seem to be the most urgent problem in the Bangkok.

ACKNOWLEDGEMENTS

The authors wish to thank Drs. Za-Chieh Moh, E.W. Brand and J.D. Nelson who initiate much of the work on Bangkok clay at AIT. Appreciation is also given to Mrs. Uraivan Singchinsuk for her assistance in the preparation of the manuscripts. Appreciation is due to Y.H. Lee, C.Y. Tsai, C. Sivandran, J.M.T. Ananda, M. Anshumali, P. Boonsinsuk, R. Essa, R. Ganeshananthan, W.H. Ho, Y.M. Ho and P.H. Kulatilake, all former graduate students at AIT, for their outstanding contribution to this paper.

REFERENCES

Ananda, J.M.T. (1980), A probabilistic approach to the stability and deformation of excavation and natural slopes. M.Eng. Thesis, Asian Institute of Technology, Bangkok, Thailand

Anshumali, M. (1980). A laboratory study of the effect of lime column stabilization on compressibility properties of Bangkok clay. M.Eng. Thesis, Asian Institute of Technology, Bangkok, Thailand.

Asaoka, A. (1978). Observational procedure of settlement prediction. Soils and Foundations, Vol. 7, No. 1.

Balasubramaniam, A.S., Sivandran, C. and Adikari, G.S.N. (1979a). Statistical evaluation of the strength characteristics of Bangkok clays. Proc. 3rd Intl. Conf. on Appl. of Statistics and Prob. in Soil and Struct. Eng., Vol. 1, pp. 198-211.

Balasubramaniam, A.S., Sivandran, C. and Ho, Y.M. (1979b). Stability and settlement of embankments in soft Bangkok clay. Proc. 3rd Intl. Conf. on Numerical Methods in Geomechanics, Aachen, West Germany, Vol. 4.

Balasubramaniam, A.S., Phota-yanuvat, C., Ganeshananthan, R. and Lee, K.K. (1981). Performance of friction piles in Bangkok subsoils, Xth Intl. Conf. Soil Mech. Found. Eng., Stockholm, Vol. 2, pp. 605-610.

Bjerrum, L. (1972). Embankments on soft ground. Proc. Spec. Conf. on Performance of Earth and Earth-Supported Structures. Purdue Univ. Vol. 2, pp. 1-54.

Boonsinsuk, P. (1974). Stability analysis of a test embankment on Nong Ngoo Hao clay. M. Eng. Thesis No. 696, Asian Institute of Technology, Bangkok, Thailand.

Christian, J.P. (1968). Undrained stress distribution. ASCE J. Soil Mech. Found. Div., Vol. 94, No. SM6.

Cox, J.B. (1973). Trial embankment studies for the Thonburi-Paktho Highway, Thailand, Lea-Geco Intl., Technical Report R-5, Bangkok, Thailand.

D'Appolonia, D.J., Lambe, T.W. and Poulos, R.G. (1971). Evaluation of pore pressure beneath embankments. ASCE J. Soil Mech. Found. Eng. Div., Vol. 97, No. SM6.

Essa, R. (1974). Stability of trial excavation in Nong Ngoo Hao clay. M.Eng. Thesis No. 700, Asian Institute of Technology, Bangkok, Thailand.

Ganeshananthan, R. (1980). A probabilistic approach to the carrying capacity of pile foundations. M.Eng. Thesis, Asian Institute of Technology, Bangkok, Thailand.

Ho, W.M. (1975). Reanalysis of Nong Ngoo Hao Test Excavation. M.Eng. Thesis No. 905, Asian Instittue of Technology, Bangkok, Thailand.

Ho, Y.M. (1976). A reanalysis of Nong Ngoo Hao Test Embankment. M.Eng. Thesis No. 906, Asian Institute of Technology, Bangkok, Thailand.

Kulatilake, P.H.S.W. (1978). Secondary compression study related to Bangkok subsidence. M.Eng. Thesis No. 1292, Asian Institute of Technology, Bangkok, Thailand.

Ladd, C.C., Foott, R., Ishihara, K., Schlosser, F. and Poulos, H.G. (1974). Stress-deformation and strength characteristics. Proc. 9th Intl. Conf. Soil Mech. Eng., Vol. 2, Tokyo.

Lee, H.J. (1982). Lime column stabilization of Bangkok clays. M.Eng. Thesis, Asian Institute of Technology, Bangkok, Thailand.

Leroueil, S., Tavenas, F., Mieussens, C. and Peignand, M., (1978b). Pore pressure in clay foundation under embankment, Part II. Canadian Geotechnical J., Vol. 15, No. 1, pp. 66-82.

Mesri, G. (1975). Discussion of new design procedure for stability of soft clays. ASCE J. Geotech. Div., Vol. 103, GT. 5, pp. 417-430.

Moh, Z.C., Brand, E.W. and Nelson, J.D. (1972). Pore pressure under a bund on soft fissured clay. Proc. Conf. on Performance of Earth and Earth-Supported Structures, Vol. 1, Purdue, Univ., pp. 243-272.

Moh, Z.C., Nelson, J.D. and Brand, E.W. (1969). Strength and deformation behavior of Bangkok clay. Proc. 7th Intl. Conf. Soil Mech. Found. Eng., Vol. 1, pp. 287-289, Mexico.

Nutalaya, P., Akagi, T., Balasubramaniam, A.S. (1979-1983) Investigation of land subsidence due to deep well pumping in the Bangkok area. AIT Research Reports.

Sivandran, C. (1975). Finite element analysis of Test Embankments and Excavation at Nong Ngoo Hao. M.Eng. Thesis No. 913, Asian Institute of Technology, Bangkok, Thailand.

Sivandran, C. (1979). Probabilistic analysis of stability and settlement of structures on soft Bangkok clay, Ph.D. Dissertation, Asian Institute of Technology, Bangkok, Thailand.

Skempton, A.W. and Bjerrum, L. (1957). A contribution to the settlement analysis of foundation on clay. Geotechnique, Vol. 7, pp. 168-178.

Tsai, C.Y. (1982). A monograph on the engineering properties of Bangkok subsoils, M.Eng. Thesis, Asian Institute of Technology, Bangkok, Thailand.

Yuen, H.K. (1975). Analysis of behavior of Nong Ngoo Hao and MIT embankments by finite element approach. M.Eng. Thesis, Asian Institute of Technology, Bangkok, Thailand.

Influence des surcharges sur la tension des ancrages

Influence of the surcharges on the tension of anchorings

F. BLONDEAU, Directeur Général Adjoint, Terrasol, France
M. CHRISTIANSEN, Ingénieur-Conseil, France

RÉSUMÉ   Quelques incidents survenus sur la tenue d'ancrages de soutènement nous ont amené à réfléchir à l'incidence des tassements induits par les surcharges sur la tension initiale de ces éléments.

Cette étude théorique présente le modèle d'interaction entre le sol (supposé élastique linéaire - plastique) et l'élément d'ancrage du soutènement (supposé élastique), et propose des abaques d'évaluation de la variation relative de tension en fonction de paramètres adimensionnels, lorsque le tassement du sol est uniforme.

INTRODUCTION

L'objet de cette étude est de trouver une explication à certaines ruptures d'ouvrages de soutènement, en analysant l'incidence du tassement du sol sur la tension des éléments d'ancrages.

La figure 1 montre un schéma typique de rideau de soutènement (pour mur de quai par exemple) ancré par un lit de tirants en tête et soumis à une surcharge. Si le sol, situé à l'arrière du rideau et traversé par la partie "libre" des tirants, tasse sous l'effet de la surcharge, le tirant subit une pression latérale et se déforme. Sa longueur augmente ainsi que sa tension. Sous certaines conditions limites de frottement longitudinal et de pression normale entre le sol et le tirant, la tension du tirant peut atteindre sa limite de rupture.

On présente, dans ce document, l'analyse du phénomène dans diverses configurations schématiques et on donne des abaques permettant de déterminer simplement l'augmentation de tension relative de l'ancrage en fonction de paramètres adimensionnels liés aux paramètres géométriques et géotechniques du site, lorsque le tassement est uniforme.

MODELISATION

On adopte les hypothèses et approximations suivantes :

- A l'origine le tirant de longueur L est tendu sous une traction T_o uniforme. Il est parfaitement flexible (rigidité transversale $EI = 0$). Le déplacement du sol s est supposé satisfaire aux conditions de la déformation plane et l'étude est faite dans le plan contenant la position initiale du tirant. Le déplacement p d'un point du tirant est

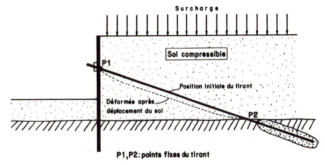

Figure 1

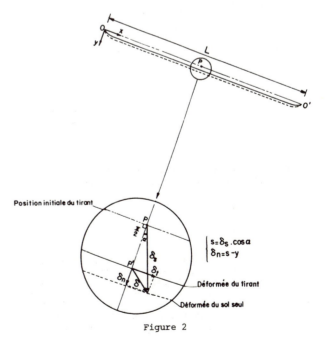

Figure 2

supposé normal à la position initial de celui-ci (fig. 2). La déformation du tirant est supposée faible pour que l'on puisse raisonner en coordonnées d'EULER dans un système d'axe OX, OY lié à sa position initiale. On définit alors les composantes normale δ_n et tangentielle δ_t du déplacement relatif sol-tirant :

$$\vec{\delta} = \vec{\delta}_s - \vec{\delta}_p$$

dans ce système d'axes. En pratique, seule la composante normale δ_n est prise en compte sous la forme :

$$\delta_n = s - y$$

avec $\quad s = \delta_s \cos\alpha$ = composante normale du déplacement du sol seul

$\quad y = \delta_p$ = déplacement du tirant

- Le comportement du tirant est supposé élastique linéaire défini par la rigidité EA de la section d'acier.

- La composante normale de l'interaction sol-tirant est de type élasto-plastique défini par la loi (fig. 3) :

$$P = E_s (s - y)$$

et $\quad P < P_\ell$

dans laquelle P est pression par unité de longueur, P_ℓ la valeur limite de P, E_s le coefficient de réaction sol-tirant.

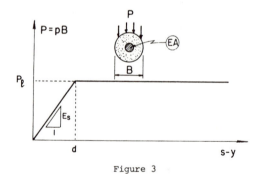

Figure 3

Le déplacement critique au-delà duquel le sol se plastifie autour du tirant est noté :

$$d = \frac{P_\ell}{E_s}$$

- La composante tangentielle de l'interaction sol-tirant est assimilée à un frottement sec défini par sa valeur f par unité de longueur, constante sur toute la longueur. Ceci revient à admettre que le déplacement relatif sol-tirant nécessaire à la mobilisation de f est très petit par rapport à d. Par ailleurs, la confi-

guration généralement adoptée pour les tirants, leur conférant une inclinaison sensible vers le bas, implique que le frottement dû au tassement du sol s'exerce de la tête vers la zone de scellement. La tête d'ancrage ainsi que le point représentatif de la zone de scellement sont supposés fixes. Toutefois, un processus itératif permettrait de prendre en compte un déplacement relatif de ces deux extrémités du tirant.

EQUATIONS D'EQUILIBRE - PRINCIPES GENERAUX DE SOLUTION

Deux conditions sont à réaliser :

Si T_x et T_y sont les composantes de la traction T s'exerçant dans le tirant déformé (T est supposé orienté vers les x positifs), l'équilibre sol-tirant se traduit par :

$$\frac{d\,T_x(x)}{dx} = -f$$

soit

(1) $\quad \begin{cases} T_x(x) = T_x(o) - f_x \\ \dfrac{d\,T_y}{dx} = -p(y) \end{cases}$

La flexibilité du tirant impose :

(2) $\quad \dfrac{T_y}{T_x} = \dfrac{dy}{dx}$

(1)+(2)→(3) $\quad T_x(o) - f(x)\ y'' - fy' = - P(y)$

L'équation (3) définit l'équilibre sol-tirant. L'allongement du tirant est déterminé par :

$$\Delta L = \frac{1}{EA} \int_o^L \left[T(x) - T_o \right] dx$$

avec $\quad T(x) = T_x(x) \sqrt{1 + y'^2}$

qui avec (1) donne

$$T(x) = \left[T_x(o) - f\,x \right] \sqrt{1 + y'^2}$$

De plus $\quad L + \Delta L = \int_o^L \sqrt{1 + y'^2}\ d_x$

ce qui conduit à l'équation d'équilibre interne du tirant :

(4) $\displaystyle\int_o^L \left[\frac{T_x(o) - fx}{EA} - 1 \right] \sqrt{1 + y'^2}\ dx = \left[\frac{T_o}{EA} - 1 \right] L$

La solution du problème passe par la résolution simultanée de (3) et (4). Compte tenu de la loi d'interaction sol-tirant, l'intégration doit être faite séparément sur les zones dites élastiques où $P_\ell < P$ et sur les zones dites plastiques où $P = P_\ell$. Certains cas simples peuvent, moyennant quelques approximations, être résolus facilement, notamment le cas du tassement uniforme décrit ci-après.

CAS DU TASSEMENT UNIFORME

Ce cas correspond à :

$$s(x) = s = C^{te}$$

Il peut être résolu très facilement si l'on admet les simplifications suivantes :

- les effets de la pression normale et du frottement sont découplés ce qui revient à admettre que l'incidence de f sur la solution de ③ et ④ est faible, ce que confirment les calculs. La tension dans le tirant est alors défini comme la somme :

$$⑤ \qquad T = T_o + \Delta T_f + \Delta T_p$$

avec T_o, tension initiale ; ΔT_f, augmentation de tension dûe au frottement seul ; ΔT_p, augmentation dûe à la pression normale. Le frottement étant supposé nul, ΔT_p est indépendant de x.

- la déformée du tirant est suffisamment proche de sa position initiale pour que l'on puisse admettre :

$$\sqrt{1 + y'^2} \simeq 1 + \frac{y'^2}{2}$$

$$T \simeq T_x$$

La valeur maximale de T_f à la tête d'ancrage vaut alors :

$$⑥ \qquad T_f(o) = f \frac{L}{2}$$

Les hypothèses simplificatrices adoptées et la symétrie de la déformée par rapport à l'abscisse L/2 conduisent à une expression mise sous forme adimensionnelle valable lorsque le sol n'est pas entièrement plastifié le long du tirant, ce qui est le cas général (fig. 4a).

$$⑦ \qquad \left[\frac{\Delta T_p}{T_o}\right]^2 \cdot \left(\frac{\Delta T_p}{T_o} + 1\right) - \Lambda_{ep} = 0$$

dans laquelle

$\Delta T_p = T - T_o$ = augmentation de tension dûe à la pression latérale

$$\Lambda_{ep} = \frac{1}{9} \cdot \frac{E_s (EA)^2 d^4}{T_o^3 L^2} \cdot \left[\left(2 \frac{s}{d} - 1\right)^{3/2} + \frac{1}{2}\right]^2$$

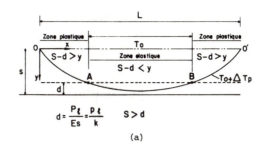

$$d = \frac{P_\ell}{E_s} = \frac{p\,\ell}{k} \qquad S > d$$

(a)

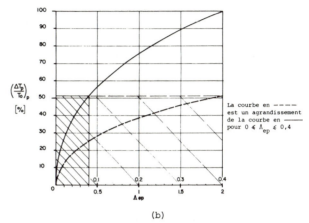

La courbe en - - - - est un agrandissement de la courbe en ——— pour $0 \leqslant \Lambda_{ep} \leqslant 0,4$

(b)

Variation relative de tension provoquée par un tassement uniforme s du sol autour du tirant lorsque le déplacement relatif sol-tirant est inférieur au déplacement d de réaction plastique dans la zone centrale.

Figure 4

$(d = \dfrac{P}{E_s}$ = déplacement sol-tirant provoquant la plastification)

L'abaque de la figure 4b donne la variation de $\Delta T_p/T_o$ en fonction de Λ_{ep}.

Le tassement critique correspondant à la plastification complète (fig. 5a) est donné par :

$$\frac{s_c}{d} = 1 + \frac{1}{8} \frac{L^2 E_s}{T_o^2} \frac{1}{1 + \left(\frac{\Delta T}{T_o}\right)}$$

dans laquelle $\Delta T/T_o$ est solution de l'équation ⑧.

$$⑧ \qquad \frac{\Delta T_p}{T_o} \cdot \left(1 + \frac{\Delta T_p}{T_o}\right)^2 - \Lambda_p = 0$$

avec $\Lambda_p = \dfrac{1}{24} \dfrac{(P_\ell \cdot L)^2 EA}{T_o^3}$

La figure 5b donne la variation de $\Delta T_p/T_o$ dans cette hypothèse. Elle représente la borne supérieure de l'accroissement de tension que peut avoir à subir le tirant.

Tant que $s < s_c$, c'est l'abaque de la figure 4 qu'il convient d'utiliser.

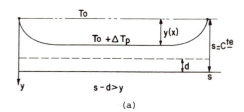

(a)

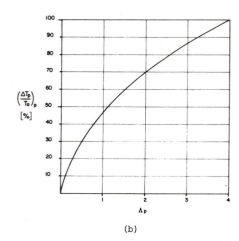

(b)

Variation relative de tension provoquée par un tassement uniforme s autour du tirant lorsque le déplacement relatif sol-tirant est partout supérieur au déplacement d de réaction plastique.

Figure 5

On note que lorsque le tassement devient important par rapport à d, le paramètre Λ_{ep} peut s'écrire :

$$\Lambda_{ep} \simeq \frac{8}{9} \frac{P_\ell \, (EA)^2}{T_o^3 \, L^2} \cdot s^3 \cdot (1 - \frac{3d}{2S})$$

On peut aussi l'exprimer à l'aide de la contrainte initiale de l'acier σ_o ($= T_o/A$)

$$(9) \qquad \Lambda_{ep} \simeq \frac{8}{9} \frac{P_\ell \cdot E^2}{\sigma_o^2 \cdot T_o \cdot L^2} \cdot s^3 \cdot (1 - \frac{3d}{2S})$$

Il apparaît clairement d'après (9) que Λ_{ep}, donc $\Delta T/T_o$ est très sensible au tassement s et que le moyen d'en réduire l'incidence, toutes choses égales par ailleurs, est d'augmenter la valeur de σ_o, c'est-à-dire de prendre des aciers de haute limite élastique et d'augmenter T_o c'est-à-dire de concentrer l'ancrage sur un faible nombre de tirants, ce qui est malheureusement contraire au souci habituel de "répartition du risque" par multiplication des éléments d'ancrage.

On note aussi que les tirants longs sont moins sensibles que les tirants courts.

Les exemples d'application courante montrent qu'une augmentation relative $\Delta T_p/T_o$ de 30 à 50 % peut être atteinte pour un tassement de l'ordre de 5 à 10 cm.

CONCLUSION

L'étude présentée ici montre que le déplacement du sol autour d'un tirant peut induire une augmentation sensible de tension de celui-ci au point d'en provoquer éventuellement la rupture. On sépare l'origine de la surtension en deux parties distinctes :

- l'effet du frottement provoqué par la composante tangentielle du mouvement. Dirigé de la tête vers le scellement, cet effet provoque une surtension relative, maximale en tête qui peut être de l'ordre de 10 à 30 % de la tension initiale ;

- l'effet de la pression provoqué par la composante normale du déplacement. Un abaque permet de déterminer très simplement l'accroissement relatif de tension dû à cet effet, dans l'hypothèse du tassement uniforme au droit de la "zone libre" du tirant.

Cet effet croît comme le cube de la valeur du tassement et peut atteindre 50 % pour 10 cm de déplacement absolu du sol (composante normale à la position initiale du tirant). Il diminue comme l'inverse du carré de la longueur libre. En cas d'augmentation sensible du tassement, la rupture du tirant intervient au voisinage de la tête d'ancrage. Pour limiter l'incidence relative de tels effets, il convient a priori d'utiliser des aciers à haute limite élastique et/ou de concentrer les ancrages sur des tirants de forte capacité.

Soil pressures on large diameter concrete pipe

Pressions du sol sur les tuyaux de grand diamètre

PAUL C. KNODEL, Chief, Geotechnical Branch, US Bureau of Reclamation, Denver, Colorado, USA

SYNOPSIS   A field study was conducted over a period of nearly 4-1/2 years to measure soil pressure distribution around two large diameter (25 feet O.D.) rigid concrete siphon pipes. One pipe was of circular, monolithic cast-in-place concrete construction while the other was circular precast, prestressed concrete pipe. Three pipe sections of each siphon were instrumented with soil pressure cells and numerous sets of readings were obtained during selected construction events. Differences were noted in soil pressure distribution around the two pipes.

INTRODUCTION

Rigid concrete pipes have for many years been designed assuming a typical bulb shaped soil pressure distribution on the pipe (Spangler, 1933). Although there have been general refinements to these analyses (Olander, 1950), there are limited data concerning actual soil pressures exerted on large rigid pipe as most of the studies in this area have been performed on rigid pipe of small diameter (Pettibone, 1966). The field study described in this paper was conducted over a period of nearly 4-1/2 years to measure actual soil pressures exerted on two large diameter (25 feet O.D.) rigid concrete siphon pipes. One pipe was of circular, monolithic cast-in-place construction while the other was circular precast, prestressed concrete pipe. The opportunity to instrument both the large diameter monolithic cast-in-place and the precast concrete siphon pipe existed on the Bureau's Central Arizona Project. Both types of pipe were designed with identical inside and outside diameters, and internal pressure capacities, and both were laid on similar foundations and had the same depth of earth cover.

INSTRUMENTATION

Three sections of pipe of each type siphon, cast-in-place and precast, prestressed were nearly identically instrumented with soil stress meters for this study. Electrical soil stress meters about 8 inches in diameter with an effective area of 42 in^2 were selected for the program. These meters are designed to provide direct measurement of pressure of fine-grained soil against a rigid structure. The meter consists of two closely spaced steel plates with the space between the plates filled with mercury; which transfers the pressure on the exposed face of the meter to

an internal diaphram, whose small deflection is detected by a strain-meter type sensing element. The exposed face of the meter is 0.540-inch-thick nickle-plated steel plate, so the meter is relatively insensitive to loading pattern. A thin layer of medium sand was, however, placed between the face of the stress meters and the backfill soil to assure uniform loading and to eliminate chance of point loading. The accuracy of the meters is 5 percent and the linearity is within 2 percent of full scale. The flexible rim of all meters was covered with a thin layer of sponge neopene when installed to isolate them from contacting the concrete. All meter faces were placed flush with the outside of the pipes.

Cast-in-Place Pipe Instrumentation

The monolithic cast-in-place concrete pipe siphon is 3,750 feet long and rests on a clayey sand (SC, SC-SM) foundation. Each monolithic pipe section has an outside diameter of about 25 feet, an inside diameter of 21 feet, and is approximately 25 feet long. Twenty-five electrical soil stress meters were placed in the three pipe sections as shown on figure 1. The soil stress meters were all placed about 4 feet from the end of each pipe section. Meters near the bottom of the pipe were placed against the soil, and concrete was placed over them. An epoxy cement was used to place meters in blockouts on the sides after the pipe was formed. Meters on the top were placed in the concrete during the pour. Pipe 57 was located between pipes 55 and 56.

Precast, Prestressed Pipe Instrumentation

The precast concrete siphon pipe was manufactured at the site. The instrumented siphon is one of seven and is about 1,600 feet long. It rests on a foundation of poorly graded sand (SP, SP-SM). Each circular precast pipe section had the following specifications:

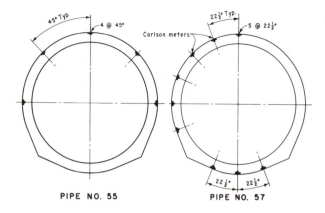

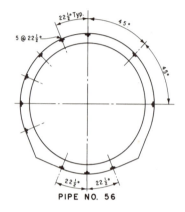

Fig. 1   Location of Soil Stress Meters for
Cast-in-Place Pipe

Inside dia	21 ft	Outside dia	24.5 ft
Pipe length	22 ft	Earth cover	5-25 ft
Weight	22 tons	Prestress wire	22 miles
Prestress tension	196,000 lb/in²		
Internal pressure	25-250 feet of head		

Two layers of prestressing wire were wrapped
on each pipe section with a 3/4-inch minimum
layer of drypack concrete between wire layers
and also over the second layer.

Twenty-seven electrical soil stress meters
were placed in the three pipe sections in an
arrangement similar to that shown on figure
1, all about 4 feet from the end of the pipe
sections. An epoxy cement was used to secure
the meters in blockouts after pipe form removal.

PIPE EXCAVATION, FOUNDATION, AND BACKFILL
PLACEMENT

The test sections for both siphons were
located where they would have the greatest
amount of backfill over the pipe, about 13 or
14 feet above the top of the siphon. The
minimum trench width for each siphon was 26 or
27 feet and the trench walls were cut at a 1:1

slope. The trench for the precast pipe was
excavated with a flat bottom while that for
the monolithic pipe was cut with a circular
cradle.

If unsuitable foundation material was encountered, it was removed to a depth of 3.5 feet
and replaced with select compacted backfill.
Also, where required, the pipe foundation was
compacted in place with heavy vibratory
rollers to improve the near invert soils to a
minimum density of 70 percent relative density
or equivalent. Average dry density of foundation materials to a depth of 6 feet beneath
the test sections, either in place or after
compaction, was about 122.4 lb/ft³ at a
moisture content of 8.9 percent. Pipe backfilling was accomplished in two steps. First,
the consolidated backfill for bedding was
placed by sluicing and vibrating the material
under the haunch area. A 3-foot lift was then
placed by jetting and vibrating the leading
edge; with vibratory sheepsfoot compactors
used farther away from the pipe. The
remaining consolidated backfill was placed
using a similar method up to a minimum depth
of (3/8) Do + 1.0 foot for the monolithic pipe
and Do/4 + 1.0 foot for the precast pipe,
where Do = the outside diameter of the pipe in
feet. Second, the remainder of the backfill
material was pushed into the siphon trench,
and the only compaction obtained was from the
construction equipment. The dry density of
consolidated backfill at the test sections
varied from 109.2 to 123.5 lb/ft³ and averaged
118.7 lb/ft³ (about 80 percent relative density) at a moisture content of 11.4 percent.
The unconsolidated backfill averaged 111.8
lb/ft³ at 8.8 percent moisture content.

INSTRUMENT READING SCHEDULE

The instrument reading schedule for both
siphons was designed to gather data so loading
conditions imposed on the pipe at various stages of construction could be investigated.

Cast-In-Place Pipe

Initial readings of all instruments were made
in March 1979 after the pipe concrete was
placed, and were continued at significant
construction loadings through March 1982.
Another set of instrument readings was
obtained in May 1983 to assess time effects on
pipe loading. Among many other sets of
readings taken, those most pertinent were
obtained immediately preceding the backfill
operation and after placement of 18 inches of
compacted backfill. Another set was obtained
after completion of compacted backfill just
prior to hydrostatic testing of the siphon.
Instruments were read frequently as the siphon
was filled and hydrostatically tested up to
maximum head. After hydrostatic testing the
siphon was emptied and the backfill operation
resumed in November 1979 until backfill
reached original ground surface. After backfill was completed in December 1979, a total
of nine sets of readings were taken periodically until March 1982. In all, 85 sets of
readings were obtained.

Precast Prestressed Pipe

For this pipe, the soil stress meters were embedded in the outside surface after manufacture and did not come in contact with the soil until the pipes were placed in the siphon trench. Forty-one sets of readings were taken over a period of about 3-1/2 years and a most recent set at about 4-1/2 years. Some of the more pertinent sets of data are discussed below. After all soil stress meters were installed in the test pipes, the instruments were read on October 31, 1978, with no load on the meters. Eighteen sets of readings were taken during placement of the test pipes in the siphon trench to record the pressures at the bottom of two pipe sections which included wheel loads of the 189-ton pipe-mobile loaded with the next 225-ton pipe section. The meters were again read after all test pipes were placed in the siphon trench with load on the invert only. Readings were taken before the start of compacted backfill on January 14, 1979, during the compacted backfill operation, and at the completion of compacted backfill on January 19, 1979. Following readings were taken during the uncompacted backfill operation on January 24, 1979, and at the completion of uncompacted backfill on January 26, 1979. Thirteen additional sets of readings were taken from March 12 through March 27, 1979, during hydrostatic testing of the siphon. Periodic readings were taken every 1 to 9 months until March 30, 1982, with the most current set of readings taken May 12, 1983.

RESULTS FROM INSTRUMENTATION PROGRAM

Plots showing distribution of soil-pipe interface pressures were prepared for selected construction loading events such as highest water level during hydrostatic pressure testing of the siphon; completion of uncompacted backfill to or slightly above original ground surface; and about 2 or more years after backfill was completed. These plots were prepared for each cross-section of instrumentation for individual pipe sections as well as for combined readings for all three test pipes. The averaged values of pressure of all radially common soil stress meters were also plotted as shown in figure 2.

Cast-In-Place Pipe

Soil pressures were consistently highest on this siphon at pressure cells 157.5° and 202.5° counterclockwise from the crown of the pipe, figure 2. Pressures recorded for cells at these locations ranged from 9.8 lb/in² with the siphon empty and 21 feet of backfill in place to 34.6 lb/in² with the siphon filled and about 39 feet of backfill in place (14 feet of backfill above the crown of the pipe).

The lowest pressures were recorded at cells located 90° and 270° counterclockwise from the crown of the pipe. The highest pressure at those locations was 6.3 lb/in² and occurred about 2 months after backfilling was completed. Soil pressures at cells located on

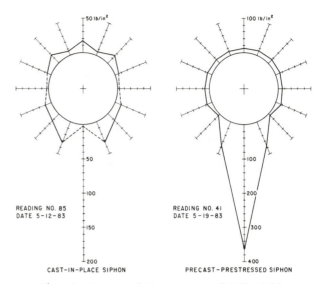

Fig. 2 Averaged Pressures of All Cells at Common Locations

the bottom (invert) of the pipes were low, a maximum of 9.0 lb/in², compared to those located 157.5° and 202.5° counterclockwise from the crown. Table I shows average pressures recorded on comparable cells from all three pipe sections for selected construction events. The six sets of soil pressure data shown in the lower part of the table correspond directly to dates and events in the upper part of the table, and the last set of data in the table is that plotted on figure 2. The cells at 90°, 180°, and 270° counterclockwise from the top of the pipes were no longer functional when the last set of readings was obtained, so the last reliable average value was plotted and this is indicated on the figure by dashed lines.

TABLE I - Average Pressure on Comparable Cells (lb/in²)

Date and Event	Cast-in-Place Siphon Pipe
8-21-79	Compacted backfill complete; 10 ft above invert; began filling siphon
10-25-79	Maximum hydrostatic head; 52 ft above invert
11-19-79	Siphon empty, backfill resumed
12-12-79	Backfill complete; 14 ft above crown
3-31-82	27-1/2 months after backfill complete
5-12-83	Most recent set of data; siphon filled

Location of cells in degrees counterclockwise from crown

0	22.5	45 & 315	67.5	90 & 270	112.5	157.5 & 202.5	180
1.7	2.8	2.2	3.0	1.1	2.0	15.6	4.0
1.6	2.7	1.7	3.2	1.7	2.4	15.8	3.1
3.6	1.7	4.0	1.8	1.6	0.6	11.6	-
17.8	10.7	13.3	10.7	5.2	5.4	23.6	-
18.0	6.1	15.9	7.1	2.0	9.4	34.6	-
17.3	6.0	15.6	6.0	-	9.8	32.1	-

Precast, Prestressed Pipe

Soil pressures recorded at all cells except those at pipe invert yielded a very uniform pressure distribution pattern. Soil pressures on the bottom of the pipe were concentrated and resulted in a bedding angle no larger than 45°, figure 2. The lowest pressures were recorded at cells 135° and 225° counterclockwise from the crown of the pipe. Table II shows average pressures recorded on comparable cells from all three pipe sections for selected construction events. As in Table I the pressure data sets correspond directly to dates and events in the upper part of the table and the last set of data is plotted on figure 2.

TABLE II - Average Pressure on Comparable Cells (lb/in^2)

Date and Event Precast, Prestressed Siphon Pipe

1-14-79 Pipes laid; no backfilling
1-19-79 Compacted backfill complete;
       8 ft above invert
1-26-79 Uncomp. backfill complete;
       13 ft above top
3-26-79 Max. hydrostatic; 32 ft above invert
3-30-82 3 years later; siphon filled
5-19-83 Most recent set of data; siphon filled

Location of cells in degrees counterclockwise from crown

0	22.5	45& 315	67.5	90& 270	112.5& 247.5	135& 225	157.5	180
-	-	-	-	-	-	-	-	241.9
-	-	-	-	-	-	-	-	219.5
11.3	12.7	12.0	10.7	7.6	8.4	1.8	34.5	364.5
12.6	14.2	15.0	13.8	9.3	14.4	4.2	55.8	377.1
12.9	14.2	12.7	13.4	13.0	17.4	4.8	72.1	360.4
11.5	13.4	14.2	12.9	13.1	15.7	4.8	73.8	362.9

With compacted backfill complete to 8 feet above pipe invert the pressure on the invert cells decreased by 22.4 lb/in^2 from that when the pipes were laid in the trench as shown by the first two data sets in Table II. This indicates good compaction of material beneath the haunch of the pipe and also represents a slight increase in bedding angle.

Cell readings were taken at pipe invert during placement with the pipe-mobile. After pipe 349 was placed, the pressure at the bottom cell was 84.7 lb/in^2. When the pipe-mobile entered pipe 349 with the next test pipe (350) the pressure increased to 191.7 lb/in^2 and dropped to 181.5 lb/in^2 with pipe 350 installed and the pipe mobile removed. Similar pressure increases were noted for each test pipe as the loaded pipe-mobile entered the previously laid pipe to lay the next section.

SUMMARY AND CONCLUSIONS

A field study was conducted over a period of nearly 4-1/2 years to measure soil pressure distribution around two large diameter (25 feet O.D.) rigid concrete pipes. One of the pipes was circular, monolithic, cast-in-place concrete and the other was circular precast, prestressed concrete pipe. Compacted backfill was placed beneath the haunch areas of the pipes to a depth of 8 or 10 feet above pipe invert. Backfill compacted only by construction equipment travel was then placed around and over the pipe to original ground surface; a height of 13 or 14 feet above the top of the pipe. Three pipe sections of each siphon were instrumented with soil pressure cells to measure soil-pipe interface pressures. Numerous sets of instrument readings were obtained during selected construction events.

Data from the cast-in-place pipe showed lowest soil pressures at pipe springline and invert, and highest at 157.5° and 202.5° counterclockwise from pipe invert. Pressures at the bottom of the pipe were low relative to those recorded at adjacent cells.

For the precast, prestressed pipe the soil pressures at all cells except those at pipe invert yielded a very uniform pressure distribution. Soil pressures on the bottom of the pipe were concentrated and resulted in a small bedding angle.

The results of this study show soil pressure distributions around pipe which vary significantly from the typically assumed bulb shaped distribution. For the cast-in-place pipe which was constructed in a shallow cradle, the measured pressures at springline and invert were quite small. The precast, prestressed pipe showed very high pressures at the invert when the pipe was laid and decreased only slightly as compacted backfill bedding was placed. The remainder of the soil stress meters for the precast pipe showed uniform soil pressures. All of the soil pressures measured reached equilibrium within a fairly short time after contruction was completed and have changed very little in the past 2 years or so. Data from this study provided valuable information about soil pressure distribution around large diameter rigid pipes and should allow for more efficient future designs.

REFERENCES

Olander, H.C. (1950). Stress Analysis of Concrete Pipe. Engineering Monograph No. 6, U.S. Bureau of Reclamation, Denver, Colorado.

Pettibone, H.C. and Howard, A.K. (1966). Laboratory Investigation of Soil Pressures on Concrete Pipe. Report No. EM-718, U.S. Bureau of Reclamation, Denver, Colorado.

Spangler, M.G. (1933). The Supporting Strength of Rigid Pipe Culverts. Bulletin 112, Iowa Engineering Experiment Station, Iowa State College, Ames, Iowa.

The effect of trenching on adjacent pipelines

L'effet d'une excavation sur les conduites voisines

K. KYROU, Water Development Department, Nicosia, Cyprus
N. A. KALTEZIOTIS, Public Works Research Centre, Athens, Greece

SYNOPSIS   One of the most common causes of ground disturbance which may induce sufficient strains in a pipe to result in fracture arises from trench excavations made alongside buried pipes. This paper aims to investigate some aspects of the adverse effect of trench excavation induced ground movements on adjacent buried pipelines by employing a three dimensional finite element model. The soil is modelled by a linear elastic incompressible solid thereby simulating a saturated clay subjected to short term unloading changes. Some typical analytical results are presented and comparisons with available field measurements are made.

INTRODUCTION

The dominant mode of failure of buried pipelines is flexural failure induced by differential movement of the surrounding ground. This may be caused by traffic, ground temperature and moisture variations or ground disturbance such as excavations. Deep trenching is one of the most common causes of ground disturbance in urban streets which are crowded with buried services. Trenches are dug alongside buried pipelines which are forced to deflect according to the horizontal and vertical differential movements of the ground.

Attempts were made to simulate this soil-pipe interaction problem theoretically using idealised elastic models. Crofts et al. (1977) simulated the problem using a discontinuous Winkler model which was based on a beam on elastic foundation approach. In the above model only the effect of horizontal movements on a long shallow buried pipeline was considered. In addition the ground displacement pattern was assumed.

The aim of this paper is to examine the nature of the ground movements induced by trenching by employing three dimensional elastic finite element models. The effect of these movements on buried pipelines is examined and useful qualitative comparisons with some available field data is presented.

GROUND MOVEMENTS INDUCED BY TRENCHING

The trench excavation was simulated using a three dimensional finite element model (Kyrou, 1980), where the soil continuum was represented by eight node solid brick elements (Fig. 1). The buried pipe was modelled using elastic beam elements having compatible nodal displacements with the surrounding soil. In the short term the soil was assumed to behave as an incompressible elastic material, implying that

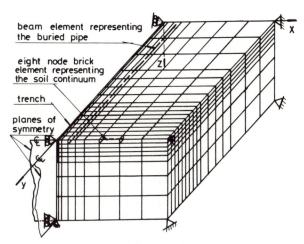

Fig. 1   Finite Element Mesh

it is fully saturated and fine grained (clay). The finite element mesh was in the form of an elastic quarter space since symmetry was assumed about the longitudinal and transverse axes of the trench. Rigid boundaries were imposed on the finite element mesh at horizontal and vertical distances sufficient to ensure that they have negligible effect on the ground movements near the trench. It was assumed that the water table is at ground surface and the water pressure prior to excavation hydrostatic. Thus the vertical total stress release at the bottom of the trench, σ_V, is $\sigma_V=\gamma H$ and the horizontal total stress release at depth z at the sides of the trench, σ_H, is

$$\sigma_H = K_0(\gamma-\gamma_w)z+\gamma_w z=\left\{K_0+(1-K_0)\frac{\gamma_w}{\gamma}\right\}\gamma z=K_{0T}\gamma z \quad (1)$$

where K_0 is the at rest earth pressure

coefficient, γ is the unit weight of saturated soil, γ_w is the unit weight of water, z is the depth from ground level and $K_{OT}=K_0+(1-K_0)\gamma_w/\gamma$ is a convenient mathematical parameter describing the insitu horizontal stresses but it is not a soil property.

In order to demonstrate the basic patterns of ground movement associated with trench construction a trench of varying length, L, was first analysed. The soil elastic modulus, E, was assumed to vary linearly with depth (i.e. $E=\lambda z$, where λ is the rate of increase of E with depth) and the trench excavation was typically represented by W/H=0.25 where W, H are the trench width and depth respectively. The calculated horizontal and vertical ground movements of the excavation face at ground level are shown in figures 2 and 3.

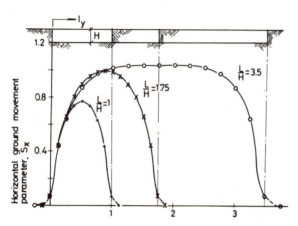

Distance from end of trench, l_y as a proportion of depth, H

Fig.2 Variation of Horizontal Ground Movement of Excavation Face at Ground Level with Length of Trench

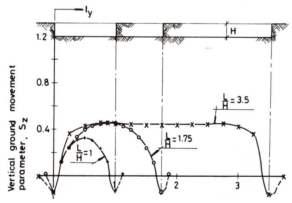

Distance from end of trench, l_y as a proportion of depth, H

Fig.3 Variation of Vertical Ground Movement of Excavation Face at Ground Level with Length of Trench

Horizontal and vertical ground movements are represented in terms of the dimensionless parameters S_x and S_z respectively, where $S=\lambda\delta/\gamma H$ and the subscripts x and z denote horizontal and

vertical movements respectively while δ denotes the excavation induced ground movements.

The following features may be noted. For small L/H ratios the ground deformation patterns for movements δ_x and δ_z follow closely a beam type deflection pattern which is typical of deep-wide excavations where the L/H ratios are small. As the ratio L/H increases no significant variation in the deformation gradient near the excavation corners occurs. However the maximum movements δ_{xmax} and δ_{zmax} increase as L/H increases from zero to approximately 2 and thereafter remain practically constant for all values of L/H>2.

It is obvious that for a short trench the pattern and magnitude of movements is governed by the restraining effect of the end of trench. For longer excavations the magnitude of movements in the central portion of the trench is governed by the restraining effect of the bottom of the excavation while the deformation gradients near the trench ends are still governed by the trench end restraint. Movements δ_x and δ_z appear to build up very rapidly near the excavation ends and these high deformation gradients are likely to have an adverse effect on pipelines buried adjacent to the trench. It should be noted that for a long trench both vertical and horizontal movements attain a maximum value approximately within a distance 1H from the trench end. The calculated horizontal elastic movements are significantly higher than the corresponding vertical movements. The maximum horizontal movement is approximately twice the maximum vertical movement and this agrees with ground movement observations reported by Gumbel and Wilson (1980).

The excavation width has a profound influence on the general pattern of ground movements and this is demonstrated by the analytical results presented in fig. 4. Owing to the increased magnitude of the uplift forces on the excavation

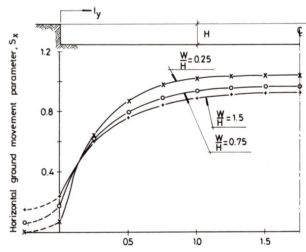

Distance from end of trench, l_y as a proportion of depth, H

Fig.4 Horizontal Ground Movements of the Excavation Face at Ground Level for Various Trench Widths

base the vertical face of the excavation at some distance from the ends is subject to some form of rotation which increases as the ratio W/H increases. Movements δ_x at the excavation end are shown to increase as the excavation width increases the deformation gradients decrease significantly and therefore narrower trenches are likely to affect more adversely nearby shallow buried pipelines.

INFLUENCE OF TRENCHING ON ADJACENT SHALLOW BURIED PIPELINES

The problem of pipe straining due to trench excavation induced ground movements is stated by considering the analytical results presented in fig. 5. The results were obtained from a soil-pipe interaction analysis where the trench was treated as long and unsupported and the soil as linear-elastic, isotropic and incompressible. The pipe analysed was quite

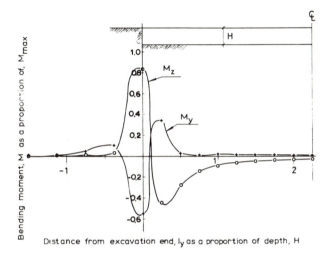

Fig.5 Normalised Bending Moments Induced in the Buried Pipe

flexible and the relative stiffness of the soil and the pipe was $E/E_pI = 10 \text{ m}^{-4}$, where E_p is the elastic modulus of the pipe and I is the second moment of area of the pipe section. The pipe was buried at a distance 0.2H from the excavation face and at a depth of 0.25H. It was assumed that full bond existed between the pipe and the soil and that the pipe joints were rigid thus allowing no rotation or independent translation of the adjacent pipe sections. The bending movements M_y and M_z induced in the buried pipe by vertical and horizontal movements respectively, are plotted as a proportion of the maximum bending moment M_{max} in fig. 5. They are shown to be of a very localised nature and they attain maximum values at approximately the same co-ordinate position. The diagrams of the bending moments M_y and M_z are shown to be very similar (although of opposite signs). When the buried pipe is forced by the retaining soil to deform laterally or vertically, the comparatively undisturbed soil at the excavation corner offers

a restraint to such movements. This introduces a high positive moment M_z and a high negative moment M_y at the excavation corner.

It is interesting to note that the maximum bending moments M_y induced by the vertical ground deformations, are quite high and in this particular case they represent about 70% of the maximum moments M_z induced by the horizontal ground deformations. At the excavation corner the pipe is subject to an abrupt change in curvature which alters its slope. Since at a certain distance from the excavation corner the ground movements tend to remain constant the pipe is forced to change curvature again thus, introducing high negative moments M_z and high positive moments M_y at a short distance from the excavations corner. For this particular case this distance is about 0.25H. Towards the centre of the excavation the moments M_y and M_z reduce to the minimum and provided the trench is long enough they will reduce to zero. These bending moments also reduce to zero towards the negative direction.

COMPARISONS WITH FIELD DATA

Observations of ground movements from instrumented trench excavations were presented by various researchers. Typical results by Symons (1980) showed that as the trench advances beyond a stationary observation point adjacent to the trench the ground movements remain unaltered and this observation agrees with the analytical results shown in fig. 2 & 3. The affect of rapid build up of movements indicated in these figures was demonstrated by observations made by Gumbel and Wilson (1980) and Symons et al. (1981). The results presented by Symons et al. (1981) showed clearly that excavation of successive trench bays and subsequent shoring does not increase the maximum movement components (see fig. 6). All

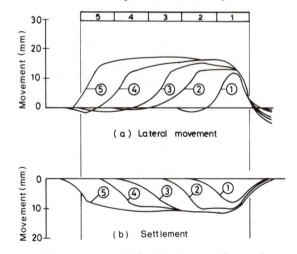

Fig.6 Measured Lateral Movement and Settlements Along a Trial Trench During Excavation of Successive Bays (After Symons et al., 1981)

observations have indicated however that removal of the shoring system and subsequent backfilling resulted in significant increase of the movement components.

Pipe strain measurements by Rumsey et al. (1981) have demonstrated a strain reversal on a pipe buried alongside an advancing trench and this agrees with the predictions of the present analytical model. Pipe strain measurements reported by Symons etl al. (1981) also compare favourably with the bending patterns of fig. 5 (see fig. 7). It should be noted that these

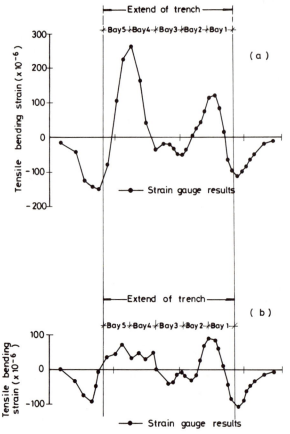

Fig.7   Bending Strains Measured in a Buried Pipeline after Excavation and Back-filling of Trench:(a) Due to Ground Settlement; (b) Due to Horizontal Movement (After Symons et al., 1981)

measurements were taken after backfilling of the trench and deviations from the theoretical patterns might have been caused by local ground yielding.

CONCLUSIONS

A method of finite element analysis has been presented which offers a means of predicting ground movement associated with trench excavation and pipe strain resulting in adjacent buried pipelines. This method can provide

realistic estimates of field behaviour provided that the soil input parameters and their distribution with depth are known.

The results presented in this paper show that the maximum horizontal and vertical elastic movements induced by trenching do not increase after a certain length of trench has been excavated. In the case where $E=\lambda z$ this length was found to be 2H. This suggests that in order to avoid underised movements during a trenching operation, trench bays should be excavated at very small lengths and effective support provided immediately.

Ground movements induced by trenching built up very rapidly near the excavation corners and they retain approximately constant values along the remaining length of a long trench. As expected the analysis has shown that bending moments induced in a adjacent buried pipe attain maximum values near the trench ends.

Field data relating to trench excavation presented by various researchers compare favourably, at least qualitatively, with the analytical predictions obtained using the elastic finite element model.

REFERENCES

Crofts, J.E., Menzies, B.K., and Tarzi, A.I. (1977). Lateral displacements of shallow buried pipelines due to adjacent deep trench excavations. Geotechnique (28), 2, 161-179.

Gumbel, J.E., and Wilson, J. (1980). Observations of ground movements around a trench excavation in London clay. Proc. Sec. Conf. on Ground Movements and Structures, 841-856, Cardiff.

Kyrou, K. (1980). The effect of trench excavations induced ground movements on adjacent buried pipelines. Ph. D. Thesis, University of Surrey, England.

Rumsey, P.B., Cooper, I., and Kyrou, K. (1981). Ground movement and pipe strain associated with trench excavation. Repair of sewerage systems, ICE, 91-101, London.

Symons, I.F. (1980). Ground movements and their infuence on shallow buried pipes. The Public Health Engineer, (8), 4, 149-153, London.

Symons, I.F., Chard, B., and Carder, D.R. (1981). Ground movements caused by deep trench excavation. Repair of sewerage systems, ICE, 73-100, London.

Developments in soft ground engineering in Singapore

Des progrès techniques en sol mou à Singapour

S. L. LEE, Department of Civil Engineering, National University of Singapore, Singapore
G. P. KARUNARATNE, Department of Civil Engineering, National University of Singapore, Singapore
K. W. LO, Department of Civil Engineering, National University of Singapore, Singapore
K. Y. YONG, Department of Civil Engineering, National University of Singapore, Singapore
V. CHOA, Department of Civil Engineering, National University of Singapore, Singapore

SYNOPSIS   Soft ground engineering is one of the prominent areas of construction activities in Singapore. Consequently, considerable interest is attached to this field of research which is highlighted in four different projects described in this paper.

INTRODUCTION

The considerable recent economic growth in South-East Asia is reflected in its boom in construction, particularly in Singapore. This is manifested by a large number of high-rise buildings incorporating several basements needing stable excavations in thick deposits of soft marine clay. In addition, the proposed Mass Rapid Transit system of Singapore will encounter problems of tunnelling in, and track support on soft ground. Furthermore, efforts are continuing in expanding the land area of Singapore Island through reclamation, problems faced in this sphere of activity being two-fold: stabilisation of deep deposits of soft clay usually associated with land reclamation and the alternate means of reclamation without resorting to the use of sand as a traditional reclamation material. Aspects of the above recent developments in soft ground engineering in Singapore are summarised in this paper.

Soft clay found in Singapore almost invariably belongs to the marine member of the Kallang formation. The distribution and geotechnical properties of this formation are well documented [Tan and Lee (1977)]. It usually varies in thickness from 10 m to 15 m near estuaries and reaches as deep as 40 m in some other areas. A relatively thin stiff clay layer, formed by dessication, exists within the soft clay at depths varying from 5 m to 25 m. The soft marine clay has an undrained shear strength ranging from 10 kPa to 40 kPa and a sensitivity of 4 to 6. The other major source of soft ground problem is the occurrence of peaty soil deposits of variable thickness.

DYNAMIC REPLACEMENT AND MIXING (DRM) OF PEATY CLAY WITH SAND

In June 1983, field trials were conducted at the Bishan Depot of Singapore's Mass Rapid Transit System to determine the feasibility of improving the insitu peaty deposits by dynamic replacement and mixing (DRM) with sand using standard dynamic consolidation (DC) equipment. A limited number of projects based on a similar approach had previously been carried out [Techniques Louis Menard, (1979), Ramaswamy

et al (1979), Aziz et al, (1980) and Varaksin (1981)], although under less stringent ground conditions.

At the trial zone (Fig. 1), some 6 m of waterlogged, peaty clay was underlain by stiff residual soils. The treatment process consisted of first clearing the trial zone, then laying a sand blanket of 1 m thickness on the prepared surface. Next, DRM was applied by tamping additional sand charges into the peaty clay using a 15T DC pounder at locations marked with crosses in Fig. 1. Altogether, 15 blows of 225T-m input energy each were applied over

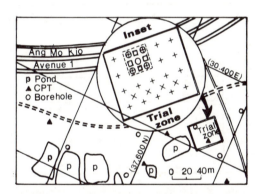

Fig. 1 Site Layout and Trial Zone

each pass. Three such low energy sand replace-ment passes were needed to drive sand columns of approximately 4 m surface diameter tapering to 2 m base diameter some 4.2 m into the peaty clay. The sand blanket was then built up to 3 m and the remaining low energy prints - albeit 10 blows only per print - carried out to "stitch" the subsoil together. Finally, 35 high energy blows of 300T-m each were imparted to the sand columns at locations marked with circles to effect additional replacement as well as mixing - by a process resembling claquage - of the insitu peaty clay with sand. A comprehensive account of the field trials is given by Lee et al (1984a).

As a result of DRM, the ground beneath the trial zone was transformed into a relatively

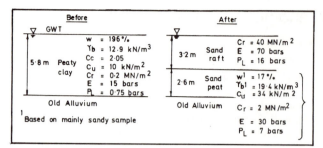

Fig. 2 Ground Conditions Before and After DRM

stiff upper sand "raft" with pockets of sandy peat of about 3.2 m thickness, followed by 2.6 m of sandy peat, as shown in Fig. 2. The formation of these layers with improved properties was evident in borehole spoil. Some 1.78 m of primary consolidation, estimated as the volume of replacing sand per unit area of treated surface, was effectively enforced. By deducting this settlement from the theoretical total settlement of 2 m due to primary consolidation, based on initial insitu soil properties and a surcharge of 3.7 m applied to the trial zone after DRM, a net settlement of 22 cm was anticipated. The latter estimate indeed compares well with field settlements monitored up to the present time (Fig. 3). The implication that potential secondary compression of the original peaty clay has been negated by

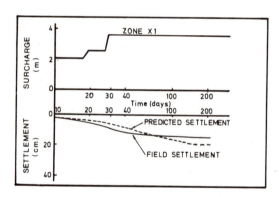

Fig. 3 Field Settlement versus Long-term Prediction

mixing with sand is confirmed by the settlement-log (time) plot of Fig. 3. Thus, DRM has been proven to effectively enforce primary consolidation and negate the effects of secondary compression of peaty clay at Bishan site to the extent that, within the 5-month limitation set aside for ground treatment, residual settlements may be rendered inconsequential.

DEEP EXCAVATION IN SOFT CLAY

A number of deep excavations carried out in soft clay in Singapore for the construction of basements of highrise buildings are usually supported by vertical sheet piles braced with cross struts. In view of the growing need for construction of deep basements in soft clay,

there is an urgent need to examine the factors that caused ground movements at a number of excavation sites.

Limitations in current design methods

Current methods of calculating horizontal strut loads in braced excavations in soft clay using apparent earth pressure distributions of Terzaghi and Peck (1967) or Peck et al (1974) disregard the influence of the thickness of soft clay that might extend below the base of excavation. The toe of sheet piles should preferably penetrate stiff soil for stability. In cases where the stiff soil for sheet pile embedment is found at a considerable depth below the soft clay, bending moment in the sheet piles can be very large and yielding of the support system becomes an important issue. In fact, Peck (1969) reported that experiences in Mexico City and Oslo had shown that large strut loads could occur where base heave was a major problem. Similar observations were made by Clough and Reed (1984) in the San Francisco Bay area.

To overcome the above shortcoming, a method of analysing the excavation support system in deep deposits of soft clay was proposed by Lee et al (1984b). The primary purpose of this method is to minimise the sheet pile displacement and to avoid yielding of the sheet pile support system by obtaining a statically admissible and safe solution which is a lower bound. The proposed method was used to estimate the strut load and the maximum bending moment of the sheet piles in a two-basement excavation project in soft clay.

Excavation site and support system

The site in the city centre is bounded by roads with heavy traffic on three sides and a six-storey building on the fourth side as shown in Fig. 4. FSP III-A sheet piles with a section modulus of 1520 cm^3/m and a yield strength of 300 N/mm^2 were installed around the site to a depth of about 30 m below the existing ground surface.

Excavation work for the two-basement construction has to be carried out to a maximum depth of 11 m, extending through a 2 m layer of fill into a 21 m thick layer of soft marine clay

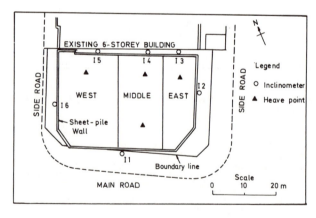

Fig. 4 Site Plan and Location of Instrumentation

with average shear strength of 20 kPa. Sheet piles penetrated about 7 m in the stiff clay underlying the soft marine clay. Given the type of sheet piles and the existing soil conditions, six levels of struts were recommended. Horizontal spacings of the struts were either 4.5 or 6.0 m. By considering the effects of a net active pressure below the excavation from the soft marine clay, the method by Lee et al (1984b) gave design strut loads generally higher than that determined by Peck (1969).

Excavation was carried out over the whole site for the first three levels of struts after which only the middle area was excavated further in three stages to the formation level. After a 3 m concrete base slab was constructed, excavation continued simultaneously in the East and West areas. Because of the larger area, the West side was further subdivided into two halves to reduce the time lapse between initiation of each stage of excavation and strutting.

Lateral ground movement

Lateral movement of the sheet pile wall was monitored with 6 inclinometers installed just behind the sheet piles at locations shown in Fig. 4. The maximum movements ranged from 105 mm at inclinometer I3 to 188 mm at inclinometer I1. The deflections would have been greater in the existing weak subsoil conditions if not for the presence of a large number of steel H-piles driven at 1.5 m centre to centre spacing all over the site to support the 36-storey superstructure. These closely-spaced piles act as a 'negative' surcharge in reducing base heave.

The lateral wall movement at I1 at the end of each successive excavation stage is plotted in Fig. 5. The maximum movement of the sheet piles generally occurred within 1 m to 2 m below the excavation level. The rate of lateral movement observed between initiation of each stage of excavation and strutting ranges from 1 mm/day to 2 mm/day.

The maximum lateral movement was observed to increase with excavation until the installation of the next level of struts. Each strut, as soon as it is inserted and preloaded, served to restrict movement of the sheet piles until the initiation of the next stage of excavation. Therefore, it is imperative that the time lapse between the initiation of each stage of excavation and strutting be kept to a minimum.

Strut loads

Four Geonor-type Vibrating Wire Strain Gauges were installed on the steel struts at each level; two on a longitudinal strut and the other two on a transverse strut. Strut load increased rapidly as the excavation progressed and as soon as the next strut was installed, the load remained fairly constant or decreased slightly. The maximum measured strut loads observed at each level near I6 up to the 5th level of excavation are shown in Fig. 6. Values of the strut loads predicted from the pressure diagrams suggested by Peck (1969) and the design values determined by the method proposed by Lee et al (1984b) are also shown.

It can be seen that the design values determined by the method of Lee et al (1984b) generally gave 30% to 40% higher loads than the measured values. This discrepancy can be attributed to the 'negative' surcharge effects of the closely-spaced piles mentioned earlier.

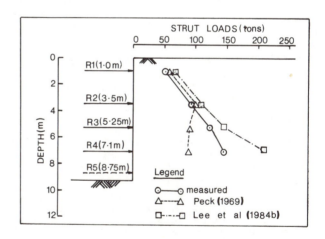

Fig. 6 Strut Loads Acting on Support System near Inclinometer I6

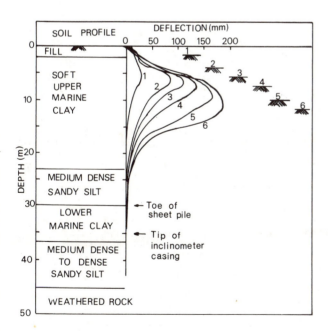

Fig. 5 Lateral Movement of the Sheet-pile Wall at Inclinometer I1

The behaviour of a braced excavation depends upon the construction procedure adopted. Because the influence of the construction factors are difficult to evaluate, predictions of ground movement in excavations in soft clay becomes unreliable. However, excessive movements can be minimised by adequate strutting, providing adequate sheet pile section and sufficient penetration into stiffer soil and minimising the time lapse between the initiation of each stage of excavation and strutting.

For estimation of strut loads the earth pressure distribution above and below the excavation level should be considered especially where a thick layer of soft clay is present. Preliminary studies have indicated that the method proposed by Lee et al (1984b) can be used to estimate the maximum strut load for limit state condition. From the point of view of stability of the support system, a program of instrumentation to monitor strut loads and deflection of the sheet-pile wall is necessary to maintain the safety of the excavation support system and to control ground movement.

CLAY-SAND RECLAMATION SCHEME

Some parts of the coast line of Singapore have been reclaimed from the sea for industrial, housing and recreational purposes. About 6.5% of new land is thus far added to the 617 sq km island state of Singapore. Dredged sand from the sea bed and the soil from the excavations of inland construction constituted the material used in the reclamations. With the depletion of sand deposits in the Singapore waters new sources of material suitable for land reclamation have been sought.

Studies have been concentrated on the feasiability of using marine clay as a reclamation material. Research carried out in the last two years has shown that soft marine clay from the seabed, when hydraulically dredged and pumped in slurry form through a pipe line, can be sandwiched between carefully "sprinkled" thin sand layers in reclamations. A substantial percentage of sand can be saved without resorting to expensive soil treatment.

Laboratory studies

Singapore marine clay whose main mineralogical constituent is Kaolinite has the following range of in-situ geotechnical properties: W_L = 70% to 90%, W_p = 20% to 30%, natural water content = 50% to 80%, clay size particles = 30% to 40%. ratio of undrained (vane) shear strength to effective over-burden pressure = 0.2 to 0.4, sensitivity = 4 to 6, $C_c/(1 + e_o)$ = 0.25 to 0.42, over-consolidation ratio = 1.1 to 1.2.

During the laboratory phase of studies marine clay was thoroughly mixed to a consistency of 600% water content and pumped into perspex cylindrical tanks, 1 m high and 200 mm - 300 mm in diameter. Sand was also pumped into the cylinders at about 30% solid content. Two methods of pumping sand and clay were employed: (a) simultaneous discharge and (b) alternate discharge. More than 85% of clay sedimentation was permitted before discharge of the next quantity of clay or sand.

The results of vane shear strength of marine clay for simultaneous and alternate discharges are shown in Fig. 7 for a range of composition by dry weight of clay to sand of 10 : 90 to 40 : 60. During simultaneous discharges of sand and clay, sand settles first resulting in the formation of sand layers followed

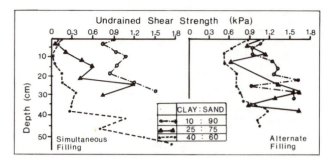

Fig. 7 Variation of vane shear strength of clay slurry and sand

by clay. When discharged alternately sand particles can be allowed to impregnate the upper part of soft clay after a 3-day period of clay sedimentation, when the excess pore pressure due to self weight consolidation has dissipated in the upper 200 mm of sedimented clay. The vane shear strength of the resulting clay : sand mixture tends to be uniform and higher than that of clay when discharged simultaneously with sand.

A model tank 1 m x 1 m x 0.5 m reclaimed by hydraulically discharging clay and sand at 40 : 60 showed that sand can be spread over the sedimented clay after 3 days. After sprinkling 30% of sand at this stage followed by the balance in a day or two after, a sand layer with a thickness in excess of 100 mm can be formed. It is important to form clean sand layers sandwiching between thin clay layers in order to accelerate the consolidation of clay in reclamations.

Pilot test

The laboratory results were extended to a pilot test in an existing large reclamation project in which a test pond 20 m x 10 m at the base and 3.5 m high was constructed. The base was covered with a sand blanket and side slopes of 1(v) : 2(H) were also made with sand. Marine clay was dredged and pumped hydraulically using a 100 hp pump from a distance of 100 m in the sea until a thickness of 1 m of clay was formed at the bottom of the pond. This system without any mechanical agitation yielded an average of 4.5% concentration of clay which was dredged from the sea bed upto a depth of 2 m. Five days afterwards sand was discharged into a perforated drum which was moved continuously over the water in the pond in order to sprinkle the sand uniformly over the clay. Initially, 10% of the total sand load was used followed by the balance 90% of sand two days later. The rate of sprinkling was about 200 kg/sq m per minute. A thin-walled piston sample at this stage indicated that 40% of the total sand had penetrated into soft clay through a distance of 120 mm. A clear layer of 180 mm of sand was found to have formed on top of soft clay. The shear strength of soft clay measured with a vane shear apparatus before pumping sand was 0.5 to 1 kPa.

The pore pressure monitored in soft marine clay

layer dissipated very fast. With a shorter drainage length of 0.5 m consolidation is estimated to be completed in 10 to 20 days. Therefore the additional surcharge necessary to increase the shear strength of clay can be placed and increased quite fast, first under water through hydraulic pumping and then through conventional means.

Method of Prototype Reclamation

In a prototype reclamation, soft clay layers should be kept to a maximum thickness of about 1 m sandwiched between sand layers so as to accelerate natural consolidation. The uppermost clay layer should be about 2 m below the proposed ground level so that with an extra surcharge of 2 m to 3 m an effective stress of 60 to 80 kPa can be applied and the clay can be improved to a strength of 15 kPa.

The use of marine clay for land reclamation on sea bed does not weaken such reclamations if carried out as described above. If the sea bed is to be treated for excessive settlement, the fill clay will be automatically treated. The material saving is very significant, the amount depending on the availability and cost of sand.

CONSOLIDATION OF CLAY UNDER RECLAMATION

Thick marine clay deposits underlying reclamations have been frequently treated with vertical drains and surcharged to reduce excessive differential settlement before construction of roads, runways and other structures. At Changi Airport where the runway was treated in the above manner a stagnation of pore pressure with continuing surface settlement was recorded. This phenomenon was partly attributed to the retardation of pore pressure dissipation by the high pore pressure built up in the clay under the surcharge overwidth and in the adjacent untreated area of recent reclamation (Choa et al, 1981). A numerical analysis using finite difference method was used to back analyse the Changi Airport results and to study the effect of drain treatment and surcharge widths on the the rate of surface settlement.

Method of Analysis

By combining the equations for equilibrium, geometric compatibility, stress-strain relationship and continuity, three governing equation in terms of u, v and σ (displacements in the x and y directions and excess pore pressure respectively) were derived for a plane strain consolidation of compressible medium with a finite thickness loaded by an infinite strip load:

$$C_1 \frac{\partial^2 u}{\partial x^2} + C_2 \frac{\partial^2 u}{\partial y^2} + C_3 \frac{\partial^2 v}{\partial x \partial y} - \frac{\partial \sigma}{\partial x} = 0 \qquad \ldots (1)$$

$$C_1 \frac{\partial^2 v}{\partial y^2} + C_2 \frac{\partial^2 v}{\partial x^2} + C_3 \frac{\partial^2 u}{\partial y \partial x} - \frac{\partial \sigma}{\partial y} = 0 \qquad \ldots (2)$$

$$\frac{k_x}{\gamma_w} \frac{\partial^2 \sigma}{\partial x^2} + \frac{k_y}{\gamma_w} \frac{\partial^2 \sigma}{\partial y^2} = \frac{\partial^2 u}{\partial t \partial x} + \frac{\partial^2 y}{\partial t \partial y} \qquad \ldots (3)$$

where $C_1 = \frac{E(1-\mu)}{(1+\mu)(1-2\mu)}$, $C_2 = \frac{E}{2(1+\mu)}$,

$C_3 = \frac{E}{2(1+\mu)(1-2\mu)}$, E = elastic modulus,

μ = poisson's ratio, k_x, k_y = permeability in the x and y directions, γ_w = unit weight of water and t = time.

After non-dimensionalising and writing the equations in finite difference form, a system of linear equations in the form $[A]\{X\} = \{B\}$ where $x = <u\,v\,\sigma>^T$ was assembled for the boundary value problem. The equations were solved by Gaussian elimination and Crank-Nicholson's scheme was used to time step after initialising the problem. The computer programme was written for permeable or impermeable and rough or smooth top and bottom boundary conditions. Load increment could be applied with respect to time. Vertical and horizontal permeablity and elastic constants could be varied in both vertical and horizontal directions and their magnitudes could be varied with respect to time enabling the analysis of multilayered soils. Variable finite difference mesh was used to save computer storage space. To simulate the effect of vertical drains the soil with drains was approximated to a soil with an equivalent increased vertical permeability. The equivalent vertical permeability was obtained by equating the average degree of consolidation of two cylinders of soil; one with horizontal flow to a central well and vertical flow to a free draining surface and the other with an equivalent vertical permeability with vertical flow only. The resulting relationship is

$$k_v' = \frac{32}{\pi^2 \mu_s} \left(\frac{H}{D}\right)^2 k_h + k_v \qquad \ldots (4)$$

where k_v' = equivalent vertical permeability, k_h and k_v = permeability of the soil in the horizontal and vertical directions respectively, H = half thickness of layer between two free draining surfaces, D = diameter of soil cylinder and μ_s = a term proposed by Hansbo (1981) involving the diameters of soil cylinder, drain and smeared zone, and the horizontal permeabilities of smeared and undisturbed soil.

Influence of Drains and Surcharge Widths

A study of the effect of drained-treatment width and surcharge width showed that these parameters significantly affect the rate of surface settlement. Fig 8 shows the variation of the normalised vertical displacement; $Ev/(pH)$, with respect to time factor ($T = kEt/(\gamma_w H^2)$) and normalised distance from the axis of symmetry, x/H (where E = elastic modulus, p = applied pressure, v = vertical displacement, H = thickness of soil layer, k = permeability, t = time, γ_w = unit weight of water) for a very wide strip load for drain treatment widths, d/H. The symbols k_{y1}, k_{x1},

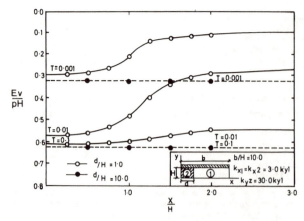

Fig. 8 Variation of vertical displacement with distance from the treated area

k_{y2} and k_{x2} are the vertical and horizontal permeabilities in zones 1 and 2 respectively. The retardation effect on the settlement due to back pressure form zone 1 on zone 2 can be observed for $d/H = 1$ even after a considerably large time after load application.

Numerical analysis has shown that the back presure from the clay under the surface over-width and the surrounding recent reclamation can significantly affect the settlement in the zone treated by drains. This effect should therefore be taken into account in designing and interpreting results of soil treatment works employing vertical drains and surcharge particularly when such works are carried out in recently reclaimed land underlain by thick deposits of soft clay where excess pore pressure within the clay has undergone relatively small degree of dissipation.

ACKNOWLEDGEMENT

The first three projects described in this paper were supported by the Ministry of Trade and Industry under research grant C/81/04-06. The assistance given by Singapore Engineering and Consultancy Services Pte Ltd, Mass Rapid Transit Corporation of Singapore and Telecommunication Authority of Singapore is gratefully acknowledged. Parts of these research studies were carried out by Chew Soon Hoe, Chua Lai Heng, V Ganeshan and John Ooi while working for higher degrees at the National University of Singapore.

REFERENCES

Aziz, M.A., Ramaswamy, S.D., Daulah, I., and Lee, S.L. (1980), Treatment of Peaty Soils, Proc. 6th South East Asian Conf., Soil Engrg., 431-446, Taipei.

Choa, V., Karunaratne, G.P., Ramaswamy, S.D., Vijiaratnam, A. and Lee, S.L. (1981), Drain Performance in Changi Marine Clay, Proceedings, 10th ICSMFE, 3, 623-626, Stockholm.

Clough, G.W. and Reed, M.W. (1984), Measured behaviour of braced wall in very soft clays. ASCE, J. Geotech. Engng. Div., (110), GT1, 1-19.

Hansbo, S. (1981), Consolidation of Fine-Grained Soils by Prefabricated Drains, Proc. 10th ICSMFE, 3, 677-682, Stockholm.

Lee, S.L., Lo, K.W., Karunaratne, G.P. and Ooi, J. (1984a), Improvement of Peaty Clay by Dynamic Replacement and Mixing, Proc. JSS MFE/NUS/AIT Seminar on Soil Improvement and Construction Techniques in Soft Ground. 208-214, Singapore.

Lee, S.L., Yong, K.Y., Karunaratne G.P. and Swaddiwudhipong, S. (1984b), Analysis of excavation support system in soft clay. Proc. JSSMFE/NUS/AIT Seminar on Soil Improvement and Construction Techniques in Soft Ground, 60-65, Singapore.

Peck, R.B. (1969), Deep Excavations and Tunnelling in Soft Ground. Proc. 7th ICSMFE, State-of-the-Art Volume, 225-290, Mexico.

Peck, R.B., Hanson, W.E. and Thornburn, T.H. (1974), Foundation Engineering. 2nd Ed., 514 pp, John Wiley and Sons, Inc., New York.

Ramaswamy, S.D., Aziz, M.A., Subrahmanyam, R.V., Abdul Khader, M.H. and Lee, S.L. (1979), Treatment of Peaty Clay by High Energy Impact. ASCE J. Geot. Eng. Div. (105), 957-967.

Tan, S.B. and Lee, K.W. (1977), Engineering geology of the marine member of Kallang Formation in Singapore. Proc. Int. Symp. on Soft Clay, 77-80, Bangkok.

Techniques Louis Menard, S.A. Singapore (1979), Improvements of Peaty Soils by Dynamic Consolidation Method. Report No. TLM/ID/262/79/Jg.

Terzaghi, K. and Peck R.B. (1967), Soil Mechanics in Engineering Practice, 2nd Ed., John Wiley and Sons, Inc., New York.

Varaksin, S. (1981), Recent Development in Soil Improvement Techniques and their Practical Applications. Sols Soils, 38/39, 7-32.

Effects of backfilling at shield work in soft cohesive soil

Effets du remblai lors du creusement au bouclier dans des argiles

A. MORI, Professor, Department of Civil Engineering, Waseda University, Japan
H. AKAGI, Lecturer, Department of Civil Engineering, Waseda University, Japan

SYNOPSIS   Rational design of the injection method to the tail void for backfill is required to protect surface and subsurface installations from the damage caused by ground movements associated with shield tunneling in the soft ground. In this paper, the effects of backfill injection at shield work in soft cohesive soil are examined using the results of finite element analysis in view of the consolidation of disturbed cohesive soil. It is concluded that the most effective method is to inject the suitable backfill materials at the same time as the occurrence of the tail void.

INTRODUCTION

It is very important to prevent ground settlement associated with shield work in soft ground. Much of the magnitude of settlement can be related with the tail void (clearance between the tailpiece and lining). It is inevitable that large settlement could occur, unless suitable injection to the tail void for backfill might be performed. There are two types of settlements associated with unsuitable injection to the tail void at shield work in soft cohesive soil. The first is the instantaneous settlement accompanied by invasion of surrounding soil into the tail void on account of delayed timing for injection. The second is the longtime settlement owing to consolidation of cohesive soil disturbed by ground displacements mentioned above. Moreover, when the greater volume of backfill materials than that of the tail void may be injected, the surrounding soil will be pushed back and the ground surface will heave. Then the consolidation settlement due to soil disturbance caused by this heave of the ground could occur. The instantaneous ground displacement and consolidation settlement due to soil disturbance result in final settlements after backfilling.

In this study the ground movements associated with shield tunneling and backfill injection are obtained from finite element analysis in view of the consolidation of disturbed cohesive soil. In the analysis, shield work in typical alluvial deposit is supposed. It is investigated what differences in final settlements can be resulted from the variation of the timing for backfill injection or soil conditions.

CONSOLIDATION OF DISTURBED COHESIVE SOIL

The displacements and strains of cohesive soil associated with shield tunneling and backfill injection seem to be great enough to break the

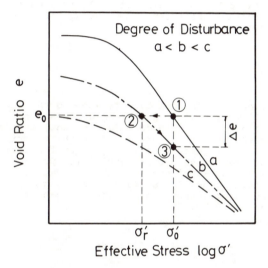

Fig.1 Change of Consolidation Curve due to Soil Disturbance

bonds between particles and change their microstructure, as Peck suggested (1969). Hence, disturbed zone of soil can be created surrounding the tunnel and delayed settlement of the ground surface will take place owing to consolidation of disturbed cohesive soil.
The mechanism of this consolidation of cohesive soil due to its disturbance is illustlated as follows. In Fig.1, typical oedometer test results are shown for undisturbed soil a, slightly disturbed soil b and completely remolded soil c. If shield tunnel is driven in soft cohesive soil corresponding to the normally consolidated state at point ① on undisturbed line a, the cohesive soil adjacent to the tunnel will be disturbed under constant void ratio e_0. The state of this soil will move to point ② on line b, since the effective stress decreses to σ_r' due to soil disturbance. The state of total stress applied

to the surrounding soil seems to recover the initial K_0 condition (at rest) gradually after backfilling. Therefore, the effective stress increases up to σ_0' along line ⓑ and the state of soil will arrive at point ③. In other words, the void ratio of the soil decreases by Δe under constant effective overburden pressure σ_0' and the consolidation of disturbed soil can take place.

Volume decrease α owing to this consolidation of disturbed cohesive soil can be represented by Eq.(1).

$$\alpha = \frac{\Delta e}{1+e_0} = \frac{Cc'}{1+e_0} \cdot \log \frac{\sigma_0'}{\sigma_r'} = \frac{Cc'}{1+e_0} \cdot \log R \quad (1)$$

where Cc' is the compression index for line ⓑ and R ($= \sigma_0'/\sigma_r'$) is the measure for the magnitude of soil disturbance, named disturbance ratio.

This consolidation of disturbed cohesive soil has been studied in detail by the authors (1983). It has been shown from a number of experiments and theoretical considerations that the disturbance ratio R can be defined by Eq.(2), using the magnitude of shear strain $\gamma(\%)$ during deformation under constant void ratio.

$$R = k \cdot \gamma + 1 \quad (2)$$

in which k is the constant related to the susceptibility of soil to disturbance. This constant k is considered to be dependent on soil type or differece in soil structure. From the experiments, the magnitude of k is greater for soils having greater values of sensitivity St. For soils having equal values of St, the value of plasticity index Ip is smaller, the magnitude of k is greater. Hence, the constant k can be represented by Eq.(3).

$$k = 0.33 \cdot Ip^{-0.37} \log St \quad (3)$$

The values of the compression index Cc' of disturbed soil have been examined experimentally. It is appropriate to use the value of Cc' for natural soil obtained by Eq.(4).

$$Cc' = 0.3 \cdot Cc \quad (4)$$

where Cc is the value of compression index of natural soil at undisturbed state.

Therefore, volume decrease α owing to the consolidation of disturbed cohesive soil can be obtained by Eq.(5), by substituting Eqs.(2), (3), and (4) into Eq.(1).

$$\alpha = \frac{0.3Cc}{1+e_0} \cdot \log((0.33 \cdot Ip^{-0.37} \log St)\gamma + 1) \quad (5)$$

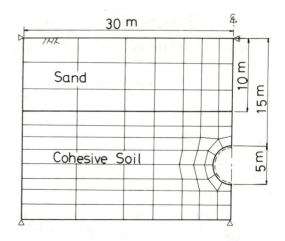

Fig.2 Finite Element Model

TABLE I Input Data for Analysis (instantaneous)

Young's Modulus	Poisson's Ratio		Unit Weight
E (kN/m^2)	Sand	Cohesive Soil	γ_t (kN/m^3)
294Z + 1764	0.333	0.475	15.7

TABLE II Input Data for Analysis (consolidation)

Type	Ip	St	Cc	e_0
I	30	10	0.4	1.4
II	30	20	0.5	1.6
III	30	30	0.7	2.0
IV	30	30	1.0	2.0

FINITE ELEMENT ANALYSIS

Finite element model used in this analysis is shown in Fig.2. This model corresponds to typical alluvial deposit, where the upper layer is 10 m thick saturated sand and the lower is saturated cohesive soil. Shield tunnel (Diameter = 5 m) is driven in the cohesive soil, thereafter backfill injection to the tail void is performed. The ground movements associated with shield tunneling are obtained from finite element analysis under plane strain condition, where the material of ground is assumed to be isotropic-elastic. Input data used in the analysis of instantaneous ground displacements associated with shield tunneling are shown in Table I. In Table II input data necessary to obtain the consolidation settlement are shown, where four types of cohesive soil are supposed. Each of them has different magnitudes of volume decrease α owing to consolidation, when disturbed to the same degree (same magnitude of shear strain).

At first, the instantaneous ground movements accompanied by invasion of the surrounding soil into the tail void on account of delayed timing for injection are obtained, where 5 cases of timing for injection are supposed. In each case the initial total stress applied to the soil adjacent to the tail void can be released to a given degree and the surrounding soil may invade the tail void according to this stress change. Therefore, the delayed timing for injection can be represented by the degree of stress release at the tail void or the volume of soil invaded into the tail void. At the same time, the magnitude of shear strain γ_i for each element in the cohesive soil can be calculated. Hence, the magnitude of consolidation settlement due to soil disturbance caused by ground movements associated with the stress release at the tail void can be obtained by using Eq.(5).

It is assumed that the tail void will be completely filled with backfill materials and the injecting pressure may be applied uniformly to the inner surface of the soil. The injection volume of backfill materials will be varied by changing the magnitude of injecting pressure within 1.7 times of the overburden pressure at the crown of the tunnel. In each case, the ground displacement (the magnitude of shear strain γ_b) associated with backfill injection can be obtained.
The magnitude of shear strain γ_b caused by backfill injection is added to the value of shear strain γ_i caused by stress release at the tail void for each element in the cohesive soil. As a result, the consolidation settlement can be obtained by summing up α over the disturbed area of cohesive soil, after backfilling.

INFLUENCES OF INJECTION TIMING AND SOIL TYPE

In Fig.3, the relations between the magnitudes of surface settlements at center line and the degrees of stress release for each type of cohesive soil are shown. In this figure, tail void contraction is the ratio of the volume of the soil invaded into the tail void to the inherent volume of the tail void. Hence, 100 % of tail void contraction corresponds to the situation

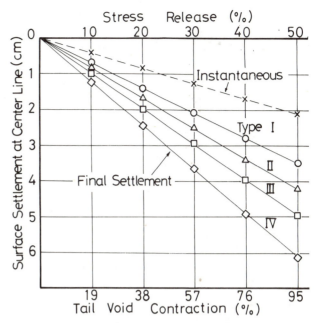

Fig.3 Relations between Surface Settlements at Center Line and Degrees of Stress Release

that the tail void is filled completely with the surrounding soil.
It is evident that the magnitude of final settlement increases owing to the consolidation of disturbed cohesive soil caused by ground movements on account of delayed timing for backfill injection, dependent on soil type.
The values of ground loss in 5 cases of stress release are shown in Table III for each soil type. The ratio of the ground loss owing to the consolidation of disturbed cohesive soil to the instantaneous ground loss accompanied by invasion of the surrounding soil into the tail void seems to be constant for the same type of cohesive soil.

SURFACE DISPLACEMENTS AND INJECTION VOLUME

The instantaneous and final surface displacements are shown in Figs.4(a) and (b), when the backfill materials equivalent to 99 % and 193 % of the inherent volume of the tail void are injected in case of 30 % of stress release (57 % of tail void contraction). Although the ground surface will heave immediately after backfill injection, delayed settlement will occur owing to the consolidation of disturbed cohesive soil.
The relations between the injection volume of backfill materials and the instantaneous and final surface displacements at center line in case of 10 % of stress release are shown in Fig.5.
It is noted that the greater magnitude of consolidation settlement takes place, the greater volume of backfill materials is injected. The preventive efficiency of backfill injection against ground settlement is sufficient in every type of soil and every degree of stress release within 100 % of injection volume. It is interesting to note that the influences of backfill

TABLE III Values of Ground Loss in 5 Cases of Stress Release for Each Soil Type

Stress Release(%)		10	20	30	40	50
Instantaneous(m³)		0.067	0.135	0.202	0.269	0.336
Type I	Delayed*)(m³)	0.051	0.102	0.151	0.200	0.247
	Ratio (%)	76	76	75	74	73
Type II	Delayed(m³)	0.077	0.152	0.225	0.297	0.367
	Ratio (%)	115	113	111	110	109
Type III	Delayed(m³)	0.106	0.209	0.309	0.406	0.501
	Ratio (%)	158	155	153	151	149
Type IV	Delayed(m³)	0.151	0.298	0.441	0.580	0.716
	Ratio (%)	225	221	218	216	213

*)Delayed means ground loss due to consolidation.

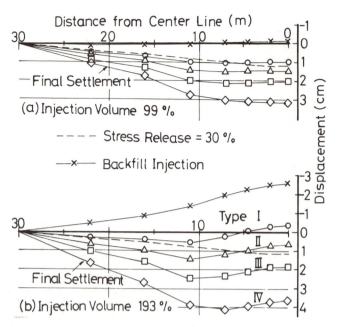

(a) Injection Volume 99 %

- - - - Stress Release = 30 %

——×—— Backfill Injection

(b) Injection Volume 193 %

Fig.4 Instantaneous and Final Surface Displacements associated with Backfill Injection

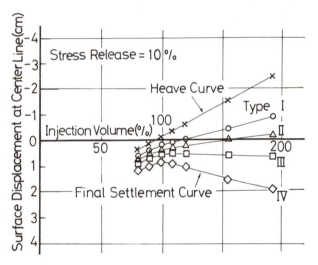

Fig.5 Relations between Injection Volume of Backfill Materials and Surface Displacements
at Center Line

becomes insufficient or harmful, when the backfill materials greater than the volume of the
tail void are injected in the types of cohesive
soil as type III or type IV. It is impossible
to reduce the magnitude of final settlement
less than 2 cm by means of backfill injection
in such types of cohesive soil, if 30 % or 50 %
of initial stress may be released on account of
delayed timing for injection.
Therefore, it is most effective to inject the
suitable backfill materials at the same time as
the occurence of the tail void. Even if it is
supposed to be injected ideally in practice, the
geometric shape of injected materials isn't
necessarily uniform. Moreover, the ground movements take place at the cutting face of the tun-

nel. As a result, the consolidation settlements
could occur due to soil disturbance caused by
these ground movements. Hence, it seems practical to regard these situations as equivalent to
the delayed timing for backfill injection.

CONCLUSION

In this study, the ground displacements associated with shield tunneling and backfill injection in the soft ground are obtained from finite
element analysis in view of the consolidation
of disturbed cohesive soil under various conditions.
Based on the results of this finite element analysis, it is concluded that :

1. Large delayed settlements could occur owing
to consolidation of the disturbed cohesive soil
adjacent to the tunnel associated with shield
tunneling and backfill injection.

2. The magnitude of final settlement can not be
reduced by injecting the backfill materials
greater than the inherent volume of the tail
void dependent on types of cohesive soil, if the
timing for backfill injection may be delayed.

3. It is most effective to inject the suitable
backfill materials at the same time as the occurence of the tail void.

It is indispensable to examine the results obtained here from the viewpoint of the measurements
in the field. However, it is very difficult to
pick up the magnitudes of ground movements associated with backfill injection only.
Therefore, it is significant to investigate the
ground movements using the method adopted in
this analysis. The results obtained here seem to
be useful guidelines for the injection method to
the tail void for backfill at shield work in the
soft cohesive soil.

ACKNOWLEDGEMENTS

Thanks are due to Tokyo Electric Power Company
Inc., which sponsored this research.

REFERENCES

MORI, A., and H. AKAGI (1983).   Consolidation
    phenomena of normally consolidated clays due
    to the disturbance caused by undrained shear.
    Proc. J.S.C.E., No.335, July, 117-125
    (in Japanese).

Peck, R.B. (1969).   Deep excavation and
    tunneling in soft ground.   State of the Art
    Report, 7th Int.Conf.Soil Mech.Found.Engg.,
    225-290, Mexico.

A braced sheetpile excavation in soft Singapore marine clay

Excavation dans les argiles marines molles de Singapour à l'abri d'un rideau de palplanches butonnes

S. B. TAN, Deputy Director, Public Works Department, Singapore
S. L. TAN, Higher Executive Engineer, Public Works Department, Singapore
Y. K. CHIN, Engineer, Public Works Department, Singapore

SYNOPSIS   In Singapore, the growing need for landspace has in recent years necessitated deeper and larger basement excavations. It is not uncommon that ground movements and stability problems associated with excavation in soft soils have endangered and caused damage to surrounding property. This paper presents instrumentation results of the 2 level basement excavation for the Ministry of the Environment Building project. Ground movements, larger than expected, were recorded in the areas where the factor of safety against base heave was low. High strut loads were also measured at a few strut locations. Generally, the measured strut loads agreed with the values calculated using Peck's (1969) empirical envelop. The results from the Finite Element analysis using a hyperbolic stress-strain model compared favourably with the measured field response.

INTRODUCTION

The sub-structure contract for this project called for the design and construction of a 2 level basement in soft marine clay. The location of the site relative to Scotts Road, Cairnhill Road and Cairnhill Garden (a twelve storey residential block of flats) is shown in Fig 1. The excavation area measured 110m by 70m. The depth of excavation varied from 6.4m to 7.5m at the pile cap locations. The proposed support system comprised interlocking steel sheetpiles (type YSP III and IV) braced by 3 levels of bolted struts. The sheetpile lengths ranged from 12m to 24m. A comprehensive instrumentation program was adopted to monitor the performance of the temporary support system and the resulting ground movements. This provided an important check on the validity of the design assumptions and also yielded useful field data for comparison with various theories.

SOIL CONDITION

Geologically, the site is located in a former tributary of the Bukit Timah river valley system. As shown in the subsoil profile in Fig 2, soft marine clay deposit of considerable thickness exists as two distinct upper and lower members at the Scotts Road side.

The geotechnical properties of Singapore Marine

Clay are well documented by Tan & Lee (1977) and Tan (1983). The Lower Member, having been exposed to the atmosphere and weathering agents during a period of low sea levels in the Pleistocene, has a lower moisture content and a stiffer consistency (especially so in its top 1-2m) than the younger Upper Member. The relevant soil data are summarised in Table 1.

EXCAVATION PROCEDURE

The reduced level (RL) of original ground varied from 102.5 to 103.6m. The excavation procedure for the various stages is outlined below:

Stage 1: Excavate to RL 101.1 to install the 1st level struts.

Stage 2: Excavate the central area to RL 99.15 leaving a 10m wide earth berm around the entire site. Excavate through the berm to install the 2nd level struts.

Stage 3: Excavate in strip to RL 97.8 to install the 3rd level strut. Excavation in the central area was permitted subject to leaving a minimum 20m wide berm against the sheetpile.

Stage 4: Excavate in panels to RL 96.1 to enable the casting of basement slab/pile caps.

INSTRUMENTATION AND OBSERVED BEHAVIOUR DURING EXCAVATION

The field instrumentation consisted of inclinometers for monitoring lateral sheetpile movements, settlements gauges and survey points for vertical and lateral ground movements, vibrating wire strain gauges for strut loads, piezometers for pore water pressures, water standpipes for water table level, and tiltmeter and precise levelling to determine the effects of excavation on the adjacent building. The type and location of instruments and the survey plan layout are illustrated in Fig 1.

	W %	PI %	Cu** KPa	Eu* KPa	γ KN/m³
Upper Marine Clay	100	70	14.5-18	150-300 Cu	14.8
Lower Marine Clay	65	45	18-22	300-600 Cu	15.8

Table 1. Soil Data for Marine Clay
* from Duncan and Buchignani 1976
** from field vane tests.

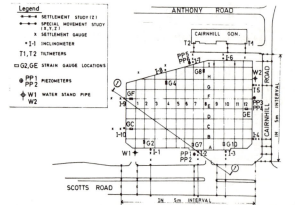

Fig. 1   LOCATION OF INSTRUMENTS AND SURVEY POINTS

the soft clay extends for considerable depths, the sequential lateral wall movements increased rapidly with the depth of excavation. The maximum movement occurred below the excavation bottom. This trend of behaviour, which is typical of base heaving, is also reported in other well documented projects (e.g. Clough (1984)). In contrast, in the other areas where the soft clay is of limited depth, the maximum lateral deflections were significantly smaller and occurred at or above the excavation bottom. Throughout the excavation phase, it was observed that the lateral sheetpile deflections were creeping on an average of 1mm a day. It is possible that these creep deflections occurred in relation to the on-set of large zones of plastic yielding in the clay; the rate of creep increasing with decreasing factor of safety against base heave.

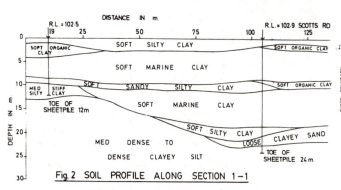

Fig. 2 SOIL PROFILE ALONG SECTION 1-1

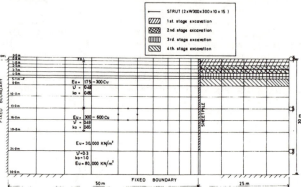

Fig 3   FINITE ELEMENT MESH

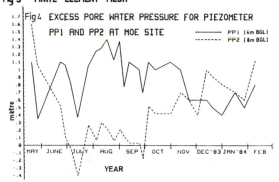

Fig4 EXCESS PORE WATER PRESSURE FOR PIEZOMETER PP1 AND PP2 AT MOE SITE

The maximum values of lateral deflections, strut loads and ground settlements at various stages of excavation are summarised below.

Stages of Excav.	Max lateral deflection (mm)	Max strut load ** (kN)	Max ground settlement (mm)
1st	160 (I-7)	-	117(1m from I-7)
2nd	152 (I-1)	550 (G7)	180(1m from I-1)
3rd	200 (I-1)	1300(G7)	225(1m from I-1)
4th	400 (I-3)*	2280(G10)	400(5m from I-7)

*Excavated depth = 7.5m, **minus initial preload

The profiles of lateral deflections and magnitude of strut loads at various stages of excavation for I-2, I-9, G7 and GF are presented in Figs 5, 6, 7, 8 respectively. The settlement patterns for Scotts Road and Cairnhill Road are plotted in non-dimensional form in Fig 11. Peck's (1969) settlement zones are included for comparison. Fig 4 shows the excess pore water pressures recorded from piezometers 1 and 2. The initial reading indicated an excess which was probably caused by the driving of steel H piles. During the first stage of excavation, the cantilever sheetpile wall deflected significantly (160mm) near I-7. The total excavated depth at this location (including a 1m surcharge of the driveway) was estimated to be 3m. In other areas, where the excavated depth was less than 2m, the lateral deflections were substantially smaller. For the first stage of excavation, the maximum depth should have been limited to $\frac{2 \; Cu}{\gamma}$ = 2m. Along Scotts Road side, where

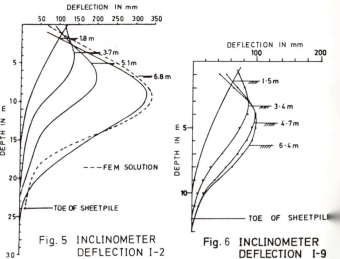

Fig. 5 INCLINOMETER DEFLECTION I-2

Fig. 6 INCLINOMETER DEFLECTION I-9

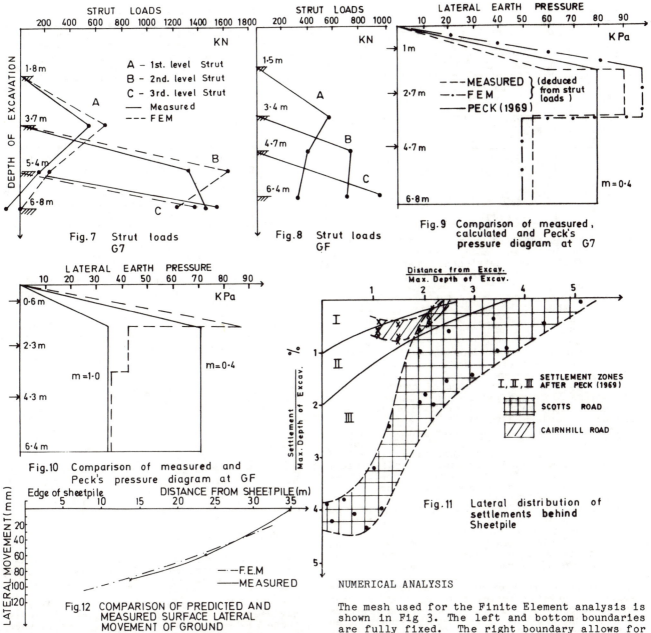

Fig. 7 Strut loads G7

Fig. 8 Strut loads GF

Fig. 9 Comparison of measured, calculated and Peck's pressure diagram at G7

Fig. 10 Comparison of measured and Peck's pressure diagram at GF

Fig. 11 Lateral distribution of settlements behind Sheetpile

Fig. 12 COMPARISON OF PREDICTED AND MEASURED SURFACE LATERAL MOVEMENT OF GROUND

The maximum measured settlement occurred next to the sheetpile wall; the magnitude being approximately equal to the maximum lateral deflection. Along Scotts Road side, noticeable settlements were observed to a distance of five times the depth of excavation.

The use of 10m wide earth berms proved to be quite effective in controlling the lateral movement of the sheetpile. However, this control was only temporary as the eventual removal of the berms resulted in large deflections.

The measured pore water pressures indicated a typical trend of a decrease in excess pressure during excavation which was reported by Clough (1984). This trend reflects the unloading effect of the excavation. After preloading, an increase in excess pore water pressure was observed.

NUMERICAL ANALYSIS

The mesh used for the Finite Element analysis is shown in Fig 3. The left and bottom boundaries are fully fixed. The right boundary allows for vertical movement only. The struts are pin-connected to the mesh nodes. The stiffness of the strut is calculated based on per m length of wall. A non-linear hyperbolic stress strain behaviour of the soil is adopted for analysis. The tangent modulus is changed incrementally according to the expression

$$E_t = \left[1 - R_f \frac{(\sigma_1 - \sigma_3)}{2\, Cu} \right]^2 Eu$$

The parameter R_f is taken to be 0.95 which is typical for most clays. Failure of the soil element occurred when $[\sigma_1 - \sigma_3] > 2\, Cu$ or when $\sigma_3 < 0$ (tensile condition). After failure a low modulus (Eu = 1 kN/m²) is used. Unloading and reloading of the soil is handled by setting $E_t = Eu$. The results of the analysis are shown in Fig 5, Fig 7 and Fig 9.

DISCUSSION

As shown below, the ratio of the maximum lateral deflection to the excavation depth increases rapidly with a decrease in the factor of safety as defined by Terzaghi (1943). This is to be expected as base heaving and plastic yielding of the subsoil begin to dominate response as the factor of safety approaches 1. (Clough, 1984).

Loca-tion	Depth H (m)	Terzaghi's Equation	F cal-culated	Max de-flection δH(mm)	$\frac{\delta H}{H}$ %
I-2	6.8	$F = \dfrac{NcCu}{H(\gamma - Cu/D)}$	0.88	330	4.9
I-9	6.4	$F = \dfrac{NcCu}{H(\gamma - Cu/0.7D)}$	1.5	100	1.6

Peck (1969) classified three distinct settlement zones for different soil conditions. Fig 11 shows that the settlement pattern along Cairnhill Road side falls under zone II. Along this side, the soft clay extends to only a limited depth below the excavation bottom. In contrast, the settlement at Scotts Road side is classified under zone III which is for the case of soft clays extending to considerable depths below excavation bottom. The measured maximum settlements are larger than generally reported. This could be attributed to three main factors. Firstly, creep movements were occuring during lapses between the completion of excavation and strutting. This was partly unavoidable in view of the large volume of excavation involved. Secondly, several third level struts were overstressed and in one situation one row of third level strut (along Grid 10) buckled slightly. It would appear that the stiffness of support system was inadequate. Thirdly, heavy constructional traffic loading along Scotts Road side could also be a contributory factor.

The damaging effects of ground movements on unsupported aprons and walls were significant within a distance of 2H from the sheetpile wall. Cairnhill Gardens (on piled foundation) showed no signs of structural damage even for lateral sheetpile deflections of up to 350mm.

The design strut load at G10 basing on Peck's empirical pressure envelop is 2200 kN whereas the measured value is 2840 kN. The difference between the two is approximately equal to an initial preload of 560 kN. This suggests that preloads should be taken into account in the design of struts. Fig 9 and 10 show equivalent pressure diagrams evaluated from strut loads at GF and G7. At the location of the 1st and 2nd level struts, the equivalent pressure deduced from the measured strut loads is slightly higher than Peck's empirical pressure envelop based on m=0.4. However, in most cases, the empirical envelop appears to give reasonable estimates of the strut loads.

The inclinometer readings before and after preload show that preloading does not push the soil back by more than 5mm. It appears that preloading is marginally effective when applied to flexible sheetpile walls. However, one visible advantage of preloading is the removal of any slackness in the system which can be potential sources of movement.

The hyperbolic model gives results that are in close agreement with measured values (Figs 5,7,9). The predicted surface lateral movements at various distances from the sheetpile agree well with the measured values (see Fig 12). To study the surface settlements, an interface element should be introduced to allow for slippage.

CONCLUSIONS

1. Excavation beyond the critical depth in soft Singapore Marine Clay can result in very large ground movements.

2. Where the factor of safety is low, creep movement can be significant. In such a case, careful planning to reduce the time lapse between excavation and strutting is important.

3. The advantage of preloading in reducing ground movements was not observed in this project. It appears that the design of strut loads should take into account the magnitudes of preloads.

4. Earth berms serve the purpose of reducing lateral deflection of the sheetpiles. Casting of basement slab in alternate strips in conjunction with the use of earth berms can also reduce ground movements.

5. Instrumentation is a very essential part of any excavation project.

ACKNOWLEDGEMENT

The authors wish to thank the Director of Public Works for his kind permission to publish this paper.

REFERENCES

Clough, G.W. and Reed, M.W. (1984). "Measured Behaviour of Braced Wall in Very Soft Clay", Journal of Geotechnical Engrg, ASCE,Vol 110,No.1

Duncan, J.M., and Buchignani, A.L. (1976). "An Engineering Manual for Settlement Studies," Geotech. Engrg. Report, Dept. of Civil Engrg., Univ. of California, Berkeley.

Peck, R.B. (1969). "Deep Excavations and Tunnelling in Soft Ground." Proc. 7th Int. Conf. Soil Mech. Found. Eng.,Mexico City, State-of-Art.

Tan, S.B. and Lee, K.W. (1977). "Engineering Geology of the Marine Member of the Kallang Formation in Singapore", Proc. Int. Sym. on Soft Clays, Bangkok, 75-88.

Tan, S.L. (1983). "Geotechnical Properties and Laboratory Testing of Soft Soils in Singapore", International Seminar on Construction Problems in Soft Soils, Singapore.

Terzaghi, K.(1943)."Theoretical Soil Mechanics", John Wiley & Sons, Inc., New York, N.Y.

Session 5B
Geotechnical engineered construction
B. Earth strengthening

Séance 5B
Construction employant le génie géotechnique
B. Renforcement des ouvrages en terre

Strengthening of a structural fill by claquage

Renforcement d'un remblai structural par claquage

A. ARCONES, Civil Engineer, Empresarios Agrupados, Madrid, Spain
E. RUIZ DE TEMIÑO, Civil Engineer, Empresarios Agrupados, Madrid, Spain
A. SORIANO, Ph.D., Civil Engineer, Empresarios Agrupados, Madrid, Spain

SYNOPSIS Some heavy buildings of a large facility have been built on structural fills. Recording of movements of the foundations has shown the need for some method of reducing long term settlements. From different earth-strengthening procedures, the "claquage" method was chosen for a large scale field test to be performed before applying it to the solution of the problem. Cement-bentonite was used as grout in the fill, creating a network of seams crossing each other to increase the strength of the fill and reduce its compressibility.

Properties of the soil before and after the treatment, results of several laboratory and "in situ" tests, data from a large plate load test with a diameter of 5 m and a detailed survey of the distribution of grout lenses within the fill are reported in this paper. This method of earth strengthening which is presently being applied to the current structural fills at the facility.

INTRODUCTION

The design of structural fills as direct foundations for close buildings when their bases are situated at different levels, is a common practice. Other alternatives usually involve higher costs.

In spite of constructing these backfills with a good and intense compaction and in spite of obtaining high densities, it may occur that, for some type of backfilling materials, subsequent loads on the fill induce creep phenomena or long term settlements that can cause future problems.

This paper describes a method of strengthening earthfills which creates a network of grout lenses, crossing each other in different directions. Injection is performed by means of claquage. This method not only increases the density of the fill material, acting as a preload, but also gives a framework to supplement the soil structure and assist in transmitting the loads to the fill foundation.

To investigate the effectiveness of such a procedure, a large model test of a structure founded on a structural fill has been constructed. It consists of a rigid circular mat 5 m in diameter loaded to the same pressure as that of the actual buildings. Testing of this method includes, in addition to the model test, a detailed survey of the claquage lenses obtained through exploration pits excavated after the injections as well as several "in situ" tests (plate load tests, cross-hole tests, "in situ" densities, etc.) and laboratory tests which, compared with similar tests run before the treatment, allowed for a quantification of the effectiveness of this method.

THE STRUCTURAL FILL

Natural Ground Conditions

The place where the buildings associated with the structural fill were built was originally levelled. It was formed by a thick deposit of heavily preconsolidated soils. Foundations of some buildings required excavations up to depths of approximately 10 to 15 metres whereas others were to be founded close to the grade level. Excavated soils were used as backfilling materials and some buildings have their foundation resting directly on these structural backfills which in addition is of variable thickness.

The natural soil deposit was formed during the Miocene as a product of erosion of granite and gneiss and the subsequent transport and deposition in horizontal layers, as they are found today. The depth of the bedrock (a conglomerate) is about 100 to 110 m as known by seismic refraction surveying and by some deep boreholes drilled through the soil deposit.

The grain size distribution of these soils changes from one level to another as the conditions of climate were variable in the geologic times of their formation. The clay content (particles with a size of less than two microns) is quite homogeneous, irrespective of the other properties, and varies between 4 and 17%, except in the case of very few samples. These soils appear as a mix of more or less fine grains of silica sands and a random percentage of clays. The dominant clay is montmorillonite and there is a significant proportion of mica, with a minor content of kaolinite and chlorite.

The soil deposit was heavily consolidated partly by the load of the eroded overburden and partly by dessication. The water level, although not clearly marked, is some 5 to 10 m below the ground surface. "In situ" dry densities were close to 1950 kg/m^3 near the surface (up to depths of 10 m) and some increase with depth (about 50 kg/m^3 for each 10 m increment in depth) was noticed from laboratory testing. The natural water content of the uppermost soils, of more interest for this study, varied from 7.5 to 19% (average value 13%) depending on the nature of the soil at each level.

The compressibility of the top layers of this deposit was studied through field tests ("in situ" plate load tests on the horizontal and vertical directions) and through laboratory test (consolidation and triaxial tests). On the basis of these testing and taking into account the experience of the behaviour of structures founded on these soils, which are very common in the central part of Spain, it was estimated that, for vertical loads, the soil would respond with a modulus value of approximately 1.5 x 10^5 kPa for loads applied at depths of approximately 5 m and with a modulus 5000 kPa larger for each metre of additional depth.

Construction of the Fill

The use of the product of excavations in this deposit as backfilling material was thoroughly studied by careful "in situ" and laboratory testing as well as the construction of fill areas for testing. The excavated soils were first piled in an attempt to exclude those whose fine content appeared larger. Afterwards, this soil pile was studied by random sampling inside pits and trenches opened within the pile.

The grain size distribution of samples taken from different depths at some fourteen locations within the pile of excavated soils lay within the narrow range indicated in Fig. 1.

The water content was quite close to that of the natural deposit, i.e. from 9 to 14%. Only the external crust of the pile had a lower water content, close to 8%.

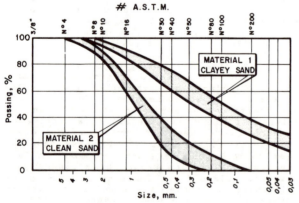

Fig. 1 - Grain-size Distribution of Borrow Materials

The first trial to extend and compact this material failed to achieve the required densities (95% of MP) due to the excessive water content (an average of some 3.5% above optimum). To solve this problem, a method was indicated by mixing these soils with clean sands taken from a far borrow pit, since weather conditions at this location did not warrant the natural dry-out of the clayey sands from the excavations.

The grain size distribution of the clean sands is also illustrated in Fig. 1. They were formed by rounded siliceous particles and their natural water content had an average value of 5.7%. The proportions of the mix were established as 70% natural clayey sands from the excavated soils and 30% clean sands. Results from MP control testing of the mix gave maximum dry densities ranging from 2,070 to 2,130 kg/m^3 at optimum water contents of 7.3 to 8.8%.

Under these circumstances, the construction of the structural fill proceeded according to the specification of achieving at least 95% MP with water contents deviating less than 3% from the optimum. Results of control testing during the construction of the structural fills gave an average value of the dry density of 97.3% of maximum MP and the average water content was 0.4% above optimum.

The evaluation of settlements for the heavy buildings to be founded on this structural fill was performed well in advance when the design of the foundations not included the removal and replacement of natural soils. Under these circumstances, the estimated settlements were of approximately a few centimetres and were acceptable within the limits of future operation. The fact of remolding the natural soils by excavation, mixing, backfilling and compaction changed the compressibility of the soils. On further testing, the estimated modulus of the natural soils, mentioned as being approximately 1.5 x 10^5 kPa, decreased to values of approximately 1.3 x 10^4 kPa (about ten times lower).

Testing after Construction

The excessive settlement of the buildings and the increase thereof over a long period, motivated a very detailed exploration to check the structural fill characteristics. This exploration was very extensive and only a summary of the main findings is given in Table 1.

This comparison shows that the unexpected behaviour of the buildings was not due to a significant deviation from the construction specification.

Consolidation tests, run with block samples taken on exploration pits at different depths (the thickness of the fill varied from 0 to 12 metres), gave similar results as that run prior to construction. A typical result is included in Fig. 2. These tests (a total of 37 were run at this phase of the study) were interpreted on the basis of the Schmertman method to obtain the estimated "in situ" com-

TABLE I - AVERAGE VALUES OF SOME CHARACTERISTICS OF THE STRUCTURAL FILL

	Construction Control	Check after 5 years
Fines (200 ASTM), %	25	35
Liquid limit, %	28	28
Plasticity index, %	10	8.4
Specific gravity grains, kN/m^3	26.1	26.3
Dry density (laboratory), kg/m^3		1930
Water content (laboratory), %		8.4
Dry density ("in situ"), kg/m^3	2020	2050
Water content ("in situ"), %	8.5	7.8

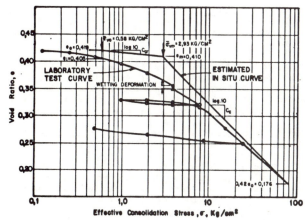

Fig.2 - Tipical Result of Consolidation Test

pression curve. The preconsolidation pressure, induced by the compaction force, was estimated as close to 300 kPa. The compression index below and beyond this pressure was C_s = 0.013 and C_c = 0.11, although a considerable scatter was seen in this data (maximum and minimum values of C_s were 0.027 and 0.007 and for C_c were 0.23 and 0.07, respectively).

Cross-hole tests were also run on this structural fill after construction. The most significant values of these results are:

- V_s = 483 m/s (standard deviation 50 m/s)

- V_p = 917 m/s (standard deviation 104 m/s)

THE METHOD OF EARTH STRENGTHENING

Two main buildings at the facility have suffered settlements well over those acceptable for regular operation mainly because of the associated titling towards the zones of the larger thickness of the structural fills. A method to repair these buildings should at least stop future settlements and, if possible, relevel part of the inclination of the building.

Some methods of underpinning were thought of but none was acceptable since they interfered with the operation of the facility which was starting up at that time. Among different methods of ground improvement available (Mitchel and Katti, 1981) squeezing grout into the soil (claquage) was selected for the fill tests since it appeared to be the simplest method and has a good background of experience in Spain (Escario and Rodríguez, 1983; Escario, 1983).

Compaction grouting (Brown and Warner, 1972; ASCE, 1977) was kept as the second choice in case the claquage proved to be inappropriate after field testing.

The injection by claquage (Cambefort, 1977) consists of pressing a suitable mix of cement and bentonite into the ground through a grout pipe with regularly spaced sleeves used one at a time. Breaking the soil with initial high pressures opens a seam through which the grout may propagate under moderate pressure. Control of the grout pressure and the viscosity of the grout mix allows the heave of the foundations to be controlled. The initial pressures necessary to start the claquage process, the opening of the plane of the fracture, the quantities of grout mix to be injected, etc., are parameters whose theoretical determination is not possible now. Only field tests and past experience were considered reasonable bases to design the procedure.

The extrapolation of the observed settlement of the buildings indicated that a future change in volume of the fill of more than 0.5% should be expected if no action were taken. The purpose of the injection should be, at least, to bring about this change in volume and, if possible, to inject more so that the verticality of the buildings may be partly recovered. On the basis of these data, and taking past experience into account, the objective of the grout operation was fixed to inject about 5% in volume of a mixture with the following characteristics:

- Cement	> 400 kg per m^3 of mix
- Bentonite	$\approx$ 6% of cement by weight
- Viscosity (marsh cone)	35 to 70 s
- Rigidity	> 0.4 kPa at 4 h
- Free water	< 3%
- Strength	> 10^3 kPa at 28 days

First, a vertical wall should be injected to contain the foundation filler grout, with a limiting pressure of 100 kPa for each metre of depth.

GROUT TESTING

The preliminary work was performed in an area close to the foundation of the buildings where the thickness of the fill was about 8 m. The ground was covered by 10 concrete mats with a surface area of 2 x 2 m each, and a thickness of 0.40 m, in order to prevent, to some degree, the grout from escaping to the surface. A total of 19 grout pipes were installed and the grouting was carried out in four different phases.

Once the grouting was finished, the grouted soil was excavated over an area of 7 x 3 m to a depth of 5 m and the distribution of grout seams within the fill, their thickness, the grout paths, etc., could be observed and mapped

The main conclusions derived from this preliminary field test were the following:

- Grouting through points at depths of less than 3 m causes the mix to leak to the surface at very low grout pressures. Confinement of the ground surface would be required if grout is needed in shallow areas.
- The thickness of grout seams appears to be very variable, but 5 to 10 mm lenses are frequent. Some planes of the fracture appear parallel to others creating a sandwich type of grout and soil with a thickness of several centimetres.
- A good part of the grout mix is distributed along inclined and subvertical fracture planes although there are many horizontal grout seams of large thickness, particularly close to the ground surface.

BUILDING FOUNDATION MODEL

To model the conditions of the fill below the buildings to be subjected to treatment, a concrete mat was constructed, as shown in Fig. 3. To simulate the building foundation pressures, the concrete mat was loaded by means of seven anchor cables fixed at a sufficient depth in natural ground. Each of these cables was designed for a total capacity of 2,500 KN. The mat was poured at a depth of 2 m (the

same as the actual buildings) and close to the buildings, resting on the same structural fill.

Prior to any grouting operations, a load was applied to the mat and settlements were recorded by high precision levelling using the same references (anchored at a depth of 40 m in the ground) being used to monitor building movements. Control of movements was followed at several points on the mat surface. The two extreme values of the settlement records (maximum and minimum settlements) are shown as a function of time and load, in Fig. 4.

The first phase of grout was injected to create a vertical curtain to laterally confine the soils below the foundation. For that purpose, a double crown of vertical tubes was installed around the perimeter of the circular model mat. A total volume of 78.07 m^3 of grout was inserted into this vertical curtain wall. During this phase of the grouting operations, the mat was permanently loaded at a constant pressure of 300 kPa by minor adjustment on the anchor cables (whose load changed slightly with these movements).

After that, grout holes were driven from the grout chamber beneath the mat and the pipes with grout sleeves were installed. Injection below the mat was carried out in two phases, separated by a waiting period of ten days. A total volume of 49.3 m^3 was grouted.

Movements of the mat were carefully recorded and are shown in Fig. 5. A small settlement of about 1 mm was observed in the initial stages when grouting the perimeter tubes, but soon the movements were directed upwards. A total heave of 6 mm took place while grouting the vertical grout tubes and an additional 33 mm heave was recorded while grouting beneath the mat. No settlements were noticed due to drilling operations to perforate horizontal holes for installation of the grout tube.

Once the grouting was finished, a waiting period was established to allow the grout mix to harden, after which the mat was subjected to a load test by increasing the load up to 700 kPa and performing unloadin-greloading cycles. Movements during this phase of the model test are shown in Fig. 6. Maximum settlement for this part of the load was less than 3 mm.

INSPECTION AFTER TESTING

To study the effects of the grout on the fill, a test pit of 2 x 2 x 2 m was excavated after removal of the model concrete mat. Excavation was carried out by horizontal levels, each with a depth of 25 cm, so that all grout seams appearing at the bottom of the test pit could be carefully mapped. Drawings were made at each of the nine stages of the excavations, as well as of the vertical walls. The length, thickness and orientation of each grout seam was measured and a computer data bank was created to handle this information. A report on the statistical distribution of grout planes inside the fill is being prepared by the authors. As an example, a sketch of the grout lenses in one of the vertical walls of the test pit is included in Fig. 7.

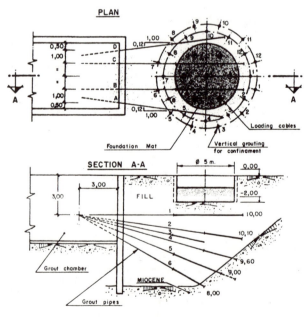

Fig. 3 - Lay-out of Field Model Test

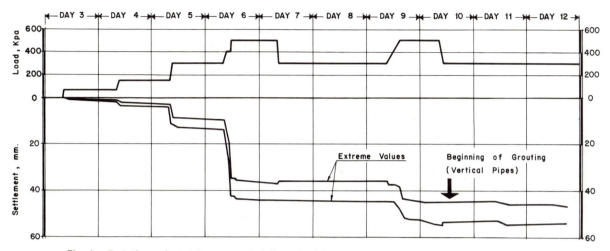

Fig. 4 - Evolution of Settlements. Building Model Load Test. Before Treatment.

The material taken from this pit was analyzed as a sample of 8 m³. A special grain size distribution test was designed to separate grout material from the fill and, in this manner, it was possible to determine that the weight of grout within the sample was 3.01% of the total weight. The heave of the mat during injection was equal to a change in volume of about 0.5% so that only a small proportion of the grout entered the fill by raising the concrete mat; the main part of the grout had to squeeze the soil and reduce its volume. The dry density of the soil in the large sample was 2097 kg/m³, so a slight increase was observed over the dry densities prior to grouting. The water content was 11.4%.

Five plate load tests, with a rigid circular plate 750 mm in diameter, were run at different depths at the bottom of the test pit and other exploration trenches within the treated soils. Comparison with a similar test run prior to grouting gave an average modulus which was three to four times greater.

Cross-hole tests were repeated after treatment. The main results were:

- V_s = 628 m/s (standard deviation 46 m/s)

- V_p = 995 m/s (standard deviation 81 m/s)

Similar changes due to grouting were obtained by Serrano and Cuellar (1979) at a different site.

CONCLUSIONS

The work described in this paper is still under way and final conclusions will be obtained when it finishes. However, from the data shown throughout the text of this paper, some preliminary conclusions may be reached.

The method described here is applicable to reducing the settlement of heavy structures founded on structural fills through a rigid mat, even when the building is in operation.

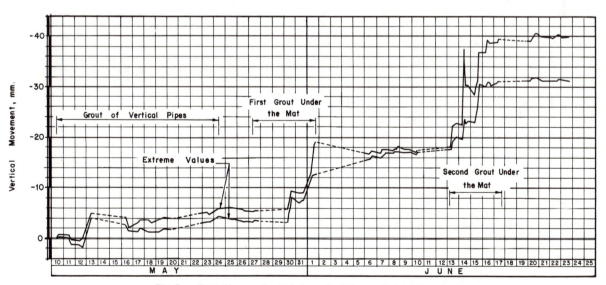

Fig. 5 - Evolution of Heaving. Building Model Grout Test

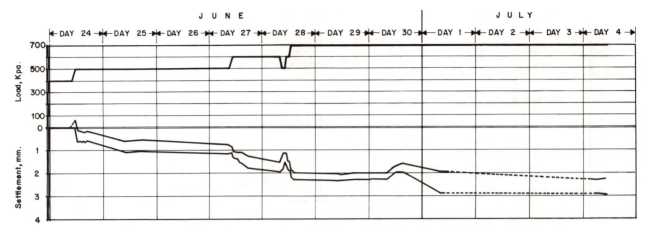

Fig. 6 - Evolution of Settlements. Building Model Load Test. After Treatment

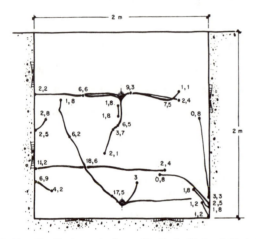

Fig.7 - Distribution of Grout. Vertical Wall of Test Pit.
(Numbers indicate grout thickness in mm.)

No settlements are induced by grouting (drilling, washing, injection, etc.) and the heave can be controlled by limiting pressures and grout volumes. The method can be applied in its entirety from outside the buildings without any constraint on the regular operation thereof.

The main effect of the grout is a reduction in the compressibility of the structural fill. This fact is due to an increase in the preconsolidation pressure of the soil and the creation of a network of grout seams, crossing in all directions, which assist in supporting the loads. The reduction in compressibility has been measured as approximately four times for loading new, additional loads.

The method is suitable for soils with a high fine content where the use of other types of grout is not possible. The conclusions of this work are, restricted to soils similar to those where the tests were carried out.

REFERENCES

ASCE Committee of Grouting (1977). "Slabjacking. State of the Art Report". Journal of the Geotechnical Engineering Division. Vol. 103, N° 6T9, September.

Brown, D.R. and Warner, J. (1972). "Compaction Grouting". Proc. Journal of the Soil Mechanics and Foundation Division ASCE. Vol. 99, N° SM8, August.

Cambefort, H. (1977). "The Principles and Applications of Grouting". The Quarterly Journal of Engineering Geology. Vol. 10, pp. 57-95.

Escario, V. (1983). "Ground Improvement Related to Soil Liquefaction. Squeeze and Compaction Grouting". Proc. VIII, European Conference on Soil Mechanics and Foundation Engineering, Helsinki.

Escario, V., Rodríguez Ortiz, J.M. and Muzás, F. (1983). "Improving Defective Foundations in Gypsum Ground by Cement Bentonite Grouting". VIII European Conference on Soil Mechanics and Foundation Engineering, Helsinki.

Mitchel, J.K. and Katti, R.K. (1981). "Soil Improvement State of the Art Report". X International Conference on Soil Mechanics and Foundation Engineering, Stockholm.

Serrano, A.A. and Cuellar, V. (1979). "Influence of Grouting on the Dynamics Properties of the Foundation of a Nuclear Power Plant". VII European Conference on Soil Mechanics and Foundation Engineering, Brighton. Vol. 2, pp. 271-279.

The performance of sand compaction piles

La performance de pieux de sable compacté

K.F. BRONS, Technical Director, International Foundation Group BV, Gouda, Netherlands
H. DE KRUIJFF, Project Engineer, International Foundation Group BV, Gouda, Netherlands

SUMMARY

The design of sand compaction piles is usually based on two relatively simple principles. One is the stability of the individual sand column, carrying the major part of the load increase and supported by the surrounding compressible material, carrying a small percentage of the load increase. The other principle is the assumption that columns and softer material will be subject to equal vertical deformation, leading to a stress concentration on the sand columns.
After installing a number of sand compaction piles for a crude oil tank in Rotterdam Ports area, pressure gauges were placed on top of the piles and in between, together with a number of piezometers in the compressible strata.
During the water test of the tank, the instrumentation was monitored and the results are compared with the technical design. During the installation of the sand compaction piles a marked increase in pore pressure occurred. The load concentration factor was not as high as anticipated, the settlements for the centre of the tank were close to the calculated values.

INTRODUCTION

The application of sand compaction piles usually aims at the reduction of the compression and the increase of the shear strength of soft strata. The function of sand piles is to form a rigid raster of columns on which the load is concentrated. A well-compacted layer is usually placed on top of the sand piles in order to obtain a better load concentration on the piles by arching. During the installation of the sand piles the pore pressures are increased, however, due to the relatively close spacing of the sand columns and the high permeability, the dissipation of the excess pore pressures takes place at a high rate.

DESIGN CRITERIA

The design of a subsoil improvement with sand compaction piles is a relatively simple matter. For the design the following steps are taken:

1. The settlement of the tank for the intreated soil is calculated with the aid of the results of the laboratory tests.

2. On the basis of the data as supplied by the tank manufacturer concerning the acceptable settlements and differential settlements for the tank centre and the tank perimeter, the percentage of the settlement in the untreated condition that can be tolerated, is established, and consequently the load that can be applied on the original soil. This criterion leads to the equation:

$$(1) \quad \Delta p_s \cdot A_{col} + \Delta p_c (A - A_{col}) = \Delta p \cdot A$$

3. The compression of the sand column will be equal to that of the surrounding softer material:

$$(2) \quad \frac{\bar{s}}{h} = m_{vs} \cdot \Delta p_s = m_{vc} \cdot \Delta p_c$$

4. The horizontal stability of the sand columns is governed by the horizontal support of the surrounding soft strata. The horizontal deformation is reduced by introducing $\lambda_p = 1$ for the load increase Δp_c and $\lambda_{p_c} = tg^2 (45 + \frac{\phi'_c}{2})$ for the clay layer under the influence of the tank pad.

$$(3) \quad \lambda_{as}(\gamma_s \cdot h' + \Delta p_s) - 2c'_s \sqrt{\lambda_{as}} =$$
$$\lambda_{pc}(\gamma_c \cdot h') + 2c'_c \sqrt{\lambda_{pc}} + \lambda_p \cdot \Delta p_c$$

In the formulas (1), (2) and (3) the following symbols have been introduced:

Δp_s	=	pressure increase on sand column (kPa)
Δp_c	=	" " " clayey material (kPa)
Δp	=	" " " due to tank load (kPa)
A_{col}	=	cross-section of sand column (m²)
A	=	area, covered by a sand column (m²)
$\bar{s}$	=	acceptable settlement (m)
h	=	thickness of xompressible layer (m)
m_{vs}	=	compressibility of sand column (kPa)⁻¹
m_{vc}	=	" " " clayey material (kPa)⁻¹
λ_{as}	=	coefficient of active soil pressure in sand
λ_{pc}	=	coefficient of passive soil pressure in clay (consolidated)
λ_p	=	coefficient of passive soil pressure in clay (unconsolidated)

c_s', c_c' = cohesion in sand and clay

γ_s = unit weight of sand (kN/m³)

γ_c = " " " clay (kN/m³)

h' = critical depth of sand column (m)

The depth for which the horizontal stresses are compared, is usually taken as 2 pile diameters below the top of the sand pile in order to be below the zone that is influenced by the constraining effect of the horizontal shear stresses between the top layer and the sand column.
Formula (3) is to be adjusted when the groundwater table influences the soil stresses.

For the centre of the tank the design is governed by the three equations above. For the edge an overall stability analysis is to be added. For this condition usually the residual load Δp_c is introduced only on the untreated soil; the shear resistance of the sand columns is neglected. The weight of the compacted sand layer should be introduced as well.

SOIL DATA

The instrumented foundation in the Rotterdam Ports area was to be built in a reclaimed area (fig. 1). The original groundlevel at 2 m - D.L. was covered with approx. 5 m of material, obtained from maintenance dredging works of the River Meuse, covered again with 1 m of sandy material. This was done approximately 10 years before the construction of the tanks, so consolidation of the material under its own weight was completed, but further loading would lead to considerable settlements.

The groundwater table was 2 m + D.L.
The area was to be excavated to 3 m + D.L. and the compacted tank pad to be placed again to a level, varying between 4,0 m + D.L. and 4,5 m + D.L. The applied load during the water test was 193 kN/m².
The settlements would have been 1,0 - 1,2 m for the tank centre without soil treatment and 0,6 - 0,8 m for the tank perimeter.
The allowable settlements for the tank centre were 0,6 m (60%) and 0,3 - 0,4 m for the edge (50%).

DESIGN

a. On the basis of the available equipment the shaft diameter was selected: D = 0,56 m. (A_{col} = 0,25 m²)

b. Δp_c = 0,6 Δp = 116 kPa (for the tank centre)

c. h = 7,75 m

d. m_{vc} = 7,3 · 10⁻⁴ (kPa)⁻¹ (lab. test results)
   m_{vs} = 0,125 · 10⁻⁴ (empirical value)

e. ϕ_c' = 20° λ_{pc} = 2,04 γ_c = 16,5/6,5 kN/m³
   c_c' = 0

   ϕ_s' = 40° λ_{as} = 0,22 γ_s = 19/11 kN/m³
   c_s' = 0

   h_1' = 2,07 m γ_s = 19 kN/m³ γ_c = 16,5 kN/m³
   h_2' = 0,87 m γ_s = 11 kN/m³ γ_c = 6,5 kN/m³

From (2): 0,125 · 10⁻⁴ · Δp_s = 7,3 · 10⁻⁴ · 116

Δp_s = 6774 kPa

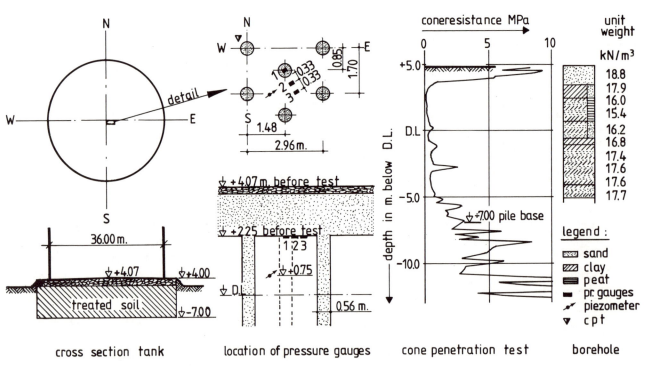

Fig. 1   Soil data and location of instruments

From (3): 0,22 (2,07 x 19 + 0,87 x 11 + Δp_s)

       = 2,04 (1,82 x 19 + 0,25 x 16,5 +

       0,87 x 6,5) + 16

       Δp_s = 890 kPa

With (1): 890 x 0,25 + 116 (A - 0,25) = 193 x A

       A = 2,5 m²

It is shown that the stability criteria lead to a lower load in the sand column than the compression criteria. This means that by a load increase in excess of that in accordance with form (2) the settlement is increasing due to a shear deformation in the sand pile.

Summary Design for the tank centre:

a. A pattern of equilateral triangles is selected with sides of 1,7 m or 1,48 m x 1,7 m (2,5 m²).

b. Pressure increase in the clay due to water testing p_c = 116 kPa.

c. Pressure increase on the sand column due to water testing p_s = 890 kPa.

MEASUREMENTS

In order to improve the knowledge about the reliability of the method of design, a number of pressure gauges was installed on top of the sand columns and in between (fig. 1).
The necessary devices were concentrated underneath the centre of the tank, so that the influence of shear deformations along the edge of the tank could be neglected. Piezometers were installed to record the development of the pore pressures in the various stages.
The piezometer readings are shown in fig. 2.

During a short period of time the pore pressures are excessively high, in fact higher than the total soil stress.
A certain heave (approx. 20% of the volume of sand introduced) was observed. The phenomenon of increased pore pressures and heave during the installation of displacement piles is well known. In the case that the sand columns are to act as drain only and the spacing is wider than in the present case, the pore water dissipation is affected seriously by this effect in combination with a possible remoulding and peripheral smear. For the compaction sand piles the spacing is small in view of the desired bearing capacity of the grid of sand columns, hence the pore water dissipation is a relatively fast process.
The pressures as measured on the piles and in between for one of the instrumented tanks are shown in fig. 3 together with the piezometer results. The maximum pressure on the column is increasing under the influence of the tank load from 140 kPa till 780 kPa or by 640 kPa, and between the columns from 30 kPa till 180 kPa. The pressure height at 0,75 m + D.L. is increasing from 1,25 m + D.L. till 3,5 m + D.L. The balance of loads should ten be

    193 x 2,5 $\overset{\bullet}{\sim}$ α (640 x 0,25 + 150 x 2,25)

  or   483 $\overset{\bullet}{\sim}$ α (160 + 338)

        483 $\overset{\bullet}{\sim}$ α · 498

          α = 0,97

The measured load corresponds very well with the applied load of the water ballast.
A small excess pore pressure is still present at the end of the water ballasting. Further pore water dissipation would have led to an increase of the load on the piles and on the clay,

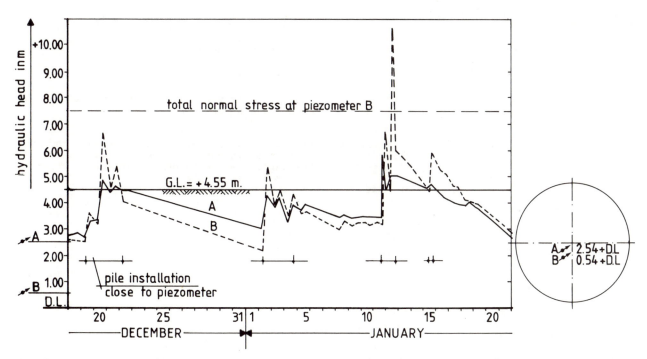

Fig. 2 Piezometer readings during pile installation

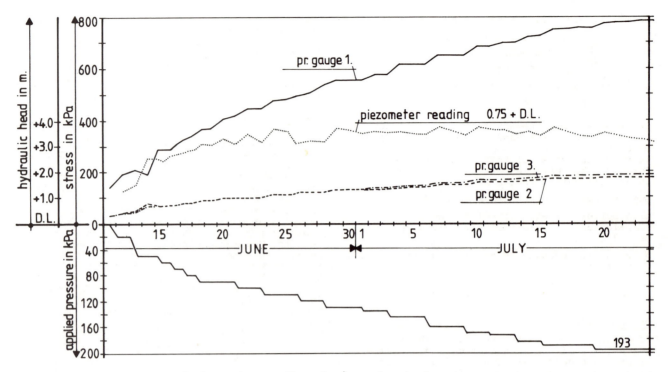

Fig. 3 Pressure gauge and piezometer readings during water test

with the major part on the columns in view of the shape of the load-settlement curve of the clayey material.

The settlement of the tank centre after the water test amounted to 0,62 m.

The additional settlement that would have occurred if the water test would have been continued till more or less full consolidation, is negligible.

DISCUSSIONS OF THE RESULTS

The design of the sand compaction piles resulted in a ratio for

$$\frac{\Delta p_s}{\Delta p_c} = 7,67$$

Actual pressure measurements resulted in a ratio of 4.25. This ratio is considerably lower than the calculated value. The measured settlement is close to the calculated value.

The compressibility of the sand column must be higher than the design value.

$$m_{vs} = \frac{S}{h \cdot \Delta p_s} = \frac{0,62}{7,75 \times 640} = 1,25 \times 10^{-4} \ (kPa)^{-1}$$

For the clay material the calculation can be checked

$$m_{vs} = \frac{S}{h \cdot \Delta p_c} = \frac{0,62}{7,75 \times 150} = 5,33 \times 10^{-3} \ (kPa)^{-1}$$

During the installation of the sand compaction pile the soil around the pile is compacted to a certain extent. According to the observations a heave occurred that corresponded with 20% of the volume of the compacted mud columns. The remaining 80% of the volume was absorbed by the surrounding strata in the shape of a densified cylinder. This observation makes the design more complicated, as it would lead to a load distribution over three separate zones. As an approximation the reduction of m_{vc} can be calculated

$$m_{vc}' = m_{vc} \frac{2,50}{2,50 + 0,8 \times 0,25} = 0,93 \ m_{vc}$$

The design value should then be

$$m_{vc}' = 0,93 \times 5,9 \times 10^{-4} \ (kPa)^{-1}$$

This value is very close to the value that has been found during the measurement

$$(5,33 \times 10^{-4} \ (kPa)^{-1}),$$

particularly in view of the fact that the consolidation is not yet completed at the end of the water testing throughout the full thickness of the clayey strata.

Compaction by blasting in offshore harbour construction
Compactage par explosif dans la construction d'un port en mer

R. CARPENTIER, Dr. ir., Chief Engineer, Belgian Geotechnical Institute, Zwijnaarde, Belgium
P. DE WOLF, ir., Senior Engineer, Ministry of Public Works, Coastal Service, Ostend, Belgium
L. VAN DAMME, ir., Senior Engineer, Ministry of Public Works, Coastal Service, Ostend, Belgium
J. DE ROUCK, ir., Chief Engineer, Harbour and Egg Consultants, Haecon N.V., Ghent, Belgium
A. BERNARD, ir., Project Engineer, T.V. Zeebouw-Zeezand, Knokke-Heist, Belgium

SYNOPSIS   The paper gives a description and the results of in situ densification tests by blasting in the sand foundation layers of the breakwaters of the new outer harbour under construction at Zeebrugge on the Belgian coast.   Use was made of buried charges lowered into the sea-bottom from a small drilling platform.

INTRODUCTION

Since 1976 a new outer harbour is under construction at Zeebrugge on the Belgian coast (Fig.1). The harbour is protected against the rather rough sea conditions of the North Sea by breakwaters of the rubble mound type constructed on a sand foundation. Over large lengths of the breakwaters the bearing capacity of the upper in situ soil layers was insufficient. These layers are dredged and replaced by relatively coarse dumped sea sand. The quality of the dumped sand foundation was evaluated by means of CPT tests performed from small jack-up platforms. In as far as the used evaluation criteria, based on the results of the CPT tests, were not fulfilled, deep compaction of the dumped sand layer was carried out by lowering vibrating probes from a jack-up platform into the ground (De Wolf et al., 1983).

Although deep compaction with a vibrating probe has given satisfactory results, a program was set up to examine the feasibility of in situ densification of the foundation layers in the given offshore circumstances using explosives.

Densification of loose cohesionless deposits by blasting for foundations of dams and other structures was described by Lyman (1942), Kummeneje and Eide (1961), Hall (1962), Wild and Haslam (1962), Prugh (1963), et al.. However the most detailed treatment of the subject was provided by Ivanov (1967, translated to English in 1972) who described extensive Russian experience with surface, deep, and underwater densification on numerous projects. Despite the economic attractiveness of in situ densification using explosives (Mitchell, 1970) very little data on the subject have been published in the technical literature in recent years (Klohn et al., 1981 ; Pilot et al., 1981).

Most of the applications of in situ densification using explosives are situated on land. Only a few publications deal with underwater densification (Ivanov, 1967 ; Dembicki et al., 1980) using charges loaded in water and exploded above the surface of the soil.

In the application of the method of in situ densification by blasting at Zeebrugge, use was made

of buried charges lowered into the sea-bottom from a small drilling platform.

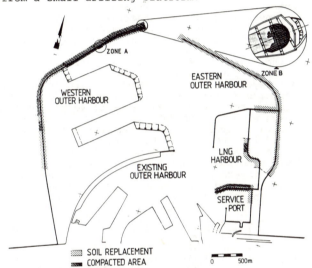

Fig.1 - Lay-out of the new outer harbour at Zeebrugge.

ENVIRONMENTAL CONDITIONS

The blasting program is carried out in the two zones A and B (Fig.1) of the north western breakwater, some 3 to 3.5 km outside the seawall. In zone A the sand foundation layer was dumped up to the level Z - 6.0 and covered with gravel up to the level Z - 5.0. In zone B the sand was dumped up to the level Z - 9.0 and covered with gravel up to the level Z - 8.0.

In the harbour area MLWS is situated at the level Z + 0.32, and MHWS at the level Z + 4.62, thus presenting waterdepths of about 5.5 m to about 12.5 m over the test areas.

At the time of the tests the significant wave height amounted to about 2 m, and the mean water current at mean tide was 1.34 m/s increasing up to 1.6 m/s at high tide in the area of the north western breakwater.

Due to the nature of the sea-bottom the water is charged with fine material and the visibility in the water is nil.

SOIL CONDITIONS

After dredging the top loose sands and soft clays, a 3.5 m (zone B) to 6 m (zone A) thick sand layer was realized by dumping sea sand in the dredged trench. The dumped sand layer was protected against erosion with a 1 m thick dumped gravel layer.

A typical grain size distribution curve of the dumped sand in the test areas is given in Fig.2.

Although special precautions were taken during dredging and dumping, a more or less clayey transitional layer could not completely be avoided at the bottom of the dredged trench (see for instance Figs. 4 and 11).

The underlying natural soil in zone A (Fig.4) was a rather dense sand with a less resistant layer with varying thickness up to about 2 to 3 m at a depth of about 11 m underneath the sea-bottom. In zone B (Fig.11) the underlying natural soil was a medium dense to dense sand with different less resistant inclusions at varying depths.

At the time of the design, shell borings had shown the sandy nature of the underlying natural soil layers. However, a more detailed investigation with continuous undisturbed sampling after blasting revealed the existence of very thin clay lenses with thicknesses of a few mm in the less resistant layer in zone A and in the natural ground in zone B, and which were not distinguished in the earlier performed shell borings. In Fig.2 also some grain size distribution curves of the layers of sand with thin clay lenses are given, showing the more or less influence of the clay lenses on the grain size distribution.

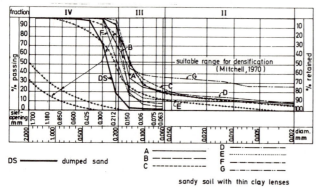

Fig.2 - Grain size distribution curves of the dumped sand in the test areas and of the sand layers with thin clay lenses.

In Fig.2 also the range of soil grain sizes suitable for densification by vibroflotation and according to Mitchell (1970) also by blasting, is represented. From Fig.2 it follows that the grain size distributions of the natural layers containing thin clay lenses are very near to the lower boundary of suitability for densification by blasting. However, the grain size distribution of the dumped sand is completely situated in the suitable range.

DESIGN OF THE BLASTING PROGRAM

A program was set up to examine the feasibility of densification by blasting of the dumped sand layer and part of the underlying natural soil in the given offshore conditions. The total thickness of layer taken into consideration amounted to about 14 m in zone A and about 11 m in zone B.

As suggested by Ivanov (1980) for considerable thickness of layer, the technique of layer by layer structure destruction was chosen, considering separately the dumped sand layer and part of the underlying natural soil layer.

Ivanov (1967 ; 1980) presents empirical relationships for single concentrated charges relating size of charge, depth of charge and spacing of blast holes based on extensive field and laboratory test data. However, no clear information is presented in the literature about size and depth of two concentrated charges placed at different depths in the same blast hole.

The empirical relationships of Ivanov were used as guidelines in preparing the blasting program and resulted in selecting the basic parameters for the upper charges in the blast holes : size of charge, depth of charge and grid spacing.

For the lower charge in a blast hole, about the same size as for the upper charge was chosen. The depth of the lower charge was selected considering that the upper layer was liquefied by the upper charge and thus could be neglected when the lower charge was detonated ; in this reasoning the lower charge was detonated within one to two seconds after the detonation of the upper charge.

The sequence of blasting was planned bearing in mind that successive blasts are more effective than a single large one or several small ones detonated simultaneously (Hall, 1962 ; Prugh, 1963 ; Mitchell, 1970). For the time interval between successive blasts at least 4 hours was chosen as suggested by several authors (Hall, 1962 ; de Groot and Bakker, 1971).

The blasting program was carried out in two stages. Stage 1 was a test stage and consisted of a grid of 25 blast holes over an area approximately 1540 meters square to confirm : the size and depth of the charges, the grid spacing, the amount of densification, the feasibility of the method in the given offshore conditions.

The Stage 1 test blasting program confirmed that the choice of the parameters was suitable for soil and environmental conditions at this site and consequently the same rules were used for the Stage 2 blasting program which was the production stage.

SETUP OF CHARGES

Explosive

A high explosive "Blastogel" with a density of 1.4 kg/dm³, primarily composed of nitroglycerine (50-60 %) and containing no ammonium nitrate was used. This explosive has initially a good water resistance but deteriorates under water in about one month. Blastogel has an equivalence factor of 1.0915 with regard to TNT. Blastogel was delivered in cylindrical blocks Ø 85 mm of 5 kg mass.

Firing system

As the electrical firing system and the use of detonating cord were excluded for under water blasting, the non electrical firing system NONEL was chosen, being waterresistant and presenting sufficient strength against water currents and accidental pull.

Charges

The upper and lower charges of one vertical were prefabricated on the deck of the drilling platform. A scheme of the prefabricated charges is given in Fig.3.

Circuit

For sake of security each charge was fitted with two detonators NONEL with suitable delay. The four NONEL tubes of the upper and lower charges of one blast hole were connected together above the waterlevel with the NONEL tubes of the charges placed in other boreholes of the same blasting series. An electric detonator was then coupled to the bundle of NONEL tubes and was detonated from a blasting initiator placed on the deck of the drilling platform.

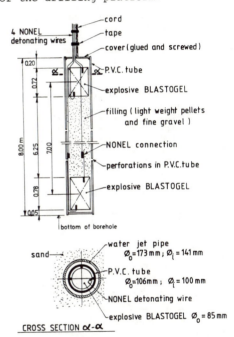

Fig.3 - Prefabricated couple of charges in zone A.

STAGE 1 TEST BLASTING PROGRAM

The test blasting program was carried out directly in the foundation layers of the north western breakwater (zone A in Fig.1).

The total test area of 81 x 38 m^2 was divided into two squares of 40.5 x 38 m^2, the first one serving as a trial area for a first choice of the blasting parameters and to obtain practical experience with the execution procedure in the given offshore circumstances, the second one serving for the eventual adaptation of the blasting parameters.

The subsoil conditions before blasting were obtained from CPT tests. Fig.4 shows a typical subsoil profile at the Stage 1 test site.

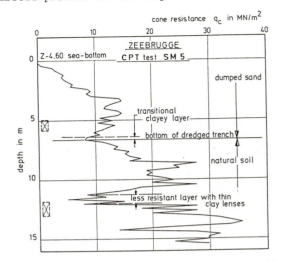

Fig.4 - Typical CPT test in zone A before blasting.

The lay-out for the Stage 1 blasting test program is shown in Fig.5. It contains 25 blast holes in a square grid of 7.5 m side, divided in 4 successive blast series as indicated in Fig.5. It was planned to make and charge the holes of each series after blasting the foregoing series.

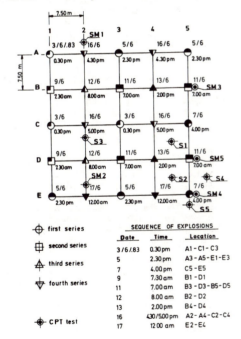

Fig.5 - Lay-out for the Stage 1 blasting test program.

The explosive charges were placed at depths of 5 m and 12 m below the sea-bottom in 173 mm diameter holes.

In blast series 1 and 2 an upper charge of 5.5 kg of Blastogel and a lower charge of 6.0 kg of Blastogel were used. In series 3 and 4 both upper and lower charges were increased with 0.5 kg of Blastogel to take into account an increase in density caused by the former blast series.

In the Stage 1 blasting program two jetting rigs were used on the drilling platform for making the charge holes. The water jet pipe served also as a casing and held the hole open while the charge was placed. Each charge, prepared on the deck of the drilling platform, was lowered into the casing by its own weight down to the bottom of the jetted hole. The casing was then withdrawn and the hole was not backfilled above the upper charge.

Blast series 1 consisted of 9 blast holes to be jointly detonated. However, already after execution of four holes it revealed that it was impossible to keep the installed NONEL tubes intact due to the strong changing currents and the movements of the drilling platform over the test site. It therefore was decided to make and blast the holes in groups of maximum four holes of the same series. The final sequence of blasting is indicated in Fig.5.

In the Stage 1 test the total soil volume of $40.5 \times 38 \times 14 = 21.546$ m^3 was improved by detonating 297.5 kg of Blastogel, or 13.8 g of Blastogel per m^3 of soil.

An attempt was made to measure the settlements of the sea-bottom after each blast series. However this had to be disregarded due to several practical reasons (lack of visibility in the water, rough sea conditions, out of plumb of the settlement stakes by the blasting or by pushes of the spuds of the drilling platform).

No pore pressure readings were made. Observations of small geysers of water and gas could only be made at the water surface.

As an indirect method of assessing the soil improvement after blasting a number of CPT tests were performed to estimate the increase in density of the sand after each blast series.

STAGE 1 BLASTING RESULTS

Before starting the blasting program a series of 5 CPT tests (prefix SM) was performed. At different intermediate stages a total of 4 CPT tests was performed. A few days after the last detonations a series of 5 CPT tests (prefix S) was performed. The locations of all CPT tests SM and S in the test area are given in Fig.5.

The virgin CPT tests SM showed comparable results although with some local differences from one vertical to another. For comparison purposes the boundaries of the minimum and maximum cone resistances measured in the five tests SM are represented in Fig.6 with the bottom of the dredged trench as a reference line.

The CPT tests S1 to S5 are performed from the fifth day after the last blasting. Taking into account the location of the tests (Fig.5), the results are compared in Figs. 7 and 8. In Fig.7 the maximum and minimum cone resistances of the four tests S1, S2, S4 and S5 are compared with the results of the nearby virgin tests SM 4 and SM 5. In Fig.8 the maximum and minimum cone resistances of all tests S1 to S5 are compared

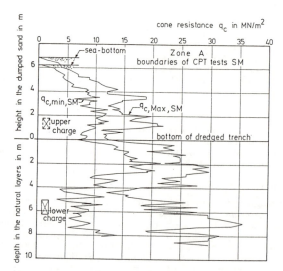

Fig.6 – Boundaries of minimum and maximum cone resistances measured in 5 CPT tests in zone A before blasting.

with the minimum and maximum cone resistances of all virgin tests SM 1 to SM 5.

From Fig.8 it can be stated that in the dumped sand layer the minimum cone resistances after blasting are situated between the minimum and maximum cone resistances of the virgin tests, while the maximum cone resistances after blasting are higher than the maximum cone resistances of the virgin tests. From Fig.7 it can be stated that in the dumped sand layer the minimum cone resistances after blasting are situated in the same range as the cone resistances of the virgin tests SM 4 and SM 5, but that the maximum cone resistances after blasting are much higher.

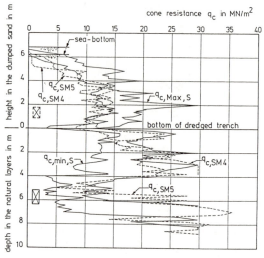

Fig.7 – Comparison between minimum and maximum cone resistances of CPT tests S1, S2, S4 and S5 after blasting, and CPT tests SM4 and SM5 before blasting.

From Fig.7 it can be stated that for the natural soil layers the maximum cone resistances after blasting are in the same range as the maximum cone resistances of the virgin tests. The minimum cone resistances after blasting however, are

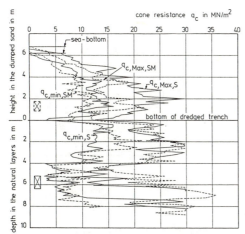

Fig.8 - Comparison between min. and max. cone resistances of tests S1 to S5 after blasting, and min. and max. cone resistances of tests SM1 to SM5 before blasting.

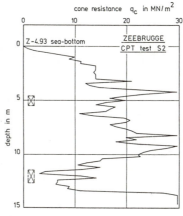

Fig.9 - Results of CPT test S2 in zone A after blasting.

much lower. It must however be remarked that test SM4 reached only a few metres into the natural soil layers. From Fig.8 it can be concluded that the minimum cone resistances after blasting are only localy lower than the minimum cone resistances in the virgin tests which can be due to local differences from one vertical to another.

The following conclusions were drawn from the results of the CPT tests after blasting
- Although already rather high cone resistances were measured in the dumped sand layer before blasting, still higher cone resistances were obtained by blasting ;
- The results of an intermediate CPT test performed in the immediate vicinity of a blast hole one hour after detonation confirmed that a liquefied zone was created around the blast hole ;
- Intermediate CPT tests indicated that even within a period of at least 18 hours after detonation the influence of the blasting was still noticeable in the natural soil layer with thin clay lenses. Control tests thus have to be performed after sufficient time after blasting.
- The results of CPT tests S1 to S5 performed from the fifth day after blasting do not indicate a marked influence on the cone resistances in the natural soil layers. Even the minimum cone resistances remained unchanged which is to be attributed to the influence of the thin clay lenses ;
- In general a more homogeneous cone resistance diagram than in the virgin tests was obtained after blasting (see for instance the results of tests S2 in Fig.9 and SM5 in Fig.4).

STAGE 2 BLASTING PROGRAM

The stage 2 blasting program was carried out in the foundation layers at the extremity of the north western breakwater (zone B in Fig.1) having in view a high production rate of in situ densification by blasting. The jack-up platform was equiped with three jetting rigs and the platform was moved in parallel lanes in order to minimize handling of the platform anchors.

The charge holes are jetted in parallel lines at distances of 7.5 m and the explosive charges are placed at depths of 4.5 m and 9.0 m below the sea-

bottom. Blasting is executed in a triangular pattern, the charges at the corners of one triangle are detonated at least four hours after detonation of the charges of the adjacent triangle. The principle of the arrangement for Stage 2 blasting is shown in Fig.10. In a first pass of the platform in one lane the charges of triangles i-1,i, i+1,... are detonated consecutively ; the charges of triangles j-1, j, j+1,... are detonated consecutively in a second pass of the platform in the same lane. In the first pass an upper charge of 4.0 kg Blastogel and a lower charge of 5.0 kg of Blastogel were used. In the second pass both upper and lower charges were increased with 0.5 kg of Blastogel. After all charges of one lane were detonated, the platform was moved to the adjacent lane. In this way the same volume of soil was influenced by different blasts at different times.

By working continuous shifts, twenty fours a day and seven days a week a total surface area of about 14 000 m^2 was compacted over a period of fifteen days. Compaction was carried out over a thickness of layer of about 11 m using about 15.3 g of Blastogel per m^3 of soil. In the compacted area 242 borings with a total length of 2180 m were carried out in water depths varying between about 8.5 m and 12.5 m. 2300 kg of explosives were detonated.

No pore pressure readings were made and no settlements were measured.

The increase in density of the sand after blasting was evaluated by performing a number of CPT tests from the jack-up platform.

STAGE 2 BLASTING RESULTS

Before starting the blast program, two CPT tests D62 and D63, shown in Fig.11, are performed.

After completion of the whole blasting program over an area of 13.612 m^2, 4 CPT tests numbered S10 to S13 are performed. In Fig.12 the boundaries of the maximum and minimum cone resistances of these tests are compared with the results of the two virgin tests D62 and D63. The tests after blasting indicate a rather high increase of the cone resistances in the dumped sand layer. In the underlying natural layer also the maximum measured values are somewhat higher after blasting.

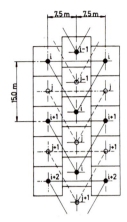 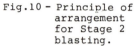

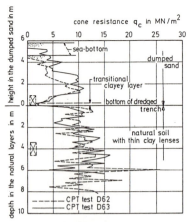

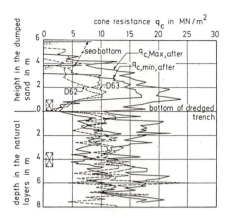

Fig.10 - Principle of arrangement for Stage 2 blasting.

Fig.11 - CPT tests D62 and D63 in zone B before blasting.

Fig.12 - Min. and max. q_c values of tests S10 to S13 after blasting with tests D62 and D63 before blasting.

However, above the level of the lower charge, the minimum cone resistances in the tests S10 to S13 after blasting are of the same magnitude as the minimum cone resistances in the virgin tests D62 and D63. As the receding peaks in the CPT diagrams in the natural soil layer are caused by thin clay lenses, it can be concluded that the existence of thin clay lenses has a great influence on the final result of an in situ densification by blasting.

CONCLUSIONS

The in situ densification of rather loose, saturated, granular soils by the use of explosives has provided an effective and economical means of improving the properties of the deposit in the given offshore conditions.

The presence of thin clay lenses has an important influence on the efficiency of the blasting technique.

Although data are available (Ivanov 1967 ; 1980) to guide the engineer in planning an in situ densification program by blasting, a prediction of the in situ behaviour of loose granular deposits when treated by blasting is difficult. A full scale field test is necessary to determine the design parameters : area of influence, degree of densification, rate of pore pressure dissipation, size of charge and minimum blast hole spacing required.

For the moment insufficient data are available for the technique of layer by layer structure destruction and further experience in this field has to be gathered.

Densification by blasting has given satisfactory results in the dumped sand layer at Zeebrugge although a mean cone resistance of 15 MN/m^2 was demanded by the Owner.

The blasting technique has been economically competitive with the compaction technique by vibrating probes in the given offshore conditions at Zeebrugge.

REFERENCES

de Groot, W., and Bakker, J.G. (1971). An investigation for compaction with explosions (in Dutch). LGM-mededelingen (14), 3, 65-89.

Dembicki, E., Kisielowa, N., Nowakowski, H., and Osiecimski, R. (1980). Compactage des fonds marins sableux à l'explosif. Proc. Int. Conf. on Compaction, 1, 301-305, Paris.

De Wolf, P., Carpentier, R., Allaert, J., and De Rouck, J., (1983). Ground improvement for the construction of the new outer harbour at Zeebrugge, Belgium, Proc. 8th ECSMFE, 2, 827-832, Helsinki.

Hall, C.E. (1962). Compacting a dam foundation by blasting. ASCE J. Soil Mech. and Found. Div. (88), SM3, 33-51.

Ivanov, P.L. (1967). Compaction of noncohesive soils by explosions. Translated from Russian in 1972. U.S. Dept. of Commerce TT70-57221.

Ivanov, P.L. (1980). Consolidation of saturated soils by explosions. Proc. Int. Conf. on Compaction, 1, 331-337, Paris.

Klohn, E.J., Garga, V.K., and Shukin, W. (1981). Densification of sand tailings by blasting. Proc. 10th ICSMFE, 3, 725-730, Stockholm.

Kummeneje, O., and Eide, O. (1961). Investigation of loose sand deposits by blasting. Proc. 5th ICSMFE, 1, 491-497, Paris.

Lyman, A.K.B. (1942). Compaction of cohesionless foundation soils by explosives. ASCE Transactions (107), 1330-1348.

Mitchell, J.K. (1970). In-place treatment of foundation soils. ASCE J. Soil Mech. and Found. Div. (96), SM1, 73-110.

Pilot, G., Colas des Francs, E., Puntous, R., and Queyroi, D. (1981). Compactage par explosif d'un remblai hydraulique. Proc. 10th ICSMFE, 3, 757-760, Stockholm.

Prugh, B.J. (1963). Densification of soils by explosive vibrations. ASCE J. Constr. Div. (89), CO1, 79-100.

Wild, P.A., and Haslam, E.F. (1962). Towers and foundations for project EHV. ASCE J. Power Div. (88), PO2, 69-111.

Chemical grouting in Taipei Basin

L'injection de produits chimiques pour le Bassin de Taipei

BENJAMIN P. C. CHI, Chief Engineer, Ret-Ser Engineering Agency, Taipei, Taiwan
JIANN-SHI YANG, Chief, R&D Section, Office of the Chief Engineer, Taiwan

SYNOPSIS   For the construction of the sewage mains in Taipei City, modern grouting techniques, such as co-axial double rod, Tube-a-Manchette, and jet grouting methods, are widely used to
supplement the excavation of shield tunnelling. By a systematic chemical grouting program, the
seepage of underground water is reduced and the cohesion of the soil is improved, permitting the
successful execution of the shield tunnelling method. The soil properties prior to and after
grouting are studied both in the laboratory test and the in-situ test. One innovative chemical
grouting technique that was developed through these studied by the research program also is
discussed in the paper.

INTRODUCTION

Taipei City is located on alluvium deposits in
former riverbeds, that is, poor stratified subsoil constituted by a complicated formation of
clay, silt, sand, rotten wood and other material;
and the ground water table is high. Thus, soil
stabilization constitutes one of the most important problems for underground construction.

To meet the needs of rising prosperity, the municipal government of Taipei decided to extend
its sewage main system. The Min Tsu Road sewage main section is from the De Hwa Sewage
Treatment Plant to the intersection of Min Tsu
Road and Sung Chiang Road. (Fig. 1) The total
length is 2558m. The sewer tunnel has an outer
diameter of 4.5m and an inner diameter of 3.6m
and is 9m in average, below the ground level.
The tunnel is excavated by two closed type mechanical shields with compressed air.

From the site investigation, the strata under-

neath the Min Tsu Road are very complicated.
Concerned about the air leakage of the compressed air, settlement caused by dewatering, and the
safety of neighboring structures, many engineers
see chemical grouting as the only solution to
providing watertightness and stability of the
existing soil. Along the route, 15 places were
evaluated in order to be grouted by three grouting techniques: (1) a flash-setting method with
co-axial double rod, (2) a slow-setting method
with Tube-a-Manchette, and (3) a jet grouting
method with ultra high pressure.

GEOLOGICAL CONDITION

The geological investigation and test of this
project included: (1) Bore hole drilling: 37
bore holes spaced 100m per hole. (2) 21 sets of
in-situ permeability tests. (3) 3 sets of air
permeability tests. The investigation and test
results were as follows:

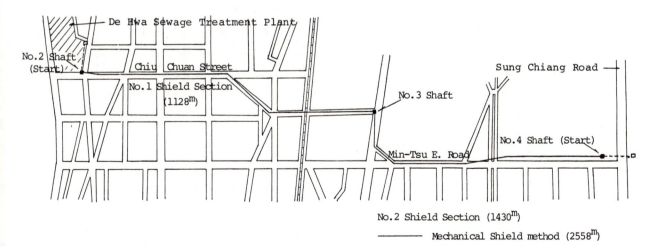

Fig. 1 Layout of Sewerage Mains at Min Tsu Road Section, Taipei

1. Soil condition : soil passed through in this project can be divided into five layers.

   1st layer : 2-7m backfill.
   2nd layer : 2-3m yellowish-brown, soft, silty clay.
   3rd layer : 1-2m greyish-brown, soft, clayey silt.
   4th layer : 5-10m loose-to-medium, grey, silty sand with sandy silt or silty clay.
   5th layer : 5m medium-to-dense, grey, sandy silt and clayey silt.

2. ground water level : 0.9-4.3m below ground surface.

3. test result :

   (1) in-situ permeability coefficient:
       2.61×10^{-4} - 2.67×10^{-2} cm/sec
   (2) in-situ air permeability coefficient:
       12.2 - 2730×10^{-3} cm/sec
       leakage coefficient: 1.02 - 1.3
   (3) N=1-30, generally about 10
   (4) $c=0-0.26$ kg/cm^2, $\phi=10.5°-43°$
   (5) $q_u=0.08-1.82$ kg/cm^2
   (6) $m_v=5.0 \times 10^{-4}$ - 1.63×10^{-1} cm^2/kg
       $C_v=4.0 \times 10^{-4}$ - 1.4×10^{-3} cm^2/sec
   (7) $c_{cu}=0-1.9$ kg/cm^2, $\phi_{cu}=9°-14°$
   (8) laboratory permeability coefficient:
       2.78×10^{-7} - 3.45×10^{-3} cm/sec

APPLICATION OF FLASH-SETTING METHOD

The flash-setting grouting method with a co-axial double rod was developed in Japan. In Taiwan, LAG (Limited Area Grouting) and DDS (Double-tube Drilling Seepage) are used. In this project, the grouting work is shown underneath by data:

(A) Grout Mixing Ratio

solution A (liter)		solution B (liter)		
silicate 100	total 200	inorganic hardening agent	20-22kg	total 200
water 100		water	balance	

(B) Pumping Design

pumping ratio	pumping pressure	discharge rate
< 40%	3-5kg/cm^2	< 20 1/min

(C) Pattern of Grouting Holes

   The spacing of drilling holes is 0.8-1.0m and the arrangement is rectangular in shape.

(D) Grouting Control

   (1) recording: Sophisticated electronics pressure and flow measuring and recording units are adopted to record the grouting result for analysis.
   (2) tracing: Phenolphthalein solution is sprayed on the excavation face to measure the penetration of silicate grout.

From the execution of shield tunnelling, the flash-setting grouting technique has proven satisfactory.

APPLICATION OF SLOW-SETTING GROUTING METHOD WITH TUBE-A-MANCHETTE

In 1982, the contractor, RSEA decided to use Tube-a-Manchette to grout an area which contained 10 kinds of underground telephone, power, water supply, and gas lines in three dimension directions and thus did not permit the use of the co-axial double rod grouting method.

(A) Grout Mixing Ratio

type of grout	material	mixing ratio
sleeve grout	bentonite	25-35 kg/m^3
and	portland cement	250-350 kg/cm^3
B/C grout	water	balance
chemical	silicate	200-250 1/m^3
	hardener 600 C or E	50-55 1/m^3
grout	water	balance

(B) Execution of the Work

Drilling for Tube-a-Manchette is performed by Atlas Copco 601-00 drilling rig with OD72 drilling bit and 3.5in casing tube. The spacing of drilling holes is 1.25-1.3m in square pattern. For a critical area, inclined guide tubes are installed precisely before drilling. The spacing of the bottom of sleeve tubes must not exceed 1.2m. Under these conditions, the grouting result can be effectively obtained. The setting time of chemical grout is limited to 40-60min. The effectiveness of grouting is mainly controlled by volume, but sometimes by pressure. To prevent the sleeve pipe from being an obstacle when the shield machine bores through the grouted area, a specially designed electric cutting device was developed to cut the PVC sleeve pipe into a 10cm long piece.

(C) Pumping Design

type of grout	pumping ratio	pumping pressure	discharge rate
B/C grout	5-10%	5-10 kg/cm^2	350 1/hr
chemical grout	40-15%	5-25 kg/cm^2	250 1/hr

(D) Grout Tracing

Fluorescence photographs are taken to observe the penetration route of silicate gel.

APPLICATION OF JET GROUTING METHOD WITH ULTRA HIGH PRESSURE

For shield tunnelling under the Hsin Sheng N. Road sewage channel, the Japanese JSP (Jumbo Special Pile) method was used to strength the soil. The pressure was 180-220kg/cm^2 and the effective diameter of JSP grouting was 65-80cm.

The mixing ratio of the grout was as follows:

ratio (liter)			ratio (liter)	
silicate	250	total	250	total
water	250	500	250	500
cement	400kg	total	150kg	total
bentonite	—	500	60kg	500
water	374		437	

The result of jet grouting showed the technique is not suitable for the shield tunnelling method, although the jet grouting section was safely excavated by the shield machines.

NEW ACCELERATING AGENT FOR HARDENER 600

Because of the tight schedule for shield tunnelling and executing the pioneer test of the new grouting technique, an inorganic, non-toxic, liquid accelerating agent was developed. When the accelerating agent is added to Hardener 600, it can shorten the setting time of silicate from over ten minutes to several seconds. The phenomenon of syneresis of the gel is the same as that of the gel without the accelerating agent. The new agent is pumped by DDS or LAG equipment. The mixing ratio of the grout is:

solution B (liter)	accelerating agent	6.5	8	
	Hardener 600	16	16	total 200
	water	balance		
solution A (liter)	silicate	100		total 200
	water	100		
setting time (sec.)		8-10	5-6	

Both lab test and field use have proven that the properties of the new accelerating agent are stable and reliable.

MODIFIED TIP ARRANGEMENT

The tip arrangement is a very important end device of flash-setting grouting method from which two solutions are mixed and the grout is pumped out into the ground. From experience, the steel ball type tip arrangement of DDS equipment has four disadvantages: (1) the grout is often blocked at the tip, causing a cleaning problem; (2) the installation of tip arrangement is not convenient; (3) after installation the steel ball, the discharge rate is decreased; and (4) sometimes the mixing of two solutions at the mixing chamber of the tip arrangement is not complete, and thus the grouting effect is not satisfied. After continuous improvement, a modified tip arrangement was developed, and has proven satisfactory.(Fig.2)

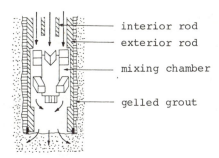

- interior rod
- exterior rod
- mixing chamber
- gelled grout

Fig.2 Modified Tip Arrangement

DEVELOPMENT OF TWO-STEP GROUTING METHOD

Through this project, we have found some problems that need to be solved for the Tube-a-Manchette method and flash-setting method:

(A) Disadvantages of Tube-a-Manchette

(1) It is very expensive and complicated.

(2) If the construction procedure can not be done continuously and simultaneously, especially in the crowded city where the job site has limited space, the high frequency of interruption of grouting work always raises the cost.

(3) Dilution and diffusion of grout may occur where underground flow water is existed.

(4) The cutting procedure of the manchette tube created an extra cost to the contractor.

(5) It is not suitable for small or emergency grouting work.

(B) Disadvantages of Flash-Setting

(1) A satisfactory drilling pattern is difficult to arrange for the area where complicated underground pipelines exist especially where the inclined drilling hole is required; therefore, the grouting results can not be effectively controlled.

(2) The phenomenon of syneresis of the inorganic grout is much more serious than that of the gel of Hardener 600, and the duration of the inorganic gel is much shorter. The compressive strength of the Hardener 600 gel is stronger than that of the flash-setting gel.

(3) Because of the short gelling time of flash-setting, the grout cannot fully penetrate the subsoil and the effect of reducing permeability is not achieved.

In order to overcome the disadvantages of both methods, the method of "two-step grouting" was initiated,(Fig.3) which consists of co-axial double rod grouting equipment with the modified tip arrangement combined with Hardener 600 and the new accelerating agent. The grouting procedure is as follow:

(1) The LW grout is pumped to fill the large voids of the subsoil.

(2) The flash-setting grout made from Hardener 600 and the new accelerating agent is pumped to become "chemical packer."

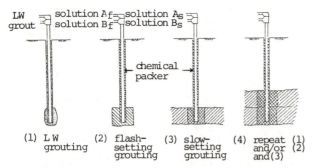

Fig.3 Operation Procedure of Two-Step
       Grouting Method

(3) The slow-setting grout by Hardener 600 is pumped to achieve the purpose of homogeneous penetration grouting.

(4) The operation procedure is repeated by (1) and/or (2) and (3) step by step, so that the subsoil is completely improved by grouting. If the soil condition is not suitable for LW grout, procedure (1) is not adopted. Step (2) and step (3) act as the main role of this technique and thus called "two-step grouting."

The ingredients of the chemical grout of "two-step grouting" are:

type of grout	solution A	solution B	setting time
flash-setting	solution A_f	solution B_f	1-60 sec.
	silicate	Hardener 600	
	water	accelerating agent	
slow-setting	solution A_s	solution B_s	1-60 min.
	silicate	Hardener 600	
	water		

Because successful grouting still depends largely on engineering experience, a large number of in-situ grouting tests for "two-step grouting" have been taken to study the new method. From the data observed, the results seem positive.

CONCLUSION

From the grouting work of Min Tsu Road, Taipei, much experience has been acquired by the engineers. The two-step grouting method with effective grouting control by modern electronic instruments has proven to be a good solution to alluvium grouting work. Developing simple operated grouting equipment and versatile chemicals, as the ones described here, is the responsibility of professional grouting engineers.

REFERENCES

Hoshiya, M. et al.(1982). A New Grouting Material of Non-Alkaline Silica Sol. Proc. of the Conference on Grouting in Geotech Eng. 378-393, New Orleans.

Stabilization of creeping slopes by dowels

Stabilisation des pentes en état de fluage par des goujons

G. GUDEHUS, Professor of Civil Engineering, Institute of Soil Mechanics and Rock Mechanics, University of Karlsruhe, FRG
W. SCHWARZ, Research Associate, Institute of Soil Mechanics and Rock Mechanics, University of Karlsruhe, FRG

SYNOPSIS   Creeping slopes in stiff clay can be stabilized by using dowels made of concrete or steel. The stabilization results in a reduction of the creep rate to a level which is harmless to superstructures. The dowels transmit the stabilizing force from the substratum to the creeping soil. The lateral load on the dowels is assumed to increase linearly up to a maximum value with the displacement relative to the surrounding soil. The design of the stabilization is carried out assuming the dowels as elastic beams with a constant coefficient of lateral subgrade reaction.

INTRODUCTION

In a creeping slope the soil moves slowly downhill. Typical creep velocities are from 0.1 mm per month to 5 cm per month. Usually the ground-water table lies near the surface. The creep velocity decreases and sometimes the creep nearly stops with lowering of the ground-water table. When the water table is raised, creeping begins again. Even small cuts or fills can induce movement of a slope.

Structures on a creeping slope will be influenced by this movement to some extent. A flexible structure, for example an asphalt road, a pipe or a cable, will be unable to resist the movement and will be damaged in due course. In the case of a stiff or inflexible foundation, as e.g. an anchored diaphragm wall or a deeply founded abutment, the soil movement will be slowed down until the build-up of earth pressure due to the creeping soil destroys the structure. Structures of moderate stiffness, as e.g. dwelling-houses, follow the movement while getting increasing cracks.

Usually a creeping slope consists of nearly saturated, stiff clay to a depth of 5 to 15 m - or even deeper. In the transition zone (the thin shear zone) between the moving soil and the stable layer, the water content is usually higher than in the surrounding soil. Often the clay is fissured and therefore the permeability is quite uneven.

In southern Germany creeping slopes are very common. Fig. 1 shows the morphology of a typical creeping slope; the trees are bent and the ground surface is ruckled. From experience people have known about the difficulties in these regions and have avoided to build structures on creeping slopes. Today, however, we often want to construct buildings, roads, and railways in such places. For this to be feasible, geotechnical engineers must provide solutions that are safe, acceptable environmentally, and economic.

Many structures have had to be abandoned because slope movement was ignored. On the other hand it usually requires enormous strength - and therefore high cost - to stabilize a creeping slope totally. In this context stabilization of a creeping slope means reducing the velocity to

Fig.1   Typical creeping slope

a level which is harmless to structures. Structures on stabilized slopes must be designed so that the remaining movement will not damage them.

Stabilizing the slope by reducing the angle of the slope can be successful but this is not feasible in most cases. Even a deep drainage does not work in all cases. If a slope is stabilized by drainage and the ground-water table sinks quickly, then the vegetation may be damaged. On the other hand, if the drainage works too slowly, the drains will be damaged by the soil movement; in addition the drains must have a high capacity and they may become sealed by the soil. Electrochemical methods - such as electric osmosis, kataphoresis and grouting - have sometimes been applied succesfully, but their action is not well understood and their design needs some further research and development.

Reinforcement by inserting piles increases the mechanical strength of a slope. If the prevailing loading of the piles is transverse shearing strength, this technique is called dowelling.

Soil dowelling is a rather old invention. In the last 10 years dowels of various diameters and materials have been used. In some cases they have been successful, and in other cases they have not (Sommer 1978, Wichter & Gudehus 1983, Fukuoka 1977).

At the Chair of Soil Mechanics and Foundation Engineering of Karlsruhe University a new design method for dowelling has been devised. The method is briefly outlined in this paper while the formulas, diagrams, and programs can be found in other publications (Schwarz 1984). The method has been tested by means of large scale field tests and by back-calculations. As a result, dowels can now be designed more economically and with greater safety. However, the development of this method is still in progress and further research is needed.

DESIGN METHOD

Considering the creeping slope as a rigid body of weight W which slides on an inclined surface (s. Fig. 2) we obtain the shear force T as

$$T = W\sin\beta \qquad (1)$$

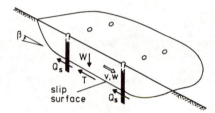

Fig. 2   Creeping slope with dowels

The force T is decreased by the forces Q_S carried by the dowels, and consequently the creep velocity is decreased from v_O to v_1. The latter reduction follows from the assumption that soil is a viscous fluid with a strongly non-linear viscosity which obeys Leinenkugel's (1976) law:

$$T_1 = T_O(1 + I_v \ln (v_1/v_O)) \qquad (2)$$

The viscosity index I_v has values between 0.01 and 0.06 and can be obtained from triaxial tests with variable rates of deformation. Using equ.2 one obtains the number of dowels as

$$n_D = -I_v \ln(v_O/v_1) W\sin\beta/Q_S \qquad (3)$$

When designing the stabilization the values I_v and $W\sin\beta$ are given whereas the ratio v_O/v_1 must be chosen according to the requirements of the structures on the slope. The objective is now to determine the resulting dowel force $n_D Q_S$ for the most economical and safe stabilizing effect. That means:

- the dowels should not be damaged during the design life of the structure. On the other hand they need not be stronger than necessary

- the resisting load from the dowels should be introduced into the soil as early as possible.

The lateral load H depends on the relative displacement u−w as shown in Fig. 3.

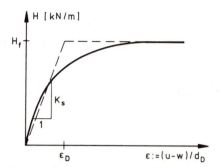

Fig. 3   Load-displacement diagram between dowel and soil

Experiments have shown that the load-displacement curve of Fig. 4 can be approximated by the two dashed straight lines. The maximum lateral load H_f and the coefficient of subgrade reaction K_s are given by the following equations (Gudehus, 1984):

$$H_f \approx 5c_u d_D \qquad (5)$$

$$K_s \approx 5c_u/\varepsilon_D \qquad (6)$$

where c_u is the undrained cohesion, d_D is the pile diameter and ε_D a characteristic strain (usually between 0.02 to 0.10) for the soil being considered. The values of c_u and ε_D can be obtained either from special investigations or from experience of similar situations. Different values occur above and below the slip surface.

To describe the mechanical behavior of a dowel, it is necessary to know the lengths h_o and h_u (above and below the slip surface), the bending stiffness $E_D I_D$ and the ultimate bending moment M_T. The relationship between the displacement w and the horizontal load H is given by the following differential equation:

$$E_D I_D u^{IV} = H \qquad (7)$$

It is assumed that the displacement inside the creeping part of the slope is constant (i.e. it behaves as a rigid body). Now it is useful to introduce the so-called elastic lengths above (o) and below (u) the shear zone:

$$l_{o,u} = \sqrt[4]{\frac{4 E_D I_D}{(K_s)_{o,u}}} \qquad (8)$$

Depending on whether the ultimate load H_f is reached or not the general solutions of equ. (7) are given by:

$$u = C_{1i} + C_{2i} z + C_{3i} z^2 + C_{4i} z^3 - \frac{H_f}{24 E_D I_D} z^4 \qquad (9)$$

and

$$u = \cosh \frac{z}{l} (C_{5i} \sin \frac{z}{l} + C_{6i} \cos \frac{z}{l})$$
$$+ \sinh \frac{z}{l}(C_{7i} \cos \frac{z}{l} + C_{8i} \sin \frac{z}{l}) + \hat{w} \qquad (10)$$

respectively.

The up to 24 constants C_{ij} are determined from the boundary and continuity conditions by solving a system of linear equations. The following equations define $\hat{w}$ and l:

$$\hat{w} = \begin{cases} w & \text{for} \quad O \leq z \leq h_o \\ O & \text{for} \quad z > h_o \end{cases}$$

$$l = \begin{cases} l_o & \text{for} \quad O \leq z \leq h_o \\ l_u & \text{for} \quad z > h_o \end{cases} \qquad (11)$$

The ranges for the equations stated above are determined iteratively.

Three special cases can be distinguished:

<u>Big dowels</u>: For high values of d_D it usually turns out that h_o/l_o and h_u/l_u are both less than 1. The example of Fig. 4 shows that the displacement of the pile is mainly tilting rather than bending. The lateral pressure on the upper and lower parts of the dowel is almost linearly distributed in accordance with the assumption of a linearly elastic subgrade. Usually, the ultimate lateral pressure and the ultimate bending moment are not reached because there is not enough relative displacement w-u during lifetime of the dowel. Therefore the big dowel is not economic. An example of this case (3 m dowels) is given in the paper of Sommer (1978).

The behaviour of <u>small dowels</u> is normally found when $h_o/l_o > 3$, and $h_u/l_u > 3$. As shown in Fig. 4 a small dowel is deflected into an S-shape both in the upper and the lower parts. For distances exceeding l_o and l_u above and below the shear zone respectively, no lateral load is exerted, i.e. there is no relative displacement between pile and soil. An upper part with a length below l_o is loaded by the full ultimate lateral resistance. The transverse force of the dowel (at the level of the shear plane) is obtained from the ultimate bending moment approximately as:

$$Q \leq M_T/(1.3 \, c_u \, d_D) \qquad (12)$$

Although their strength is fully utilized, small dowels are often uneconomic, since only a small section of them is stressed. Moreover, a large number of dowels is needed and this leads to high installation costs.

The <u>optimum dowel</u> has h_o/l_o and h_u/l_u values between 1 and 3. This ensures the optimum utilization of the pile strength and the soil strength (s. Fig. 4).

The optimization has been carried out by a computer program given by Schwarz (1984). However, for a preliminary design the diagrams given by Gudehus (1984) may be used as well. The optimum diameter is roughly 5 % of the depth to the slip surface.

When using this design method the design should ensure that the chosen dowels are as easy to install as possible and are distributed in such a way that the soil cannot flow between them. It should be noted that the dowel action only occurs after a lapse of a time which is needed for the displacement to mobilize a sufficiently high lateral force. Analytical expressions and extrapolation methods to predict this behavior have been given by Schwarz (1984).

The success of the design is very sensitive to the values chosen for the parameters needed in the analysis. These values should be reduced by appropriate factors of safety. In difficult

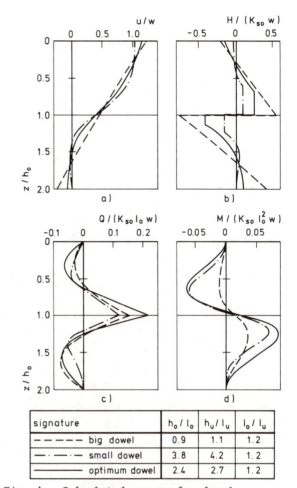

signature		h_o/l_o	h_u/l_u	l_o/l_u
– – – – –	big dowel	0.9	1.1	1.2
–·–·–·–	small dowel	3.8	4.2	1.2
———	optimum dowel	2.4	2.7	1.2

Fig. 4   Calculated curves for dowels
      a) deflection   b) lateral load
      c) transverse force d) bending moment

situations the success of the stabilization should be checked by control measurements (such as geodetic and inclinometer measurements).

CASE STUDIES

a) <u>Landslide at Dautenheim</u>
A 8 m high fill embankment for the motorway A 61 was erected on a slope with an angle of 5°. After some years significant creeping began. The position of the sliding surface was identified by means of inclinometer measurements (s. Fig. 5) and was found to be located in a stiff tertiary clay ($c_u \approx 150 \text{ kN/m}^2$, $I_v \approx 0.03$).

The landslide was stabilized by two rows of 1.5 m diameter dowels. The distribution of the dowels is shown in Fig. 5. The former creep rate of 0.1 to 0.15 cm/day was reduced to a rate which was not measureable over the period of a few months. Possibly the lowering of the ground water table also contributed to this result.

b) <u>Large scale field test Geislingen(I)</u>
A slope with an angle of 18° to 20° in a stiff, fissured jurassic clay ($c_u = 150 \text{ kN/m}^2$, $I_v = 0.035$) was cut for a railway track 100 years ago.

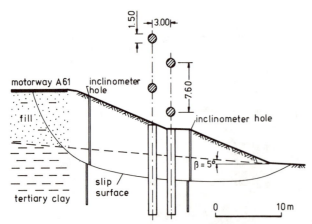

Fig. 5   Dowelling at Dautenheim

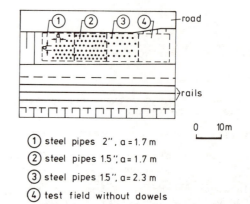

(1) steel pipes 2″, a = 1.7 m

(2) steel pipes 1.5″, a = 1.7 m

(3) steel pipes 1.5″, a = 2.3 m

(4) test field without dowels

Fig. 7   Situation of the test field
Geislingen (II)

There have been creep movements since then. On this site a field test for dowelling was carried out.

Fig. 6 shows the cross section of the slope, the mechanism of failure (detected by inclinometer measurements) and the two rows of dowels. The latter were made of reinforced concrete with a diameter of 0.4 m. Within a control interval of 25 weeks the creeping velocity was reduced from 4.7 mm/month to about 1.3 mm/month. Since then, for financial reasons, no further measurements have been carried out. A detailed description of this project has been given by Schwarz (1984).

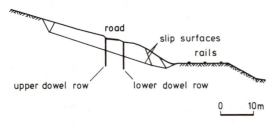

Fig. 6 Cross section of the test field
Geislingen I

c) Large scale field test Geislingen(II)

A part of the slope described above was stabilized with "grouted" dowels. Steel tubes of 1.5' and 2' diameter were introduced into pre-bored holes. The latter were sealed with a suspension of cement and silica. Four different dowel distribution densities were tested (s. Fig. 7).

The success of the stabilization depended on the dowel distribution density. The test with the lowest dowel-density was not stabilized at all. In the other tests a reduction of the creep velocity was achieved. As expected with the small diameter dowels, the stabilization set on quickly, but later the dowels were destroyed due to the progressively increasing load. For more details s. Wichter & Gudehus (1984).

REFERENCES

Fukuoka, M. (1977).   The Effects of Horizontal Loads on Piles due to Landslides. Proc.Spez.Sess.10, IX. ICSMFE, Tokyo.

Gudehus, G. (1984).   Seitendruck auf Pfählen in tonigen Böden. Geotechnik 7, pp. 73-84.

Leinenkugel, H.J. (1976).   Deformations- und Festigkeitsverhalten bindiger Erdstoffe. Experimentelle Ergebnisse und ihre physi-kalische Deutung. Veröff. Inst.f.Bodenmech. u.Felsmech., Univ. Karlsruhe.

Schwarz, W. (1984).   Verdübelung toniger Böden. Veröff.Inst.f.Bodenmech.u.Felsmech., Univ.Karlsruhe.

Sommer, H. (1978).   Zur Stabilisierung von Rut-schungen mit steifen Elementen, Berech-nungen und Messungen. Bautechnik 55, 9, Berlin, pp. 304-311.

Wichter, L. & Gudehus, G. (1984).   Injektions-verdübelungen. Tiefbau/Ingenieurbau/ Straßenbau, 2, pp. 62-68.

Large scale lime treatment of pavement subgrades

Grande échelle chaux traitement de pavement fondement

J. J. HENEGHAN, Vice President, Foundation Engineering, Wahler Associates, Palo Alto, California, USA
J. I. LANDAZURI, Principal Engineer, Wahler Associates, Palo Alto, California, USA

SYNOPSIS   The paper presents a case history of the use of large scale lime treatment of subgrade soils for structural support of roadways designed for heavy traffic applications in Pleasanton, California. The paper discusses the selection of design criteria, lime treatment operations, benefits and problems encountered, and recommendations for future use of lime treatment in similar soils.

INTRODUCTION

Lime stabilization of roadways for improvement of foundation conditions has been used on projects of increasing size and complexity since the Romans. This paper discusses the design considerations, benefits of use, construction operations and problems encountered with the use of both granular quicklime and of "DOLO-CHEM" lime, a locally available, inexpensive by-product of extracting magnesium hydroxide from Dolomitic quicklime using a rich magnesium seawater as a hydrating liquid.

DESCRIPTION OF PROJECT

The Hacienda Business Park, a development of Prudential Insurance Company/Callahan-Pentz Properties, lies near a strategic intersection between Interstates 580 and 680 in Pleasanton, California, approximately 30 miles east of San Francisco. The Hacienda Business Park is planned to be one of the largest masterplanned, high-technology business parks in the United States and will ultimately cover almost 1,000 acres of land. During the planning for Phase I, which consists of 570 acres, considerable attention was given to the traffic impacts of the business park, both during and after the construction of the roadway improvements within the business park and in the general area surrounding it.

The existing roadway pavements around the business park, prior to construction of the new improvements, were built on the bases of then existing traffic conditions. The Pleasanton area has undergone considerable growth and, because of future traffic needs, the streets around the Hacienda Business Park were redesigned for high traffic volumes. A number of large quarries that supply aggregate base and subbase products operate several miles southeast of the project area. However, truck load limits on several of the access roads to the

project were required by the City of Pleasanton, in order to limit deterioration of the roadway pavements.

Furthermore, timely supply of aggregate subbase material was not certain, given the large volume required in a relatively short period of time. Lime treatment of the native subgrade soils, which generally consist of highly plastic, expansive clays (CH per USCS classification) was therefore considered for this project, in order to limit the amount of imported aggregate materials for road construction. The difference in unit cost, between lime treating the native soils and using imported material for subbase, was very small. Therefore, cost was not a consideration in the selection of the alternative. However, lime treating the soils allowed the work to continue even during periods of inclement weather.

The average physical and engineering properties of the native soils at the project site are as follows:

In-Situ Water Content	18%
Liquid Limit	59
Plastic Limit	23
Plasticity Index	36
Percentage Passing No. 200 Sieve	96
Percentage Passing the 0.002 mm	39
Maximum Dry Density* (pcf)	102.5
Optimum Moisture Content*	19.7%

*Compaction Standard: California Test Method 216

The construction of the business park required that the existing access roads surrounding the park and the internal roadway system be designed for high traffic indices, reflecting heavy truck use. Traffic indices varying from 7 to 10 were required.

The locations of the streets where lime-treated soils were used in the pavement section are shown on Figure 1.

A total of approximately 9 miles of road were

lime treated during construction of the Phase I public improvements. All lime-treatment work was performed by the Ralph Esterly Company Inc. of San Martin, California.

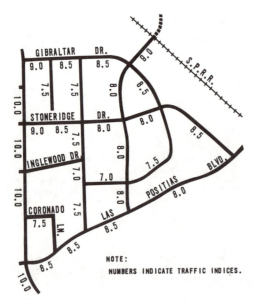

Fig. 1 Traffic Indices for Project Streets

DESIGN CONSIDERATIONS

The Traffic Index and the R-Value (Resistance Value) of the subgrade soils are the most significant factors affecting pavement design by the California Method of Flexible Pavement. This method incorporates the resistance of the soil to prevent plastic deformations under imposed wheel loads, as reflected by the R-Value and the expansion pressure of the subgrade soil. In non-expansive soils, the design R-Value is determined from the exudation pressure data, whereas, in expansive soils, the design R-Value may be determined by the expansion pressure. The thickness design relationship is:

$$T = \frac{0.0032(TI)(100-R)}{G_f}$$

Where: T = Thickness of Pavement Section (in feet)
TI = Traffic Index
R = Design R-Value
G_f = Gravel Equivalent Factor

As shown by this equation, pavements built on subgrades with low R-Values require significantly thicker sections than those built over subgrades with high R-Values. The R-Value of the native subgrade soils ranges from about 5 to 8. Based on these R-Values and the required traffic indices, pavement sections were recommended as shown in Table I.

When the native subgrade soils were treated with 4 percent quicklime (by weight) in the laboratory, the R-Value increased to values ranging from 55 to 72. Figure 2 summarizes the laboratory test results, showing the effect of

quicklime on the R-Value of the soil. The cure time for the tests shown on Figure 2 was overnight, as required by California Test Method 301. Chemical analyses of the subgrade soils indicated the sulfate contents to be below the levels considered detrimental to the long-term performance of the soil-lime mixture. It is generally believed that soils with more than 0.5 to 1.0 percent of sulfates are not suitable for lime stabilization. The sulfate content of on-site clays ranges from 0.01 to 0.07 percent.

TABLE I

Pavement Design

Traffic Index	Alternative Sections	Asphaltic Concrete (inches)	Class 2 Aggregate Base (inches)	Class 2 Aggregate Subbase (inches)	Lime Treated Subgrade (inches)
7.0	A	3.0	6.5	12.0	---
	B	3.0	6.5	---	12.0
8.0	A	3.5	8.0	13.0	---
	B	3.5	8.0	---	13.0
9.0	A	4.5	8.0	15.5	---
	B	4.5	8.0	---	15.5
10.0	A	5.0	9.5	17.0	---
	B	5.0	9.5	---	17.0

Notes:
1) All layers in compacted thickness
2) Lime treated subgrade includes 4% lime by weight

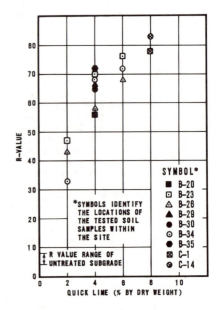

Fig. 2 Effect of Quick Lime on R-Value

In order to reduce truck traffic over city streets and the quantity of imported aggregate for roadway construction, and to allow construction during the winter months, lime-treated native soils were recommended as an alternative to the aggregate subbase.

The R-Value test, conducted in accordance with California Test Method 301, and the laboratory compaction test, performed in accordance with California Test Method 216 (Cal-Impact), were used to control the lime treatment operations in the field. A minimum R-Value of 50 (required for aggregate subbase) was established as the criteria for control.

A laboratory testing program was undertaken to determine the minimum recommended percent of granular quicklime to be used with the on-site native materials. At the request of the Contractor, "DOLO CHEM" lime was subsequently considered. However, because of the reduced amount of Calcium Oxide (CaO) in the "DOLO CHEM" lime product, a substantially greater percentage of "DOLO CHEM" lime than granular quicklime was required to achieve the same field R-Value. The addition of 8 percent "DOLO CHEM" produced R-values of only 9 to 16, whereas the addition of 8 percent "DOLO CHEM" and 3 percent quicklime produced R-values in excess of the required 50 R-value. In addition, more variability in field R-Value results were obtained in using the less expensive "DOLO CHEM" lime, probably due to the waste by-product nature of the material. Therefore, where "DOLO CHEM" lime was to be used, a hybrid design, using a minimum of 8 percent "DOLO CHEM" lime followed by 3 percent granular quicklime (by weight) was established as the criteria to achieve the required minimum R-Value of 50. The Contractor eventually decided to discontinue the use of "DOLO CHEM" after the initial stage of the project and proceeded using quicklime.

The chemical composition and gradation of the two limes are as follows:

Dolomitic Quicklime	"DOLO CHEM"
CaO+MgO = 95%	Mg = 38%
CaO = 57%	CaO = 42%

The gradation characteristics of the Dolomitic Quicklime are:

Sieve	Percent Passing
3/8"	98-100
No. 100	0-25
No. 200	0-15

Where granular quicklime alone was to be used, a minimum of 4 percent quicklime (by weight) was required. In general, an additional 1 percent quicklime was added in the field to the minimum stipulated, based on the laboratory testing, to allow for inefficiencies in large-scale construction operations.

The project was controlled by an end result specification, and the work was rejected if the minimum 50 R-Value was not achieved after the required mixing and pulverizing.

LIME TREATMENT OPERATIONS

All pavement construction, materials selection, and lime treatment were performed in general accordance with the Caltrans Standard Specifications, (State of California, Department of Transportation).

A total of 180,000 cubic yards of soils, over 9 miles of roadways, were lime-treated by the Ralph Esterly Company using specialized equipment, primarily consisting of several Gator Soil Stabilizers, manufactured by Ray Go, Inc. Upon the addition of lime, several passes of the equipment were made until the pulverization of the native clays achieved the Caltrans requirements limiting the maximum size particle. In general, where the required thickness of lime-treated subbase exceeded 12 inches, a two-stage operation was undertaken. Considerably more difficulty was encountered in achieving the required R-Value where "DOLO CHEM" lime was used. Minimal difficulties were encountered where the granular quicklime, meeting Caltrans specifications, was used, and no safety problems were encountered with either the application of granular quicklime or the "DOLO CHEM" lime.

Over 200 R-Value tests and about 20 compaction curves were carried out during construction for control purposes. Where the test results indicated R-Values less than the minimum required, more lime was added until the required R-Value was obtained.

The range and distribution of field R-value tests for the project is summarized as follows:

Range of Field R-Value	Percent of Total Tests
Less than 30	0.5
31 to 40	3.7
41 to 50	6.4
51 to 60	27.3
61 to 70	34.8
71 to 80	22.5
81 to 90	4.8
TOTAL	100.0

The general variation of R-value with field moisture content is shown on Figure 3.

The wide ranges of R-value for the same water content can be attributed to variations in the dry density of the soil, in the treated soils and in the amount of lime added.

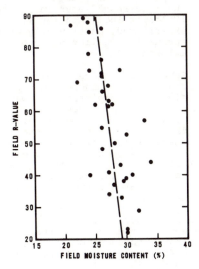

Fig. 3 R-Value vs. Field Moisture Content

SUMMARY

The large scale lime stabilization for structural support of roadways designed for heavy traffic applications at the Hacienda Business Park in Pleasanton, California, was undertaken in an area where only limited application of lime stabilization had previously been attempted. The extensive work was performed with minimum inconvenience to surrounding homeowners and businesses. Assessment of the completed project reveals a number of benefits and problems, associated with the use of lime-treated materials, and several recommendations are believed to be applicable to the future use of lime stabilization in similar soils.

BENEFITS AND PROBLEMS

A number of benefits can be attributed to the use of lime to replace aggregate subbase on this project and can be summarized as follows:

(i)   Disposal of a considerable amount of native clay off-site was eliminated.

(ii)   Import of considerable aggregate-base material was not required.

(iii)   Traffic noise and anticipated roadway deterioration due to heavy truck traffic was minimized.

(iv)   Inconvenience to surrounding homeowners and business was reduced.

Several problems were encountered during the construction operations and can be similarly summarized as follows:

(i)   Some difficulty was experienced in achieving consistent R-Value results with the use of "DOLO CHEM" lime.

(ii)   Considerable difficulty in keeping heavy truck traffic off newly compacted lime-treated areas during the required 72-hour curing period (Caltrans Specifications), was experienced, particularly where sprinkling in lieu of an oil seal was allowed.

(iii)   Several instances of minor roadway cracking has been observed since the completion of roadway construction. These locally cracked areas account for considerably less than ½ percent of the total length of roadways lime-treated, and have generally been investigated and attributed to reflective cracking due to general shrinkage of the lime-treated structural roadway section.

Based upon our experience with the lime stabilization work at the Hacienda Business Park, the following recommendations are considered appropriate for the future use of lime stabilization on similar soils:

(i)   The use of granular quicklime, meeting Caltrans specifications should be used exclusively for structural application. "DOLO CHEM" lime should be limited to uses associated with "drying up" a site.

(ii)   An oil seal should always be added immediately after compaction of the lime-treated material, in order to maintain the moisture and to discourage the use of the newly constructed roadway by heavily loaded construction vehicles.

(iii)   Considerable care should be undertaken to maintain the moisture of the lime-treated soils, in order to reduce the possibility of shrinkage. Particular care should be used to verify that the soils immediately adjacent to the roadway section being lime-treated have sufficient moisture to avoid drawing moisture out of the lime-treated soils, thereby contributing to the possibility of reflective shrinkage cracks in the asphaltic concrete near the curb and gutter.

ACKNOWLEDGEMENTS

The writers wish to thank the Prudential Insurance Company/Callahan-Pentz Properties, Pleasanton, the developers, the City of Pleasanton, and Oliver DeSilva Inc., the general contractor, for their assistance and support during the course of the work.

REFERENCES

Dumbleton, M.J. (November 1962). "Lime-Stabilized Soil for Road Construction in Great Britain", Roads and Road Construction.

Sherwood, P.T. (February 1962). "The Effects of Sulphates on Cement and Lime Stabilized Soils", Roads and Construction.

State of California, Division of Highways (June 1969). "Effects of Hydrated Lime in Treating Soil".

Transportation Research Board, National Academy of Sciences (September 1976). "Transportation Research Circular, State of the Art: Lime Stabilization".

U.S. Department of Transportation, Federal Highway Administration (October 1979). "Soil Stabilization in Pavement Structures, A Users Manual".

Limit equilibrium analysis of reinforced soil walls

Analyse des murs en terre renforcée par équilibre limité

R. A. JEWELL, Head of Reinforced Soil Group, Binnie & Partners, Consulting Engineers, London, UK

SYNOPSIS   Innovations are proposed for the limit equilibrium analysis of reinforced soil. The forces required for equilibrium in the soil are separated from the forces made available by reinforcement layers. A triangular distribution for required horizontal stress across potential slip mechanisms is suggested. This allows analysis where the mobilised soil shear strength is chosen and the required forces distributed to the reinforcement layers. Back analysis of instrumented reinforced soil walls indicate agreement with measured force distributions in metallic strip reinforcements, and overall face movements in a case with polymer reinforcement. A curve representing overall compatibility between soil and reinforcement strains indicates how design assumptions affect the expected maximum strains at equilibrium. One intriguing result is that the locus linking points of maximum reinforcement force depends on the reinforcement length, bond characteristics and the soil properties and appears not to be the consequence of a single worst potential failure mechanism as currently thought.

INTRODUCTION

Fresh studies on limit equilibrium analysis have been carried out stimulated by wider applications of reinforced soil, including the reinforcement of clay slopes with polymer materials. A method of analysis giving a consistent pattern for steep slopes was found, and a design procedure with charts has been proposed for slopes up to β = 80°, Jewell, Paine and Woods (1984). The method is reviewed here as it might apply to the vertical case, and may assist where polymer reinforcements and lower quality fills are contemplated. The attraction is that simple, conventional parameters describe the soil and reinforcement. The method offers guidance on the selection of reinforcement spacings and lengths, and provides a basis for choosing safety factors and for the estimation of deformations.

METHOD OF ANALYSIS

The analysis separates the forces required to provide the desired state of equilibrium in the soil and the set of forces made available by the inclusion of reinforcement layers.

The required forces are independent of the reinforcement and depend on the soil properties, pore water pressures, slope geometry and surcharge loading. The gross horizontal force required to maintain equilibrium on a potential slip mechanism may be calculated by applying forces external to the slope or wall face to provide equilibrium. Analysis of a full set of mechanisms in the soil assuming a fixed magnitude of mobilised soil shear strength defines two surfaces, Fig 1. The locus of zero required force defines the zone in the soil where reinforcement forces are required to maintain equilibrium. The most critical mechanism passing through the toe separates a zone at the face where uniformly high reinforcement forces are required, from a zone of decreasing required forces. The magnitude of required reinforcement forces and the position of the two surfaces in Fig.1 depend on the value of mobilised soil shear strength.

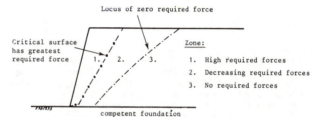

Fig.1. Zones of required force for equilibrium (Case 4:1 slope φ = 35°)

The value of available force at a point along a reinforcement layer depends either on the mobilised bond stress or the reinforcement material properties, Fig. 2. Ultimately the limiting maximum force is governed by the reinforcement strength. For design, a factored long term strength or the force which would develop a limiting allowable strain would be selected for calculation.

Reinforcement distribution

Where there is sufficient bond, the force in extensible (polymer) reinforcement depends on the magnitude of extension which is directly controlled by strain in the adjacent soil. In contrast, the force in inextensible (metallic) reinforcement is governed by the soil stresses.

The spacing of reinforcement layers should ideally be chosen so that each can maintain the soil locally at or below the desired stress ratio. This concept, and

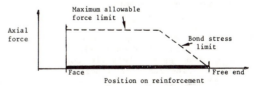

Fig.2. Envelope of maximum available force , for full load connection to face

empirical findings from limit equilibrium analyses, indicate that for slopes up to β = 80° the gross horizontal force can be represented as a triangular distribution of required horizontal stress across a slip mechanism , Fig. 3, Jewell et al (1984). Thus equal strength reinforcement layers should ideally be spaced as an inverse function of depth so that each would be equally loaded, Fig. 3.

This spacing arrangement would be appropriate for both extensible and inextensible reinforcement, and should provide equal loading of the reinforcement layers and a balanced improvement through the soil.

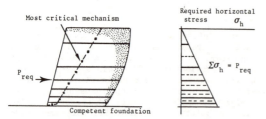

Fig.3. Triangular distribution of required force, and reinforcement spaced to carry equal loads (Case 4:1 slope φ = 35°)

Slip mechanisms

As discussed by Jewell et al (1984) two-part wedge mechanisms with zero interslice roughness are considered both convenient and suitable for the analysis. They have the merit of simplicity, do not require complex assumptions about interslice forces (about which little is currently known for reinforced soil) and adequately model the basic mechanics of reinforced soil. Mechanisms emerging at the toe and at points up the front face are examined.

Analytical procedure I

This first procedure mirrors the convention for unreinforced analyses, and progresses by trial and error. The soil geometry and reinforcement layout are chosen. Design strength parameters for the soil(s) and maximum available force envelopes for the reinforcement layers are selected. A safety factor on any slip mechanism may then be calculated by iteration, reducing the soil strength and the available force on intersected reinforcement layers by the same (lumped) safety factor. The reinforcement length and spacing may be adjusted on the basis of the results until the required safety factor is achieved on all mechanisms.

Analytical procedure II

The second procedure is more cumbersome, but more useful for back analysis. In this case a fixed magnitude of mobilised soil shear strength is assumed, and the gross force required for equilibrium on any slip mechanism is distributed to the reinforcement layers intersected.

The distribution method adopted is to divide the gross force between the reinforcement layers in proportion to the area of the stress triangle supported by each layer, Fig. 3. The force at a point in any layer is limited to that available through bond, and should this value be exceeded the remainder is redistributed to the other layers in proportion as before.

An inadequate reinforcement arrangement which would cause collapse is indicated in one of two ways. A slip mechanism may be found for which excess required force cannot be allocated to the reinforcement layers because of bond limitations. Alternatively, the force at a point on a reinforcement may exceed the maximum allowable limit. (Forces causing overstress should not be redistributed to adjacent reinforcements).

LOCUS OF MAXIMUM FORCES FOR WALLS

Analysis using procedure II for a frictional soil wall reinforced by layers at an ideal spacing extending back to the locus of zero force gives the same pattern of force in each reinforcement layer, Fig. 4a. Each reinforcement supports the same uniform force in the front zone of the wall, and the force decreases gradually to zero at the locus of zero force. Varying the spacing from the ideal alters the magnitude of force but does not change the pattern of the force profile in the reinforcement layers.

Truncation of the reinforcement to give a practical arrangement of (say) equal lengths alters the force profile and destroys the uniformity, Fig. 4b. The resulting force profile shapes then depend on reinforcement bond characteristics, truncation length and the soil properties. The trend is for a peak force to occur in a reinforcement layer and at a point closer to the face than the most critical mechanism through the toe. In the lower layers the reinforcement carries additional forces shed due to lack of bond from the upper layers. The point of peak force moves markedly towards the wall face in the upper reinforcement layers, particularly for metallic strip reinforcement, directly as a result of bond stress limits, Fig. 4c.

The resulting locus linking the points of maximum force no longer represents a single slip mechanism, as assumed in the design rules for reinforced earth walls Schlosser et al (1983). Rather it appears to be a consequence of equilibrium being maintained on all potential mechanisms. The consistent position of the locus of maximum force found for compact frictional soil walls reinforced by uniformly spaced metallic strips should not be expected in fills of lower shear strength or for reinforcements which can develop their design forces over short bond lengths.

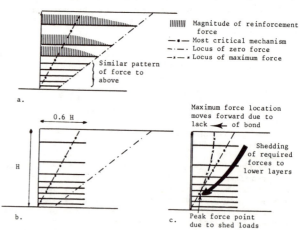

Fig.4. a.Ideal reinforcement layout and forces
b. and c. Truncated layout and resultant force redistribution (Case φ = 35°)

COMPARISON WITH MEASURED BEHAVIOUR

Centrifuge models

Conventional metallic strip reinforced walls have been tested by Bolton and Pang (1982). Four identical models were constructed and detailed reinforcement force measurements taken. Results are given at 63 g acceleration, close to failure for the 202 mm high model walls, or the equivalent 12.73 m high prototype . The test parameters are summarised in Table 1. The sand of unit weight 16.9 kN/m^3 had a measured average peak strength $\phi = 45°$, and bond coefficient with the reinforcement $\mu = 0.6$, measured at a stress level equivalent to 63 g in the model.

These values of parameters were used in a procedure II analysis to calculate the force distributions in the reinforcement layers. Results at three levels below the wall crest are compared with the measured forces, Fig. 5. Good agreement was found for layers away from the influence of the wall base. In the lower reinforcement layers horizontal loading of the soil by facing panels constrained at their contact with the base would provide part of the required force, thus reducing the amount needed from the reinforcement. Bolton and Pang have commented correctly that extreme care should be taken before relying on this phenomenon to reduce the required reinforcement forces at the wall base.

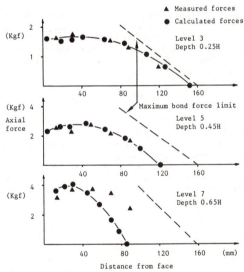

Fig.5. Comparison of measured and calculated reinforcement forces for centrifuge tested models

Dewsbury trial wall, Yorkshire

A 6 m high trial wall with rigid full height facing beams and reinforced with orientated grid reinforcement (Tensar SR2) was built in the summer 1983 using a compacted sandstone fill, Fig. 6a. Measurements were made of outward face movements.

The distribution of force in each grid reinforcement layer was calculated using the procedure II analysis and assumed mobilised strengths for the compacted granular fill $\phi' = 35°$ and $40°$. The overall extension of each layer was calculated from the force

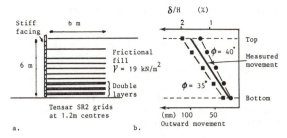

Fig.6. Dewsbury trial wall layout with measured and calculated face movements

distribution and a simplified linear load extension relationship for Tensar SR2 with 30 kN/m load causing 10% extension , which represents behaviour under sustained loading in the trial, (see Netlon Limited 1984). A straight line was fitted through the set of calculated extensions to represent the constraint of the rigid full height facing panels. The results are shown in Fig. 6b, and bound the measured movements. It is interesting to note the relatively small magnitude of outward movement , even though relatively extensible reinforcement was used .

Table 1. Details for the reinforcement in the model wall tests described (Bolton & Pang 1982)

Length	160 mm	vertical spacing	20 mm
width	4 mm	horizontal spacing	80 mm
Strength	4.8 kgf		

STRESS CONCENTRATION IN WALLS

For slope angles steeper than 80° a rigid block analysis for the reinforced zone indicates increased vertical stresses in the front half of the wall. Increased stresses have been directly measured , Schlosser et al (1983). The origin of the stress concentration may be identified with truncation of reinforcement length from the "ideal" case, Fig.4a. The truncated reinforced zone must support the wedge of unreinforced soil behind it, Fig. 4b. This results in overturning forces on the reinforced zone.

The results of limit equilibrium analysis clearly show increased force magnitudes in lower reinforcement layers towards the face , due to load shedding from higher layers, but these are less than would be anticipated from the local increase in vertical stress calculated with a rigid overturning block. The discrepancy could perhaps be resolved by a more sophisticated limit equilibrium formulation which examined moment equilibrium. Alternatively, the rigid block analysis may be unrealistically conservative.

For the present, however, it would be prudent to allow for extra reinforcement in the lower front portion of walls as indicated by the rigid block analysis to avert any possibility of local stress concentration triggering premature failure by reinforcements breaking. Such a provision is not required for slopes of 80° to 85° (depending on soil and pore water pressure parameters) for which the rigid block analysis does not indicate an increase in vertical stresses at the toe. There may be consequent savings on reinforcement quantities from building steeply sloping rather than vertical reinforced abutments .

COMPATIBILITY FOR EXTENSIBLE REINFORCEMENT

The response of granular soil to compressive loading may be represented by a relationship between mobilised frictional strength (or stress ratio) and tensile strain, Fig. 7a. Tensile testing of polymer reinforcements under sustained loading can provide a load extension relationship appropriate to long term sustained loading, which may be represented on an isochronous load extension curve, Fig. 7b.

The relationship between maximum gross required force and mobilised soil strength can be determined for a given soil geometry. Greater forces are required where there is lower mobilised shear strength. From the soil characteristics the calculated gross required force may be related to tensile soil strain as shown plotted in Fig. 7c.

In turn the gross available force for extensible reinforcement depends directly on the soil tensile strain, the reinforcement characteristics and the number of reinforcement layers. The gross available force may similarly be plotted against soil tensile strain as shown in Fig. 7c.

The critical state strength for the soil has been suggested for designs with extensible reinforcement, Jewell et al (1984), McGown et al (1984). The lesser of the long term strength under conditions in the ground, or the sustained load which would cause no more than 8% to 10% extension at the end of the design life, would be an appropriate limit to the maximum available force for polymer reinforcement . The compatibility curve shown in Fig. 7c indicates that with a lumped safety factor 1.3 to 1.5, designs based on this combination of parameters may typically reach equilibrium at relatively low reinforcement extensions of the order 2% to 4% . The resulting outward face movements would then be well within typical construction tolerances.

CONCLUSIONS

The findings presented in the paper confirm that routine limit equilibrium analysis can be effective in modelling the observed behaviour of reinforced soil, and for design. The separation of required and available reinforcement forces is helpful to the analysis. The following are significant .

1. Equal strength reinforcement layers should be spaced approximately as the inverse of depth to provide maximum and uniform benefit.

2. Ideally the reinforcement layers would extend back to the locus of zero force, Fig. 1. The practical (and more efficient) use of shorter reinforcement lengths causes load shedding to lower reinforcement layers.

3. The locus of points of maximum reinforcement force varies in position depending on the reinforcement length and bond characteristics, and the soil and pore water pressure parameters.

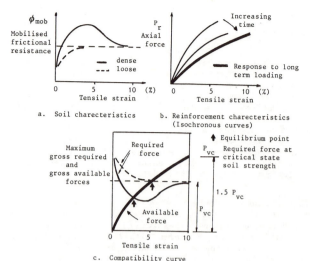

a. Soil charecteristics

b. Reinforcement charecteristics (Isochronous curves)

c. Compatibility curve

Fig.7. Soil and reinforcement charecteristics used to indicate strain compatibility

The locus of maximum force appears not to represent a single worst slip mechanism, but rather to be the consequence of equilibrium on many potential slip mechanisms.

4. A compatibility curve has been shown to help match soil characteristics and polymer reinforcement properties so that sufficient reinforcement layers can be selected to provide equilibrium within allowable strain and deformation limits.

ACKNOWLEDGEMENTS

The contributions of N. Paine, who developed the concept of a compatibility curve, and R.I. Woods, who completed computational studies, are gratefully acknowledged. West Yorkshire Metropolitan County Council are thanked for permission to publish results from the Dewsbury trial.

REFERENCES

Bolton M.D. & Pang P.L.R. (1982). Collapse limit states of reinforced earth retaining walls. Geotechnique 32. No. 4. 349–367.

Jewell R.A., Paine N. & Woods R.I. (1984). Design methods for steep reinforced embankments. Proc. Symp. on Polymer Grid Reinforcement in Civil Engineering. London, March.

McGown A., Paine N. & DuBois D.D. (1984). The use of geogrid properties in design. Proc. Symp. on Polymer Grid Reinforcement in Civil Engineering. London, March.

Netlon Limited (1984). Test methods and physical properties of Tensar geogrids. Technical guidelines.

Schlosser F., Jacobsen H.M. and Juran I (1984). Soil reinforcement. General Report. Proc. 8th Eur. conf. Soil Mech. Fndn. Engng., Vol.3, Helsinki.

First application of anchored earth

Première utilisation de la terre ancrée

C. J. F. P. JONES, Assistant Director, West Yorkshire Metropolitan County Council, UK
R. T. MURRAY, Ground Engineering Division, Transport and Road Research Laboratory, Berkshire, UK
J. TEMPORAL, Ground Engineering Division, Transport and Road Research Laboratory, Berkshire, UK
R. J. MAIR, Principal, Geotechnical Consulting Group, London, UK

SYNOPSIS   The first application of the Transport and Road Research Laboratory's Anchored Earth System for use on a road scheme was constructed in Yorkshire during 1984 as part of the Otley By-Pass Trunk Road.

The retaining structure is 100m in length and has a height of 6.5m. In addition to supporting a small road embankment the wall acts as an abutment for a pedestrian footbridge.

In this paper details are presented of the general principles of anchored earth, the design method and the construction procedure used at Otley, together with some results of the measurements taken to record the initial behaviour of the structure.

INTRODUCTION

Silver Mill Hill retaining wall forms part of the new Otley By-Pass. Over part of its length the new road occupies an existing railway cutting which was excavated in 1860 and abandoned in 1965. The 100m wall is situated in this cutting and retains a shallow embankment carrying an access road; at its highest elevation of 7m it also acts as an abutment for a reinforced concrete footbridge, Fig 1. The ground into which the railway cutting was excavated descends relatively steeply from the Chevin to the River Wharfe. Land sliding is common on the whole site. This takes the form of rotational slips in the upper part accompanied by shallower solifluction movements over the lower slopes extending to the railway cutting. The use of earth reinforcing techniques was considered to be appropriate to the site and Silver Mill Hill was constructed using anchored earth as this offered economic advantages over a conventional reinforced earth solution.

The essential difference between anchored earth and other reinforcing techniques concerns the method by which resistance to earth pressures is achieved. With reinforced earth, resistance is usually mobilised by friction between soil and reinforcing elements. In anchored earth, resistance is mobilised primarily by development of bearing pressures around an anchor at the end of a straight shaft generally circular in cross-section.

There is a corresponding difference in the load-deflection characteristics of an anchor and a reinforcing strip.

The principles of anchored earth were developed at the Transport and Road Research Laboratory (TRRL) where laboratory trials were conducted at both model and full scale, Murray and Irwin (1981). In addition TRRL commissioned centrifuge tests at Cambridge University; these tests have been reported by Bolton (1981). These initial studies indicated potential benefits for anchored earth.

Various forms of anchor can be used, one of the most efficient being triangular, formed from mild steel reinforcing bar (Fig 2).

The economic advantage of an anchor derives from the ease with which it can be formed from common rebar and the economy in the use of material which the element offers relative to the anchor loads carried. An anchor formed from round bar also offers the smallest surface area, an advantageous feature when protecting the element against corrosion. In addition the anchor offers the potential of using indigenous fill, which may be less costly than the selected fill often specified with earth reinforcing systems.

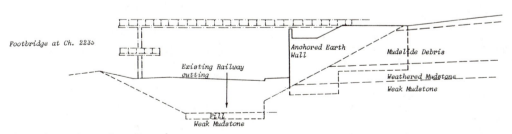

Fig 1. Section through anchored earth wall at Ch.2250

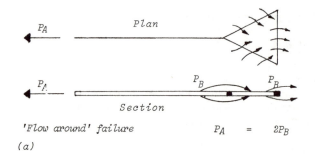

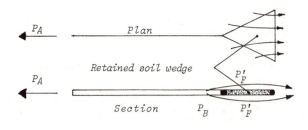

'Flow around' failure $P_A = 2P_B$

(a)

'Retained wedge' failure $P_A = P_B + 2P'_F$

(b)

Fig 2. The components and shearing mechanisms of a triangular anchor

THEORY

The ultimate load of an anchor corresponds to either:

(i) the anchor pulling through the soil, or
(ii) structural failure of the anchor.

Model tests suggest that there are two alternative mechanisms for shear around a triangular anchor element, Fig 2. In the first soil flows around the two leading members and the back member of the anchor as it is pulled through the soil, in this case:

$$P_A = 2P_B \qquad (1)$$

In the second mechanism a triangular wedge of soil is retained within the anchor, shear occurs on the top and bottom of the triangular wedge and supplements the bearing failure at the two leading members of the anchor; in this case:

$$P_A = P_B + 2P'_F \qquad (2)$$

The value of P_B may be taken as analogous to the bearing pressure on a deep strip footing. The following design expression (appropriate to $\Phi' = 35^{0}$) was selected from a number of approaches:

$$P_B = 4K_p\sigma_v' \, Bt \qquad (3)$$

where B = the length of the back bar of the anchor which is used to define anchor size.
    K_p= coefficient of passive earth pressure
    t = diameter of anchor bar

A lower bound case for P'_F may be taken as:

$$P'_F = A\sigma_v' \tan \phi' \qquad (4)$$

where A = plan area of a triangular anchor
    σ_v'= vertical effective stress
    Φ' = the peak angle of shearing resistance measured in a shear box

A lower bound value of P_A is acceptable for design using the lesser of expressions (1) or (2). In the case of Silver Mill Hill retaining wall the capacity of the anchors used was confirmed by pull-out tests using full scale anchors embedded in the proposed backfill. The results of these pull-out tests generally confirmed the use of the formula ($P_A = 2P_B$) for most of the anchor sizes used at Otley. For the larger (more flexible) sizes, the tests indicated that the upper value for P_A given by expression (2) may be more applicable, since the anchor can deform sufficiently to lock in place the sand enclosed by the triangle (Fig 2b). Measured displacements required to develop full working load in the anchors were less than 10mm for all the anchors specified. The tests also indicated that the structural strength of the anchors was not exceeded.

ANALYSIS

Silver Mill Hill wall was designed in accordance with Department of Transport Design Memorandum for Reinforced Earth, BE3/78, modified to cover the use of anchors rather than strip reinforcement, Jones (1984). Anchors 5m long formed from 20mm diameter cold worked steel having back bar lengths (B) of 650mm, 900mm and 1200mm were determined from the analysis. The smaller anchors were used in most of the wall structure, and the 900mm and 1200mm anchors placed adjacent to the footbridge bankseat. Spacing of the anchors was generally 500mm vertically and 1200mm horizontally. As this was the first use of anchored earth a good quality cohesionless fill was specified.

To check the semi-empirical analysis provided by memorandum BE3/78 which is based upon the assumption of a tie-back wedge failure hypothesis, a finite element analysis was conducted. This analysis, which simulated the construction sequence of the anchored earth structure, was performed by treating the backfill as an elasto-plastic material capable of dilating during shear with an angle of dilation equal to half the angle of shearing resistance Φ'. Rather than providing direct predictions of the behaviour of the Silver Mill Hill wall, the purpose of the analysis was to examine how anchored earth might behave and to compare various methods of predicting anchor forces and earth pressures.

The properties assumed for the wall and backfill are tabulated in Fig 3. For simplicity the foundation soil in the finite element analysis was assumed rigid. A rigid prop was modelled at the top of the wall facing unit: this was released after the simulated completion of the backfilling in accordance with the actual construction technique used.

The presence of the anchors was modelled by using the novel concept of tied degrees of freedom. As the backfill behind the wall was constructed in layers, the installation of an anchor was simulated by typing the horizontal degree of freedom of the node on the front of the wall at the elevation of the anchor with the corresponding node at the same elevation but located 5m from the facing, corresponding to the rear of the anchor. The predicted anchor force distribution after prop release, i.e. after completion of the wall, is shown in Fig 3, together with the results from the tieback wedge analysis. The prop force, which developed as construction was simulated, reached a value of 4.5kN/m for a 6m wall. The horizontal earth pressures predicted by the finite element analysis were a little greater than those corresponding to active condition (angle of wall friction $\delta = 0^0$), Fig 4.

Properties assumed for backfill:

γ = 20 kN/m^3
ϕ' = 35^0
E = 3.9x10^{4}kN/m^2
γ = 0.3

Properties assumed for prestressed facing panels:

E = 30x10^{6}kN/m^2
γ = 0.15

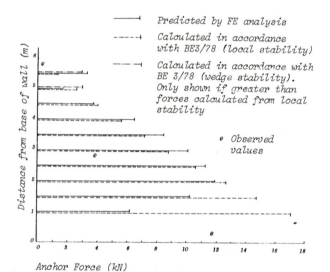

Fig 3. Anchor force distribution predicted by finite analysis and tieback wedge analysis

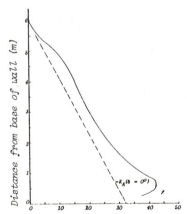

Fig 4. Horizontal stress acting on facing unit (kN/m^2) predicted by finite element analysis

CONSTRUCTION

The wall was designed and built using the York Method (Jones, 1978) for earth reinforced structures, using a full height prestressed facing panel. Internal movement of the fill and anchors relative to the facing was provided by having a slotted connection between the anchor and the facing panel, Fig 5, as proposed in the original TRRL design.

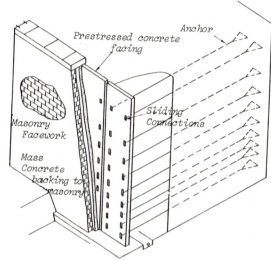

Fig 5. Isometric of anchored length of construction using full height facings

The full height panels were erected prior to the placing of the fill and held in place by push/pull props. The fill was placed and compacted in layers not exceeding 200mm with the anchors being inserted at appropriate levels (Fig 6). The anchors were held in place by passing their threaded end through the facing slots and fixing with a nut and washer. The props were removed after all fill had been placed. In the final form the wall will be stone faced to protect the connections used to conform with local environmental conditions. See reference above.

Fig 6.

An anchor being prepared for installation

MEASUREMENT

During construction instrumentation was installed into three panels, two were chosen close to the footbridge bankseat where the wall is 6.2m high and the third where the wall is 5.6m high. Measurements have been taken of anchor loads, of horizontal earth pressures on the facing units and of the deflection of the facing panels in the vertical and horizontal directions. Preliminary results for the facing panels adjacent to the bankseat are shown in Figures 7,8 and 9 for the period before the bankseat and bridge were constructed. The backfill in this section had a dry density, after compaction, of 2.23Mg/m^3 and a moisture content of 3.9%.

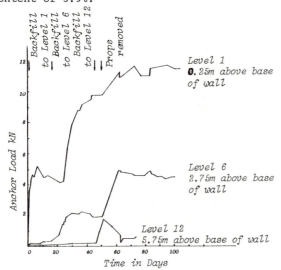

Fig 7. Anchor Loads v time for panels 60 and 61

Figure 7 shows that the loads on the anchors steadily increased after back filling and then rose sharply when the construction props were removed. The loads then became constant but will increase when the bankseat and bridge are constructed. For comparison purposes, the steady state values after removal of the props have been plotted on Fig 3 where it can be seen that the observed distribution and that produced on the basis of BE3/78 are of the same form. The observed values are smaller, of course, most probably as a result of the actual value of Φ' being larger than assumed.

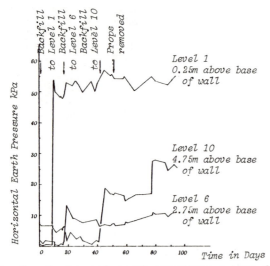

Fig 8. Horizontal earth pressures v time for panels 60 and 61

The horizontal earth pressures acting on the units are shown in Fig 8.

Whereas the anchor loads increased with increasing depth, the same trend is not shown in the earth pressure data. It would appear that anchor loads provide a better indication than the horizontal earth pressure of the forces acting within the structure.

Figure 9 shows that the deflections of the facing units increased steadily up to the time that the props were removed and then remained essentially constant. The vertical settlement recorded was 9mm; the outward horizontal movement was 21mm at the top of the wall and 7mm near the base. These are consistent with a rotation about the base of the wall of 0.2°

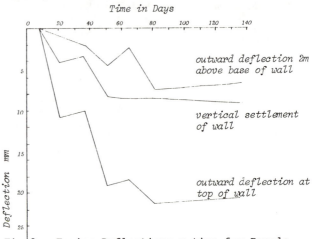

Fig 9. Facing Deflections v time for Panels 60 and 61

ACKNOWLEDGEMENTS

Silver Mill Hill Retaining Wall was designed for the Department of Transport by West Yorkshire Metropolitan County Council in co-operation with the Transport and Road Research Laboratory. Geotechnical Consulting Group provided the Category III Check on the design. The finite element analysis was undertaken by Dr. D.M. Potts and Dr. D.W. Hight at Imperial College. The Contractor was A.F. Budge & Co,.
The views expressed in this paper are those of the Authors. Some of the work described in this paper forms part of the programme of research of TRRL and is published by permission of the Direct

REFERENCES

Bolton, M.D. (1981) Centrifuge model tests on TRRL anchored earth system. A report to the Transport and Road Research Laboratory. University of Cambridge Engineering Dept.,

Jones, C.J.F.P. (1978) The York Method of Reinforced Earth. ASCE Symposium on Earth Reinforcement. Pittsburgh.

Jones, C.J.F.P. (1984) Reinforced Earth and Soil Structures. Pub. Butterworths.

Murray, R.T. and Irwin, M.J. (1981 A preliminary study of TRRL anchored earth. TRRL Supplementary Report SR674.

Les soutènements par clouage – Etude sur modèles numériques

Numerical study of nailed soil retaining structures

I. JURAN, Dr.Ing., CERMES, Ecole Nationale des Ponts et Chaussées, Paris, France
S. SHAFIEE, Elève-chercheur, CERMES, ENPC, Paris, France
F. SCHLOSSER, Professor, ENPC, Paris, France

RESUME Le clouage est une technique de renforcement des sols en place par des inclusions passives. Cette communication présente une étude théorique sur modèles numériques du comportement des soutènements par clouage. On examine l'effet des divers paramètres et notamment de phases de construction, de la rigidité des inclusions, et de leur inclinaison sur les efforts mobilisés dans les inclusions ainsi que sur le déplacement de la paroi d'excavation.

INTRODUCTION

Le clouage est une technique de renforcement des sols en place par des inclusions passives. Dans les soutènements en sols cloués les renforcements sont soit placés dans des forages et scellés par injection sur toute leur longueur, soit enfoncés par un système de vibropercussion. La surface extérieure du massif est généralement protégée par une couche de béton projeté (10 à 15 cm d'épaisseur) ou par des panneaux préfabriqués.

L'interaction sol-inclusion est essentiellement réalisée par le frottement mobilisé sur les interfaces et le comportement d'un soutènement en Sol Cloué présente donc une certaine analogie avec celui d'un mur en Terre Armée. Cependant, il existe des différences fondamentales entre ces deux systèmes. Outre le fait que la Terre Armée consiste à renforcer un matériau granulaire rapporté alors que le clouage est un renforcement du sol in-situ, ces différences concernent essentiellement : le procédé de construction(un mur en Terre Armée est construit en remblayant alors qu'un soutènement par clouage est construit en déblayant) et la rigidité à la flexion des inclusions (dans un mur en Terre Armée celles-ci sont flexibles et ne travaillent donc qu'à la traction alors que dans le cas du clouage elles peuvent avoir une certaine rigidité à la flexion et résister alors à la fois à la traction, au cisaillement et à la flexion).

Pour étudier les conséquences de ces différences sur le comportement de l'ouvrage, on a effectué une étude paramétrique sur modèles numériques en utilisant un programme des éléments finis. Cette communication présente les résultats principaux de cette étude ainsi qu'une comparaison qualitative de ces résultats théoriques aux résultats expérimentaux des essais sur modèles réduits tridimensionnels des murs en Terre Armée et en Sol Cloué effectués au C.E.R.M.E.S.(Juran et al,1984).

MODELISATION NUMERIQUE

La Figure 1 montre le modèle et les conditions aux limites considérées. Il s'agit d'un mur de hauteur 5 m, ayant 5 lits d'inclusions, de lon-

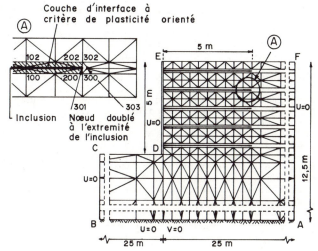

FIGURE 1 - LE MODELE NUMERIQUE ET LES CONDITIONS AUX LIMITES

gueur 5 m, espacées verticalement et latéralement de 1 m. La limite horizontale inférieure du modèle (AB) est considérée comme un substratum rigide parfaitement rugueux (déplacements horizontaux (u) et verticaux (v) nuls). Sur les limites verticales (BC, DE, FA) les déplacements horizontaux (u) sont supposés nuls. Le programme utilisé permet une simulation bidimensionnelle des phases successives de construction (excavation ou remblaiement, mise en place des inclusions et du parement, etc...).

Le sol est considéré comme un matériau élasto-parfaitement plastique, ayant le critère de plasticité de Coulomb et les caractéristiques suivantes : poids volumique : γ = 16 kN/m^3 ; angle de frottement interne : ψ = 30° ; coefficient de Poisson : ν_{sol} = 0,33 ; module de Young : E_{sol} = 10 000 Kpa ; coefficient de poussée du sol au repos : K_O = 0,5.

Les inclusions (barres de diamètre φ = 50 mm) et les éléments du parement (épaisseur - 0,1 m) sont modélisés en utilisant des éléments de flexion (poutres élastiques), à deux noeuds et à six paramètres. Ces éléments ont un module de Young $E = 2.10^8$ kPa et un coefficient de Poisson ν=0,25.

La nature bidimensionnelle de cette analyse conduit à modéliser les lits d'inclusions en utilisant des plaques équivalentes, dont la largeur est égale à l'espacement horizontal (e) entre les inclusions (Juran et al, 1983). Les caractéristiques (E_{eq} ; I_{eq}) et l'épaisseur (t_{eq}) de ces plaques sont déterminées en considérant respectivement une rigidité équivalente à la traction ($E_{eq} . S_{eq} = E . S$; où : S et S_{eq} sont respectivement la section de l'inclusion et celle de la plaque) et une rigidité équivalente à la flexion ($E_{eq} . I_{eq} = E . I$; où : I et I_{eq} sont respectivement le moment d'inertie de l'inclusion et celui de la plaque).

Les interfaces sol-parement et sol-inclusion sont modélisées en considérant deux approches : la première admet une adhérence parfaite entre le sol et les inclusions se traduisant par une continuité des déplacements entre les noeuds des éléments du sol et ceux des inclusions ; la deuxième permet de simuler les déplacements relatifs entre le sol et les inclusions en modélisant leur interface par des éléments à critère de plasticité orienté (Frank et al, 1982). Tant que la résistance au cisaillement de ces éléments n'est pas entièrement mobilisée les deux noeuds ont les mêmes déplacements ; lorsque la résistance au cisaillement est atteinte un déplacement tangentiel se produit sous une contrainte de cisaillement ultime constante. Par ailleurs, on assure la continuité des déplacements horizontaux (u) et verticaux (v) du sol de part et d'autre de cette couche d'interface (par exemple, sur la Figure 1, on a : $u_{100} = u_{102}$ et $v_{100} = v_{102}$). De plus, les extrémités des inclusions dans le sol sont modélisées en utilisant des noeuds doubles ; cela permet d'assurer une discontinuité entre le sol et l'inclusion et d'empêcher ainsi l'apparition des tractions aux extrémités libres de l'inclusion.

ETUDE PARAMETRIQUE SUR LE COMPORTEMENT DES SOUTENEMENTS EN SOL CLOUE

On présente ci-après les résultats relatifs à l'effet du procédé de construction, de la rigidité des inclusions, et de leur inclinaison sur les efforts développés dans les inclusions et sur les déplacements du parement.

Effet du procédé et de phases de construction

La Figure 2a montre les distributions des tractions le long des inclusions dans un soutènement en Sol Cloué. Ces distributions sont calculées en simulant les 5 phases successives de construction (excavation, mise en place des inclusions et du parement, etc...) illustrées sur la Figure 2b, et en considérant respectivement les deux approches de modélisation de l'interface sol-inclusion décrites précédemment : adhérence parfaite et couche d'interface à critère de rupture orienté.

On remarque que la modélisation de l'interface sol-inclusion a un effet sensible sur l'allure de ces distributions ainsi que sur la valeur de leur maximum. L'utilisation du critère de rupture

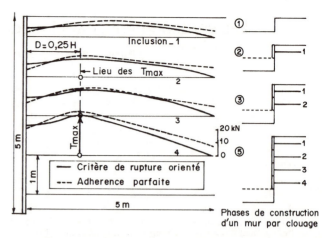

FIGURE 2 - DISTRIBUTIONS DES TRACTIONS LE LONG DE INCLUSIONS DANS UN SOUTENEMENT PAR CLOUAGE

orienté et des noeuds doubles aux extrémités des inclusions permet d'obtenir des distributions de tractions analogues à celles mesurées dans les ouvrages réels (Cartier et Gigan, 1983). Des résultats comparables sont également obtenus sur le modèle numérique du mur en Terre Armée. Ces distributions théoriques des tractions présentent les aspects suivants :

. La force de traction dans un lit d'inclusions n'est pas maximale sur le parement.
. La ligne des tractions maximales sépare le mur en deux zones : la zone active, près du parement où les contraintes de cisaillement mobilisées su les interfaces sol-inclusion sont dirigées vers l'extérieur ; la zone résistante, où l'inclusion est retenue par les contraintes de cisaillement qui sont dirigées vers l'extérieur. En liant ces deux zones les inclusions confèrent au massif en sol renforcé une cohésion apparente, fortement anisotrope, qui est proportionnelle à leur résistance à la traction et à leur densité.
. Les lignes des tractions maximales dans les soutènements en Sol Cloué et dans les murs en Terre Armée sont similaires. Elles sont verticales dans la partie supérieure du mur et leur distance du parement est proche de 0.3 H (H étan la hauteur du mur).

La Figure 3 montre l'effet du procédé de constru tion sur les déplacements du parement et sur les valeurs des tractions maximales. Afin d'étudier l'influence de phases de construction on a considéré d'une part une construction par une seule phase et d'autre part une construction par 5 pha ses successives (voir Figure 2b). On remarque que dans le cas de la Terre Armée la prise en compte des phases de construction successives n' qu'un effet très faible sur le comportement du mur alors que dans le cas du clouage les phases de construction ont une influence significative sur les déplacements du parement et sur les trac tions maximales dans les inclusions.

Ces résultats montrent que le comportement du mur dépend sensiblement du procédé de construction et de l'histoire des sollicitations qui en résultent. Toutes choses étant égales par ailleurs, l'excavation dans le cas du clouage conduit à des déplacements (y) du parement plus importants, en particulier en tête du mur, et à de tractions maximales (T_{max}) plus élevées dans les

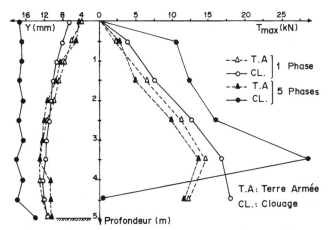

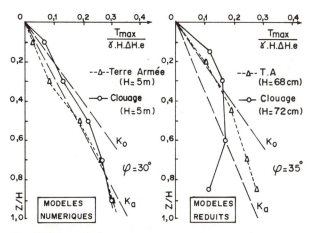

FIGURE 3 – EFFET DU MODE DE CONSTRUCTION : A/DE-
PLACEMENT DU PAREMENT;B/TRACTIONS MAXI-
MALES

FIGURE 4 – DISTRIBUTIONS THEORIQUE ET EXPERIMEN-
TALE DES TRACTIONS MAXIMALES

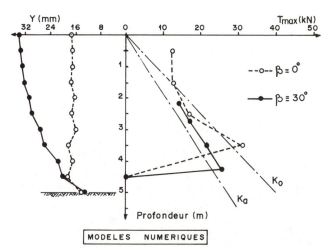

FIGURE 5 – EFFET DE L'INCLINAISON DES INCLUSIONS:
A/DEPLACEMENT DU PAREMENT;B/TRACTIONS
MAXIMALES

inclusions que le remblaiement d'un mur en Terre Armée. Ces différences peuvent être expliquées en considérant les champs des vecteurs de déplacement dans les deux ouvrages. On remarque que le remblaiement produit essentiellement des tassements alors que l'excavation produit essentiellement des déplacements horizontaux entraînant la mise en traction des inclusions.

Pour comparer les résultats théoriques avec les observations sur les modèles réduits des murs en Sol Cloué on a simulé les phases de construction de ces modèles (voir Juran et al, 1984). Cela revient à considérer une excavation dans un massif en sol renforcé en admettant que lors de chacune des phases d'excavation la mise en place du parement et des inclusions précède la déformation du sol.

Les Figures 4a et 4b montrent respectivement les distributions expérimentales et théoriques des tractions maximales (T_{max}) dans les inclusions des modèles réduits des murs en Terre Armée et en Sol Cloué. Ces tractions sont données sous forme adimensionnelle en utilisant le paramètre $T_{max}/(\gamma.H.\Delta H.e)$ (où γ est le poids volumique du sol ; H est la hauteur du mur ; ΔH et e sont respectivement les espacements vertical et horizontal entre les inclusions). Malgré les différences entre les modèles physiques et les modèles numériques considérés on peut noter pour le cas du clouage un certain accord qualitatif entre la théorie et l'expérience. La distribution des tractions maximales n'est pas linéaire ; en tête du mur elle correspond à la poussée du sol à l'état K_O alors que dans le bas du mur elle est inférieure à la poussée du sol à l'état limite plastique, caractérisé par le coefficient K_a. On note cependant que les simulations numériques conduisent à sous estimer les tractions maximales dans les armatures en tête du mur en Terre Armée.

Effet de l'inclinaison des inclusions

La Figure 5 montre l'effet de l'inclinaison β des inclusions sur les déplacements du parement et sur les valeurs des tractions maximales dans un soutènement par clouage. On remarque qu'en inclinant les inclusions vers le bas on augmente considérablement les déplacements du parement en tête du mur. L'inclinaison a pour effet

de réduire les valeurs de tractions maximales dans les inclusions ; celles-ci correspondent à la poussée du sol à l'état K_O et se rapprochent de la poussée à l'état limite K_a lorsque l'inclinaison augmente.

La Figure 6a montre que l'inclinaison des inclusions vers le bas entraîne une inclinaison du lieu des tractions maximales et un élargissement correspondant de la zone active. Comme le montre la Figure 6b ce résultat est en accord avec les observations sur les surfaces de rupture, passant par les points de cassure des inclusions, dans les modèles réduits. On note également que l'étude de la propagation des zones plastiques dans le massif en Sol Cloué montre que celles-ci se propagent dans la zone active au fur et à mesure qu'on augmente l'inclinaison des inclusions. On remarque que ces zones plastiques sont limitées par une surface qui est quasiment perpendiculaire aux inclusions et qui est généralement proche du lieu des tractions maximales. Cette surface constitue à la fois une surface de glissement potentiel pour le sol et une surface de rupture potentielle pour les inclusions.

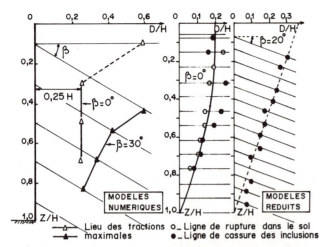

FIGURE 6 - EFFET DE L'INCLINAISON DES INCLUSIONS
SUR LE LIEU DES TRACTIONS MAXIMALES

Effet de la rigidité à la flexion

Pour étudier l'influence de la rigidité à la flexion des inclusions on a considéré trois rigidi-
tés différentes correspondant respectivement à:
$I = 0$; $I = I \varnothing 50$; et $I = 10 I \varnothing 50$ (où $I \varnothing 50$
est le moment d'inertie d'une barre de diamètre
$\varnothing = 50$ mm).

On remarque que la butée latérale du sol sur l'inclusion de part et d'autre de la surface de glissement potentiel délimitant la zone active, provoque une mobilisation de la résistance de l'inclusion à la flexion. Cette mobilisation dépend
sensiblement des déplacements du sol perpendiculairement aux inclusions ; or, ceux-ci restent
très faibles par rapport aux déplacements horizontaux qu'entraînent la mise en traction des
inclusions. Par conséquent, comme le montre la
Figure 7a, les valeurs des efforts tranchants(T_c)
mobilisés dans les inclusions restent nettement

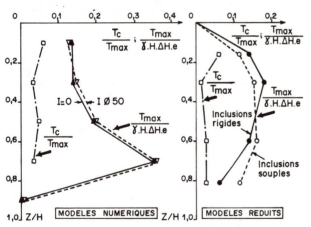

FIGURE 7 - EFFET DE LA RIGIDITE DES INCLUSIONS
SUR LES TRACTIONS MAXIMALES

inférieurs à celles des efforts de traction correspondants. On note également que l'influence
de la rigidité sur les déplacements du parement,
sur le lieu des tractions maximales et sur les
valeurs de ces tractions est pratiquement négli-
gleable. Comme le montre la Figure 7b, ces résul-

tats théoriques sont en accord avec les observations sur le comportement avant rupture des modè-
réduits des murs en Sol Cloué. En effet, les efforts tranchants mesurés dans les inclusions sont
nettement inférieurs aux efforts de traction correspondants et la rigidité à la flexion n'a d'effet significatif ni sur les déplacements du parement ni sur les valeurs des tractions maximales.

Cependant, les essais ont permis de mettre en évidence l'influence de la rigidité sur le mécanisme de rupture du modèle qui se produit par rotation de la zone active entraînant un déplacement
important du sol perpendiculairement aux inclusions. On observe qu'à la rupture la mobilisation
des efforts tranchants dans les inclusions a pour
conséquences d'élargir la zone active et de réduire la hauteur critique du modèle.

CONCLUSIONS

Cette étude permet de tirer des conclusions con-
concrètes sur l'effet des divers paramètres sur
le comportement des soutènements en Sol Cloué. On
note en particulier que l'inclinaison des inclusions a une influence sensible sur les déplacements du parement et sur les lieux des tractions
maximales. Par ailleurs, la rigidité à la flexion
des inclusions n'a pratiquement aucun effet sur
le comportement de l'ouvrage sous charges de service.

En comparant les résultats théoriques aux observations sur les modèles réduits on peut conclure
qu'en dépit des différences entre les modèles
physiques et les modèles numériques considérés
ces derniers constituent une modélisation ration-
nelle des soutènements en sol renforcé. Cependant
les conclusions qu'on en tirer ne semblent
être significatives que tant que les déplacements
du sol dans le massif renforcé restent assez faibles. Par ailleurs, il est à présent nécessaire
de vérifier les conclusions de cette étude par
des expérimentations sur des ouvrages réels.

REMERCIEMENTS

Les auteurs remercient M. P. HUMBERT du LCPC et
M. F. SCHLOSSER, Professeur à l'ENPC, pour leur
aide et leurs conseils ainsi que le Département
des Voies Nouvelles de la SNCF pour sa participation au financement de cette recherche.

REFERENCES

Cartier G., Gigan J.P. (1983) Experiments and Observations on soil nailing structures. Proceeding of the 8th Conf. of the E.C.S.M.F.E., Helsinki.

Frank R., Guénot A., Humbert P. (1983) Numerical
analysis of contact in geomechanics, Compte-
rendu du 4ème Colloque Int. sur les méthodes
numériques en géomécanique. Edmonton, 1982.

Juran I., Shafiee S., Schlosser F., Humbert P.,
Guénot A. (1983) Study of soil-bar interaction
in the technique of soil nailing. Proc. of the
8th Conf. of the E.C.S.M.F.E., Helsinki.

Juran I., Beech J., Delaure E.(1984) Etude expérimentales sur modèles réduits du comportement
d'un soutènement en sol cloué, compte-rendu du
Coll. Int. sur le renforcement des Sols et des
Roches, Paris.

Design parameters for deep stabilized soil evaluated from in-situ and laboratory tests

La détermination des paramètres dans le laboratoire et in-situ pour le sol stabilisé par la consolidation dynamique

K. KUJALA, Research Assistant, University of Oulu, Finland
H. HALKOLA, Geotechnical Engineer, Geotechnical Department of the City of Helsinki, Finland
P. LAHTINEN, Senior Research Engineer, Technical Research Centre of Finland, Espoo, Finland

SYNOPSIS   Deep stabilization has been used and researched in Finland since 1974 and the experiences have so far been good. However, especially the question how to evaluate the parameters of the stabilized object and choice of proper design methods still require further research. With the determination of the design parameters, esp.of shear strength and compressibility, the aim has been to evaluate these in laboratory using samples taken in-situ. This has not, however, proved to be easy. Samples mixed in laboratory have in some cases given values deviating greatly from in-situ measured values, mostly so that the in-situ values are greater. In addition to differences in the mixing process, the laboratory-blanded samples also deviate in respect to temperature and pressure from the stabilized column made in-situ.Especially the temperature proved essential in the strengthening of the column. By imitating the temperature forming in the columns in the laboratory testing procedure, the laboratory results significantly better correlate to the in-situ values. The present paper gives research results on the effect of temperature on strengthening, as well as comparisons on how humus and sulphur content is decreasing the strength of lime stabilized clay and, also observations on the effect of air, formed in the column during construction, on the compression of the column.

INTRODUCTION

Deep stabilization is a good technique for strengthening of foundations on soft clay, for improving slope stability and for decreasing settlements. The deep stabilization technique used on Finland was invented in Sweden in 1967. (Broms, Boman 1978).

Deep stabilization has been used in Finland on building projects for about ten years with constantly increasing and diversifying applications. Follow-up measurements have been carried out during several years on many deep stabilization projects. In order to analyze the projects and control the measurement methods, comparative calculations have been performed (Lahtinen, Vepsäläinen, 1983), (Lahtinen, 1984). The research has been carried out also on actual building projects. Subjects of research were:
- various applications of deep stabilization
- various stabilizing agents and the effects of their quantities
- the suitability of laboratory and in-situ research equipment
- the effect of the composition of clay on the strengthening
- the effect of the temperature on the strengthening
- the determination of design parameters of deep stabilized soil
- the suitability of calculation and measurement methods.

The determination of design parameters of deep-stabilized soil has proved to be a most demanding task. The definition of the parameters evaluated from samples mixed in laboratory seems to lead to too great a dispersion and too small values compared to the values obtained from in-situ measurements. The present paper deals with the latest results obtained in the clarification work on the determination of design parameters in Finland.

DETERMINATION OF DESIGN PARAMETERS FROM LABORATORY TESTS

The mechanical properties of deep stabilized soil depend on the physico-chemical properties of the soil to be stabilized and on those of the stabilizing agent, and on the strengthening time and conditions. The shear strength of clays stabilized in laboratory varied at age 1 year from 10 to 100 kPa (Kujala, 1984). Sediments of the Litorina Sea, to which a high humus content, in addition with a high sulphur content is characteristic, showed only little strength gain with stabilization. Also the strength of very heavy clays remained poor.The best strengthening soils were silty clays with low content humus. For design purposes, strength and deformation parameters as well as the optimum amount of stabilizing agent have to be defined for each soil type of the site to be improved by deep-stabilization, using test samples stabilized in laboratory. It was, however, peculiar to the laboratory determined design parameters that they were often significantly lower than those obtained from columns stabilized in-situ. The worst correlation was in general found for the modulus of elasticity (Figure 1).

The effect of temperature

The difference between the parameters of the laboratory and in-situ stabilization is mainly

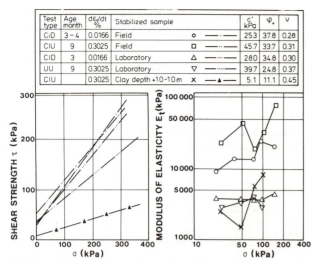

Test type	Age month	dεᵥ/dt %	Stabilized sample		c' kPa	φ.	ν
CiD	3 – 4	0.0166	Field	o	25.3	37.8	0.28
CIU	9	0.3025	Field	□	45.7	33.7	0.31
CiD	3	0.0166	Laboratory	△	28.0	34.8	0.30
UU	9	0.3025	Laboratory	▽	39.7	24.8	0.37
CIU		0.3025	Clay depth +10–1.0 m	x	5.1	11.1	0.45

Fig.1. Shear strength and modulus of elasticity of clay limestabilized in laboratory and in-situ.

caused by the temperature during the early strengthening period. The binding agent used with deep stabilization is unslaked lime, which strongly reacts with water by releasing heat. The temperature of the lime columns in-situ varies greatly (Figure 2).

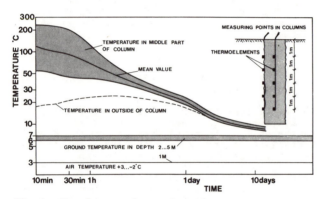

Fig.2. The temperature of a lime column as the function of time.

Maximum temperature of about 240°C were measured. The temperature in the columns evens out slowly and still after two weeks it is some degrees above that of the surrounding soil. In laboratory conditions similar early strengthening temperatures are not reached, because the stabilizing agent is usually mixed with a mechanical mixer in open vessels giving quicker temperature equalization and heat dissipation.

The higher the temperature the stronger it effects the strength and deformation parameters of stabilized soil (Figure 3). Raising the temperatures from +7°C to 20°C will increase the shear strength about 4 times and the modulus of elasticity close to 5 times. In order to receive better correlation between laboratory and in-

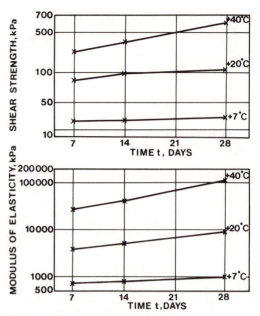

Fig.3. The effect of temperature on shear strength modulus of elasticity of lime-stabilized clay.

situ parameters, the temperatures of the test samples should in the early strengthening period better correspond to the temperature of the in-situ column. Figure 4 gives a summary of the test results where the early strengthening temperatures have been changed to correspond with the temperatures of the in-situ columns. This gives a much better correlation of test results.

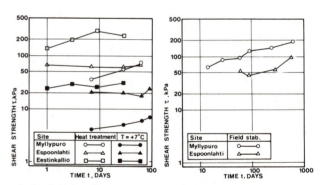

Site	Heat treatment	T = +7°C
Myllypuro	o——o	●——●
Espoonlahti	△——△	▲——▲
Eestinkallio	□——□	■——■

Site	Field stab.
Myllypuro	o——o
Espoonlahti	△——△

a) Stabilized in laboratory   b) Stabilized in-situ

Fig.4. Strength of stabilized clays as a function of time.

The strong effect of the temperature on strength and compressibility is based on the changes in the mineralogy of the stabilized soil. This can be observed among other things as mineral differences for instance between temperatures +7° and +20°C (Kujala, 1984). The effect of the temperature can also be seen in the micro structure of the clay as a strong aggregation of clay particles into regularly shaped hexagonal plates.

The proportion of air in the columns

Due to the construction of the lime columns they contain a lot of air, the proportion of which in the volume change tests was nearly half of the total volume change (Figure 5). It is essential to the air content of the lime columns that most of it slowly leaves the column at a certain stage of loading. Here several local fractures occur in the micro structure of the stabilized soil, settling the granular framework and pressing the air from the sample. Greater than calculated settlements have thus been observed in certain deep stabilization sites, when the dimensioning of the stabilized soil was based on the elasto-plastic model (Lahtinen, 1984). The reason for these greater settlements may therefore be the amount of air leaving the columns when the load has exceeded a certain limit value.

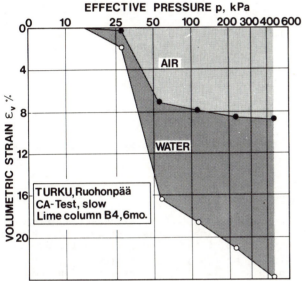

Fig. 5. Proportion of air in the volume change of a lime column in an anisotropic volume change test.

IN-SITU INVESTIGATIONS

Stabilization control and measuring shear strength

Control soundings are used for observation of the deep satbilized soil after the stabilization work is completed. The purpuse of the soundings is to investigate the quality of the stabilized soil and also the strength increase. In Finland investigations are performed using a purpose designed column-penetrometer (Torstensson, 1980) and special vane-bore for calibration of the penetration-test results (Halkola, 1983). Also a screw-plate compressometer (Janbu et al, 1973) is used. The results of the control soundings show that in clay areas, where the humus content is < 2 % and the sulphur content < 0.1 %, the strength increase (CaO as stabilizing agent) is almost similar (Figure 6, black points). When the humus and sulphur content is high, the strength increase is evidently smaller (Figure 6, white points).

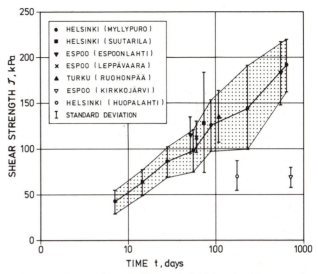

Fig.6. Strength of lime-stabilized columns at different times.

Demands for the quality of the stabilization-work

Sounding results in different stabilization sites show that standard deviation of the strength of the stabilized soil is remarkable. The values for standard deviation have been observed to vary between 15 - 60 %. The scatter of the results depends on the stabilization equipment used and also on the stabilization site. It is recommendable to investigate at last 3 columns even in the smallest stabilization sites. In larger projects the suitable amount for investigated columns is 1 - 3 °/oo of all columns in the project. Usually control-soundings are made when the stabilized columns are 1 - 3 months of age. In the case the standard deviation of the sounding results exceeds 25 %, it is necessary to investigate more thoroughly how the stabilization work has succeeded for instance by taking samples from the columns. It is also possible to lift a whole column for an inspection (Broms et al., 1978).

Settlement behavior of deep-stabilized soil

The purpose of deep stabilization is to increase the shear strength and also to reduce the compressibility of the soil. So far it has proved to be difficult to obtain reliable design parameters, due to poor correlation between in-situ and laboratory results. Deformation modulus (E_u) for design purposes are usually obtained applying deformation results of already completed stabilized structures (Lahtinen et al., 1983). The modulus of elasticity of lime-stabilized columns in clayey ground in the Helsinki area has been observed to vary within the range of E = 15 000 - 25 000 kPa. The humus and sulphur content was low in the observed sites, and structures on stabilized areas were built when lime-columns were 3 - 9 months of age.

Also a screw-plate compressometer (with weights) has been used to determine the deformation moduli. With the screw-plate compressometer it is possible to load soil at different depths without excavations. Results of two screw-plate tests made in lime-stabilized columns are presented in figure 7. The calculated moduli of elasticity in the example are E = 22 000 kPa for a stabilized column 270 days of age and E = 170 000 kPa for a column 1000 days of age. Results of settlement observation at a test embankment in the same area (Helsinki, Myllypuro) have also been applied to calculate the moduli. These have been observed to vary within the range of E = 11 000 - 26 000 kPa. The stabilized columns were approximately 270 days of age when the test embankment was built. In screw-plate tests a Ø 160 mm plate is normally used, and because of the small effective depth of the vertical stress, local changes in the strength of a column affects strongly the results.

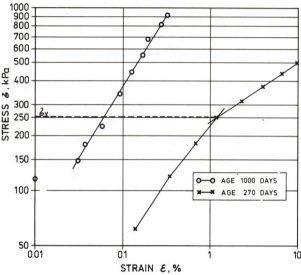

Fig.7. Example of screw-plate compressometer tests in lime-stabilized columns.

The creep-limit of a single column can also be obtained applying screw-plate results. When the creep-limit (σ_y) of a column is exeeded, the deformation strongly increases (Figure 7). In some cases it has proved to be very difficult to determine creep-limits from the screw-plate test results. The creep-limit is then considered to be the stress σ_y at a relative strain of ε = 1 %.

In the near future, the long-term settlement behaviour of stabilized columns will be investigatred when the creep-limit is exeeded. It is expected that the air present in the micro structure of a column would be pressed out and cause large secundary compression. The total settlement of a stabilized area can then be equal to the settlement of an unstabilized area.

CONCLUSIONS

1.The research, in which in-situ and laboratory investigations have been compared, shows very clearly that if the parameters of deep stabilized soils are determined in the laboratory, the samples have to be stored at the same temperature which exist in the lime columns. Heat treatment makes it also possible to determine the development of strengthening of deep stabilized soil.

2.The composition of clay (especially the contents of sulphur and humus) have significant effect on the strengthening of lime stabilized soil. In the soft clays of the Helsinki area the strength gain has been relatively consistent when the content of sulphur is < 0.1 % and the content of humus < 2 %.

3.Investigation of lime columns in-situ has been involved for development of suitable equipments. The column-penetrometer and column vane-bore have proved to be good investigation equipments to determine the strength and its variation on lime columns. For the evuluation of compressibility the screw-plate compressometer has proved to be a most suitable toal.

4.During the construction of the lime columns rather much air remains entrapped. When the load of a lime column exceeds the creep load the settlements are speeded up apparently and at the same time air and water is compressed out to an increasing amount. Local fractures occur in the micro structure of the lime-column, and the column looses at least partly and temporarily its bearing capacity.

ACKNOWLEDGEMENTS

The writers wish to express their appreciation to the sounding personnel of the Geotechnical Department of the City of Helsinki as well as to the student of technology Juha Korpi's valuable assistance.

REFERENCES

Broms, B., Boman, P. (1978). Stabilization of soil with lime columns, Design handbook.Royal Institute of technology, Stockholm, Sweden.

Halkola, H. (1983). In-situ investigations of deep stabilized Soil. Proc. 8th Conf. on ECSMFE, Helsinki, Finland.

Janbu, N., Senneset, K. (1978). Field compressometer-principles and application. Proc. 8th Conf. on ICSMFE, Moscow, USSR.

Kujala, K. (1984). Faktorer som inverkar på djupstabiliserade jordars mekaniska egenskaper Nordiska Geoteknikermötet, Linköping, Sweden.

Lahtinen, P. (1983). Djupstabiliseringens dimensionering. Nordisk Seminarium om djupstabilisering, Espoo, Finland.

Lahtinen, P. (1984). Calculating the Settlements on a deep stabilized site. Proc. 8th Conf. on ECSMFE, Vol 3, Helsinki, Finland.

Lahtinen, P., Vepsäläinen, P. (1983). Dimensioning deep stabilization using the Finite Element Method. Proc. 8th Conf. on ECSMFE, Helsinki, Finland.

Torstensson, B-A. (1980). The "BAT lime column proble" for in-situ testing of quality of lime columns. Linden Alimak AB, Skellefteå, Sweden.

Research on tiebacks anchored in cohesive soils

L'investigation des tirants ancrés dans les sols argileux

HARALD LUDWIG, Schnabel Foundation Company, Bethesda, Maryland, USA
DAVID E. WEATHERBY, Schnabel Foundation Company, Bethesda, Maryland, USA
HARRY SCHNABEL, Schnabel Foundation Company, Bethesda, Maryland, USA

SYNOPSIS   Load tests were performed on instrumented tiebacks anchored in a variety of cohesive soils. The results of the test program indicate that currently accepted testing procedures can be used to verify the short-term, load-carrying capacity of tiebacks anchored in cohesive soils and evaluate their long-term, load-carrying capacity.

INTRODUCTION

Tiebacks anchored in cohesive soils may exhibit significant time-dependent movements, while ones anchored in coarse-grained soils have exhibited negligible time-dependent movements at their working loads. In spite of these differences, tieback tests and acceptance criteria developed for tiebacks anchored in coarse-grained soils are applied to tiebacks anchored in cohesive soils.

Research was conducted on tiebacks anchored in cohesive soils to: (1) investigate the load-carrying behavior of straight-shafted, tiebacks, (2) determine whether or not the commonly used testing procedures are suitable for tiebacks anchored in cohesive soils, and (3) determine what type of acceptance criteria could be used in conjunction with the tests.

TIEBACK DESCRIPTION AND SITE CONDITIONS

Bar tendons with weldable strain gauges were used. The tiebacks were installed using a 305-mm (12-in.) diameter, hollow-stemmed auger. The tendon was inserted inside the auger prior to drilling the hole. Once the hole was drilled, grout was pumped down the auger as it was extracted.

Table I lists pertinent data for all of the tiebacks used in this study, and Table II gives the soils data for the four test sites.

TABLE I

Tieback Data

Tieback Number	Unbonded Length (m)	Anchor Length (m)	Max. Test Load (kN)	Failure Load (kN)
622-1	6.0	9.2		779
622-2	10.2	4.5	881	
638-1	2.7	9.2		775
597-3	0.0	15.9	596	
715-1	6.7	9.2	837	
715-3	6.9	9.2	837	
715-4	11.1	4.6	837	

TEST PROGRAM

Each tieback was subjected to a creep test or a performance test in accordance with the procedures outlined by Weatherby (1982), wherein a series of cyclic loads was applied to the tieback by means of a centerhole hydraulic jack. The peak load of each successive load cycle was greater than its predecessor. At the end of each load cycle, the load was released to a nominal alignment load. In the creep test, the peak load of each load cycle was held constant for periods ranging from 10 minutes to 1000 minutes. In the performance test, only the maximum load was maintained constant. At each load and during each load-hold, displacement of the tendon was measured and recorded to the nearest .025mm (.001-in.). During the test, the strain gauges were automatically read using a thirty channel strain indicator.

Figure 1 contains the load-displacement curves for each of the tiebacks studied. To simplify the presentation of the data, only the displacements corresponding to the maximum load in each cycle were plotted. The vertical

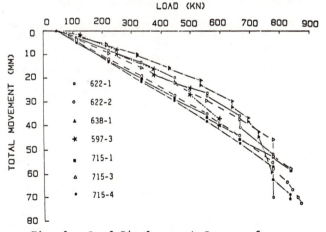

Fig. 1: Load-Displacement Curves of Several Straight-Shafted Tiebacks Anchored in Different Cohesive Soils

TABLE II

Soils Data

Site No.	Tieback No.	Soil Description	Atterberg Limits PL	LL	Natural Water Content	Undrained Shear Strength (kPa)
1	622-1, 2	Stiff-to-very-stiff, slightly overconsolidated sandy, clayey silt (MH)	46%	60%	45-56%	56 a/
2	638-1	Stiff-to-very-stiff, slightly overconsolidated silty clay (CL)	18%	37%	19%	130
3	597-3	Layered soil profile ranging from a medium-to-stiff, silty clay (CL-CH) to a fine sandy silt (ML), to a very dense, silty fine sand (SM)	18%	26%	24%	153 b/
4	715-1, 3, 4	Medium, slightly overconsolidated silty clay (CL)	20%	35%	24%	67

a/ Soil was interlaced with black seams along which it failed in unconfined compression tests.
b/ Soils data pertains to the silty clay stratum.

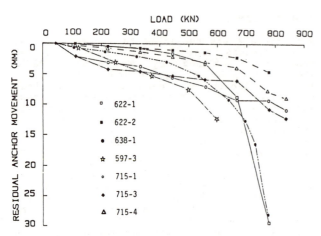

Fig. 2: Residual Anchor Movement Curves of Several Straight-Shafted Tiebacks Anchored in Different Cohesive Soils

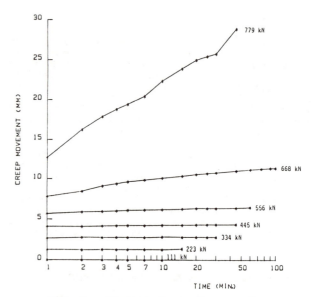

Fig. 3: Typical Creep Curves of a Straight-Shafted Tieback Anchored in Cohesive Soil

lines in each curve represent the creep movement that occurred during each load-hold.

Figure 2 contains the load-residual anchor movement curves for each tieback studied. The residual anchor movement or inelastic movememt is defined as the displacement corresponding to each alignment load. The elastic movement or recoverable movement of the tieback is the difference between the total displacement of the tieback and the residual anchor movement.

Figure 3 shows the creep curves for tieback 622-1. Creep curves are used to evaluate the long-term, load-carrying capacity of tiebacks anchored in cohesive soils. The time-dependent or creep movements are plotted on a semi-logarithmic scale as a function of time. For each load, the creep movement per logarithmic cycle, creep rate, is determined by computing the slope of a best fit straight line drawn through the data points. The creep rates as a function of load can be plotted.

Figure 4 shows the creep rate curves for the creep tested tiebacks studied.

Figure 5 shows the distribution of strain in the tendon of tieback 622-1. Assuming that the anchor grout cracks, the load in the tendon will be proportional to the strain in the tendon. Grout cracking over most of the anchor length was observed in a tieback unearthed at the same site. The shaded areas on the curves represent the change in strain that occurred during the creep test load-holds. Some of the fluctuations in strain along the unbonded length of the tendon are likely a result of bending, particularly at the higher loads. The slopes of the strain distribution curves in the anchor length are non-linear, thereby indicating a non-linear transfer of load from the anchor to the soil. The total movement of the tieback can be

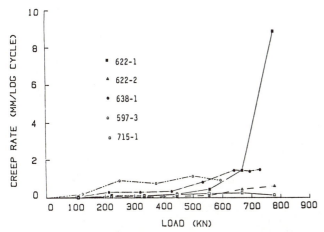

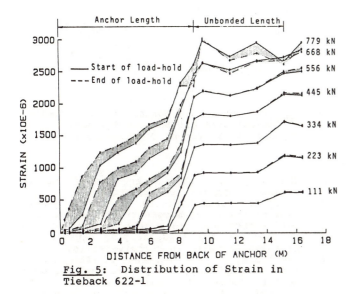

Fig. 4: Creep Rate-Load Curves of Several Straight-Shafted Tiebacks Anchored in Different Cohesive Soils

Fig. 5: Distribution of Strain in Tieback 622-1

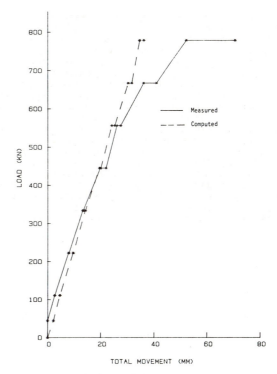

Fig. 6: Measured and Computed Total Movement of Tieback 622-1

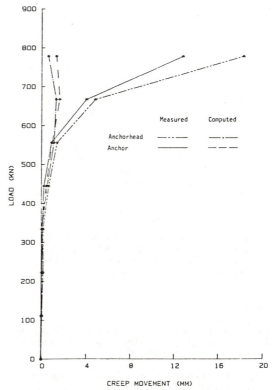

Fig. 7: Measured and Computed Creep Movement of Tieback 622-1

calculated by integrating the strain gauge data shown in Figure 5. Figure 6 shows a comparison of the computed and measured total movements. For loads less than 556 kN, the measured and computed movements show good agreement. At the 668 kN and 779 kN loads, the total measured movement deviates from the computed movement. This indicates that the back of the anchor had begun to move through the soil when the 668 kN load was applied. Tieback 638-1 showed similar behavior.

A comparison of the measured and computed creep movements of tieback 622-1 in Figure 7 also shows that the back of the anchor had begun to move through the soil at 668 kN. The good agreement in measured and computed creep movements prior to the 668 kN load indicates that creep movements measured at the anchorhead reflect the movements occuring in the anchor.

Figures 8 and 9 show the residual anchor movements and the creep rates plotted as a function of normalized load. The applied loads were normalized by dividing them by the maximum load applied to the tieback. For tiebacks 622-1 and 638-1 the maximum load was the failure load. For loads greater than 70 to 80 percent of the ultimate load, the residual anchor movement increased rapidly. The two tiebacks that failed exhibited residual anchor movements greater than 25.4-mm (1-in.), and the other tiebacks had residual movements less than 13mm (0.5 in.). For the tiebacks studied, failure occurred when their creep rates reached 1.5 mm/logarithmic cycle (0.06 in./logarithmic cycle). For loads less than 80 percent of the ultimate load, no creep rates in excess of 1.0 mm/logarithmic cycle (0.04 in./logarithmic cycle) were measured.

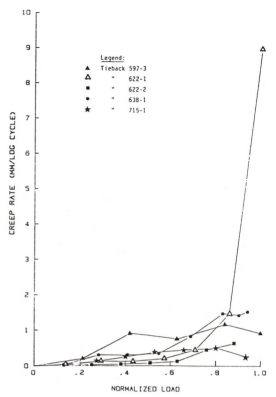

Fig. 9: Creep Rate-Normalized Load Curves of Several Straight-Shafted Tiebacks Anchored in Different Cohesive Soils

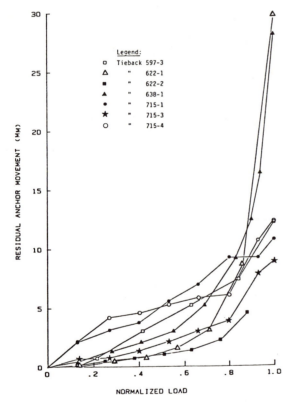

Fig. 8: Residual Anchor Movement-Normalized Load Curves of Several Straight-Shafted Tiebacks Anchored in Different Cohesive Soils

CONCLUSIONS

Tests performed on seven instrumented hollow-stem-augered tiebacks anchored in cohesive soils indicate that:

1) The distribution of load transfer along the anchor is non-linear.
2) Time-dependent tieback movements are associated with a redistribution of load in the anchor.
3) The back of the anchor moves before ultimate capacity is obtained.
4) Creep movements measured at the anchorhead reflect the creep movements of the anchor.
5) Performance and creep testing can be used to evaluate the load-carrying capacity of tiebacks anchored in cohesive soils.
6) Overloads of 125 percent of the design load coupled with creep rate and residual anchor movement guidelines may be sufficient to ensure acceptable long-term performance of similar straight-shafted tiebacks.
7) For the particular tiebacks tested, a residual anchor movement less than 13 mm (0.5 in.) and a creep rate less than 1.5 mm/logarithmic cycle (0.06 in./logarithmic cycle) indicated satisfactory behavior.

REFERENCES

Weatherby, D.E., Tiebacks, Report No. FHWA/RD-32/047 U. S. DOT, Washington, DC, 1982.

Densification of a decomposed landfill deposit

Densification d'un dépôt d'ordures ménagères dans lequel le processus de décomposition de matières putréfiables est complet

R. G. LUKAS, Senior Principal Engineer, STS Consultants, Ltd., Northbrook, Illinois, USA

SYNOPSIS   A decomposed municipal waste landfill deposit was improved by different compaction techniques for support of a regional shopping center, consisting of one and two-story buildings plus surrounding parking lots and driveways. In the fill areas, the landfill was compacted to adequate densities by conventional earth-moving and compacting equipment. In the cut and transitional areas, the load-bearing areas were improved by means of dynamic compaction. The improvement was sufficient to limit settlements of footings with column loads ranging from 1,000 to 1,500 kN to values on the order of 1 to 2 cm.

INTRODUCTION

During 1975 to 1977, a regional shopping center was constructed in Chicago on a former landfill deposit. The buildings consisted of one and two-story reinforced concrete structures with column loads on the order of 1,000 to 1,500 kN. The shopping center occupied a 215,000-m² site. The landfill deposits were compacted by conventional earth moving equipment in the fill areas and densified by means of dynamic compaction in the cut and transitional areas. The depth of landfill below final grade ranged from 9 to 18 m. The buildings were constructed with footings supported on the landfill and with slabs-on-grade.

PRE-CONSTRUCTION CONDITIONS

Beginning in 1919, natural clay was removed from this site and used for making bricks. Over a period of approximately 30 years, this resulted in a lowering of the site to depths ranging from 15 to 18 m below surrounding street grade. The deep excavation was filled with refuse in an uncontrolled manner. The refuse consisted of municipal waste, demolition debris, wood products from removal of dead trees, and miscellaneous materials. Open burning occurred in the pit at isolated locations from heat generated during the decomposition. The landfilling operations ceased in

1947 and left a profile similar to that shown on Figure 1. At the south end of the site, the landfill was piled to a height of about 37 m above street grade while at the north end of the site, the pit remained open. Leachate accumulated in the lower portion of the pit and was periodically pumped into the city sewer system.

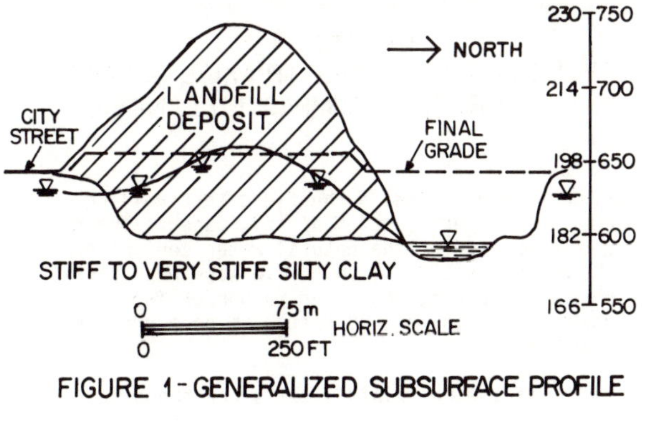

SITE PREPARATION

In order to balance the cut and fill operations, the surface elevation for the shopping center development was set at street grade near the north end of the project site and approximately 6 m above street grade at the southern end. Approximately one-million cubic meters of landfill was removed from the southern end of the site and filled into the northern end. The fill material was hauled by conventional earth scrapers and compacted in maximum lifts of 30 cm. The compacted fill was intended to form a suitable subgrade for building and roadway construction. At the southern end of the site and in the transition areas between the cut and fill, dynamic compaction was utilized to densify the upper portion of the landfill deposit. The most crucial zone for densification was the transition area because the deposits in this region had not been pre-loaded by the height of the former landfill, nor was any compaction applied during filling operations.

DESCRIPTION AND PROPERTIES OF THE LANDFILL DEPOSITS

At the time of construction, the landfill had decomposed to a material that can best be described as a well-graded granular material containing fines, making the soils slightly cohesive. The grain size gradation of a typical sample is shown in Figure 2. Approximately 40% of the sample is in the sand-size range with 20% each of silt and gravel. About 15% is classified as clay. In addition, there were large chunks of concrete, occasional timbers, numerous bottles, rubber tires, and pieces of metal in the fill deposit. No organic materials such as paper or rubbish were identified within these deposits. Atterberg limits tests performed upon the portion passing the No. 40 sieve yielded a liquid limit of 31 and a plasticity index of 7. According to the Unified Soil Classification System, this

FIGURE 1 - GENERALIZED SUBSURFACE PROFILE

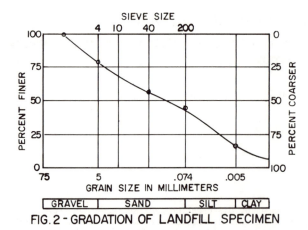

FIG. 2 - GRADATION OF LANDFILL SPECIMEN

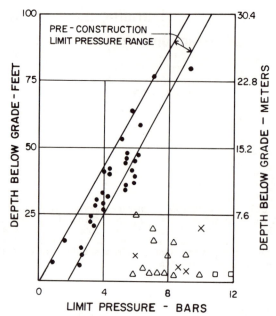

KEY : • TESTS IN NORMALLY CONSOLIDATED LANDFILL
× TESTS IN CONVENTIONAL COMPACTED LANDFILL
□ TESTS IN TEST SECTION 2
△ TESTS IN DYNAMICALLY COMPACTED LANDFILL

FIGURE 3

PRESSUREMETER TEST RESULTS

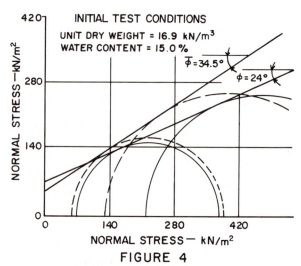

FIGURE 4

CONSOLIDATED UNDRAINED TRIAXIAL SHEAR TEST
ON LABORATORY COMPACTED LANDFILL

specimen would be SC bordering on SC-SM. The natural water content of the fill was on the order of 15 to 27% above the prevailing water table and about 20 to 30% below the water table.

Monitoring of boreholes with gas measuring devices indicated that combustible gas was not present within the landfill which is another indication that the organic matter had decomposed. A gas venting system that was originally thought necessary was not provided beneath the slabs.

The Standard Penetration Resistance Values were quite erratic and were frequently as low as five blows per 30 cm to depths as great as 20 m below grade. Higher Standard Penetration Resistance Values were encountered at certain levels, presumably on larger obstructions within the fill.

Pressuremeter tests were performed within boreholes extending through the fill. Typical limit pressure values plotted against depth are shown on Figure 3.

The tests shown by the solid dots represent the tests performed in advance of construction. Most of the tests fall within a band labelled "Preconstruction Limit Pressure Range".

This range indicates the self-bearing limit pressure for this deposit; i.e., the limit pressure for a normally consolidated landfill deposit at varying depths below grade. This band represents a lower bound of limit pressure from which to compare the limit pressure of compacted fills. Compaction will induce preconsolidation of the fill deposit so the limit pressure of compacted fills should be higher than this range. The difference between the limit pressure of the compacted fill and the lower bound range will depend upon the degree of compaction achieved. Previously, the self-bearing limit pressure for a sand has been reported as 6 bars (1) and for a silt as 4 bars. Unfortunately, these values were not correlated to the confining pressure of the overburden.

Undisturbed specimens of the landfill could not be obtained with shelby tube piston samplers because of the large size debris within the landfill as well as the extremely loose condition of this deposit. To obtain additional information on the shear strength parameters of densified landfill, two large diameter (30 cm) specimens were compacted and tested in a triaxial chamber. The specimens were compacted to a unit dry weight of 16.9 kN/m³ which corresponds to 95% of the

maximum density obtained in the field test rolling discussed in the next section of this paper. The specimens were compacted at the natural water content of the fill which was 15%. Each sample was then saturated by the backpressure method prior to performing a consolidated undrained triaxial, $\overline{CU}$ test with pore pressure measurements.

The results of the $\overline{CU}$ triaxial tests are shown in Figure 4.

The drained angle of shearing resistance, $\bar{\phi}$, was 34.5⁰ with a cohesion intercept, $\bar{c}$, of 39 kN/m². The friction angle, $\bar{\phi}$, is typical for a granular soil containing a significant portion of silt (2). The cohesion intercept is higher than anticipated and is attributed to the clay size particles within the landfill.

CONVENTIONAL COMPACTION RESULTS

Because of the erratic nature of the fill and high amount of large size particles, laboratory moisture-density tests were not performed. The maximum unit dry weight for compaction purposes was determined in advance of construction by field compaction test sections. Three test sections were initiated to determine the compaction characteristics of the landfill deposits at different locations. Site material was spread out to a thickness of 30 cm over a width of 6 m and length of 15 m. At each test section, one portion of the strip was compacted with a self-propelled vibratory roller. The remaining portion was compacted with a 104-cm diameter sheepsfoot roller pulled by a dozer. Three lifts of site materials were placed and compacted at each test section.

All three test sections behaved in a similar manner, so only the test results from test section 2 are shown in Figure 5. The vibratory roller resulted in a unit dry weight of 17.8 kN/m³ after five passes. The sheepsfoot roller resulted in low and erratic compacted unit weights ranging from 13 to 14 kN/m³. The feet of the compactor tended to loosen the deposit as they lifted from the landfill which was detrimental to obtaining good compaction. The vibratory roller was then selected for the construction. In the future building areas, a minimum compacted density of 95% of 17.8 kN/m³ was established. In future parking areas, the specified compaction was 90% of 17.8 kN/m³.

Three pressuremeter tests were performed at a depth of 0.6 m below grade within the compacted test section. The pressuremeter modulus was found to range from 120 to 130 bars with limit pressures ranging from 11 to 13 bars. This represents a vast improvement over the "in-situ" conditions. As shown in Figure 3, a comparable limit pressure of 11 bars would not be attained within a normally consolidated landfill unless the overburden were greater than about 30 m.

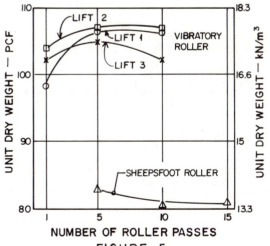

NUMBER OF ROLLER PASSES

FIGURE 5

EFFECT OF ROLLER PASSES ON COMPACTED DENSITY

For a comparison with compacted areas, 37 field density tests were performed on uncompacted site landfill deposits. The lowest unit dry weights were found to range from 7 to 8 kN/m³ for a cinder and ash. The typical unit dry weight of landfill ranged from 11.7 to 14.2 kN/m³. Based upon these unit weights, a volumetric shrinkage of 17% was calculated.

Earthwork operations started in September, 1975. Field density tests were performed on each lift of soil. The compacted densities were found to range from 90 to 95% of 17.8 kN/m³. Fortunately, the cut and fill operations occurred above the water table and the water content of the landfill was near optimum for compaction. Some blading and drying was undertaken prior to compaction. Discing could not be undertaken because the large debris in the landfill frequently broke the discs. Where cuts were made below the water table in the transition area, the fines in the landfill made the fill unworkable. It was necessary to stockpile the fill to allow it to dry before compaction.

During November, 1975, wet and cold weather conditions developed and the degree of compaction declined to less than 90%. Since the winter months were approaching and less favorable conditions were anticipated, the remaining fill was stabilized with western coal flyash containing a high lime content. The flyash was spread from trucks and mixed by blading. The flyash content ranged from 6 to 10% by weight and this was sufficient to reduce the water content by about 4 to 6% prior to compaction. With this procedure, the compacted densities once again exceeded 90% of 17.8 kN/m³. The following year, it was observed that some cementation occurred as a result of this stabilization. Approximately the uppermost 6 m of the fill was stabilized with the flyash.

It was originally anticipated that some of the landfill from the cut areas would be unsuitable for fill, either because of high organic content or large debris. However, all the landfill was found acceptable so none was removed from the site.

Following completion of the earthwork operations on November 22, 1975, 12 settlement observation plates were embedded in the landfill where the thickness of compacted landfill ranged from 9 to 18 m to measure post-construction settlement. Elevation readings were taken four times per month until February, 1976. The majority of the settlement occurred within the first month following completion of filling, and almost no settlement occurred after January 8, 1976.

In the building areas where 95% compaction was achieved, the post-construction settlements were on the order of .4 to .5% of the height of the fill. In parking areas, the degree of compaction was relaxed to 90% and the settlements were on the order of .7 to .9% of the height of fill. These compressions are typical for granular deposits (3).

DYNAMIC COMPACTION

Dynamic compaction was undertaken using a 6-tonne weight dropped from a height of 11 to 12 m. In the compacted fill areas, the dynamic compaction was applied only at the footing locations to further improve the deposits. In the cut and transitional areas, dynamic compaction was undertaken on a grid basis throughout the entire building area plus 3 m beyond with a 2-m spacing between the center of the impacts. This was followed by additional impacting at the footing locations. The applied

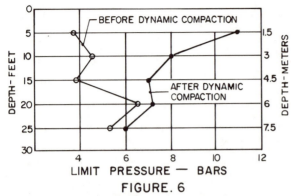

FIGURE. 6

INCREASE IN LIMIT PRESSURE DUE TO DYNAMIC COMPACTION

energy ranged from 130 ton-meters/meter^2 (Tm/m^2) in the slab area to 260 Tm/m^2 in the footing areas. Details of the dynamic compaction were presented in an earlier paper (4).

Soil borings and pressuremeter tests were completed following dynamic compaction to determine the degree and depth of improvement. The results of the pressure-meter tests at a typical footing location are summarized in Figure 6. In this area, there was a cut of about 8 to 10 meters prior to dynamic compaction. Improvements to depths of about 6 m were noted. This was considered to be a satisfactory depth improvement since the deep seated deposits had been previously densified by the landfill that was removed from these areas.

Typically, limit pressures of 5 to 10 bars and modulus values of 50 to 100 bars were achieved within the depth range of 1 to 6 m below grade. Typical limit pressure test results are shown on Figure 3. The limit pressures following dynamic compaction or roller compaction were not as high as measured in the test section where the the limit pressures ranged from 11 to 13 bars and the pressuremeter modulus ranged from 120 to 130 bars. This is attributed to the lower degree of compaction in the mass fill than was attained in the test section. However, a minimum limit pressure of 5 bars or modulus of 50 bars was considered acceptable for this project to produce the proper bearing capacity and limit settle-ment to tolerable values.

At a few isolated locations, the landfill was so weak or wet that the weight would become buried below the landfill surface following impact. At these locations, crushed stone fill was deposited within the craters and dynamic compaction resumed until satisfactory resis-tance was obtained. Weaker-than-normal support condi-tions were also encountered at the boundaries of the landfill and natural clay deposits. Some arching of the landfill may have occurred, thereby resulting in a looser condition of the landfill immediately adjacent to the near-vertical faces of the clay deposit. At all but a few isolated locations, it was not necessary to place granular fill at the surface of the landfill to provide a mat for the weight to impact into. Following dynamic compaction, the landfill was levelled by pushing the fill from between the craters into the craters. The surface area was then densified by making three passes with a fully loaded dump truck.

In the cut and transition areas, the average ground depressions following dynamic compaction ranged from

30 to 50 cm. This ranged from about 5 to 10% of the thickness of the deposit that was densified. In the fill area where flyash stabilization and conventional compaction was undertaken, the crater depths were only on the order of 20 cm and the average ground depression only about 7 cm. This is attributed to the cementation that occurred within the landfill from the flyash as well as from higher compacted densities in the fill.

PERFORMANCE

Settlement readings were taken on footing foundations in both one and two-story buildings as the structures were constructed and for one to two months thereafter. Measured settlements were on the order of 1.5 to 2 cm which was the magnitude predicted based upon an antici-pated pressuremeter modulus of 50 to 60 bars that would be achieved following dynamic compaction or conventional compaction.

CONCLUSIONS

After the organic material has decomposed, landfill deposits can be classified as suitable materials for engineered construction. At this site, the landfill behaved similar to a granular soil with fines and a slight cohesion.

The landfill deposits at this site were compacted by different methods. In fill areas, thin lifts of con-trolled fill were compacted by conventional compaction equipment consisting of a vibrating roller. Compacted densities ranging from 90 to 98% of 17.8 kN/m^3 were achieved.

In cut and transitional areas, the landfill deposits were compacted by means of dynamic compaction. Pressure-meter modulus values ranging from 50 to 100 bars and limit pressures ranging from 5 to 10 bars were achieved within the zone of improvement.

Both methods of densification were sufficient to limit settlement for one to two-story buildings to values on the order of 1.5 to 2 cm.

REFERENCES

(1) Menard, L., "Interpretation and Application of Pressuremeter Test Results", Sols Number 26, 1975., p. 40.

(2) Peck, R.B., Hansen, W.E., and Thornburn, T.H., "Foundation Engineering", 2nd Edition, John A. Wiley & Sons, 1974.

(3) Department of the Navy, Bureau of Yards and Docks, Design Manual DM-7, Soil Mechanics-Foundations and Earth Structures, February, 1962.

(4) Lukas, R.G., "Densification of Loose Deposits by Pounding", ASCE Journal of the Geotechnical Engi-neering Division, Vol. 106, No. GT4, April, 1980.

Effect of surface reinforcing of soft soils

Effet du armement superficiel des sols moux

B. MAJES, Assistant, Edvard Kardelj University, Ljubljana, Yugoslavia
D. BATTELINO, Lecturer, Edvard Kardelj University, Ljubljana, Yugoslavia

SYNOPSIS   The behaviour of reinforced footing on soft subsoils has been analyzed by the
finite element method. The soil has been treated as a hypoelastic-plastic body and the reinforcement as an elastic membrance. Linear elements of the reinforcement are compatibly bound with the
triangular mesh of the soil body. Data of some model tests have been used for the verification of
the computer program. From the application of the program for a road embankment lying on a soft
clayey layer the following conclusions could be drawn:

(1) The geotextile membrance restrains the lateral displacements of the subsoil, favourably
     modifies the displacement pattern reducing somewhat maximum settlements and increases the
     bearing capacity.

(2) In a poorly permeable undrained soils the reinforcing effect is particularly pronounced in the
     initial consolidation phase of prevailing distortional displacements.

(3) The finite element method is a useful tool for predicting the reinforcing effect.

INTRODUCTION

In order to increase the bearing capacity of
soft soils under road embankments the transverse
reinforcement of the footing has been applied
for hundreds of years. In the past, trunks,
branches or fascines were mainly used for this
purpose. In recent years metal reinforcing grids
have also been used to some extent. However,
geotextiles seem to have replaced most of the
ancient materials, at least in the industrial-
ized countries (Eggestad, 1983).

In the past such strengthening constructions were
governed only by experience. Modern trends are
to put criteria for their need and suitability
on the base of computation procedures that take
into account soil and reinforcement properties
as well as the conditions for their cooperation.

In this paper we shall endeavour to contribute
to the elaboration of such criteria through a
finite element analysis. The soil will be treated as a hypoelastic-plastic body with the Mohr-
Coulomb failure criterium, and the reinforcement
as an elastic membrane having a certain tension
strength. The procedure described in the next
chapter will first be verified by its application to the data of some model tests and then
used for predicting the effects of the surface
reinforcement of soft soils under a road embankment.

In the present phase of our investigations the
viscous properties of materials will be neglected. The consolidation which is governed by the
hydraulic seepage resistance will be considered
only by separate analyses of the reinforcing
effect in the beginning phase of pure distorsion-
al deformations and in the phase at the end of
primary consolidation. The effect of the number
of reinforcing layers will be elucidated as well.

NUMERICAL PROCEDURE

The computer program for the numerical analysis
according to the finite element method has been
elaborated for plane strain states. The contour
of the compatible network of finite elements can
be arbitrary provided that it is composed of
straight lines between external nodes of triangular elements into which the soil body has been
discretized; the network can include the embankment and several soil layers. The triangular
elements have six degrees of freedom. The reinforcement is continuously composed of linear
elements with four degrees of freedom; their
nodes coincide compatibly with the nodes of the
finite element mesh of the soil body. On the
contour of the soil body either nodal forces or
nodal displacements or partly forces and partly
displacements can be prescribed.

The hypoelastic stress-strain relationships for
soils are expressed as non-linear relationships
between octahedral values of strains (ε^0, γ^0)
and stresses (σ^0, τ^0):

$$\varepsilon^0 = \varepsilon^0(\sigma^0, \tau^0) \quad , \quad \gamma^0 = \gamma^0(\tau^0, \sigma^0) \qquad (1), (2)$$

either by analytical functions or by sets of
coordinate values using splines for interpolation. Equation (2) includes the failure states
at which the shear strains tend to infinity.
Equations (1) and (2) yield the corresponding
relationships between the tangent values of the
compression (K) and shear (G) moduli resp. and
the octahedral stresses:

$$K = K(\sigma^0, \tau^0) \quad , \quad G = G(\tau^0, \sigma^0) \qquad (3), (4)$$

whereby

$$K = (1/3)/(\partial\varepsilon^0/\partial\sigma^0), \quad G = 1/(\partial\gamma^0/\partial\tau^0) \quad (5), (6)$$

In soils the strains are deduced from displacements according to the first order theory.

For the reinforcement linear stress-strain relationship has been taken, the tension strength representing the limit of the elastic behaviour. According to the membrane character of the reinforcement, the second order theory has been applied.

Neither consolidation nor viscous properties have been considered in the present phase of our analysis.

MODEL TESTS

The reinforcement effect has been illustrated by some tests in a model kit 28 cm high, 29.7 cm wide and 150 cm long. Into this kit a remoulded saturated silty clay of very high compressibility was placed in layers of 3 cm up to the height of 18 cm ; the upper surface of each layer was colored. The surface of the highest layer was covered by a 3 cm thick layer of fine sand. A rigid wooden plate b = 29 cm wide and l = 9.5 cm long was put onto the sand in the middle of the kit. The average pressure below the plate was first 3.5 kPa and increased in time intervals of 24 hours by 7 kPa .

Two test series have been performed: the first without the fabric, the second with the fabric put in a length $3\,l$ = 28.5 cm on the clay surface before covering it with sand. The product of the modulus of elasticity E_r and the thickness a of the fabric was $a\,E_r$ = 1350 kN/m .

The water content of the clay was determined at the placing (w_{in}) and at the end (w_{end}) of each test series. The following values were ascertained (1st , 2nd series):

$$w_{in} = 35.7 \ , \ 44.3 \ \% \ , \quad w_{end} = 44.7 \ , \ 44.6 \ \% \ .$$

On one of both longitudinal lateral plexiglass plates of the kit a network of vertical and horizontal lines was marked in order to facilitate the registration of the displacements of coulored interlayer surfaces. In both test series the displacements were observed up to the failure load reaching the values of q_f = 24.5 and 38.5 kPa respectively.

Since the model scales cannot be successfully realized, the model test results cannot be directly applied for prediction of the behaviour of a prototype. Nevertheless, the comparison of measured displacements with computed values obtained by using the material properties and data of model tests, can serve for the verification of the suitability of the numerical procedure. In our concrete case the following assumptions could be taken: (1) the displacements developed in undrained conditions (Poisson's ratio close to 0.50), (2) the model soil can be considered as an ideal elastic-plastic body with deformation modulus E_s obtained in the domain of approximately linearly increasing settlements (q = 10.5 kPa) of the unreinforced soil, and with the cohesion c (at ϕ = 0) according to Prandtl's solution and corresponding to the load q at which the settlements started to increase with acceleration (q = 24.5 kPa). - Since the

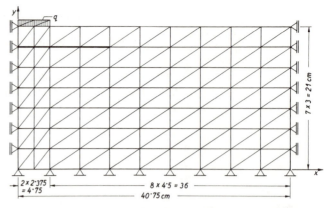

Fig.1   Model test: network of finite elements and boundary conditions.

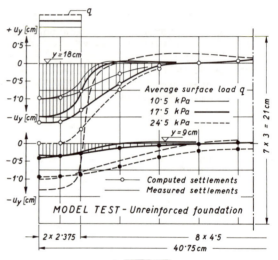

Fig.2   Model test: without fabric. Comparison of computed and observed settlement diagrams.

water content and with it the deformability could not be kept quite constant in successive test series, the E_s modulus in the second series (reinforced footing) was deduced from the settlements in the load axis at q = 17.5 kPa . The following values were obtained:

$$E_{s1} = 42 \text{ kPa} \ , \quad E_{s2} = 65 \text{ kPa} \quad \text{(both values at}$$
$\nu = 0.48$), $c_1 = c_2 = 4.8$ kPa .

The comparison of measured settlements and those computed with E_{s1} for the first series (unreinforced soil) and E_{s2} resp. for the second series (reinforced soil with $a\,E_r$ = 1350 kN/m), with c = 4.8 kPa , ν = 0.48 for both series, is presented by diagrams $u_y = \{u_y(x)\}_{y=18 \text{ cm}}$ in Figs 2 and 3 resp. while Fig.1 presents the finite element mesh used and the boundary conditions; the rigid loading plate was discretized in four triangular elements of very high stiffness ($E_q = 5 \cdot 10^8$ kPa at $\nu_q = 0$). For both series the settlement diagrams are presented for three load intensities: $q = 10.5$, 17.5 and 24.5 kPa . In the second test series (Fig.3) (reinforced soil) the computed settlements approach satisfactorily the measured values. The discrepancies in the first series (without fabric) are probably mainly due to the effect of the penetration of the rigid plate through the sandy covering layer (confer Tcheng, 1957). In greater depths the difference between computed and measured values is not important even in the unreinforced soil. (For the level $y = 9$ cm the comparison is presented in Fig.2.)

The local safety has been defined by the quotient τ_f^o / τ^o , τ^o being the octahedral shear stress and τ_f^o its failure value: $\tau_f^o = (2\sqrt{2}/3) \, c$ (confer equation 9 for $\phi = 0$). For the load $q = 17.5$ kPa the isolines τ_f^o / τ^o are presented in Fig.4 for the unreinforced soil and in Fig.5 for the reinforced soil. The favourable effect of the reinforcement on the increase of the bearing capacity is evident.

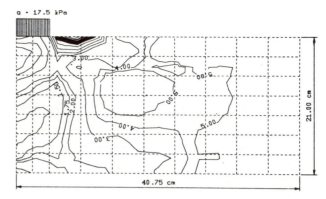

q · 17.5 kPa

Fig.5 Model test: with fabric. Isolines
τ_f^o / τ^o at $q = 17.5$ kPa .

In general the above comparisons confirm the applicability of the elaborated computer program.

APPLICATION TO A ROAD EMBANKMENT

The above described and verified computer program was applied to a symmetric trapezoidal road embankment (width 9 + 2 x 9 = 27 m) put directly on a very compressible saturated silty clay of 9 m thickness lying on a horizontal rigid base. The tangent compression (K) and shear (G) moduli of the clay could be expressed by the following analytical functions:

$$K = a + b \, \sigma^{0\cdot} \quad (\sigma^{0\cdot} \text{ positive for tension}) \quad (7)$$

$$G = f(\tau_f^o - \tau^o) \quad (8)$$

with the following parameter values:

$a = 100$ kPa , $b = -8$, $f = 5.27$
τ_f^o is the octahedral shear stress at failure:

$$\tau_f^o = \{2\sqrt{2} \cos\phi' / (3 - \sin\phi')\}(c - \sigma^{0\cdot} \tan\phi') \quad (9)$$

$c = 7$ kPa , $\phi' = 25^o$

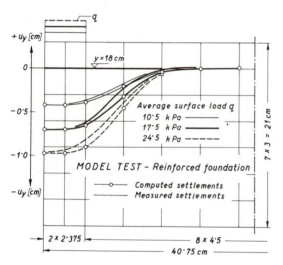

q · 17.5 kPa

Fig.3 Model test: with fabric. Comparison of computed and observed settlements.

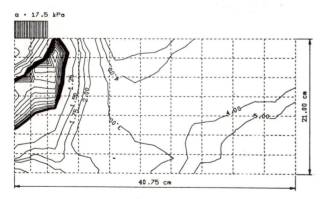

q · 17.5 kPa

Fig.4 Model test: without fabric. Isolines
τ_f^o / τ^o at $q = 17.5$ kPa .

The initial stress state corresponds to the void ratio $e_0 = 2.92$ in stressless state and to the earth-pressure coefficient at rest $K_0 = 0.667$. The discretization of the soil layer into a network of triangular finite elements and the boundary displacement conditions are shown in Fig.6 . The discretization is denser near the surface between the depths 0.30 , 0.60 and 0.90 m representing the levels of the triple reinforcement by non-woven geotextile with the value $a \, E_r = 4350$ kN/m . The single reinforcement by the same membrane was placed in the depth 0.60 m and the double one on the levels 0.30 and 0.90 m . The unit weight of the embankment fill has been taken 20 kN/m^3 ; the embankment profile was not included into the network of finite elements; its weight has been considered to be transferred on the soil by surface nodal forces linearly proportional to the height of the fill above the nodes. The reinforcements have been laid along the entire fill-soil contact and on both sides by 9 m outside the foot of the embankment.

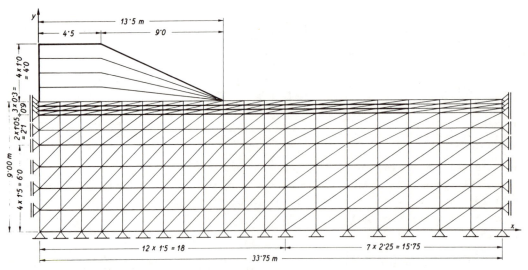

Fig.6   Road embankment. Network of finite elements and boundary conditions.

With the above defined material properties , displacements, strains and stresses in the soil have been computed for several embankment heights up to 6 m . For the heights 1 , 2 and 4 m the resulting settlement diagrams $u_y = \{u_y(x)\}_{y=9}$ m are presented in Fig.7 ; two alternatives have been considered: the unreinforced soil and the triply reinforced soil. For heights 1 and 2 m the reduction of settlements by reinforcement is not important and could hardly justify the costs of reinforcement. The settlements of the 4 m high embankment are too large to be tolerated; neither do they allow the application of the first order theory. (The program can, however, easily be extended to allow for large deformations, similarly as by Boutroup and Holtz, 1983.)

Now, the above presented "drained" analysis can give a definite answer concerning the safety of

the embankment and the role of the reinforcement only in cases when the consolidation is forwarded by vertical drainage, event. combined with preloading, and on condition the loading proceeds slowly enough. Even in such cases the speed of the pore-pressure dissipation has to be taken into account at least by an approximate analysis. For undrained and non-preloaded soils a rough evaluation of displacements and safety can be made by combining the "drained" and "undrained" analysis. For the latter the total stress-strain relationships have to be applied as deduced from undrained triaxial or biaxial tests. Since the undrained displacements occur at unchanged porosity and since during the consolidation the spheric deformations are accompanied by additional deviatoric displacements, the final settlements approach the values obtained by superposing undrained and drained displacements.

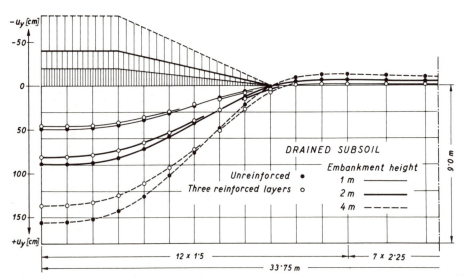

Fig.7   Road embankment: drained conditions. Comparison of settlements of unreinforced and of triply reinforced soil surface: for three different embankment heights.

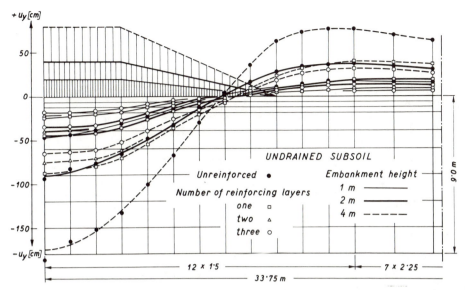

Fig.8   Road embankment: undrained conditions. Comparison of settlements for three embankment heights (1 , 2 and 4 m) and for four reinforcement alternatives: unreinforced soil, single, double and triple reinforcement.

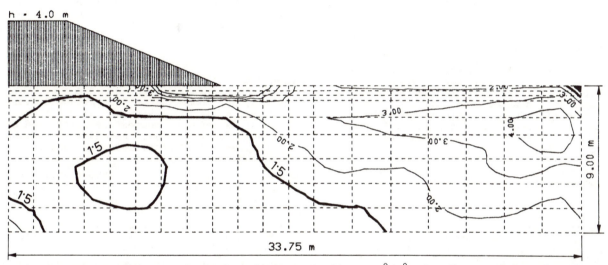

Fig.9   Road embankment: undrained conditions. Isolines τ_f^o/τ^o for the unreinforced soil at the embankment height 4 m .

Missing analytical expressions for the undrained behaviour of the same soil we have repeated the above presented "drained" analysis with unchanged $G = G(\tau^o, \sigma^o)$ relationship at $\nu = 0.499$, reducing the strength parameters to $c = 5$ kPa , $\phi = 12^o$. The resulting settlement diagrams are presented in Fig.8 for the unreinforced as well as for all three reinforced alternatives (one, two and three reinforcement layers). The diagrams prove favourable reinforcement effect up to the embankment height 4 m with modest yet pronounced decrease of settlements with increasing number of reinforcement layers.

For the embankment height 4 m , Fig.9 represents isolines τ_f^o/τ^o (τ_f^o according to equation

9) for the unreinforced soil, and Fig.10 for the single reinforcement. The comparison proves the favourable effect of reinforcement on the increase of safety.

DISCUSSION AND CONCLUSIONS

Additionally the described computer program was applied to the case treated in the foregoing chapter with the only difference that down to the depth 0.90 m below the fill-soil contact the silty clay was replaced by a fine sand with a constant deformation modulus E_c = 20 000 kPa at $\nu = 0.3$. Already at the height 1 m of the embankment plastification (τ_f^o/τ^o < 1) began to

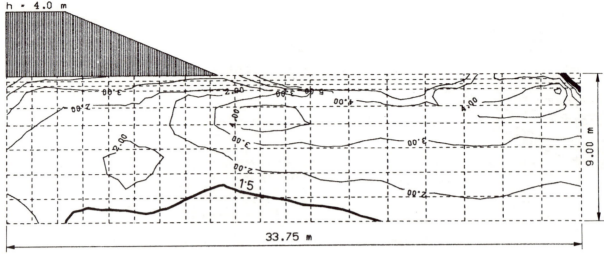

Fig.10   Road embankment: undrained conditions. Isolines τ_f^0/τ^0 in the case of single
reinforcement, height 4 m .

develop in the sandy cover, provoked probably by
large horizontal displacements of the clay in
the contact surface. In the program of further
investigations we intend to introduce special
interface elements between the fabric and adjacent soil as well as along contacts between
soils of very different deformation properties
allowing for slip along interfaces. Such interface elements have already been developed by
Barksdale & all., 1983, while Brown and Poulos,
1981, take into consideration the slip along
the soil-reinforcement interfaces only after
full mobilization of friction; constant resistance is assumed thereafter (see also Mitchell
and Katti, 1981).

With the above indicated limitations the present
study permits the following conclusions:

(1) The geotextile membrane restrains the lateral
    displacements of the subsoil, favourably mo-
    difies the displacement pattern reducing
    somewhat maximum settlements and increases
    the bearing capacity (in accordance with
    Schlosser & all., 1983).

(2) In poorly permeable undrained soils the rein-
    forcing effect is particularly pronounced in
    the initial consolidation phase of prevail-
    ing distortional displacements.

(3) The finite element method is a useful tool
    for predicting the reinforcing effect.

ACKNOWLEDGEMENT

This study has been made at the Civil Engineering
Department of the Edvard Kardelj University in
Ljubljana in the scope of the research project
"Design criteria and predictive techniques for
embankments on soft soils" supported by the
Research Community of Slovenia and the US Department of Transportation, Federal Highway Administration, and supervised by Prof. L. Šuklje. The
authors wish to thank Prof. Šuklje for his valuable assistance.

The grant of the Road Community of Slovenia and
the friendly aid of Mr. Z. Breška in adjusting
the computer program for the graphical presentation of local safety isolines are gratefully
acknowledged.

REFERENCES

Barksdale, R., Robnett, Q., Lai, J. and Zeevart-
   Wolff, A. (1982). Experimental and theoretical behavior of geotextile reinforced aggregate soil systems. Second International
   Conference on Geotextiles, Las Vegas,
   375-380.

Boutrup, E., and Holtz, R.D. (1983). Analysis
   of embankments on soft ground reinforced
   with geotextiles. Proc. 8th Eur. Conf. Soil
   Mech. Found. Engg, (2), 469-472, Helsinki.

Brown, B.S., and Poulos, H.G. (1981). Analysis
   of foundations on reinforced soil. Proc.
   10th ICSMFE, (3), 595-598, Stockholm.

Eggestad, Å. (1983). Improvement of cohesive
   soils. State-of-the-art report. Proc.
   8th Eur. Conf. Soil Mech. Found. Engg, (3),
   991-1007, Helsinki.

Mitchell, J.K., and Katti, R.K. (1981). Soil
   improvement - General report (preliminary).
   10th ICSMFE , General Reports, State-of-the-
   art Reports, Lectures, 163-171, Stockholm.

Schlosser, F., Jacobsen, H.M., Juran, I. (1983).
   Soil reinforcement. General report. Proc.
   8th Eur. Conf. Soil Mech. Found. Engg,
   (3), 1159-1180, Helsinki.

Tcheng, Y. (1957). Fondations superficielles en
   milieu stratifié. Proc. 4th ICSMFE, (1),
   449-452, London.

Soil strengthening using randomly distributed mesh elements

Renforcement de sol par éléments de grillage distribués au hazard

A. MCGOWN, Reader, University of Strathclyde, Scotland, UK
K. Z. ANDRAWES, Senior Lecturer, University of Strathclyde, Scotland, UK
N. HYTIRIS, Research Assistant, University of Strathclyde, Scotland, UK
F. B. MERCER, President, NETLON Ltd., UK

SYNOPSIS

The paper considers the influence of randomly distributed polymeric mesh elements on the strength
of a granular soil. Their action is to interlock particles and groups of particles together to
form a coherent matrix. 150mm diameter drained triaxial tests and small scale footing tests both
show that the mesh elements improve the strength of the soil at all strain levels, even very
small strains.

INTRODUCTION

Recently undertaken research into the use of
randomly distributed polymeric mesh elements
in soils, MERCER et al (1984), has shown that
the meshes interlock with the soil particles
and produce a strengthening at the meso-scale.
As with soil strengthening by roots, WALDRON
(1977), and by man-made fibres, ANDERSLAND AND
KHATTAR (1979), HOARE (1979), LEFLAIVE (1982)
and GRAY and OHASHI (1983), the ductility and
permeability of the soil are not reduced and a
relatively homogeneous composite is produced.
The principal advantage of using mesh elements
is their interlock action. This occurs at two
levels with the ribs of individual mesh elements interlocking with groups of soil particles to form an aggregation of particles, Fig.
1(a), then adjacent aggregations interlocking
to form a coherent matrix, Fig. 1(b). Numerous types of mesh elements are now being
tested in a range of soil types and the practical problems of supplying and mixing them
with different soils in various situations are
being investigated. However, in order to
demonstrate the operational mechanisms and
levels of soil improvement to be gained from
the use of these materials, this paper will
only describe triaxial and model footing test
data obtained using one mesh type mixed with
one soil type.

MATERIALS TESTED

Soil: The soil used is a processed fluvio-
glacial sand known as Mid-Ross sand. It has
sub-angular particles ranging in size from
0.05 to 7.0mm diameter with a uniformity coefficient of 5.

Mesh Elements: The mesh is manufactured from
polypropylene using the NETLON extrusion process. It has a mass per unit area of $52g/m^2$,
filament thicknesses of 0.5mm (M.D.) and
0.48mm (X.M.D.) and openings 6.7 x 7.1mm.
The maximum tensile strength of the mesh when
tested as 200 x 100mm specimens, at a constant
rate of strain of 2 per cent per min. and
temperature of 20°C was 3.5 kN/m (M.D.) and

3.8 kN/m (X.M.D.). For the tests reported in
this paper, the mesh was cut into elements
50 x 50mm.

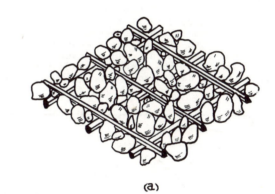

(a)

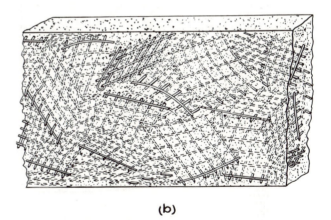

(b)

Fig. 1. THE INTERLOCK MECHANISM FOR MESH
ELEMENTS
(a) Interlock with groups of particles
(b) Interlock of adjacent aggregations

TRIAXIAL TESTS

To determine the fundamental stress-strain behaviour of soil-mesh mixtures, drained triaxial tests 150mm diameter x 200mm high with lubricated ends, were carried out on Mid-Ross Sand alone and when it was mixed with various proportions of mesh elements. The sand with or without the mesh elements, was compacted and tested in a dry state. The type and level of compactive effort was equivalent to the standard Proctor compaction but was carried out in a specially prepared split mould. The achieved dry densities of sand and sand-mesh mixtures varied from 1800 to 1849 kg/m^3 the sand alone having an average of 1827 kg/m^3 and the sand-mesh mixtures having the same or a slightly greater average density. Cell pressures used ranged from 10 to 300 kN/m^2 and the tests were conducted at a constant rate of strain of 0.05 per cent per minute.

Test Series A: A large number of triaxial tests were conducted on the soil alone. The deviator stress-axial strain behaviour of the sand recorded in these tests was then used as the basis of comparison for the behaviour of the sand when mixed with various proportions of mesh elements.

Test Series B: These were conducted on sand with 0.18 per cent of mesh by dry weight of soil, which is 66 m^2 of mesh per m^3 of soil (66m^2/m^3). Figure 2 shows the relationship between deviator stress and axial strain for the sand with and without these mesh elements, when tested at different cell pressures. It clearly shows that the mesh increased the deviator stress developed at all strains, even

at very small strains, and that peak stresses in the sand-mesh mixture occurred at slightly higher axial strains than for the sand alone. To illustrate these improvements Mohr failure envelopes for the sand with and without the mesh elements were constructed for peak stress conditions as shown in Fig. 3(a). Equivalent envelopes, based on mobilised stresses at 1.0 and 15.0 per cent axial strains were also produced, Fig. 3(b), to show the improved behaviour of the composite at low and high strain conditions. From these and similar envelopes at different constant axial strains, the increase in shear resistance ($\Delta \tau$) can be plotted against normal stress (σ) for both peak stress and constant axial strain conditions, as shown in Figs. 4(a) and (b) respectively. The peak stress condition does not fit exactly the pattern shown for constant axial strain conditions as it compares stresses developed at unequal axial strains.

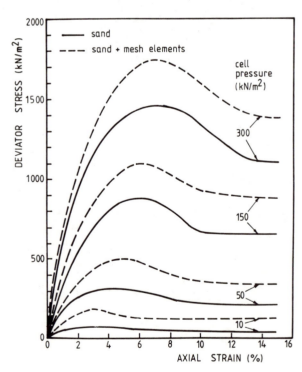

Fig. 2. RELATIONSHIPS BETWEEN DEVIATOR STRESS AND AXIAL STRAIN FROM DRAINED TRIAXIAL TESTS

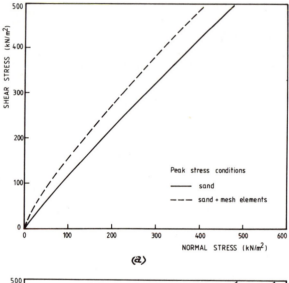

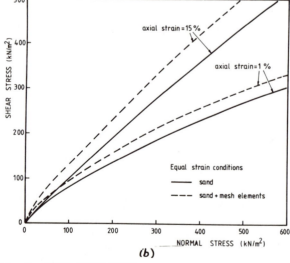

Fig. 3. MOHR ENVELOPES
(a) At peak stress conditions
(b) At 1 and 15% equal strain conditions

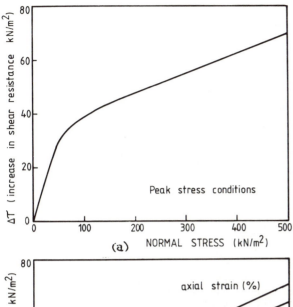

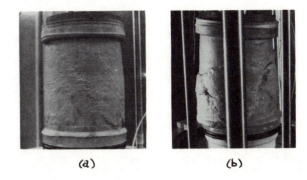

Fig. 5. THE DEFORMED TRIAXIAL SAMPLES AT LARGE STRAINS
(a)   Sand alone
(b)   Sand with mesh elements

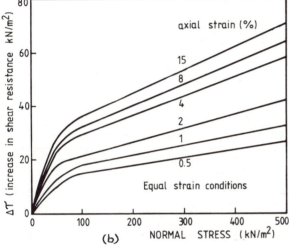

Fig. 4. INCREASE IN SHEAR RESISTANCE WITH NORMAL STRESS
(a)   At peak stress conditions
(b)   At equal strain conditions

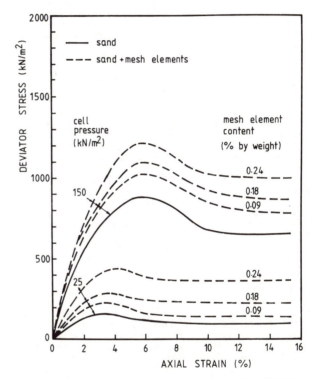

Fig. 6. RELATIONSHIPS BETWEEN DEVIATOR STRESS AND AXIAL STRAIN FOR DIFFERENT PROPORTIONS OF MESH ELEMENTS

The behaviours indicated by the data from Test Series A and B clearly demonstrate the ability of the mesh elements to generate tensile strain resistance from the beginning of the test. The tendency for the improvements to level-off at high axial strains is believed to be associated with the soil alone and soil-mesh composite both approaching their state of constant volume. Further drained triaxial tests on saturated samples in which volume changes can be measured to investigate this phenomenon are planned, but photographic records of the forms of soil alone and soil-mesh test specimens when both are at large strains, Figs. 5(a) and (b), illustrate the changes in overall deformation characteristics that the mesh content imposes on the sand as it is strained. Thus the sand with mesh elements has both different strength and deformation characteristics from the sand alone.

Test Series C: As an indication of the influence of the proportion of mesh elements mixed

with the sand, further tests were conducted using the same mesh elements as before, but in the proportions of 0.09, 0.18 and 0.24% by weight of soil which are 33,66 and 90 m^2/m^3 respectively. The data obtained for these three mesh proportions are shown in Fig. 6 for 25 and 150 kN/m^2 cell pressures. As indicated in this diagram the improvement in deviator stress is related to the proportion of mesh elements present. Obviously it will be important to determine the actual quantitative relationship between the proportion of mesh and improvement achieved, for the design of soil-mesh mixtures.

MODEL FOOTING TESTS

In order to ensure that the improvements measured in the triaxial tests could be measured
in a simple soil-mesh system, model footing
tests were undertaken. The test tank was
glass-sided and 640mm long x 300mm deep x 75mm
wide. It was filled with dry Mid-Ross Sand
placed in a dense state. A smooth metal footing 75 x 75mm was pushed into the soil at a
constant rate of penetration of 1mm/min. Tests
were conducted on sand alone and on sand overlain by a layer of sand-mesh mixture with 0.18%
($66m^2/m^3$) of mesh elements, the depth of this
layer varying in each test from 0.5 to 4.0
times the breadth of the footing. Each test
was repeated at least twice and the data
obtained are shown in Fig. 7(a). Once again
very large improvements were obtained at all
strain levels from the use of the mesh elements. These improvements are indeed very
similar to those measured in the triaxial tests
in terms of both strength and deformation
characteristics and confirm that the improvements measured in the triaxial testing are not
specific to that test.

When unloading the footing tests, a further
significant difference was observed between
the behaviour of the sand and the sand-mesh
mixture, as indicated in Fig. 7(b). This shows
that where a layer of the sand-mesh mixture
was present, almost 20 per cent of the imposed
vertical settlement was recovered, which was 4
times that for the soil alone. This was
probably due to the partial recovery of the
strains in the mesh elements and this improved
system elasticity could well prove to be a very
important property of soil-mesh mixtures,
particularly where repeated loading is
involved. For this reason, cyclic triaxial and
plate bearing tests are now planned on soil-
mesh layers to investigate their deformation
characteristics under repeated loading
conditions.

CONCLUSIONS

The use of randomly distributed polymeric mesh
elements in Mid-Ross Sand has been shown to
greatly improve its strength and beneficially
alter its deformation properties. Triaxial
tests using other soil types mixed with the
mesh show that similar levels of improvement
are obtained. The proportions of the mesh
elements present in any mixture have also been
shown to be important and tests using different
types, sizes and shapes of mesh show that the
tensile load-strain behaviour, flexural
stiffness, rib shapes and sizes and opening
sizes of the mesh are all important factors
influencing the behaviour of the soil-mesh
mixture.

ACKNOWLEDGEMENTS

The work described in this paper has been
carried out at the University of Strathclyde
with the financial support of Netlon Ltd. It
is based on fundamental research conducted by
F. Brian Mercer and patent applications have
been filed in a large number of countries.

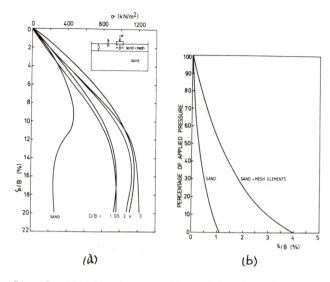

Fig. 7. EFFECT OF DEPTH OF SAND/MESH LAYER ON
THE LOAD SETTLEMENT BEHAVIOUR
(a)   Load-settlement behaviour
(b)   Recoverable settlements.

REFERENCES

Andersland, O.B. and Khattak, A.S., (1979).
Shear Strength of Kaolinite/fibre soil
mixtures. Int. Conf. on Soil Reinforcement:
Reinforced Earth and Other Techniques. (1).
11 - 16. Paris.
Gray, D.H. and Ohashi, H. (1983). Mechanics of
fibre reinforcement in sand. Jour. of Geot.
Eng. ASCE. 109. 3. 335 - 353.
Hoare, D.J. (1979). Laboratory study of
granular soils reinforced with randomly
oriented discrete fibres - a laboratory study.
Int. Conf. on Soil Reinforcement: Reinforced
Earth and Other Techniques. 1. 47 - 52. Paris.
Leflaive, E. (1982). The reinforcement of
granular materials with continuous fibres.
Proc. 2nd Int. Conf. on Geotextiles. 3 721-726.
Las Vegas.
Mercer, F.B. Andrawes, K.Z., McGown, A., and
Hytiris, N. (1984) A new method of soil
stabilisation. Proc. Sym. Polymer Grid Reinf.
in Civil Eng. London. March. Paper 8.1. 7pp.
Waldron, L.J. (1977). The shear resistance of
root-permeated homogenious and stratified
soil. Jour. Soil Sci. Soc. Amer. 41.843 - 849.

Soil improvement using wick drains and preloading

Amélioration du sol en utilisant la mèche des tuyaux avant le chargement

KEITH E. ROBINSON, Dames & Moore, Johannesburg, South Africa
MICHAEL M. EIVEMARK, Robinson Dames & Moore, Vancouver, Canada

SYNOPSIS   This paper describes the use and benefits of wick drains to improve the settlement response of a soft clayey silt in Vancouver, Canada. The use of these vertical drains reduced site development costs to three-quarters, or less, of alternative procedures, while reducing construction time by two to four months and minimizing potential instability at the edge of the fill.

An extensive monitoring programme was implemented to assess the effectiveness of the vertical drains, control the speed of fill placement and determine when the preload would be removed. The results on the monitoring programme are presented, herein, and confirmed the benefits of the wick installation alternative.

INTRODUCTION

On December 15, 1982, the decision was made to construct three warehouses near the Fraser River in Vancouver, Canada, to replace warehouses located within the proposed development of EXPO 86 in downtown Vancouver. Because of the need to quickly develop the EXPO site, the current tennants of the warehouses had to be relocated to their new quarters by December 15, 1983.

The site chosen, by B.C. Hydro & Power Authorities - Railway Division, the property owners and landlords for the warehouses, was adjacent to the main railway line within the old floodplain of the Fraser River. Three adjacent sites were chosen, as shown on Fig.1, for a total site area of 3.9 hectares. The three buildings would occupy 0.61 hectares with the surrounding areas used for parking, driveways and landscaping.

All three buildings were designed to have raised slab grades (about 1.2 m above final yard grade) to accommodate truck and rail loading and unloading. Structural loads from the buildings would average 5 kPa, and the average, long-term floor loading would be 24 kPa. Final yard grade for the three sites was established at Elevation 3.1 m.

SITE AND SOIL CONDITIONS

Sites 1 and 2 were essentially flat-lying, with ground level before foundation improvement varying from Elevation 2.4 to 2.6 m. Both areas were previously used for temporary storage of lumber and scrap metal. Site 3 consisted of part of a cultivated field. The surface of the parcel varied in elevation from 1.7 to 1.9 m.

During the course of the field programme, 16 borings were completed to depths of up to 60 m, to assess subsurface conditions. On the basis of the field work, the soil stratigraphy is relatively uniform across the sites, except for variations in thickness of the upper soft soil zone and the existence, or not, of a surface fill covering. Surficial soils consist of about one to 1.5 m of fill and gravel, except at Site 3, over topsoil. A soft to medium stiff, organic, clayey silt extends to depths of four to 9.5 m below existing site grade. In some areas, particularly the northeast part of Site 1, some organic zones exist in the clayey silt.

Beneath the clayey silt, and extending to a depth of about 24 m, is a dense sand layer, which contains some random lenses of softer silt. Below the sand, to a depth of at least 60 m, is a soft to stiff, clayey silt with sand layers. A typical soil profile is shown to 12.5 m depth for Boring 8 on Fig.2, from near the centre of the building on Site 1.

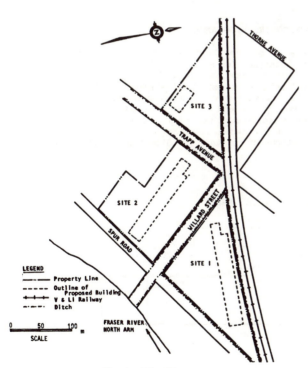

LEGEND
———— Property Line
----- Outline of Proposed Building
←┼→ V & LI Railway
-··-··- Ditch

0   50   100 m
SCALE

THORNE AVENUE
SITE 3
TRAPP AVENUE
VILLARD STREET
SITE 2
SPUR ROAD
SITE 1
FRASER RIVER NORTH ARM

Fig.1 Site Plan

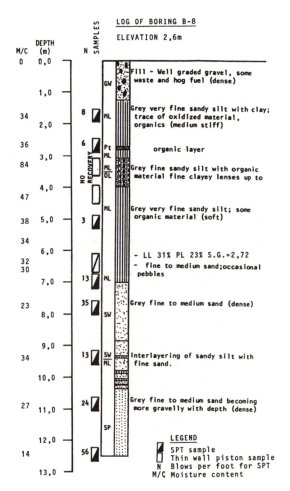

Fig.2 Typical Boring Log - Site 1

An extensive laboratory testing programme was undertaken to assess strength, consolidation and plasticity of the upper soft soils and the interlayered materials below 24 m depth. Results indicated that the upper soils were effectively normally consolidated, although some previous random loading had occurred on Sites 1 and 2 as a result of bulk storage. The deeper soils were also at close to normal consolidation conditions. However, these deeper soils would be much less effected by the anticipated areal loading. Resultant settlements, from the deep soils, would have little or no impact on structures as differential movements would be very low. For average conditions at Site 1, where the soft soils were deeper than at the other sites, the percent consolidation plot with time shown on Fig.3 was estimated from the laboratory tests.

FOUNDATION DESIGN ALTERNATIVES

Without special treatment, building settlements would be up to 750 mm with 300 mm differential movements across a 20 m width. The flexible steel structures would accommodate up to 150 mm settlements, according to the designers. Three alternatives were investigated to reduce post construction settlements to less than 150 mm.

(i)   A super-preload up to 6.4 m above the raised floor slab.

(ii)   A normal preload of four m with wick drains.

(iii)   A pile supported building and floor slab.

The second alternative was chosen because costs (about $700,000 Canadian 1983) were significantly less, with the pile alternative the most expensive, and the wick drains would reduce preload time from an estimated six months, to one to two months.

MONITORING PROGRAMME

Because of the short period available for preloading, the potential for edge instability and the concern about effectiveness of the wick drains, a comprehensive monitoring programme was instigated. This consisted of 44 settlement plates, 36 movement hubs, 16 pneumatic tip piezometers (placed at the middle of the upper compressible zone), and two screw-plate settlement gauges (placed below the upper clayey silt). The locations of monitors for Site 1 are shown on Fig.4.

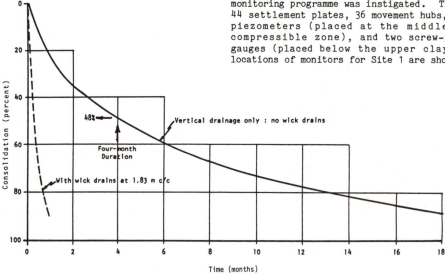

Fig.3 Average Rate Of Consolidation - Site 1

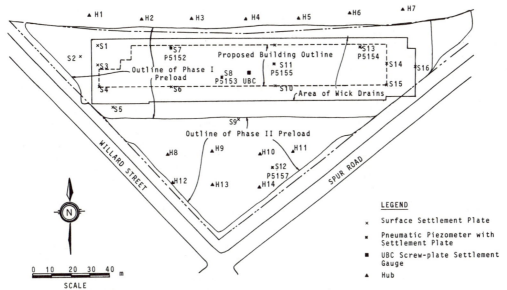

Fig.4 Monitoring Positions and Wick Coverage - Site 1

All monitoring devices were recorded at least once a day during the critical stages of filling. Piezometers were recorded as often as once an hour when a thick layer of fill approached a monitoring position.

WICK DRAIN INSTALLATION

The design pattern for installation of wick drains was triangular at 1.83 m centres along rows and 1.83 m between rows. The pattern was extended three to eight m beyond the sides of the building perimeters (depending on available space) and up to 15 m beyond the ends. This was to ensure consolidation well beyond the building walls and to assist in pore pressure dissipation at the edges of the relatively high preload fills. The coverage of wick drains at Site 1 is shown on Fig.4.

Wick drains consisted of a sleeve of porous, synthetic fibre surrounding a corrugated plastic band. This permitted water to seep into the hollow space of corrugations to relieve pore water pressure. The wick was about 100 mm wide by 5 mm thick and was supplied in 150 m rolls. The wicks were installed with a hollow-core mandrel suspended from a boom attached to a backhoe. The wick threaded inside the mandrel, which hydraulically "stitched" the wick into the ground.

Installation was initially slow for Site 1 because of the miscellaneous fill layer up to 1.5 m thick. When the mandrel encountered large pebbles or wood debris, it would not penetrate through the fill. This problem was solved by ripping furrows through the fill with a single ripper blade on the back of a bulldozer. This was done for each row of wicks at Sites 1 and 2. Site 3, where there was no fill, did not require ripping, although a 600 mm thickness of clean sand fill had to be placed before the wick machine could safely traverse the soft, saturated surface soils.

The wick installation was completed in 16 working days averaging about 9 hours per day, including a few breakdowns. A total of 26,175 m of wick were installed to depths of four to 9.5 m at 4328 locations. As the initial estimates of installation depth were slightly

greater and the spacing was also increased slightly, the total order for wick drains was 30,000 m at an installed cost of $104,000 Canadian.

FILL PLACEMENT

Material for site grading and preload fill was obtained from a dredged sand stockpile adjacent to the Fraser River about 6 km from the site. The fill was very uniform fine to medium sand with less than 10 percent silt, generally less than 5 percent. The preload was designed to load the original site grade with a pressure of about 100 kPa, two-thirds greater than the anticipated building plus slab loading plus site grading fill load of 60 kPa.

The preliminary design included placing the preload fill to the final lines and grades over the entirety of each site in one phase. On review, it was determined that this approach would result in an excess of fill at the time of removal of about 150,000 tonnes above what was required for site grading fill. Because no initial construction activities were planned for the yard areas at each site, it was decided to preload in two phases:

(i)   the building area and an approximate 12 m wide berm at each site; and

(ii)   the yard area at each site.

This approach resulted in achieving the required pre-construction settlements very quickly under areas where construction was planned, and wick drains had been installed, while allowing perimeter areas for driveways and parking to be preloaded more slowly during building construction. The re-use of some of the preload fill reduced the amount of excess fill at the end of final preloading to about 100,600 tonnes of the 151,800 tonnes placed during Phase I.

Fill placement for the Phase I preloading was regulated to three lifts per site, with a four-day lapse between lifts. This schedule was implemented to allow monitoring of the results of surcharging and to prevent slope and/or foundation failures occurring around the perimeter of the fills. The three lifts of fill were constructed to Elevations 4.3, 6.4, and 8.3 m respectively. Preload fill was placed sequentially on Sites 1, 2 and 3. Filling was accomplished in one month. To minimize potential stability problems, the edge of the fill was stepped with one or two intermediate benches or berms, depending on whether the site had already been covered with fill (Sites 1 and 2), or not (Site 3), and the available space.

Phase II was initiated two to three months after Phase I was complete, depending on building schedules, with preload being redistributed into the yard areas of each site to Elevation 4.3 m. Excess fill was removed from the area. A third phase involved the removal of excess yard area preload after six months or until the yard area was required for paving.

RESULTS OF MONITORING

Monitoring of settlement and pore pressure during preloading was undertaken to follow the progress of foundation compression, assess the adequacy of the design assumptions, and determine when subsequent phases of site work could be initiated. For the purposes of this paper, and for simplicity, only monitoring related to Site 1 are discussed in detail. A summary is provided for all three sites.

Settlement Markers

The settlement trends induced by preloading are summarized on Fig.5, which presents the typical range of settlements for Site 1 plotted as a function of the logarithm of time. In each case, the curves eventually formed a straight-line portion, indicative of long-term, secondary compression. Fig.6 presents a normal time plot of settlement marker 13 along with fill height and piezometric pressures.

As shown on Fig.5 settlements at Site 1 varied from 360 to 810 mm, during the Phase I preload. The minimum settlement was recorded along the southern edge of the preload, while the maximum values occurred along the northern edge, increasing toward the east end. This corresponds well with the variation in soft soil conditions of six to 9.5 m at Site 1 and the near surface organic zones encountered toward the southeast corner of the building. At the time of preload removal, the long-term settlement rate varied from 75 to 130 mm per log cycle of time. Based on the screw-plate settlement markers, deep-seated settlements were in the order of 40 to 60 mm.

The observed settlements compared favourably with the values estimated based on the field and laboratory investigation. Larger than predicted settlements occurred toward the eastern end of the preload, indicating a more compressible material or a thickening of the compressible zone. The available boring records suggest a combination of both factors.

The results indicated that 90 percent of theoretical, primary consolidation was achieved within 16 days of completion of construction of the preload. A best-fit, theoretical curve is shown on Fig.6 in normal time and Fig.7 for log time.

A summary of estimated and actual preload induced settlements for the three sites is provided in Table 1.

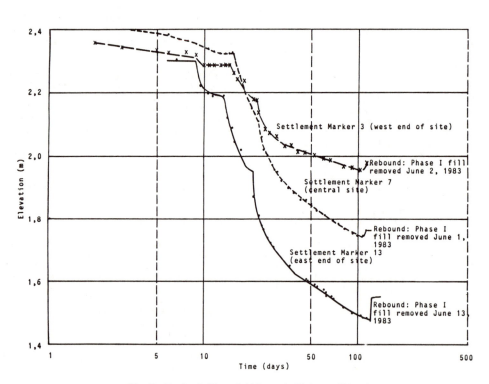

Fig.5 Typical Time-Settlement Plots - Site 1

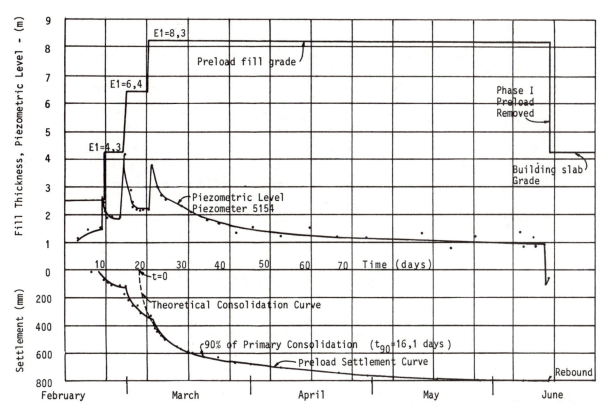

Fig.6 Time vs Settlement, Pore Pressure and Fill Height S13 - Site 1

TABLE 1

Settlement Range

Site	Estimated	Actual
1	400 to 680	360 to 810
2	350 to 560	150 to 240
3	500 to 850	300 to 450

Movement of Hubs

Hubs were installed in the Site 1 yard area to detect peripheral effects of the Phase I building preload, prior to placement of Phase II fill. During two months of measurement, the recorded difference in elevation of the hubs increased between six and 15 mm. For this magnitude of deflection, it is not possible to determine whether heave actually occurred, or whether the records are within the range of survey error.

Similarly, markers established along the railway track to the north of Site 1, to monitor vertical and horizontal movements, indicated a general decrease in level of between ten and 30 mm, and no noticeable horizontal movement. The downward movement is probably due to settlement induced by the railway ballast, combined with nominal area effects of the preload fill.

Piezometers

At Site 1, the response of the pneumatic piezometers to preload fill was distinct. For each metre of fill added, the piezometers registered between 0.8 and 1.8 m of additional pore pressure, peaking about half a day after completion of fill placement. The decay of pore pressure after loading took place over 10 to 20 days, more or less consistent with the rate of compression indicated by the settlement curves (Fig.6). When the Phase I fill was removed, the piezometers showed a minor drop in pore pressure. However, the change in pore pressure was not correlative to the amount of preload removed. This is as expected, because pore pressures had already decayed to the effective level of the local groundwater table.

CONCLUSIONS

From the results of monitoring settlement markers and piezometers, the required settlements under the preload fill were generally obtained within one month after construction of the preload. The installation of the wick drains was responsible for the accelerated response. Without wick drains, a similar magnitude of settlement would require up to two years of preloading. This pattern was verified by the settlement markers placed in the yard areas beyond the influence of the wick drains. For this project, wick drains provided an effective means for achieving preload settlements within a shortened construction schedule.

From the observed settlements during Phase I, original predictions tended to be conservative for Sites 2 and 3 (40 to 60 percent of actual) and reasonable for Site 1. In the northeast area of Site 1 it is likely that more significant thicknesses of organic soil exist that caused greater than originally estimated settlements (about 20 percent more settlement than predicted). The rate of primary consolidation compared favourably with

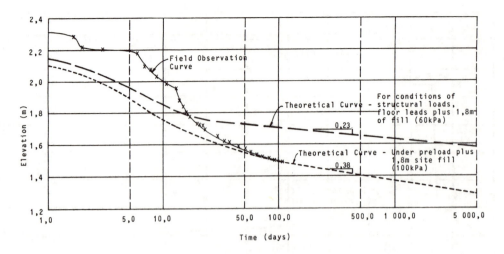

Notes: 1. The main difference between the theoretical consolidation
           curves and the observed settlement curve is related to
           the staged construction of the preload fill.

        2. Curves show long term settlements rate estimates.

Fig.7 Time-Settlement Plot S13 - Site 1

rates computed from coefficients of consolidation and
formula developed for wick installations.

Differences between predicted settlement and observed
settlement at Sites 2 and 3 are concluded to reflect
some preconsolidation due to previous loading (Site 2),
or dessication during geologic history. Local variation
in gradation, i.e. less compressible, more permeable
material, also may account for the conservative
estimates.

After reviewing the results of settlement induced by
preloading, the predicted post-construction settlement
under the building on Site 1 would vary from 40 to 140
mm, not including a small amount of relatively uniform
settlement resulting from long term compression of the
deep clay zones. Post-construction settlements under
the proposed buildings on Sites 2 and 3 would vary from
25 to 60 mm and 50 to 100 mm, respectively, excluding
deeper soil effects.

These post-construction settlement estimates were
acceptable to the building designers. Both the owners
and designers were very satisfied with the results of
preloading using wick drains, particularly because the
site development work was completed at least two months
(and probably closer to four months) faster than any
alternative scheme would have taken. In addition site
development costs were 56 to 74 percent of the estimated
cost of the alternatives.

Hardening of soil improved by deep mixing method

Durcissement des sols améliorés par la méthode du mélange en profondeur

S. SAITOH, Research Engineer, Takenaka Technical Research Laboratory, Tokyo, Japan
Y. SUZUKI, Research Engineer, Takenaka Technical Research Laboratory, Tokyo, Japan
K. SHIRAI, Research Engineer, Takenaka Technical Research Laboratory, Tokyo, Japan

SYNOPSIS   The deep mixing method (DM method) for strengthening thick deposits of weak sedimentary soil by mixing, in-situ with a strengthening agent is now widely used in Japan. The authors have studied the mechanism which produces this strengthening. The result of their study indicate that adsorption and the pozzolanic reaction in the soil as well as the reaction of the strengthening agent itself, contribute greatly to the increase in strength of the various soils. This provides a uniform basis for explaining the complicated soil strengthening process and explains why the same treatment used in different soils produces a wide variation in results.

INTRODUCTION

The method of strengthening weak clay soils by mixing in situ with a dry type hardening agent was developed about 1975 simultaneously in Sweden and Japan. The hardening agent used in both cases was quicklime. Later, in Japan, ordinary Portland Cement was used as the hardening agent and it was applied as a slurry (i.e. mixed with water) rather than in dry form. This appeared to produce a more uniform mixture of the hardening agent with the in situ soft soils which increased both strength and uniformity in the improved soil. Due to its superior performance in these areas, this method was accepted and used widely throughout Japan especially in marine projects.

Various engineering properties of cohesive soil improved by mixing with a ordinary Portland Cement slurry were reported by Kawasaki et al. (1981 and 1983). However, these reports failed to explain fully why the same improvement procedure applied to different soils produced varying results. In order to determine this it is important to attempt to define the mechanism that produces the soil strengthening by studying the characteristics of the strengthened soil in relation to the in situ soil properties and the characteristics of the hardening agent. The authors consider that the improved soil consists of hardened cement particles and also soil particles hardened as a result of the pozzolanic reaction between the soil and products of the cement hardening process and intend to identify the mechanism by which this occurs.

PROPERTIES OF SOILS AND CEMENTS USED IN TESTS

Samples from 3 kinds of marine clay soils and 3 other soils having a relation to the clays in the marine soils were used in the testing. The marine clay soils samples were taken from Yokohama, Osaka and Imari. The other soils were kaolin, bentonite and a volcanic ash type clay ("Kanumatsuchi").

TABLE   I

Properties of Soil Used

Name of Sample / Properties	Marine Clay			Kanuma-tsuchi	Kaolin	Ben-tonite
	Yoko-hama	Osaka	Imari			
Specific Gravity	2.776	2.674	2.632	2.495	2.715	2.978
Water Content (%)	100	100	90	100	130	1020
Liquid Limit (%)	88.0	65.7	70.4	NP	50.8	461.4
Plastic Limit (%)	31.9	22.4	24.2	NP	31.6	25.1
Plasticity Index	56.1	43.3	46.2	—	19.2	436.3
Sand Content (%)	9.9	28.5	2.2	6.5	0	0
Silt Content (%)	44.0	26.1	44.5	51.1	35.1	31.3
Clay Content (%)	46.1	45.4	53.3	42.4	64.9	68.7
Humus Content (%)	0.6	0.3	0.5	0.1>	0.1>	0.1>

The physical and chemical characteristics of the soil samples are shown on Table I. The mineral content of the marine soils (clays) used, based on the "X-ray Powder Diffraction Method" proposed by Oinuma were reported by Kawasaki et al. (1983) and are not repeated in this paper. The content of amorphous materials in the soils was determined by the "Weight Loss at 200°C Method" proposed by Kitagawa (1977) and was 9.6, 4.1 and 4.1 percent respectively for the Yokohama, Osaka and Imari soils provided that the grain size of the samples was under 74 μm.

The hardening agent used in the tests was a mixture of ordinary Portland Cement (OPC) and blast furnace slag (slag) blended at various ratios. This mixture was selected because it is quite often used in actual construction projects in Japan. The "Blaine Fineness" of OPC and slag was 3300 and 3410 (cm^2/g) respectively.

CHEMICAL REACTION BETWEEN SOIL AND HARDENING AGENTS, AND SCHEMATIC ILLUSTRATIONS OF IMPROVED SOIL

The Chemical reactions between a cohesive

soil, ordinary Portland Cement and blast-furnace slag and their reaction products, in general, are shown in Fig. 1. When OPC is used as a hardening agent, the following reactions occur: (a) hydration of OPC producing $Ca(OH)_2$ (b) adsorption of $Ca(OH)_2$ by clay (or a cation exchange reaction) until the clay is saturated with $Ca(OH)_2$ and from that point (c) the pozzolanic reaction between clay and $Ca(OH)_2$ will occur. When a mixture of slag and OPC is used as a hardening agent, slag hydration due to alkaline activation of $Ca(OH)_2$ occurs in addition to the above-mentioned reactions. In both cases, $Ca(OH)_2$ produced by hydration of OPC plays an important role in the hardening of the improved soil.

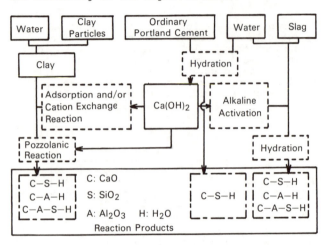

Fig. 1 Chemical Reaction between Soil and Hardening Agents

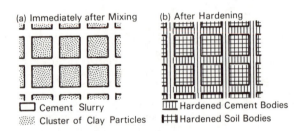

Fig. 2 Schematic Illustrations of Improved Soil

It is proposed to illustrate the conditions of hardening with the schematic diagrams shown in Fig.2 above. Fig. 2(a) shows the condition immediately after mixing a cohesive soil and a hardening agent slurry. It is considered that even if the cohesive soil and hardening agent slurry are thoroughly mixed, clay particles will form into clusters which will be surrounded by the slurry. Fig. 2(b) shows the condition after cohesive soil and hardening agent slurry have formed a hardened body. Here the hardening agent slurry shown in Fig. 2(a) produces hydrated calcium silicates, hydrated calcium aluminates, $Ca(OH)_2$, etc., and forms hardened cement bodies. The pozzolanic reaction between the clay and the $Ca(OH)_2$ produced by the cement hydration reaction produces hardened soil bodies. It

is considered as shown in Fig. 2 that the strength of the improved soil will depend upon the strength characteristics of both types of hardened bodies.

STRENGTH CHARACTERISTICS OF HARDENED SOIL BODIES AND HARDENED CEMENT BODIES

Strength characteristics of the hardened soil bodies are governed by the $Ca(OH)_2$ adsorption and the pozzolanic reactivity of the soils. The hydration of OPC produces $Ca(OH)_2$ which is first adsorbed by the clay to the point of saturation. This adsorption does not produce an appreciable increase in the soil strength. If additional $Ca(OH)_2$ is available after saturation the pozzolanic reaction between the clay and this free $Ca(OH)_2$ will occur. The pozzolanic reaction will produce a dramatic increase in the strength of the soil. Thus as $Ca(OH)_2$ is added to a clay in increasing amounts, the point where a dramatic increase in soil strength occurs indicates the point where the soil is saturated by the $Ca(OH)_2$ and the pozzolanic reaction has started. The dosage at that point then will indicate the maximum amount of $Ca(OH)_2$ that can be adsorbed by the soil.

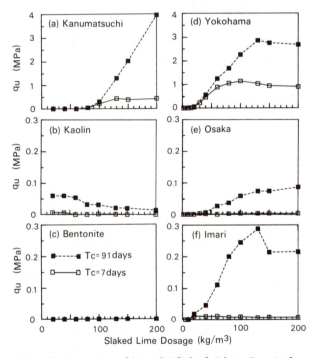

Fig. 3 Test Results of Slaked Lime Treated Soil

Fig. 3 indicates the strength/dosage relationship of the test soils which have been treated with $Ca(OH)_2$ (Slaked Lime). The dosage of slaked lime was increased from zero to 200 kg/m³ for all six soils. As can be seen, the Kanumatsuchi soil (whose main constituent is allophane, one of the amorphous clay minerals) displays the greatest adsorption with a saturation point of between 80 and 100 kg/m³ of $Ca(OH)_2$. This is followed by the three marine clay soils which all have lower adsorption capacities. The kaolin and bentonite indicate no capacity for Ca(OH)$_2$ adsorption.

The pozzolanic activity of the soil can be judged by the increase in strength of the soil after adsorption saturation has been reached. In this respect, the Kanumatsuchi, and Yokohama soils show a high pozzolanic reactivity while the remaining 4 soils were rather low. [Please note that the strength scales on Figs. 3(a) and 3(d) are different that those on Figs. 3(b), 3(c), 3(e), and 3(f).] These strength also appear to corresponded to the amorphous material contents of the soils.

For the strength characteristics of the hardened cement bodies in the improved soil, the test results reported by Maruyasu et al. (1970) as shown in Fig. 4 will apply. Fig. 4 indicates compressive strength of cement mortor where the hardening agent consists of various blends of OPC and slag.

The figure suggests that hydration of slag is slower than that of OPC. Also, as the quantity of slag increases, the quantity of Ca(OH)$_2$ (which is generated by the hydration of the OPC) becomes smaller which produces a finer microstructure. Strength characteristics of the hardened cement bodies in the DM improved soil are considered similar to those shown in Fig. 4.

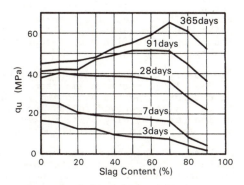

Fig. 4   Test Results of OPC-Slag Mortar (after Maruyasu et al.)

RESULTS OF UNCONFINED COMPRESSION TESTS OF VARIOUS SOILS AND THEIR DESCRIPTION

Strength tests were conducted on test specimens of soils treated with a hardener composed of a blend of OPC and slag. The hardener was applied as a slurry with three hardener dosage rates (200, 150 and 100 kg/m^3) and with a water/hardener ratio at a constant 60%. The persentages of OPC and slag composing the hardener were varied. Test results are shown in Figs. 5 and 6. By examining Figs. 5 and 6 two main features are apparent as follows:
  (i) The OPC/slag ratio which provides the maximum unconfined compressive strength in the improved soil varies according to the type of soil, dosage of hardening agent and age.
  (ii) The effects of the improvement vary according to the soil type even among

soils with nearly the same relative water content treated with identical dosages of hardening agent.
We shall attempt to explain the experimental results shown in Figs. 5 and 6 by means of schematic diagrams (Fig. 7), using the characteristics of hardened cement and hardened soil bodies. The assumptions used are as follows:
  (i) The improved soil consists of hardened cement and hardened soil bodies.
  (ii) The strength characteristics of the hardened cement bodies are in accordance with Fig. 4.
  (iii) The strength characteristics of the hardened soil bodies are in accordance with Fig. 3.
  (iv) Hydration of OPC generates calcium hydroxide amounting to 25% of its weight.
  (v) The calcium hydroxide generated is first adsorbed by the clay then the remainder is used in pozzolanic reactions and slag hydration.

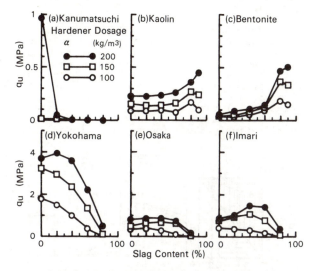

Fig. 5   Test Results of Improved Soil (Tc = 7 days)

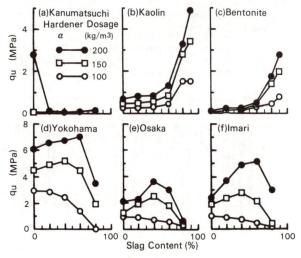

Fig. 6   Test Results of Improved Soil (Tc = 91 days)

(vi) Only a trace quantity of calcium hydroxide is required for slag hydration.

Fig. 7 (a) shows the state of hydration, after long aging, of hardening agents with various blending ratios of OPC and slag. For example, the blend corresponding to the line A-A is slag 40% and OPC 60%. At the hardening agent dosage of 200 kg/m^3 this means OPC 120 kg/m^3 and slag 80 kg/cm^3. In the OPC hydration, 30 kg/m^3 (= 120 × 0.25) of calcium hydroxide is generated, 15 kg/m^3 of which is adsorbed in the clay, and the remaining 15 kg/m^3 is used in pozzolanic reactions and slag hydration. The line B-B indicates the boundary between occurrence and non-occurrence of slag hydration. At line C-C the blend is 80% slag and 20% OPC. Since the quantity of calcium hydroxide generated is small (10 kg/m^3), it is entirely adsorbed by the clay, and all the slag remains unhydrated. On the basis of Fig. 7(a), the strength of the hardened cement bodies, hardened soil bodies and improved soil are illustrated in Fig. 7 (b), (c) and (d) respectively.

With reference to Fig. 7 (a), we can determine that the OPC/slag ratio which provides maximum unconfined compressive strength in the improved soil increases as (a) less adsorption of slaked lime in the soil occurs or (b) as larger dosages of hardening agent are applied or (c) with greater age.
Figs. 8 (a) thru (d) show the diagrams for the various soils as in Fig. 7(a). We can explain qualitatively the strength of improved soils

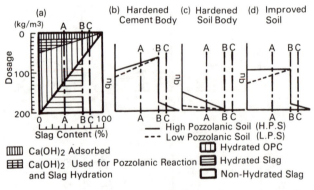

Fig. 7 Diagram for Description of Strength of Improved Soil [Dosage of Hardening Agent (α) = 200 kg/m^3]

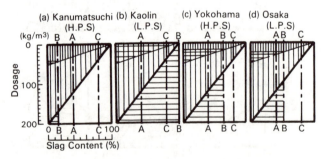

Fig. 8 Diagram of Description of the Strength of Various Improved Soils [Dosage of Hardening Agent (α) = 200 kg/m^3]

shown in Fig. 5 and Fig. 6 on the basis of Fig. 8, though the detailed explanation will be abbreviated.

CONCLUDING REMARKS

The points which have been clarified by the present research are summarized below.

i) The idea that the soil improved by the DM method consists of hardened soil bodies and hardened cement bodies, can adequately explain, in a unified manner, the strength characteristics of improved soils for various types and quantities of cement as well as various types and qualities of soil. In the future, this approach may be expected to provide a semiquantitative or quantitative method of estimating strength by considering the ratio of the contributions of the hardened soil and hardened cement bodies.

ii) In the case of soils with lower pozzolanic reactivity, the strength characteristics of the hardened cement bodies largely govern the strength characteristics of the improved soil. On the other hand, soils with higher pozzolanic reactivity produce stronger hardened soil bodies and finer hardened cement bodies by reacting with the calcium hydroxide generated by the hydration of the cement contained in the hardening agent. Therefore, all other factors being equal, greater strength is manifested in soils with high pozzolanic reactivity.

iii) The adsorption and pozzolanic reactivity of the clay constitute important factors in understanding the hardening characteristics of improved soils. Solidification tests of clay using slaked lime are effective in providing these data.

iv) As hardening agents in the deep mixing method, ordinary Portland Cement and Portland Blast-Furnace Slag Cement are more advantageous than quick lime and slaked lime from the viewpoint of wide applicability to various types of soil.

REFERENCES

Kawasaki, T., Niina, A., Saitoh, S., Suzuki, Y. and Honjyo, Y., (1981), Deep Mixing Method Using Cement Hardening Agent, Proc. 10th ICSMFE, Vol. 3, pp. 721-724, Stockholm
Kawasaki, T., Saitoh, S., Suzuki, Y. and Babasaki, R., (1983), Ground Stabilized by Deep Mixing Method, Proc. 7th ARC, SMFE, Vol. 1, pp. 249-254, Haifa.
Kitagawa, Y., (1977), Determination of Allophane and Amorphous Inorganic Matter in Soils, Bulletin of the National Institute of Agricultural Sciences (in Japanese with a summary in English), No. 29
Maruyasu, T., Kobayashi, K. and Sakamoto, Y., (1970), Studies on Portland Blast-Furnace Slag Cement Concrete, Concrete Library (in Japanese), No. 25

Analyse de stabilité d'ouvrages en sols renforcés

Stability analysis of reinforced soil structures

J. SALENÇON, Professeur, ENPC, Ecole Polytechnique, Laboratoire de Mécanique des Solides, Palaiseau, France
P. DE BUHAN, Ingénieur des Ponts et Chaussées, ENPC, Laboratoire de Mécanique des Solides, Palaiseau, France

RÉSUMÉ On présente une méthode pour l'analyse de stabilité des ouvrages en sols renforcés, fondée sur la modélisation macroscopique du sol par un matériau homogène anisotrope. Traitant le cas particulier d'un talus en sol purement cohérent renforcé par un sol de cohésion plus grande, on montre que la stabilité de cet ouvrage peut être analysée comme celle d'un talus en sol purement cohérent anisotrope, pour laquelle une méthode générale à caractère cinématique a été proposée antérieurement. La mise en oeuvre pratique est faite sur deux exemples. La comparaison des résultats obtenus avec ceux issus d'une méthode souvent utilisée dans la pratique met en évidence l'intérêt de la méthode d'homogénéisation pour le dimensionnement d'ouvrages en sol renforcé et attire l'attention sur les risques de surestimation importante du facteur de stabilité liés à l'emploi d'une méthode classique.

1 - INTRODUCTION

Les analyses de stabilité d'ouvrages en sols renforcés se font actuellement par des méthodes "à la rupture" transposées de celles utilisées classiquement pour les ouvrages constitués de sols naturels homogènes et isotropes. On a montré dans des publications récentes comment la théorie du calcul à la rupture permet d'interpréter de façon mécaniquement rigoureuse ces méthodes classiques (Salençon et Coussy, 1979) et d'en concevoir de nouvelles pour l'étude d'ouvrages constitués de sols naturellement anisotropes (Salençon et Tristán-López, 1981).

On se propose ici, par une application de la théorie du calcul à la rupture d'abord au niveau du matériau "sol renforcé", puis au niveau de l'ouvrage lui-même, de construire et de mettre en oeuvre une méthode d'analyse de stabilité simple et performante dans laquelle l'ouvrage sera modélisé comme constitué d'un matériau "sol renforcé" homogène et anisotrope.

Laissant de côté tous les développements théoriques disponibles par ailleurs, l'étude est présentée à propos de l'analyse de stabilité d'un talus en sol cohérent renforcé par un sol de cohésion plus grande (renforcement du type "argile stabilisée à la chaux"), traitée comme un problème bidimensionnel.

2 - LE PROBLÈME ÉTUDIÉ

On s'intéresse à l'étude de stabilité d'un talus de hauteur h et d'angle β, constitué d'un sol purement cohérent (cohésion C_1) renforcé par des couches verticales d'un sol plus cohérent (cohésion $C_2 > C_1$). Le problème ainsi défini peut être étudié dans la plan Oxy (figure 1).

En désignant par e_i l'épaisseur des couches du sol de cohésion C_i (i = 1,2), les rapports $\lambda_i = e_i/e$ (où $e = e_1 + e_2$) représentent les proportions respectives de chacun des sols. On suppose par ailleurs que le contact entre le sol en place et le sol de renforcement est à adhérence parfaite.

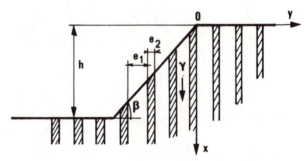

Figure 1 : Stabilité d'un talus en sol renforcé.

Les deux sols sont pesants, de même poids volumique γ, qui constitue ainsi l'unique paramètre de chargement de l'ouvrage.

On sait d'après un résultat classique que la stabilité d'un tel ouvrage ne peut être assurée que si le facteur adimensionnel $K = \gamma h/C_1$ (facteur de stabilité) demeure inférieur à une valeur critique K^+ qui, par des considérations d'analyse dimensionnelle, se met nécessairement sous la forme :

$$(\gamma h/C_1)^+ = K^+(\beta, C_2/C_1, \lambda_2/\lambda_1, e/h) \qquad (1)$$

On s'attachera plus particulièrement ici à déterminer K^+ (ou tout au moins à en approcher la valeur) lorsque le rapport e/h tend vers zéro :

$$K_o^+ = \lim_{e/h \searrow 0} K^+, \qquad (2)$$

c'est-à-dire en pratique lorsque l'épaisseur des couches du sol renforcé peut être considérée comme faible devant la hauteur du talus, longueur de référence de l'ouvrage.

3 - FONDEMENTS THÉORIQUES DE LA MÉTHODE D'HOMOGÉNÉISATION

3.1 La difficulté à déterminer K_o^+ tient essentiellement à la nature hétérogène du sol constituant l'ouvrage. Il paraît dès lors naturel, compte tenu de l'hypothèse formulée précédemment (e/h ↘ 0), de chercher la solution d'un problème homogène associé (figure 2) défini par les mêmes paramètres de géométrie (β, h) et de chargement (γ) que dans le problème initial, mais pour lequel le sol renforcé est modélisé du point de vue macroscopique comme un *matériau homogène anisotrope* défini par son critère de rupture macroscopique. Celui-ci n'est fonction que des cohésions respectives des deux sols (C₁,C₂) ainsi que de leur proportion volumique.

Pour ce talus homogène, la stabilité est également régie par le facteur adimensionnel (γh/C₁) qui doit être inférieur à une valeur limite que l'on notera K_{hom}^+, fonction de C₂/C₁ et λ₂/λ₁.

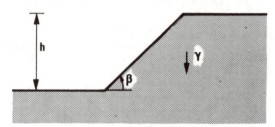

Figure 2 : Talus homogène associé.

3.2 La détermination du critère de résistance macroscopique du matériau "sol-renforcé" peut être effectuée par voie théorique : de Buhan et Salençon (1983) ont donné la formulation mécanique précise de ce problème et la méthode de construction explicite. Dans le même cadre et indépendamment, Suquet (1983) a pu démontrer un résultat très général qui se traduit dans notre exemple par l'inégalité suivante :

$$K_{hom}^+ \geqslant K_o^+ \tag{3}$$

c'est-à-dire que la valeur critique du facteur de stabilité de l'ouvrage "homogénéisé" défini au paragraphe 3.1 est supérieure à celle de l'ouvrage réel. Ce résultat, qui ne va manifestement pas dans le sens de la sécurité, se révèlera néanmoins d'une importance décisive par la suite.

4 - CRITÈRE DE RÉSISTANCE DU MATÉRIAU "SOL RENFORCÉ"

4.1 Le critère de résistance du matériau homogénéisé "sol renforcé" obtenu dans le cadre défini ci-dessus apparaît comme du type *cohérent anisotrope*. Son expression est la suivante :

$$\sigma_M - \sigma_m - 2\,C(\alpha) \leqslant 0 \tag{4}$$

où σ_M (respectivement σ_m) désigne la contrainte

principale majeure (respectivement mineure), comptée positivement en compression, à laquelle est soumis un élément représentatif de sol renforcé, et α est l'inclinaison de la direction de σ_M par rapport à l'orientation des couches (figure 3). La *cohésion anisotrope* C(α) qui apparaît dans ce critère, peut s'écrire :

$$C(\alpha) = C_1 \cdot \rho(\alpha,\ \lambda_2/\lambda_1,\ C_2/C_1) \tag{5}$$

où ρ est un facteur sans dimension, supérieur ou égal à 1, qui caractérise le renforcement du sol. Sa valeur est maximale pour α = 0° et 90°, et minimale pour α = 45° :

$$C(0°) = C(90°) = C_1 \cdot \frac{1 + (\lambda_2/\lambda_1)\,(C_2/C_1)}{1 + (\lambda_2/\lambda_1)} = r\,C_1 \tag{6}$$

$$(\rho = r)$$

$$C(45°) = C_1 \qquad (\rho = 1) \tag{7}$$

Le diagramme polaire ρ(α) = C(α)/C₁ est représenté sur la figure 3.

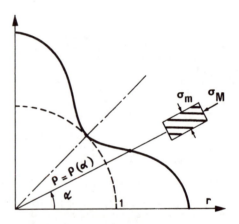

Figure 3 : Diagramme polaire de cohésion du sol renforcé.

4.2 Il est intéressant de pouvoir comparer ce critère avec celui de Bishop (1966), également de type cohérent anisotrope, employé pour décrire l'anisotropie de rupture de certaines argiles naturelles. On identifie pour celà les valeurs des cohésions relatives aux deux critères obtenues pour les angles de 0°, 45° et 90°. L'expression de la cohésion pour le critère de Bishop devient alors :

$$C(\alpha) = C(45°) \cdot [\,r \cdot \cos^2 2\alpha + \sin^2 2\alpha\,] \tag{8}$$

La comparaison des diagrammes polaires de cohésion montre une assez bonne coïncidence des deux critères pour des valeurs de r proches de 1,7 (figure 4-a). Ils sont par contre nettement distincts pour les autres valeurs de r, en particulier lorsque r devient supérieur à 2 (figure 4-b).

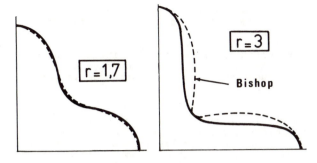

Figure 4 : Comparaison avec le critère de Bishop.

5 - ANALYSE DE STABILITÉ DU TALUS HOMOGÈNE ASSOCIÉ

Ce procédé d'homogénéisation permet donc de ramener l'étude de stabilité de l'ouvrage en sol renforcé à celle d'un ouvrage homogène constitué d'un sol obéissant au critère (4). Salençon et Tristán-López (1981) ont exposé le principe de la méthode cinématique utilisant des mécanismes de rupture par blocs rigides pour l'analyse de stabilité de ce dernier type d'ouvrages en matériau homogène purement cohérent anisotrope ; ils ont montré en particulier que la ligne de discontinuité de vitesse qui sépare le bloc en mouvement du reste du massif est nécessairement circulaire (figure 5).

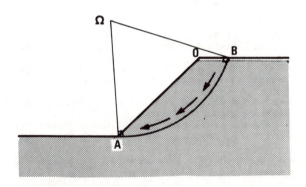

Figure 5 : Mécanisme de rupture circulaire.

L'utilisation de la méthode cinématique nécessite la connaissance des fonctions "π" associées au critère de résistance. Celles-ci ont été calculées par Zghal (1983) pour le critère (4) et l'on peut ainsi déterminer une valeur par excès de K^+_{hom} soit K^m_{hom} :

$$K^m_{hom} \geqslant K^+_{hom} \qquad (9)$$

Les résultats obtenus sont présentés à la figure 6 sous forme d'abaques donnant K^m_{hom}/r en fonction de r et de λ_2/λ_1, et pour deux valeurs d'inclinaison du talus : $\beta = 90°$ (talus vertical), $\beta = 45°$.

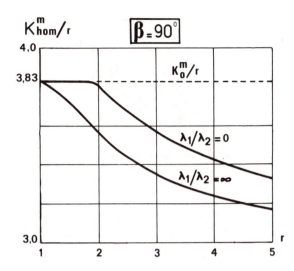

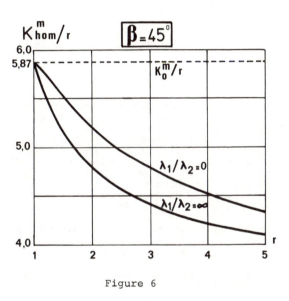

Figure 6

On remarque que l'on retrouve bien pour r = 1 et $\beta = 90°$ (talus vertical constitué d'un sol homogène de cohésion C_1) le résultat classique dû à Taylor : $K^m_{hom} \approx 3,83$.

6 - COMMENTAIRES ET CONCLUSION

6.1 - Comparaison avec une méthode classique (Alimak Lime Column Method, 1980)

Une méthode utilisée habituellement pour le dimensionnement de pentes ou de talus en sols renforcés consiste à vérifier directement la stabilité de l'ouvrage hétérogène vis-à-vis de la rupture circulaire (figure 7), en particulier lorsque le rapport e/h tend vers zéro. Il est clair que ce type de calcul permet d'obtenir un majorant de K^+_0 noté K^m_0 :

$$K^m_0 \geqslant K^+_0 \quad . \qquad (10)$$

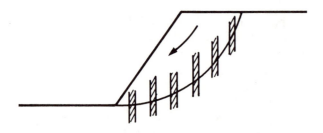

Figure 7 : Méthode classique d'analyse de
stabilité d'un talus en sol renforcé.

Dans notre exemple, on montre que ce majorant
est toujours proportionnel à r (par exemple
$K_o^m \approx 3,83$ r pour $\beta=90°$), et on trouve qu'il est
supérieur à celui obtenu par la méthode d'homogénéisation (voir abaques figure 6), soit :

$$K_o^m \geqslant K_{hom}^m \qquad (11)$$

On tire alors de la combinaison de (9) et (11)
et de l'inégalité de Suquet (3), la double inégalité :

$$K_o^m \geqslant K_{hom}^m \geqslant K_o^+ \qquad (12)$$

Ce résultat important signifie que pour la *même
famille de mécanismes de rupture* (cercles de
glissement), la méthode d'homogénéisation fournit une meilleure approche par excès de K_o^+ que
la méthode classique. Cette dernière conduit en
effet au même majorant que celui que l'on ob-
tiendrait à l'aide de mécanismes de rupture circulaire pour un talus constitué d'un sol homo-
gène et *isotrope* de cohésion $rC_1 = \lambda_1 C_1 + \lambda_2 C_2$
(moyenne pondérée des cohésions des deux sols).

En fait, rejoignant en cela l'intuition mécanique, la méthode d'analyse proposée rend bien
compte de l'anisotropie macroscopique du matériau "sol renforcé", ce qui explique qu'elle
conduise à de meilleurs résultats dans les analyses de stabilité.

6.2 *Exemple pratique de dimensionnement.*

Ainsi pour un talus d'inclinaison $\beta = 45°$, constitué d'un sol homogène de cohésion C_1, les deux
méthodes donnent évidemment le même majorant de
K_o^+ :

$$K_o^+ \leqslant 5,87$$

Le sol en place est alors renforcé par un sol de
cohésion $C_2 = 10\ C_1$ (ordre de grandeur de l'augmentation de cohésion d'une argile stabilisée à
la chaux) dans une proportion de 10% ($\lambda_1 = 0,9$,
$\lambda_2 = 0,1$) d'où r = 1,9.

La méthode classique donne alors $K_o^m \approx 11,15$ soit
un accroissement de 90% de la valeur critique du
facteur de stabilité du talus ; la méthode d'homogénéisation donne quant à elle $K_{hom}^m \approx 9,27$ ce
qui montre que l'accroissement du facteur de stabilité dû au renforcement du talus ne sera en
réalité pas supérieur à 58% : *ainsi pour un talus dont le coefficient de sécurité serait ini-
tialement de 0,67, le renforcement permettra une*

*amélioration de ce coefficient jusqu'à 1,04 et
non jusqu'à 1,25 comme indiqué par la méthode
classique.*

Ce résultat illustre bien le risque de surestimation de la stabilité d'un ouvrage en sol renforcé que comporte l'utilisation de la méthode
classique.

6.3 Plusieurs prolongements de cette méthode
sont envisageables : on peut par exemple préciser le rôle joué par les conditions de résistance aux interfaces entre le sol en place et le
sol de renforcement (supposées être à adhérence
parfaite dans notre étude). Il serait également
possible d'étudier dans le cadre de la méthode
d'homogénéisation d'autres types de renforcement.

RÉFÉRENCES

SALENÇON, J & COUSSY, O (1979) "Analyse de la
    stabilité des remblais sur sols mous," C.R.
    symp. Int. Méc. Sols, Oaxaca (Mexique), Mars
    1979, Vol I, 145-153.

SALENÇON, J & TRISTAN-LOPEZ, A (1981) "Stabilité
    d'ouvrages en sols cohérents anisotropes," C.R
    Xe Cong. Int. Méc. Sols, Stockholm, Vol III,
    515-518.

de BUHAN, P & SALENÇON, J (1983) "Définition et
    calcul d'un critère de rupture macroscopique
    pour le matériau multicouche," Coll. Int.
    CNRS "Critères de rupture des matériaux à
    structure interne orientée," Grenoble (Fran-
    ce).

SUQUET, P (1983) "Analyse limite et homogénéisa-
    tion," CRAS, t. 296, série II, 1355-1358.

BISHOP, A.W. (1966) "The strength of soils as engi-
    neering materials," Geotechnique, 16, 2, 89-130.

ZGHAL, A. (1983) "Stabilité d'ouvrages en maté-
    riaux composites," Mémoire de D.E.A., Labora-
    toire de Mécanique des Solides, (Palaiseau),
    ENIT, (Tunis).

LIME COLUMN METHOD. Document de la société Lin-
    den-Alimak, Suède, 1980.

Soil fracturing – An injection method for ground improvement

Sol fracturant – Une méthode d'injection pour l'amélioration des sols

HERBERT SAMOL, Member of GKN Keller GmbH, Ground Engineering Contractors, Offenbach, FRG
HEINZ PRIEBEL, Dipl.-Ing., Member of GKN Keller GmbH, Ground Engineering Contractors, Offenbach, FRG

SYNOPSIS

Using the grouting method, i.e. the injection of fluid slurries into the voids of the soil, an improvement is achieved with regard to impermeabilization and strengthening. In rock or stiff cohesive soil this grout fills gaps, cracks and fissures and in noncohesive soil the pores between the grains. However, these injections do not disturb the soil structure because fluids are used with low viscosity, which penetrate the voids by relatively low injection pressure. The technology is widely known by many publications and numerous applications.

Contrary to injections, which scarcely influence the structure of the soil, the improvement by soil fracturing is based on the intentional cracking of the soil by the injected fluids. The application is generally restricted to cohesive soils with low permeability, which are not suitable for conventional grouting. The filling of horizontal and vertical cracks with set grout results in

       - a supporting network,
       - a soil compaction and consolidation,
       - intentional heave after saturation and compaction.

Since there are only a few criteria for design, performance and quality control, the application for soil fracturing requires above average knowledge and experience. As examples, the readjustments of two different buildings are presented.

SEWAGE PLANT DORNBIRN

Project and Subsoil Conditions

The sewage plant at Dornbirn, Vorarlberg/ Austria, was enlarged with a biological-chemical cleaning stage. The chosen area was formerly covered by a swamp. In recent years it was used to deposit garbage and debris. The subsoil is very problematic for any kind of structures because it consists of geologically young and very varying estuary deposits. Up to approximately 10 m depth there are soft to very soft peat and silt-clay layers. Laboratory tests show constrained moduli of generally less than 1 MN/m^2.
In the strata below, the organic content is decreasing and sandy-gravelly layers are encountered but the bearing capacity is only slightly increasing with depth. The fine-grained layers between 10 and 20 m depth show constrained moduli of less than 3 MN/m^2. The maximum boring depth was approximately 40 m, and no significant change was observed. In addition to the varying stratification, the ground water conditions are also affected to a disadvantage, because there are artesian water tables.

Foundation and Settlement Behaviour

In view of the bad subsoil conditions, all parts of the sewage plant, including the connecting pipe-lines required special foundations. For the two rather large aeration basins each 80,8 m long and 43,6 m wide the upper soft layers were improved by stone columns. By this process the varying strata were considerably homogenized in order to achieve fairly uniform settlements, induced by the lowering of the ground water table. Moreover stone columns could not possibly fail, because the load from the basin was not in excess of the initial overburden. However, during and after the construction period one of the basins suffered from differential settlements. It was observed that the outer edge - in relation to the entire plant-settled considerably. Especially the corner section, resulting from the arrangement of the expansion joints of the foundation raft had settled in an order exceeding the allowable limit of approx. 4 cm. When re-adjustment measures were started at the end of January 1982, maximum settlement amounted to 73 mm (Fig. 1)

The main reasons for this unfavourable development has to be seen in the following facts. Due to a former real estate border the area was primarily covered with less overburden and thus less pre-consolidated. In addition it was filled subsequently which implied unforeseen load.

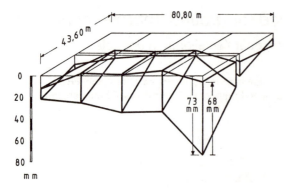

Fig. 1:   Schematic graph of the settlement
          and heave of the aeration basin

Preliminary Works

The re-adjustment by soil fracturing should
not disturb or even destroy a drainage
system which had to assure safety against
uplift in case of empty basin. Therefore,
the stone columns, which normally represent
drainage paths, had to be sealed in their
upper portions below the drainage and above
the soil fracturing injection level. This
sealing was performed by jet grouting, which
was considered to reach the stone columns
even if the borings deviated somewhat. The
sealing works included 14 x 3 borings at
the frontal edge and 88 x 2 borings alongside (Fig. 2).

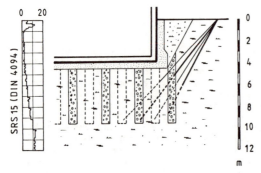

Fig. 2:   Scheme of the borings for the sealing
          of the stone columns including a
          sounding before the re-adjustment

Altogether approximately 150 m^3 grout were
injected at a rate of 300 kg blast-furnace
cement and 200 kg limestone powder per
1000 l water, stabilized by 25 kg bentonite.
It is selfexplanatory that during the jet
grouting procedure, as well as during the
following soil fracturing works, the drainage system was constantly observed.

Re-adjustment

The soil fracturing works included 4 x 5
borings at the frontal edge and 11 x 5 bor-

ings alongside the basin. These borings
were equipped with injection pipes suited
for injections at three stages minimum within the lower portion (Fig. 3).

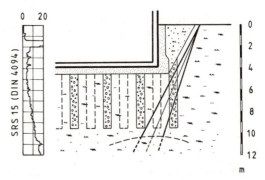

Fig. 3:   Scheme of injection pipes including
          a sounding after re-adjustment

A total of approximately 450 m^3 grout were
injected at a rate of 400 kg blast-furnace
cement and 800 kg limestone powder per
1000 l water, stabilized by 25 kg bentonite.
Measurements of heave, inclination of the
walls and width of the joints were carefully
taken and the quantity of grout was limited
accordingly. Due to little overburden and
soft soil, the pressures were low except for
the immediate bursting of the valves, but
sounding before and after the re-adjustment
proved to have a compaction effect (Fig. 2
and 3). Undesireable leaking of the grout
at the surface were prevented by fast-setting
admixtures.

Conclusions

The soil fracturing process proved to be
suitable for the re-adjustment of a large
basin of a sewage plant. The works took two
and a half months, including all preliminary
efforts. At the longitudinal edge of the
basin settlements were more or less completely adjusted. The remaining slight inclination of the frontal edges was left to
compensate the effect of the filling of the
basins (Fig. 1). However, the corner of the
basin, which was mainly affected by settlements, was lifted by 68 mm (Fig. 4).

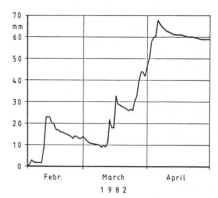

Fig. 4:
Heave at the
corner of
the basin

VEB BUNA, SCHKOPAU

Basic Situation

An 18 m high building of a chemical plant, which was erected in 1978 for VEB Buna Schkopau, GDR, suffered considerably from settlements. Mainly affected were nine columns of the steel skeleton structure founded on single footings at different depths. Differential settlements of these footings led to an inclination that endangered the production plant. First steps taken for stabilization consisted of a re-inforcement of the steel supports.

Subsoil Conditions

According to the investigation report and the results of additional core borings the subsoil varies from noncohesive to cohesive layers with partly organic components. Glacial drift immediately below the footings is underlain by loamy gravelly sand and silt to sandy silt with varying content of lignite (Fig. 5).

Aforementioned layers were also tested in a laboratory and the results indicated that the stratification possesses sufficient bearing capacity.

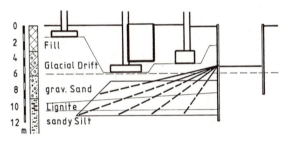

Fig. 5: Schematic graph of the foundation including injection pipes

Reasons for Settlement

From a broken pipeline an unknown quantity of highly concentrated caustic soda solution seeped unnoticed into the ground. It effected chemical reactions with the lignite which partly led to a nearly complete loss in bearing capacity. The resulting settlements amounted to a maximum of 106 mm at

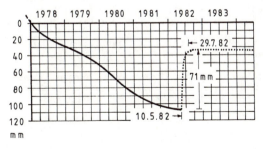

Fig. 6: Settlement and heave at column D-6

column D-6 before the re-adjustment measures were started.

To establish adequate measures to improve the subsoil comprehensive investigations were carried out, to include core borings, dutch cone soundings and laboratory tests. They confirmed a remarkable solvent effect on the lignite. The test samples were partly of very soft consistency. The analysed concentration of caustic soda solution amounted to 4 percent of weight. This value was so high that further lignite dissolution could be expected.

Re-adjustment Measures.

Any measures for solving the problem were not allowed to disturb or hinder, interrupt or even stop the running production process of the plant. Therefore, most possibilities had to be omitted, such as:

        soil substitution
        mini - piles
        pile foundations
        pipe protection slabs
        jet grouting

Due to low permeability of the strata to be improved even conventional grouting was out of the question. Thus the proposal of GKN Keller to improve the subsoil by soil fracturing was accepted.

Injection Material

Preliminary qualification tests with customary grouts were performed. They showed that with the prevailing conditions, cement would fail as matrix because chemical reactions would prevent the setting. Therefore the elements of the Joosten-process were used which have been approved for decades. Hereby the setting results from the immediate production of calcium silicate when highly concentrated water glass is mixed with calcium chloride to neutralize remaining caustic soda solution in the soil. In addition aluminium sulphate was injected which also precipitates silicates from the water glass. To enrich the grout with solids, the water glass was admixed with limestone powder at a ratio of 1:1.

Performance Scheme

Due to many installations and various fittings which should not be distroyed, the work was executed from a ditch 28,5 m long and 5,5 m wide (Fig. 1). Approximately 150 nos. of duplex-injectionpipes were inserted into the area to be treated in a fan-shaped arrangement. The volume of soil was estimated in the order of 1250 m³. Laterally the area was bounded by the sheet pile wall of aforementioned ditch and the remaining bounds were achieved by diaphragm injections which were executed with aluminium sulphate as means for setting and neutralizing. Furthermore an injected cover of approximately 1 m thickness was carried out to avoid uncontrolled fracturing in the vicinity of the footings and to provide an adequate load distribution. Surplus pore water in the soil or from the grout was pumped from relieve and drainage borings which also served as observation holes.

Performance

The soil fracturing works were carried out with hydrostatic pumps in different stages and passes through the injection pipes. Construction period was from March 10th to August 12th, 1982. The saturation phase was already achieved after few days. After that, position and output of the injection was adjusted to the intended heave of 9 footings within tolerances of 1 to 2 mm. Altogether the columns were lifted as follows:

Column	4	5	6
B	12 mm	8 mm	3 mm
C	28 mm	35 mm	30 mm
D	39 mm	61 mm	71 mm

The maximum heaves were attained at the columns D-4 and D-6 (Fig. 7). At the beginning the heave per shift was approximately 2 mm. This was more and more reduced with growing values.

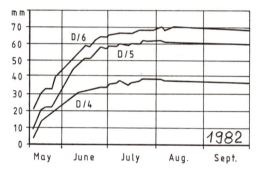

Fig. 7:   Heave of the columns in row D

In total the following quantities of grout-materials were injected:

304 m^3 highly concentrated water glass
203 m^3 electrolytical solutions
 75 m^3 stone powder
582 m^3

With rates of 5 to 15 l/min the injection pressures were 5 to lo bars at the beginning, and at the end, after frequently repeated injection phases, at 10 to 25 bar, depending on the efficiency of the pumps. The pressures to burst the valves and to start the soil cracking increased from 10 to 40 bar accordingly.

Quality Control

Finally qualification tests were performed. Therefore, 4 core borings were executed with complete core recovery. The visual examination and in-situ tests proved soil-fracturing to be a successful method for treatment in the present case (Fig. 8).
Laboratory tests completed the in-situ observations. From core samples the relevant characteristics were determined:
-bulk density
-compressive strength
-moisture content
-remaining alkalinity
-loss-on-ignition

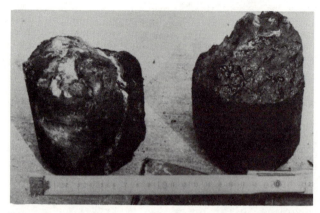

Fig. 8:   Cores from the improved lignite

The very soft layers of lignite were drained and compacted so much that the bearing capacity was higher than initially. Furthermore the existence of ramified cracks, filled with set groud, were proved within the cohesive layers and the lignite, forming a permanent load supporting frame.

Conclusions

Summarizing it can be stated that

- the bearing capacity of the soil was regained,
- all soil characteristics were improved,
- the intended heave was achieved,
- the readjustment will be lasting.

References:

Kutzner, Chr., Über die mechanischen Eigenschaften der mit Silikatgaben injizierten Erdstoffe, Bautechnik 1968, S. 86-97

Henri Combefort, "Injection des sols", Übersetzung Bodeninjektionstechnik 1969, Bauverlag Wiesbaden, Germany

Ruppel, G. Ausführung von Injektionen in Lockergestein, Bergbauwissenschaften 1970, S. 285-290

Neumann, H., Die Entwicklung der Injektionstechnik, Erzmetall 1972, S. 16-25

Bonzel, J. u. Dahms, J., Über den Einfluß des Zementes und der Eigenschaften der Zementsuspensionen auf die Injizierbarkeit in Lockergesteinsboden, Beton Verlag, 1972

Douglas, R. Warner, J., Compaction Grouting Journal Soil Mechan. 1973, S. 589-600

Ulrichs und Samol, Untersuchungen zur Feststellung der Haltbarkeit eines chemisch verfestigten Kies-Sandes, Tiefbau, 1977/6

Interaction of soil and buried rigid structure

Interaction entre le sol et une structure enterrée rigide

M. TERASHI, Chief of Soil Stabilization Lab., Port & Harbour Research Institute, Japan
M. KITAZUME, Research Engineer, Port & Harbour Research Institute, Japan
M. YAJIMA, Third District Port Construction Bureau, Ministry of Transport, Japan

SYNOPSIS   Deep Mixing Method has been applied in Japan to reinforce soft clay by manufacturing an extraordinary stiff treated soil mass in-situ. Interaction of soft alluvial soil and the treated soil walls resting on reliable stratum is investigated to improve current design procedure. It is known from the centrifuge model test that the external forces are carried solely by the treated soil walls, that the magnitude and distribution of contact pressures at the surface of treated soil mass are dependent on the magnitude of factor of safety against external stability, and that the pressures change with time due to consolidation process of soft soil.

INTRODUCTION

Deep Mixing Method(DMM), a deep in-situ admixture stabilization using cement slurry, has been developed in Japan to reinforce soft alluvial clays. In practice, huge treated soil mass whose shear strength exceeds 1 MPa is formed to support superstructure. Due to the large difference of the engineering characteristics between treated soil and untreated soft soils, treated soil mass is assumed to behave as a rigid structure buried in soft ground. In the present article, interaction between soft soil and this rigid buried structure manufactured by DMM is investigated. Special attention is paid to the time dependent change of earth pressure and pore water pressure acting on the surface of rigid structure of wall type.

CURRENT DESIGN PROCEDURE

Stability analysis of the improved ground is currently carried out in two stages. The first stage is an "external stability" of a buried rigid structure in which four modes of failures are examined; sliding, over-turning, bearing capacity and extrusion. The second stage is an "internal stability" of a structure in which induced stresses should be limited to be lower than the allowable strength of treated soil. Design loads considered both in the external and internal stability analyses are mass forces, active and passive earth pressures and other external forces exerted onto the boundary of the structure. Above mentioned design concept is derived for simplicity by analogy with the design procedure of a gravity type structure such as a concrete retaining structure. Details of the current design procedure and mechanism of extrusion failure have already been reported by Terashi et al(1983).

In the current design procedure examining different modes of failure independently, optimum design must be found out by trial and error. An example of these calculations for the most common

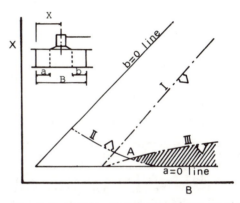

Fig.1 Determination of Optimum Design

application of DMM is shown in Fig.1. In the case, superstructure is a revetment composed of gravel mound and concrete caisson supporting the earth pressure caused by sea reclamation. Superstructure is to be constructed on a soft clay layer underlain by reliable bearing stratum of dense sand as shown in the upper left corner of the figure. First approximation of the shape of treatment in this trial calculation is shown by dotted line. To obtain necessary factor of safety, width B of treated soil mass is increased by changing distances a and/or b. Three lines in the figure are suggesting the minimum extent of treated soil mass which satisfy the requirement of sliding of the buried structure (line I), induced shear stress at the toe of a buried structure (II), and also shear stress in the vertical plane in front of superstructure (III). Hatched zone satisfies all the requirements and point A is the optimum. In this particular example, over-turning, bearing capacity and extrusion are not the governing factor. As shown, usually, one or two modes become critical factors in determining the shape and extent of treated soil mass. Arrow on each line shows a direction toward higher factor of safety.

From the example calculation it must be easily

understood that the optimum design (point A) is
sensitive to the determination of design loads
on the boundary and the magnitude of factor of
safety. It is natural to take two dimensional
active and passive earth pressures as design
load for external stability, as long as a buried
structure is two dimensional and is resting on a
reliable stratum as in the above example. However, it is questioable to apply the same critical earth pressures for the internal stability
analysis of a structure whose external stability
has been already satisfied. When a rigid buried
structure is three dimensional, even for the
external stability, further consideration is
required for the pattern of failure and for the
determination of design loads. Extrusion failure
is the typical three dimensional failure (Terashi, et al,1983). When a rigid buried structure
is floating in the soft clay, the magnitude and
distribution of contact pressure would be highly
dependent on the mode of displacement of a rigid
structure.

To avoid too much conservative design, (i) clear
understanding of the design loads acting on
boundaries of a buried structure, (ii) improvement of the accuracy of calculation for each
mode of failure and (iii) selection of adequate
factor of safety for each mode and establishment
of appropriate allowable strength for treated
soil are required. However, there has been no
attempt to obtain reliable field data on the
behavior of superstructure and a buried structure since the first application of DMM in 1976.

CENTRIFUGE MODELING OF A BURIED RIGID STRUCTURE

Model study of a superstructure and improved
ground is carried out using large geotechnical
centrifuge at Port & Harbour Research Institute.
Details of the centrifuge are described by Terashi et al(1984). Present model tests have no
particular prototype and the purpose is to know
the interaction between soft soil and extraordinary stiff treated soil mass of wall type
resting on a reliable stratum.

test procedure

Soft clay ground is modeled by kaolinite whose
liquid limit, plastic limit, and Gs are 71.5 %,
32.9 % and 2.58 respectively. Bakelite stiff
enough to model treated soil whose density is
1.39 g/cm^3 is used to model a rigid buried
structure. Toyoura standard sand which is uniform fine sand with Uc = 1.33, D_{10} = 0.12 mm and
G_s = 2.64 is used to model underlying sand layer
and fill material. Concrete caisson is modeled
by cement mortar with density = 1.71 g/cm^3.
Due to the selection of these materials,
consolidation of clay ground and instrumentation
for contact pressure measurement are carried out
with ease.

Long walls of a model rigid buried structure
(Fig.2) is placed on the sand layer in the
prescribed position in the strong box. Kaolinite
remolded by vacuum mixer at water content of
approximately 150 % is poured on the sand layer
and preconsolidated at 10 kPa in the laboratory
under 1 G. Following preconsolidation, strong box
is disassembled to embed short walls in-between
long walls and to place targets for photographic

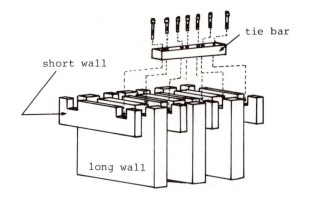

Fig.2 Model of Treated Soil Walls

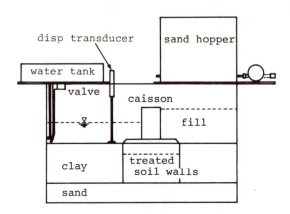

Fig.3 Setup of Model Ground

measurement on the side of clay. Strong box is
reassembled, mounted on a swinging basket of
centrifuge and brought into 50 G field. In this
stage, short walls are set between long walls
independently from long walls so as to allow
free consolidation of the soft clay in-between
long walls. Thus a clay ground normally
consolidated in general and lightly overconsolidated at top surface is prepared after
a long run of centrifuge. Centrifuge is once
stopped to connect long and short walls tightly
as it is the case of actual improvement and to
place mound and caisson in place. Acceleration
is increased again and back filling is carried
out using sand hopper under the steady acceleration of 50 G. Setup of model ground and
strong box is shown in Fig.3.
Transducers for total earth pressure (TEP) and
pore water pressure (PWP) are fixed in the bakelite walls to measure the pressure change at the
interface between a rigid structure and soft
soil. A limited number of transducers for TEP
and PWP are set on the sand layer in-between
long walls to measure reaction of soft soils and
on clay surface to measure fill pressure and
water pressure.

test conditions

Centrifuge tests were carried out for two model
grounds both of which are designed to satisfy
external stability. In both cases, depth of clay

is 10 cm, long walls reach to underlying sand layer(height of long wall is also 10 cm), height of short wall is 3 cm, thickness of long wall is 2 cm and that of short wall is 1 cm. Difference is in the width of long wall; width of long wall is 10 cm for case A and 15 cm for case B. It means the factor of safety against external stability is higher in case B. Factor of safety for sliding is 1.0 for case A and 1.4 for case B.

test results

The change of total earth pressure and pore water pressure in the first flight are shown in Fig. 4. In this and in the following figures, triangles & bars show the positions of TEP & PWP cells. Before this flight clay ground was preconsolidated only at 10 kPa. Total vertical stress in the clay ground practically equals to TEP and PWP measured at the surface of the rigid buried structure immediately after acceleration up to 50 G. At the end of consolidation under 50 G, measured PWP equals to static water pressure and measured TEP showed the increase of effective horizontal stress due to consolidation.

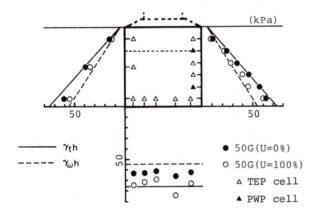

Fig.4 Pressure Distribution
(Modeling of N.C. Clay)

K_0 coefficient obtained by the experiment is approximately 0.35 which is a little bit smaller value compared with laboratory test result carried out separately. With consolidation process, TEP measured at the bottom of long walls slightly increased. This phenomenon is a result of negative skin friction along long walls due to self weight consolidation of clay ground which never would happen in reality.

The placement of superstructure on top of a buried structure gives rise to no change of TEP and PWP in the soft soils in-between long walls. It suggests that the applied external load is carried solely by long walls.

Measured TEP and PWP during filling stage is the major concern in the present study. TEP and PWP underneath the fill respond quickly to filling and whose magnitude is quite reasonable in case B (Fig. 5b). However, in case A, TEP and PWP underneath the fill respond only to first filling (Fig. 5a). As is already explained in the previous section, factor of safety for sliding in case A is around unity. Disagreement between applied vertical stress and measured pressure increment in the case A seems to be due to the horizontal displacement of a buried structure. TEP and PWP on the front of a buried structure shows negligibly small increase with filling in both cases. The pressure increase with filling and decrease with the consolidation of clay is shown in Fig. 5c.

Change of horizontal pressure with time and change of contact pressure distribution at the bottom of long wall is clearly shown in Fig. 6. Increment of resultant vertical force calculated from the measured contact pressures agrees well with the vertical increment of external force. Fig. 7 shows the TEP and PWP measured in-between the long walls. As shown in the figure, pressures increase with back filling. Immediately after the filling, the distribution of induced pressure increment is linear decreasing from

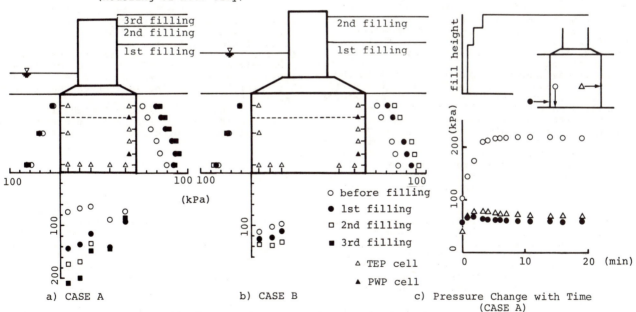

a) CASE A   b) CASE B   c) Pressure Change with Time
(CASE A)

Fig.5 Mesured Pressure in the Filling Stage

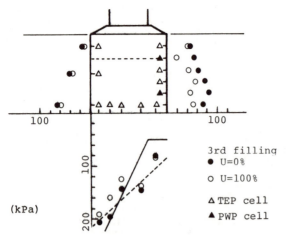

Fig.6 Pressure Re-distribution
due to Consolidation

3rd filling
● U=0%
○ U=100%

△ TEP cell
▲ PWP cell

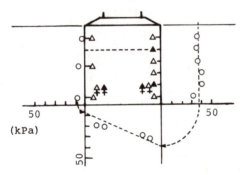

Fig. 7 Pressure Increment between Walls

heel to toe of the buried structure. Most of this pressure increment disappears with time. It seems that the pressure distribution is dependent solely on the difference of excess pore water pressure between the front and rear of a structure and hence it disappears with dissipation of excess pore water pressure underneath the filling. These evidences suggest that the external force is carried mostly by the rigid buried structure. However, no strong evidence of large stress concentration is found from the measured pressure on long walls along the vertical plane at the heel. Therefore, in the external stability analysis of wall type improvement except extrusion, two dimensional earth pressure is applicable as design loads along the vertical planes at the heel and toe of a buried structure. Horizontal force acting on soft clay in-between the long walls is considered to be transmitted to long walls by adhesion. The force carried by long walls is finally transmitted to bearing stratum.

Contact pressure at the bottom of long walls is calculated by assuming that the buried structure is rigid and it seats on the elastic springs. As is already described, the resultant vertical stress at the bottom of the long walls agrees well with the vertical external force and mass force. However the calculated contact pressure distribution based on the horizontal component of earth pressure (solid line in Fig. 6 for U= 100 %) is steeper than measured one. This is probably because no account was taken for the

vertical component of earth pressure from the fill, shear stress induced in the clay layer on the surface of a buried structure to restrain the rotational movement at the instance of loading, and the negative skin friction in the long run. Contact pressure distribution taking account of vertical component of earth pressure of the fill material and the negative skin friction acting on the treated soil walls is shown by dotted line in Fig. 6 also for U = 100 %. The similar trend is obtained from the elasto-plastic FEM calculation simulating the model tests.

Loading test on a full scale improved ground of wall type was carried out by the Third District Port Construction Bureau in collaboration with Port & Harbour Research Institute. Loading was applied by gravel mound, concrete caisson and back filling as in the case of centrifugal model test. The test was ended by the sliding of super-structure. Measurement of displacement of buried structure and superstructure, contact pressures and strains inside the treated soil mass has been carried out successfully until the end of the test. Obtained data also support the findings of the present study. Yajima and Terashi (1984) have reported the details.

CONCLUSION

Interaction between soft soil and a rigid buried structure sitting on the reliable stratum is studied by means of centrifuge modeling. From the study, it is known that the design load condition is sensitive to relative movement of a rigid buried structure to surrounding soft soils.

Conclusions drawn from the present study are as follows.
i) Design load condition in "internal stability" should not be the critical active and passive earth pressures.
ii) When the margin of safety against external stability is sufficiently large, K_0 pressure must be taken as design load at the front of a rigid buried structure.
iii) Underneath the fill, earth pressure must be calculated as a sum of effective horizontal stress and excess pore water pressure. It means that the rate of filling influences the loading condition.
iv) In the analysis of internal stability, it is reasonable to consider that all the external forces are carried by a rigid buried structure.

REFERENCES

Terashi, M., Kitazume, M. and Tanaka, H. (1984) Application of PHRI Geotechnical Centrifuge., Submitted to International Symposium on Geotechnical Centrifuge Modeling, Tokyo, April.
Terashi, M., Tanaka, H. and Kitazume, M. (1983) Extrusion Failure of Ground Improved by the Deep Mixing Method. Proc. 7th Asian Regional Conf. on SMFE, 1, 313-318, Haifa.
Yajima, M. and Terashi, M. (1984) Full Scale Loading Test on the Improved Ground by DMM. Submitted to JSSMFE Symposium on the Strength and Deformation of Composite Ground, Tokyo, Oct., '84.

Construction of a railway embankment by displacement of deep soft clays and silts

Construction d'un quai de chemin de fer par déplacement des argiles molles et des limons

D. L. WEBB, Senior Partner and Head of Geotechnical Division, Webb & Partners, Consulting Engineers, Durban, South Africa

SYNOPSIS

Construction of a wide railway embankment by end tipping of sand to displace slurry and soft clay up to 16 m deep is described. From the results of limit state analysis, model tests, post construction boreholes and settlement records it is shown that this project has been successful. Procedures for placing the sand fill are given.

1. INTRODUCTION

During the construction of the Richards Bay Harbour Works in 1970 large quantities of sand were excavated from an area of coastal sand dunes near the estuary of the Mhlatuze River for the construction of a railway embankment across the bay. This formed a lagoon 10 hectares in extent with an average depth of about 15 m below LWOST (low water ordinary spring tide), Figure 1.

The lagoon subsequently became filled to a level of approximately -1 m LWOST by an accumulation of fine sand silt and clay slurry. This occurred partly as a result of natural silting up, during periods of flooding of the lagoon, and partly as a result of disposing of dredged material from the Richards Bay Coal Terminal by pumping it into the lagoon. Although the material near the bed of the lagoon, particularly the more sandy material, had consolidated slightly during the ensuing 10 years, the bulk of the soil material in the lagoon, above its sand bed, consists of low strength clayey silt or slurry.

In 1980 a railway embankment 80 m wide and 1800 m long across the lagoon was planned as part of the further development of a railyard for Phase 3 of the Richards Bay Coal Terminal A number of construction methods were considered which involved placement of embankment fill in layers by conventional earth moving machinery or by pumping. However, difficulties soon became apparent. The soft clay slurry in the lagoon would not be able to support a sand embankment greater than 0,5 m in height without a bearing capacity failure. Sand pumping through pipes on floating pontoons would not achieve the very flat slopes and uniform spread of sand required. The proposed embankment was to be constructed to an elevation of 4,50 LWOST and the resulting consolidation settlements were expected to reach some 3 m or more over a period of 10 to 20 years. Removal of the slurry by dredging was ruled out on the grounds of both cost and the absence of a suitable site for the disposal of the dredged material. Bog blasting methods were also considered but were rejected on account of the massive scale of the operation and the uncertainties involved. The method finally adopted was the displacement method involving end-tipping of sand to form an advancing face the full width of the embankment.

2. SITE INVESTIGATION

Seven borings with standard penetration tests were put down at the site of the proposed

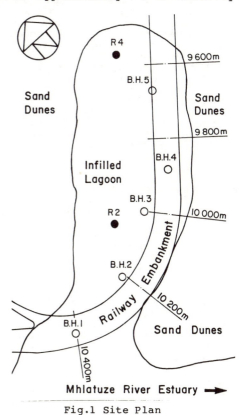

Fig.1 Site Plan

embankment at the positions shown in Figure 1. This method, however, was not sensitive enough to measure the low strengths of the silts and clays and thus vane shear tests were carried out next to each borehole at intervals down to the original sand bed of the lagoon. Piston samples were taken from boreholes 3, 4 and 5 for laboratory determination of Atterberg limits and shear strength characteristics. The general succession of sediments in the lagoon is

Sea/lagoon water	Depth of water varies with tide between 0,5 and 1,5 m
Dark grey, extremely soft sandy and silty clay, slurry.	Extends to between −4 and −7 LOWST
Dark grey/brown extremely soft slightly sandy silty clay	Varies in thickness between 3 and 6 m increasing to 9 m near centre of proposed embankment
Dark green/grey soft to firm silty sandy clay	Extends to bed of lagoon at centre of embankment but not found to any extent elsewhere.
Light grey/green medium to dense sand. Original bed of the lagoon	Encountered at elevations ranging between −16,7 m and −9,5 m LWOST

A representative cross-section through the proposed embankment is illustrated in Figure 2 which shows that there is a variation in the level of the sand bed of the lagoon.

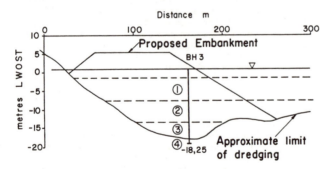

South-East   North-West

① Very dark grey and dark brownish grey, extremely soft, very silty CLAY.

② Dark grey to brownish grey, very soft, slightly sandy to sandy, silty CLAY.

③ Dark grey to dark greenish grey, very soft to soft, silty, very sandy CLAY.

④ Light grey and light greenish brown, loose to medium dense, fine and medium grained SAND.

▽ Average Lagoon Water Level.

Fig.2   Cross-Section at Chainage 9800

The variation in moisture content and Atterberg limits with depth, for all the boreholes, is plotted in Figure 3. It is seen that water contents of slurry vary, within fairly narrow limits, around 180 percent. In the underlying sandy and silty clays the insitu water contents decrease with depth but are generally well above the liquid limits which is to be expected for the soft silty clay still consolidating under its own mass. Vane shear strengths, in Figure 4, reflect a consistent increase with depth.

The average ratio between undrained strength and effective overburden pressure, c_u/p' is about 0,14 compared with a value of about 0,17 for normally consolidated clays obtained from Skempton's equation

$$c_u/p' = 0.11 + .0037PI \qquad (1)$$

A series of immediate undrained triaxial compression tests was carried out on cylindrical specimens cut from the piston samples. However, in some cases the clay was so soft that the specimens collapsed during preparation. The remoulded strengths, shown in Figure 4, indicate a sensitivity of about 4.

The plasticity index of the infill sediments ranges between 16 and 33 and the compression index ranges between 0,4 and 0,53.

In terms of effective stress the cohesion intercept, c', of the silty or sandy clays underlying the upper few metres of slurry ranges between zero and 15 kN/m^2 and σ' ranges between 29,2 and 32 degrees. Average values are c' = 5,5 kN/m^2 and φ' = 30,7. Corresponding parameters for the dune sand at the bottom of the lagoon are c' = 1 kN/m^2 and φ' = 31 degrees. A similar sand was used for the construction of the embankment. Drained box shear tests were carried out on dune sand mixed, in various proportions, with sandy silty clay slurry to establish whether there would be any significant reduction in c' and φ' in the event that the sand fill became mixed with slurry during end tipping into the lagoon. As to be expected it was found that, in the fully drained state, admixtures of slurry had little effect on the shear strength of the sand.

3. SCALE MODEL TESTS

A detailed analysis of stability was carried out to establish the minimum height of embankment required to initiate a shear failure in the clayey sediments in the lagoon, and progressively displace them, as the face of the embankment advanced. The results indicated that proposed height of the embankment of 4,5 m above LWOST would be sufficient to induce the required shear failure and displacement. However, the exact mode of failure could not be predicted accurately from the limit state analysis and a scale model was constructed to investigate it in the laboratory.

The model was constructed to a scale of 1 in 50 in a perspex tank 1800 mm long and 500 mm high. The tank was carefully filled with

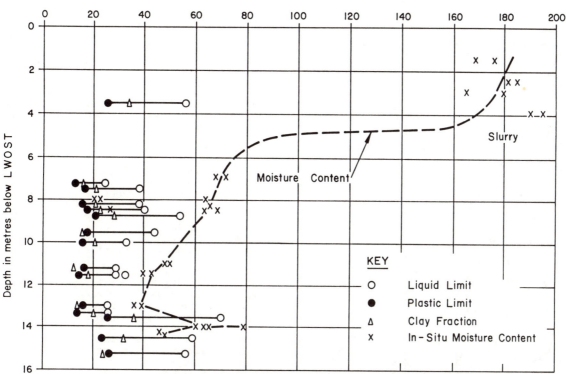

Fig.3 Atterberg Limits and Water Contents

successive layers of bentonite slurry each mixed to a predetermined shear strength to simulate the layers of sediment in the lagoon. Each layer was given a different colour so that its deformation could be readily plotted after failure of the model embankment. Although ideal equivalent densities could not be achieved in the bentonite model, the results of the tests did provide valuable information on the dynamic behaviour of the system as the model sand embankment advanced, as listed below.

3.1 It was found that both the shallow slurry and the underlying very soft clay provided significant lateral support to the advancing dry sand fill.

3.2 The slope of the sand fill, both above and below the surface of the sediments decreased markedly as the height of the sand fill was increased above the surface of the slurry.

3.3 When the slurry was pumped out of the perspex tank the at-rest slope of the sand fill reduced to about 1 vertical in 5 horizontal.

3.4 The amount of slurry trapped under the sand fill appeared to vary at random. However, from the results of both the model tests and the laboratory box shear

tests on mixtures of slurry and sand, it was apparent that small amounts of slurry which became mixed with the sand fill were not likely to have a serious adverse effect on the performance of the embankment.

3.5 The sand fill did not displace the lower zone of very soft model clay. This had the highest undrained shear strength equivalent to approximately 10 kN/m^2.

3.6 Hydraulic placement of the model sand embankment indicated that flow of the saturated sand was likely to take place along the lower horizons of of firmer clay, resulting in a very flat embankment slope.

From an assessment of the behaviour of the model it was considered that some 15 to 25 percent of sandy silty clay or slurry would be trapped in the mass of the sand embankment close to the bed of the lagoon, and be mixed to a certain extent with the sand fill. On that basis post construction settlements were estimated to range, at random, between about 250 and 550 mm over a period of 1,5 to 3 years. Effects of secondary consolidation and lateral creep are expected to increase these settlements by about 25 percent over a further 10 years.

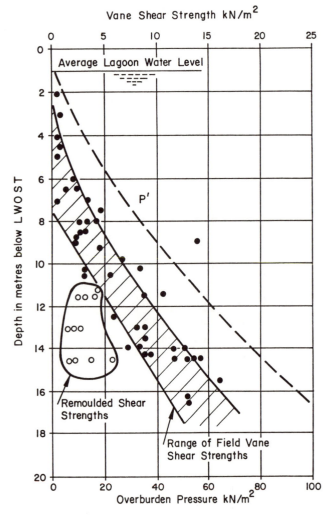

Fig.4 Vane Shear Strengths

At the beginning of the contract the embankment was advanced at an initial face height of a metre above high water level but as mud build-up occurred in front of the fill the face height was gradually raised to 3,5 m above high water which is + 5,5 LWOST and a metre above final formation level as originally specified.

As the gap between the two advancing faces of the fill narrowed it became necessary again to raise the level of the fill near the face. Over the final 150 m of each of the two lengths of embankment the height of fill at the face was increased to 3 m above final design level of 4,5 LWOST. The approaching faces were inclined in plan at an angle of 45 degrees to the centre line of the embankment to aid lateral displacement of slurry and soft clay. Prior to placement of fill the level of the surface of the mud in the lagoon was 0 metres LWOST. On completion of the embankment, however, the mud level in the lagoon had risen by approximately 2,5 m.

Owing to the construction program the excess sand could be left in position to accelerate settlement for only a few weeks before it was dozed over the edge of the embankment. This procedure was adopted to increase the stability of the edge of the embankment, and to consolidate any undisplaced clay, and to provide a wider shoulder as protection to the main embankment which is subject to wave action in times of high water or flood.

Some as-built details to the embankment are shown in Figure 5.

5. POST CONSTRUCTION SITE INVESTIGATION

Twenty six boreholes and twelve Dutch probes were put down along the embankment and across it, from shoulder to shoulder, to determine the mud profile under the fill. Particular attention was paid to the area where the north and south fills met to establish whether any significant amount of mud had been trapped there. A representative cross section is shown in Figure 6. Most of the soft clay appears to have been displaced, particularly where temporary surcharging, to heights of 1 to 3 metres above final design level, was employed. Tne shape of the sand/mud interface in Figure 5 was established from the results of hand shear vane tests carried out on the embankment slope and from a floating raft on the mud next to the embankment.

Levelling studs in concrete bases were placed on a grid pattern over the embankment immediately after removing the excess sand. During the following 8 months the maximum recorded settlement was 290 mm. This occurred where the embankment flanks the estuary mouth, and is attributed to lateral spreading of the fill as the displaced mud spreads and takes up a lower level under the action of tidal forces. Rate of settlement here had decreased to 20 mm per month after 8 months.

At the southern end of the embankment where the face height was initially only 2 metres

Because of these features of the proposed embankment and the anticipated random variation in settlement due to variation in the depth and the mechanical properties of the slurry and underlying soft clay, it wasrecommended that the embankment be placed to a level 1,0 m above the required final formation level. From the behaviour of the model it was expected that the increased height of the embankment, during construction, would also increase the efficiency of the displacement operation and accelerate settlement. Surplus sand would be removed later, down to required formation level.

4. CONSTRUCTION OF THE EMBANKMENT

The embankment was constructed in two portions simultaneously, from the north and south ends of the lagoon. The maximum quantity of sand placed in one month was 422 000 cubic metres using 15 scrapers, 7 dozers and 33 trucks. Total volume was 1,3 million cubic metres.

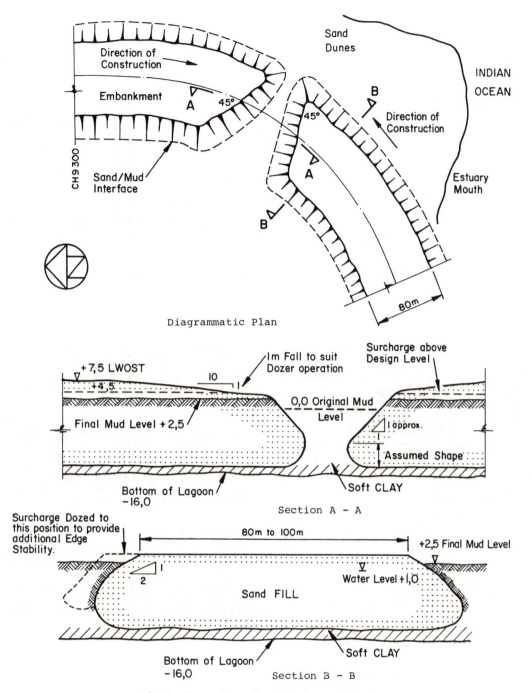

Diagrammatic Plan

Fig.5 Procedure for Placing Sand Fill

above mud level settlements of up to 165 mm were recorded after 8 months, but by that time the rate of settlement had reduced to 4 to 8 mm per month.   Over the major part of the embankment, constructed by the full face displacement method, corresponding settlements are less than 75 mm and were continuing at a reducing rate of between 1,5 and 3,5 mm per month after 8 months.

6. CONCLUSIONS

Both the model study and the monitored behaviour of the wide railway embankment itself, during placement and after completion, have shown that the displacement method of construction is practical and economical in deep very soft clay and slurry.   The short placement period of some 5 months on this project

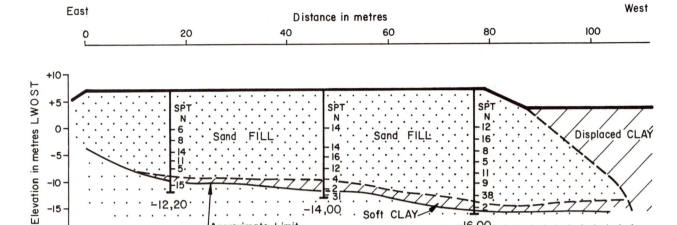

Fig.6 Cross-section after Construction at Chainage 9670

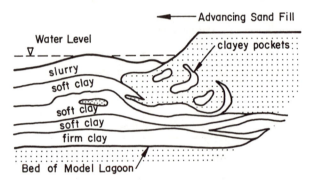

Fig.7 Representative Cross-section Through Model

resulted in substantial cost savings, and the method obviated the very expensive alternative of dredging the lagoon.

The soft clay and slurry provided significant permanent support to the submerged sand with the result that the side slopes were steeper than anticipated.

The placement water content of the sand averaged about 12 percent and it was found that this had not increased very much in samples taken from below water level in the embankment several months after placement. This is attributed to the low permeability of the clay in contact with the sand fill below water level.

As the mud level in the lagoon rose it became necessary to increase the height of the advancing face of the embankment. The resulting temporary surcharge of 1 to 3 m had the effect of accelerating the settlement of the embankment and the lateral deformation of the soft clays surrounding the sand fill. Settlement of the embankment after removing

the surplus sand has been relatively small. It has averaged about 30 mm in 8 months except in two localised areas, discussed in Section 5, where settlements of up to 165 and 290 mm have occurred for other predictable reasons.

Although some soft clay became trapped in the sand fill in the model tests, Fig 7, there was little evidence of soft clay being trapped in the fullscale fill. However, a layer of soft clay 1 to 3 m thick remained in place on the bed of the lagoon beneath 15 m to 20 m of sand fill, Fig 6. This was also apparent in the model.

ACKNOWLEDGEMENT

Permission, given by the Richards Bay Coal Terminal Company (Pty) Limited, for this paper to be published is gratefully acknowledged. Assistance on this project by the author's colleagues D.M.J. Silk, K.N. Mival and A.W. Robinson was much appreciated.

Session 5C
Geotechnical engineered construction
C. Applications of geotextiles

Séance 5C
Construction employant le génie géotechnique
C. Applications de géotextiles

Dimensionnement d'ouvrages renforcés par géotextiles

Designing geotextile reinforced earthwork

Ph. DELMAS, Ingénieur, Laboratoire Central des Ponts et Chaussées, Paris, France
J. P. GOURC, Maître de Conférences, IRIGM, Université de Grenoble, Grenoble, France
H. PERRIER, Ingénieur, Centre d'Expérimentations Routières, Rouen, France

RESUME   Le développement des géotextiles, depuis une dizaine d'années, est directement lié aux avantages tant hydrauliques que mécaniques lors de leur introduction dans les sols. La présente communication traite du renforcement mécanique, en prenant pour exemples d'applications, la chaussée provisoire sur sol mou ainsi que le massif multicouches en sol renforcé.

INTRODUCTION

Dans cette communication, un calcul des renforcements par géotextile est proposé, où l'accent sera mis sur l'influence de la déformabilité relativement importante de ce type d'inclusions. Nous définirons ainsi un nouveau concept de rupture dont le critère ne sera pas lié uniquement à la résistance à la traction de l'armature, mais aussi à la déformation admissible de l'ouvrage en terre renforcé.

I - CHAUSSEES PROVISOIRES SUR SOL MOU, RENFORCEES PAR GEOTEXTILE

I-1 Modélisation

C'est une étude sur modèle effectuée à l'Université de Grenoble qui a permis, de mieux schématiser le mécanisme de renforcement en grandes déformations, de proposer une méthode de dimensionnement et d'étendre cette méthode au cas des remblais et massifs multicouches en respectant les règles de similitudes (5).

Le problème est considéré comme bidimensionnel et étudié à l'échelle 1/3. La cuve d'essai est parallélépidique (largeur 2,30 m - hauteur 0,80 m- épaisseur 0,30 m). La couche de roulement est simulée par une couche de gravette (ϕ = 48°) d'épaisseur H, le sol mou de fondation par une argile (c_u = 10 kPa). Le géotextile, placé à l'interface entre les deux couches, a une largeur totale (L = 1 m). Le passage de camions à 15 kM/h est simulé par le chargement cyclique (P_m = 140 kPa - f = 1 Hz) d'une plaque de largeur (B = 0,25 m). Soit r l'enfoncement de la plaque, appelé orniérage. L'étude a été complétée par des essais cycliques à différents P_m et des essais pseudo-statiques, à vitesse d'enfoncement constante.

Nous présentons ci-après les résultats obtenus pour différents géotextiles. Ces matériaux sont caractérisés mécaniquement par leur module de traction K reliant la tension T à la déformation relative ε dans un essai de traction simple (T = K.ε), et leur angle de frottement ϕg sol-textile.

Le diagramme de la fig.1 se rapporte au chargement cyclique du modèle de chaussée, renforcé par ces différents géotextiles ou non renforcé (0 géot.") : soit r l'orniérage obtenu pour N cycles charge-décharge. Il apparaît clairement que la résistance à la fatigue de la chaussée croît avec le module K du géotextile.

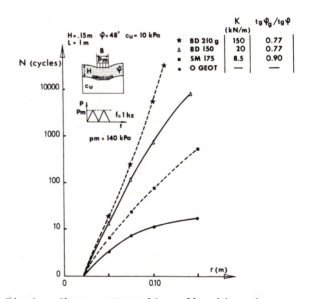

	K (kN/m)	tg ϕ_g /tg ϕ
★ BD 210 g	150	0.77
△ BD 150	20	0.77
■ SM 175	8.5	0.90
● O GEOT		

Fig.1 - Chargement cyclique d'un bicouche Influence du module K du géotextile

Un comportement similaire se retrouve pour des essais de poinçonnement pseudo-statiques à vitesse d'enfoncement constante (3). Soit p_s (r) la pression statique moyenne sous la plaque. On retiendra l'influence croissante du géotextile avec l'orniérage. Des essais de poinçonnement cyclique effectués pour différentes charges maximales p_m (fig.2) nous ont permis de montrer que, pour une même structure de chaussée (H, B, ϕ, c_u) et un géotextile donné, le comportement à la fatigue d'une chaussée renforcée pouvait être caractérisé par (6) :

$$p_m = \frac{\alpha_1 (r)}{[\log N + \alpha_2 (r)]^2} + \alpha_3 (r)$$

Par ailleurs, nous avons montré (4) qu'il existe une pression limite de fatigue qui pouvait être approchée à l'aide d'un simple essai de poinçonnement pseudo-statique (soit in-situ, un essai de plaque). [$P_{m\ell}$ (r) = α_3 (r) ; $P_{m\ell}$ (r) > 0,60. p_s (r)] permet une bonne corrélation avec les résultats de la fig.2 .

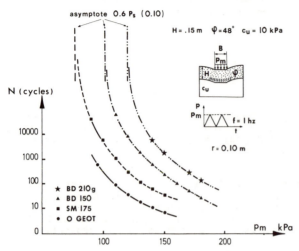

Fig.2 - Critère de fatigue expérimental type pour bicouches renforcés (r = 0.10 m)

I-2 Calcul théorique de l'effet de renforcement

Le cas des bicouches (sol pulvérulent sur sol cohérent) a déjà été étudié par différents auteurs : la couche pulvérulente joue un rôle répartiteur des contraintes de poinçonnement (ξ_{do}).

Une inclusion textile jouera un double rôle :

- <u>augmentation de l'effet répartiteur</u> : tg ξ_d > tg ξ_{do} par mise en compression horizontale de la couche pulvérulente.

- <u>effet membrane</u> (2) - (5) : un géotextile est un matériau souple qui ne peut mécaniquement que reprendre des efforts suivant son plan.

Nous avons simulé théoriquement le passage de véhicules sous la forme d'un double poinçon (fig.3) :

- <u>effet répartiteur</u> : augmentation Δp_R de la pression maximale sous la double plaque

$$\Delta p_R = p^{max} (B^*/H, E/H) - p_O^{max} (B_O^*/H, E/H)$$

p_O^{max} est obtenu à partir d'un calcul en analyse limite. Pour notre exemple numérique ci-après (fig.4), nous avons considéré le cas moyen (ξ_{do} = 5° ; ξ_d = 15°).

- <u>effet membrane</u> : nous adoptons le principe d'une surpression normale au géotextile, uniforme par tronçons (soit une déformée circulaire, en accord avec les essais sur modèle).

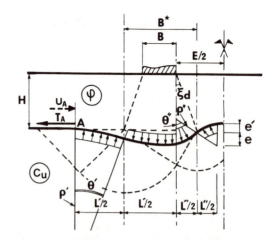

Fig.3 - Mécanisme du renforcement d'une chaussée sur sol mou, par géotextile

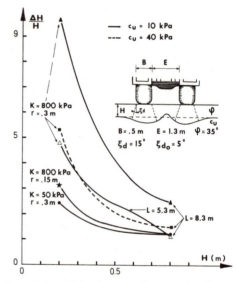

Fig.4 - Gain d'épaisseur de couche de roulement lié à l'utilisation d'un géotextile

La tention T est uniforme dans la partie du géotextile en membrane : T = T_A . Latéralement à A et A' le géotextile est ancré (comportement en ancrage du type élastoplastique) et soumis à un glissement u_A permettant d'équilibrer tension en membrane et tension d'ancrage (T_p est la tension maximale d'ancrage). L'augmentation Δp_M de la pression maximale sous la double plaque s'écrit :

$$\Delta p_M = T (\sin \theta' + \sin \theta'')$$

On peut présenter les résultats obtenus, sous forme d'un gain d'épaisseur pour la couche de roulement grâce à l'inclusion textile, en égalant la portance du bicouche renforcé (H, ϕ, c_u) et la portance du bicouche non renforcé (H$_O$, ϕ, c_u) soit $\Delta H = H_O - H$ le gain d'épaisseur de couche de roulement relatif à l'utilisation d'un géotextile (fig.4).

Ce gain d'épaisseur augmente nettement avec le module K du géotextile et l'ornièrage admissible.

1-3 Expérimentation sur site réel

Dans le prolongement de ces recherches, l'expérimentation grandeur nature réalisée au Laboratoire Régional des Ponts et Chaussées de Nancy avait pour but de comparer l'efficacité de différentes structures de renforcement (nappe courte, nappe longue, bi-nappe, conteneur, géotextile tissé ou non tissé). Le trafic a été réalisé à l'aide d'un camion, possédant un essieu de 130 kN, et roulant à 20 km/h.

L'analyse de l'évolution de l'ornière en fonction du nombre de passages (fig.5) confirme les résultats obtenus sur modèle réduit (à comparer à la fig.1) :

- Meilleur comportement de la chaussée pour un module K supérieur (BD280, K = 40 kN/m et T 250, K = 200 kN/m de même largeur totale L = 4,5 m).

- Meilleur comportement de la chaussée pour un géotextile mieux ancré (t 205, K = 200 kN/m - L = 4,50 m et L = 7,00 m).

- Bon comportement pour des structures bi-nappes associant des géotextiles de modules relativement faibles (2 x BD210, K = 35 kN/m, L = 5,30 m meilleur que t 205, K = 200 kN/m, L = 7,00 m).

Ces essais en vraie grandeur ont aussi permis de mettre en évidence des phénomènes difficilement modélisables tels que l'abrasion importante du géotextile supérieur dans les structures bi-nappes et le fonctionnement sur sol de fondation hétérogène.

II - MASSIFS MULTICOUCHES

Le renforcement multicouches d'ouvrages en terre par géotextile date de 1969 (8). Cette technique tend actuellement à se développer. Citons la réalisation récente d'un massif renforcé, sur la RN19 à Langres, étudié par le Laboratoire Régional des Ponts et Chaussées de Nancy (fig.6) (10).

II-1 Expérimentation sur site réel

Un ancien mur de soutènement subissait depuis plusieurs mois des désordres (rotation autour de l'arête extérieure) liés à l'importance des efforts horizontaux induits par une circulation de camions intense et en courbe, associée à de faibles caractéristiques mécaniques pour le remblai situé derrière le mur.

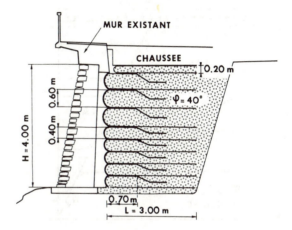

Fig.6 - Massif multicouches derrière un mur de soutènement à Langres. Expérimentation du L.P.C. de Nancy

La solution a consisté à supprimer la poussée sur le mur au moyen d'un massif renforcé par géotextile. Cependant, les tolérances étroites sur les déformations admissibles au niveau de la chaussée, ont permis de mettre en relief la carence des méthodes usuelles de dimensionnement quant à l'estimation des déformations. Peu de publications abordent ce problème (1).

II-2 Estimation théorique des déformations d'un massif multicouche

Pour un ouvrage type (H = 6 m, γ = 18 kN/m^3, ϕ = 30°, p = 40 kPa - géotextile :

T admissible = 36,5 kN/m, ϕg = 21°) (fig.7), nous donnons le résultat du dimensionnement obtenu par trois méthodes classiques (la méthode B consiste à supposer que l'effort de poussée des terres est repris par les armatures). On aboutit à des différences importantes (respectivement 66 - 50 et 89 m^2/ml de géotextile).

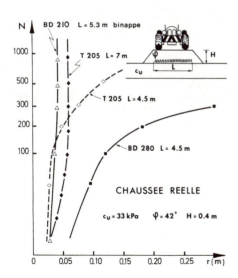

Fig.5 - Expérimentation de chaussée sur site réel : évolution du nombre de passages en fonction de l'ornièrage pour différentes structures renforcées

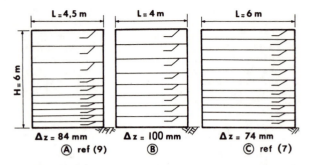

Fig.7 - Profil du massif multicouches dimensionné par trois méthodes différentes

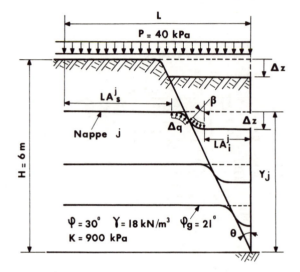

Fig.8 - Massif multicouches : estimation des déformations

La méthode proposée ici a pour but de permettre une comparaison de différents dimensionnements à partir du calcul des déformations (déplacement vertical Δz) nécessaires dans chaque cas à la stabilisation de l'ouvrage dont les valeurs sont indiquées sur la fig. 7.

Nous adoptons le même principe que dans le chapitre I, de la membrane ancrée, (longueur d'ancrage L_{Ai} et L_{As}. Le décrochement Δz d'équilibre est tel qu'il permet de vérifier l'équilibre local de chaque nappe et l'équilibre global du coin de rupture (fig.8).

Cette méthode fera l'objet d'une publication indépendante.

CONCLUSION

La confrontation d'essais sur modèles réduits et en vraie grandeur a permis de développer une méthodologie de calcul permettant de prendre en compte la spécificité du renforcement par géotextile, en particulier la souplesse et les déformations des ouvrages ainsi renforcés.

REFERENCES BIBLIOGRAPHIQUES

(1) Blanchier A., Gielly J.- Etude de la stabilité des talus en remblais renforcés par des géotextiles, 2è Congrès International des Géotextiles, Las Vegas, 1982.

(2) Delmas Ph. - Sols renforcés par géotextiles. Premières études. Thèse Docteur-Ingénieur, Université Scientifique et Médicale de Grenoble, I.R.I.G.M., Décembre 1979.

(3) Gourc J.P., Matichard Y., Perrier H., Delmas Ph. - Capacité portante d'un bicouche, sable sur sol mou, renforcé par géotextile, 2è Congrès International des Géotextiles, Las Vegas, 1982.

(4) Gourc J.P., Perrier H., Riondy G., Rigo J.M., Perfetti J. - Chargement cyclique d'un bicouche renforcé par géotextile, 2è Congrès International des Géotextiles, Las Vegas, 1982.

(5) Gourc J.P. - Quelques aspects du comportement des géotextiles en mécanique des sols. Thèse de Docteur-es-Sciences, Université de Grenoble, Décembre 1982.

(6) Gourc J.P., Perrier H., Riondy G. - Unsurfaced roads on soft subgrade : mechanism of geotextile reinforcement, 8ème Congrès Européen de Mécanique des Sols, Helsinki, Mai 1983.

(7) Haliburton A. - Use of engineering fabrics in transportation related applications. Draft for Federal Highway Administration Review. (Washington - Octobre 1981).

(8) Puig J., Vautrain J. - Remblai expérimental de Caen. Bulletin de Liaison des Laboratoires des Ponts et Chaussées, n° 41, Novembre 1969.

(9) Smith G.N. - Principles of reinforced earth design. Symposium on Reinforced earth and other composite soil techniques. Edinburgh Septembre 1977. TRRL Supplementary Report 457.

(10) Delmas Ph., Favre J.M., Lehman M., Matichard Y., Prudon R., Rebut P. - Renforcement par géotextile d'un mur de soutènement sur la RN19 à Langres. Revue générale des Routes et Aérodromes. Juin 1984.

The shear strength behaviour of certain materials on the surface of geotextiles

La résistance à la rupture au cisaillement de différents matériaux à la surface de feuilles plastiques

J. FORMAZIN, Director, VEB SBK Wasserbau, KB Baugrund Berlin, Berlin, GDR
C. BATEREAU, Head of the Laboratory, VEB SBK Wasserbau, KB Baugrund Berlin, Berlin, GDR

SYNOPSIS   The growing application of geotextiles in building embankments, slopes and earth walls requires investigation into interfacial shear strength behaviour of geotextiles and the materials in contact with them.   Most frequent combinations under investigation were

                    geotextile - synthetic watertight foil
                    geotextile - prefabricated concrete slab
                    geotextile - soil

THEORETICAL ASPECTS

Provided the technologically caused roughness of the surface of the soil subgrade is neglected, the following basic contact situation may be assumed (Batereau, 1982; Richter, 1972):

- There is no toothing at all at the interface. The surfaces of both materials are ideally smooth.

- Toothing at the interface is caused by the roughness of the materials. The effectiveness of the toothing depends on the normal stress due to the high deformability of the geotextile.

Shear consists of the following processes:

- friction without deforming or destroying the surfaces of the materials

- friction with partial or complete destruction of the surfaces of the materials

The initial shear strength is the greater the higher the mutual toothing of both shear planes is.   A declining growth of the shear strength is found with rising stress and an increasing percentage of the destruction of the materials (Figure 1, graph 2).

When the toothing is caused only by normal stress, there is an increaseing growth of the shear strength in the range of minor stress (Figure 1, graph 3), while the decline of the growth of the shear strength as shown in Figure 1, graph 2 can be observed with further growing stress.   The kind and degree of toothing between

        geotextile and prefabricated concrete slabs and soil, respectively

depend on the following factors:

- synthetic fabrics, surface structure, and thickness of the geotextile

- surface roughness of the prefabricated concrete slab

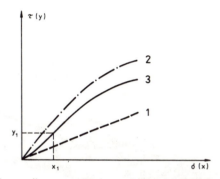

Assumption: no adhesion and cohesion, respectively

$1 \quad \tau = m \cdot d$

$2 \quad \tau = m \cdot d^n$

$3 \quad \tau = A \cdot \ln\left(\frac{d - x_1}{B} + \sqrt{\left(\frac{d - x_1}{B}\right)^2 + 1}\right) + y_1$

Fig. 1 Possible laws for interfacial shear strength

- grain size, grain-size distribution, grain shape, and compactness of the soil

Creeping deformation was minute and therefore neglected.

TESTING PROCEDURE AND RESULTS

A special flat-shear apparatus (Batereau, 1982) with a shear box which was used parallel was built to carry out investigations under clearly defined, uniform conditions:

- The geotextile is completely fastened in a frame.

- The testing was made in water-saturated conditions.

- The range of normal stress under investigation was

$$\delta_N = 0.01 \text{ to } 0.05 \text{ MN/m}^2.$$

- The load was raised every other minute.
- 20 steps of load increment were planned to attain a rupture of the materials.

The testing results of geotextile and the above-mentioned contact materials have in principle proved the correctness of the correlations for the shear strength at the interface shown in Figure 1.   The following results were attained:

Combination

   geotextile - synthetic watertight foil

This combination is of importance in building river and canal constructions when watertight foils are laid out parallel to the slops and geotextiles are used as a protective layer. Testing results (Fig. 2) show that there are remarkable differences depending on the materials of the foils.

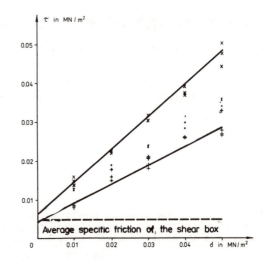

Fig. 3   Interfacial shear strength between synthetic bonded fibre fabric and prefabricated concrete slabs with differing surface roughness

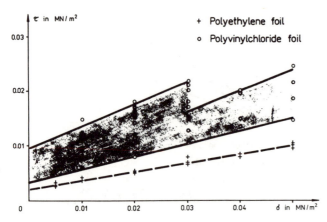

Fig. 2   Interfacial shear strength between different synthetic fabrics and watertight polyethylen and polyvinylchloride foil, respectively

With polyethylene foil with a very smooth surface all contacting geotextiles under investigation yield an almost constant shear strength at the interface, while the values are strongly varying with polyvinylchloride foil with smooth surface.   Due to the testing procedure the friction of the shear box can be neglected in this combination.

Combination

   geotextile - prefabricated concrete slab

The interfacial shear strengths in this combination (Fig. 3) vary greatly. The main cause for these variations is the roughness of the surface of the concrete slab. Detailed investigations to determine a parameter of roughness failed.

The following visual assessment has stood its practical test:

smooth: The surface of the concrete feels polished. Due to even moulds it has got a non-shining glazed surface. Roughness occured only as bubbles which were curved to the inside. These surfaces were produced by plastics, or steel or similar moulds. Smoothed concrete surfaces. The surface of the slab mainly consists of clean grains of aggregates (smoothed rocks without cement slurry coating).

rough: The surface of the concrete feels rough. Aggregates at the surface have a high roughness and a rough coating of cement slurry. These surfaces were produced by sawn wooden moulds; the concrete was coarsely trimmed by means of a plank.

This shows that preliminary assessment of the interfacial shear strengths is only possible to a limited extent, the same as in the combination of two synthetic elements.   In contrast to the first combination a medium specific friction of the shear box must be considered. There was no measurable adhesion between the synthetic fabric and the concrete slab.

Combination

   geotextile - soil

In this case one must further distinguish between

   geotextile - cohesive soil and
   geotextile - cohesionless soil.

No decline in the interfacial shear strength against the angle of shear within cohesive soil was found in the tests with a combination with cohesive soil.

TABLE

Interfacial shear strength values for water saturated conditions

Material in contact with geotextile	Kind of geotextile	μ
Polyethylene foil - smooth -	Synthetic bonded fibre fabric	0.16
Polyvinylchloride - smooth - foil	Synthetic bonded fibre fabric	0.25 to 0.45
Prefabricated - smooth - concrete slab	Synthetic bonded fibre fabric	0.45 to 0.60
- rough -	" " " "	0.60 to 0.80
Soil $d_5 \geq 0.063$ mm d_{50}		
0.2 to 2.0 mm	Synthetic bonded fibre fabric	0.70
2.0 to 5.0 mm	" " " "	0.60
5.0 to 10.0 mm	" " " "	0.50
0.2 to 2.0 mm	woven and knitted fabric	0.60
2.0 to 5.0 mm	" " " "	0.50
5.0 to 10.0 mm	" " " "	0.40

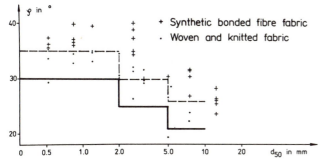

Fig. 4 Interfacial shear strength between different geotextiles and non-cohesive soil with differing grain size

Further tests therefore centred on a combination with cohesionless soils. Measurements of the influence of normal stress have shown that most practical considerations can assume linear τ - σ - relations. Extrapolation of the test values is not permissible. The grain size of the non-cohesive soil (Fig. 4) in contact with the synthetic fabric decisively influences the interfacial shear strength. In the tests the void ratio of the soil was e = 0.83. All fractions used, with a d > 0.1 mm, had smooth, partly rounded edges.

CONCLUSIONS

Interfacial shear tests made in the above-mentioned combinations allow for the following conclusions:

- Conclusions for interfacial shear strength values for the above-mentioned combinations from specific parameters of materials can only be rough estimations. On-the-spot shear tests will also be necessary in the future.

- Friction coefficients given in the table can be used for rough calculations.

- On-the-spot interfacial shear tests should always be made in the range of normal stress which will actually act on the interface in the finished construction.

- Linear dependence in evaluating the tests yields adequately exact results for practical purposes.

- Extrapolation to ranges of stress which were not under investigation is only possible to a limited extent. If non-linear behaviour is to be expected extrapolated values must not be used for ultimate calculations.

REFERENCES

Batereau, C. (1982). "Zur Normalspannungs-abhängigkeit der Grenzflächenscherfestig-keit". Neue Bergbautechnik, 12. Jg., Heft 9.

Batereau, C. (1982). "Versuchsdurchführung zur Bestimmung der Grenzflächen-scherfestigkeit zwischen flächenförmigen Kunststoffelementen und Lockergestein". Bauinformation Wissenschaft und Technik, Jg. 25, Heft 3.

Richter, H.-C. (1972). "Gleit- und Scher-verhalten ebener und unebener mechanisch wirksamer Trennflächen". Zeitschrift für angewandte Geologie, 18. Jg., Heft 6.

Bearing capacity of a geotextile-reinforced foundation

Capacité d'appui d'une fondation géotextile-armé

VITO A. GUIDO, Ph.D., P.E., Assistant Professor, Civil Engineering, Cooper Union School of Engineering, New York, NY, USA
G. L. BIESIADECKI, Structural Engineer, Mueser, Rutledge, Johnston & DeSimone, New York, NY, USA
M. J. SULLIVAN, Geotechnical Engineer, Frank H. Lehr Associates, East Orange, New Jersey, USA

SYNOPSIS   The use of geotextiles as a reinforcing element in soils has gained widespread use throughout the world. One application of geotextile reinforcement is below shallow foundations. Presented herein are the results of laboratory model tests used to study the bearing capacity of shallow foundations reinforced with geotextiles. The parameters studied were the effect on the bearing capacity of a square footing of depth below the footing of the first layer of reinforcement, the vertical spacing of the layers, the number of layers, the width size of the sheet of geotextile reinforcement and the tensile strength of the geotextile. For the tests performed, the bearing capacity of the soil reinforced with geotextiles was increased by a factor greater than three.

INTRODUCTION

The present concept of reinforced earth is due largely, in part, to the work of Henri Vidal (1966). Although the original work done by Vidal used galvanized metal strips as the reinforcing material, geotextiles can be used effectively. Reinforced earth has been used successfully in retaining walls, and roadbed and embankment stabilization. Its application to shallow foundation problems has been studied experimentally by Binquet and Lee (1975), Akinmusuru and Akinbolade (1981), Biesiadecki (1983), and Sullivan (1984). This paper will investigate the experimental study carried out by the authors on the effect on the bearing capacity of a square footing on sand reinforced with a geotextile.

EXPERIMENTAL LABORATORY MODEL

The model tests were performed in a square stiffened plexiglass box 1.22m wide with a depth of 0.92m. Two series of tests were performed for a total of 70 tests, 25 from Series A and 45 from Series B. Each series used a different uniformly graded sand. In Table I are shown the properties of the two sands used. A 0.31m square footing was used. A vertical load was applied to the footing through the use of a hydraulic jack and hand pump. The load was applied in small increments and the resulting footing displacement measured by two dial gages, placed at opposite corners of the footing. The differential settlement recorded by these gages was very small for all tests performed. The geotextiles used as reinforcing material are shown in Table II. All model tests were performed with square sheets of geotextiles. A parameter defined as the width ratio, b/B; where b is the width of the geotextile and B is the width of the footing was required. The square sheets of geotextile were placed concentrically under the square footing. The geometry of the model is shown in Fig. 1.

TABLE I

Properties of the Sands Used in Model Tests

	Series A Tests	Series B Tests
Uniformity Coefficient, C_u	2.5	1.9
Effective Size, D_{10},m	8.6×10^{-5}	8.6×10^{-5}
Median Size, D_{50},m	1.8×10^{-4}	1.5×10^{-4}
Specific Gravity	2.63	2.66
Minimum Dry Unit Weight,γ_{dmin},kN/m^3	13.45	13.10
Maximum Dry Unit Weight, γ_{dmax},kN/m^3	16.45	15.65
Dry Unit Weight γ_d , kN/m^3	14.80	14.26
Relative Density, Dr, %	50	50
Angle of Internal Friction, ϕ',$^\circ$	35	36

In order to obtain the full benefits of a geotextile behaving as reinforcement, sufficient deformation of the fabric is required to mobilize the fabrics' tensile stress. These deformations can be obtained in a soil which is relatively loose. However, placement of the soil in the test model with relative densities less than 50%, with repetitiveness from test to test, was very difficult. Therefore, a relative density of 50% was used, which is in the medium compact density range. In addition, a soil at relative densities greater than 50% would not have exhibited the increase in bearing capacity, due to fabric reinforcement, as dramatically.

TEST RESULTS

The effect of five parameters on the bearing capacity of a square footing on a soil reinforced with geotextiles was studied:

1. The depth below the footing of the first

layer of reinforcement, u. This was expressed as a dimensionless ratio u/B, where B is the width of the footing.
2. The vertical spacing of the layer of reinforcement, Δz. A dimensionless ratio of $\Delta z/B$ was used.
3. The number of layers of reinforcement, N.
4. The width size, b, of the square sheet of reinforcement, expressed in dimensionless form as b/B.
5. The tensile strength of the geotextile used as reinforcement.

TABLE II

Geotextiles Used in Model Tests

Manufacturer	Fabric Trade Name	Structure	Thickness $\times 10^4$ (m)	Tensile Strength (kN)
E.I.DuPont de Nemours & Co.	Typar 3401	Nonwoven	3.8	0.67
Crown Zellerbach	Fibretex 400	Nonwoven	27.9	1.16
Mirafi Inc.	600X	Woven	7.6	1.33
Phillips Fibers Corp.	Supac 8 NP	Nonwoven Staple	22.9	1.47
Burlington Industrial Fabrics	Bi-tech 3013	Woven	7.6	1.78
Hoechst Fibers Industries	Trevira Spunbond S1155	Nonwoven	53.3	2.16

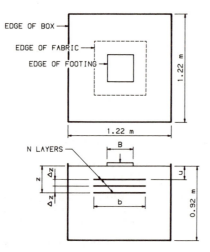

Fig. 1 Geometry of Model

Except for those tests, where the effect of the tensile strength of the geotextile was investigated, all model tests were performed using the Dupont Typar 3401. In no model test was a fabric ever torn or damaged in any way due to load application. Reference tests for both the Series A and Series B tests were performed for the case of no fabric reinforcement. For the Series A tests, the ultimate bearing pressure,

q_o, for the unreinforced sand was 82.7 kPa at a settlement, s, of 0.015m, or s/B of 0.05. The Series B tests had an ultimate bearing pressure, q_o for the sand of 99.3 kPa at 0.019m of settlement, or s/B of 0.063. Binquet and Lee (1975) introduced a term, bearing capacity ratio (BCR), for convenience in expressing and comparing test data:

$$BCR = q/q_o \qquad (1)$$

where q_o is as defined above and q is the bearing pressure of the reinforced soil at a settlement corresponding to the settlement at the ultimate bearing pressure for the unreinforced soil. Typical load-settlement curves, for Series A tests, are shown in Fig. 2 for different values of N.

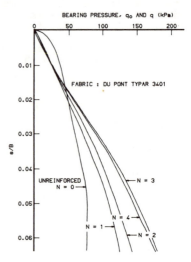

Fig. 2 Load-Settlement Curves for Series A Tests, u/B=0.5, $\Delta z/B$=0.25 and b/B=2

Since the soil is at a relative density of 50% and can be classified as having a medium compact density, the load-settlement curve for the unreinforced soil (N=0) has a shape similar to that for a general shear failure mode. It does not exhibit an abrupt curvature into a vertical tangent because the soil is not in the compact to very compact density range. The load-settlement curves for the reinforced soil(N>0) have the classical shape for a local-shear (punching) failure mode; this was substantiated when u was less than 0.051m and the top layer of fabric visibly had the outline of the footing impressed into it. Since radial tensile stresses develop in the soil directly beneath the footing, dissipating with depth, the fabric reinforcement placed directly beneath the footing is in tension preventing the general-shear failure mode to take place. In order to obtain maximum benefit from a geotextile functioning as reinforcement, sufficient deformation of the fabric is required to mobilize its tensile stress. As is shown in Fig. 2 for small settlements, s/B less than 0.017, the load-settlement curve of the unreinforced soil indicates that it is stiffer than the reinforced soil. At small deformations, the full benefits of the presence of the fabric are not exhibited since the fabric has not deformed sufficiently, whereas, the presence of the fabric has changed the failure mode from one of general-shear to one of local-shear as indicated above. For this reason, the unreinforced soil is stiffer than the reinforced soil at small settlements. However, at settlements where s/B is greater than 0.017, the load-settlement curve for the unreinforced soil is to the left of those for the reinforced soil. The fabric has deformed sufficiently to mobilize its tensile stress thereby increasing the loading carrying capacity of the soil above that of the unreinforced condition.

Effect of the Depth of the Top Layer and the Vertical Spacing of the Layers of Reinforcement-

If the reinforcement is kept within the effective depth (z/B=1), with the depth of the bottom layer of reinforcement at a value equal to B, the vertical spacing of the layer is tied directly to the number of layers and the depth of the top layer of reinforcement by

$$\frac{\Delta z}{B} = \frac{1-(u/B)}{N-1} \tag{2}$$

In Fig. 3 are shown the results for Series B tests, of varying the depth of the first layer of reinforcement, and $\Delta z/B$ varying with N and u/B according to Eq. (2). For a given value of N as u/B increases ($\Delta z/B$ decreases) the BCR decreases to a value at which a further increase in u/B does not change the BCR. This would indicate that beyond a critical depth, the effect of the location of the top layer of reinforcement is offset by the decrease in vertical spacing of the layers for a constant value of N (the density of the number of layers within a given volume of soil is increasing). In addition, for a given value of u/B as N increases ($\Delta z/B$ decreases) the BCR increases. Therefore, the effect of the two parameters u/B and $\Delta z/B$ on the bearing capacity cannot be considered separately, only concurrently.

Effect of the Number of Layers of Reinforcement-

In Fig. 4 is shown the variation of the BCR with the number of layers, N. Fig. 4a is for Series A tests with b/B=2, and Fig. 4b is for Series B tests with b/B=3. For both of these curves when N=4 the depth of the bottom layer of reinforcement is at 1.25B. As the number of layers increase from 0 (unreinforced) to 3 there is a steady increase in the BCR, however, as the number of layers increases above 3 there is little change in the BCR. This is true for both Series A and Series B tests. These results are similar to those observed by Binquet and Lee (1975), and Akinmusuru and Akinbolade (1981). In addition, when N=3 the botton layer of reinforcement is at a depth of z=B indicating that the placement of reinforcement below a depth B yields no added improvement in the bearing capacity. The soils for Series A and Series B tests had q_o = 82.7 kPa and 99.3 kPa, respectively. One would expect that the Series A tests would exhibit larger increased benefits in bearing capacity due to reinforcement than the Series B tests. A comparison of Figs. 4a and 4b would indicate a sharper increase in the BCR with N and a higher peak value of the BCR for the Series A tests than the Series B tests; even though b/B of the Series A tests is smaller than the b/B of the Series B tests.

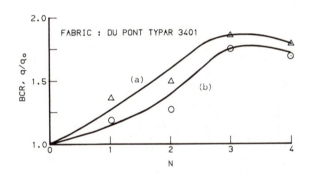

Fig. 4 BCR Variation With Number Of Reinforcing Layers, u/B=0.5 and $\Delta z/B$=0.25; (a) Series A Tests and b/B=2, (b) Series B Tests and b/B=3

Effect of the Width Size of the Square Sheet of Reinforcement -

Since a zone exists beneath the footing in which radial tensile stresses develop, fabric placed within this zone will also be in tension. This fabric in tension reinforces the soil and increases the bearing capacity of the soil above the unreinforced condition (BCR increases). If fabric is placed outside this zone, it will be in compression and serve only as anchorage; it does not contribute to the reinforcing aspects of the soil. Therefore, to increase the width of the fabric beyond an optimum value would yield no benefits of reinforcement. The curve in Fig. 5 shows the variation in BCR with the width ratio b/B for Series A tests. As b/B varies from 0 (unreinforced) to 2.5 the BCR steadily increases, however, as the b/B approaches 3 there is little change in the BCR. This indicates that for given values of u/B, $\Delta z/B$ and N an optimum width ratio can be obtained to yield the optimum BCR.

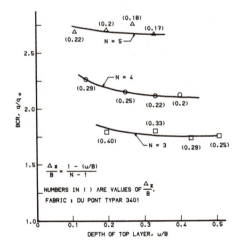

Fig. 3 BCR Variation With Depth Of Top Layer For Series B Tests, b/B=3 And Bottom Layer Of Reinforcement at z=B

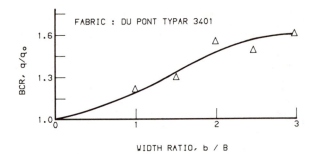

Fig. 5 BCR Variation With Width Ratio For Series A Tests, u/B=0.5, Δz/B=0.25 and N=2

Effect of Tensile Strength of Geotextile – The reinforcements themselves must be able to support tensile forces while the soil sustains compressive and shearing stresses. Therefore, the tensile strength of the reinforcement is an important parameter, with increased BCR expected with increasing tensile strength. In Fig. 6 is shown the variation of BCR with tensile strength. As the tensile strength increases there is a steady increase in the BCR, this is true for both the Series A and Series B tests. It was indicated above that the unreinforced ultimate bearing pressure for the Series A tests was less than that for the Series B tests, therefore, it would be expected that the tensile strength of the fabric would have a greater effect on the BCR for the Series A tests than for the Series B tests. Fig. 6 indicates this. Some of the points in Fig. 6 are below the curves drawn, indicating a bearing pressure that is too low. These points are for fabrics with large thicknesses (as shown in Table II), therefore, the fabrics are more compressible and the settlement registered on the dial gages is not due solely to the displacement of the soil but also the compression of the fabric. This would yield load-settlement curves where the bearing pressures would be too low for a given settlement.

SUMMARY AND CONCLUSIONS

This paper has described two series of laboratory model tests to investigate the bearing capacity of a square footing on a geotextile reinforced sand. The results presented have shown that five parameters have a substantial effect on the bearing capacity; the depth below the footing of the first layer of reinforcement, the vertical spacing of the layers, the number of layers, the width size of the sheet of geotextile, and its tensile strength. It was shown that the parameters u/B, Δz/B, and N are closely related if the reinforcement is kept within the effective depth (z/B=1) with the depth of the bottom layer of reinforcement at a value equal to B. In addition, similar trends in BCR values as a function of the above mentioned parameters for two different sands were obtained, indicating that these trends are not specific for one sand only. This study has given a better understanding of the geotextile reinforced earth slab, where none previously existed.

REFERENCES

Akinmusuru, J.O., and Akinbolade, J.A. (1981). Stability of Loaded Footings on Reinforced Soils. ASCE J. Geo. Engg. Div. (107), GT6, 16320, June, 819-827.

Biesiadecki, G. L. (1983). A Study of the Bearing Capacity and Settlement Characteristics of Shallow Foundations Reinforced with Geotextiles. Master's thesis presented to The Cooper Union, School of Engineering, N.Y., N.Y.

Binquet, J. and Lee, K.L. (1975). Bearing Capacity Tests on Reinforced Earth Slabs. ASCE J. Geo. Engg. Div. (101), GT12, 11792, Dec., 1241-1255.

Sullivan, M.J. (1984). Parameters Affecting the Bearing Capacity and Settlement Characteristics of Shallow Foundations Reinforced with Geotextiles. Master's thesis presented to the Cooper Union, School of Engineering, N. Y., N.Y.

Vidal, H. (1966). La Terre Armee, Annales de l'Institut Technique de Batiment et des Traux Publics, July-Aug., 888-936.

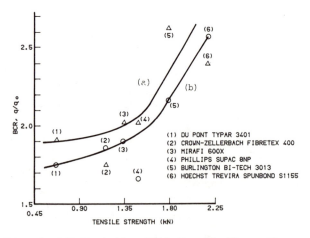

(1) DU PONT TYPAR 3401
(2) CROWN-ZELLERBACH FIBRETEX 400
(3) MIRAFI 600X
(4) PHILLIPS SUPAC 8NP
(5) BURLINGTON BI-TECH 3013
(6) HOECHST TREVIRA SPUNBOND S1155

Fig. 6 BCR Variation With Tensile Strength, u/B=0.5, Δz/B=0.25, b/B=3, and N=3; (a) Series A Tests, (b) Series B Tests

Stability of earth structures reinforced by geotextiles

Sur la stabilité des murs de soutènement renforcés au géotextile

H. MOUST JACOBSEN, Ph.D., Soil Mechanics Laboratory, University of Aalborg, Denmark

SYNOPSIS   The stability of retaining walls or embankments can be improved by means of horizontal layers of inclusions. Several authors have analysed the method theoretically and have proposed calculation methods based on circular slip analyses. Failure occurs in a very narrow zone surrounded by rather stiff soil bodies. This failure mechanism has been studied in a special shear box using a sand-geotextile element. The long term creep of the geotextile has also been investigated in a test series including a very long lasting plane strain tensile test with constant load.

INTRODUCTION

Use of geotextiles as a reinforcing element in earth retaining structures or in embankments is rather attractive because of its low cost and uncomplicated installation. However, such structures have so far mainly been built for experimental purposes. Geotextiles have until now been used in temporary roads and some small roads situated on soft subsoils to improve the bearing capacity of the road and to separate the subsoil from the road base. The reason is, that the long term reduction in the strength of the geotextile is still an open question, which must be answered before use of geotextiles in important permanent constructions, or the allowable tensile forces should be reduced considerably making the construction too expensive.

Design of an earth retaining structure reinforced by several layers of geotextile comprises

construction of surface elements
calculation of stresses in the circular shaped geotextile membranes behind the surface elements
calculation of overlapping length and anchor length
calculation of the vertical spacing of the geotextile layers.

This paper restricts itself to the stability problem shown in the circle in Fig. 1. Since the failure takes place along a curved surface the plane of shear failure may assume different angles α relative to the horisontal layer of the geotextile. This problem also appears in the design of embankments and slopes.

The soil used in reinforced earth structures is normally sand. The failure mechanism has therefore been studied in the laboratory by performing tests with sand and a non-woven geotextile in a special shear box developed for this purpose (Fig. 5). The same phenomenon has been studied earlier in tests performed on clay-geotextile specimens (Snaith, Bell and Dubois 1979).

PROPERTIES OF THE SOIL

The sand used in all tests is a pure quarts sand with fairly angular grains, called Lund no 0. The grain size distribution is quite uniform as can be seen in Fig. 2. The void ratios in the loosest and densest state are e_{max} = 0.82 and e_{min} = 0.56. The tests are performed with a mean void ratio of 0.57. Since the sand is very dense and the stress level rather low the internal angle of friction is high. The angle of friction measured in the triaxial apparatus is $\phi = 50°$ at $\sigma_3' = 5$ kPa and $\phi = 48°$ at $\sigma_3' = 10$ kPa. The angle of dilatation $\nu \sim 17°$.

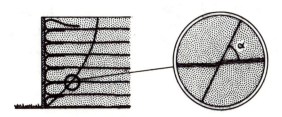

Fig. 1. Stability failure in reinforced soil.

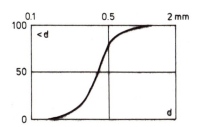

Fig. 2. Grain size distribution of sand.

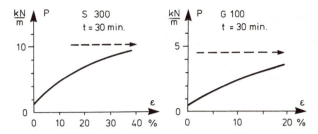

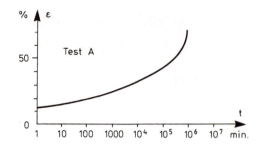

Fig. 3. Plane strain tensile tests with geotextiles.

PROPERTIES OF THE GEOTEXTILE

The geotextile used are all made by Fibertex in Denmark. They are non-woven, needle-punched and thermic bonded under compression and are composed of polypropylene. The quality mainly used in the test series is the so-called S300 with a unit weight of 300 g/m². In a few tests a weak geotextile, G100, were used with a unit weight of only 100 g/m². The short term tensile strengths of S300 and G100 in plane strain is 12 and 4 kN/m, respectively.

Plane strain tensile tests have also been performed at a stress rate corresponding to that in the shear box test. The load was applied stepwise and kept constant for half an hour and after five to six steps the geotextile broke. (Fig. 3).

LONG TERM STRENGTH OF A GEOTEXTILE

In order to study the long term reduction of the strength of a geotextile stressed by a constant load a test series has been carried out in the plane strain tensile apparatus. The geotextile was loaded stepwise until failure and during a test the duration of each step was as constant as possible. But the step length t_s varied from test to test beginning with $t_s = 4$ min., succeding with $t_s = 16, 60, 1400$ and 4000 min. and ending up with a test, which is still continuing after $t = 1000000$ min. (2 years). The time curve is shown in Fig. 4 and the test seems now to be very near its end. In Fig. 4 is also plotted the strength of the geotextile against t_s. The relationship between the strength of the geotextile P_t and the duration of the constant load is a logarithmic function:

$$P_t = P_{max}(1 - s \cdot log_{10}t_s)$$

P_{max} is the strength of the geotextile, when loaded with time intervals of 1 min. It is found to correspond closely to the short term tensile strength measured at the factory. The long term reduction s is 7% per decade. With an estimated life time for a retaining wall or an embankment of 20 years the strength should be reduced with 50%.

It is worth noting that this result could have been achieved even if the maximum duration of the constant load had been only one to three days. In other words, a standard method comprising tests with $t = 4$ min., 100 min. and 1000 – 4000 min. could be a practical tool for design purposes.

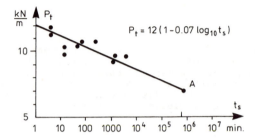

Fig. 4. Long term behaviour of geotextile S300.

THE TESTING APPARATUS

A special shear box has been developed in order to study the stabilizing effect of a geotextile embedded in sand. The sand specimens were dry and prepared by the pluvial compaction technique. The surface of the specimen was horizontal during the layering and therefore the geotextile has to be mounted horizontally, just as in practice. The sand-geotextile specimen represents an element in the backfill of a retaining wall (compare Fig. 5 and 1) or in an embankment. The sand specimen is 175 mm x 100 mm x 150 mm in size. It is situated between two circular end platens, which can be rotated in such a way that the shear surface assumes angles of 30°, 60° or 90° with the horizontal plane. Inside the two end platens some small wheels prevent deformations in the transverse direction of the geotextile. The geotextile can be fixed by two jaws corresponding to a perfect anchoring of the geotextile, or the two jaws can allow the geotextile to move freely into the sand corresponding to a very short anchor length. The sand specimen is loaded by means of weights, representing typical overburden pressures corresponding to the load of 3-5 m of

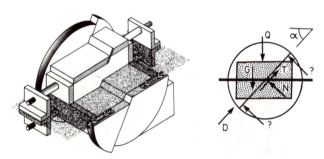

Fig. 5. Shear box with inclining failure surface.

sand. It is possible to prevent horizontal movements between the upper pressure head and the end platens in order to study the effect of the movements in the sliding soil mass. The sand-geotextile specimen was sheared at a deformation rate of 0.12 mm/min. The maximum shear deformation was 28 mm. Fig. 5 also shows the principle of calculation. The known quantities are the

dead load of weights Q, the weight of the sand and the moving part of the apparatus G, the external shearing force D producing shear deformations. Unknown quantities are the shearing force T in the failure surface and the force N normal to the failure surface. T is easily calculated from

$$T = (Q + G)\sin\alpha - D$$

but N remains unmeasured.

A test series includes four test types

1. Dummy tests.
2. Sand tests without any geotextile.
3. Tests with fixed geotextile.
4. Tests with movable geotextile.

EXPERIMENTAL RESULTS

The tests carried out until now are grouped into six test series, including tests with $\alpha = 30°$, 60° and 90° and vertical loads $\sigma_n \sim 40-45$ kPa and 80-85 kPa. A test series includes as a minimum four test types and ten tests: Dummy tests without sand and geotextile, control tests with sand, tests with movable geotextile and tests with fixed geotextile. A test series with $\alpha = 30°$ and $\sigma_n \sim 40-45$ kPa is shown in Fig. 6.

Dummy tests

The friction between the different parts of the apparatus which pass over each other during the test is minimized by using rubber membranes and silicone grease. The lasting friction is measured in special tests without sand and geotextile as shown in Fig. 6 or after a normal test in an uncleaned apparatus.

Control tests

Tests performed with sand specimens serve as control tests. The angle of internal friction can be calculated and compared with results from triaxial tests. However, it is a little complicated since the two quantities measured is a normal stress on a horizontal surface and a shear stress in another surface inclining α degrees, as indicated in Fig. 7.

First τ_s can be plotted against σ_n as shown in Fig. 7. Proportionality between τ_s and σ_n can be obtained by adding the attraction $c\cot\phi = 11$ kPa to all values of σ_n.

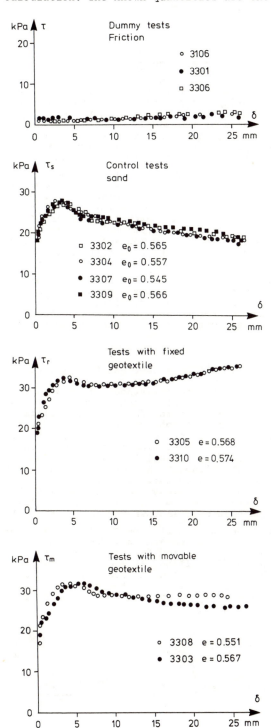

Fig. 6. Tests with $\alpha = 30°$ and $\sigma_n \sim 40-45$ kPa.

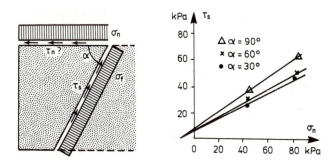

Fig. 7. Control tests with sand.

Assuming homogeneous stress distribution in the specimen the Mohr's circle can be used to illustrate the problem (Fig. 8). The inclining surface is the plane of zero extension, which is represented by the point F. The angle ν in Fig. 8 is the angle of dilatation. The point representing the horizontal surface is found by turning F 2α clockwise. For a fixed value of α and τ_s/σ_n ϕ depends on the choise of ν as shown in Fig. 8. The intersection between the curves with different values of α gives $\phi = 54°$ and $\nu = 14°$. This agrees well with triaxial test results mentioned earlier in this paper, taking into account the differences between plane and axisymmetrical states. The apparent cohesion is 8 kPa and may be effected by testing technique.

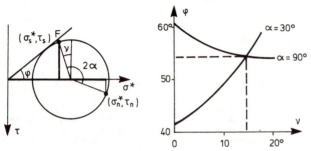

Fig. 8. Determination of strength properties of sand.

Tests with fixed geotextiles

The maximum reinforcing effect is obtained when the ends of the geotextile don't move. As observed in Fig. 6 the shearing resistance of sand τ_s decreases during the test while the shearing resistance of sand with fixed geotextile τ_r is slightly increasing. The improvement factor τ_r/τ_s is then increasing during the test.

Values of τ_r and τ_s are shown in Fig. 9, corresponding to a shear deformation $\delta = 10$ mm. It is seen, that the sand-geotextile element acts as a frictional material with an increased internal friction, but with the same cohesion as that of the sand.

The improvement factor τ_r/τ_s is also shown in Fig. 9 and compared with test results from [6]. The improvement factor depends on the intersection angle α. It is interesting to notice that the plane of principal tensile strain is horizontal for $\alpha = 45 + \nu/2 \approx 52°$, theoretically causing maximum of improvement.

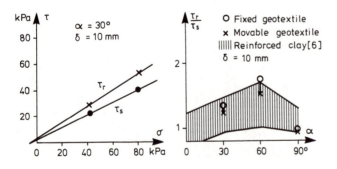

Fig. 9. Comparison between tests with sand, tests with reinforced sand and tests with reinforced clay.

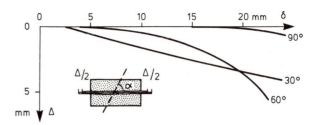

Fig. 10. Retraction of movable geotextile.

Tests with movable geotextiles

The minimum reinforcing effect is obtained if the anchor length is very small, for instance if the overlapping length between two textiles is too short. Tests with an anchor length of half the length of the sample result in a minimum improvement factor (Fig. 9). The difference between the improvement factors for fixed and movable geotextiles increases when δ exceeds 10 mm.

The movement of the geotextile into the sample is shown in Fig. 10. At $\alpha = 30°$ the movements begin after a shear deformation δ of 2 mm, for $\alpha = 60°$ after $\delta = 8$ mm and for $\alpha = 90°$ the movements are very small even after 20 mm. In agreement with these observations the test series shows that the improvements for $\alpha = 30°$ takes place almost from the beginning; but for $\alpha = 60°$ the improvement begins after $\delta = 2-3$ mm.

These tests show that even if the anchor length is very short the geotextiles still improves the soil. A possible failure plane near the border of the reinforced zone will then be forced to take place outside the reinforced zone.

INTERACTION BETWEEN SAND AND GEOTEXTILE

When the shearing resistance of sand beneath shallow foundations or behind smooth retaining walls is exceeded the failure takes place in failure zones of considerable extent. It is possible to place the geotextiles inside the failure zone, most conveniently orientated in the direction of principal tensile strain (McGown et al. 1978), although the most practical location is horizontal. In this case the effect of reinforcement can be measured in triaxial tests with horizontal layers of geotextile (Broms 1977) or in the unit cell (McGown and Andrawes 1977).

This paper deals with instability of a normal retaining wall or embankment. The failure takes place in very narrow failure zones surrounded by rather stiff soil bodies and is normally assumed to follow a circle or a logarithmic spiral. The failure mechanism around the geotextile is rather complicated as shown in Fig. 11. During failure

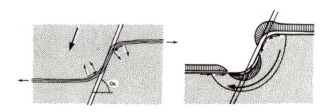

Fig. 11. Local instability near intersection point.

the geotextile is forced into the direction of the failure plane. At point A the bending of the geotextile increases the normal shear stresses between geotextile and sand and reduces the tensile forces in the geotextile outside the failure area. When the failure plane is very steep the necessary anchor length is reduced essentially. (Fig. 10 α = 90°). At point B the bending reduces the stresses between the geotextile and the sand below. If the geotextile and the sand above is removed, it results in a sand slope loaded with the interaction forces from the geotextile. The removed part can be seen by turning Fig. 11 upside down. The slope may during the overall stability failure be unstable and the rotation of the geotextile reduced.

STABILIZATION BY GEOTEXTILES

The development of the additional shear force ΔT produced by the geotextile can be studied in the shear box as already shown in Fig. 6. The results of extensive test series are shown in Fig. 12 a) and b), whereas Fig. 12 c) and d) show results from a few more tests carried out to obtain further information.

Fig. 12 a) and b) show ΔT corresponding to a movement of δ = 10 mm and 20 mm respectively. The stabilization is evidently a friction phenomenon. The strength of the geotextile limits the value of ΔT but does not normally influence its actual value.

Tests with sand in its loosest state can be seen in Fig. 12 c), and shows some reduction of ΔT. It is also observed in tests with more extensible geotextile (Fig. 12 d)). The reduction is of course expectable, but it seems to be very small, only 10-20%. If further investigations show the same tendency, it should then be possible to use such results as shown in Fig. 12 over a wide range of sand densities and geotextile modules.

CONCLUSIONS

The stability of a slope, a retaining wall or an embankment can be improved by horizontal layers of geotextiles. The spacing of the layers depends on the long term creep strength of the geotextile and the interaction between geotextile and soil which takes place in a narrow failure zone surrounded by rather stiff soil bodies.

The long term creep strength has been studied in a plane strain tensile apparatus, showing that the strength is a logarithmic function of time. After a loading period of 2 years the strength is reduced to 60% of its initial strength specified by the factory.

The interaction between soil and geotextile in a narrow failure zone has been studied in a special shear box developed for this purpose. The main result is that the reinforcing mechanism is a frictional phenomenon as shown in Fig. 12. It means that the local influence of a geotextile is proportional to the overburden pressure until the additional shearing force ΔT reaches its maximum value at a certain depth, where the strength of the geotextile is fully utilized. The strength of the geotextile limits the size of the reinforcing construction, but the improvement of the soil has to be taken into account by

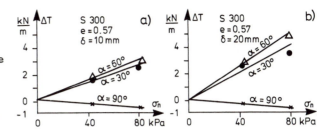

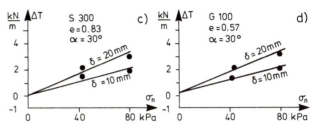

Fig. 12. Shear force introduced by fixed geotextile.

calculating the additional mean shear stress between every two layers, and then determine higher angles of internal friction in the soil-geotextile elements.

Strength improvement of a dense sand like that mainly used in this study is not possible in practice. The imposed deformations in the geotextile are bigger than the peak strength deformation in the sand. The improvement caused by geotextiles is then followed by a reduction in the strength of the sand. In the tests which correspond to a heavily reinforced sand the strength of the sand-geotextile system nearly kept its strength during shearing (Fig. 6).

Strength improvement of a loose sand is easy, since the strength of both the sand and the geotextile still increases continuously even after large deformations.

REFERENCES

[1] Broms, B.B. (1977): Triaxial tests with fabric-reinforced soil. Proc. Int. Conf. on Use of Fabrics in Geotechnics. 3, 129-133. Paris.

[2] Ingold, T.S. (1982): An analytical study of geotextile reinforced embankment. Sec. Int. Conf. Geotextiles. 683-688. Las Vegas.

[3] McGown, A., Andrawes, K.Z. (1977): The influence of non-woven fabric inclusions on the stress strain behaviour of a soil mass. Proc. Int. Conf. on Use of Fabrics in Geotechniques, 161-166, Paris.

[4] McGown, A., Andrawes, K.Z., Al-Hasani, M.M. (1978): Alteration of soil behaviour by the inclusion of materials with different properties. Ground Eng. Vol. 11. Paris.

[5] Murray, R.T. (1982): Fabric reinforcement of embankments and cuttings. Sec. Int. Conf. Geotextiles. 707-713. Las Vegas.

[6] Snaith, M.S., Bell, A.L., Dubois, D.D. (1979): Embankment construction from marginal material. C. R. Coll. Int. Renf. d. Sols, Paris.

Sol renforcé par des fils continus: le Texsol

Soil reinforced with continuous yarns: the Texsol

E. LEFLAIVE, Laboratoire Central des Ponts et Chaussées, Paris, France

RESUMÉ

Les avantages fondamentaux de l'emploi des géotextiles dans les ouvrages en terre -résistance, ductilité, continuité, capacité de drainage et de filtration- peuvent être obtenus tridimensionnellement par l'association de sols et de fils continus.

La communication décrit le procédé Texsol breveté et développé par les Ponts et Chaussées ainsi que le travail de recherche et de développement des applications effectué au sujet de cette technique. Les techniques de fabrication, les mécanismes de comportement et les propriétés du matériau sont présentés ; avec du sable, une cohésion de 100 à 200 kPa est obtenue avec un dosage pondéral en fil de 1 pour mille.

Les applications en cours de développement concernent les remblais, les routes, les voies ferrées, les barrages et les ouvrages sous-marins.

Depuis plus de dix ans, le développement des géotextiles illustre les avantages de l'introduction des fibres synthétiques dans les sols dans tous les domaines de la géotechnique. Sur le plan mécanique, le géotextile est un élément de continuité qui modifie le transfert des contraintes et la répartition des déformations, d'où une profonde modification du comportement du sol aussi bien sous l'effet des charges statiques que répétées.

Sur le plan hydraulique, les milieux fibreux ont la particularité de pouvoir présenter des porosités très élevées, associées à des diamètres de filtration faibles, avec par conséquent des propriétés très intéressantes pour le drainage et la filtration. De plus, le fait d'éviter les discontinuités dans les déformations est également un avantage important vis-à-vis du risque d'érosion interne.

Le développement des géotextiles s'est fait jusqu'à présent surtout sous la forme de nappes, c'est-à-dire de grandes surfaces de faible épaisseur, auxquelles on peut ajouter quelques applications particulières comme les drains verticaux, ou certaines tentatives d'armatures textiles que l'on peut considérer, par rapport à la masse du sol, comme des éléments à une dimension. A trois dimensions, on a réalisé des massifs multicouches constitués de nappes de géotextiles intercalées entre des couches de sol. On a cependant encore peu utilisé de composite sol-fibres à trois dimensions, dans lequel l'association du milieu granulaire et des éléments fibreux est suffisamment intime pour constituer un matériau que l'on puisse considérer comme homogène.

On peut pourtant penser que les ressources potentielles du mariage sol-fibres, évoquées brièvement ci-dessus, peuvent donner à un tel matériau des propriétés intéressantes.

Au cours de ces dernières années, le L.C.P.C. a entrepris des recherches sur la faisabilité d'un tel matériau ; les premières études ont abouti au dépôt d'un brevet et la recherche actuelle porte sur les propriétés de ce matériau et sur le développement de ses applications. L'idée est de réaliser le mélange le plus intime possible d'un sol, tel qu'un sable par exemple, et de fils continus ; on a appelé Texsol le résultat de cette association. Cette communication résume les études faites et présente le premier cas concret d'application, de dimensions encore modestes.

PRINCIPE DU PROCEDE

Le principe du mélange d'un matériau granulaire et de fils continus consiste à projeter un ou plusieurs fils, par voie pneumatique ou hydraulique, sur le matériau granulaire en mouvement, par exemple à l'extrémité d'une bande transporteuse, à la sortie d'un tuyau de remblai hydraulique, ou plus généralement à la sortie de tout système de transport ou d'épandage. On obtient alors un mélange tridimensionnel désordonné de fils et de particules solides ayant des propriétés mécaniques et hydrauliques intéressantes qui sont décrites plus loin.

Dans ce qu'il a d'essentiel, le principe du procédé est donc d'associer à un matériau discontinu à frottement interne des éléments continus souples, dans une disposition géométrique désordonnée et tridimensionnelle. Il se distingue donc nettement :

- des composites où les éléments continus sont noyés dans une masse à laquelle ils sont liés par adhérence ;

- des associations sol-armatures où ces dernières

sont disposées de façon régulière et rectiligne, dans un sens déterminé et avec des espacements grands par rapport aux dimensions des particules du sol ;

- des mélanges utilisant des fibres coupées.

Les différences avec les procédés ci-dessus, qui apparaissent au niveau des composants et de leur mode d'association, se traduisent aussi au niveau du comportement, ainsi qu'on le verra plus loin.

ETUDES EXPERIMENTALES

Les premiers essais de laboratoire ont été faits par projection pneumatique de fil sur du sable entraîné dans un courant d'eau ; les premiers essais à plus grande échelle, portant sur quelques mètres cubes, ont été réalisés par projection du fil à l'eau sur du sable déversé par une bande transporteuse.

A ce stade, des essais assez simples et surtout qualitatifs ont été faits pour avoir une idée du comportement du Texsol et en estimer l'intérêt éventuel. En laboratoire, on a fait des essais de compression simple et des essais de poinçonnement qui se sont révélés très encourageants. Des essais plus élaborés ont alors été réalisés, dont les résultats sont indiqués ci-dessous.

Essais de poinçonnement

Ces essais ont été effectués suivant la procédure de l'essai CBR, sur des matériaux secs. Pour le sable seul, l'essai a donné la valeur de 37 (avec surcharge). Avec un pour mille de fil la valeur obtenue est de 65 ; elle atteint 100 pour un dosage de 3,5 pour mille.

Essais de compression simple

Des éprouvettes de 100 mm de diamètre et 200 mm de haut ont été fabriquées directement dans des moules avec un dispositif de fabrication spécial, étant donné que le carottage normal d'une éprouvette dans un massif n'est pas possible en raison de la présence des fils. Les résistances en compression simple mesurées ont été trouvées approximativement proportionnelles au dosage en fil, avec une valeur de 300 à 400 kPa pour un pour mille en poids.

Essais triaxiaux

Les essais ont été réalisés sur trois sables différents, sur des éprouvettes à l'état lâche et à l'état compacté, avec des dosages compris entre 1,4 et 2 pour mille, et des éprouvettes de sable seul, sans fil. Il s'agissait d'essais consolidés drainés, avec des valeurs de la contrainte horizontale comprises entre 50 et 500 kPa.

A l'état compacté on obtient un maximum, puis une décroissance du déviateur dans les éprouvettes avec fils comme dans les éprouvettes sans fil. (Fig. 1). Une différence du processus de rupture est cependant que la déformation axiale au maximum du déviateur de contrainte pour les éprouvettes avec fils est beaucoup plus élevée que pour les éprouvettes sans fils, atteignant 6 à 8 % contre 2 à 4 %.

Du point de vue de la résistance mécanique,

Fig. 1 - Eprouvette de Texsol rompue à l'essai triaxial

la présence du fil se traduit par l'apparition d'une cohésion de 150 à 250 kPa pour les dosages de 1,4 à 2 pour mille, pour les éprouvettes compactes. Pour les éprouvettes lâches, la cohésion mesurée est plus faible, inférieure à 100 kPa.

Essais triaxiaux à chargements répétés

Ces essais ont été faits pour s'assurer que, même avec un sable concassé, la répétition des charges n'amenait pas une fatigue prématurée due au cisaillement des fils.

Les conditions d'essai étaient les suivantes : teneur en eau 12 % ; poids volumique sec 18 kN/m³ ; étreinte latérale 50 kPa ; déviateur dynamique = 0,4 - 0,46 - 0,5 ou 0,64 fois le déviateur de rupture statique ; nombre de cycles 10^5 ; fréquence 0,5 Hz jusqu'à 200 cycles, 1 Hz jusqu'à 2 000 cycles, 5 Hz jusqu'à 10^5 cycles ; dosage en fil voisin de 2 pour mille.

On a constaté une déformation axiale cumulée augmentant linéairement en fonction du logarithme du nombre de cycles, avec une déformation axiale finale comprise entre 2,5 et 6 % (sauf dans le cas où le déviateur atteignait 0,64 fois le déviateur de rupture en statique, et où il y a eu rupture en cours d'essai).

Ce comportement en fatigue est donc normal, sans abrasion particulière des fils. Deux éprouvettes avec fils ont été rompues statiquement après avoir subi 10^5 cycles ; leur résistance a été trouvée de 55 % plus élevée que les éprouvettes équivalentes non soumises aux chargements répétés, ce qui provient de leur consolidation.

Une autre constatation faite au cours de ces essais concerne le module de déformation du matériau. Les différents modules mesurés sont dans l'ensemble un peu plus élevés lorsqu'il y a présence de fils, mais pas dans une forte proportion. Les modules tangents à l'origine de chaque cycle ne sont pas, en moyenne, plus élevés avec fils.

En conclusion de ces essais, on constate que l'adjonction de fils continus souples à un matériau granulaire a pour effet de lui conférer une cohésion importante en augmentant sa capacité de déformation à la rupture, mais sans accroître de façon notable le module du matériau dans le domaine des petites déformations.

AVANTAGES ESSENTIELS DU MODE DE LIAISON PAR FILS

Par rapport aux liants travaillant par adhérence, l'efficacité d'une liaison par fils ne dépend pas de la granularité du matériau granulaire, alors qu'une granularité contenant aussi peu de vides que possible est nécessaire pour bien utiliser un liant travaillant par adhérence.

Ce mode de liaison permet par conséquent de traiter des matériaux naturels de granularité creuse, qui ne seraient pas susceptibles d'un traitement classique sans correction granulométrique.

Par ailleurs, la liaison par fils d'un matériau très creux permet d'obtenir un matériau résistant mais conservant une forte perméabilité. On peut en effet considérer que la perméabilité n'est pas affectée par la présence des fils, puisque ceux-ci n'occupent qu'une fraction négligeable du volume des vides (de l'ordre de 1 % pour un dosage de deux pour mille).

Du point de vue hydraulique, la présence d'un réseau de fils au sein du matériau constitue, à condition que le fil utilisé soit assez fin et le mélange, assez régulier, un filtre tridimensionnel incorporé dans la masse, qui améliore la résistance à l'érosion interne du matériau granulaire initial. Il faut en effet bien noter que, même pour des dosages pondéraux aussi faibles que un pour mille, la longueur de fil par unité de volume traité est très importante si l'on utilise des fils de titres courants dans l'industrie textile. C'est ainsi par exemple que pour un matériau de densité sèche 1,7 traité à un pour mille par du fil de 100 décitex, la longueur de fil est de 17 cm/cm³ ; pour des dosages et des titres différents, cette longueur est proportionnelle au dosage et inversement proportionnelle au titre. (Fig. 2).

Fig. 2 - Eprouvette Texsol avec deux pour mille de fil (après congélation puis rupture)

Du point de vue mécanique, en plus de la possibilité de traiter un matériau de granularité creuse, le procédé présente l'avantage unique de pouvoir réaliser un matériau résistant non rigide, par conséquent non fragile, et pouvant s'adapter à des déformations, problème souvent posé par les ouvrages de génie civil.

Il présente enfin la caractéristique de ne pas exiger de temps de prise.

MECANIQUE DE LA LIAISON PAR FILS CONTINUS

Les mécanismes par lesquels des fils continus souples incorporés à un milieu granulaire modifient son comportement mécanique sont différents de ceux qui interviennent dans un composite à matrice continue, et de ceux qui sont responsables de la tenue d'un système du type de la terre armée.

Une première observation est que, pour un matériau où les fibres ne sont liées que par frottement et non par adhérence, les longueurs d'ancrage que l'on peut calculer pour des états courants de contraintes, en supposant qu'il y a un bon contact entre les fibres et le sol, sont de l'ordre de la dizaine de centimètres ou du mètre. Il en résulte donc que des fibres coupées de quelques centimètres, comme celles que produit couramment l'industrie textile, ne peuvent pas être efficaces, alors qu'elles peuvent l'être dans un composite où les fibres sont noyées dans une matrice continue à laquelle elles sont liées par adhérence.

Une deuxième observation est que l'hypothèse d'un "bon contact" entre les fibres et le sol granulaire, faite pour calculer la longueur d'ancrage, n'est pas vraisemblable si l'on tient compte de la flexibilité et des dimensions transversales d'un fil textile et du fait que les fibres n'occupent qu'un volume de l'ordre de 1 % du volume des vides du milieu granulaire. On ne peut donc pas, dans ce cas, faire l'hypothèse, comme dans la terre armée, que la contrainte normale moyenne régnant au sein du milieu s'applique à la surface de l'armature et calculer la contrainte tangentielle possible à partir du coefficient de frottement. On peut au contraire considérer, à la limite, que les fibres textiles serpentent à l'intérieur du réseau des vides du milieu granulaire sans être serrées au sein de ce milieu.

En fait, cette hypothèse est probablement elle-même excessive, mais on doit supposer que le fil n'est serré au sein du milieu que de points en points et que, par conséquent, la contrainte moyenne qui règne dans le milieu n'est transmise que partiellement au fil, et que l'effort tangentiel disponible correspondant n'est lui-même que partiel.

On pourrait alors, à ce stade de l'analyse, douter de l'efficacité du procédé, même avec des fils continus dont la longueur d'ancrage disponible n'est pas limitée. En fait, le procédé est efficace, car deux autres mécanismes interviennent dans son fonctionnement :

- le premier mécanisme est lié à la tortuosité du fil. Chaque fil présente de nombreuses sinuosités ; lorsqu'un fil est mis en tension, des forces de frottement se développent dans les zones incurvées et introduisent une résistance qui croît en fonction de la tension appliquée sur le fil, à condition que quelques efforts localisés, au moins minimes, s'opposent à son glissement. Ce mécanisme, lié à la courbure, est celui que l'on retrouve utilisé par exemple dans la marine pour retenir un navire par une corde avec la force d'un seul homme, en enroulant la corde autour d'une borne d'amarrage ;

- le second mécanisme est lié à l'entrecroisement des fils. Si la tension exercée sur une boucle tend à déplacer le fil transversalement par rapport à lui-même, il rencontre immédiatement d'autres fils qui s'opposent à ce déplacement et auxquels se transmettent des efforts, mettant ainsi en jeu de nouvelles zones du matériau.

Les deux mécanismes décrits brièvement ci-dessus ne sont présents ni dans les composites à matrice continue ni dans la terre armée. Le matériau décrit dans cet article est donc bien entièrement distinct de ces deux conceptions.

Un dernier cas, présentant apparemment une analogie avec ce matériau, est celui des couches géotextiles constituées de boucles de gros filaments à forte raideur qui s'enfoncent dans le sol et permettent l'ancrage d'un filtre ou donnent au sol une certaine raideur élastique.

Ce cas est profondément différent de celui présenté dans cet article, car il s'agit seulement d'une couche de 2 ou 3 cm d'épaisseur et non d'un matériau en masse, et parce que, dans une telle couche, les boucles ont une forte rigidité en flexion associée à une très faible résistance en traction (il s'agit de filaments non étirés amorphes), alors que dans le matériau il s'agit de fils multifilament parfaitement souples qui travaillent en tension.

DEVELOPPEMENT

Le développement de ce matériau est actuellement poursuivi au sein des Laboratoires des ponts et chaussées, notamment par le Centre d'expérimentations routières de Rouen (C.E.R.), le laboratoire régional de Rouen et le Centre d'études et de construction de prototypes (C.E.C.P.) de Rouen également.

Un petit chantier a été réalisé en novembre 1982 à Caudebec-en-Caux. Il s'agissait du glissement

Fig. 4 - Le remblai de Caudebec en cours de réalisation

de la moitié supérieure d'une falaise de craie altérée, sur une hauteur de 6 mètres, dont la réparation était nécessaire à la fois pour protéger l'espace situé plus bas et pour rétablir un chemin piétonnier à la partie supérieure.

Un remblai en Texsol (voir figure 3) de 6 mètres de haut avec un talus incliné à 60 ° sur l'horizontale a été construit sur une dizaine de mètres de longueur. Le matériau de base est du sable de Seine auquel il a été ajouté 2,3 pour mille de fil continu polyester 330 décitex 60 brins de résistance 36 cN/tex. La réalisation a été faite en utilisant une machine à béton projeté pour la mise en place du sable et avec projection manuelle du fil entraîné par un courant d'eau sous pression (Fig. 4).

Le comportement du remblai, sur lequel n'a été placée aucune protection extérieure, est excellent, aucun mouvement ni érosion n'ont été observés.

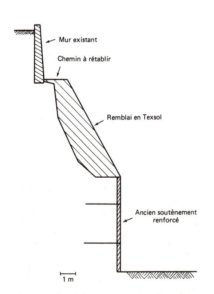

Mur existant

Chemin à rétablir

Remblai en Texsol

Ancien soutènement renforcé

1 m

Fig. 3 - Coupe de l'ouvrage de Caudebec

Règles et normes pour l'emploi des géotextiles, durabilité

Rules and standards for the use of geotextiles, durability

J. PUIG, Laboratoire Régional des Ponts et Chaussées, Toulouse, France
E. LEFLAIVE, Laboratoire Central des Ponts et Chaussées, Paris, France
B. LECLERCQ, Institut Textile de France, Paris, France
J. P. GOURC, Université de Grenoble, France
D. FAYOUX, CEMAGREF, France

RESUMÉ

Le développement de l'emploi des géotextiles dans les ouvrages en terre implique de pouvoir prévoir et calculer le comportement des ouvrages comportant des géotextiles. Cela exige d'une part une connaissance chiffrée des performances des matériaux et d'autre part des règles d'emploi et des méthodes de calcul appropriées. Depuis plusieurs années le Comité Français des Géotextiles a travaillé dans ce sens. La communication présente les méthodes de mesure normalisées adoptées pour les caractéristiques mécaniques et hydrauliques des géotextiles (normes françaises AFNOR) et fait la synthèse des règles techniques actuellement publiées et en vigueur pour le choix des géotextiles dans la réalisation de différents types d'ouvrages en terre. La durabilité des géotextiles a également été étudiée à partir d'une campagne de prélèvement dans plus de trente ouvrages après des années de fonctionnement. L'ensemble des constatations porte sur l'évolution des propriétés hydrauliques et mécaniques et permet de conclure positivement pour l'emploi des géotextiles dans les ouvrages à longue durée de vie.

I - INTRODUCTION

Les géotextiles sont apparus en France dès 1970 et au cours des années suivantes ils ont été utilisés sur de nombreux chantiers de terrassement et d'ouvrages en terre. Le nombre des produits disponibles est devenu rapidement assez important, les géotextiles proposés étant variés et différant selon le polymère constitutif, le type de fabrication textile (tissés, non-tissés), la masse surfacique, etc. Par ailleurs, il était clair que selon les cas les fonctions du géotextile étaient différentes, ou tout au moins que la fonction principale n'était pas la même d'une application à une autre, l'accent pouvant être mis sur le rôle de séparateur, de filtre, de renfort ou sur celui de drain. Il était donc nécessaire, pour choisir dans chaque cas un produit techniquement adapté et économique afin d'éviter les échecs et les dépenses inutiles, de définir les caractéristiques des produits convenant à chaque application. Cet objectif a entraîné une double démarche : d'une part définir les fonctions et les qualités requises des géotextiles dans les différentes situations où ils sont utilisés, d'autre part se donner les moyens de caractériser les produits et de mesurer leurs propriétés de façon correcte. L'action correspondante a été menée à l'initiative et avec la coordination du C.F.G. (Comité Français des Géotextiles devenu depuis 1983 le Comité Français des Géotextiles et Géomembranes), association réunissant :
- les principaux services publics concernés,
- des établissements d'enseignement et de recherche,
- des bureaux d'études,
- les producteurs et distributeurs de géotextiles,
- des entreprises de génie civil.

Il a abouti à des bases communes de spécifications et d'essais actuellement utilisés en France.

La difficulté de la tâche provenait de la relative complexité des fonctions simultanées remplies par les géotextiles dans de nombreux cas, de la nécessité de prendre en compte les conditions de mise en oeuvre et le comportement dans le sol, notamment le risque de déchirure, et enfin de ce que les essais traditionnels textiles convenaient mal, dans l'ensemble, aux besoins des utilisateurs des travaux publics.

La première étape a été de se mettre d'accord sur la terminologie permettant de les décrire, une liste de termes textiles a été établie, qui permet aux utilisateurs de comprendre, en termes clairs, la signification du vocabulaire spécifique aux géotextiles.

La deuxième étape a été de constituer la liste des caractéristiques descriptives pour l'identification d'un produit : désignation commerciale, nature du polymère, type de textile, dimension des fibres, masse surfacique, épaisseur en sont les points principaux.

La terminologie et la fiche descriptive-type ont été enregistrées et publiées par l'Association Française de normalisation (AFNOR) [1].

Il a fallu ensuite définir des essais aptes à caractériser les géotextiles en fonction de leurs sollicitations dans les ouvrages, fournir des recommandations aux utilisateurs pour leur emploi et s'assurer que leur durabilité est compatible avec la durée de vie des ouvrages.

II – PROPRIETES DE BASE DES GEOTEXTILES

Pour les essais, qui sont maintenant normalisés, le choix du Comité s'est arrêté sur les propriétés mécaniques et hydrauliques suivantes:

2.1. Résistance à la traction (en KN/m) et allongement à l'effort maximal (en %)

Le choix de l'essai de référence pour caractériser un géotextile en traction a donné lieu à de nombreuses recherches [2] [3]. L'essai retenu actuellement normalisé [1], est proche d'un essai de traction en déformation plane (Fig.1), il est relativement simple à réaliser et les valeurs obtenues sont physiquement interprétables et suffisamment précises pour être utilisées dans des calculs de dimensionnement.

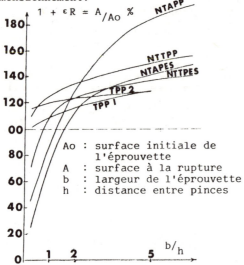

Ao : surface initiale de l'éprouvette
A : surface à la rupture
b : largeur de l'éprouvette
h : distance entre pinces

Fig.1 Variation de $1 + \epsilon R = \dfrac{A}{Ao}$ en fonction de b/h pour des tissés et non-tissés

Il est réalisé sur des éprouvettes de grandes dimensions (100 mm entre pinces et 500 mm parallèlement aux pinces b/h = 5), ce qui est une des conditions indispensables pour que la déformation dans le sens perpendiculaire à la traction ($\epsilon 2$) soit faible. La vitesse de déplacement est de 50 mm/min. ± 5 mm/min. L'allongement à l'effort maximal est exprimé par une valeur conventionnelle qui recoupe bien les valeurs d'allongement mesurées dans les essais où le géotextile est inclus dans un sol : $\epsilon R = \epsilon 1 + \epsilon 2 + \epsilon 1 . \epsilon 2$.

2.2. Résistance au déchirement

Le risque de détérioration par déchirement est une notion très importante pour l'emploi des géotextiles en génie civil. L'essai normalisé [1] permet de la mesurer effectivement, il est réalisé sur des éprouvettes trapézoïdales de grande dimension (bases 670 et 225 mm, hauteur 445 mm), la déchirure amorcée de 50 mm est au milieu de la petite base.

2.3. Perméabilité

La mesure de la perméabilité des géotextiles est assez délicate mais indispensable. En plus des difficultés habituelles à cet essai, la très forte perméabilité de nombreux géotextiles a pour conséquence que l'effet de perte de charge propre à l'appareillage peut être très sensible. La recherche dans ce domaine[2]a permis de retenir les conditions expérimentales garantissant une mesure correcte de la perméabilité de Darcy k, correspondant aux conditions d'écoulement classiques dans les ouvrages en terre.

Suivant le type d'application, il sera utile de connaître la perméabilité normale au plan du géotextile (kn) afin de déterminer dans leur emploi comme filtre la surpression qu'ils occasionnent (surpression inversement proportionnelle à la permittivité $\frac{kn}{e}$) ou leur aptitude à laisser s'écouler un certain débit d'eau dans leur plan, propriété capitale pour caractériser leur pouvoir drainant, Transmissivité (kt.e).

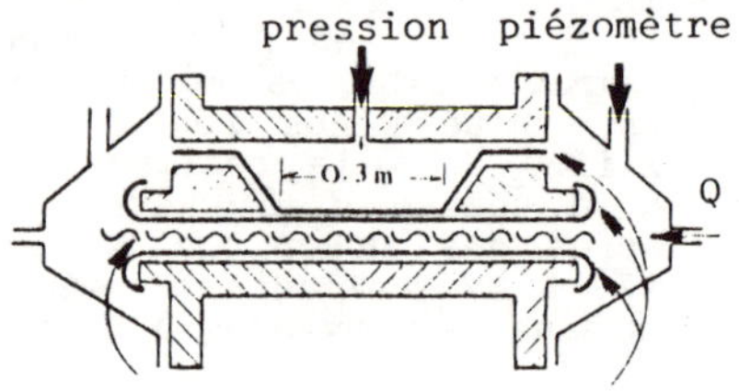

pression piézomètre

géotextile à tester   membrane latex

Fig.2 Perméamètre pour la mesure de kt

Les essais normalisés sont réalisés dans un perméamètre sous un gradient hydraulique assez faible (domaine de mesure $Re < Re^c$) avec de l'eau désaérée. Pour la mesure de la perméabilité kt une contrainte de 2×10^5 Pa est appliquée sur le géotextile.

2.4. Ouverture de filtration

La détermination de la porométrie d'un géotextile, théoriquement possible pour une grille ou un géotextile tissé, est beaucoup plus complexe pour un non-tissé où le nombre de cheminements possibles à partir d'un point d'entrée est très grand. En pratique, il est plus simple et suffisant de connaître la taille des plus grands pores du géotextile, appelée "ouverture de filtration". Cette valeur est déterminée au moyen d'un essai de filtration hydraudynamique en faisant passer au travers du géotextile un matériau de granulométrie connue en suspension dans l'eau. L'ouverture de filtration est par convention exprimée par le d.95 du passant.

III – AUTRES PROPRIETES

Un certain nombre d'utilisations impliquent une connaissance précise d'autres propriétés. Leurs mesures nécessitent des matériels d'essai sophistiqués et font appel à des processus opératoires lourds et délicats. Le C.F.G. dans le but de parvenir à une certaine homogénéité des procédures, facteur indispensable au développement de l'emploi des géotextiles, a retenu dans son programme à venir :
- l'étude complète du comportement en traction

(coefficient de Poisson, effet d'une contrainte de confinement, comparaison entre comportement au sec et au mouillé, module de cisaillement...)
- la détermination des propriétés utiles au dimensionnement d'ouvrages renforcés (Fluage, frottement, perforation, comportements aux sollicitations localisées, déchirure dynamique).
- le comportement filtrant en présence d'un sol pour des conditions particulières d'écoulement.

IV - ECHELLE DE CLASSIFICATION

Pour des ouvrages courants, la connaissance des quatre propriétés de base est suffisante pour permettre le choix du produit le mieux adapté à un emploi donné. L'échelle de classification proposée par le C.F.G. comporte douze classes pour chacune des propriétés mesurées suivant les normes d'essai en vigueur. Un géotextile donné y est représenté par une classe différente pour chacune de ses caractéristiques.

V - CHOIX DES PRODUITS ET DIMENSIONNEMENT

5.1. Généralités

Pour chaque utilisation, la démarche consiste à définir les propriétés du géotextile mises en jeu, en fonction de son rôle dans l'ouvrage, on procède ensuite à l'analyse des sollicitations qu'il supporte et des interactions avec le sol. Cette analyse débouche sur la prise en compte de paramètres propres au type d'ouvrage permettant de déterminer les caractéristiques des géotextiles à retenir. Dans les applications courantes, les utilisateurs souhaitent une méthode de dimensionnement simple et rapide ne faisant intervenir ni calculs compliqués ni essais spéciaux. La méthode proposée est utilisable non seulement par des bureaux d'études, mais aussi par le chef de chantier qui doit résoudre rapidement un problème imprévu.

5.2. Propriétés à prendre en compte

Les propriétés du géotextile à prendre en compte sont fonction du rôle que le géotextile doit assurer dans l'ouvrage.

5.2.1. Séparation - Anticontamination

Le géotextile sépare deux couches de matériaux, l'ensemble est peu soumis à la percolation d'eau. Toutefois un minimum de perméabilité est nécessaire pour permettre les mouvements d'eau occasionnels. La continuité du géotextile à l'interface est essentielle, celle-ci implique non seulement une certaine résistance à la traction, mais surtout une déformabilité compatible avec celle du sol. De plus la résistance à la déchirure doit être suffisante pour éviter tout risque de propagation d'une déchirure à partir d'une coupure localisée.

5.2.2. Filtration

Le rôle du géotextile situé dans une zone soumise à une percolation d'eau perpendiculairement à la nappe, est de laisser passer l'eau tout en maintenant les particules de sol. C'est le cas pour les géotextiles autour des tranchées et tapis drainants, sur les berges de rivière et parements de barrage, entre le sol et le parement en enrochement, dalles de béton, etc ... La continuité est bien sûr primordiale, mais de plus le produit doit être plus perméable que les sols environnants et avoir une porométrie adaptée pour retenir les particules de sols entrainées par l'eau.

5.2.3. Drainage

La continuité doit être assurée dans le sens de l'écoulement. La perméabilité et l'épaisseur du géotextile (mesurée sous une contrainte égale à celle existant dans l'ouvrage) doivent être suffisantes pour évacuer le débit voulu sous une charge suffisamment faible. Le drain ne doit pas se colmater. S'il est monocouche sa porométrie doit être appropriée. Il est possible aussi de séparer les fonctions drainage et filtration en utilisant une partie drainante grossière protégée par des parties filtrantes plus fines.

5.2.4. Renforcement mécanique

Les paramètres principaux à prendre en compte sont la résistance, la déformation et le module du géotextile soumis à la traction, le coefficient de frottement sol-textile et éventuellement les caractéristiques de fluage.

Toutefois, ces deux derniers paramètres ne sont pas pris en compte dans les tableaux de dimensionnement courants. Le module est pris en compte de façon implicite dans le dimensionnement en jouant sur les caractéristiques à la rupture.

5.3. Evaluation pratique des sollicitations

L'évaluation pratique des sollicitations qui sont fonction du rôle du géotextile et des caractéristiques propres de l'ouvrage est faite en prenant en compte les paramètres particuliers au type d'emploi :
- désignation précise de l'ouvrage (par exemple : tranchée drainante, piste, etc...)
- structure de l'ouvrage et position du géotextile (par exemple : structure de piste comportant un ou deux textiles, géotextiles sous une couche drainante) ;
- caractéristiques des sols de part et d'autre du géotextile (sol support, matériaux d'apport ...) ;
- sollicitations externes sur l'ouvrage: trafic, charges, etc ...

5.4. Dimensionnement

On obtient en croisant tous ces paramètres un très grand nombre de cas. On ne retient que les cas vraisemblables où l'emploi d'un géotextile est justifié. Ces cas sont portés dans un répertoire ou un tableau qui renseigne immédiatement l'utilisateur et donne la référence du dimensionnement. Celui-ci est présenté le plus souvent sous forme de tableaux utilisant les échelles de classification et indiquant les valeurs minimales ou maximales recommandées pour chaque cas. Ces valeurs correspondent à des cas moyens et peuvent être modulées, pour chaque cas particulier, en tenant compte de l'analyse du rôle de géotextile et de ses sollicitations. Pour certaines applications où l'attribution de classes a priori n'est pas possible, des méthodes de détermination sont proposées (écoulement hydraulique, filtration, renforcement).

VI - FASCICULES DE RECOMMANDATIONS DU C.F.G.

Pour faciliter l'utilisation de ces règles de dimensionnement, un fascicule de recommandations est établi pour chaque type d'utilisation [4]. Les publications existantes concernent les ouvrages suivants :
- pistes, voies à faible trafic, couches de forme,
- aires de stockage et de stationnement,
- voies ferrées,
- géotextiles sous remblais,
- espaces verts, terrains de sport et de loisirs,
- systèmes de drainage et de filtration.

Chacun de ces fascicules utilise la démarche définie ci-dessus et fournit le dimensionnement du géotextile. Ils contiennent en outre des indications particulières à chaque type d'ouvrage. Enfin, un fascicule général traite de la mise en oeuvre, de l'agrément et du contrôle des géotextiles. Bien qu'ils n'aient pas de caractère obligatoire ces fascicules sont distribués comme documents techniques et recommandés pour l'établissement des clauses contractuelles par plusieurs administrations dans leurs services (ministère de l'Agriculture, ministère de l'Urbanisme, ministère des Transports).

VII - DURABILITE

Le problème de la durabilité des géotextiles se pose chaque fois qu'ils sont introduits dans des ouvrages. Les études sur les polymères qui entrent dans leur fabrication fournissent des éléments de réponse à leur comportement vis-à-vis des agents chimiques, de la chaleur ou des rayonnements, mais elles ne permettent pas de prédire complètement leur durabilité dans les conditions d'utilisation où les contraintes sont à la fois d'ordre mécanique et chimique.

Au cours d'une action menée avec le support financier du Ministère de la Recherche et de l'Industrie [5] et [6] environ 200 utilisations de géotextiles dans divers ouvrages mis en oeuvre entre 1969 et 1975 ont été référencées. Une sélection des chantiers représentatifs des diverses conditions d'emploi (remblais, pistes et couches de formes, filtre-drains, parement de barrages) a permis la constitution d'un échantillonnage d'une trentaine de géotextiles aiguilletés de polyester et polypropylène prélevés suivant un protocole bien déterminé et qui ont été caractérisés sur les plans mécanique, chimique et hydraulique.

Cette étude a permis tout d'abord de constater que les géotextiles étaient là où ils avaient été placés une dizaine d'années auparavant et qu'ils avaient parfaitement rempli leurs rôles.

Sur le plan des propriétés mécaniques la plus grande partie des géotextiles n'accuse pas de perte de plus de 30 % des valeurs initiales, que ce soit de la résistance ou de l'allongement à la rupture. Comme le montrent les tests de simulation d'enfouissement, cette réduction n'est à attribuer qu'en partie à l'action propre de l'environnement (10 à 15 %), le restant est dû aux contraintes mécaniques de mise en oeuvre.

Sur le plan chimique aucune modification significative n'a été observée si ce n'est exceptionnellement un cas de légère hydrolyse de polyester en milieu présentant un pH fortement acide (phosphogypse).

Sur le plan hydraulique des observations au microscope sur des lames minces obtenues à partir de coupes de géotextiles ont pu mettre en évidence des colmatages qui ne sont jamais au degré de 100 %. Les mesures de perméabilité font apparaître que la permittivité des géotextiles pollués peut être divisée par un facteur de l'ordre de 30 à 60. Cependant ils conservent une perméabilité importante par rapport à celle des sols en place qui leur permet de continuer à assurer la fonction de drainage. Ils ne semblent donc pas pouvoir constituer une barrière de continuité hydraulique entre le sol en place et les matériaux d'apport.

CONCLUSIONS

L'action du C.F.G. en matière de recherche a permis de déboucher rapidement sur la mise au point d'essais normalisés permettant une comparaison valable entre produits et donnant des valeurs fiables pour les projeteurs qui disposent par ailleurs de règles d'emploi établies pour les cas les plus courants.

Les résultats positifs obtenus sur la durabilité des géotextiles autorisent leur emploi dans des ouvrages à longue durée de vie.

REFERENCES

[1]AFNOR Septembre 1983 - G 38000 - G 38010 à G 38017 - G 38050 - France

[2]Second Congrès International des Géotextiles LAS VEGAS Août 1982 I.F.A.I. (U.S.A.)

[3]Gourc J.P. (1982) Comportement Géotextiles en mécanique des sols. Thèse Docteur ès Sciences. Université de Grenoble (France)

[4]Fascicules de Recommandations pour l'emploi des Géotextiles. Edition CFG. ITF (France)

[5]Etude du vieillissement des Géotextiles. 1983 Contrat M.I.R. 792340558 ITF (France)

[6]Leclercq B., Sotton M., (1983) La durabilité des Géotextiles. Edana. Congrès Index Genève

Geotextile reinforced land reclamation in the Bay of River Vantaa, Helsinki

La réclamation des terres du Baie de la Rivière Vantà, Helsinki, à l'aide de géotextiles

H. G. RATHMAYER, M.Sc. (Civ. Eng.), Senior Research Engineer, Technical Research Centre of Finland, Geotechnical Laboratory, Espoo, Finland

O. E. KORHONEN, M.Sc. (Civ.Eng.), Division Manager, Geotechnical Department of the City of Helsinki, Helsinki, Finland

SYNOPSIS   The City of Helsinki is reclaiming land for a recreation area in the bay of river Vantaa. On the 15 to 43 m thick mud and soft clay deposits of the shoreline single and twin embankments have to be erected. The consolidation process will last for 2 to 6 centuries. The overall stability of the shore is improved with woven polypropylene geotextile reinforcement. Short term tensile strength properties of 150 / 120 and 500 / 80 kN/m and in the long term a load take up reminder of 25% of failure load at 7% elongation are required. Design principles, results of in-situ and laboratory tests and problems encountered with their evaluation are presented. The chosen design and working methods are backed up by observations made at a 400 m long trial embankment and at earlier constructed reinforced embankments in the same area.

INTRODUCTION

The west shore of the bay of river Vantaa in Helsinki has for several decades been used as a dump. Owing to poor subsoil conditions (soft mud and clay deposits 15 ... 43 m thick), high filling levels of surplus material and lack of proper design the stability of this shore line is today insufficient. Slide planes have formed down into the soft deposits, some failures have occurred and the shore is in continuous motion towards the sea.

New plans call for the building of a recreation and harbour storage area. Over a distance of about 2200 metres a new shore line is to be built and it will run at most 200 m out from the present shore line. The depth of water in the future shore area will vary between 1 and 2,5 m.

The shore line is planned to be constructed mainly by means of floating reinforced embankments. The area behind them will be filled with masses of surplus material.

A first trial section of the reinforced floating embankment, 400 m long, was constructed in autumn 1983. At this section two different types of reinforcement and the proper installation technique were tested. New sections are planned to be built during the winter period 1984/85.

The design is backed up also by most valuable information gained from settlement observations of old and recent fills in the area, by inclinometer measurements and by observations made since summer 1982 at four test embankments reinforced in different ways.

SITE CONDITIONS

The subsoil at the west shore of the bay of river Vantaa bay consists of 15 to 43 m thick mud and soft postglacial clay layers. Heavy soil and ceramical waste masses, dumped during

several decades without proper design, rest on top of these layers. The water depth varies on the area under construction between 1,0 and 1,5 m.

The ongoing movements of these fills towards the bay are controlled with about 20 settlement rods and at the most critical area also by aid of inclinometer measurements. The settlement rates observed are up to 70 mm/year, the horizontal movement rates have reached values of up to 20 - 50 mm/month. At a depth of 20 m under the fills a failure zone has been mobilized. An impression of the instability of the area can be obtained from Figure 1 showing observed horizontal movements.

A design map of the shore is presented in Figure 2 showing the new recreation area and the harbour storage plant. The new shore line will have a length of about 2,2 kilometres behind which an area of approx. 200 000 m^2 has to be filled up.

The site investigations consisted besides of routine testing methods, as vane tests, Swedish weight sounding and sampling of undisturbed samples for further laboratory testing, also of more sophisticated in situ testing at the new

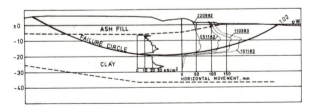

Fig. 1. Example of horizontal movements caused by uncontrolled fill. West shore of river Vantaa Bay, Helsinki.

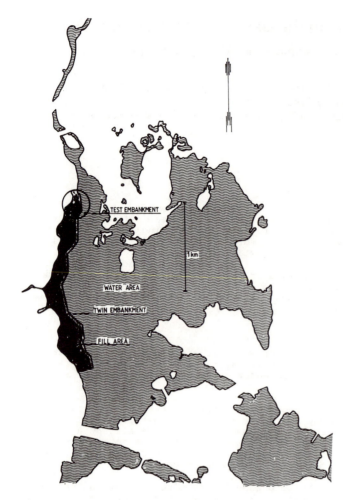

Fig. 2. Map of the new shore line.

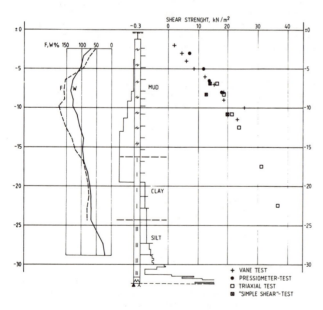

Fig. 3. Typical soil profile.

shore line. To clear up anisotropy and drained shear parameters of the soft soil layers pressuremeter tests and slowly rotated vane tests, using different size and shape of the vane blade, were performed.

In the slowly rotated vane tests the maximum shear stress was reached after 110 ... 160 minutes. The measured shear strength values were only about 60 - 70 % of those measured with routine procedure.

The strength and deformation properties were also determined from triaxial tests and simple shear tests. The triaxial tests were made as anisotropically consolidated undrained tests.

The shear parameters above level -12,0 N.N. varied in the limits of c' = 1,8 - 7,9 kN/m^2 and ρ' = 22,0° - 32,0°. Below level -12,0 N.N. the limits were c' = 1,4 - 3,8 kN/m^2 and ρ' = 21,4° - 24,2° respectively. Also bearing plate tests were performed using different plate sizes. A typical soil profile is shown in Figure 3.

THE FLOATING EMBANKMENT SOLUTION

Single and twin embankment

The floating embankments are designed to be constructed by aid of geotextile reinforcement.

The reinforcement is required to act conjointly with the soil. The strength of the soil and of the reinforcement should be mobilized simultaneously. The reinforcement is located on top of the mud layer. A sand layer of a thickness of 0,3 - 0,5 m in thickness on top of the geotextile shall protect the reinforcement. The embankments are built of crushed rock.

At the northern end of the construction area the relatively better soil conditions allow the use of single floating embankments. Twin embankments are used where the thickness of the clay deposit is exceeding 25 meter. Typical sections of the embankments are illustrated in Figure 4.

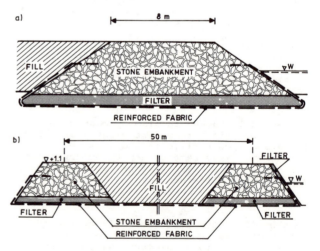

Fig. 4. Cross sections of the single and twin embankments.

Design principles

The design of the embankments is based on the strength and deformation properties of the soft clay deposit as well as on the thickness of it. For stability reasons the fill levels of the embankments may vary between +1,0 and + 1,2 m above medium sea level, in some sections the fill hight may rise up to +2,0 m.

The settlement predictions are based mainly on triaxial test results and also on oedometer test results.

The initial settlement of the embankment was estimated to be in the range of 450 - 600 mm (after construction the measured settlement was in the range of 300 - 700 mm).

The stability of the embankments is strongly dependent on the progress of settlements. The stability calculations were made by $\rho = 0$ and c' - ρ' -methods for different construction stages and time periods. Especially three periods were controlled in the design. The initial stage for the period t = 0-1 years, the medium consolidated stage for t = 20-30 years and the final stage at t = 100 years. For different thicknesses of the clay deposits the required 90% consolidation times are given in Table 1.

Table 1. Time for 90 % consolidation as function of clay thickness.

Thickness of clay (m)	90 % consolidation time (years)
20	200
25	310
30	450
35	610

For the different design periods one has to consider the progress of settlements, the pore pressure development, the increase of the shear strength of the soil and the demanded corrections of the top level of the embankments.

The main conclusions of this design procedure were:
- Good knowledge of both short term and long term soil properties is essential for all design stages.
- The creep and relaxation behaviour of the reinforcing geotextile has to be taken into account.
- The deformation and strength properties of soil and geotextile reinforcement have to be adequately mobilized. For purpose of design the stress-strain properties of both soil and geotextile have to be known also as a function of time.

The principles of the combined action between soil and reinforcement is illustrated in Figure 5. Corresponding to the deformation behaviour of the clay the reinforcement strains may vary between 6 and 10 %. The principles of embankment design with reinforcement to improve the stability is illustrated in Figure 6.

As to be seen from Fig. 6 has the reinforcement also to be anchored.

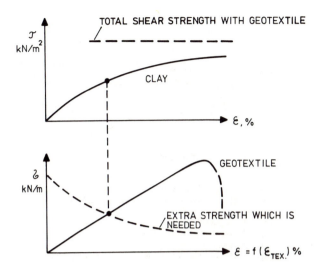

Fig. 5. Combined action of clay and reinforcement.

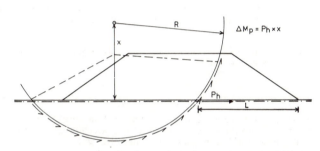

Fig. 6. Adopted design principles for reinforced embankment.

An example of long term stability calculations is given in Table 2. The anchor length L is calculated assuming that there are only cohesion forces acting on the reinforcement-clay-interface.

Table 2. Example of stability calculation.

M_{act} kN m/m	M_{STAB} kN m/m	ΔM_{STAB} kN m/m	R m	X m	P_h kN/m	L m	F -
6645	8446	1522	19	9	169	53	1,5

M_{act} = active moment
M_{STAB} = restoring moment
ΔM_{STAB} = restoring moment activated by reinforcement
R = radius of failure circle
X = vertical distance between circle pole and reinforcement
P_h = required force of reinforcement
L = anchoring length
F = factor of safety

The loading scheme and stability situation during the construction period is shown in Fig. 7.

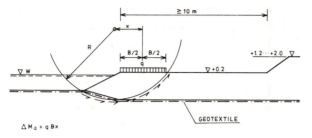

Fig. 7. Situation during construction period.

In the design of the working phase the following parameters of influence on the stability have to be observed.
- Height of embankment
- Weight of working machines
- Sea water table
- Strength of seams in the reinforcement.

The demanded properties of reinforcement are in crosswise direction of the embankment:
- long term (t>100 years) tensile strength 160 - 190 kN/m (twin embankment) and 60 - 80 kN/m (single embankment
- short term tensile strength 500 - 600 kN/m (twin embankment) and 150 - 200 kN/m (single embankment).

In longitudinal direction the demanded tensile strength is 60 - 80 kN/m.

TRIAL EMBANKMENT

A trial embankment was built in the northern part of the bay of river Vantaa in autumn 1983. The length of the test embankment was constructed as a single embankment shown in Figure 4 a. The water depth was during the construction period about 1,0 - 1,5 metres. The thickness of the layers of mud and clay varied between 15 and 20 metres.

The trial embankment was mainly reinforced with two layers of Terram 85 K. The tensile strength of this fabric is 150 kN/m, according to the manufacturer. These reinforcements were tested in the Geotechnical Laboratory of the Technical Research Centre of Finland.

To study the behaviour of this trial embankment during the construction period the following instrumentation was installed:
- settlement rods
- horizontal settlement tubes
- pore pressure gauges
- inclinometer tubes.

The observed settlements were in the range of 300 - 700 mm during the first 6 months. Most of the measured settlement is regarded as initial settlement.

The pore pressure reached after three months its highest value; this was about 90 % of the total weight of the embankment.

The inclinometer measurements show a horizontal displacement of the embankment of about 60 mm. Probably the fill behind the embankment (Figure 8) is pushing it horizontally.

The arrangement of the instrumentation is shown in Figure 8.

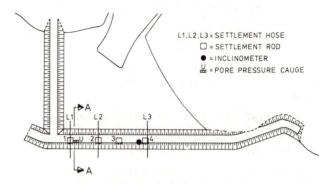

Fig. 8. Map of trial embankment.

Some of the results are presented in the Figures 9 and 10.

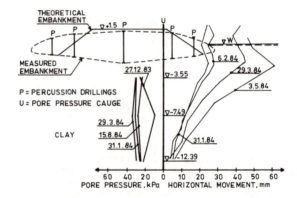

Fig. 9. Measured pore pressures and horizontal movements.

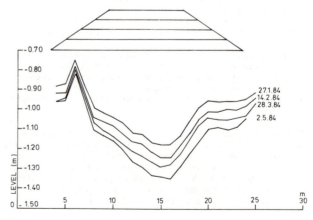

Fig. 10. Measured settlements.

CONSTRUCTION SEQUENCE

The reinforcement was placed on the mud layer with the help of a set of 7 - 10 pontoons. The largest dimensions of the fabric were 218 metres in width and 50 metres in length. Some parts of the fabric were installed with the help of light motor boats. The reinforcement was covered with a thin sand layer (0,3 - 0,5m) which had to act as a filter and to protect the geotextile. Sand and also crushed rock was spread out with a scoop of an excavator.

In the first stage the top level of the embankment was raised up to the sea level. Then the edges of the fabric were turned up on the embankment. Thereafter the embankment was raised to the designed height. The water area behind was filled with waste materials (moraine, silt, soft clay, etc.).

The fabric sheets were jointed together by sewing. Part of the sewing operation was done at the manufacturing plant, the rest of the joints were sewed on the pontoon. The joints were sewed with a portable stitcher and using an overlap of approximately 0,10 m in the seams. The handling of the reinforcement and some of the construction operations are shown in Figures 11 and 12.

REINFORCEMENT OF THE TEST SECTION

Material requirements

As the design calculations have shown, it is necessary to use reinforcement to achieve a sufficient factor of safety for the construction stage and during the time of consolidation. For a rotational failure the direction perpendicular to the embankment axis is dominant. Assuming a 25 % level of long-term strength for polypropylene (PP) woven geotextiles the required short-term tensile strength level was assessed to 150 - 200 kN/m at break, 60 - 80 kN/m of which have to be mobilized at a strain level not exceeding 7 %. For ensuring safe installation progress the tensile strength requirements in the direction of the embankment axis (weft direction of the geotextile) were assessed to 65 % of the above mentioned requirements. Full strength mobilisation had to be guaranteed for the seams (joints), also.

A first selection of suitable woven geotextiles was based on out-of-plane strength testing with the pull-out cone test according to NORDTEST testing procedure NT Build 242 and on strip tensile tests (50 mm strip width) performed as CRS tests with strain rate of 100 mm/min.

The reinforcing geotextile installed was the Terram 85 K type. This fabric has an ultimate strength of about 150 kN/m in warp and 120 kN/m in weft direction. The corresponding strains at failure are roughly 30 % in warp and 20 % in weft direction. The strength mobilized at a strain level of 7 % was between 60 and 65 kN/m.

TESTING PROCEDURES AND RESULTS

Cone pull out tests

The tests were performed according to the NORDTEST testing procedure NT Build 242. The test gives an indication of the out-of-plane strength properties as a function of tensile strength in both warp and weft directions and of the weaving structure.

Permeability

The water permeability of the offered geotextiles was tested with constant head flow tests using pressure heads varying between h = 0,5 m and 1,56 m.

Fines retention

The ability of the woven geotextiles to retain fines was tested according to the BAW (Bundes-anstalt für Wasserbau, Karlsruhe, F.R.Germany) testing procedure for soil type 4 in turbulent flow. The soil used in these propeller tests was a clayey silt taken from the site of installation.

PROBLEMS ENCOUNTERED WITH THE PREDICTION OF LONG TERM BEHAVIOUR OF REINFORCING GEOTEXTILES.

As far as testing of high strength woven geotextiles is concerned there are at present no generally accepted standardized testing procedures available for a fair comparison of materials manufactured from different raw materials.

Testing rate

According to existing standards for tensile strip testing the time to reach break may vary between 20 and 30 seconds. As some of the

Figures 11 and 12. Embankment under construction

materials are quite sensible to the rate of testing (strain rate) and knowing the differences in the elongation at break, fabrics made of polypropylene have to be tested at a much higher strain rate as e.g. polyester fabrics. The strain rates may vary between 100 and 200 %/min. On the other hand soil strength parameters which are determined at strain rates of 2 %/min (for granular soils) or essentially slower ones for cohesive soils (varying between 0.2 %/min to 0.0002 %/min), are used for the geotechnical design.

Testing temperature

Textile testing should according to DIN 50014 be performed at temperature and humidity controlled conditions, using either 20°C and 65 % R.H. or 23°C and 50 % R.H.. In the authors' opinion testing climate should reflect the in-soil conditions, which in Finland would mean soil temperatures of +8...+9°C and wet testing.

For many applications the knowledge of strength properties at frost temperatures is essential. Unfortunately only little or no information is available from the material suppliers on the influence of low temperatures on the strength properties of fabrics.

Clamping

For high strength technical fabrics the clamping technique is playing an essential role for achieving of repeatable failure strength values. Simple pressure clamping technique has proved to be unsufficient, when the tensile strength values exceed about 45 kN/m. Slippage in the clamps might occur, strain measurements get inaccurate.

Long-term properties

Long term loading tests with Terram 85 K samples were started in March 1984. Strips of 50 mm width from both warp and weft directions are loaded statically under controlled temperature conditions, using a temperature of +10°C. The

load levels were chosen between 60 and 95 % of failure load. The results of these tests are presented in Fig. 13. With a load level of 95 % of average failure load one sample failed after 2 months of loading. All the other samples are still intact after 6 months of loading. This information gives a good backfeed for stability considerations. The excess pore pressure at the site has exceeded its maximum and consolidation of the subsoil is in progress.

Stress relaxation

A test series to study stress relaxation of the fabric material at working loads and temperatures is intended to be started in autumn 1984. The strain level in these tests will be 7 %. These tests could provide the designer with the essential information, how long the loading capacity of 25 % of failure strength is available at strains less than 7 %.

REFERENCES

BAW (1978). Vorläufige Richtlinien für die Prüfung und Dimensionierung von textilen Filtern im Verkehrswasserbau. Bundesanstalt für Wasserbau, Karlsruhe, F.R.G.
NT Build 242 (1984). Nonwoven Geotextiles. Plunger pull out test. NORDTEST, Helsinki, Finland.

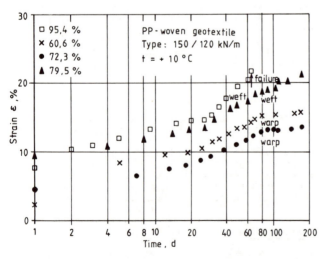

Fig. 13. Creep behaviour of PP woven geotextile at +10°C.

Interface response of geotextiles

Interface réponse de géotextiles

S. K. SAXENA, Professor and Chairman, Civil Engineering Department, Illinois Institute of Technology,
Chicago, Illinois, USA
J. S. BUDIMAN, Research Assistant, Civil Engineering Department, Illinois Institute of Technology,
Chicago, Illinois, USA

ABSTRACT

This paper presents the results of a study to evaluate the interface friction between geotextiles
and soil or ballast. A knowledge of interface friction is necessary to estimate the restraining
characteristics of a geotextile, i.e., the minimizing of lateral restraint under horizontal loads.
The study involved two kinds of geotextiles -- a woven type, Celanese 600X and nonwoven type,
Monsanto C-34. All tests were performed in a specially designed direct shear machine where a 25.4
cm x 25.4 cm (10 in x 10 in) specimen of material can be tested.

INTRODUCTION

A wide variety of synthetic fiber textiles are
being used in soil and construction these days.
Those which allow the water to pass while retaining fine particles of soil are called "geotextiles" and those which use impermeable liners
are called "geomembranes". The objective of
this investigation was to evaluate the interface
behavior of geotextiles under soil-geotextile-
ballast system, typical to be found in railway
tracks. The difference in behavior of woven
type and nonwoven type was also a part of the
investigation. A knowledge of interface-
friction is important for the engineering works
wherein geotextiles are used. All the investigations were conducted by a specially designed
Direct Shear Apparatus. The design of which
was also a part of the research.

It may be pointed out that previous studies of
soil-geotextile friction were conducted by
Myles (1982) using Leighton Buzzard sand and
needle-punched polypropylene, heat-bonded poly-
propylene/polyethelene, heavy-weight woven
polyester and light-weight woven polypropylene.
A comparison has been made of his apparatus and
that developed for this study; however, a comparison of his results and the results of this
study would not provide any meaningful contribution in view of the variation of the soils
and geotextiles used. Nonetheless, where possible, a comparison of the results of both
studies has been attempted.

DESCRIPTION OF SHEAR APPARATUS

A specially designed Direct Shear Apparatus was
fabricated to perform the experiments and investigate the interface friction behavior. Most
elements of this apparatus were made of aluminum
and are shown in Fig. 1. The Screw Jactuator
(Fig. 1-1) drives the horizontal load and displacement. The jack has a driving capacity of

10 tons. The Jactuator is mounted to the
chassis, (Fig. 1-24) through frames that consist of aluminum plate and angle section steel.
The Jactuator itself is driven by a gear motor,
(Fig. 1-2). The input shaft of Screw Jactuator
is 2.54 cm (1 in) and the output shaft of the
gear motor is 1.9 cm (0.75 in), hence a Morse
coupling with different bore holes at each side
is used to couple the gear motor and the Jactuator. The gear motor is mounted to the base
plate (Fig. 1-27) of the chassis. To control
the speed range of the gear motor, control box
(Fig. 1-3) is used.

The magnitude of the horizontal load which is
driven by the Jactuator is calibrated through
a loading cell (Fig. 1-4). The strain of the
load cell indicates the horizontal load applied.
The load cell connects the Jactuator and the
saturation tank (Fig. 1-6). The saturation tank
has a wall of 6 mm (0.25 in) thick and its base
plate is 19 mm (0.75 in) thick. The side walls
of the shear box are 13 mm (0.5 in) thick, front
and rear walls are 2.54 cm (1 in) thick. The
use of more rigid walls in the front and rear is
to eliminate or minimize the deflection while
shearing.

The shear box consists of upper and lower boxes
(Fig. 1-11 and 1-12). The base of the lower box
is tied by bolts to the base of the saturation
tank and will move together with the saturation
tank, whereby the upper box is fixed to the
holding bar (Fig. 1-8). Since the saturation
tank is connected to the Jactuator that moves
with a constant rate of speed, the lower box
which is tied to the saturation tank will also
move, and the relative shears will be at the
interface of the lower box and upper box. During preparation of the sample, the upper box
and lower box were tied together. This is done
by putting bolts through the guiding grooves.
The guiding grooves also prevent any sway movement during the shear. The holding bars consist of two angle sections of steel which are
supported and tied to the columns (Fig. 1-20).

The columns are of square structural steel tubes. An appropriate gap could be provided between the upper box and lower box to eliminate friction during shear by providing a couple of washers or shims (Fig. 1-5) between the top of the columns and the holding bars before they are bolted together. The thickness of the washers or shims depends on the gap needed to separate any contacts at the interface of the upper box and lower box.

The geotextiles (Fig. 1-17), can be fixed either to the lower box or upper box by means of clamping to the four edges of the box with aluminum strip clamps (Fig. 1-9). A 51 mm (2 in) thick end plate (Fig. 1-10) is needed in the rear side to prevent any contacts between the ballast and the rear wall of the lower box and upper box is indicated by a dial gage (Fig. 1-7). The dial gage is mounted to the saturation tank while the arm is touching the upper box. The saturation tank bears on two bearings (Fig. 1-21). The bearings rest on roundways stainless steel shafts (Fig. 1-22). The dual roundway mounting block forming a V-shape support system prevents the lateral or sideways movement. Hence, only forward and backward movements are allowed. The shafts are supported by support rails (Fig. 1-23).

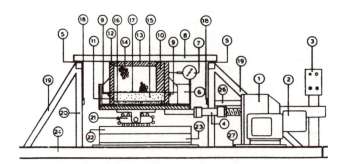

Figure 1. Direct Shear Apparatus

Legend for Figure 1.

1. Screw Jactuator	15. Soil or ballast
2. Gear motor	16. Sand layer
3. Control box	17. Fabric
4. Loading cell	18. Limit switch
5. Washers/shims	19. Bracings
6. Saturation tank	20. Columns
7. Dial gage	21. Bearings
8. Holding bars	22. Shafts
9. Clamps	23. Support rails
10. End plate	24. Chassis
11. Lower box	25. Guiding groove
12. Upper box	26. Bars
13. Top plate	27. Base plate
14. Ballast or soil	

The limit switch is attached to each side of the columns to prevent any damage if the saturation tank hits the columns. When the saturation tank touches the limit switch, the electricity to the motor will be automatically cut off. All these components are put together on an aluminum chassis which consists of 6 channels providing required stiffness yet are light in weight.

Figure 2. Direct Shear Apparatus in Vertical Loading Machine

To apply the vertical load, the direct shear apparatus can be put into any of the vertical loading machines with necessary spacing as shown in Fig. 2. The load can be applied to the specimen through a rigid aluminum top plate (Fig. 1-13).

The salient differences in Myles' (1982) and the IIT Shear Apparatus are as follows: The size of the lower and upper boxes in IIT shear apparatus is 25.4 cm x 25.4 cm (10 in x 10 in) while the upper box of Myles which contains sand is only 10 cm x 10 cm (3.9 in x 3.9 in). The IIT Shear Apparatus allows the forward and backward movement while that by Myles allows only backward movement. The rate of strain in IIT Shear Apparatus is 0.76 mm/min (0.03 in/min) while the rates used by Myles were 10 mm/min, 25 mm/min and 75 mm/min (3.93 in/min, 9.84 in/min and 29.53 in/min) though the rate of strain can vary from 5 mm per minute to 100 mm per minute. Saturation of sand and ballast can be accomplished in IIT Shear Apparatus, however the very low rate of application of shear displacement ensures that at the interface all stress measurements are effective. In Myles' apparatus the fabric is firmly glued to a 1 cm thick wooden plate which is the top portion of the lower box and there appears no provision to saturate the sand.

PROGRAM OF INVESTIGATION

The geotextiles consisted of two types - a woven type, Celanese 600X and a nonwoven type - Monsanto C-34, and were tested in the soil-geotextile-ballast system under direct shear. The friction on both interfaces of the geotextiles was investigated - soil-geotextile and ballast-geotextile interfaces. The geotextile was clamped downward to the lower box to evaluate the interface friction between ballast-geotextile and was clamped upwards to the upper box for the soil-geotextile interface.

In these studies an "undisturbed" state is defined as one wherein the soil-synthetic fiber textile interface in the shear box is being subjected to the initial application of shear in one direction. The sheared sample when subjected to stress reversal (opposite to initial shear direction) is supposed to be tested in a "disturbed" state.

Soil Used in the Investigation: The soil used for this investigation was sandy clay synthesized in the laboratory with 50% kaoline clay, 45% Ottawa sand, and 5% bentonite. The specific gravity of the soil was 2.66 with liquid limit of 40% and a plasticity index of 28%. The Standard Proctor Test provided the optimum water content of 16% with a dry unit weight of 17.6 kN(m³ (112 pcf)). The angle of internal friction obtained from consolidated-undrained triaxial tests was 12.6° with a cohesion of 7.8 kPa (1.1 psi). The limestone ballast used in the study had a dry unit weight of 20.0 kN/m³ (128 pcf). The angle of friction obtained from a consolidated undrained test was 39.8° with no cohesion. The grainsize distribution of the soil and ballast is the same as reported by Saxena and Chiu (1982).

Testing Procedures: At the base of the lower box 1.27 cm (0.5 in) uniform moist sand was used instead of a porous stone, (Fig. 1-16). The porous stone of the same thickness was unable to withstand the applied normal pressures. The soil was mixed with 18.5% by weight of water and was compacted in the assembled shear box with a Standard Proctor hammer for 89 blows per layer of 3.8 cm (1.5 in) thick. The 89 blows were used because it provides an equivalent energy of the Standard Proctor Test. The total thickness of soil layers was 7.6 cm (3 in).

The upper box was then removed and the soil exceeding above the top of the lower box was trimmed. The geotextile was clamped to the box. As stated earlier, for evaluating the ballast-geotextile interface friction, the geotextile was clamped downward to the lower box and for evaluating the geotextile soil interface friction, it was clamped upward to the bottom of the upper box. The geotextile was clamped at four edges to the box. The upper and lower boxes were tied keeping an appropriate gap between the upper and lower boxes. This was done by putting shims at the guiding grooves before bolting. To eliminate the friction between the ballast and inner walls, the inner walls were greased and then ballast was placed in the shear box. The ballast was compacted by the Standard Proctor hammer with 89 blows per layer of 3.8 cm (1.5 in) thick for 5 layers.

All tests were conducted with the shear box placed into the saturation tank and water added to the saturation tank to saturate the sample. All tests were conducted with vertical normal loads of 68.9, 137.8 and 206.7 kN/m² (10, 20 and 30 psi). During shear, the vertical and horizontal displacements and shear force was recorded. The initial shear was applied until a horizontal displacement of about 4.5 to 5 cm (1.8 in to 2 in) was achieved. This concluded the test of a sample in the "undisturbed" state. The direction of shear was then reversed and the experiment repeated to study the interface friction in the "disturbed" state.

TEST RESULTS

The results of the investigations are graphi-

cally presented. Fig. 3 shows the threshold shear force of soil-geotextiles interface for the two geotextiles - Celanese 600X (woven) and Mansanto C-34 (nonwoven) in the "undisturbed" and "disturbed" state for three vertical pressures. The threshold interface friction of soil-geotextiles in both cases is reached at a relatively large displacement of 1.52 cm (0.6 in). The residual strength does not vary significantly from peak strength. In the disturbed state, the shear strength is lower compared to

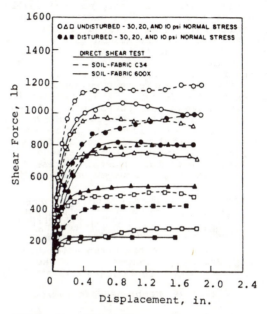

Figure 3. Shear Force vs Horizontal Displacement for Soil Geotextiles

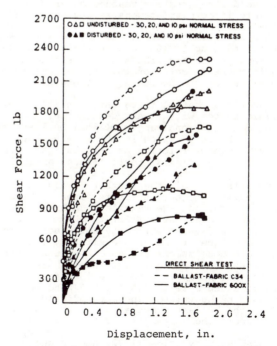

Figure 4. Shear Force vs Horizontal Displacement for Ballast Geotextiles

the undisturbed state; displacements are needed to reach the threshold strength. For Monsanto C-34, the curves for disturbed state are flatter compared to those from the undisturbed condition. Fig. 4 presented the shear strength versus displacement of ballast-geotextile interface for both geotextiles. The interface strengths with ballast are much higher compared to that of soil and so also are the relative displacements (to reach peak strengths). It appears from Fig. 4 that perhaps the interface strengths in disturbed state may eventually reach closer to that of an undisturbed state especially for higher vertical pressures; however, the displacement needed to reach peak strengths are going to be large. This is because during the initial shear (undisturbed) application, the geotextile moves with the lower box at the edges where it is clamped, while at the center, the friction of ballast-fabric resists the movement of fabric until a threshold shear force is mobilized. The relative displacement of the fabric to the lower box is more at the central portion and less near the edges, thus making the lateral strands deformed in a curved shape the threshold stress (see Fig. 5). The test in a "disturbed" state begins with

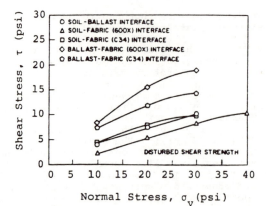

Figure 6. Interface Friction vs Normal Stress - "Undisturbed" State

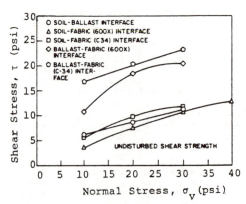

Figure 7. Interface Friction vs Normal Stress - "Disturbed" State

| Initial Shape | After First Shear (Undisturbed) | After Second Shear (Disturbed) |

Figure 5. Membrane Deformation

the geotextile in a curved shape and the shear force will invert the membrane shape in an opposite direction. For both geotextiles, the threshold strengths are reached after a relatively large displacement regardless of the normal pressure, about almost 4.06 cm (1.6 in). In the disturbed state, geotextile C-34 looses its strength up to 40% because the ballast during shear pulls the fibers of geotextile causing it to badly deteriorate, and perhaps is responsible for the decrease of strength.

In addition, control tests were run for a soil-ballast system without any geotextile. The interface frictional angle of soil-ballast was found to be 14.1° which is the same as the internal angle of friction of soil-ballast interface found by triaxial tests (Saxena and Chiu).

A comparison of all the tests to evaluate the contribution of geotextiles is given in Figs. 6 and 7. The soil-geotextile C-34 interface strengths are almost similar to that of the soil-ballast system while the soil-geotextile 600X interface strengths are slightly lower. The above conclusions are good for "undisturbed" and "disturbed" states. The results also indicate that ballast-geotextile interface strengths decrease to 40% for C-34 and about 20% for 600X being thinner and more brittle (than C-34), the ballast penetrates into it, and at those spots the geotextile is torn during shear.

The sand used by Myles (1982) had an angle of friction of 38° and the angles of friction of

sand-geotextiles were found to be 35.5°, 34°, 38° and 32° for needle-punched, heat-bonded heavy-weighted woven and light-weight woven respectively. The rates of application of displacement used by Myles did not appear to make a difference in the angles of friction. Compared to these, the angles of friction of soil geotextiles in this study were 27.5° and 22.2° for C-34 and 600X respectively in their "undisturbed" state and reduced to 23.8° and 17.2° respectively in the "disturbed" state.

REFERENCES

Saxena, S. K. and Chiu, Y. S. (1982), "Evaluation of Fabric Performance in a Railroad System", Proceedings of the International Conference on Geotextiles, August 1982, Las Vegas, Nevada, pp. 489-490.

Budiman, J. S. (1981, "Behaviour of Soil-Fabric-Ballast System Under Static Shear Conditions," Master's Thesis, Illinois Institute of Technology, Civil Engineering Department, Chicago, Illinois

Myles, B. (1982), "Assessment of Soil-Fabric Friction by Means of Shear," Proceedings of the International Conference on Geotextiles, August 1982, Las Vegas, Nevada, pp. 787-791.

Transmission of linear tensile forces by means of fabrics

La prise de forces de traction linéaires par des tissus de construction enterrés

H. SCHEFFLER, Dr.sc.techn., Hochschuldozent für Bodenmechanik, Technische Hochschule Leipzig, GDR
E. FRITZSCHE, Dipl.-Ing., Oberassistent, Technische Hochschule Leipzig, GDR
M. KERREIT, Dr.-Ing., Wissenschaftlicher Mitarbeiter, VEB Verkehrs- und Tiefbaukombinat Leipzig, GDR

SYNOPSIS   For super-lightweight construction in the form of composite fabric structures a flexible soil-buried anchorage made of fabrics has been developed. The underlying experimental tests as well as the analysis pattern and the practical utilization are being described. Experiences from the erection of experimental buildings are being given. The angular anchor developed is especially suitable to carry forces from air-supported structures into non-cohesive soil. If the limits of utilization of the present labour code are followed the pull-out tests required by now are no longer necessary.

INTRODUCTION

Geofabrics used as soil reinforcement have the task to give "tensile strength" to non-cohesive soils. The effect of soil reinforcement is based on the fact that primarily occurring soil deformations cause strains and thereby tensile forces, too, in the reinforcement by means of friction bond between fabric and soil. Thus the reinforcement guarantees the stability of the composite system. Reversing this principle of reinforcing it is possible to anchor a primarily tensioned fabric in the soil by utilizing the friction bond mentioned above.

TASK

Structures in which technical textiles in the form of structural fabrics (i.e. materials with well-defined requirements of high-quality and reliability) are used as the basic building element have been increasingly applied worldwide for about 30 years. Thus air-supported structures (in the following designated as ASS) have a central place in the field of composite fabric construction. Their space-enclosing membrane consists of structural fabrics. Their stability is acquired by a pressure difference between the enclosed air and the atmosphere outside the structure. The thus developing stabilizing pressure as well as the active lateral wind load result in tensile stresses inside the structure. Along the edge of the membrane they occur as linear tensile edge forces. For ASS of medium span (< 40 m) representing the majority of such structures in the German Democratic Republic these tensile forces are smaller than 15 kN/m. Depending on the geometry of the membrane and the distribution of the imposed load the direction of these forces in relation to the horizontal line varies.

The tensile edge forces must be carried by the anchoring structure. Internationally plenty of possibilities are known (Herzog, 1976), (Kerreit, 1984). Most frequently concrete counterweights in the form of precast concrete elements which are joined together or monolithic concrete strips are used (as shown in Fig. 1), and, to a smaller extent, also screwing-in piles, arrowhead type piles and spreading steel piles are used. Using a concrete counterweight the disadvantages are as follows:

- In the design principle a contradiction arises between the extremely light membrane and the necessary mass volume for the anchorage elements: In an ASS over a rectangular plan with the dimensions of length = 45 m, width = 20 m, height = 8 m there is a mass volume of the membrane of about 1.5 t versus about 190 t of the required self-weight concrete anchorage. The expense of transport capacity resulting is disproportionately high.

- The linear tensile force of the membrane is concentrated into single forces with the help

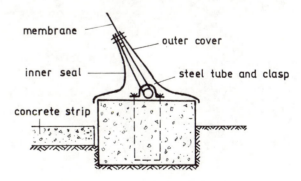

Fig. 1   Section through the concrete counterweight

of special structural elements (e.g. steel tubes and clasps, as shown in Fig. 1). In the example given above some 0.8 t of steel are required.

To guarantee a strict observance of the structural lightweight principle in the erection of ASS the research team TEXTILVERBUNDBAU at the TH Leipzig/Sektion Ingenieurbau has been developing a flexible soil-buried anchorage. In this research project special emphasis has been laid on the following targets:

- Optimum design of the anchor form with a view to the load-bearing behaviour and the placing technique.
- A special dimensioning process adapted to the anchorage of variable tensile forces shall be developped. Its validity is to be examined and confirmed by full scale tests in order to eliminate the pull-out tests so far necessary for anchorage structures.

EXPERIMENTAL TESTS

Previously carried out small-scale model experiments proved an angular anchor as shown in Fig. 7 to be the most suitable variant with a view to placing technique and load bearing capacity as well as to material expenditure.

Field Tests

As a fabric-type anchorage material the PVC-coated polyamid fabric SPA 360 canvas was used which has for a long time also been used in the erection of ASS. Its tearing strength is 3,500 N/5 cm. The angular anchor cut out from this material had the following dimensions: width 'b' = 3,000 mm; horizontal length 'l_H' = 1,200 mm and 1,500 mm; burying depth 't' = 1,200 mm. The so-dimensioned anchor was subjected to pull-out tests in the experimental process shown in Fig. 2. The pulling angle was 'ϑ' = 55° and 90° in relation to the horizontal line. In this test the anchor was buried in a conventionally graded moist sand. Its most significant soil physical parameters were:

- medium grain size d_{50} = 0.77 mm
- coefficient of uniformity U = 3.2

- bulk density γ = 18 kN/m^3
- capillary cohesion c' = 3 kPa
- efficient friction angle Φ' = 36°

In each of the 15 full-scale tests which have been carried out the load-relevant displacements of the anchor head, the elongations and deformations of the canvas as well as soil raisings were measured for the single load increments. Prior to the determination of the possible ultimate tensile force 'Z_{Gr}' of the fabric anchor the service load ($\leq$ 15 kN/m) was repeatedly entered for three times. The most significant test results are:

- Failure of the anchor results from passing beyond the frictional limit between fabric and soil. The anchor will be pulled out.
- In the anchor dimensions studied the ultimate tensile forces 'Z_{Gr}' which were achieved varied between 20 kN/m and 30 kN/m.
- Under inclined tension and on increase of the horizontal anchor length 'l_H' the ultimate tensile forces rise markedly.
- Anchor head displacements of ultimately 135 mm horizontally and 90 mm vertically occuring in the service load range are neglegible for the operation of ASS.
- Horizontally upward anchor raisings in the service load range are mainly caused by strains in the anchor fabric. These raisings decrease in relation to the number of load cycles.

Friction tests

Since the load bearing behaviour of the soil anchor is based on the friction between fabric and soil a quantitative study of the specific frictional resistance between the coated canvas material and the non-cohesive soil was necessary. These tests which were carried out by means of specially developed pull-out devices in three non-cohesive soils are generally described in (Fritzsche et al., 1984) and in a more detailed way in (Kerreit, 1984). From an evaluation of 152 individual tests the following conclusions may be drawn:

- In the soil area studied for building works the density of the soil and water saturation do not affect the frictional coefficient μ^*.

1 fabric anchor, 3 m wide
2 main traverse
3 traverse system
4 dynamometer
5 traverse guiding
6 portable jack
7 support to enable the incline
8 support for dial gauges (soil raisings)

Fig. 2   Installation for field test

- For a fractional range of $0.2 \leq d_{50} \leq 2.6$ mm $\mu^* = 1.0$ may be assumed as the lower limit value of the confidence interval (95 per cent statistically determined safety) and may be given as a value for analysis.

DIMENSIONAL DESIGN OF FABRIC ANCHOR

The displacement analysis of the loaded anchor determined from the field tests serves as the basis for the model of analysis.

To analyze the load bearing capacity of the anchor the latter is separated into five ranges of influence due to the displacement characteristics as shown in Fig. 3.

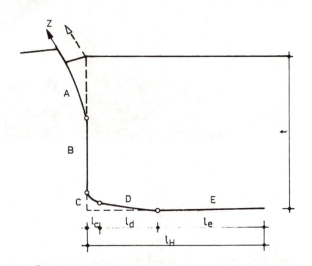

Fig. 3   Displacement of the loaded angular anchor

A - range of inclined tension; B - undisturbed vertical range; C - range of clearly defined change of force direction; D - raised horizontal range with friction on the upper side; E - horizontal range with friction on both sides

For reasons of simplification it is assumed in the model of analysis that in ranges A to C the anchor force 'Z' is only changed in its direction and is not reduced due to non-existing friction. Thus when entering range D force 'Z' becomes effective in full scale. In ranges D and E which are fully loaded by the soil, the tensile force of the anchor is diminished by friction. Fig. 4 demonstrates the balance in these ranges. To calculate the load-depending dimensions in range D the horizontal line component of the resulting friction force 'R_d' is entered at the rear of the range. This is done analogous to the simplifying representation of Fig. 5.

As a supporting line in range D results:

$$z(x) = 2\tan(x - \frac{x^2}{2l_d}) \qquad (1)$$

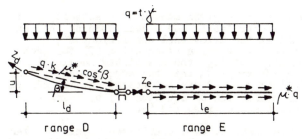

Fig. 4   Balance of forces in the D and E ranges

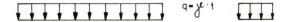

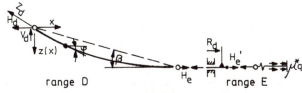

Fig. 5   Simplified model of range D

from which follows as a first derivation:

$$\frac{dz(x)}{dx} = 2\tan\beta(1 - \frac{x}{l_d}) \qquad (2)$$

The edge forces 'H_d' and 'V_d' are:

$$H_d = H_e = \frac{ql_d}{2\tan\beta} ; \quad V_d = q \cdot l_d \qquad (3)$$

Friction force 'R_d' originating in range D but acting only at the rear of the range due to Fig. 4 is:

$$R_d = q \cdot l_d \cdot k \cdot \mu^* \cdot \cos^2\beta \qquad (4)$$

For forming the canvas of length 'L' in range D the initial length 'l_d' must be elongated:

$$\int_0^L dL = l_d + \int_0^L \frac{z(x)}{E} dL + \Delta l_e \qquad (5)$$

With $F(z) = H_d/\cos\varphi$; $dL = dx/\cos\varphi$; $H_e' = H_e - R_d$ and

$$\Delta l_e = \frac{H_e'^2}{2E \cdot \mu^* \cdot q} = \frac{q \cdot l_d^2}{2E \cdot \mu^*} \left[\frac{1}{2\tan\beta} - \frac{k \cdot \mu^*}{1 + \tan^2\beta} \right]^2 \qquad (6)$$

as well as with equations (2) and (3), equation (5) can be integrated, resulting in

$$\frac{1}{2}\left[2\tan\beta \sqrt{1 + 4\tan^2\beta} - \ln(\sqrt{1 + 4\tan^2\beta} - 2\tan\beta) \right] =$$

$$2\tan\beta + \frac{q \cdot l_d}{E}\left[1 + \frac{4}{3}\tan^2\beta\right] + \frac{q \cdot l_d \cdot \tan\beta}{E \cdot \mu^*} \cdot$$

$$\left[\frac{1}{2\tan\beta} - \frac{k \cdot \mu^*}{1 + \tan^2\beta} \right]^2 \qquad (7)$$

With both, a given module of elasticity E of the anchor fabric and a soil loading 'q', as well as the frictional coefficient μ^*, by iterative solution of equation (7) for each quantity of 'l_d' the associated inclination angle β and with this the edge forces 'Z_d' and 'H_e' of range D can be determined. The numerical evaluation of equation (7) by means of a desk computer resulted in:

- The quantity of the utilized module of elasticity of the anchor fabric notably affects 'l_d' and 'β', but does hardly affect the horizontal length 'l_d' and 'l_e' required for carrying a certain tensile force as shown in Fig. 6.

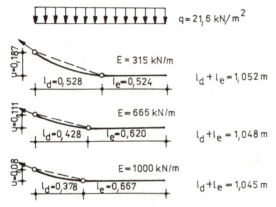

Fig. 6   Module of elasticity and horizontal anchor length 'l_d' and 'l_e'

- The raisings in the anchor range D are higher in the calculation than in the test which may result from the fact that the experimentally determined and applied module of elasticity of the fabric only insufficiently represents the mechanical behaviour of the soil anchor's fabric material. At present the strain behaviour of fabrics can only be studied according to the specifications of the textile industry, i.e. as a simple uni-axial tensile strip test without taking into account the soil contact.

- The correspondence of the limit tensile forces in field tests and in the calculation with a maximum variation of four per cent can be regarded as very good.

As a result of the calculations carried out a dimensioning diagram has been worked out which unsophisticatedly provides a quick determination of the required anchor dimensions depending on the anchor force.

PRACTICAL APPLICATION OF SOIL FABRIC ANCHORS

The result of the studies undergone is a specification on the application of soil fabric anchors in building practise. According to this specification the anchorage is only possible in

sites in which the existing soil meets the following criteria:

- Index of organic admixtures < 0.05

- The soil must be composed of a proportion of less than 15 per cent of particles with a grain size smaller than 0.06 mm and a proportion of less than 25 per cent with a grain size larger than 30 mm.

To examine and confirm the theoretical results in practise in 1980 and in 1983 two air-supported structures with fabric anchors have been erected as experimental buildings (see Fig. 7).

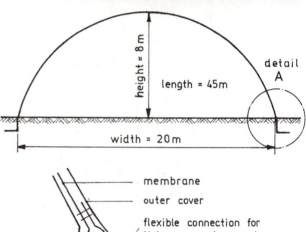

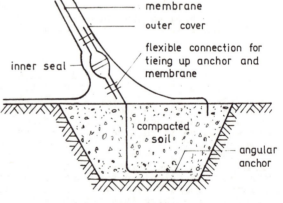

detail A

Fig. 7   Experimental structure, 1980

Experience gathered by now may be summarized as follows:

- To avoid any problems in the later connection of the membrane to the fabric anchor structure it is a decisive presupposition for the latter to fit accurately into the previously defined ground-plan. This is achieved by a simple auxiliary assembling device which ensures the anchor head against displacement when backfilling and compacting the soil in the circumferential anchor ditch.

- Unavoidable inaccuracies are most suitably to be compensated for at the corners. These are backfilled only after the stabilization of the membrane.

- The type of anchorage described has proved successful in long-time operation for four years. During this period the exchange of the membrane has been tested likewise. For the canvas material used a maximum service life of 15 years is assumed when applied for soil anchorage.

CONCLUSIONS

(1) For strict application of the principle of lightweight construction the linear tensile forces of air-supported structures may be safely carried into the soil using a flexible angular fabric anchor buried in the soil.

(2) Full-scale tests in non-cohesive soil have shown that failure of the anchorage results from a situation when the frictional resistance between fabric and soil passes beyond its limit value. The anchor is pulled out.

(3) The stresses arising in the angular range may result in the formation of sliding planes in the soil. This phenomenon is secondary as compared to the failure of the anchor due to friction.

(4) Dimensioning the soil fabric anchor is possible with a design method which assumes a frictional failure of the anchorage. The correspondence of the ultimate tensile forces in field tests and in the calculation with a maximum variation of four per cent can be regarded as very good. The practical use of the design method developed can be rendered favourable to the user by dimensioning diagrams. Such a diagram has been worked out and is ready to use for the anchors in sand which were examined.

(5) When applying the soil fabric anchors in building practise emphasis is to be laid on strictly observing the previously given anchor form by means of an auxiliary assembling device. Ensuring the anchor head against displacement when backfilling and compacting the soil in the circumferential ditch is an essential prerequisite to connect the anchor to the membrane of the ASS without any difficulty.

(6) If the regulations and limits of application in the "Specification on the Use of Flexible Soil Anchors for Air-Supported Structures in Non-Cohesive Soil" are strictly followed the pull-out tests hitherto required for anchorage structures are no longer necessary.

ACKNOWLEDGEMENTS

The authors thank the VEB Textil- und Veredlungsbetrieb Neugersdorf comprised in the VEB Kombinat Technische Textilien Karl-Marx-Stadt, GDR, for having financially supported these studies. The field tests were made possible by active support of KB Industriebau Bautzen within VEB BMK Kohle und Energie, GDR.

REFERENCES

Fritzsche, E., Kerreit, M., Scheffler, H.(1984). Biegeweiche Erdverankerung für Tragluft-hallen. 1. Nationales Symposium "Geotextilien im Erd- und Grundbau", Mainz 28./29. März 1984. Forschungsgesellschaft für Straßen- und Verkehrswesen, Köln 1984. 159-164.

Herzog, Th. (1976). Pneumatische Konstruktionen. Hatje-Verlag, Stuttgart.

Kerreit, M. (1984). Beitrag zur Verankerungstechnik im extremen Leichtbau. Dissertation A 1984, Technische Hochschule Leipzig, DDR-7030 Leipzig, Karl-Liebknecht-Str. 132.

Design of reinforced embankments for Great Yarmouth Bypass

L'étude des remblais renforcés pour la rocade de Great Yarmouth

D. WILLIAMS, C. H. Dobbie & Partners, Ipswich, UK
R. L. SANDERS, C. H. Dobbie & Partners, Ipswich, UK

SYNOPSIS   The paper presents the effective stress design methods developed for reinforced embankments on the Great Yarmouth Bypass.   The design methods are discussed in relation to total stress methods and the properties of the very soft underlying soils.   The performance of the embankments is outlined with an account of a localised failure, passing through the reinforcement. It is concluded that the use of effective stress methods can produce cost effective reinforced embankment designs.

INTRODUCTION

Embankments reinforced with geogrids and geotextiles have been constructed for the Great Yarmouth Western Bypass in Norfolk, England. The embankments vary in height between 2.0 and 8.0m and consist entirely of imported granular fill.   They are underlain by soft and very soft alluvial deposits to a depth of 22m.   The history of the site and the construction of the embankments have been presented previously, together with some performance data (Williams 1984).

The concept behind the design was to construct embankments for which stability analyses employing total stress ($\emptyset=0$) criteria, neglecting the reinforcement, result in end of construction safety factors between 0.8 to 1.0.   The reinforcing members were not intended to provide means for steepening side slopes, but were considered to be an economic means of increasing foundation safety factors.

The majority of analytical methods used for reinforced embankments reported in recent literature employ limit equilibrium methods applied to circular arc surfaces and total stress criteria. In order to adopt such a method for the Great Yarmouth embankments, reinforcement would be required to increase the embankment safety factor from 0.8 to 1.3.   While it appears acceptable to use reinforcement to increase safety factors from say 1.1 to 1.3, increases from below unity appear inexpedient.

In addition to stability, the design for a road embankment over deep alluvial deposits must take account of consolidation of the deposits and effects of residual settlement on the completed road.   In order to prevent the occurrence of excessive residual settlement, periods for settlement are often incorporated into the construction programme between filling and road laying stages. Such periods may be reduced by surcharging, whereby the embankment is constructed to a greater height than ultimately required.   It then becomes possible to include cessation periods in embankment raising to allow porewater pressure dissipation.   Taking account of the increase in strength of the subsoil brought about by porewater dissipation, the embankment design is no longer governed by total stress concepts but is controlled by effective stresses. It appears logical then, where factors of safety are less than unity for a $\emptyset=0$ analysis, to combine effective stress criteria with reinforcing inclusions to provide adequate safety factors throughout the construction period.

At Great Yarmouth the dissipation of excess porewater pressure during and subsequent to embankment construction was promoted by vertical band drains installed in the underlying alluvial deposits.

DESIGN DEVELOPMENT

Milligan and La Rochelle (1984) note, for embankments constructed over soft clay foundations with factors of safety using a $\emptyset=0$ analysis in the range 1.2 to 1.3, lateral strains are several percent and settlement about 10 percent of the embankment height.   They further note, where settlement is expected to exceed 10 percent, the design should include a detailed assessment of strain and limit equilibrium methods for reinforced embankments must be used with caution.

In order to assess such strains, determine actual performance characteristics and check the proposed design, trial works were undertaken along the line of the proposed road.   These comprised of the construction of a 5m high embankment in two 2.5m lifts over a geotextile reinforced foundation.   This embankment was constructed along the line of a much narrower former railway embankment, which is closely followed by the proposed road (Fig 1).   Two 2.5m high filling phases were separated by a cessation of 10 weeks duration to permit dissipation of excess porewater pressure.   During the first phase construction and the cessation, settlements and lateral strains in excess of 20 percent and

12 percent respectively of the embankment height were recorded without failure. The rate of construction was controlled by stability analyses using values of porewater pressure and effective stress parameters inferred from triaxial tests. Further control of construction rates was provided by observations of the rates of settlement and lateral strain.

In view of the high values for settlement and lateral strain measured during the trial works, the effective stress analysis was extended for the design of the further Great Yarmouth embankments, utilising the results from back analyses of the trial embankment.

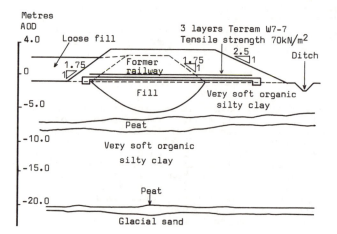

Fig. 1   Simplified Trial Embankment Section

DESIGN METHOD

Three modes of failure were considered (Fig 2)
(1) internal lateral strains causing tensile failure of the reinforcement
(2) circular and non circular failure through the reinforcement and
(3) plastic flow of the foundation

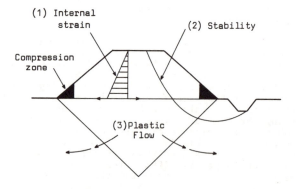

Fig. 2   Failure Modes

Internal lateral strains

In accordance with recent literature it was assumed that the reinforcement must be capable of resisting a horizontal force approximated by the Mohr Coulomb active pressure equation.

$$Pa = 0.5 \gamma H^2 \tan^2 (45 - \phi/2) \qquad (1)$$

Where γ is the density of the fill and H is the current embankment height.

Furthermore the reinforcement was terminated within the embankment avoiding the zones of zero or compressive strain (McGown et al 1978).

Circular and non circular failure

Using the effective stress design approach developed during the trial works and the rigorous method for stability analysis developed by Sarma (1973), the reinforcement was considered as a cohesive layer after Fowler (1982), or as a resisting moment after Jewell (1982). These approaches were used to equate the porewater pressures around a failure surface, the tensile strength for the reinforcement and the factor of safety. Similar relationships were established for the two methods, however, neither takes account of the disrupting effect a geotextile has on the failure surface. Given adequate bond, a stiff geotextile inclusion reduces the shear stress on the adjacent soil and thereby causes the failure plane to penetrate deeper. This lengthening of the failure plane increases the factor of safety, although in this case no appreciable increase in subsoil shear strength with depth exists.

It was postulated that for a low embankment, reinforcement would steepen the classic shear plane inclination through the embankment to greater than $45-\phi/2$. It was considered that due to the gradual method of filling and compaction of the granular fill, specified in the design, tension cracks would only appear as a result of the development of a failure plane in the foundation.

Plastic flow of the foundation

Stability and bearing capacity failures are known to have taken place during construction of the railway embankments and the site of these failures is traversed by the new road. Site investigation confirmed that the 4m high railway embankment on the poorest soils, in part constructed upon a brushwood mat, caused plastic flow of the subsoil and fill material punched to a depth of 7.0m (Fig 3). In order to prevent a repeat or reactivation of these punching failures, the bearing capacity was analysed using a simplified effective stress approach:

Terzaghi's bearing capacity equation:

$$qf = cNc + \gamma zNq + \tfrac{1}{2} B\gamma N\gamma \qquad (2)$$

can be expressed in terms of effective stress to give:

$$qf = c'Nc + p' (Nq - 1) + \tfrac{1}{2} B\gamma' N\gamma + P \qquad (3)$$

where $p' = \gamma z - u$ and $\gamma' = \dfrac{\gamma z - u}{z}$

For an embankment above original ground level P=0, and the equation becomes

$$qf = c'Nc + (\gamma z - u) (Nq - 1) + \tfrac{1}{2} B \dfrac{(\gamma z-u)}{z} N\gamma \qquad (4)$$

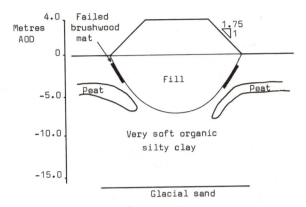

Fig 3.   Former Railway Embankment
(Bypass chainage 2100)

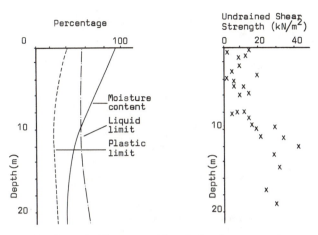

Fig 5.   Soil properties - backswamp area

Equation (4) can be solved to give values of porewater pressure (u) for bearing capacity failure.

This approach was used to back analyse the trial and establish values of c' and Ø' for the subsoil.   The method was then used to relate porewater pressure with factors of safety and with controls placed upon lateral movement and settlement, used to control filling rates.

Incorporation of design method

Variations in soil profile, embankment height, the position of the former railway and the requirements for the finished road, resulted in a variety of different levels of reinforcement, construction rates and settlement period durations.   Within the scheme various side roads were given lower design and end of construction requirements than the trunk road with the embankment design modified accordingly.

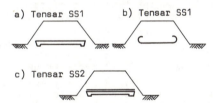

a) Tensar SS1   b) Tensar SS1

c) Tensar SS2

Fig 4.   Design variations: a) roundabout chainage 2100 b) Industrial access road c) Embankments over 3m high

PERFORMANCE

The great majority of the 5000m length of reinforced embankment in the scheme performed in accordance with design predictions.   However, to report on the total scheme is beyond the scope of the present paper which will concentrate solely on the area of the poorest subsoil.   This area thought to be a backswamp to a former river estuary, contains increasingly organic deposits and forms the site of greatest settlement of the former railway embankment.

A roundabout lies in the centre of this area on an embankment 2.5m high which includes 2 geogrid layers (Fig 4a).   An industrial access road and cycleway connecting onto the roundabout includes a single geogrid layer (Fig 4b).   Identical filling sequences were used for both sections

based upon instrument readings under the roundabout.   The roundabout was safely constructed to full height in 15 weeks including 2 short cessation periods, however, the cycleway embankment suffered a rotational slip failure along one side approximately 30m long at a height of 1.9m.   Soil properties for the backswamp area are shown in Fig 5.

Lateral strains

Lateral strains measured across the width of the embankement throughout the area under consideration were in the order of 10 percent of the height or between 1 and 2 percent of the width. At the slip these figures were not exceeded due to the rotational nature of the movement. Investigation of the slip revealed a clean break in the geogrid with the shear plane passing through at 90°.   The geogrid either side of the break showed no apparent distress and a stitched joint some 100mm distant, displayed no signs of having been subjected to excessive tension. The break appeared to be a form of local shear failure of the geogrid with no destructive tensile component.   It is postulated that tensile forces induced by the shear force are extremely localised and transferred by bonding to the fill material, due to the high normal stress on the geogrid and surrounding fill.

Stability analysis

Porewater pressures in the vicinity of the slip were found to be in excess of those under the roundabout and exceeded those used in design. Fig 6 shows the mode of failure and the soil properties measured along the failure plane.

Back analysis of the slip using the effective stress approach gives a factor of safety of 0.9. Similar analyses for the roundabout give a factor of safety of 1.1 whilst total stress analyses show factors of safety of 0.8 and 0.9 respectively.

Plastic flow

The large railway embankment failures have not been reactivated or repeated and settlements are in accordance with predictions based upon elastic analysis.   Fig 7 shows relationships between the porewater and settlement rates.   It can be seen that settlement rates increase rapidly when porewater pressure limits calculated using equation (4) were approached and exceeded.

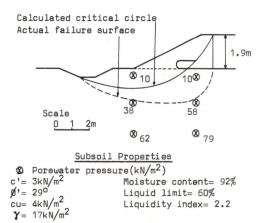

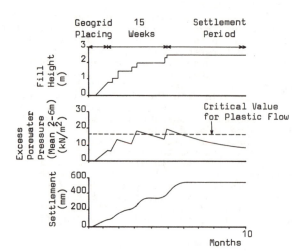

Fig 6. Cross Section of Failure and Measured Soil Properties

Fig 7. Backswamp Area (Ch2100)
(a) Filling Rate (b) Excess porewater pressure (c) Settlement

CONCLUSIONS

By combining the benefits induced by disrupting a potential failure plane using layers of reinforcement, with those of effective stress analyses, cost effective reinforced embankments have been constructed.

In addition to reinforcement and effective stress analyses controlling the stability of the embankments, similar approaches have also been used to reduce settlement by controlling plastic movement of the foundation, using a modified bearing capacity analysis.

Tensile forces induced in a geogrid reinforced

embankment at failure have been shown to be extremely localised with rupture taking place in the form of a shear failure.

The design approach and control exercised during construction have been successful in preventing a repeat of the failures which occurred previously on this site.

ACKNOWLEDGEMENTS

The scheme was designed and supervised by C.H.Dobbie and Partners, Consulting Engineers. The works were undertaken by May Gurney and Co. Limited.

The authors wish to thank all persons involved in the design and construction of the works and in the preparation of this paper.

The paper is given by permission of Mr.D.I.Evans BSc Tech MSE C Eng Director (TP) Eastern Region, Department of Transport.

REFERENCES

1) Engineers reports on the construction of the Lowestoft Junction Railway for the Midland and Great Northern Railways, Joint Committee. (1901 - 1904).

2) Fowler, J. (1982). Theoretical design considerations for fabric reinforced embankments. Proc. 2nd Int. Conf. on Geotextiles, Vol. 3, Las Vegas.

3) Jewell, R.A. (1982). A limit equilibrium method for reinforced embankments on soft foundations. Proc. 2nd Int. Conf. on Geotextiles, Vol. 3, Las Vegas.

4) McGown, A., Andrawes, K.Z. and Al-Husani, M.M. (1978). Effect of inclusion properties on the behaviour of sand. Geotechnique (28) 3. 327-346.

5) Milligan, V. and La Rochelle, P. (1984). Design methods for embankments over weak soils. Proc. Symp. on Polymer Grid Reinforcement in Civil Engineering.

6) Sarma, S.K. (1973). Stability Analysis of embankments and slopes. Geotechnique (23)3.

7) Terzaghi, K. (1943). Theoretical soil mechanics, John Wiley and Sons, New York.

8) Williams, D. (1984). Reinforced embankments at Great Yarmouth Bypass. Proc. Symp. on Polymer Grid Reinforcement in Civil Engineering.

9) Williams, D. (1984). Design and construction of the Great Yarmouth Trial Embankment. C.H.Dobbie and Partners Internal Report. Unpublished.